Aviation Maintenance Technician Series

Airframe

Dale Crane

Terry Michmerhuizen
Technical Editor
School of Aviation Sciences
Western Michigan University

Aviation Supplies & Academics, Inc.
Newcastle, Washington

Aviation Maintenance Technician Series: Airframe
Second Impression

Aviation Supplies & Academics, Inc.
7005 132nd Place SE
Newcastle, Washington 98059-3153

Cover photo © Jaime Villaseca/The Image Bank

Photo credits: p. 6—Aerostar International, Inc.; p. 20—Raisbeck Engineering; pp. 25, 28—Cessna Aircraft Company; p. 28—Piper Aircraft; p. 29—Beech Aircraft Corporation; p. 158—Miller Electric Manufacturing Co.; p. 159—The Lincoln Electric Company; p. 235—Beech Aircraft Corporation; p. 251—Heatcon Composite Systems; p. 422—Joe Finelli; p. 423—Cessna Aircraft Company; p. 449—Aircraft Braking Systems Corporation; pp. 573, 574—Simpson Electric Company; p. 574—John Fluke Manufacturing Company, Inc.; p. 751—American Avionics; p. 848—courtesy of Dayton-Granger, Inc. (Kuflic Photography); pp. 849, 850—courtesy of Dayton-Granger, Inc. (Ring Photography).

Illustration credits: pp. 41, 237—line drawings courtesy Grumman Corporation; p. 156—drawing source courtesy The Lincoln Electric Company; p. 314—illustration courtesy Chadwick-Helmuth Company, Inc.

Sections of some chapters are excerpted from previous publications, and have been used with permission: pp. 202–203, "Poly-Fiber Covering and Painting Material" courtesy Poly-Fiber Aircraft Coverings, Riverside, California; pp. 205–207, sections of the Superflite System manuals; pp. 205–207, Ceconite 7600 procedures provided by Blue River Aircraft Supply, Harvard, Nebraska.

ISBN 1-56027-267-8
ASA-AMT-A

Library of Congress Cataloging-in-Publication Data

Crane, Dale.
    Airframe / Dale Crane; Terry Michmerhuizen, technical editor.
      p.   cm.—(Aviation maintenance technician series)
    Includes index.
    ISBN 1-56027-153-1
    1. Airframes—Maintenance and repair. I. Title. II. Series.
TL 671.9.C663 1994
629.1346—dc20
                       94-22063
                       CIP

CONTENTS

AVIATION SUPPLIES & ACADEMICS, INC.

PREFACE

Aviation maintenance technology has undergone tremendous changes in the past decades. Modern aircraft, with their advanced engines, complex flight controls and environmental control systems, are some of the most sophisticated devices in use today, and these marvels of engineering must be maintained by knowledgeable technicians. The Federal Aviation Administration, recognizing this new generation of aircraft, has updated the requirements for maintenance technicians and for the schools that provide their training. The FAA has also instituted an Aviation Maintenance Technician Awards Program to encourage technicians to update their training.

New technologies used in modern aircraft increase the importance of maintenance technicians having a solid foundation in such basic subjects as mathematics, physics, and electricity. The *Aviation Maintenance Technician Series* has been produced by ASA to provide the needed background information for this foundation and to introduce the reader to aircraft structures, powerplants, and systems.

These textbooks have been carefully designed to assist a person in preparing for FAA technician certification, and at the same time serve as valuable references for individuals working in the field. The subject matter is organized into categories used by the FAA for the core curriculum in FAR Part 147, Aviation Maintenance Technician Schools, and for the Subject Matter Knowledge Codes used in the written tests for technician certification. In some cases in the ASA series, these categories have been rearranged to provide a more logical progression of learning.

This textbook is part of the ASA series of coordinated maintenance technician training materials. The series consists of the *General, Airframe,* and *Powerplant* textbooks with study questions, the *Fast-Track Test Guides for Aviation Mechanics,* exam software for Aviation Maintenance Technician tests, the *Oral and Practical Exam Guide,* the *Dictionary of Aeronautical Terms,* and the *Aviation Mechanic Handbook.*

Continued

To supplement this fundamental training material, ASA reprints the FAA Advisory Circulars AC 43.13-1A and 2A *Acceptable Methods, Techniques, and Practices Aircraft Inspection, Repair, and Alteration,* and semiannually updated excerpts from the Federal Aviation Regulations that are applicable to the aviation maintenance technician.

Dale Crane

ACKNOWLEDGEMENTS

A series of texts such as this *Aviation Maintenance Technician Series* could never be compiled without the assistance of modern industry. Many individuals have been personally helpful, and many companies have been generous with their information. We want to acknowledge this and say thank you to them all.

Aeroquip Corporation, *Jackson, MI*

Aerostar International, *Sioux Falls, SD*

Airborne Division, Parker Hannifin Corporation, *Elyria, OH*

Aircraft Braking Systems Corporation, *Massillon, OH*

American Avionics, *Seattle, WA*

Beech Aircraft Corporation, *Wichita, KS*

Biddle Instruments, *Blue Bell, PA*

Blue River Aircraft Supply, *Harvard, NB*

Cessna Aircraft Company, *Wichita, KS*

Chadwick-Helmuth Company, Inc., *El Monte, CA*

Christie Electric Corp., *Gardena, CA*

Dayton-Granger, *Fort Lauderdale, FL*

DeVilbiss Ransburg Industrial Equipment, *Maumee, OH*

Evergreen Weigh, Inc., *Lynwood, WA*

General Electric Aircraft Engines, *Cincinnati, OH*

Grayhill, Inc., *La Grange, IL*

Grumman Corporation, *Bethpage, NY*

Heatcon Composite Systems, *Seattle, WA*

Hobart Brothers Company, *Troy, OH*

Lincoln Electric Company, *Cleveland, OH*

John Fluke Manufacturing Company, *Everett, WA*

Machida, Incorporated, *Orangeburg, NY*

Maule Air, Inc., *Moultrie, GA*

Micro-Surface Finishing Products, *Wilton, IA*

Miller Electric Manufacturing Company, *Appleton, WI*

Monsanto Chemical Company, *St. Louis, MO*

NASA Lewis Research Center, *Cleveland, OH*

Northrop Corporation, *Pico Rivera, CA*

Optronics Engineering, *Goleta, CA*

Piper Aircraft Company, *Vero Beach, FL*

Poly-Fiber Aircraft Coatings, *Riverside, CA*

Raisbeck Engineering, *Seattle, WA*

Randolph Products, *Carlstadt, NJ*

Simpson Electric Company, *Elgin, IL*

Superflite, *Elk Grove Village, IL*

Technical Chemical Company, *Dallas, TX*

Teledyne Battery Products, *Redlands, CA*

Zetec, Inc., *Issaquah, WA*

A very special thanks goes to Terry Michmerhuizen, Leard Wylie, and Robert Aardema of the School of Aviation Sciences of Western Michigan University for their careful editing, critiquing, and many suggestions.

A special thanks goes to David Jensen and Pete Owsley of Heatcon® Composite Systems of Seattle, Washington, for their valuable input and their editing of the section on Composite Construction.

BASIC AERODYNAMICS

Continued

1

BASIC AERODYNAMICS

Basic Fixed-Wing Aerodynamics

The Beginnings of Flight

People have dreamed of taking to the air since the earliest observers watched the graceful flight of birds. It was only natural the first thoughts of flight assumed a need for flapping wings. In Greek mythology, Daedalus and his son Icarus escaped from Crete by making wings of feathers held together with wax. Icarus was so enamored of flight, he flew too close to the sun. The wax melted, and he plunged into the sea and drowned.

The earliest experimental flying machines emulated the bird, using flapping wings for propulsion. These machines, or "ornithopters," were unsuccessful. The first successful heavier-than-air flying machines were built and flown by the Chinese centuries before Christ, kites held in the air by the same aerodynamic forces that sustain modern airplanes and helicopters.

Two Types of Lift

Two types of lift raise aircraft against the force of gravity: aerostatic and aerodynamic. Aerostatic lift is produced when the weight of air displaced by the aircraft is greater than the weight of the aircraft. Aerodynamic lift is produced when movement of the aircraft through the air forces down a weight of air greater than the weight of the aircraft.

Aerostatic Lift

While the Chinese were flying kites and raising objects with the kites' aerodynamic lift, most experiments in Europe were of an aerostatic nature. In November of 1783, the Montgolfier brothers launched a manned hot-air balloon from Paris, France. Between the two world wars of the twentieth century, huge lighter-than-air flying machines carried aloft thousands of persons and transported tons of cargo, and in 1929 the German *Graf Zeppelin* made a round-the-world flight of more than 21,000 miles.

During the 1920s and 1930s, the U.S. Navy experimented with several huge lighter-than-air flying machines, using two of them, the *USS Akron* and the *USS Macon*, as flying aircraft carriers. Interest in lighter-than-aircraft was dealt a serious blow on May 6, 1937, when the German airship *Hindenburg* burned as she docked at the U.S. Naval Air Station in Lakehurst, New Jersey. Strained diplomatic relations between the ruling parties in Germany and the

ornithopter. A heavier-than-air flying machine that produces lift by flapping its wings. No practical ornithopter has been built.

Zeppelin. The name of large rigid lighter-than-air ships built by the Zeppelin Company in Germany prior to and during World War I.

United States meant the Germans did not have access to helium gas (only found in commercial quantities in the United States). They used the extremely flammable hydrogen gas to lift the Hindenburg.

Experimental work with large lighter-than-air machines continues today, and gas-filled blimps frequently advertise above our cities. The most common lighter-than-air aircraft, though, are hot-air balloons. Made of modern high-strength synthetic fabrics, these aircraft use propane burners to heat the air.

blimp. A cigar-shaped, nonrigid lighter-than-air flying machine.

Figure 1-1. *The modern hot-air balloon uses the same type of aerostatic lift that carried two aeronauts aloft in France more than two centuries ago.*

Aerodynamic Lift

Most modern aircraft employ aerodynamic lift, which requires relative movement between the air and the aircraft.

To create aerodynamic lift, a specially shaped surface, called an airfoil, is moved through the air. A low pressure is produced above its surface, and a relatively high pressure is produced below it. This pressure differential deflects the air downward, and the mass of the air forced down is balanced by an equal force that pushes upward on the airfoil. This upward force is the aerodynamic lift.

Properties of the Atmosphere

The atmosphere is the layer of gases that surrounds the earth from its surface to a height of about 22 miles. These gases consist of a mixture of nitrogen and oxygen with a small percentage of other gases, including water vapor.

In the troposphere, the lowest layer of the atmosphere, all our weather exists. The troposphere extends from the surface to about 36,000 feet, and in this layer, the temperature and pressure decrease steadily as the altitude increases.

Immediately above the troposphere is the stratosphere, which extends to the upper limit of the atmosphere. The temperature in the stratosphere remains constant at -56.5°C (-69.7°F), but the pressure continues to decrease. The boundary between the troposphere and the stratosphere is called the tropopause.

Standard Atmospheric Conditions

The ICAO (International Civil Aeronautical Organization) standard atmosphere is a hypothetical condition whose parameters have been accepted by international agreement as representative of the atmosphere surrounding the earth for the purposes of aircraft design and performance calculations, and for the calibration of aircraft instruments.

aerodynamic lift. The force produced by air moving over a specially shaped surface called an airfoil. Aerodynamic lift acts in a direction perpendicular to the direction the air is moving.

airfoil. Any surface designed to obtain a useful reaction, or lift, from air passing over it.

ICAO Standard Atmosphere

Parameter	British Units	Metric Units
Pressure, P_0	2116.22 lb/ft² 29.92 in. Hg	$1.013250 \cdot 10^5$ N/m² 760 mm Hg
Temperature, T_0	518.67°R 59.0°F	288.15°K 15.0°C
Acceleration due to gravity, g_0	32.1741 ft/sec²	9.80665 m/sec²
Specific weight, $g_0 \rho_0$	0.76474 lb/ft³	1.2230 kg/m³
Density, ρ_0	0.0023769 lb-sec²/ft4	0.12492 kg-sec²/m4

Figure 1-2. *Conditions of the standard ICAO atmosphere*

In practical flight conditions, air pressure is measured in terms of altitude rather than inches of mercury or pounds per square inch. The altimeter is an absolute-pressure gage, or barometer, that measures the pressure of the air and indicates the altitude at which that pressure exists.

When the barometric scale of the altimeter is set at the standard sea-level pressure, 29.92 inches of mercury, the indication is called pressure altitude.

Density altitude, used to determine the amount of lift produced by an airfoil and the amount of power produced by an engine, is found by correcting pressure altitude for nonstandard temperature.

Bernoulli's Principle

Aerodynamic lift is produced by the relative movement between an airfoil and the air. Air is a viscous fluid: it "wets," or tends to adhere to, any surface over which it flows.

An airfoil like the one in Figure 1-3 is shaped in such a way that the air flowing over its upper surface finds the surface dropping away from it, and it must speed up. The air flowing below the airfoil finds the surface rising into its path and it is forced to slow down.

In 1738, the Swiss physicist Daniel Bernoulli explained the relationship between potential and kinetic energy in the air as it flows over an airfoil. Air's potential energy relates to its pressure, and kinetic energy to its velocity. The sum of potential and kinetic energy in the air is its total energy.

Bernoulli's principle explains that if the total energy in the air flowing over an airfoil remains constant, any increase in its velocity will cause a corresponding decrease in its pressure.

Since the air flowing over the top of the airfoil speeds up, its pressure decreases, and air flows down to fill the low pressure. The air flowing under the airfoil is slowed down and its pressure increases. Air is forced away from the high pressure. The net result is that the air flowing around the airfoil is forced downward. (*See* Figure 1-4.) The weight of forced-down air is exactly balanced by the force pushing upward on the airfoil, aerodynamic lift.

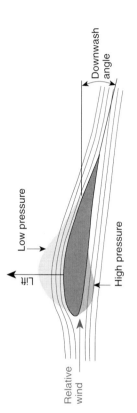

Figure 1-4. *Aerodynamic lift is produced by a relatively low pressure above the airfoil surface pulling air down to the surface, while a relatively high pressure below the surface forces the air away. The mass of the air deflected downward is balanced by an equal upward force on the airfoil.*

pressure altitude. The altitude in standard atmosphere at which the pressure is the same as the existing air.

density altitude. The altitude in standard air at which the density is the same as that of the existing air.

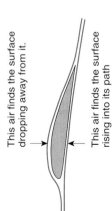

This air finds the surface dropping away from it.

This air finds the surface rising into its path

Figure 1-3. *The air flowing over the upper surface of this airfoil finds the surface dropping away, and is forced to speed up. The air flowing below the airfoil finds the surface rising into its path, and is forced to slow down.*

kinetic energy. Energy that exists because of motion.

potential energy. Energy possessed in an object because of its position, chemical composition, shape, or configuration.

downwash. Air forced down by aerodynamic action below and behind the wing of an airplane or the rotor of a helicopter. Aerodynamic lift is produced when the air is deflected downward. The upward force on the aircraft is the same as the downward force on the air.

Axes of an Aircraft

An aircraft in flight is free to rotate about three axes: the longitudinal, or roll axis; the lateral, or pitch axis; and the vertical, or yaw axis. *See* Figure 1-5.

Forces Acting on an Aircraft in Flight

Four basic forces act on all aircraft in flight. During straight and level, unaccelerated flight, these forces are balanced and act through the aircraft's center of gravity. *See* Figure 1-6.

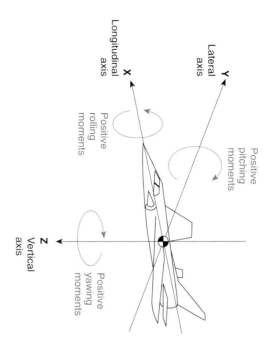

Figure 1-5. *An airplane in flight is free to rotate about its longitudinal, lateral, and vertical axes. These three axes are mutually perpendicular, and all pass through the aircraft's center of gravity.*

Thrust

The propeller or jet stream of an airplane, and the forward vector of the lift produced by a helicopter's rotor, provide thrust, or a force that causes forward movement. Thrust for a glider and for an airplane under reduced power, is produced by the forward component of lift and weight caused by the aircraft's downward flight path. *See* Figure 1-7.

When the thrust line is above the center of gravity, an increase in thrust rotates the airplane nose-down about its lateral axis. A decrease in thrust lets the airplane rotate nose-upward.

Lift

Lift is the total upward force produced by the aerodynamic reaction of the air flowing over the airfoil-shaped surfaces of the aircraft. The lift force is perpendicular to the relative wind, and may be tilted by varying the amounts of lift produced by each wing panel. Lowering the left aileron while raising the right aileron changes the shape of the wing airfoil, increasing the lift on

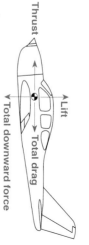

Figure 1-6. *Four basic forces act on an airplane in flight: a forward force of thrust, an upward force of lift, a rearward force of drag, and a downward force made up of weight and an aerodynamic down load on the tail.*

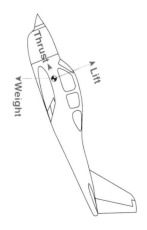

Figure 1-7. *When an airplane is in a power-off glide, the thrust is produced by the forward component of the lift and weight vectors.*

the left side of the airplane and decreasing the lift on the right side. The airplane rolls to the right and the lift tilts. Lift now has two components: one vertical and one horizontal. *See* Figure 1-8. It is this horizontal component of lift that causes an airplane to turn.

Weight

The weight of an airplane is the total pull of gravity. Weight acts through the center of gravity directly toward the center of the earth. Weight is the greatest part of the downward force on airplanes, but there are also other downward forces.

An airplane's downward tail load changes with its airspeed, and may be adjusted so all the downward forces are exactly equal to the upward forces. The combination of the downward forces moves the center of gravity to the same location as the center of lift, and the airplane balances about its center of gravity. *See* Figure 1-9.

For the airplane to remain at the same altitude, the total upward force must equal the total downward force. When the airplane is turning, centrifugal force causes a horizontal movement away from the center of the turn. This centrifugal force adds vectorially to the aircraft's weight to produce a resultant weight that is greater than the lift. If the lift is not increased as the airplane turns, the upward force will not equal the downward force, and the airplane will descend in the turn.

Drag

An airplane's drag is the sum of the forces that hold it back against the forward force of thrust. There are two basic drag forces: induced drag, which is produced by the same factors that produce aerodynamic lift, and parasite drag, which is caused by all factors not producing lift.

Induced drag, which is affected by the angle of attack, increases as the airspeed decreases. Parasite drag increases as the airspeed increases. The total drag is the sum of the induced and parasite drags. Total drag is least at the point where induced and parasite drags are equal.

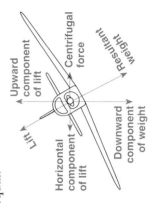

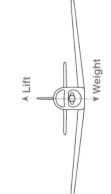

In straight and level trimmed flight, the lift exactly balances the weight.

In turning flight, centifugal force adds to the weight, and if the lift is not increased, the downward component of weight will be greater than the upward component, and the airplane will descend.

Figure 1-9. *Forces acting on an airplane in straight and level flight and turning flight.*

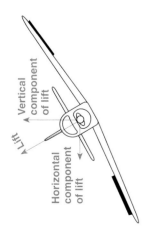

Figure 1-8. *Lift acts in a direction that is perpendicular to the lateral axis and may be tilted by rolling the airplane about its longitudinal axis. When the lift is tilted from its true vertical, it produces both a vertical and a horizontal component.*

induced drag. Aerodynamic drag produced by an airfoil when it is producing lift. Induced drag is affected by the same factors that affect induced lift.

parasite drag. A form of aerodynamic drag caused by friction between the air and the surface over which it is flowing.

angle of attack (α). The acute angle formed between the chord line of an airfoil and the direction of the air that strikes the airfoil.

trimmed flight. A flight condition in which the aerodynamic forces acting on the control surfaces are balanced and the aircraft is able to fly straight and level with no control input.

Development of the Aerodynamic Forces

Five factors affect aerodynamic lift and induced drag:

- Shape of the airfoil section
- Area of the airfoil
- Air density
- Speed of the air relative to the airfoil surface
- Angle between the airfoil and the relative wind (the angle of attack)

Notice that two of these factors relate to the airfoil, two to the air, and one to the relationship between the two. The direction of the lift produced by the wing is always perpendicular to the direction of the relative wind.

Airfoil Sections

Aerodynamic lift depends on the shape of the airfoil section and on the airfoil surface area. Figure 1-10 shows a typical subsonic airfoil section and some of the more important terms related to its shape.

The mean camber (H) is a line drawn midway between the upper and lower cambers, and its curvature is one of the most important factors in determining the aerodynamic characteristics of the airfoil. The maximum camber (F) of a typical low-speed airfoil is about 4% of the length of the chord line, and is located about 40% of the chord length behind the leading edge. The maximum thickness (E) is about 12% of the chord length and is located about 30% of the chord length behind the leading edge.

relative wind. The direction the wind strikes an airfoil.

mean camber. A line that is drawn midway between the upper and lower camber of an airfoil section. The mean camber determines the aerodynamic characteristics of the airfoil.

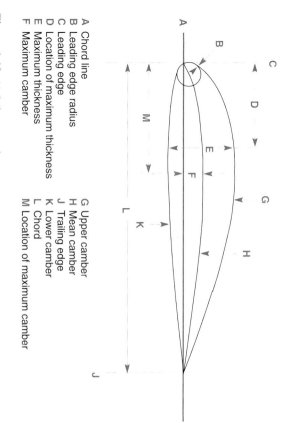

A Chord line
B Leading edge radius
C Leading edge
D Location of maximum thickness
E Maximum thickness
F Maximum camber
G Upper camber
H Mean camber
J Trailing edge
K Lower camber
L Chord
M Location of maximum camber

Figure 1-10. *Airfoil nomenclature*

center of pressure. The point on the chord line of an airfoil where all of the aerodynamic forces are considered to be concentrated.

The center of pressure is the point on the chord line of an airfoil at which all of the aerodynamic forces are concentrated. The lift vector acts from the center of pressure in a direction that is perpendicular to the relative wind, and the drag vector acts from this same point in a direction parallel to the relative wind.

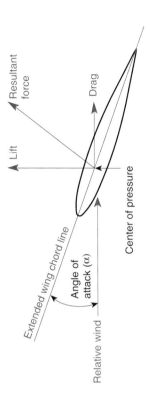

Figure 1-11. *The center of pressure of an airfoil is that point on the chord line at which the aerodynamic forces are considered to be concentrated.*

The center of pressure of a subsonic airfoil is typically located somewhere around 30% to 40% of the chord line back from the leading edge. On an asymmetrical airfoil, the center of pressure moves forward as the angle of attack increases, and backward as it decreases. On a symmetrical airfoil, the center of pressure does not move, but remains in essentially the same location as the angle of attack changes.

Figure 1-12 shows an evolution of airfoil shapes. The earliest airfoils were deeply cambered, and some were not even covered on the bottom. The shape was copied from a bird's wing. The next major step in airfoil development was the Clark-Y airfoil, the standard airfoil section through the 1920s and into the 1930s. The National Advisory Committee for Aeronautics (NACA), the ancestor of today's NASA, developed much more streamlined airfoils that allowed a smoother flow of air and greater lift with less drag. These airfoils included both symmetrical and asymmetrical sections.

When airplanes such as the Lockheed Lightning of World War II fame began flying in the transonic range, their subsonic airfoil sections left much to be desired. Shock waves formed, increasing drag and destroying control. Further study developed the supersonic airfoils, with their maximum thickness about midway back and their equally sharp leading and trailing edges. The supercritical airfoil evolved next, with its blunter leading edge and flatter upper surface. This airfoil section reduces the velocity of the air over the upper surface and delays the extreme drag rise that occurs as the airfoil approaches the speed of sound.

shock wave. A pressure wave formed in the air by a flight vehicle moving at a speed greater than the speed of sound. As the vehicle passes through the air, it produces sound waves that spread out in all directions. But since the vehicle is flying faster than these waves are moving, they build up and form a pressure wave at the front and rear of the vehicle. As the air passes through a shock wave it slows down, its static pressure increases, and its total energy decreases.

12

The NASA-developed GAW-1 and GAW-2 low-speed airfoils have the same downward cusp at the trailing edge that the supercritical airfoil has. These airfoils were developed for general aviation aircraft, and they give a wing a higher L/D ratio by increasing the lift and decreasing the drag.

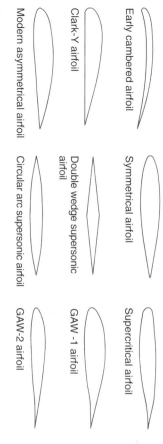

Figure 1-12. *Airfoil types*

Early cambered airfoil

Clark-Y airfoil

Modern asymmetrical airfoil

Symmetrical airfoil

Double wedge supersonic
airfoil

Circular arc supersonic airfoil

Supercritical airfoil

GAW -1 airfoil

GAW-2 airfoil

Aerodynamic Lift

To find the amount of aerodynamic lift produced by an airfoil, use the formula in Figure 1-13. When the air density is expressed as a density ratio (σ) between standard air density at sea level and the density of the existing air, and the velocity of the air is expressed in knots, the dynamic pressure (q) of the air in pounds per square foot is found with the formula in Figure 1-14. Notice that the lift is affected by the square of the airspeed. Doubling the airspeed increases the lift four times.

Figure 1-13. *Formula for finding aerodynamic lift*

$$L = C_L q S$$

L = aerodynamic lift in pounds
C_L = coefficient of lift from characteristic curve for the angle of attack specified
q = dynamic pressure in pounds per square foot
S = airfoil surface in square feet

$$q = 0.00339 \, \sigma \, V^2$$

q = dynamic pressure in pounds per square foot
0.00339 = a constant that allows knots to be used as the velocity
σ = density ratio as found in Figure 1-15
V = true airspeed in knots

Figure 1-14. *Formula for finding the dynamic pressure*

cusp. A pointed end.

symmetrical airfoil. An airfoil that has the same shape on both sides of its center line.

asymmetrical airfoil. An airfoil section that is not the same on both sides of the chord line.

density ratio (σ). The ratio of the density of the air at a given altitude to the density of the air at sea level under standard conditions.

dynamic pressure (q). The pressure a moving fluid would have if it were stopped. Dynamic pressure is measured in pounds per square foot.

knot. A measure of speed equal to one nautical mile per hour.

Figure 1-15 is an excerpt from the International Civil Aviation Organization (ICAO) Standard Atmosphere Chart. As the altitude increases, the density of the air decreases, but the temperature and the speed of sound decrease only to an altitude of 36,089 feet, and then stabilize. This altitude is the beginning of the stratosphere.

Altitude feet	Temperature °F	Temperature °C	Density Slugs / ft³	Density ratio σ	Speed of sound knots
Sea level	59	15	.002378	1.000	661.7
1,000	55.4	13	.002309	0.9711	659.5
5,000	41.2	5.1	.002049	0.8617	650.3
10,000	23.3	-4.8	.001756	0.7385	638.6
20,000	-12.3	-24.6	.001267	0.5328	614.6
30,000	-47.9	-44.4	.000890	0.3741	589.5
36,089	-69.7	-56.5	.000706	0.2971	573.8
40,000	-69.7	-56.5	.000585	0.2462	573.8
50,000	-69.7	-56.5	.000362	0.1522	573.8

Figure 1-15. *Excerpts from the ICAO Standard Atmosphere Chart*

The information required about the airfoil is its shape and its area. Figure 1-16 shows a typical set of characteristic curves for a specific shape of airfoil. Such curves are available for every airfoil section.

The coefficient of lift (C_L), the coefficient of drag (C_D), and the lift over drag (L/D) curves are the most important characteristics. These curves let you find the appropriate coefficients, or dimensionless numbers, for the airfoil at each angle of attack.

Notice that the C_L curve increases steadily from 0 at 0° angle of attack until, at an angle of attack of 20°, it suddenly drops off. This is the critical angle of attack at which the air ceases to flow smoothly over the top of the wing, and the wing stalls.

The C_D curve is relatively flat from 0° up to about 3° and then turns sharply upward and continues to increase with the angle of attack. You can find the values for the L/D curve by dividing the C_L by the C_D for the particular angle of attack. For example, at an angle of attack of 6°, the C_L is approximately 0.5 and the C_D is 0.04. Divide C_L by C_D to find that the L/D ratio for 6° is 12.5. This is the high point of the L/D curve, or the L/D_{MAX}. *See Figure 1-16.*

coefficient of drag. A dimensionless number used in the formula for determining induced drag as it relates to the angle of attack.

coefficient of lift. A dimensionless number relating to the angle of attack used in the formula for aerodynamic lift.

L/D ratio. A measure of efficiency of an airfoil. It is the ratio of the lift to the total drag at a specified angle of attack.

stall. A flight condition in which an angle of attack is reached at which the air ceases to flow smoothly over the upper surface of an airfoil. The air becomes turbulent and lift is lost.

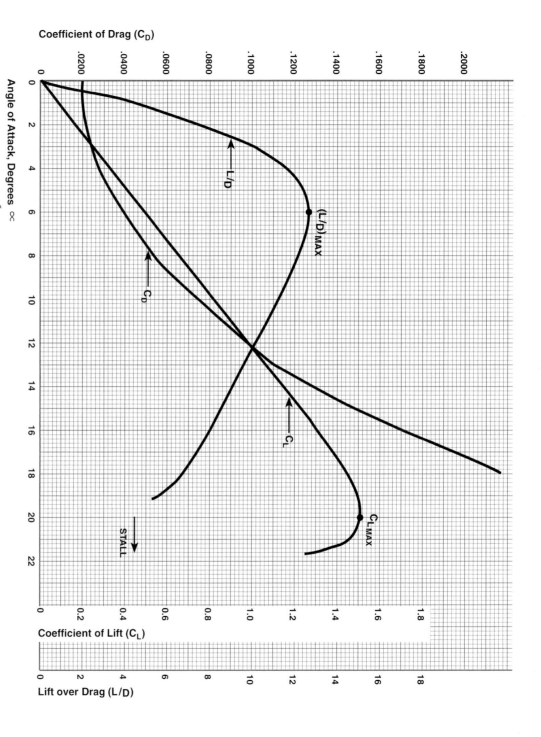

Figure 1-16. *Aerodynamic characteristics curves for a typical subsonic airfoil*

Find the amount of lift produced by a wing by following the steps shown in Figure 1-17.

Known values

Angle of attack = 16°
True airspeed = 60 knots
Density altitude = 1,000 feet
Wing area = 170 square feet

Find

Lift produced in pounds

Procedure

1. Find the coefficient of lift:
   In Figure 1-16, locate 16° along the angle of attack scale at the bottom of the chart. Follow this line upward until it intersects the C_L curve. From this point, follow a line to the right until it intersects the C_L index. This occurs at 1.3.

2. Find the dynamic pressure:
   Use the ICAO Standard Atmosphere Chart in Figure 1-15 to find the density ratio at 1,000 feet. Follow the horizontal line for 1,000 feet to the right to the density ratio column. $\sigma = 0.9711$
   Use the formula in Figure 1-14 to find the dynamic pressure:
   $q = 0.00339 \; \sigma \; V^2$
   $= 0.00339 \times 0.9711 \times 60^2$
   $= 11.85$ pounds per square foot

3. Find the aerodynamic lift:
   Use the formula in Figure 1-13.
   $L = C_L q S$
   $= 1.3 \times 11.85 \times 170$
   $= 2,618.8$ pounds

Figure 1-17. *Finding the lift produced by a wing*

Induced Drag

Notice that the C_D curve in Figure 1-16 increases greatly with the angle of attack, but the angle of attack needed to produce a given amount of lift decreases as the airspeed increases. The induced drag, therefore, decreases with an increase in airspeed, as shown in the typical drag curve in Figure 1-19 on Page 18.

$D = C_{D} q S$

D = induced drag in pounds
C_D = coefficient of drag from characteristic curve for the angle of attack specified
q = dynamic pressure in pounds per square foot
S = airfoil surface in square feet

Figure 1-18. *Formula for finding the induced drag, in pounds, produced by an airfoil*

Parasite Drag

Parasite drag is caused by the friction of the air flowing over the surface of an aircraft, and it increases with the airspeed. Figure 1-19 shows the way induced drag and parasite drag change with airspeed. At low airspeed, such a high angle of attack is required that the induced drag is extremely high, but the air friction, or parasite drag, is low. As the angle of attack decreases and the airspeed increases, the induced drag decreases rapidly and the parasite drag increases. At the angle of attack that produces the maximum L/D ratio, induced and parasite drag are the same. The total drag, which is the sum of induced and parasite drags, drops until the drags become equal and then rises.

As airspeed increases, the total drag increases just a little more slowly than the parasite drag until the airspeed reaches the transonic range. At this speed, the formation of shock waves on the surface, caused by compressibility, produces a rapid increase in the total drag. (See "Basic High-Speed Aerodynamics" beginning on Page 37.)

There are special forms of parasite drag. Profile drag is parasite drag produced by the skin friction as the air flows over it, and is present on an airfoil even when it is not producing lift. Form drag is the parasite drag caused by the form of the object passing through the air, and it is less a factor for streamlined bodies than for bodies that have other than streamlined shapes. Interference drag is the part of the parasite drag caused by air flowing over one portion of the airframe interfering with the smooth flow of air over another portion. Interference drag is minimized by the installation of fairings or fillets where the two surfaces or components join at an angle.

Flight at High-Lift Conditions

Airplanes need a high forward speed to produce enough lift to become airborne. Much research has gone into developing an aircraft that can maintain its lift at a low forward speed. This practical problem has, of course, been solved with the helicopter.

The coefficient of lift of an airfoil increases smoothly with the angle of attack until the critical angle of attack is reached. At this point, the air ceases to flow smoothly over the upper surface of the airfoil, and lift is lost. This condition is called a stall. *See* Figure 1-16 on Page 15.

An airplane stalls when it reaches its critical angle of attack, which can occur at almost any airspeed. If the airplane is heavily loaded, it requires such a high angle of attack for normal flight that there is very little margin left for the changes in angle of attack that occur while flying in turbulence.

Unintentional stalls and spins have plagued airplane operators since the beginning of flight. These can occur if an airplane is making a slow, high angle-of-attack approach for landing, and the pilot kicks the rudder to align the airplane with the runway. Both wings are operating at a high angle of attack, and when the rudder moves suddenly, the airplane yaws. The angle of attack of the wing moving forward is increased until this wing stalls.

compressibility effect. The sudden increase in the total drag of an airfoil in transonic flight caused by formation of shock waves on the surface.

profile drag. Aerodynamic drag produced by skin friction. Profile drag is a form of parasite drag.

form drag. Parasite drag caused by the form of the object passing through the air.

interference drag. Parasite drag caused by air flowing over one portion of the airframe interfering with the smooth flow of air over another portion.

fairing. A part of a structure whose primary purpose is to produce a smooth surface or a smooth junction where two surfaces join.

fillet. A fairing used to give shape but not strength to an object. A fillet produces a smooth junction where two surfaces meet.

spin. A flight maneuver in which an airplane descends in a corkscrew fashion. One wing is stalled and the other is producing lift.

The angle of attack of the wing moving backward is not increased and it continues to produce lift. The airplane enters a spin, and, if at low altitude, crashes.

Airplanes can also stall at high airspeeds. If an airplane is in a dive and the pilot tries to recover by pulling the control wheel back suddenly, the angle of attack will increase to the point that the airplane stalls.

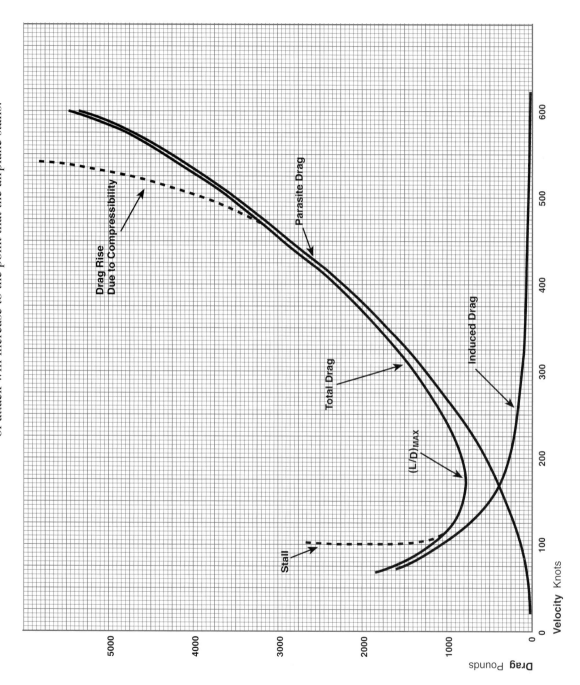

Figure 1-19. *Typical airplane drag curve*

Ground Effect

When an airplane flies at a height above the ground of less than one-half its wing span, the air forced down is deflected, which effectively increases the angle of attack without increasing the induced drag. This deflected air is called ground effect.

It is possible for the pilot to take off in a heavily loaded airplane at too low an airspeed. The decreased induced drag lets the airplane get airborne, but when the pilot climbs above the ground effect, the induced drag increases until the airplane drops back to a lower height. Pilots must drop the nose and pick up additional airspeed under these conditions, so the high angle of attack is not needed.

Effect of High-Lift Devices

An airplane can fly in a high-lift condition without stalling if the pilot can use wing flaps to modify the camber, or curvature, of the airfoil in flight. The various types of flaps are discussed in Chapter 4. The purpose of all flaps is the same: to increase the camber of the wing so it can operate with a higher angle of attack without the airflow over the top surface becoming turbulent and breaking away.

When the flaps are lowered and the camber is increased, both the lift and the drag are increased. Most flap installations are designed in such a way that the first half of flap extension increases the lift more than the drag, and partial flaps are used for takeoff. Lowering the flaps all the way increases the drag more than the lift, and full flaps are used for landing.

Boundary Layer Control

Air is viscous and clings to the surface over which it flows. At the surface, the air particles are slowed to near-zero relative velocity. Above the surface the retarding forces lessen progressively, until slightly above the surface the particles have the full velocity of the airstream. The air immediately above the surface is called the boundary layer.

Air flowing over a smooth flat surface begins, as shown in Figure 1-20, by flowing in a smooth layer-like fashion with no air particles moving from one level to another. This is called laminar flow. Friction between the air and the surface uses part of the energy in the air, and the boundary layer thickens, becomes unstable and turbulent, and creates a great deal of drag. See Figure 1-20 on the next page.

ground effect. The increased aerodynamic lift produced when an airplane or helicopter is flown nearer than a half wing span or rotor span to the ground. This additional lift is caused by an effective increase in angle of attack without the accompanying increase in induced drag, which is caused by the deflection of the downwashed air.

boundary layer. The layer of air that flows next to an aerodynamic surface. Because of the design of the surface and local surface roughness, the boundary layer often has a random flow pattern, sometimes even flowing in a direction opposite to the direction of flight. A turbulent boundary layer causes a great deal of aerodynamic drag.

laminar flow. Airflow in which the air passes over the surface in smooth layers with a minimum of turbulence.

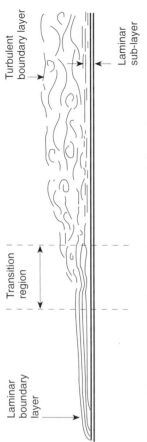

Laminar boundary layer

Transition region

Turbulent boundary layer

Laminar sub-layer

Figure 1-20. *Development of boundary layer on a smooth flat surface*

Boundary layer is studied by attaching hundreds of short tufts of wool yarn to the surface of a wing and photographing them in flight. At low angles of attack, most of the tufts lie flat against the surface and straight across the wing. But as the angle of attack is increased, some of the tufts behind the thickest part of the wing begin to wave back and forth and up and down. Some of them even wave around and point forward. These tufts show the turbulence in the boundary layer. *See* Figure 1-21.

Since a turbulent boundary layer causes a definite increase in drag and usually leads to airflow separation, much study has been made to find ways of minimizing it. Slots and slats force high-energy air from below the wing into the upper-surface boundary layer at high angles of attack. This allows for a higher angle of attack before the airflow separates. Slotted and triple-slotted flaps are used to duct high-energy air over the upper surface of the flaps when they are extended, which prevents the air separating from their surface.

A more extensive method of boundary layer control involves sucking the boundary layer from the surface so that the smooth air above it can flow nearer the surface. The wing surface has a series of small slots in its upper skin, and these slots open into a series of channels inside the wing that are connected to a suction pump. The turbulent air in the boundary layer is removed and the smooth air is pulled down to the surface.

slat. A secondary control on an aircraft that allows it to fly at a high angle of attack without stalling. A slat is a section of the leading edge of the wing mounted on curved tracks that move into and out of the wing on rollers.

slot. A fixed, nozzle-like opening near the leading edge of an airplane wing ahead of the aileron. A slot acts as a duct to force air down on the upper surface of the wing when the airplane is flying at a high angle of attack. The slot allows the airplane to fly at a high angle of attack before it stalls, and the slot is located ahead of the aileron, so the aileron will remain effective throughout the stall.

wing fences. Vertical vanes that extend chordwise across the upper surface of an airplane wing to prevent spanwise airflow.

Figure 1-21. *Tufts attached to the upper surface of these wings are used to study the boundary layer. Notice the wing fences, the dark objects parallel to the wing chord. These fences prevent the air flowing spanwise.*

Vortex Generators

Vortex generators are small low-aspect-ratio airfoils, such as those seen in Figure 1-22. They are installed in pairs on the upper surface of a wing, on both sides of the vertical fin just ahead of the rudder, and on the underside of the vertical stabilizer. They pull high-energy air down to the surface, which energizes the boundary layer and prevents airflow separation until the surface reaches a higher angle of attack.

Vortex generators are installed on the wing of an airplane ahead of the aileron in one row, about one-third of the way back from the leading edge. This is the point where the air begins to reach sonic velocity when the airplane is cruising in the transonic flight range. Another row is installed about one-third of the way forward of the trailing edge, where the air returns to subsonic speed. These generators are mounted in complementary pairs at such an angle that the vortex from one aids the vortex of its companion.

The pressure between the generators in a pair is higher than the pressure on the outside, and the air spills over and forms a tight swirl, or vortex. High-energy air is caught in the vortex and pulled down to the surface, where it energizes the sluggish boundary layer, delays the onset of shock-induced separation, and aids in maintaining aileron effectiveness at high speeds.

vortex generator. Small low-aspect-ratio airfoils installed in pairs on the upper surface of a wing, on both sides of the vertical fin just ahead of the rudder, and on the underside of the vertical stabilizers of some airplanes. Their function is to pull high-energy air down to the surface to energize the boundary layer and prevent airflow separation until the surface reaches a higher angle of attack.

vortex. *pl.* **vortices.** A whirling motion in a fluid.

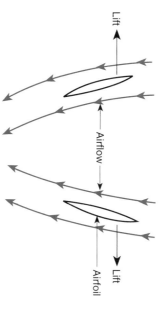

Top view

Lift

Airflow

Airfoil

Lift

Airflow

Airfoil

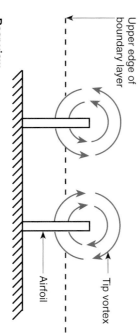

Rear view

Upper edge of boundary layer

Airfoil

Tip vortex

Figure 1-22. *Vortex generators pull high-energy air down to the surface to energize the boundary layer and reduce drag.*

Vortex generators mounted on the wings improve flight characteristics at high speed, but those on the empennage improve flight characteristics at low speed. The generators mounted on both sides of the vertical fin prevent flow separation over the rudder during extreme angles of yaw, as would occur if rudder application was delayed after an engine failure at low airspeed. Vortex generators mounted on the lower surface of the horizontal stabilizer ahead of the elevators prevent flow separation over the elevator at low airspeed.

Effect of Wing Planform

The planform of a wing is its shape as viewed from directly above, and it affects the aircraft's flight performance. The two most important characteristics of wing planform are its aspect ratio and taper.

The aspect ratio is the ratio of the length, or span, of a wing to its width, or chord. With all else equal, an increase in aspect ratio decreases the drag, especially at high angles of attack. A sailplane is a high-performance glider that operates at slow airspeed and high angle of attack, and all modern sailplanes have very high-aspect-ratio wings.

The planform also has a pronounced effect on the stall progression. Figure 1-23 shows an exaggerated view of several basic wing planforms and the way stalls progress on each. The rectangular wing has the most desirable stall progression. The stall begins at the wing root and progresses outward, so the air still flows smoothly over the ailerons when the wing loses enough lift to cause the nose to drop. The elliptical wing has the most efficient planform, because it produces the minimum amount of induced drag for a given aspect ratio. But it has two disadvantages that prevent its wide acceptance: it is difficult and expensive to construct, and the stall progression is inferior to that of a rectangular wing.

A wing with a moderate taper has many of the advantages of an elliptical wing, and is less costly to construct. Its stall characteristics are similar to those of the elliptical wing. When the taper is increased, the stall characteristics become adverse, with the stall beginning near the tip and progressing inboard. This progression causes the loss of aileron effectiveness, and thus lateral control, while lift is still being produced by the inboard portion of the wing.

Slots and Stall Strips

Some wings stall in such a way that the airflow breaks up ahead of the aileron while the wing is still producing lift. This causes a loss of lateral control. Two methods of preventing this problem have been used on small- and medium-size general aviation airplanes: slots and stall strips.

Some airplanes have a fixed slot just behind the leading edge of the wing ahead of the aileron, like that in Figure 1-24. At a high angle of attack, air flows through this slot and is forced down over the upper surface, letting the wing reach a higher angle of attack before the area ahead of the aileron stalls.

empennage. The tail section of an airplane.

yaw. Rotation of an aircraft about its vertical axis.

stall strip. A small triangular metal strip installed along the leading edge of an airplane wing near the wing root. Stall strips cause the root section of the wing to stall before the portion of the wing ahead of the ailerons stalls.

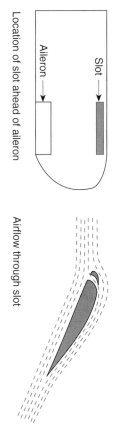

Location of slot ahead of aileron

Slot

Aileron

Figure 1-24. *A fixed slot in the leading edge of the wing ahead of the aileron forces high-energy air down over the aileron and prevents this portion of the wing from stalling before the inboard portion of the wing stalls.*

Airflow through slot

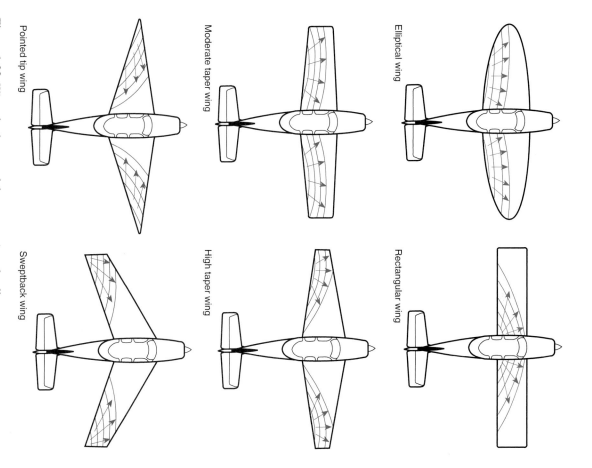

Figure 1-23. *Wing planforms and the progression of stalls*

Elliptical wing

Moderate taper wing

Pointed tip wing

Rectangular wing

High taper wing

Sweptback wing

A simpler fix for a wing that stalls in the aileron area before the root stalls is to install a stall strip, as in Figure 1-25. This is a small triangular strip of metal attached to the leading edge of the wing root. As the angle of attack increases, the stall strip disturbs the air and causes the root of the wing to stall before the tip stalls. The nose of the airplane drops before lateral control is lost.

Figure 1-25. *A stall strip forces the root of the wing to stall before the tip area stalls. This allows the pilot to have lateral control during the stall.*

Stall strip

Wing-Tip Vortices

An airplane in flight has a low pressure above the wing and a high pressure below, and some of the high-pressure air flows from the bottom to the top around the wing tip and produces a strong swirl of air called a vortex. Energy is lost in the vortices, and steps have been taken to minimize them. One effective step is the use of a high aspect ratio. Figure 1-26 shows the planforms of three wings with the same area but different aspect ratios. The low-aspect-ratio wing is the least effective, because a large percentage of its surface is in the tip loss area.

External fuel tanks mounted on wing tips and tip plates on the ends of the wings prevent air spilling over the tip and causing vortices. Winglets minimize losses due to vortex generation. Winglets, small upturned vertical surfaces mounted on the wing tips, reduce drag by reducing the spanwise flow of air, therefore reducing vortices. *See Figure 1-27.*

aspect ratio. The ratio of the length, or span, of an airplane wing to its width, or chord. For a nonrectangular wing, the aspect ratio is found by dividing the square of the span by the wing by its area.

Aspect Ratio = span² ÷ area

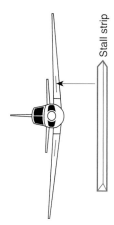

Tip loss area

Wing-tip vortices

Wing with low-aspect ratio has large percentage of its area in tip loss area, and produces strong wing-tip vortices.

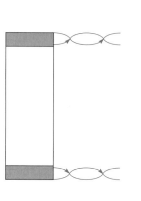

Wing with medium-aspect ratio has less tip loss area and weaker vortices.

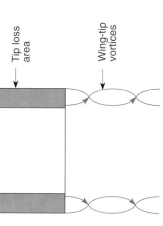

Wing with high-aspect ratio has the least tip loss area and weakest vortices.

Figure 1-26. *An increase in the aspect ratio of a wing decreases the amount of energy that is lost in wing-tip vortices.*

Figure 1-27. *Winglets extend upward from the wing tips of many modern airplanes to reduce drag and increase the L/D ratio by minimizing wing-tip vortices.*

Stability and Control

The development of the airplane was delayed by two problems: how to achieve stability and how to achieve control. Before the Wright brothers' successful flight in 1903, others had flown, but none had their success in controlling their aircraft.

"Stability" relates to maintaining the desired flight attitude with a minimum of pilot effort, and "control" involves rotating the airplane about one or more of its three axes.

Static Stability

The tendency of an aircraft to try to return to straight and level flight after it has been disturbed from this condition is called static stability.

If the nose of an airplane that has positive longitudinal static stability is forced up or down, and the controls are released, established forces bring the nose back to level flight. If the airplane has neutral static stability, the nose will stay displaced but will neither get further from its disturbed condition nor try to return to level flight. An airplane with negative static stability will deviate further from a condition of level flight and make no effort to return.

static stability. The characteristic of an aircraft that causes it to return to straight and level flight after it has been disturbed from that condition.

Positive static stability about an airplane's lateral axis causes it to return to level flight after the control has been moved to drop a wing, and then released. Positive static stability about the vertical axis causes the airplane to straighten out and point into the relative wind after a rudder pedal has been depressed and then released. Neutral and negative static stability about these axes have the same effect as they have about the longitudinal axis. *See* Figure 1-28.

Dynamic Stability

Static stability is the production of a restorative force to bring the aircraft back to a condition of straight and level flight after it has been disturbed. Dynamic stability is the decrease of these forces with time.

For example, if the nose of an airplane that has positive static and positive dynamic longitudinal stability is forced down and the control released, the nose will rise, but will go beyond level flight into a nose-up attitude. From this position, static stability will cause the nose to drop, but again it will pass through level flight to a nose-down position, although not as low as the original displacement. The oscillations caused by these restorative forces will decrease, and the airplane will return to its level-flight attitude. These oscillations are plotted in Figure 1-29.

An airplane with positive static stability and neutral dynamic stability will continue to oscillate with the same displacement. One with positive static and negative dynamic stability will have divergent oscillations, and the intensity of the oscillations will increase with time.

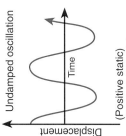

Damped oscillation

(Positive static)
(Positive dynamic)

An airplane with positive static and positive dynamic stability will oscillate with damped oscillations if it is disturbed and the disturbance is removed.

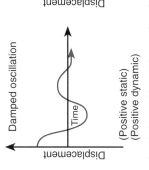

Undamped oscillation

(Positive static)
(Neutral dynamic)

An airplane with positive static and neutral dynamic stability will oscillate with an undamped oscillation.

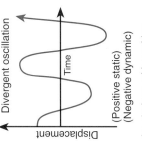

Divergent oscillation

(Positive static)
(Negative dynamic)

An airplane with positive static and negative dynamic stability will oscillate with divergent oscillation when disturbed.

Figure 1-29. *Dynamic stability*

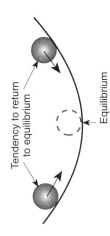

A ball has **positive static stability** when in a trough. If moved up the walls of the trough and released, it will roll back to the bottom, which is its position of equilibrium.

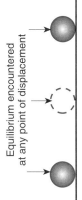

A ball has **neutral static stability** when on a flat plane. When moved from its position of displacement, it will not try to move farther away, neither will it try to return to its original position.

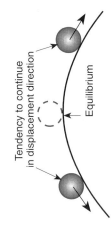

A ball has **negative static stability** when on a ridge. When released from its position of equilibrium (on the top), it will continue to move farther from its position with no added disturbance.

Figure 1-28. *Static stability*

damped oscillation. Oscillation whose amplitude decreases with time.

divergent oscillation. Oscillation whose amplitude increases with time.

undamped oscillation. Oscillation that continues with an unchanging amplitude once it has started.

Longitudinal Stability

Longitudinal stability is stability along the longitudinal axis and about the lateral, or pitch, axis. A longitudinally stable airplane will maintain level flight without requiring the pilot to continually operate the controls.

An airplane has longitudinal stability because of the relationship between its center of gravity and center of lift. Figure 1-30 shows an airplane with its center of lift behind its center of gravity (CG). The nose-down rotation that would result is counteracted by a nose-up force caused by the downward aerodynamic load on the tail.

The nose-down force caused by the CG's position ahead of the center of lift is fixed and does not change with airspeed. But the tail load is speed dependent—the higher the airspeed, the greater the downward force on the tail. If the airplane is trimmed for level flight with the pilot's hands off the controls, and a wind gust causes the nose to drop, the airplane will nose down and the airspeed will increase. As the airspeed increases, the tail load increases and pulls the nose back to its level flight condition. If the nose is forced up, the airspeed will drop off, and the tail load will decrease enough to allow the nose to drop back to level flight. *See* Figure 1-30.

Flying wing airplanes usually have a large amount of sweepback, and since they have no tail, their longitudinal stability is produced by washing out the tips of the wing. The speed-dependent downward aerodynamic force at the wing tip is behind the center of lift, and it produces the same stabilizing force as that produced by a conventional tail.

Static stability causes an airplane to return to a condition of straight and level flight when it has been disturbed from this condition. This is good for most airplanes, but not for highly maneuverable military fighter aircraft. These aircraft are designed with what is known as relaxed static stability, and have little or no static stability. The airplane must be flown at all times, an almost impossible task for the pilot. To overcome this limitation, airplanes with relaxed static stability have sophisticated electronic stability augmentation systems that compensate for the lack of natural static stability.

Longitudinal Control (Rotation About the Lateral Axis)

When an airplane is trimmed for straight and level flight at a fixed airspeed, all the aerodynamic forces are balanced and no control forces are needed. But the airplane can be rotated nose upward about its lateral axis (pitch up) by increasing the downward tail load, or nose downward (pitch down) by decreasing the tail load.

The most generally used pitch control for an airplane is the fixed horizontal stabilizer with a movable elevator hinged to its trailing edge. When the control wheel or stick is pulled back, the trailing edge of the elevator moves up and increases the down load on the horizontal tail surface. The tail moves down and rotates the airplane nose-up about its lateral axis. *See* Figure 1-31.

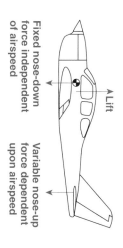

Figure 1-30. *Longitudinal stability is produced by the relationship between the center of gravity and center of lift, and by the downward aerodynamic load on the tail.*

flying wing. A type of heavier-than-air aircraft that has no fuselage or separate tail surfaces. The engines and useful load are carried inside the wing, and movable control surfaces on the trailing edge provide both pitch and roll control.

stabilator. A flight control on the empennage of an airplane that acts as both a stabilizer and an elevator. The entire horizontal tail surface pivots and is moved as a unit.

Some airplanes use a stabilator for pitch control. *See* Figure 1-32. This is a single-piece horizontal surface that pivots about a point approximately one-third of the way back from the leading edge. When the control wheel is pulled back, the leading edge of the stabilator moves down and increases the downward force produced by the tail. This rotates the nose up. When the wheel is pushed in, the nose of the stabilator moves up, decreasing the tail load, and the airplane rotates nose down.

Figure 1-31. *This airplane uses a conventional horizontal stabilizer and elevators for longitudinal stability and control.*

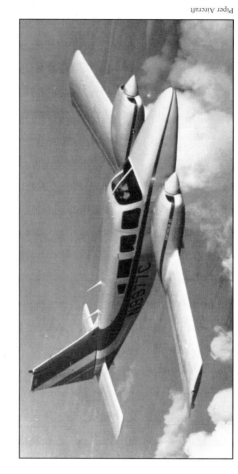

Figure 1-32. *This airplane uses a stabilator for longitudinal stability and control.*

Longitudinal control is achieved on the V-tail Beech Bonanzas with two fixed and two movable surfaces arranged in the shape of a V. Moving the control wheel in and out actuates the movable surfaces together so they act as elevators and rotate the airplane about its lateral axis. When the rudder pedals are moved, the movable surfaces move differentially and act as a rudder to rotate the airplane about its vertical axis. The movable surfaces on this type of empennage are called ruddervators.

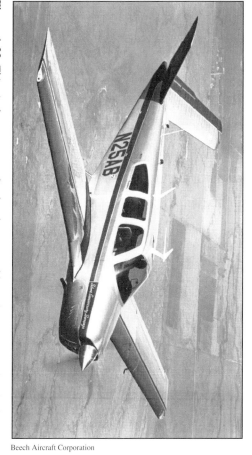

Beech Aircraft Corporation

Figure 1-33. *This airplane uses two fixed and two movable surfaces arranged in the form of a V for longitudinal stability and control*

Lateral Stability

Most airplane wings tilt upward from the fuselage, and this upward angle, called dihedral, gives the airplane lateral stability. If the airplane shown in Figure 1-34 is flying along with the pilot's hands and feet off of the controls, and a wind gust causes the right wing to drop, the air striking the descending right wing will increase its angle of attack, and the air striking the rising left wing will decrease its angle of attack. Since lift is determined by the angle of attack, the uneven lift will bring the airplane back to level flight.

Lateral Control (Rotation About the Longitudinal Axis)

Balanced aerodynamic forces cause a properly designed and trimmed airplane to fly straight and level with hands and feet off of the controls. The lift produced by the wings is equal.

ruddervators. The two movable surfaces on a V-tail empennage. When these two surfaces are moved together with the control yoke, they act as elevators, and when they are moved differentially with the rudder pedals, they act as the rudder.

dihedral. The positive angle formed between the lateral axis of an airplane and a line that passes through the center of the wing or horizontal stabilizer. Dihedral increases the lateral stability of an airplane.

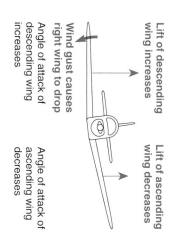

Lift of descending wing increases

Lift of ascending wing decreases

Wind gust causes right wing to drop

Angle of attack of descending wing increases

Angle of attack of ascending wing decreases

Figure 1-34. *Dihedral produces lateral stability. When the right wing drops in flight, its angle of attack increases, and the angle of attack of the left wing decreases. Increasing the angle of attack increases the lift, and the wings return to level flight.*

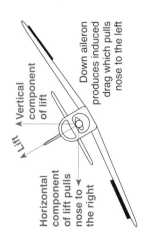

Lift

Vertical component of lift

Horizontal component of lift pulls nose to the right

Down aileron produces induced drag which pulls nose to the left

Figure 1-35. *The horizontal component of lift pulls the nose of a banked airplane around in a turn. When the bank is started, the down aileron produces enough induced drag to temporarily start the nose moving in the wrong direction.*

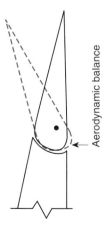

Aerodynamic balance

Figure 1-36. *A Frise aileron minimizes adverse yaw by extending the nose of the up-aileron below the lower surface of the wing to produce additional parasite drag. This counteracts the increased induced drag caused by the lowered aileron on the opposite wing.*

adverse yaw. A condition of flight at the beginning of a turn in which the nose of an airplane momentarily yaws away from the direction in which the turn is to be made.

differential ailerons. An aileron system in which the aileron moving upward deflects more than the one moving down. The additional upward movement produces enough parasite drag to counteract the induced drag caused by the lowered aileron. Differential ailerons are used to minimize adverse yaw.

When you want to roll the airplane to the right, turn the control wheel to the right. The aileron on the right wing moves up, decreasing the camber, or curvature, of the right wing and decreasing the lift it produces. At the same time, the aileron on the left wing moves down, increasing the camber of the left wing and increasing the lift it produces. The difference in lift produced by the two wings rolls the airplane to the right.

Turning Flight

An airplane is turned by rotating it about its longitudinal axis. Look at Figure 1-35. When the airplane is rolled to the right, the lift produced by the wing, which acts perpendicular to the lateral axis, now has a horizontal component that pulls the nose around to the right.

But when the left aileron moves down to increase the lift on the left wing and start the bank, it also increases the induced drag that pulls the nose to the *left*. As soon as the wing rises, the lift tilts, and its horizontal component pulls the nose around to the right as it should.

The movement of the nose in the wrong direction at the beginning of a turn is called adverse yaw. It is minimized by the use of differential aileron travel. The aileron moving upward travels a greater distance than the aileron moving downward. The extra upward travel creates just about enough parasite drag to counteract the induced drag caused by the lowered aileron. Another way to minimize adverse yaw is to use Frise ailerons, as shown in Figure 1-36. The hinge of the aileron is set back from the leading edge so that when the aileron is deflected upward, its nose extends below the bottom wing surface and produces parasite drag.

At the beginning of a turn, the rudder is used to rotate the airplane about its yaw axis to start the nose moving in the correct direction. As soon as the bank is established, the adverse yaw force disappears and the rudder is neutralized.

Many large jet transport airplanes have two ailerons on each wing and flight spoilers to assist in roll control. The outboard ailerons are locked in their faired, or streamline, position when the trailing edge flaps are up. The inboard ailerons and the flight spoilers provide enough roll control for high-speed flight, but when the flaps are lowered, the inboard and outboard ailerons work together to provide the additional roll control needed for low-speed flight.

Flight spoilers are hinged surfaces located ahead of the flaps. They are used in conjunction with the ailerons to assist in roll control. When the ailerons are deflected, the flight spoilers on the wing with the up-aileron automatically extend to decrease the lift on the wing that is moving down and to produce additional parasite drag to overcome any adverse yaw. When a large amount of aileron is used, the spoilers account for about 70% of the roll rate.

Directional Stability

Stability about the vertical axis is called directional stability, and it causes the nose of the airplane to turn into the relative wind when it has been disturbed from this condition. Directional stability is achieved primarily by the weather-vane tendency of the vertical fin. Figure 1-37 shows that when the airplane is flying straight into the relative wind, the air flows evenly around the fin, and there is no sideways force on the tail. But if a wind gust strikes the airplane and forces the nose to the right, the air striking the vertical fin gives it an angle of attack that increases the lift on the right side and pulls the tail around until the airplane is headed back into the relative wind.

An airplane's propeller forces the air to rotate around the fuselage in a corkscrew-like manner. This causes the air to strike the vertical fin in such a way that produces an angle of attack resulting in a sideways force to the right. To prevent this yawing force, most single-engine propeller-driven airplanes have the leading edge of the vertical fin offset a few degrees to the left. This places the fin directly into the relative wind when the airplane is flying at its normal cruising airspeed with the engine turning at a specific RPM.

The Effect of Sweepback

One of the problems with high-speed aerodynamics is the compressibility factor, which causes shock waves to form on the wing. With the leading edge of the wing swept back, compressibility can be delayed to a higher airspeed. But sweepback also has an effect on directional stability.

When an airplane with a swept-back wing is struck by an air gust that causes the nose to yaw to the left, as is shown in Figure 1-38, the right wing moves forward into the wind and the left wing moves back. More air is now flowing straight back across the right wing, producing more induced drag than the left wing, so the nose is pulled back to the right.

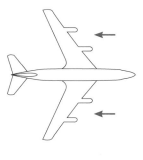

Figure 1-38. *Effect of sweepback on directional stability*

When an airplane with swept-back wings is flying straight into the wind, the lift and drag on both sides are equal.

When an airplane yaws to the left, the right wing produces more induced drag than the left, and the airplane tends to straighten into the relative wind.

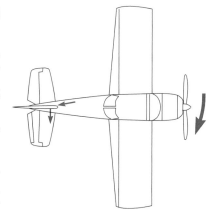

Figure 1-37. *Directional stability*

When a wind gust forces the nose to rotate to the right, air strikes vertical fin in such a direction, it creates an aerodynamic force that pulls the tail to the right and corrects the yaw.

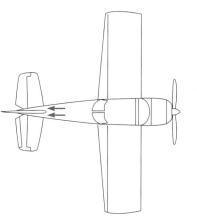

When airplane is flying straight into relative wind, air strikes both sides of vertical fin evenly and there is no force to the side.

spoilers. Flaps that may be extended from the upper surface of a wing to destroy lift. Spoilers are used on some airplanes to assist the ailerons in providing roll control and to produce drag that allows the airplane to descend at a steep angle without gaining excessive airspeed.

Dutch Roll

Sweptwing airplanes sometimes encounter a condition in which the airplane oscillates about both its longitudinal and vertical axes at the same time. This is known as Dutch roll. When the airplane is disturbed in flight in such a way that a wing drops, both the dihedral and the sweepback work together to restore the airplane to straight and level flight. But if the dihedral effect is strong with respect to the static directional stability, an oscillation is set up that is uncomfortable to the occupants. Airplanes that have this problem are usually equipped with a yaw damper, a special automatic flight control device that senses the Dutch roll and applies corrective rudder action to prevent or at least greatly attenuate it.

Dutch roll. A coupled oscillation about an airplane's lateral and vertical axes.

Directional Control (Rotation About the Vertical Axis)

The rudder is used on an airplane only to rotate it about its vertical axis. An airplane is turned by tilting the lift vector with the ailerons and not by using the rudder. The rudder is used only at the beginning of the turn to overcome the adverse yaw and start the nose moving in the correct direction and for such flight conditions as crosswind takeoffs and landings.

Some airplanes have eliminated the movable rudder entirely, and others have connected it to the aileron controls through springs so that when a turn is started, the rudder automatically moves in the correct direction.

STUDY QUESTIONS: BASIC FIXED-WING AERODYNAMICS

Answers begin on Page 58. Page numbers below refer to chapter text.

1. Lift produced by a body displacing a greater weight of air than its own weight is called _____ lift. *Page 5*

2. Lift produced by the reaction caused when a mass of air is deflected downward is called _____ lift. *Page 5*

3. The lowest layer of our atmosphere is called the _____. *Page 7*

4. The layer of our atmosphere that is typified by the temperature of the air remaining constant as the pressure continues to drop is called the _____. *Page 7*

5. The type of altitude measurement used to determine the amount of lift produced by an airfoil or the performance of an aircraft engine is _____ altitude. *Page 8*

6. The principle of physics that states that if the total energy in the air moving over an airfoil remains constant, any increase in its velocity will result in a corresponding decrease in its pressure, is called _____ principle. *Page 8*

7. The three axes about which an aircraft can rotate are:

a. _____

b. _____

c. _____

Page 9

8. The four basic forces that act on an aircraft in flight are:

a. _____

b. _____

c. _____

d. _____

Page 9

9. If the propeller shaft is above the center of gravity of an airplane, addition of power will cause the nose to pitch _____ (upward or downward). *Page 9*

10. The total lift required by an airplane in a turn must be increased to compensate for the added _____ force caused by the turn. *Page 10*

11. There are two downward forces that act on an airplane in level flight. These are caused by the weight and by the _____. *Page 10*

12. The center of pressure remains in essentially the same location as the angle of attack changes on a/an _____ (asymmetrical or symmetrical) airfoil. *Page 12*

13. Five factors that affect aerodynamic lift are:

a. _____

b. _____

c. _____

d. _____

e. _____

Page 11

14. The angle of attack at which the air no longer flows smoothly over the top of the wing and the wing stalls, is called the _____ angle of attack. *Page 14*

Continued

15. The point on the chord line of an airfoil at which all of the aerodynamic forces may be considered to be concentrated is called the _____. *Page 12*

16. Find the number of pounds of lift produced by a wing with the airfoil shown in Figure 1-16, and an area of 200 square feet, when the angle of attack is 6° and the true airspeed is 150 knots while flying at 10,000 feet. Lift is _____ pounds. *Page 16*

17. If the airspeed is doubled, with no other variable condition changing, the lift produced by an airfoil will increase _____ times. *Page 13*

18. The direction of lift produced by an airfoil is _____ (parallel or perpendicular) to the direction of the relative wind. *Page 12*

19. Interference drag, profile drag, and form drag are all types of _____ (induced or parasite) drag. *Page 17*

20. Induced drag _____ (increases or decreases) as the airspeed _____. *Page 16*

21. Parasite drag _____ (increases or decreases) as the airspeed _____. *Page 17*

22. Three types of parasite drag are:

    a. _____ drag

    b. _____ drag

    c. _____ drag

    Page 17

23. The angle of attack at which the induced and parasite drags are the same produces the _____ (maximum or minimum) L/D ratio. *Page 18*

24. The total drag produced by an airplane in flight is _____ (least or greatest) at the point at which the induced and parasite drag are the same. *Page 18*

25. An airplane stalls only when it reaches a critically _____ (low flying speed or high angle of attack). *Page 17*

26. An airplane operating in ground effect has a/an _____ (increased or decreased) induced drag. *Page 19*

27. Wing flaps allow an airplane to fly at a high angle of attack without stalling. Flaps normally _____ (increase or decrease) the camber of the wing. *Page 19*

28. The random-flowing layer of air immediately adjacent to the surface of a wing is called the _____ layer. *Page 19*

29. Vortex generators mounted on the wings of an airplane improve flight characteristics at _____ (high or low) airspeed. *Page 22*

30. Vortex generators mounted on the empennage of an airplane improve flight characteristics at _____ (high or low) speed. *Page 22*

31. The two most important characteristics of a wing planform are its _____ and its _____. *Page 22*

32. An airplane wing that operates most efficiently at a high angle of attack has a _____ (high or low) aspect ratio. *Page 22*

33. The stall begins on a rectangular wing at the _____ (root or tip). *Page 23*

34. Longitudinal stability is stability about an airplane's _____ axis. *Page 27*

35. Lateral stability is stability about an airplane's _____ axis. *Page 29*

36. Directional stability is stability about an airplane's _____ axis. *Page 31*

37. An airplane is rotated about its lateral axis by the use of its _____. *Page 27*

38. The aerodynamic load on the tail of a longitudinally stable airplane acts _____ (upward or downward). *Page 27*

39. Dihedral is used to give an airplane _____ (lateral, longitudinal, or directional) stability. *Page 29*

40. Directional stability is achieved on an airplane by the use of the _____. *Page 31*

41. An airplane has positive longitudinal static stability when its center of gravity is _____ (ahead of or behind) the center of lift. *Page 27*

Continued

42. An airplane is rotated about its longitudinal axis by the use of its _____. *Page 30*

43. The aileron moving upward to begin a turn travels a _____ (greater or lesser) distance than the aileron moving downward. *Page 30*

44. The tendency of the nose of an airplane to start to travel in the direction opposite to that desired at the beginning of a turn is called _____ yaw. *Page 30*

45. A large airplane with two ailerons on each wing uses both ailerons in _____ (low- or high-) speed flight. *Page 30*

46. When an airplane uses spoilers to aid the ailerons in roll control, the spoiler will extend on the wing with the _____ (up or down) aileron. *Page 30*

47. An airplane is rotated about its vertical axis by the use of its _____. *Page 30*

48. The leading edge of the vertical fin on most single-engine, propeller-driven airplanes is offset to the _____ (right or left). *Page 31*

49. A simultaneous oscillation about an airplane's longitudinal and vertical axes is called Dutch roll. It is minimized on many airplanes by the use of a _____. *Page 32*

50. A horizontal tail surface that combines the functions of a stabilizer and an elevator is called a/an _____. *Page 28*

51. A movable tail surface that combines the functions of a rudder and an elevator is called a/an _____. *Page 29*

52. On a large aircraft that has two sets of ailerons on each wing, only the _____ (inboard or outboard) ailerons are used when the trailing edge flaps are up. *Page 30*

53. The rudder on an airplane _____ (is or is not) used to cause the airplane to turn. *Page 30*

Basic High-Speed Aerodynamics

Compressibility

During the latter part of World War II, airplane design had advanced to the extent that a new problem arose. High-performance airplanes such as the Lockheed Lightning could attain such high speeds in a dive that, as they approached the speed of sound, the controls lost their effectiveness and in some instances developed flutter and vibration that caused the airplane to come apart in the air. There was thought to be an insurmountable sound barrier that prevented airplanes from flying faster than the speed of sound. But on October 14, 1947, Chuck Yeager, flying the Bell X-1, flew faster than sound and proved to the world that there was no such a thing as a true sound barrier.

At this speed, the air flowing over the airplane's surfaces no longer acts as an incompressible fluid, but it actually compresses and follows the laws of compressible flow.

Compressible and Incompressible Flow

When air flows at a subsonic speed, it acts as an incompressible fluid. Figure 1-39 shows the way air flowing at a subsonic velocity acts as it flows through a converging duct. The mass of air flowing through this duct remains constant at all locations. For the same mass of air to pass through the restriction in the tube, it must speed up, and as its velocity increases, its pressure decreases. As the air leaves the restriction and enters the diverging portion of the duct, it slows down to its original velocity, and its pressure rises to its original value. The density of this subsonic flow of air does not change.

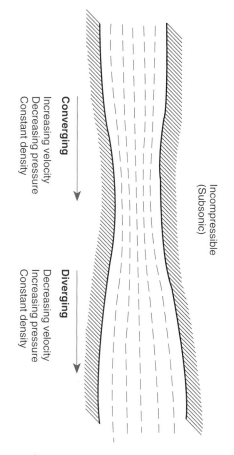

Incompressible
(Subsonic)

Converging
Increasing velocity
Decreasing pressure
Constant density

Diverging
Decreasing velocity
Increasing pressure
Constant density

Figure 1-39. *As air flows through a converging duct at speeds below the speed of sound, its velocity increases and its pressure decreases. As it leaves the restriction and enters the diverging portion of the duct, its velocity decreases and its pressure increases.*

converging duct. A duct, or passage, whose cross-sectional area decreases in the direction of fluid flow.

diverging duct. A duct, or passage, whose cross-sectional area increases in the direction of fluid flow.

When the air flows through this same converging duct at a supersonic velocity, shown in Figure 1-40, it behaves differently. It compresses and its density increases. Its velocity decreases and its pressure increases. As it flows into the diverging portion of the duct, it expands and its density decreases. Its velocity increases and its pressure decreases.

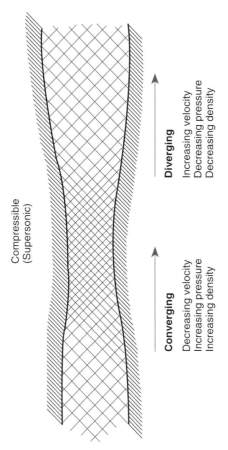

Compressible
(Supersonic)

Converging
Decreasing velocity
Increasing pressure
Increasing density

Diverging
Increasing velocity
Decreasing pressure
Decreasing density

Figure 1-40. *The flow of supersonic air through a convergent-divergent duct*

The Speed of Sound

The speed of sound is the speed at which small pressure disturbances are able to move through the air. It is determined entirely by the temperature of the air, as indicated in the chart in Figure 1-41.

High-speed flight is measured in terms of Mach number, which is the ratio of the speed of the aircraft to the speed of sound. An airplane flying at a speed of Mach 1 at sea level is flying at the speed of sound, which, according to Figure 1-41, is 661.7 knots. When it is flying at a speed of Mach .75, it is flying at 75% of the speed of sound at the existing air temperature. Airplanes that fly at these speeds have Machmeters in the cockpit that automatically compensate airspeed for the air temperature and show the pilot the Mach number at which the airplane is flying.

Altitude feet	Temperature		Speed of sound knots
	°F	°C	
Sea level	59.0	15.0	661.7
5,000	41.2	5.1	650.3
10,000	23.3	-4.8	638.6
15,000	5.5	-14.7	626.7
20,000	-12.3	-24.6	614.6
25,000	-30.2	-34.3	602.2
30,000	-48.0	-44.4	589.6
35,000	-65.8	-54.3	576.6
40,000	-69.7	-56.5	573.8
50,000	-69.7	-56.5	573.8
60,000	-69.7	-56.5	573.8

Figure 1-41. *The speed of sound in the air varies with the air temperature.*

Mach number. A measurement of speed based on the ratio of the speed of the aircraft to the speed of sound under the same atmospheric conditions. An airplane flying at Mach 1 is flying at the speed of sound.

Flight Speed Ranges

High-speed flight can be divided into four speed ranges:

Subsonic — Below Mach 0.75

All airflow is below the speed of sound.

Transonic — Mach 0.75 to Mach 1.20

Most of the airflow is subsonic, but in some areas, it is supersonic.

Supersonic — Mach 1.20 to Mach 5.00

All of the airflow is faster than the speed of sound.

Hypersonic — Greater than Mach 5.00

Subsonic Flight

In low-speed flight, air is considered to be incompressible, and acts in much the same way as a liquid. It can undergo changes in pressure without any appreciable change in its density. But in high-speed flight the air acts as a compressible fluid, and its density changes with changes in its pressure and velocity.

An airplane passing through the air creates pressure disturbances that surround it. When the airplane is flying at a speed below the speed of sound, these disturbances move out in all directions and the air immediately ahead of the airplane is affected and its direction changes before the air reaches the surface. This subsonic airflow pattern is shown in Figure 1-42.

At speeds greater than the speed of sound, the disturbances do not spread out ahead of the airplane, and there is no change in flow direction ahead of the leading edge.

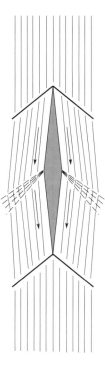

Air flowing around an airfoil at subsonic speeds deflects before it reaches the surface.

Air flowing around an airfoil at supersonic speeds is not deflected ahead of the leading edge.

Figure 1-42. *Air deflection around airfoil in flight*

subsonic flight. Flight at an airspeed in which all air flowing over the aircraft is moving at a speed below the speed of sound.

transonic flight. Flight at an airspeed in which some air flowing over the aircraft is moving at a speed below the speed of sound, and other air is moving at a speed greater than the speed of sound.

supersonic flight. Flight at an airspeed in which all air flowing over the aircraft is moving at a speed greater than the speed of sound.

hypersonic speed. Speed of greater than Mach 5 (5 times the speed of sound).

Transonic Flight

When an airplane is flying below the speed of sound in the transonic range, some of the air flowing over the airfoil has accelerated until it is supersonic and a normal shock wave forms. Air passing through this normal shock wave slows to a subsonic speed without changing its direction. The shock wave can cause the air that passes through it to be turbulent, and to separate from the wing surface. Shock-induced separation can create serious drag and control problems.

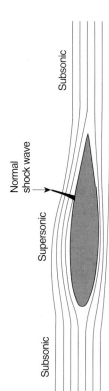

Figure 1-43. *When an airplane is flying in the transonic speed range, some air over the surface of the wing is speeded up until it becomes supersonic. A normal shock wave forms that slows the air behind it to a subsonic speed.*

Effect of Sweepback

One of the most common ways to prevent drag rise and control problems with an airplane flying in the transonic range is to sweep the wings back. Only the component of the air that flows across the wing surface perpendicular to the leading edge is involved in the production of lift. By sweeping the wing back at an angle, for example, 45°, when the airplane is flying at the speed of sound (Mach 1.0), the air flowing directly across the wing perpendicular to the leading edge is moving only at a speed of Mach 0.7. *See* Figure 1-44.

Notice in Figure 1-44 that there is a component of the air that flows in a spanwise direction. This airflow does not produce lift but it does cause problems. To minimize this spanwise flow, wing fences may be installed on the upper surface of the wing parallel to the line of flight. *See* Figure 1-21 on Page 20.

Forward-Swept Wing

The advantage gained by sweepback could also be attained by sweeping the wing forward. This has the additional advantage that the forward-swept wing stalls at the root first, eliminating the loss of lateral control experienced by a swept-back wing as it approaches a stall.

But forward-swept wings lack torsional rigidity. In other words, the wing tends to twist when high flight loads are applied. When a swept-back wing twists in flight, the wing tips wash out. Their angle of incidence, and thus the lift they produce, decreases. This decreases the load imposed on the wing. But when a forward-swept wing twists in flight, its tips wash in. Their angle of incidence increases and the loads imposed on the wing can increase until they destroy it.

normal shock wave. A shock wave that forms ahead of a blunt object moving through the air at the speed of sound. The shock wave is perpendicular to the air approaching the object. Air passing through a normal shock wave is slowed to a subsonic speed and its static pressure is increased.

angle of incidence. The acute angle formed between the chord line of an airfoil and the longitudinal axis of the aircraft on which it is mounted.

wash in. A condition in the rigging of an airplane in which a wing is twisted so that its angle of incidence is greater at the tip than at the root.

wash out. A condition in the rigging of an airplane in which a wing is twisted so that its angle of incidence is smaller at the tip than at the root.

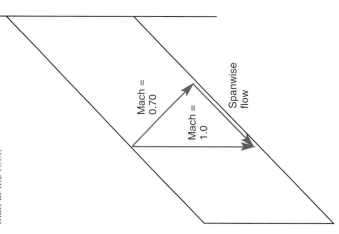

Figure 1-44. *By sweeping the wing back, the flight airspeed can be increased appreciably before the component of the air flowing directly across the wing reaches the speed of sound.*

The Grumman Corporation's new research airplane, the X-29, uses high-tech composite construction to make the forward-swept wing lightweight and so rigid that it does not twist in flight.

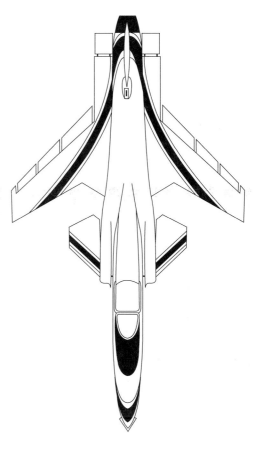

Figure 1-45. *The Grumman X-29 Advanced Technology Demonstrator exploits the advantages of the forward-swept wing because of the extensive use of composites in its aeroelastic tailoring of the wing to counteract undesirable bending stresses.*

Supersonic Airflow

When air flows over a surface at a supersonic speed, pressure waves form. There are three types of pressure waves, normal and oblique shock waves, and expansion waves.

Normal Shock Waves

Air flowing over an airfoil acts in the same way it does as it flows through a converging and diverging duct. Figure 1-46 shows that air approaching a relatively blunt-nose subsonic airfoil at a supersonic speed forms a normal shock wave, which wastes energy. When the supersonic airstream passes through a normal shock wave:

- The airstream slows to subsonic.
- The airflow direction immediately behind the wave is unchanged.
- The static pressure of the airstream behind the wave increases greatly.
- The density of the airstream behind the wave increases greatly.
- The energy of the airstream is greatly reduced.

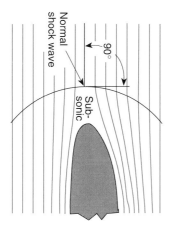

Figure 1-46. *When a supersonic airstream encounters a blunt object, a normal shock wave forms. The air immediately behind the wave is slowed to a subsonic speed.*

Oblique Shock Waves

When a supersonic airstream strikes a sharp-edged airfoil, the air is forced to turn, forming an oblique shock wave. *See* Figure 1-47. As the air passes through an oblique shock wave:

- The airstream is slowed down, but it is still supersonic.
- The flow direction changes to follows the surface.
- The static pressure of the airstream behind the shock wave increases.
- The density of the airstream behind the shock wave increases.
- Some of the energy in the airstream is converted into heat and is wasted.

oblique shock wave. A shock wave that forms on a sharp-pointed object moving through the air at a speed greater than the speed of sound. Air passing through an oblique shock wave is slowed down, but not to a subsonic speed, and its static pressure is increased.

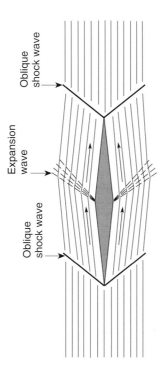

Figure 1-47. *When a sharp-edged, double-wedge airfoil moves through the air at a supersonic speed, the air is forced to turn, and oblique shockwaves form at the leading and trailing edges. At the center of the airfoil, the surface drops away from the airstream and an expansion wave forms.*

Expansion Waves

When air flows at a supersonic speed over a double-wedge airfoil like that in Figure 1-47, the air will turn to follow the surface and an expansion wave forms.

When supersonic air flows through an expansion wave:

- The airstream accelerates and the air behind the expansion wave has a higher supersonic velocity.
- The direction of flow changes to follow the surface.
- The static pressure of the airstream behind the wave decreases.
- The density of the air behind the wave decreases.
- There is no loss of energy in the airstream.

expansion wave. The change in pressure and velocity of a supersonic flow of air as it passes over a surface which drops away from the flow. As the surface drops away, the air tries to follow it. In changing its direction, the air speeds up to a higher supersonic velocity and its static pressure decreases. There is no change in the total energy as the air passes through an expansion wave, and so there is no sound as there is when air passes through a shock wave.

Answers begin on Page 58. Page numbers below refer to chapter text.

54. The speed of sound in the air is affected only by the _____ of the air. *Page 38*

55. The ratio of the speed of an airplane to the speed of sound is called _____ . *Page 38*

56. When subsonic air flows into a converging duct, its velocity
_____ (increases, decreases, or remains the same), its pressure
_____ (increases, decreases, or remains the same), and its density
_____ (increases, decreases, or remains the same).
Page 37

57. When subsonic air flows into a diverging duct, its velocity
_____ (increases, decreases, or remains the same), its pressure
_____ (increases, decreases, or remains the same), and its density
_____ (increases, decreases, or remains the same).
Page 37

58. When supersonic air flows into a converging duct, its velocity
_____ (increases, decreases, or remains the same), its pressure
_____ (increases, decreases, or remains the same), and its density
_____ (increases, decreases, or remains the same).
Page 38

59. When supersonic air flows into a diverging duct, its velocity
_____ (increases, decreases, or remains the same), its pressure
_____ (increases, decreases, or remains the same), and its density
_____ (increases, decreases, or remains the same).
Page 38

60. The velocity of air that has passed through a normal shock wave is _____
(subsonic or supersonic). *Page 41*

61. When air passes through a shock wave, its velocity is _____ (increased or decreased).
Page 41

Continued

62. When air passes through an expansion wave, its velocity is _____ (increased or decreased). *Page 42*

63. Only the component of the air flowing across the wing _____ (parallel or perpendicular) to the leading edge is involved in the production of lift. *Page 40*

64. When a forward-swept wing flexes under flight loads, the lift produced at the wing tips _____ (increases or decreases). *Page 40*

Basic Rotor-Wing Aerodynamics

The concept of rotor-wing flight was proposed as early as 1500 by Leonardo da Vinci, who made drawings and models of a "helix." The late 1800s saw several small models of helicopters that did fly, and in 1907 the French engineer Louis Breguet built a man-carrying helicopter that actually rose from the ground, but was highly unstable and had no means of control. In 1921, the U.S. Army contracted with Dr. George de Bothezat to build a helicopter, and by the end of 1922, the large four-rotor machine did actually fly.

Throughout the 1920s and well into the 1930s, hundreds of experimental helicopters were built in America and abroad with varying degrees of success. In September of 1939 Igor Sikorsky flew his VS-300, with which he solved many of the control problems that had plagued other experimenters. The VS-300 made its first flights with a main rotor and three auxiliary control rotors, but this configuration soon gave way to one main rotor and a single tail rotor, which is standard today.

Development of the helicopter was assisted greatly by the autogiro. Stall and spin accidents in fixed-wing aircraft prompted much study and experimentation aimed at finding a "safe" flying machine, and in 1920, a Spanish engineer, Juan de la Cierva, began experimenting with a rotorcraft that had unpowered rotors. An aerodynamic force produced by air flowing upward through the rotor turns it, and as it turns, it produces lift that holds the machine in the air. Cierva's first autogiro was built from an airplane fuselage with its engine and propeller. For lift, it had a freewheeling four-blade rotor mounted on a pylon above the fuselage. The propeller provided thrust to pull the machine across the ground until there was enough air flowing upward through the rotor to start it spinning. When it spun, it produced enough aerodynamic lift to raise the autogiro into the air.

The primitive autogiro had a serious fault. It would roll over in flight. In 1922 Cierva discovered that by hinging the rotor blades and allowing them to flap up and down as they rotated he could eliminate this rolling-over tendency.

autogiro. A heavier-than-air rotor-wing aircraft sustained in the air by rotors turned by aerodynamic forces rather than by engine power. When the name Autogiro is spelled with a capital A, it refers to a specific series of machines built by Juan de la Cierva or his successors.

The autogiro met with limited success, but the knowledge gained from it, especially the knowledge of flapping rotor blades, was applied to helicopter development. Many of the patents held by the Autogiro Company of America were used in early helicopters.

Aerodynamic Principles

Rotor-wing aerodynamics are more complex than fixed-wing aerodynamics for such reasons as the speed variation along the length of the rotating rotor blade, the dissymmetry of lift caused by forward flight, and the problem caused by the helicopter flying in its own downwash.

Lift, or Rotor Thrust

The lift, or thrust, produced by a helicopter rotor is similar to the lift produced by the fixed wing of an airplane. It is affected by these factors:

- The density of the air
- The square of the rotor tip speed
- The blade-lift coefficient, which is a function of the shape of the airfoil section, the blade area, and the angle of attack
- The rotor solidity

The airfoil sections used on helicopter rotors are usually symmetrical, like the one in Figure 1-48. The location of the center of pressure of a symmetrical airfoil remains relatively constant as the angle of attack changes. This is important because as the blade rotates its angle of attack constantly changes, and if the center of pressure moved, it would cause undesirable stresses and vibration.

The area used for computing the lift of a helicopter rotor system is more complex than that for a fixed-wing aircraft. The spinning rotor creates a lift-producing disc, and there are three values that are used in computing the total amount of lift: the blade area, the disc area, and the solidity ratio.

- The blade area is the area in square feet of the actual rotor blade itself.
- The disc area is the area swept by the blade as it rotates.

$$\text{Disc area} = 0.7854 \cdot \text{Blade span}^2$$

- The solidity ratio is the portion of the circular disc that is occupied by the blades, and is the ratio of the total blade area to the total disc area.

$$\text{Solidity ratio} = \text{Blade area} \div \text{Disc area}$$

The solidity ratio for a typical rotor is between 4% and 7%.

solidity. The solidity of a helicopter rotor system is the ratio of the total blade area to the disc area.

Figure 1-48. *Helicopter rotors typically use symmetrical airfoils because the center of pressure remains at a relatively constant location as the angle of attack changes.*

disc area. The total area swept by the blades of a helicopter main rotor.

The speed of a rotor blade through the air varies from its root to its tip, and it also varies with the speed of the helicopter through the air. When the helicopter is hovering in still air, the speed of the rotor blade through the air is the same on both sides of the disc.

Hovering blade tip speed = Tip speed

But when the helicopter is moving through the air, the blade that is moving in the same direction as the helicopter (the advancing blade) has a speed equal to its tip speed plus the speed of the helicopter.

Advancing blade tip speed = Tip speed + Helicopter speed

The blade moving in the direction opposite to that of the helicopter (the retreating blade) has an airspeed equal to its tip speed minus the helicopter speed.

Retreating blade tip speed = Tip speed - Helicopter speed

See Figure 1-49.

Dissymmetry of Lift

The tendency of the first autogiros to roll over when they were pulled through the air by their propellers was caused by dissymmetry of lift, which in turn was caused by the difference in airspeed between the advancing and retreating blades. Lift increases as the airspeed of the rotor increases, and the greater speed of the advancing blade gives the advancing half of the disc more lift than the retreating half. The most effective way of overcoming dissymmetry of lift is to mount the rotor blades on a hinge so they are free to flap up and down.

The advancing blade with its greater airspeed has more lift, so it flaps upward, and as it does, its angle of attack decreases and its lift decreases. The retreating blade with its lower airspeed has less lift, so it flaps downward. This increases its angle of attack and thus its lift. Rotor-flapping thus prevents dissymmetry of lift.

Torque

Newton's third law of motion states that for every action there is an equal and opposite reaction. The engine mounted in the fuselage of a helicopter drives the rotor, and the torque, or twisting movement, the engine imparts to the rotor has an equal but opposite reactive force that tries to rotate the fuselage. There are a number of ways the torque acting on the fuselage can be compensated. The engine can drive two rotors, one above the other, on concentric shafts with the rotors turning in opposite directions. The torque caused by the upper rotor is balanced by the opposite torque caused by the lower rotor. Other helicopters have two rotors mounted at an angle above the cabin and intermeshing with each other so that the torque from one rotor counteracts the torque of the other. Still other helicopters have two rotors, with one mounted on the forward end of the fuselage and the other at the aft end. By far the most

advancing blade. The blade on a helicopter rotor whose tip is moving in the same direction the helicopter is moving.

retreating blade. The blade on a helicopter rotor whose tip is moving in the direction opposite to that in which the helicopter is moving.

torque. A force that produces or tries to produce rotation.

popular configuration of helicopters uses a single main rotor, and its torque is counteracted by a small vertically-mounted rotor on the tail end of the fuselage. By changing the pitch of the tail-rotor blades with the foot pedals, the pilot can vary the amount of tail-rotor thrust to control the yaw of the fuselage about its vertical axis.

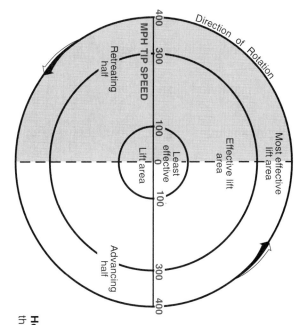

Hovering. When a helicopter is hovering, the rotor airspeed is the same on both sides of the disc.

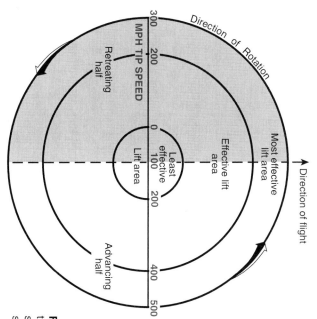

Figure 1-49. *Production of dissymmetry of lift*

Forward Flight – 100 MPH. In forward flight the airspeed of the advancing blade is its rotational speed plus the helicopter speed, while the airspeed of the retreating blade is its rotational speed minus the helicopter speed.

Autorotation

If the rotor of a helicopter is disengaged from the engine in flight, it will continue to turn and produce lift in the same way as the rotor of an autogiro. The aerodynamic force that causes this rotation is called the autorotative force, and it operates as shown in Figure 1-50.

Lift always acts perpendicular to the relative wind, and drag acts parallel to it. When air is flowing upward through the rotor of a helicopter or an autogiro, the lift vector is tilted forward, and the resultant lift is tilted ahead of the axis of rotation. The resultant lift has a horizontal component that acts forward in the plane of rotor rotation and produces an autorotative force that causes the rotor to spin. The rotor increases in speed until the drag becomes great enough to bring the resultant lift in line with the axis of rotation, and the rotor stabilizes at this speed.

Retreating Blade Stall

A rotor blade, like the wing of an airplane, stalls when its angle of attack becomes excessive. Low-speed flight of an airplane is normally limited by the stall, but the retreating blade stall of a helicopter occurs at high speed. When the helicopter is in high-speed forward flight, the advancing blade has a high airspeed and a low angle of attack, but the retreating blade has a low airspeed and a high angle of attack. When the forward speed is great enough, the angle of attack is so high that the rotor tip stalls. Increasing either the blade pitch or helicopter forward-speed causes the stall to progress inward toward the hub, and when approximately 15% of the rotor disc is stalled, the helicopter can no longer be controlled.

autorotation. Descent of a helicopter without the use of engine power. An aerodynamic force causes the rotors to rotate.

retreating blade stall. The stall of a helicopter rotor disc that occurs near the tip of the retreating blade. A retreating blade stall occurs when the flight airspeed is high and the retreating blade airspeed is low. This results in a high angle of attack, causing the stall.

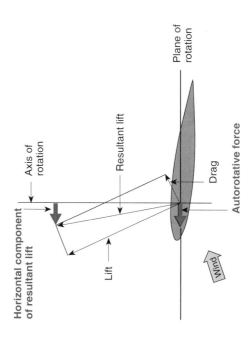

Figure 1-50. *When air flows upward through a rotor, the resultant lift has a component that acts forward in the plane of rotation and causes the rotor to spin.*

A retreating blade stall causes rotor roughness, erratic stick forces, and a stick shake whose frequency is determined by the number of rotor blades. *See* Figure 1-51.

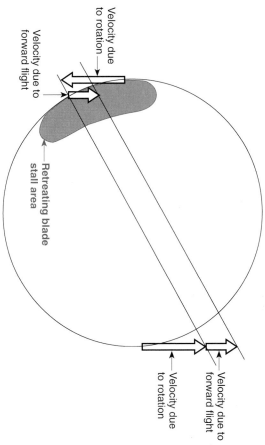

Velocity due to rotation

Velocity due to forward flight

Retreating blade stall area

Velocity due to forward flight

Velocity due to rotation

Figure 1-51. *When a helicopter is flown at a high speed, the airspeed of the tip of the retreating blade is low and its angle of attack is high. The tip of the retreating blade stalls, as is indicated by the shaded area.*

Ground Effect

It requires less power for an airplane to fly very near the surface than it does higher up, and because of the same aerodynamic principles, a helicopter can hover near the ground with less power than it can a few feet higher. This increased efficiency near the ground is caused by the phenomenon called ground effect.

When a helicopter is hovering at a height well above the ground, the downwash is not affected by the presence of the ground, and there is a vertical velocity of the air moving through the rotor disc. This vertical component, V_V, and the rotational velocity of the rotor, V_R, produce an angle of attack like that in Figure 1-52 (on the next page). But when the helicopter is hovering at an altitude of less than one-half the rotor diameter, the air strikes the ground and flows outward. This decreases its vertical velocity, and the angle of attack of the blades increases. Increasing the angle of attack for the same rotor speed increases the lift, and because the lift always acts perpendicular to the relative wind, the lift vector tilts toward the vertical.

Since a lower blade angle is used to produce the lift needed to hover, the induced drag is decreased and less power is required for the helicopter to hover. Helicopter specifications list the hover ceiling for a helicopter both in ground effect (IGE) and out of ground effect (OGE). The hover ceiling IGE is always higher than it is OGE.

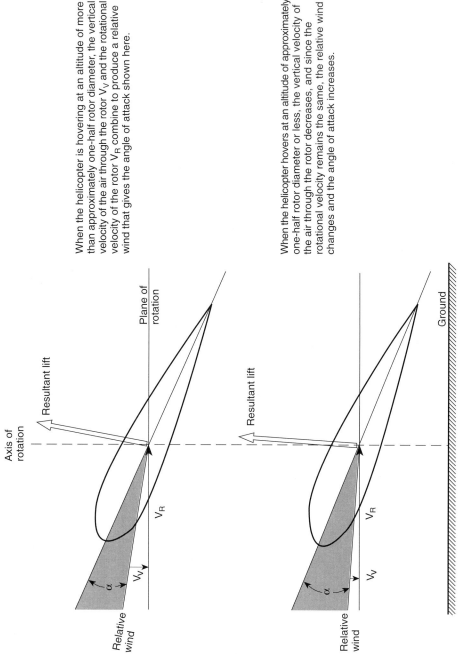

When the helicopter is hovering at an altitude of more than approximately one-half rotor diameter, the vertical velocity of the air through the rotor V_V and the rotational velocity of the rotor V_R combine to produce a relative wind that gives the angle of attack shown here.

When the helicopter hovers at an altitude of approximately one-half rotor diameter or less, the vertical velocity of the air through the rotor decreases, and since the rotational velocity remains the same, the relative wind changes and the angle of attack increases.

Figure 1-52. *Change in the angle of attack caused by ground effect*

translational lift. The additional lift produced by a helicopter rotor as the helicopter changes from hovering to forward flight.

Translational Lift

When a helicopter takes off, the pilot lifts it from the ground into a hover and then tilts the rotor disc forward with the cyclic control. The tilted lift has a horizontal component which pulls the helicopter forward. The forward motion increases the mass of air flowing through the rotor disc, and this increases the efficiency of the rotor system and the lift it produces. The increased lift caused by the beginning of forward flight is called translational lift.

Gyroscopic Precession

A gyroscope is a rapidly spinning wheel with the weight concentrated about its rim. Its spinning produces dynamic forces that are greater than the static force of gravity. One of the characteristics of a gyroscope is gyroscopic precession, which causes a force applied to the spinning wheel to be felt at a point 90° from the point of application in the direction of rotation.

The spinning rotor of a helicopter acts in the same way as a gyroscope. When the pilot wishes to tilt the rotor disc forward, the pitch of the retreating blade is increased and the pitch of the advancing blade is decreased, as shown in Figure 1-53.

gyroscopic precession. The characteristic of a gyroscope that causes it to react to an applied force as though the force were applied at a point 90° in the direction of rotation from the actual point of application. The rotor of a helicopter and the propeller of an airplane act in the same way as a gyroscope and are affected by gyroscopic precession.

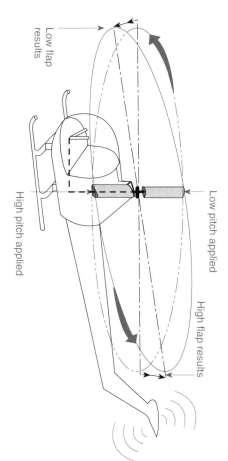

Low flap results

Low pitch applied

High flap results

High pitch applied

Figure 1-53. *The rotor of a helicopter acts as a gyroscope and is affected by gyroscopic precession. If the blade pitch is increased on the left side of the rotor, the disc will tilt forward.*

Transverse Flow Effect

In forward flight, air passing through the rear portion of the rotor disc has a higher downwash velocity than air passing through the forward portion. This is because the air passing through the rear portion has been accelerated for a longer period of time than the air passing through the forward portion. This increased downwash velocity at the rear of the disc decreases the angle of attack and the blade lift, so the lift on the rearward part of the disc is less than it is in the forward part. According to the principle of gyroscopic precession, maximum deflection of the rotor blades occurs 90° later in the direction of rotation than the force which caused it. The rotor blades will reach maximum downward deflection on the right (advancing) side and maximum upward deflection on the left (retreating) side. This transverse flow effect is responsible for the major portion of the lateral cyclic stick control required to trim the helicopter at low speed.

The unequal drag in the fore and aft portions of the disc also result in vibrations that are most noticeable at slow forward airspeeds.

Coriolis Effect

The effect that makes ice skaters spin faster when they pull in their legs or slower as they extend is called the coriolis effect. This same effect causes a rotor blade to increase or decrease its velocity in its plane of rotation as it flaps in flight.

Figure 1-54 shows the way the center of mass of a blade of a three-bladed, fully articulated rotor moves closer to the axis of rotation as the blade flaps up. As the advancing blade flaps upward, its mass moves inward, and the blade accelerates — its tip moves forward. As it flaps down on the retreating side, it decelerates — its tip moves backward. Two-bladed rotors are not so affected by the coriolis effect because they are typically underslung, and the distance between their center of mass and the rotor shaft changes less than it does with a fully articulated rotor.

Settling With Power

If a pilot tries to hover a helicopter out of ground effect at an altitude above its hovering ceiling, the helicopter descends in the turbulent air that has just been accelerated downward.

In a normal hover, all of the airflow through the rotor is downward, as seen in Figure 1-55. When the helicopter is settling with power, some air flows upward through the rotor, and this upward flow causes two sets of vortices that destroy the lift produced by the rotor.

coriolis effect. The change in rotor blade velocity to compensate for a change in the distance between the center of mass of the rotor blade and the axis of rotation of the blade as the blades flap in flight.

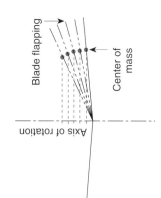

Figure 1-54. *The coriolis effect causes a rotor blade to change its velocity as its center of mass moves closer to the axis of rotation when the blade flaps in flight.*

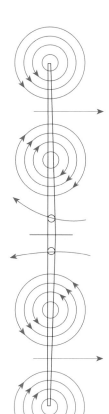

When the helicopter is hovering normally, all of the air flows downward through the rotor.

In power settling, some of the air flows upward through the center of the rotor while air is still flowing downward through the outer portion of the rotor.

The mixed airflow through the rotor causes two sets of vortices which destroy the lift.

Figure 1-55. *Airflow through a helicopter rotor during power settling*

Helicopter Flight Controls

A single-main-rotor helicopter's flight controls include the collective pitch control, the cyclic pitch control, and the antitorque pedals.

The collective pitch control changes the pitch of all rotor blades at the same time to change the total lift produced by the rotor disc. Engine power is coordinated with the collective control.

The cyclic control changes the pitch of the individual blades at a particular point in their rotation. It changes the lift around the rotor disc to tilt the disc and cause the helicopter to move forward, rearward, or to the side.

The antitorque pedals change the pitch of the tail rotor to increase or decrease its thrust to rotate the helicopter about its vertical axis.

Collective Pitch Control

The collective pitch lever is located by the left side of the pilot's seat and is operated with the left hand. This lever is moved up and down to change the pitch of all the rotor blades at the same time. Raising the collective control increases the blade pitch, the angle of attack, and the thrust, or lift, produced by the rotor disc. Increasing the angle of attack also increases the drag, and the rotor would slow down if engine power were not increased. The engine power is coordinated with the collective pitch control to increase the power when the collective pitch is increased.

Cyclic Pitch Control

The cyclic pitch control, located directly in front of the pilot and moved by the pilot's right hand, changes the pitch of the individual blades at a specific point in their rotation. This tilts the plane of the rotor disc, which gives the lift a horizontal component and pulls the helicopter in the direction the rotor is tilted. *See* Figure 1-56.

Because of gyroscopic precession, the blade pitch is actually changed 90° of blade rotation before the change is desired. For example, to tilt the rotor forward, the pitch is decreased on the advancing blade when it is at right

fully articulated rotor. A helicopter rotor whose blades are attached to the hub in such a way that they are free to flap, drag, and feather. See each of these terms;

underslung rotor. A helicopter rotor whose center of gravity is below the point at which it is attached to the mast.

collective pitch control. The helicopter control that changes the pitch of all of the rotor blades at the same time. Movement of the collective pitch control increases or decreases the lift produced by the entire rotor disk.

cyclic pitch control. The helicopter control that allows the pilot to change the pitch of the rotor blades individually, at a specific point in their rotation. The cyclic pitch control allows the pilot to tilt the plane of rotation of the rotor disk to change the direction of lift produced by the rotor.

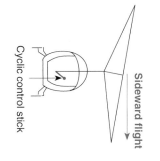

Thrust →

↑ Lift

Vertical flight

Cyclic control stick

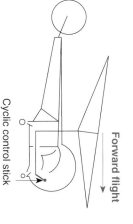

Sideward flight →

Cyclic control stick

Forward flight →

Cyclic control stick

Figure 1-56. *Moving the cyclic control changes the pitch of the main rotor blades at a point in their rotation. This tilts the rotor disc and creates a horizontal component of lift that moves the helicopter in the direction the disc is tilted.*

angles to the fuselage. On the opposite side of the helicopter, the pitch of the retreating blade is increased. These pitch changes cause the front of the rotor disc to lower and the rear of the disc to raise. *See* Figure 1-53 on Page 50.

Horizontal Stabilizer

Some helicopters have either a fixed or movable horizontal stabilizer near the tail, like the one in Figure 1-57, to hold the fuselage level in forward flight. When the cyclic pitch control is moved forward, the rotor tilts forward and the fuselage tries to follow it. Fixed horizontal stabilizers are set so that they provide the required downward force at cruise speed to keep the fuselage level and minimize the drag. Movable horizontal stabilizers are controlled by the pilot to allow the tail to rise on takeoff so the maximum amount of thrust can be used to increase the airspeed.

Antitorque Pedals

The rotor on most single-rotor helicopters rotates to the left as viewed from above. The torque reaction to this rotation causes the fuselage to rotate to the right. This torque force is compensated by thrust from the tail rotor that keeps the fuselage from rotating. The pilot controls tail rotor thrust by changing the pitch of the tail rotor blades with the antitorque pedals. *See* Figure 1-58.

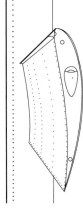

Figure 1-57. *A horizontal stabilizer on a helicopter provides a downward aerodynamic force to hold the tail down in forward flight.*

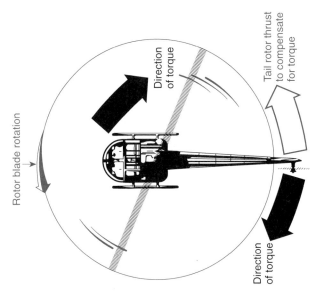

Rotor blade rotation

Direction of torque

Direction of torque

Tail rotor thrust to compensate for torque

Figure 1-58. *Torque of the engine driving the main rotor tries to rotate the fuselage to the right. This rotation is prevented by thrust from the tail rotor.*

When the pedals are in their neutral position, the tail rotor has a medium positive pitch, and the thrust from the tail rotor is approximately equal to the torque of the main rotor during cruising flight. This allows the helicopter to maintain a constant heading in level flight.

When the pilot moves the left pedal forward, the pitch of the tail rotor increases and produces additional thrust that rotates the nose to the left. When the pilot moves the right pedal forward, the pitch decreases until the tail rotor has a negative pitch. This assists the torque in rotating the nose to the right.

Sideways thrust from the tail rotor tends to pull the helicopter to the right, or causes it to drift. To counteract this tendency, the main rotor mast of some helicopters is offset to the left so that the tip-plane path has a built-in tilt that produces enough side thrust to the right to counteract the drift.

Stabilization Systems

A helicopter is statically stable, but dynamically unstable. When it is disturbed from a condition of level flight, a force is set up that tries to restore it. But this restorative force, instead of decreasing with time, increases and causes the helicopter to develop divergent oscillation.

Several types of stabilization systems have been developed to prevent this. Three commonly used systems are the stabilizer bar, the offset flapping hinge, and the electronic stability augmentation system.

Stabilizer Bar

The stabilizer bar, used for helicopters with two-blade rotors, involves two long arms with weights on their ends, mounted on a center bar so that they rotate with the rotor mast. The bar is perpendicular to the rotor blades and free to pivot with respect to the rotor mast. The weighted bar acts as a gyroscope and remains rigid in space as the helicopter pitches or rolls. *See* Figure 1-59.

The stabilizer bar continues to rotate in its original plane when the helicopter pitches or rolls. The angular difference between the stabilizer bar and the rotor mast moves the pitch change linkage in the correct direction to change the pitch of the blades and bring the helicopter back to a level flight attitude.

Offset Flapping Hinge

Moving the flapping hinge of a fully articulated rotor out away from the rotor mast, as is shown in Figure 1-60, generates stabilizing forces when the helicopter pitches or rolls. The angle of attack of the descending blade is increased and a restorative force is produced, which acts from the offset hinge and restores the helicopter to level flight. *See* Figure 1-60 on the next page.

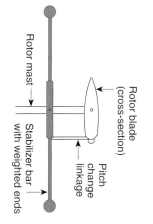

Rotor mast →

Rotor blade (cross-section)

Stabilizer bar with weighted ends

Pitch change linkage

When the rotor mast is vertical, no corrective pitch change is made.

Figure 1-59. *Stabilization with a stabilizer bar*

When the helicopter tilts, the stabilizer bar remains in a horizontal plane, and the blade pitch is changed to produce a force that restores the helicopter to level flight.

Offsetting the flapping hinge from the center of the mast increases the corrective action produced by the flapping rotor.

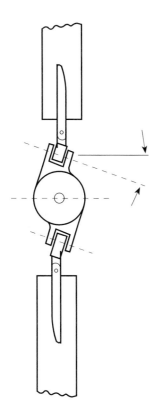

Angling the flapping hinge increases the stabilizing effect.

Figure 1-60. *Stabilization with offset and angled flapping hinges*

Electronic Stability Augmentation System

Many high-performance helicopters use an electronic stability augmentation system that senses any motion from the desired flight condition and feeds a signal back into the aircraft control system, restoring the helicopter to the desired flight attitude. A simplified block diagram of a stability augmentation system is shown in Figure 1-61.

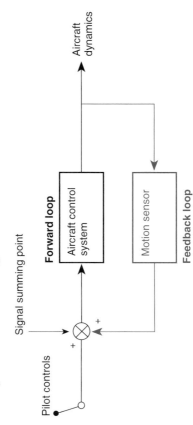

Figure 1-61. *Block diagram of a stability augmentation system*

Answers begin on Page 58. Page numbers below refer to chapter text.

65. The rotor blade on the side of a helicopter that is moving in the same direction the helicopter is moving is called the _____ blade. *Page 46*

66. The rotor blade on the side of a helicopter that is moving in the opposite direction to that of the helicopter called the _____ blade. *Page 46*

67. Helicopter rotor blades are mounted on flapping hinges to overcome the effect of _____ . *Page 46*

68. The retreating blade of a helicopter will stall when the helicopter airspeed is too _____ (high or low). *Page 48*

69. The stall of a helicopter rotor blade caused by the high angle of attack on the retreating blade begins at the _____ (hub or tip) of the blade. *Page 48*

70. When a helicopter is hovering in ground effect, the induced drag is _____ (greater or less) than it is when hovering outside of ground effect. *Page 50*

71. In order to tilt the rotor disc of a helicopter forward, the pitch of the _____ (advancing or retreating) blade is increased. *Page 51*

72. The coriolis effect causes the rotor blades to move _____ (back and forth or up and down). *Page 52*

73. The coriolis effect is most noticeable on _____ (two or three) -blade rotor systems. *Page 52*

74. When a helicopter hovers normally, the air flows _____ (upward or downward) through the rotor. *Page 52*

75. Drift caused by thrust of the tail rotor is compensated on some helicopters by tilting the main rotor a few degrees to the _____ (right or left). *Page 55*

76. The pitch of the rotor blades is changed at a particular point in their rotation by the _____ (collective or cyclic) pitch control. *Page 53*

Continued

77. The pitch of all the rotor blades is changed at the same time by the _____ (collective or cyclic) pitch control. *Page 53*

78. A helicopter usually has positive static stability and _____ (positive or negative) dynamic stability. *Page 55*

Answers to Basic Aerodynamics Study Questions

1. aerostatic
2. aerodynamic
3. troposphere
4. stratosphere
5. density
6. Bernoulli's
7. a. longitudinal
   b. lateral
   c. vertical
8. a. thrust
   b. lift
   c. drag
   d. weight
9. downward
10. centrifugal
11. tail load
12. symmetrical
13. a. shape of the airfoil
    b. area of the airfoil
    c. air density
    d. speed of the air relative to the surface
    e. angle of attack
14. critical
15. center of pressure
16. 5,520
17. 4
18. perpendicular
19. parasite
20. decreases
21. increases

22. a. form
    b. profile
    c. interference
23. maximum
24. least
25. high angle of attack
26. decreased
27. increase
28. boundary
29. high
30. low
31. aspect ratio, taper
32. high
33. root
34. lateral
35. longitudinal
36. vertical
37. elevators
38. downward
39. lateral
40. vertical fin
41. ahead of
42. ailerons
43. greater
44. adverse
45. low
46. up
47. rudder
48. left
49. yaw damper
50. stabilator
51. ruddervator

52. inboard
53. is not
54. temperature
55. Mach number
56. increases, decreases, remains the same
57. decreases, increases, remains the same
58. decreases, increases, increases
59. increases, decreases, decreases
60. subsonic
61. decreased
62. increased
63. perpendicular
64. increases
65. advancing
66. retreating
67. dissymmetry of lift
68. high
69. tip
70. less
71. retreating
72. back and forth
73. three
74. downward
75. left
76. cyclic
77. collective
78. negative

METALLIC AIRCRAFT STRUCTURES

2

Aircraft Welding **138**

METALLIC AIRCRAFT STRUCTURES

2

Sheet-Metal Aircraft Construction

The first airplanes were made with a truss structure of wood or bamboo, and the lifting and control surfaces were covered with cotton or linen fabric. This structure was lightweight, but difficult to streamline. When aircraft speeds increased to the extent that streamlining became important, the structure had to be modified, and in the late 1920s the molded-plywood monocoque structure used on the record-setting Lockheed airplanes were state-of-the-art. The next logical step in the evolution of aircraft structure was to make the monocoque structure of thin sheet metal instead of plywood. This reduced the weight and allowed mass-production of aircraft.

Aluminum alloy was the logical choice of metal for this new type of construction. Pure aluminum is weak, but during World War I, the Germans discovered that by alloying aluminum with copper, manganese, and magnesium, they could increase its strength without increasing its weight. This new alloy was called Duralumin, and it was the forerunner of the high-strength and lightweight alloys that we use in aircraft construction today.

Types of Metal Structure

To take the maximum advantage of metal, most aircraft structure is of the stressed-skin type. There are two types of metal stressed skin: monocoque and semimonocoque.

Monocoque Structure

The name monocoque means single shell, and in a true monocoque structure, all the strength of the structure is carried in the outside skin. Figure 2-1 shows a simplified view of a monocoque structure. The bulkhead and formers give the structure its shape, but the thin metal skin riveted to them carries all the flight loads.

Semimonococque Structure

Pure monocoque structure has the serious drawback that any dent or deformation will decrease its ability to carry the flight loads. To overcome this limitation, semimonococque structure as seen in Figure 2-2 is widely used. In this type of structure, bulkheads and formers still provide the shape, and the

monocoque structure. A type of structure that carries all of the stresses in its outside skin.

Duralumin. The name for the original alloy of aluminum, magnesium, manganese, and copper. Duralumin is the same as the modern 2017 aluminum alloy.

stressed skin structure. A type of aircraft structure in which all or most of the stresses are carried in the outside skin. A stressed skin structure has a minimum of internal structure.

semimonococque structure. A form of aircraft stressed skin structure. Most of the strength of a semimonococque structure is in the skin, but the skin is supported on a substructure of formers and stringers that give the skin its shape and increase its rigidity.

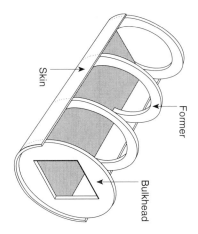

Skin

Former

Bulkhead

Figure 2-1. *A true monocoque structure has bulkheads and formers to give the structure its shape, but all of the flight loads are carried in the thin sheet metal skin.*

majority of the flight loads are carried in the skin, but stringers are installed across the formers to reinforce the skin and prevent its deforming under normal operational loads.

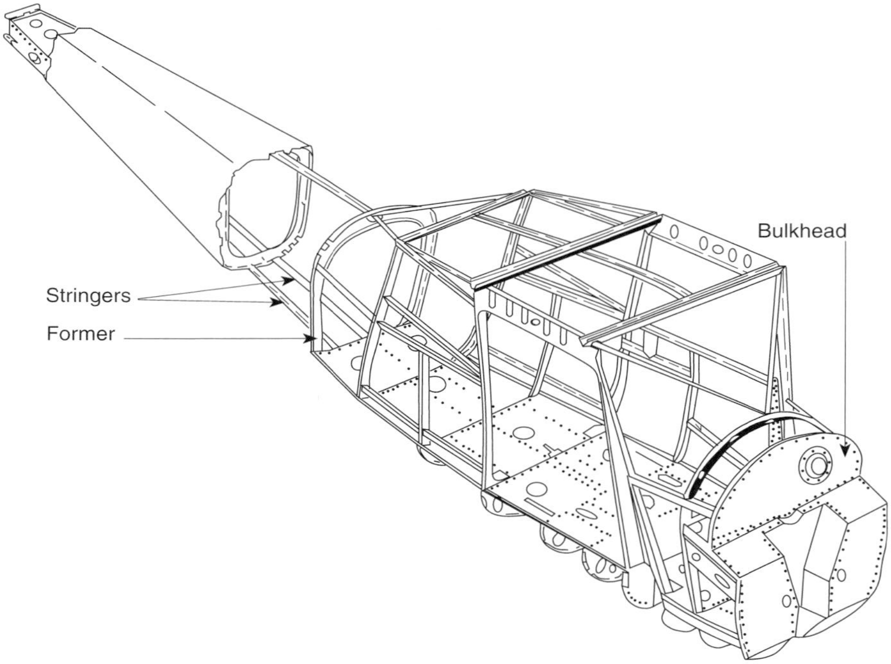

Figure 2-2. *A semimonocoque structure carries the flight loads in its outer skin, but this thin skin is backed up with stringers that extend across the formers.*

Reinforced Shell Structure

The reinforced shell structure such as the one in Figure 2-3 elaborates on the semimonocoque structure. This is the most commonly used structure in modern all-metal aircraft. The shape is provided by bulkheads, formers, and stringers, but this structure is reinforced with longerons that help carry the loads. A sheet-metal skin riveted over the structure carries a major portion of the flight loads.

bulkhead. A structural partition that divides the fuselage of an aircraft into compartments, or bays.

former. An aircraft structural member used to give a fuselage its shape.

stringer. A part of an aircraft structure used to give the fuselage its shape and, in some types of structure, to provide a small part of the fuselage strength.
Formers give the fuselage its cross-sectional shape and stringers fill in the shape between the formers.

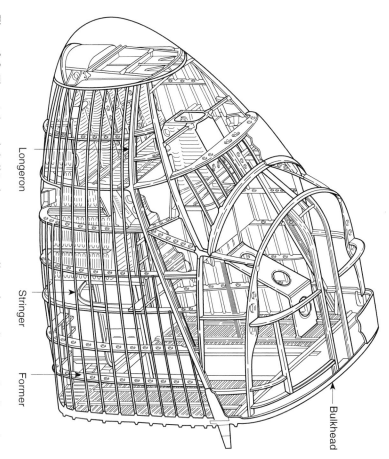

Figure 2-3. *The reinforced shell is the most generally used type of construction for modern all-metal aircraft.*

Longeron

Stringer

Former

Bulkhead

Stresses Acting on an Aircraft Structure

Aircraft are unique in their structural requirements. They must be lightweight and at the same time withstand flight loads, landing loads, and a wide range of vibration. In this study of all-metal structure, we will consider the five basic stresses that act on all physical objects: tension, compression, torsion, bending, and shear. Tension and compression are the basic stresses and the other three are combinations of these two.

A stress is a force that is set up within an object that tries to prevent an outside force changing its shape. A strain is a deformation or a physical change caused by a stress.

A material that is strained within its elastic limit will return to its original size and shape after the stress is removed, but if it has been strained beyond this limit, it will be permanently deformed.

stress. A force set up within an object that tries to prevent an outside force from changing its shape.

strain. A deformation or physical change in a material caused by a stress.

elastic limit. The maximum amount of tensile load, in pounds per square inch, a material is able to withstand without being permanently deformed.

Tension (Tensile Stress)

Tension tries to pull an object apart. Consider the hoist in Figure 2-4. The chain is under tension, or more properly stated, it has a tensile stress in it.

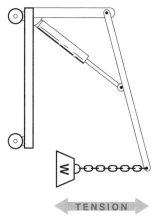

Figure 2-4. *The chain on this hoist has a tensile stress in it.*

W

TENSION

Compression (Compressive Stress)

Compression tries to squeeze the ends of an object together. The rivet in Figure 2-5 is distorted or strained by a compressive stress between the rivet gun and the bucking bar.

Torsion (Torsional Stress)

Torsion is a combination of tension and compression acting in the same object. The shaft in Figure 2-6 has a tensile stress and a compressive stress acting at 90° to each other, and they are both acting at 45° to the shaft. Propeller shafts and helicopter rotor shafts are both subjected to torsional stresses.

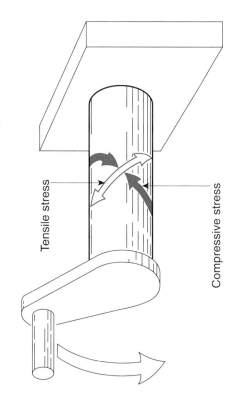

Tensile stress

Compressive stress

Figure 2-6. *This shaft is subjected to a torsional stress, which is made up of a compressive and a tensile stress.*

Bending

Bending is also made up of tension and compression. The wing of the airplane in Figure 2-7 is under a bending stress. When the airplane is on the ground, the top skin of the wing is under a tensile stress and the bottom skin is under a compressive stress. In flight these forces are the opposite. The top skin is under a compressive stress and the bottom skin is under a tensile stress.

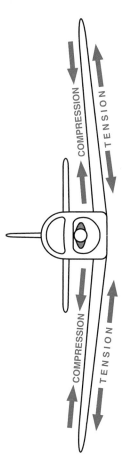

COMPRESSION

TENSION

COMPRESSION

TENSION

Figure 2-7. *In flight, the top of the wing of this airplane is under a compressive stress and the bottom is under a tensile stress. These two stresses make up the bending stress.*

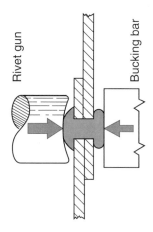

Rivet gun

Bucking bar

Figure 2-5. *The rivet shown here is strained by the compressive stress put into it when the rivet gun hammers it against the bucking bar.*

bucking bar. A heavy steel bar with smooth, hardened surfaces, or faces. The bucking bar is held against the end of the rivet shank when it is driven with a pneumatic rivet gun, and the shop head is formed against the bucking bar.

Shear

A shear stress tries to slide an object apart. The clevis bolt in Figure 2-8 is subject to a shear stress. The force on the cable puts a tensile stress in the clevis bolt toward the right while the fixed fitting puts a tensile stress into the bolt toward the left. These two tensile stresses act beside each other rather than opposite each other, and the result is a force that tries to shear the bolt, or to slide it apart.

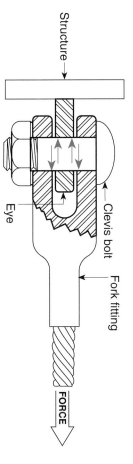

Figure 2-8. *A shear stress tries to slide the clevis bolt apart as a load is applied to the cable.*

STUDY QUESTIONS: SHEET METAL AIRCRAFT CONSTRUCTION

Answers begin on Page 167. Page numbers refer to chapter text.

1. A stressed skin structure that is made in the form of a single shell with all of its strength in its outer skin is called a _____ structure. *Page 65*

2. A structure that has most of its strength in its outer skin, but supports this skin with stringers across the formers is called a _____ structure. *Page 65*

3. The five basic stresses to which a structure can be subjected are:

    a. _____
    b. _____
    c. _____
    d. _____
    e. _____

    Page 67

4. A force that is set up within an object that tries to prevent an outside force changing its shape is called a/an _____ . *Page 67*

5. A deformation within a material caused by a stress is called a/an _____ . *Page 67*

6. A material will return to its original size and shape after a stress is removed if it has not been stressed beyond its _____ . *Page 67*

Materials for Metal Aircraft Construction

The various metals used in aircraft construction are discussed in Chapter 7 of the *General* textbook of this *Aviation Maintenance Technician Series*.

Nonferrous Metals

Aluminum alloys are the most widely used nonferrous metal in aircraft construction. In this section, these alloys are discussed along with magnesium and its alloys, and titanium.

Aluminum Alloys

Aluminum is a lightweight metal, but it does not have sufficient strength to be used as a structural material. Pure aluminum alloyed with other metals is much stronger. Aluminum alloys are susceptible to corrosion, but their high strength and light weight make them a metal of choice.

Aluminum Alloy Designation and Characteristics

Copper was the first metal used as the primary alloying element for aluminum, and copper alloys are still the most widely used. Other elements are used, as in Figure 2-9. The alloy is identified by a four-digit number with the following significance:

    First digit — Alloy type
    Second digit — Modification of alloy
    Third and fourth digits — Purity of aluminum*

*The last two digits are also used for the old designation of alloys in use before the adoption of the four-digit system.

Alloy 1100 is a low-strength, commercially pure aluminum that can be used only in non-structural applications where strength is not important.

Alloy 2024 is the most popular structural aluminum alloy.

Alloy 3003 is similar to 1100 and is used for the same types of applications. It is non-heat-treatable, but can be hardened by cold-working.

Alloy 5052 is used for welded applications such as fuel tanks and rigid fluid lines.

Alloy 6061 is used in applications where heat-treatability, ease of forming, medium strength, and good corrosion resistance are needed.

Alloy 7075 is used for high-strength structural requirements.

Heat-Treatable Alloys

Aluminum alloys are divided into two basic categories, those that can be hardened by heat and those that cannot. Both can be softened by annealing. The most widely used heat-treatable alloys are 2024, 6061, and 7075 for sheet metal, and 2017, 2117, and 2024 for rivets.

Alloy Type	Group
Aluminum 99+% pure	1xxx
Copper	2xxx
Manganese	3xxx
Silicon	4xxx
Magnesium	5xxx
Magnesium and silicon	6xxx
Zinc	7xxx

Figure 2-9. *Identification of aluminum alloys*

Solution Heat Treatment

Heat-treatable alloys are hardened by heating them in a furnace until they have reached a specified temperature throughout and immediately quenching them in water. The metal gains hardness and strength over a period of several days through the process called aging.

During the aging process, some of the soluble constituents precipitate from the supersaturated solid solution, and the strength of the material increases. The submicroscopic particles that are precipitated act as locks between the grains that resist internal slippage and distortion when a load of any type is applied.

In the process of heat-treating, the grain size is reduced when the metal is hot, and it grows as the metal cools. For maximum strength the metal must be quenched immediately after it is taken from the oven so it will have the smallest grain size possible. If there is a delay between the time the metal is removed from the oven and the time it is quenched, the grains will grow large enough for the metal to become susceptible to intergranular corrosion that forms along the grain boundaries within the metal.

Precipitation Heat Treatment

When an aluminum alloy has been solution heat-treated, it gains its full hardness and strength by natural aging, but this strengthening process may be speeded up and increased by returning the metal to the oven and heating it to a temperature much lower than that used for solution heat treatment. It is held at this temperature for up to 24 hours and then removed from the oven and allowed to cool in still air. This precipitation hardening, or artificial aging, greatly increases the strength and hardness of the metal, but it decreases the ductility; the metal becomes more difficult to bend and form.

Figure 2-10 lists the heat treatment temperatures and times for the most popular aluminum alloys.

Alloy	Solution Heat-Treatment			Precipitation Heat-Treatment		
	Temperature °F	Quench	Temper Designation	Temperature °F	Time of Aging	Temper Designation
2017	930-950	Cold water	T4			T
2117	930-950	Cold water	T4			T
2024	910-930	Water	T4			T
6061	960-980	Water	T4	315-325	18 hour	T6
				345-355	8 hour	T6
7075	870	Water		250	24 hour	T6

Figure 2-10. *Typical temperatures for heat treatment of various aluminum alloys*

solution heat treatment. A type of heat treatment for nonferrous metals in which the metal is heated in a furnace until it has a uniform temperature throughout. It is then removed and quenched in cold water.

When the metal is hot, the alloying elements enter into a solid solution with the base metal to become part of its basic structure. When the metal is quenched, these elements are locked into place.

aging. A change in the characteristics of a material with time.

Certain aluminum alloys do not have their full strength when they are first removed from the quench bath after they have been heat-treated, but they gain this strength after a few days by the natural process of aging.

precipitation heat treatment. A method of increasing the strength of heat-treated aluminum alloy. After the aluminum alloy has been solution-heat-treated by heating and quenching, it is returned to the oven and heated to a temperature lower than that used for the initial heat treatment. It is held at this temperature for a specified period of time and then removed from the oven and allowed to cool slowly.

ductility. The property of a material that allows it to be drawn into a thin section without breaking.

Annealing

Some aluminum alloys can be hardened by heat treatment while others can be hardened only by cold-working. But both types can be annealed, or softened, by heating them in an oven to a specified temperature and then cooling them slowly in the furnace or in still air. Annealing leaves the metal soft, but in its weakest condition.

Aluminum Alloy Temper Designations

The temper of an aluminum alloy is noted by a letter that follows the alloy designation. *See* Figure 2-11.

F — The metal is left as fabricated There has been no control over its temper.
T — The metal may be heat treated.
  T3 — solution heat treatment, followed by strain hardening. A second digit, if used, indicates the amount of strain hardening.
  T4 — solution heat treatment, followed by natural aging at room temperature.
  T6 — solution heat treatment, followed by artificial aging (precipitation heat treated).
  T7 — solution heat treatment, followed by stabilization.
  T8 — solution heat treatment, followed by strain hardening and then artificial aging.
  T9 — solution heat treatment, followed by artificial aging and then strain hardening.
H — The metal cannot be heat treated, but can be hardened by cold working.
  H1 — strain hardened by cold working.
    H12 — strain hardened to its 1/4-hard condition.
    H14 — strain hardened to its 1/2-hard condition.
    H18 — strain hardened to its full hard condition.
    H19 — strain hardened to its extra hard condition.
  H2 — strain hardened by cold working and then partially annealed.
  H3 — strain hardened and stabilized.
    H36 — strain hardened and stabilized to its 3/4-hard condition.
O — The metal has been annealed.

Figure 2-11. *Temper designations of aluminum alloys*

Nonheat-Treatable Alloys

Certain alloys, such as 3003 and 5052, cannot be hardened by heat treatment, but are hardened by cold-working. When these alloys are formed into sheets in the rolling mill, their strength and hardness are increased. The amount of this increase is indicated by their temper designation, as in Figure 2-11.

Nonheat-treatable alloys can be softened by annealing. When a sheet of 5052 aluminum alloy is formed by hammering or spinning, it gets hard and is likely to crack. If further working must be done, the metal may be annealed by heating it in an oven to a temperature slightly higher than is used for hardening and allowing it to cool very slowly.

Corrosion Protection of Aluminum Alloys

Pure aluminum is relatively corrosion resistant, but when it is alloyed with other elements to give it strength, it loses this resistance. The most efficient way to protect aluminum alloys from corrosion is to cover their surfaces with something that prevents air or moisture from contacting the alloy. There are

Cladding

Aluminum alloy sheets to be used as the outside skin of an aircraft can be protected from corrosion and given an attractive finish by covering a layer of pure aluminum on both of their surfaces. This resulting material is called clad aluminum and is available under such registered trade names as Alclad and Pureclad. The pure aluminum coating is about 2½ to 5% of the thickness of the alloy sheet, and it decreases the strength of the sheet somewhat, as indicated in Figure 2-14 on Page 75.

Pure aluminum cladding does not corrode, but an airtight oxide film forms on its surface and prevents any oxygen or moisture from reaching the metal. The alloy sheet is protected as long as the cladding is not scratched through.

Oxide-Film Protection

A hard, airtight oxide film may be deposited on the surface of aluminum alloy sheets by either an electrolytic or a chemical action. The electrolytically deposited film is called an anodized film. The chemically deposited film is called a conversion coating, sometimes called Alodizing after one of the popular chemicals used to form the film. Alodine. These oxide films not only protect the metal, but provide a slightly rough surface that makes it possible for a paint film to adhere.

Enamel or Lacquer Coating

Airplanes may be given an attractive and protective finish by covering the metal with a coating of enamel or lacquer. Before this type of finish will adhere to the metal, the surface must be prepared, usually with a primer. The most commonly used primers are zinc chromate, wash primer, and epoxy primer. All have special characteristics discussed in the section on "Aircraft Painting and Finishing," beginning on Page 212.

Magnesium Alloys

Magnesium alloys are lighter in weight than aluminum alloys and are used as structural materials when weight is a deciding factor. These alloys do have serious drawbacks, however. They are more reactive than aluminum alloys and are thus more susceptible to corrosion, and they are more brittle and thus more likely to crack. When a part is properly designed and the metal is protected against corrosion, it is useful as an aircraft structural material.

three ways to do this: roll a thin coating of pure aluminum on the alloy sheet; form a hard, airtight oxide coating on the surface of the metal; or cover the surface with a film of enamel or lacquer.

clad aluminum. A sheet of aluminum alloy that has a coating of pure aluminum rolled on one or both of its surfaces for corrosion protection.

Alclad. A registered trade name for clad aluminum alloy.

Pureclad. A registered trade name for clad aluminum alloy.

anodizing. The electrolytic process in which a hard, airtight, oxide film is deposited on aluminum alloy for corrosion protection.

Alodine. The registered trade name for a popular conversion coating chemical used to produce a hard, airtight, oxide film on aluminum alloy for corrosion protection.

Titanium

Titanium is expensive and difficult to work, but its ability to retain its strength when exposed to high temperatures has made it a popular material for the construction of high-performance turbine-powered aircraft.

Titanium is heavier than aluminum, but is much stronger, and it is lighter than steel of equivalent strength. Special techniques must be used when forming, drilling, or cutting titanium.

Ferrous Metals

Metals that contain iron are called ferrous metals, and most ferrous metals used in aircraft construction are some form of steel, which is iron with a specific amount of carbon and other alloying elements added.

Alloy Steels

Steel alloyed with such elements as molybdenum, chromium, tungsten, nickel, and vanadium is used in aircraft engines and landing gears, and for fittings where high strength is needed.

Corrosion-Resistant Steel

Corrosion-resistant steel is sometimes called stainless steel, and is used in thin sheets for engine firewalls and exhaust system components. The main alloying elements in this steel are chromium and nickel.

Strength of Metal Structural Materials

The strength of a metal is measured in pounds per square inch of tensile strength, and there are several types of strength.

The elastic limit, or yield strength, of a material is the maximum amount of tensile load, in pounds per square inch, a material is able to withstand without being permanently deformed. Any time a material is loaded to less than its elastic limit and the load is released, it will return to its original size and configuration.

When a piece of metal is put into a tensile testing machine and a load is applied, the metal will stretch in direct proportion to the amount of the load until its elastic limit is reached. At this point it will continue to stretch without the load being increased. When the metal stretches, its molecular structure rearranges and it becomes harder and stronger, but it will not return to its original configuration after the load is removed. If the load is increased still further, the metal will pull apart when its ultimate tensile strength is reached.

The tensile strength of steel is directly related to its hardness, and can be determined by measuring its hardness with a Rockwell hardness tester, as is described in the General textbook of this *Aviation Maintenance Technician Series*. Figure 2-12 shows the relationship between the hardness and tensile strength of steel in the range that is normally used in aircraft structure.

ferrous metal. Any metal that contains iron and has magnetic characteristics.

Rockwell C-Scale Hardness Number	Tensile Strength 1,000 psi (approximate)
50	245
49	239
48	232
47	225
46	219
45	212
44	206
43	201
42	196
41	191
40	186
39	181
38	176
37	172
36	168
35	163
34	159
33	154
32	150
31	146
30	142
29	138
28	134
27	131
26	127
25	124
24	121
23	118
22	115
21	113
20	110

Figure 2-12. *Relationship between hardness and tensile strength of steel*

The strength of aluminum alloys does not relate directly to its hardness because of the effect of the alloys. But when you know the alloy and its hardness, you can determine its temper, and by reference to a chart such as the one in Figure 2-14, find its tensile strength.

For example, if a piece of 2024 aluminum alloy has a Brinell number of 120, a check of the chart in Figure 2-13 shows that this is the hardness of 2024 in its T3 state. The table in Figure 2-14 shows that 2024-T3 aluminum alloy has an ultimate tensile strength of 70,000 pounds.

Alloy Number	Hardness Temper	Brinell Number 500 kg load 10 mm ball
1100	O H18	23 44
2014	O T6	45 135
2024	O T3	47 120
3003	O H16	28 47
5052	O H36	47 73
6061	O T4 T6	30 65 95
7075	O T6	60 150

Figure 2-13. *Brinell hardness number for various aluminum alloys*

Alloy and Temper	Minimum Ultimate Tensile Strength psi
1100-O 1100-H18	13,000 24,000
2014-O 2014-T6	27,000 70,000
2024-O 2024-O Alclad 2024-T3 2024-T3 Alclad	27,000 26,000 70,000 65,000
3003-O 3003-H16	16,000 26,000
5052-O 5052-H36	28,000 40,000
6061-O 6061-T4 6061-T6	18,000 35,000 45,000
7075-O 7075-O Alclad 7075-T6 7075-T6 Alclad	33,000 32,000 83,000 76,000

Figure 2-14. *Minimum ultimate tensile strength of various aluminum alloys*

yield strength. The amount of stress needed to permanently deform a material.

ultimate tensile strength. The tensile strength required to cause a material to break or to continue to deform under a decreasing load.

shear strength. The strength of a riveted joint in a sheet metal structure in which the rivets shear before the metal tears at the rivet holes.

bearing strength. The amount of pull needed to cause a piece of sheet metal to tear at the points at which it is held together with rivets. The bearing strength of a material is affected by both its thickness and the diameter of the rivet.

Bearing and Shear Strength

A riveted joint in a piece of sheet aluminum alloy must be designed so it will fail by the rivet shearing rather than the sheet of metal tearing. By using the charts in Figures 2-15 and 2-17 you can determine whether a riveted joint will fail in shear or bearing. When designing a riveted joint, always choose a rivet whose shear strength is near to, but slightly less than, the bearing strength of the metal sheet.

If two sheets of 0.040 aluminum alloy are riveted together with 1/8-inch 2117T rivets, and the joint is loaded until it fails, it will fail in shear. The rivets will shear and the sheets of metal will be undamaged. We know this because the shear strength of 1/8-inch 2117T rivets is 331 pounds, and the bearing strength for 0.040 aluminum alloy sheet for a ⅛-inch rivet is 410 pounds. If the same size higher strength 2024T rivets were used in this joint, the sheet would tear at the rivet holes because the shear strength of the rivet is 429 pounds, which is greater than the 410-pound bearing strength of the sheet. *See* Figures 2-15 and 2-17.

Later in the chapter when we consider the actual design of a riveted joint, we will use the chart in Figure 2-81 on Page 118 to determine whether a joint will fail in bearing or shear.

Rivet Alloy	Diameter of Rivet (inch)				
	3/32	1/8	5/32	3/16	1/4
2117T	186	331	518	745	1,325
2017T	206	368	573	828	1,472
202	241	429	670	966	1,718

Figure 2-15. *Shear strength of aluminum alloy rivets in a single-shear joint. Double-shear strength is approximately twice that shown in the chart.*

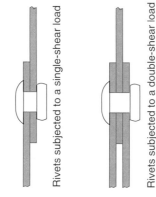

Rivets subjected to a single-shear load

Rivets subjected to a double-shear load

Figure 2-16. *Types of riveted joints*

Thickness of sheet (inch)	Diameter of Rivet (inch)				
	3/32	1/8	5/32	3/16	1/4
0.020	153	205	256	307	410
0.025	192	256	320	384	512
0.032	245	328	409	492	656
0.040	307	410	512	615	820
0.051	391	522	653	784	1,045
0.064	492	656	820	984	1,312

Figure 2-17. *Bearing strength of 2024-T3 aluminum alloy sheet*

STUDY QUESTIONS: MATERIALS FOR METAL AIRCRAFT CONSTRUCTION

Answers begin on Page 167. Page numbers refer to chapter text.

7. Identify the chief alloying agent in each of these aluminum alloys.
   a. 2024 _____
   b. 5052 _____
   c. 7075 _____
   Page 70

8. When a piece of aluminum alloy is heated in a furnace, then quenched in cold water, it is said to have been _____ heat-treated. *Page 71*

9. If there is a delay between the time the aluminum alloy is removed from the oven and it is quenched, the grains will grow to a size that makes the metal susceptible to _____ corrosion. *Page 71*

10. After a piece of aluminum alloy has been solution heat-treated, it gains strength over a period of days. This process is called _____. *Page 71*

11. After a piece of aluminum alloy has been solution heat-treated, it can be returned to the oven and held at an elevated temperature for a period of time to increase its strength. This process is called _____ heat-treating. *Page 71*

12. Another name for precipitation heat-treating is _____ . *Page 71*

13. Aluminum alloy may be annealed by heating it in an oven and then cooling it _____ (slowly or rapidly). *Page 72*

14. An aluminum alloy that cannot be hardened by heat-treating _____ (can or cannot) be annealed by heating and controlled cooling. *Page 72*

15. An aluminum alloy that has been solution heat-treated and then strain hardened has the temper designation _____ . *Page 72*

16. An aluminum alloy that has been solution heat-treated and then artificially aged has the temper designation _____ . *Page 72*

17. An aluminum alloy that has been strain hardened by cold-working to its half-hard condition has the temper designation _____ . *Page 72*

18. An aluminum alloy that has been annealed has the temper designation _____ . *Page 72*

19. Aluminum alloy 3003 _____ (is or is not) heat-treatable. *Page 72*

20. If a nonheat-treatable aluminum alloy becomes too hard while it is being worked, some of the hardness can be removed by _____ . *Page 72*

21. Pure aluminum _____ (is or is not) susceptible to corrosion. *Page 72*

22. Aluminum alloy sheet that is protected from corrosion by rolling a coating of pure aluminum on its surface is called _____ aluminum. *Page 73*

23. Clad aluminum alloy is _____ (stronger or weaker) than a sheet of unclad metal of the same alloy and thickness. *Page 73*

24. A hard oxide film that is deposited on an aluminum alloy by an electrolytic process is called a/an _____ film. *Page 73*

25. A corrosion-protective oxide film may be deposited on aluminum alloy by a chemical called a/an _____ coating. *Page 73*

26. Magnesium alloys are _____ (more or less) susceptible to corrosion than aluminum alloys. *Page 73*

Continued

27. Titanium _____ (does or does not) retain its strength when it is exposed to a high temperature. *Page 74*

28. Metals that contain iron are called _____ metals. *Page 74*

29. Steel is iron with _____ and other alloying elements added in controlled amounts. *Page 74*

30. The main alloying elements for corrosion-resistant steel are _____ and _____. *Page 74*

31. The load in pounds per square inch that causes a material to break is called the _____ tensile strength of the material. *Page 74*

32. The tensile strength of a piece of steel may be determined by measuring its _____. *Page 74*

33. A piece of steel with a Rockwell-C hardness of 40 has a tensile strength of approximately _____ pounds per square inch. *Page 74*

34. The strength of aluminum alloy _____ (does or does not) relate directly to its hardness. *Page 75*

35. A piece of 2024 aluminum alloy with a Brinell hardness of 120 has a tensile strength of approximately _____ pounds per square inch. *Page 75*

36. A riveted joint should be designed so it will fail in _____ (bearing or shear). *Page 75*

37. A riveted joint connecting two sheets of 0.032-inch 2024-T3 aluminum alloy with $3/32$-inch 2117T rivets will fail in _____ (bearing or shear). *Page 76*

Aircraft Structural Fasteners

Sheets of metal must be fastened together to form the aircraft structure, and this is usually done with solid aluminum alloy rivets. This section of the *Aviation Maintenance Technician Series* covers both solid and special rivets.

Solid Rivets

When aircraft manufacturers started building all-metal aircraft in the 1930s, different manufacturers had different favored rivet head designs. Brazier heads, modified brazier heads, button heads, mushroom heads, flat heads, and 78°-countersunk heads were all used. As aircraft construction standardized, four rivet head designs almost completely replaced all of these others. Rivets exposed to the airflow over the structure are usually either universal head MS20470, or 100°-countersunk head MS20426 rivets. For rivets used in internal structure, the round head MS20430, and the flat head MS20442 are generally used.

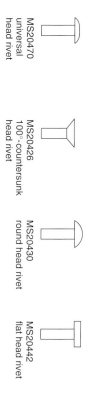

MS20470
universal
head rivet

MS20426
100°-countersunk
head rivet

MS20430
round head rivet

MS20442
flat head rivet

Figure 2-18. *Modern solid rivet design*

The material of which an aluminum alloy rivet is made is indicated by a mark on the manufactured head. Figure 2-19 shows the marks and indicates the metal or alloy of which the rivet is made.

A basic rule for rivet material selection is that you should use a rivet of the same material as the sheet metal you are joining, but this rule is not generally adhered to. Most aircraft structure is made of 2024 alloy, but 2024 rivets must be heat-treated and used shortly after they are removed from the quench. Because of this requirement, most aircraft are designed to use 2117 alloy rivets that can be driven just as they are received from the manufacturer.

When a higher strength rivet is required, use 2017 or 2024 alloy rivets. These are called "icebox" rivets, and they must be heat-treated before they are driven to prevent their cracking. Rivets of both of these alloys are heated to a specified temperature in an oven and are then quenched in water. They are soft when they are first removed from the water and may be driven immediately without cracking. But if they remain at normal room temperature for more than about ten minutes, they harden enough that they will crack. To prevent this hardening, they may be stored in a freezer at a temperature well below zero. They will remain soft enough to drive for several weeks if they are stored at a temperature of near -50°F, but they should be driven within 5 to 10 minutes after they are removed from the freezer.

icebox rivet. A solid rivet made of 2017 or 2024 aluminum alloy. These rivets are too hard to drive in the condition they are received from the factory, and must be heat-treated to soften them. They are heated in a furnace and then quenched in cold water. Immediately after quenching they are soft, but within a few hours at room temperature they become quite hard. The hardening can be delayed for several days by storing them in a sub-freezing icebox and holding them at this low temperature until they are to be used.

Head Mark		Alloy	Code
No mark	◯	1100	A
Dimple	◎	2117T	AD
Raised dot	◉	2017T	D
Two raised dashes	⊖	2024T	DD
Raised cross	⊕	5056T	B

Figure 2-19. *Head identification marks for solid aluminum alloy rivets*

Magnesium is a highly reactive metal and every reasonable precaution must be taken to prevent contact with other metals. For this reason rivets made of 5056 alloy are used to join magnesium alloy sheets. These rivets contain approximately 5% magnesium and create the least dissimilar metal problem of any of the rivets. These rivets may be driven as they are received without further heat treatment.

Rivet Dimensions

The diameter of a solid rivet is the diameter of its shank, as seen in Figure 2-20. In rivet specifications, the diameter is given in $\frac{1}{32}$-inch increments as the first dash number following the material code for the rivet.

The length of solid rivets is measured from the portion of the head that is flush with the surface of the metal sheet to the end of its shank. This length is measured in $\frac{1}{16}$-inch increments and is given in rivet specifications as the second dash number.

Rivet Identification

A solid aluminum alloy rivet is identified by a number that indicates its head shape, alloy, diameter, and length. The letters MS or AN identify the specifications under which the rivet is manufactured. The number indicates the shape of the head, the code that follows this number identifies the alloy, the first dash number is the diameter in $\frac{1}{32}$-inch increments, and the second dash number is the length in $\frac{1}{16}$-inch increments. This identification is shown in the example in Figure 2-21.

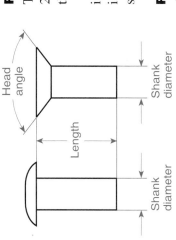

Figure 2-20. *Measurement of an aircraft solid rivet*

Head angle

Length

Shank diameter

Shank diameter

MS20470AD-4-6	
MS	Military Specifications
20470	Universal head rivet
AD	2117T alloy
-4	4/32 or 1/8-inch diameter
-6	6/16 or 3/8-inch length

Figure 2-21. *Meaning of rivet specification numbers*

Identification Number	Head Shape	Alloy	Diameter	Length
MS20426AD-4-4	100° Csk	2117T	1/8	1/4
MS20470DD-5-8	Universal	2024T	5/32	1/2
MS20430D-6-10	Round	2017T	3/16	5/8
MS20442D-4-6	Flat	2017T	1/8	3/8
MS20430A-3-4	Round	1100	3/32	1/4

Figure 2-22. *Examples of aluminum alloy rivet designation*

Solid rivets made of copper, stainless steel, and Monel are identified in a manner similar to that used for aluminum alloy rivets.

Monel. An alloy of nickel, copper, and aluminum or silicon.

Identification Number	Head Shape	Material	Head Mark
MS20427	100° Countersunk	Mild steel	Recessed triangle
MS20427M	100° Countersunk	Monel	Raised triangle
MS20427C	100° Countersunk	Copper	No mark
MS20427F	100° Countersunk	Corrosion resistant steel	No mark
MS20435	Round	Mild steel	Recessed triangle
MS20435M	Round	Monel	Raised triangle
MS20435C	Round	Corrosion resistant steel	No mark
MS20435F	Round	Copper	No mark
MS20441	Flat	Mild steel	Recessed triangle
MS20441M	Flat	Monel	Raised triangle
MS20441C	Flat	Copper	No mark

Figure 2-23. *Identification of solid rivets other than aluminum alloy*

Special Fasteners

There are many locations on an aircraft where it is not possible to reach both sides of the structure, and special blind rivets must be installed. In this section several types of blind rivets and other special fasteners that are used in place of solid rivets or bolts are discussed.

Friction-Lock Cherry Rivets

The Townsend Division of Textron, Inc., manufactures a series of blind rivets that are widely used in both civilian and military aircraft. Figure 2-24 shows two head styles of the self-plugging friction-lock Cherry rivet. The correct length of rivet is chosen and it is inserted through the holes in the sheets of metal to be joined. A special puller is clamped over the ridged stem and pulled. The tapered end of the stem is pulled into the hollow shank where it swells the shank and clamps the skins tightly together. Continued pulling breaks the stem and leaves part of it wedged tightly inside the shank. The end of the stem is cut flush with the top of the rivet head with a pair of rivet cutters.

Friction holds the stem in the rivet shank, and it can vibrate out. Because of this possibility, friction-lock rivets are not approved to replace solid rivets on a size-for-size basis, but must be one size larger than the solid rivets they replace.

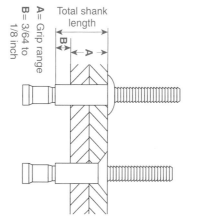

Total shank length

A = Grip range
B = 3/64 to 1/8 inch

Figure 2-24. *Self-plugging, friction-lock Cherry rivets*

rivet cutters. Special cutting pliers that resemble diagonal cutters except that the jaws are ground in such a way that they cut the rivet shank, or stem, off square.

Mechanical-Lock Cherry Rivets

A more secure rivet is the mechanical-lock Cherry rivet, as in Figure 2-25. A locking collar is swaged into the groove between the stem and the rivet head to prevent the stem from coming out of the installed rivet. A mechanical-lock rivet can replace a solid rivet on a size-for-size basis.

When the stem of this rivet is pulled, the end of the hollow stem is upset, which pulls the metal sheets tightly together and forms the upset head. Continued pulling shears the shear ring from the stem cone and allows the stem to pull up into the hollow shank enough for the stem break notch to be flush with the top of the rivet head. The puller forces the locking collar down tightly into the recess formed between the groove in the shank and the rivet head. This locks the stem in the shank, and further pulling snaps the stem off flush with the head of the rivet.

To remove a mechanical-lock Cherry rivet, follow the steps in Figure 2-26. File the broken end of the shank off smooth, and make a center punch mark in its center. Drill off the tapered part of the stem that provides the lock and, using a pin punch, pry out the locking collar. Use a drill that is slightly smaller than the rivet hole, and drill almost through the rivet head. Pry the head off of the rivet with a pin punch, and drive the rivet from the hole.

Other manufacturers produce mechanical locked rivets similar to these described. Most of them swage a collar into a groove between the stem and the rivet head to lock the stem in place as it is broken off by the pulling tool.

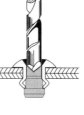

Drill off tapered part of stem.

Pry off rivet head.

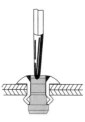

Make center punch mark in center of stem.

Drill almost through rivet head.

File end of stem flat.

Pry out remainder of locking collar.

Drive rivet from hole.

Figure 2-26. *Removal of a mechanical-lock Cherry rivet*

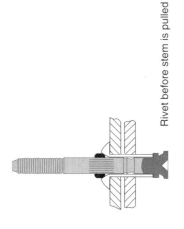

Rivet before stem is pulled

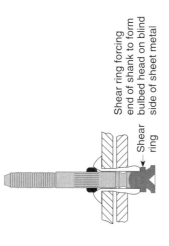

Shear ring forcing end of shank to form bulbed head on blind side of sheet metal

Shear ring

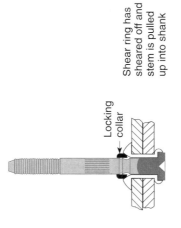

Shear ring has sheared off and stem is pulled up into shank

Locking collar

Collar has been forced down into groove in stem and stem broken off flush with rivet head

Figure 2-25. *Bulbed mechanical-lock Cherry rivets*

Threaded Rivet

When the B. F. Goodrich Company conceived the rubber de-icer boot, it discovered a need for threaded holes in the thin sheet-metal skins of the wing and tail surfaces, and answered it with the Rivnut.

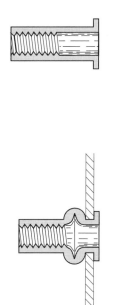

Rivnut before installation

Rivnut after it has been upset

Figure 2-27. *A Rivnut provides a threaded hole in a thin sheet metal.*

To install a Rivnut, drill the hole and cut the keyway with a special keyway cutter. Screw the Rivnut onto the threaded mandrel of a heading tool, such as the one in Figure 2-28. Insert the Rivnut into the hole with the key in the keyway and squeeze the movable handle. This upsets the Rivnut's shank, letting you turn the mandrel crank to remove the tool from the installed Rivnut.

High-Strength Pin Rivets

Modern aircraft construction techniques require as much automation as possible, and in locations where a high-strength fastener is required that is not likely to be removed in normal maintenance, a pin rivet such as the Hi-Shear rivet in Figure 2-29 may have been used. This fastener may be installed rapidly and has the same shear strength as an equivalent size structural steel bolt.

Pin rivets are installed by inserting the body of the rivet with the correct grip length through a hole that has been reamed to the correct size. The shank of these rivets does not expand to completely fill the hole as does the shank of a conventional solid rivet.

The correct grip length allows no more than $1/16$-inch of the straight portion of the shank to extend through the material, and the end of the unswaged metal collar should be slightly higher than the shearing edge of the pin. It is permissible to use a 0.032-inch steel washer between the collar and the material if necessary to position the collar.

To drive a pin rivet, hold a heavy bucking bar against the flat head and a Hi-Shear rivet set such as the one in Figure 2-30 against the collar. Impacts from the rivet gun swage the collar into the groove in the pin, and the shearing edge on the pin trims the top edge of the collar until it forms a smooth cone, as seen in Figure 2-31.

To remove a pin rivet, use a small, sharp chisel to split the collar and pry it off the pin. After removing the collar, tap the pin from the hole with a hammer.

Mandrel crank

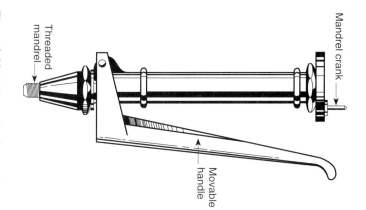

Threaded mandrel

Movable handle

Figure 2-28. *A Rivnut heading tool*

Figure 2-29. *High-strength steel pin rivets may be installed in an aircraft structure in locations that would normally use steel bolts loaded in shear.*

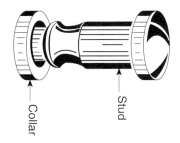

Collar

Stud

rivet set. A tool used to drive aircraft solid rivets. It is a piece of hardened steel with a recess the shape of the rivet head in one end. The other end fits into the rivet gun.

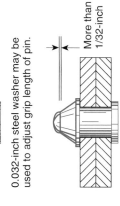

0.032-inch steel washer may be used to adjust grip length of pin.

More than 1/32-inch

Collar is overdriven. If there is more than 1/32 inch between shearing edge of pin and top of collar, collar should be removed and a new one installed.

Correctly-driven pin rivet.

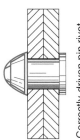

Collar is underdriven. It may be driven more.

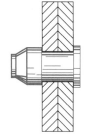

Pin is too short. Remove collar and use longer pin.

Pin is too long. Remove collar, install washer, or use shorter pin.

Figure 2-31. *Pin rivet inspection*

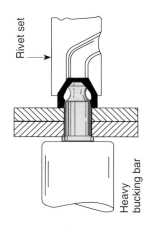

Rivet set

Heavy bucking bar

Figure 2-30. *Hi-Shear rivet set in the correct position to swage the collar into the groove of the pin.*

STUDY QUESTIONS: AIRCRAFT STRUCTURAL FASTENERS

Answers begin on Page 167. Page numbers refer to chapter text.

38. A solid aluminum alloy rivet with a dimple on its head is made of _____ alloy. *Page 79*

39. A solid aluminum alloy rivet with no mark on its head is made of _____ alloy. *Page 79*

40. A solid aluminum alloy rivet with a raised dot on its head is made of _____ alloy. *Page 79*

41. A solid aluminum alloy rivet with two raised dashes on its head is made of _____ alloy. *Page 79*

42. A solid aluminum alloy rivet with a raised cross on its head is made of _____ alloy. *Page 79*

43. Two solid aluminum alloy rivets that can be driven in the condition they are received without further heat treatment are coded _____ which is made of _____ alloy, and _____ which is made of _____ alloy. *Pages 79 and 80*

44. Icebox rivets must be heat-treated before they are driven. These rivets are made of either of two alloys; these are _____ and _____ . *Page 79*

45. The proper rivet to use for joining sheets of magnesium alloy is a rivet made of _____ alloy. *Page 80*

46. Identify the head style, alloy, diameter, and length of each of these solid rivets:

a. MS20426AD-4-4   Head _____ ,   Alloy _____ ,
                Diameter _____ ,   Length _____ .

b. MS20470DD-6-8   Head _____ ,   Alloy _____ ,
                Diameter _____ ,   Length _____ .

Page 80

47. A rivet with a raised triangle on its head is made of _____ . *Page 81*

48. Friction-lock Cherry rivets _____ (are or are not) approved to replace solid rivets on a size-for-size basis. *Page 81*

49. Mechanical-lock Cherry rivets _____ (are or are not) approved to replace solid rivets on a size-for-size basis. *Page 82*

50. The stem of a mechanical-lock Cherry rivet is held in the hollow shank by a _____ that is swaged into a groove in the stem before the stem breaks off. *Page 82*

51. A special fastener that provides a threaded hole in a piece of thin sheet metal is the _____ . *Page 83*

52. High-strength pin rivets are designed to be used for _____ (shear or tensile) loads. *Page 83*

Tools for Sheet-Metal Construction and Repair

Aircraft manufacturing requires many exotic and sophisticated tools and fixtures that allow the structure to be built with the maximum degree of interchangeability of parts among aircraft of the same design. Repair of these aircraft requires relatively simple tools, which are described here, categorized according to their function.

Layout Tools

Aircraft drawings are discussed in the General textbook of this *Aviation Maintenance Technician Series*. In a detail drawing, all of the dimensions are given that are required to manufacture a part. This information, which includes all of the needed dimensions, angles, and radii, should not be scaled from the drawing because the paper stretches or shrinks, but should be laid out directly on the metal or on a template using the dimensions shown on the drawing.

Combination Set

The combination set in Figure 2-32 is a useful layout tool. When you place the stock, or square, head against the side of a piece of material, the blade extends across it at an exact 90° or 45° angle. Use the protractor head when you need an angle of other than 90° or 45°.

Use the center head to locate and mark the center of a round object. Notice that the head is in the form of two arms at right angles to each other, and the blade intersects this angle. To locate the center of a circle, lay the blade across it with the arms of the head tight against the outside edge and draw a line along the edge of the blade. Move the tool around about 90° and draw another line crossing the one just drawn. The intersection of these lines is in the center of the circle.

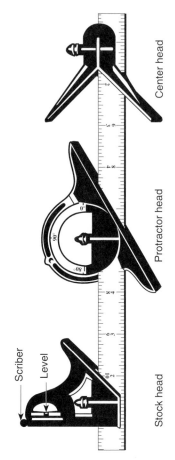

Scriber

Level

Stock head

Protractor head

Center head

Figure 2-32. *The combination set is one of the most widely used tools for sheet metal layout.*

Steel Scales

The scale on the blade of the combination set is useful for layout work, but special scales are available in both flexible and rigid steel. One handy scale for sheet metal work is flexible and rigid steel. One handy scale is graduated in common fractions of an inch and the other is in decimal fractions. The common fraction side has graduations as small as $\frac{1}{64}$ inch, and the smallest graduation on the decimal side is one hundredth of an inch, or 0.01 inch.

When using a steel scale for making a measurement, do not use the end of the scale, but rather make the measurement between two marks on the scale away from the end.

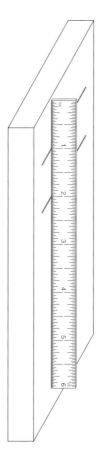

Figure 2-33. *When using a steel scale to determine the distance between two marks, do not use the end of the scale, but measure from one of its inch marks.*

One handy type of steel scale is the hook rule, seen in Figure 2-34. The inside edge of the hook is aligned exactly with the end of the scale. Place it over the edge of the object to be measured. You can make measurements quickly and easily from the edge to the marks on the scale. A hook rule is the most convenient way to get measurements from the edge when there is a radius involved.

Figure 2-34. *A hook rule is used for making measurements to the edge of a piece of material. It is especially helpful if the material has a radius or a bevel on its edge.*

Dividers

Dividers are used for transferring distances from a steel scale to the metal being laid out and for dividing a line into equal spaces, for example, when laying out a row of rivets. See Figure 2-35.

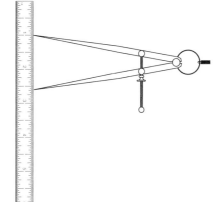

Figure 2-35. *Dividers are used to transfer distances from a steel scale to the metal being laid out.*

Marking Tools

When laying out a steel part for machining, it is acceptable practice to coat the surface of the metal with a dark blue opaque layout dye and scribe the marks with a sharp-pointed steel scriber. But this is not an acceptable practice for laying out parts on sheet aluminum or magnesium alloys. Any scribe marks in this thin sheet metal can cause stress concentrations that can lead to failure of the metal.

The best way to lay out thin sheet metal is to spray a very light coat of zinc chromate primer on the metal and mark all of the bend tangent and sight lines with a soft lead pencil. Only cutoff lines may be scribed with a steel scriber, and this is not necessary if a good sharp lead pencil is used.

If it is not desirable or convenient to spray the metal with zinc chromate primer, use an extra fine point Sharpie® permanent marker. This marking pen has a soft, sharp point and leaves a dark permanent mark on the sheet metal. These marks are considered permanent, but can be removed from the metal with a rag damp with alcohol.

Punches

Mark the exact location for drilled holes by holding the point of a prick punch at the location marked on the metal and tapping it lightly with a small hammer. The sharp point of the punch makes it easy to mark an exact location, but it does not indent the metal at the correct angle to start a drill.

After marking the locations of all drilled holes with a prick punch, enlarge the marks with a center punch. This punch is heavier than a prick punch, and its point is ground with a 60° angle, which is correct for making a twist drill start cutting. Center punches are available in sizes ranging from about three inches to five inches long. Be sure to use the punch that makes the appropriate starting indentation for the size drill you will be using.

Often when making a new piece of skin for an aircraft repair, you must use the original skin as a pattern. To do this, use a transfer punch to mark the center of the rivet holes. The end of the punch is the diameter of the rivet hole and has a sharp point in the center of its flat end. The metal sheets are held tightly together and the transfer punch is placed through a rivet hole and tapped lightly with a small hammer. The sharp point makes a small indentation like that produced by a prick punch, but at the location of the exact center of the rivet hole in the pattern.

Pin punches are used, not so much for layout, but for removing rivets after their heads have been drilled through, and for aligning sheets of metal by placing the punch through rivet holes in each of the sheets. These punches are available in sizes for most standard aircraft rivets, and all have straight shanks.

twist drill. A metal cutting tool turned in a drill press or hand-held drill motor. A twist drill has a straight shank and spiraled flutes. The cutting edge is ground on the end of the spiraled flutes.

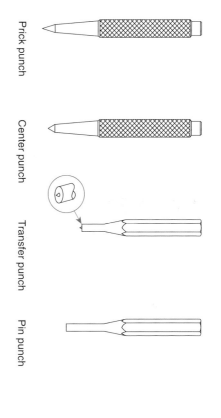

Prick punch   Center punch   Transfer punch   Pin punch

Figure 2-36. *Punches used for sheet metal layout and fabrication*

Cutting Tools

In both manufacturing and repair of sheet metal aircraft, some of the most important tools are those that cut the metal. It is extremely important to cut the metal at exactly the correct location, and to keep the edges free of cracks and burrs. This section discusses the cutting tools used in a shop first, and then the tools you as a technician will have in your personal tool chest.

Squaring Shear

The squaring shear in Figure 2-37 (Page 90) is one of the most useful tools in a sheet metal shop. These foot-operated shears normally accept a four-foot-wide sheet of thin sheet metal. The line on which the metal is to be cut is placed directly above the cutting edge of the bed of the shear, and it is held securely while the foot treadle is pressed down. Some squaring shears have a clamp near the cutting edge that allows you to clamp the metal so your fingers are not near the cutting edge when cutting small pieces of metal.

Large power-operated shears using energy stored in a flywheel to drive the cutting edge are used in steel fabrication shops to cut across sheets of heavy steel.

Throatless Shears

Throatless shears can cut across any size sheet of metal and can cut metal heavier than the foot-operated squaring shears. Their operation is much like a pair of heavy-duty, short-blade scissors. *See* Figure 2-38 on the next page.

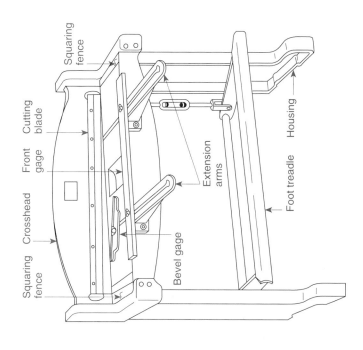

Figure 2-37. *A squaring shear for making straight cuts across sheets of thin metal*

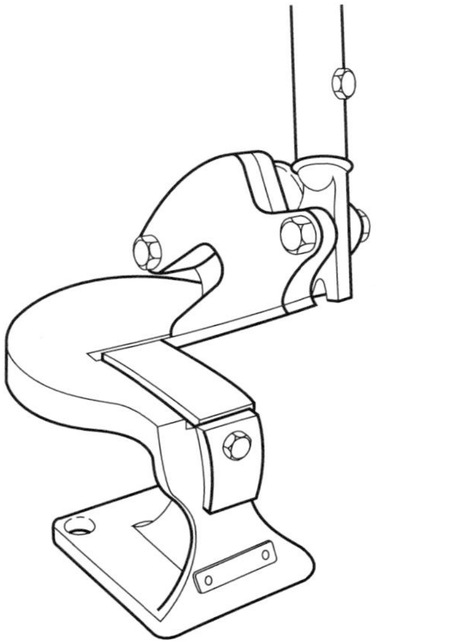

Squaring fence

Front gage

Cutting blade

Crosshead

Squaring fence

Bevel gage

Extension arms

Foot treadle

Housing

Scroll Shears

Scroll shears are used to cut irregular lines on the inside of a sheet without cutting through to the edge. The upper cutting blade is stationary, while the lower blade is moved up and down with the handle. *See* Figure 2-39.

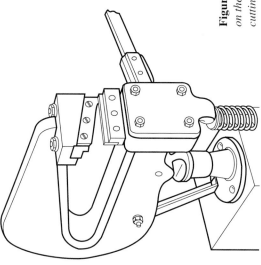

Figure 2-39. *Scroll shears are used to cut on the inside of a sheet of metal without cutting through to the edge.*

Figure 2-38. *Throatless shears cut metal in much the same way as scissors cut paper.*

Bandsaw

Metal-cutting bandsaws are extremely versatile cutting tools. You can vary the speed of the blade to provide the correct cutting speed for the type and thickness of metal being cut. You can tilt the work table to allow the blade to cut the metal at an angle.

An especially useful feature is the butt welder and grinder built into this bandsaw. When it is necessary to cut on the inside of a piece of metal without cutting to the edge, the blade can be cut and inserted into a hole drilled in the metal, and then the ends of the blade can be welded back together and ground down smooth. The blade is then reinstalled on the saw and the metal is cut.

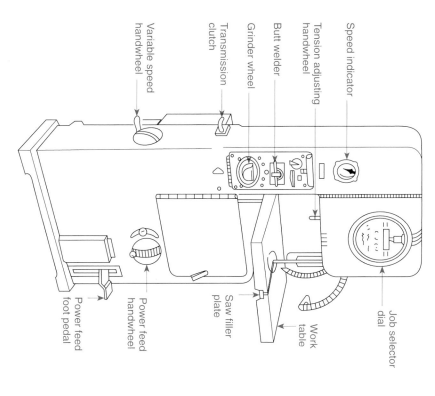

Figure 2-40. *The contour bandsaw is a versatile metal-cutting shop tool.*

Speed indicator

Tension adjusting handwheel

Butt welder

Grinder wheel

Transmission clutch

Variable speed handwheel

Power feed foot pedal

Power feed handwheel

Saw filler plate

Work table

Job selector dial

Hacksaws

The most widely used metal-cutting saw is the hacksaw that holds a narrow, flexible steel blade under tension in an adjustable frame.

Hacksaw blades are about $\frac{1}{2}$-inch wide and are available in both 10-and 12-inch lengths. Blades are available with the number of teeth ranging from 14 to 32 per inch and may be made of either carbon steel or molybdenum steel.

Molybdenum blades are called high-speed blades and are considerably more expensive than carbon-steel blades, but they last so much longer that their overall cost is actually much less.

Determine how many teeth to use by the thickness of the material being cut. As a rule of thumb, there should always be at least two teeth on the material being cut. Figure 2-41 matches the number of teeth of the blade to the work.

The proper technique for using a hacksaw is to use as long a stroke as is convenient and to apply pressure on the forward stroke only. Lift the blade away from the metal on the return stroke to prevent dulling it.

Type of Material Being Cut	Recommended Teeth Per Inch
Material with large thickness and soft material where large chip clearance is needed	14
General shop use for cutting a variety of materials	18
Material with thicknesses between 1/16- and 1/4-inch	24
Material with thicknesses up to 1/16-inch	32

Figure 2-41. *Recommended teeth per inch for hacksaw blades*

Files

After cutting the metal to almost the correct size and shape, finish it by cutting the edges with a file. A file is so familiar to most of us that we often do not realize its importance or give it the care it deserves.

The teeth that cross the file at an angle are cutting tools and must receive the same care as any other cutting tool. The cut, or coarseness, of the teeth is designated by a series of numbers or by the name of the cut. The names, ranging from coarsest to smoothest, are: rough cut, coarse cut, bastard cut, second cut, smooth cut, and dead smooth cut. The designation of the cut is the same for all sizes of files, but the teeth on a small file are closer together than the teeth of the same-named cut on a larger file.

Files with a single set of teeth crossing the body at an angle of 65° to 85° are called single-cut files, and those with two sets of teeth, one crossing at an angle of 45° and the other crossing at an angle of 70° to 80°, are called double-cut files.

Vixen files are special cutting tools whose teeth are curved across the body of the file. These files are designed to remove a rather large amount of metal with each stroke and are used only on soft metal.

If you give files a reasonable amount of care they will give good service. Always match them to the work: use the right type and size of file, and choose the degree of coarseness to give the type of cut required. Never use a file without slipping a handle over the tang to protect your hands.

file. A hand-held cutting tool used to remove a small amount of metal with each stroke.

vixen file. A metal-cutting hand file that has curved teeth across its faces. Vixen files are used to remove large amounts of soft metal.

tang. A tapered shank sticking out from the blade of a knife or a file. The handle of a knife or file is mounted on the tang.

Never store files loose in your tool chest where they can be damaged by other tools. Store them in a rack or protect them in paper or plastic envelopes. They should never be oiled but should be kept clean and dry. When a file has been used to file soft metal, remove all of the metal that has remained between the teeth by brushing with a stiff brush or file card. Remove any stubborn metal with a sharp metal pick.

When filing hard metal, raise the file on the back stroke and apply pressure only on the forward stroke. Pressure on the back stroke will dull the teeth. It is a good practice, however, when filing very soft metals such as lead or soft aluminum, to apply some pressure on the back stroke to remove chips of metal from between the teeth.

Cross filing is done by moving the file lengthwise across the work, but when a very smooth surface is required, move the file sideways across the work. This is called draw filing.

Chisels

A chisel is a simple cutting tool made of a piece of hardened and tempered tool steel. The blade of the chisel is ground with a cutting edge, and is used to shear metal by driving it into the metal with a hammer.

There are a number of types of chisels in use. The most common is the flat chisel, the cutting edge of which is ground to an angle of approximately 70°, and into a convex shape. This convex shape concentrates the forces of the hammer blows in the center of the cutting edge. *See Figure 2-43.*

Cape chisels have a narrow blade and are used to remove the head of a rivet after it has been drilled through. *See Figure 2-44.*

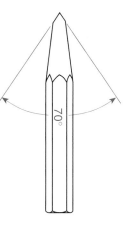

Cutting edge of a flat chisel is ground to an angle of approximately 70°.

Cutting edge is ground to a convex shape to concentrate hammer blows in the center of the cutting edge.

Figure 2-43. *A flat, or cold, chisel*

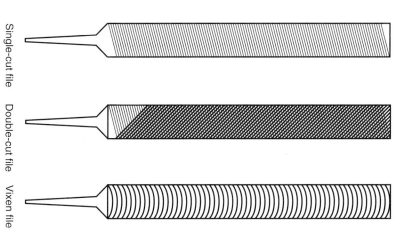

Single-cut file   Double-cut file   Vixen file

Figure 2-42. *Hand files*

Figure 2-44. *A cape chisel may be used to remove the head of a rivet after it has been drilled through.*

Deburring Tools

Any time metal is sheared or drilled, burrs are left on one side that must be removed. A smooth-cut file is a good tool for deburring, or removing these burrs, from the edges of sheets that have been sheared. A deburring tool used in production facilities uses two hardened, sharp-edged steel wheels mounted side-by-side with their edges almost touching. To deburr a piece of metal, pull the tool along the edge of the sheet with the wheels straddling the edge. The sharp edges of the wheels remove the burrs. *See* Figure 2-45.

You can make a handy deburring tool by grinding a sharp V-shaped notch in the end of a small flat file. Just pull this notch along the edges of the sheet that needs deburring and it will remove the burrs from both edges at the same time.

A countersinking tool or a large drill is good for removing burrs from the edges of a drilled hole. Be sure that you do not remove too much metal, just the burr. *See* Figure 2-46.

Drills

Twist drills are used in aircraft construction and maintenance to drill the thousands of rivet and bolt holes needed for the fasteners holding the aircraft structure together. Figure 2-47 shows the nomenclature of a typical twist drill.

Twist drill sizes are measured by three systems: numbers, letters, and fractions. The most popular drills used for aircraft sheet metal work are number drills. *See* the twist drill size chart of Figure 2-48.

burr. A sharp rough edge of a piece of metal left when the metal was sheared, punched, or drilled.

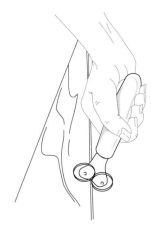

Figure 2-45. *A deburring tool used in production shops to deburr the edges of large sheets of metal.*

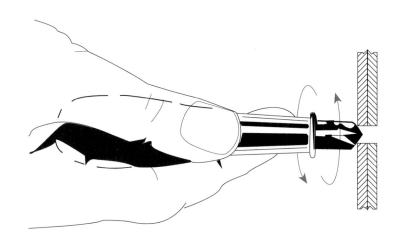

Figure 2-46. *A reamer or a large drill can be used to remove the burrs from the edge of a drilled hole.*

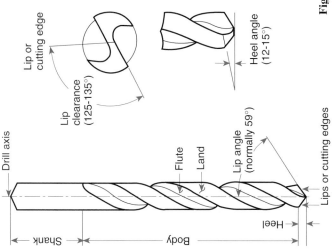

Figure 2-47. *Twist drill nomenclature*

Drill axis

Flute

Land

Lip angle (normally 59°)

Shank

Body

Heel

Lips or cutting edges

Lip or cutting edge

Lip clearance (125-135°)

Heel angle (12-15°)

Twist drill sizes

Number or Letter	Fraction	Decimal Equivalent
80		0.0135
79		0.0145
	1/64	0.0156
78		0.0160
77		0.0180
76		0.0200
75		0.0210
74		0.0225
73		0.0240
72		0.0250
71		0.0260
70		0.0280
69		0.0292
68		0.0310
	1/32	0.0313
67		0.0320
66		0.0330
65		0.0350
64		0.0360
63		0.0370
62		0.0380
61		0.0390
60		0.0400
59		0.0410
58		0.0420
57		0.0430
56		0.0465
	3/64	0.0469
55		0.0520
54		0.0550
53		0.0595
	1/16	0.0625
52		0.0635
51		0.0670
50		0.0700
49		0.0730
48		0.0760
	5/64	0.0781
47		0.0785
46		0.0810
45		0.0820
44		0.0860
43		0.0890
42		0.0935
	3/32	0.0937
41		0.0960
40		0.0980
39		0.0995
38		0.1015
37		0.1040
36		0.1065
	7/64	0.1094
35		0.1100
34		0.1110
33		0.1130
32		0.1160
31		0.1200
	1/8	0.1250
30		0.1285
29		0.1360
28		0.1405
	9/64	0.1406
27		0.1440
26		0.1470
25		0.1495
24		0.1520
23		0.1540
	5/32	0.1562

Number or Letter	Fraction	Decimal Equivalent
22		0.1570
21		0.1590
20		0.1610
19		0.1660
18		0.1695
	11/64	0.1719
17		0.1730
16		0.1770
15		0.1800
14		0.1820
13		0.1850
	3/16	0.1875
12		0.1890
11		0.1910
10		0.1935
9		0.1960
8		0.1990
7		0.2010
	13/64	0.2031
6		0.2040
5		0.2055
4		0.2090
3		0.2130
	7/32	0.2187
2		0.2210
1		0.2280
A		0.2340
	15/64	0.2344
B		0.2380
C		0.2420
D		0.2460
	1/4	0.2500
E		0.2500
F		0.2570
G		0.2610
	17/64	0.2656
H		0.2660
I		0.2720
J		0.2770
K		0.2810
	9/32	0.2812
L		0.2900
M		0.2950
	19/64	0.2969
N		0.3020
	5/16	0.3125
O		0.3160
P		0.3230
	21/64	0.3281
Q		0.3320
R		0.3390
	11/32	0.3438
S		0.3480
T		0.3580
	23/64	0.3594
U		0.3680
	3/8	0.3750
V		0.3770
W		0.3860
	25/64	0.3906
X		0.3970
Y		0.4040
	13/32	0.4062
Z		0.4130
	27/64	0.4219
	7/16	0.4375
	29/64	0.4531
	15/32	0.4688
	31/64	0.4844
	1/2	0.5000

Figure 2-48. *Twist drill sizes*

Drill Motors

Most of the holes used for sheet metal repair work are drilled with hand-held pneumatic drill motors. These are superior to electric drill motors because they are lightweight, have excellent speed control, do not overheat when they are stalled, and they do not produce sparks which could serve as a source of ignition. Since rivet guns require compressed air, compressed air lines are usually available where sheet-metal repairs are being made.

Drill Attachments and Special Drills

Aircraft are noted for requiring work in hard-to-reach locations, and holes that need drilling are no exceptions. Fortunately, snake attachments and right-angle drill motors use very short twist drills, and right-angle attachments can be used in a conventional drill motor. *See Figure 2-49.*

You can use extension drills to drill in a location that cannot be reached with a conventional short drill. If the rigid extension drill is not available, use an extra-long drill. When using a long drill of a small size, it is a good idea to slip a piece of aluminum tubing over the drill to keep it from whipping.

Snake attachment

Right-angle attachment

Drill for right-angle attachment

Figure 2-49. *Attachments for drilling holes in hard-to-reach locations.*

Extension drill that uses a long, rigid shaft and conventional twist drill.

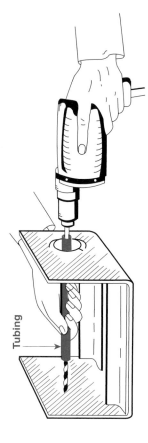

Tubing

When using small diameter, extra-long drill, place piece of aluminum tubing around drill to prevent it whipping.

Figure 2-50. *Extension drills and extra-long drills*

Forming Tools

Large sheets of metal are formed in an aircraft factory with press brakes, drop hammers, hydropresses, and stretch presses. In the smaller maintenance shops the tools described here are used to form both straight and compound curves on thin sheet metal.

Cornice Brake

The cornice, or leaf, brake is one of the most familiar brakes in a maintenance shop. The metal to be bent is clamped between the bed of the brake and the top nose bar, with the sight line marked on the metal directly below the edge of the nose bar. (This is discussed in detail in the section on metal layout and forming beginning on Page 105.) The bending leaf is lifted, bending the metal against the radius on the top nose bar.

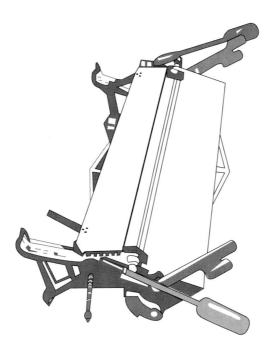

Figure 2-51. *A cornice brake is used for making straight bends across sheets of metal.*

Box Brake

A cornice brake can only bend the two opposite sides of a box, but a box, or finger, brake can bend up all four sides. A box brake is much like a cornice brake except the top nose bar is divided into sections called fingers. The brake is adjusted for the correct metal thickness and bend radius, and two opposite sides of the box are bent up. The metal is turned 90° and the fingers are adjusted so the two formed sides of the box fit between two fingers, and the final two sides of the box are bent.

cornice brake. A large shop tool used to make straight bends across a sheet of metal. Cornice brakes are often called leaf brakes.

slip roll former. A shop tool used to form large radius curves in sheet metal.

Slip Roll Former

You can bend large radius curves in a sheet of metal with a slip roll former, such as the one in Figure 2-52. These machines have three hardened steel rollers. The drive roller is rotated with a hand crank, the gripping roller is adjustable to clamp the metal between it and the drive roller so it will be pulled through the machine, and behind these two rollers is a radius roller that can be adjusted to force the metal into a curve as it is pulled through the rollers. The radius roller is adjusted to cause the metal to be slightly bent by the first pass, then the metal is passed through the rollers a second time with the radius roller moved up a bit. This makes the radius of the bend smaller. The metal may be passed through the rollers as many times as needed, and the radius roller adjusted each time until the metal has the desired bend. One end of the gripping roller can be lifted to remove the metal if it has been rolled into a complete cylinder.

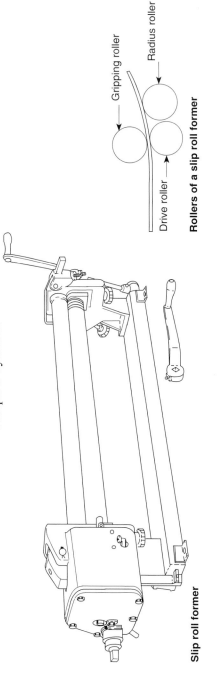

Slip roll former

Figure 2-52. *Slip roll formers are used for making large radius bends in sheet metal.*

Gripping roller

Radius roller

Drive roller

Rollers of a slip roll former

Sandbag

You can form compound curves in a piece of sheet metal by bumping it with a soft-face mallet and a sandbag. The sandbag is made of canvas or leather and filled with clean dry sand. A depression is made in the bag and the metal is bumped into the depression. Always start at the outside edges of the bend and work toward the center. Continually check the work with a template to be sure the metal takes the desired shape.

Riveting Tools

Production riveting on an assembly is done with a high-tech riveting machine that drills the hole, countersinks it, drops the rivet in place, squeezes it to the proper compression, and automatically moves over to the location for the next rivet. The riveting done in maintenance shops is not so automated and is done with a rivet gun or a hand-held compression, or squeeze, riveter.

Rivet Gun

The typical rivet gun is shown in Figure 2-53. This is a pneumatic hammer that can drive a rivet set against the rivet head. The set is held in the gun with a beehive-shaped spring that screws over the end of the gun cylinder.

Rivet guns are available in several types and shapes, shown in Figure 2-54. These guns are classified according to the speed of the blows they deliver and the shape of their handle.

Use long-stroke, slow-hitting guns to drive large, hard rivets. These guns upset the rivet with a few blows without excessively work hardening them. Use fast-hitting guns to drive smaller rivets. They give you excellent control over the blows the gun delivers.

beehive spring. A hard-steel, coil-spring retainer used to hold a rivet set in a pneumatic rivet gun.

This spring gets its name from its shape. It screws onto the end of the rivet gun and allows the set to move back and forth, but prevents it being shot from the gun.

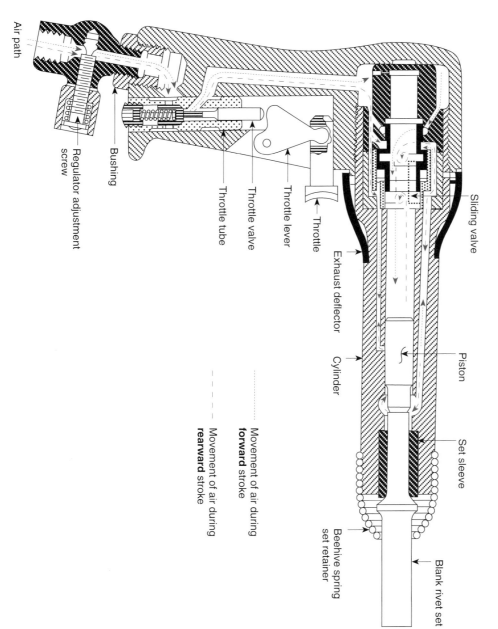

Figure 2-53. *A typical offset-handle pneumatic rivet gun*

Air path

Regulator adjustment screw

Bushing

Throttle tube

Throttle valve

Throttle lever

Throttle

Exhaust deflector

Cylinder

Sliding valve

Piston

Set sleeve

Beehive spring set retainer

Blank rivet set

·········· Movement of air during **forward** stroke

– – – – Movement of air during **rearward** stroke

Long-stroke, slow-hitting,
pistol grip rivet gun

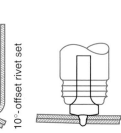

Fast-hitting, offset-handle rivet gun

Long-stroke, slow-hiting,
offset-handle rivet gun

Fast-hitting, push button rivet gun

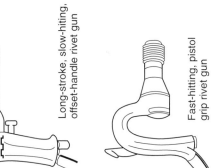

Fast-hitting, pistol
grip rivet gun

Figure 2-54. *Pneumatic rivet guns*

Rivet Gun Size	Maximum Rivet Diameter
1x	3/32 inch
2x	1/8 inch
3x	3/16 inch
4x	1/4 inch

Figure 2-55. *The rivet gun should match the size rivet being driven.*

Rivet guns are rated by size (*see* Figure 2-55), and all of these guns accept standard rivet sets that have a 0.401-inch shank.

Observe certain safety and operating rules when using a rivet gun:

- Never point a rivet gun at anyone at any time.
- Never depress the trigger of a rivet gun unless the rivet set is held firmly against the head of a rivet or against a piece of wood.
- Disconnect the hose from the rivet gun when it is to be out of use for an appreciable length of time.

Rivet Set

A rivet set is the device that actually drives the rivet. Standard rivet sets have a 0.401-inch shank that fits into the rivet gun and a cup in the end of the end of the shank that fits over the head of the rivet.

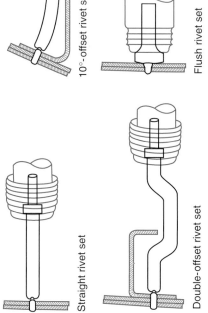

Straight rivet set

10°-offset rivet set

Double-offset rivet set

Flush rivet set

Figure 2-56. *Rivet sets*

The radius of the cup in the rivet set should be slightly greater than the radius of the rivet head. This concentrates the blows from the rivet gun and prevents the set from damaging the skin being riveted.

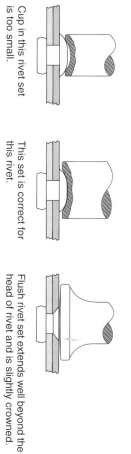

Cup in this rivet set is too small.

This set is correct for this rivet.

Flush rivet set extends well beyond the head of rivet and is slightly crowned.

Figure 2-57. *The radius of the cup in a rivet set is slightly greater than the radius of the rivet head. This allows the blows from the rivet gun to be concentrated on the rivet head.*

Bucking Bars

The rivet gun drives the rivet set against the manufactured head of a rivet, but it is the bucking bar that actually forms the shop, or bucked, head of the rivet. Bucking bars are made of hardened and polished steel and are available in many shapes and sizes. When choosing a bucking bar, match the weight of the bar with the size of the rivet.

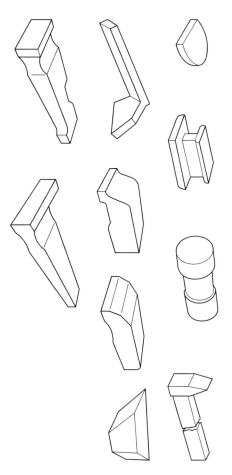

Figure 2-58. *Typical bucking bars*

Rivet Diameter (inch)	Bucking Bar Weight (pounds)
3/32	2 to 3
1/8	3 to 4
5/32	3-1/2 to 4-1/2
3/16	4 to 5
1/4	5 to 6-1/2

Figure 2-59. *Relationship between rivet size and proper bucking bar weight*

Compression Rivet Squeezers

You can use compression riveting to rapidly upset a large number of rivets reachable with a rivet squeezer. Rivets driven by this method are uniform and are not work-hardened by hammering.

The two most widely used pneumatically operated squeezers are the C-yoke and the alligator-yoke seen in Figure 2-60.

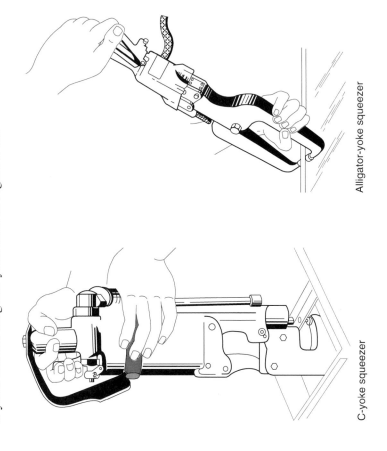

C-yoke squeezer

Alligator-yoke squeezer

Figure 2-60. *Compression rivet squeezers*

Sheet-Metal Assembly Tools

The actual riveting is a small part of the joining of sheets of metal. The layout, cutting, drilling, burring, and assembly must all be done carefully and accurately before the part is ready to be riveted.

When you have drilled, deburred and sprayed the mating parts with a corrosion-inhibiting primer, you must assemble them before riveting. You can hold the sheets together with sheet metal screws, but this is time consuming and damages the holes. It is best to use some form of patented fastener such as the Cleco fastener seen in Figure 2-61. These fasteners are quick and easy to install and remove, they hold the sheets tightly together, they are inexpensive, so an adequate number of them can be used, and they do not damage the rivet holes. They are available in sizes for all standard rivets and are color-coded to make selection of the correct size easy.

Cleco fastener. A patented spring-type fastener used to hold metal sheets together until they can be permanently riveted together.

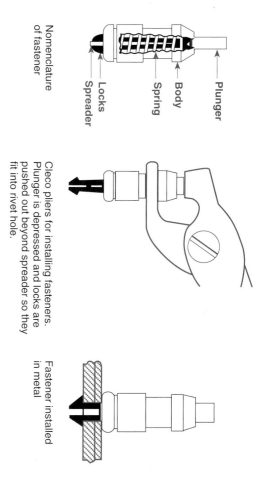

Figure 2-61. *Cleco sheet metal fastener*

Nomenclature of fastener

Plunger
Body
Spring
Locks
Spreader

Cleco pliers for installing fasteners. Plunger is depressed and locks are pushed out beyond spreader so they fit into rivet hole.

Fastener installed in metal

Figure 2-62. *Color-coding identifies the size of a Cleco fastener.*

Rivet Diameter (inch)	Cleco Fastener Color
3/32	Silver
1/8	Copper
5/32	Black
3/16	Brass
1/4	Copper

Hole Finder

When replacing a piece of aircraft skin, you must drill the holes in the skin so they line up exactly with the holes in the structure beneath it. To do this, use a hole finder, or strap duplicator. This tool is made of two straps of metal spot-welded together at one end. The open end of one strap has a drill bushing that fits the proper drill for the rivet, and the open end of the other strap has a pin that fits into the rivet hole. This pin is exactly in line with the hole in the drill bushing. To use this tool, slip the hole finder over the new skin. The pin drops into the rivet hole in the structure below the skin. The drill bushing is now exactly over the hole and you can drill the skin through the bushing.

Spot welds

Drill Bushing

Pin

Figure 2-63. *A hole finder may be slipped over the edge of a new piece of aircraft skin to position the drill directly over the hole in the original structure.*

Chip Chaser

When holes are drilled through partially assembled sheets of metal, chips are left between the sheets that can prevent the sheets from fitting tightly together. You must remove these chips with a chip chaser. These can be purchased, but you can make a good one with a worn-out hacksaw blade. Grind off the teeth and grind a notch into its edge at one end. Put a handle on the other end of the blade, and you have a very handy and effective tool. Slip the blade between the sheets and maneuver it until the chips are in the notch, then pull them out.

STUDY QUESTIONS: TOOLS FOR SHEET-METAL CONSTRUCTION AND REPAIR

Answers begin on Page 167. Page numbers refer to chapter text.

53. Layout lines should be marked on sheet metal with a _____ . *Page 88*

54. Two things that determine the correct speed for a bandsaw blade are the type of metal being cut and its _____ . *Page 91*

55. When choosing the number of teeth for a hacksaw blade, choose one that will allow at least _____ (how many) teeth to be on the material being cut. *Page 92*

56. A flat chisel is ground so its cutting angle is approximately _____ °. *Page 93*

57. Three ways of indicating the size of a twist drill are _____ , _____ , and _____ . *Page 95*

58. A number 30 twist drill is _____ (larger or smaller) than a number 50 drill. *Page 95*

59. Straight bends across a sheet of metal can be made with a _____ brake. *Page 97*

60. Straight bends with a large radius are made in a piece of sheet metal with a _____ . *Page 98*

61. Compound curves in a piece of sheet metal may be made with a soft-face mallet and a _____ . *Page 98*

62. A large-diameter hard rivet should be driven with as _____ (many or few) blows from the rivet gun as possible. *Page 99*

63. The radius of the cup in a rivet set should be _____ (greater or smaller) than the radius of the rivet head it fits. *Page 101*

64. The proper bucking bar used to drive a ⅛-inch rivet should weigh between _____ and _____ pounds. *Page 101*

65. The Cleco fastener to use in a hole for a ³⁄₃₂-inch rivet is colored _____ . *Page 103*

Layout and Forming

Laying out and forming sheet aluminum and magnesium require techniques and considerations quite different from those used in commercial sheet-metal work. Aircraft metals have high strength for their light weight, and their heat treatment makes them so brittle that they must be bent with a large enough radius that the metal is not excessively strained.

Grain of the Metal

When an ingot is rolled into a sheet of metal, the metal grains align in such a way that the maximum strength of the sheet is in a line parallel to the direction the sheet was rolled. This direction is said to be with the grain of the metal. If you look closely at the surface of a piece of aluminum alloy sheet, you can see lines that run the length of the metal. For the maximum strength of a formed, angled piece of sheet metal, make bends across the grain of the metal.

Bend Radius

When you bend a piece of metal, the material on the inside of the bend is subjected to a compressive stress and that on the outside is subjected to a tensile stress. There is a neutral plane, or neutral axis, within the metal that is not subjected to either a tensile or compressive stress. This plane lies at 44.5% of the thickness of the metal from the inside radius of the bend, but for practical purposes, the neutral plane can be considered to be in the middle of the metal thickness.

Figure 2-64 shows the minimum bend radius, measured on the inside of the bend, that can be used with the various aluminum alloys without weakening the metal.

ingot. A large block of metal that was molded as it was poured from the furnace. Ingots are further processed into sheets, bars, tubes, or structural beams.

bend radius. The radius of the inside of a bend.

neutral axis (neutral plane). A line through a piece of material that is bent. The material in the outside of the bend is stretched and that on the inside of the bend is shrunk. The material along the neutral plane is neither shrunk nor stretched.

Minimum Bend Radius for Aluminum Alloys								
Alloy	Thickness							
	0.020	0.025	0.032	0.040	0.051	0.064	0.072	0.081
2024-O	1/32	1/16	1/16	1/16	1/16	3/32	1/8	1/8
2024-T4	1/16	1/16	3/32	3/32	1/8	5/32	7/32	1/4
5052-O	1/32	1/32	1/16	1/16	1/16	1/16	1/8	1/8
5052-H34	1/32	1/16	1/16	3/32	3/32	1/8	1/8	1/8
6061-O	1/32	1/32	1/32	1/16	1/16	1/16	3/32	3/32
6061-T4	1/32	1/32	1/32	1/16	1/16	3/32	5/32	5/32
6061-T6	1/16	1/16	1/16	3/32	1/16	1/8	3/16	3/16
7075-O	1/16	1/16	1/16	3/32	3/32	3/32	5/32	3/16
7075-W	3/32	1/8	1/8	1/16	3/16	1/4	9/32	5/16
7075-T6	1/8	1/8	1/8	3/16	1/4	5/16	3/8	7/16

Figure 2-64. *Minimum bend radius for various aluminum alloys*

Setback

Setback is the distance the radius bar on the brake, such as in Figure 2-65, is moved back from the brake hinge line. For a 90° bend this is equal to the bend radius plus the thickness of the metal. For a bend of more or less than 90°, the bend radius plus metal thickness must be multiplied by the K-factor from the table in Figure 2-66.

Degree	K-Factor	Degree	K-Factor	Degree	K-Factor	Degree	K-Factor
1	0.00873	46	0.42447	91	1.0176	136	2.4751
2	0.01745	47	0.43481	92	1.0355	137	2.5386
3	0.02618	48	0.44523	93	1.0538	138	2.6051
4	0.03492	49	0.45573	94	1.0724	139	2.6746
5	0.04366	50	0.46631	95	1.0913	140	2.7475
6	0.05241	51	0.47697	96	1.1106	141	2.8239
7	0.06116	52	0.48773	97	1.1303	142	2.9042
8	0.06993	53	0.49858	98	1.1504	143	2.9887
9	0.07870	54	0.50952	99	1.1708	144	3.0777
10	0.08749	55	0.52057	100	1.1917	145	3.1716
11	0.09629	56	0.53171	101	1.2131	146	3.2708
12	0.10510	57	0.54295	102	1.2349	147	3.3759
13	0.11393	58	0.55431	103	1.2572	148	3.4874
14	0.12278	59	0.56577	104	1.2799	149	3.6059
15	0.13165	60	0.57735	105	1.3032	150	3.7320
16	0.14054	61	0.58904	106	1.3270	151	3.8667
17	0.14945	62	0.60086	107	1.3514	152	4.0108
18	0.15838	63	0.61280	108	1.3764	153	4.1653
19	0.16734	64	0.62487	109	1.4019	154	4.3315
20	0.17633	65	0.63707	110	1.4281	155	4.5107
21	0.18534	66	0.64941	111	1.4550	156	4.7046
22	0.19438	67	0.66188	112	1.4826	157	4.9151
23	0.20345	68	0.67451	113	1.5108	158	5.1455
24	0.21256	69	0.68728	114	1.5399	159	5.3995
25	0.22169	70	0.70021	115	1.5697	160	5.6713
26	0.23087	71	0.71329	116	1.6003	161	5.9758
27	0.24008	72	0.72654	117	1.6318	162	6.3137
28	0.24933	73	0.73996	118	1.6643	163	6.6911
29	0.25862	74	0.75355	119	1.6977	164	7.1154
30	0.26795	75	0.76733	120	1.7320	165	7.5957
31	0.27732	76	0.78128	121	1.7675	166	8.1443
32	0.28674	77	0.79543	122	1.8040	167	8.7769
33	0.29621	78	0.80978	123	1.8418	168	9.5144
34	0.30573	79	0.82434	124	1.8807	169	10.385
35	0.31530	80	0.83910	125	1.9210	170	11.430
36	0.32492	81	0.85408	126	1.9626	171	12.706
37	0.33459	82	0.86929	127	2.0057	172	14.301
38	0.34433	83	0.88472	128	2.0503	173	16.350
39	0.35412	84	0.90040	129	2.0965	174	19.081
40	0.36397	85	0.91633	130	2.1445	175	22.904
41	0.37388	86	0.93251	131	2.1943	176	26.636
42	0.38386	87	0.80978	132	2.2460	177	38.188
43	0.39391	88	0.96569	133	2.2998	178	57.290
44	0.40403	89	0.9827	134	2.3558	179	114.590
45	0.41421	90	1.0000	135	2.4142	180	Infinite

Figure 2-66. *K-factor for finding setback for angles other than 90°*

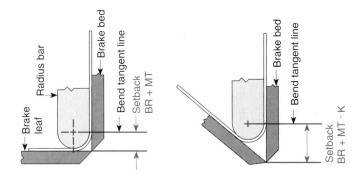

Figure 2-65. *Setback is the distance the bend tangent line is moved back from the brake leaf.*

setback. The distance the jaws of a brake must be set back from the mold line to form a bend. Setback for a 90° bend is equal to the inside radius of the bend plus the thickness of the metal being bent. For a bend other than 90°, a K-factor must be used. *See also* K-factor.

K-factor. A factor used in sheet metal work to determine the setback for other than a 90° bend.

Setback = K · (bend radius + metal thickness).

For bends of less than 90° the value of K is less than 1; for bends greater than 90° the value of K is greater than 1.

bend tangent line. A line made in a sheet metal layout that indicates the point at which the bend is started.

Bend Allowance

Bend allowance is the actual amount of material used in the bend. Find it by using a chart such as the one in Figure 2-67. In this chart, the top number in each group at the intersection of the metal thickness and bend radius is the bend allowance for a 90° bend. The bottom number is the bend allowance for each degree of bend.

Metal Thickness	Radius of Bend (inches)													
	1/32	1/16	3/32	1/8	5/32	3/16	7/32	1/4	9/32	5/16	11/32	3/8	7/16	1/2
0.020	.062 .000693	.113 .001251	.161 .001792	.210 .002333	.259 .002874	.309 .003433	.358 .003977	.406 .004515	.455 .005056	.505 .005614	.554 .006155	.603 .006695	.702 .007795	.799 .008877
0.025	.066 .000736	.116 .001294	.165 .001835	.214 .002376	.263 .002917	.313 .003476	.362 .004017	.410 .004558	.459 .005098	.509 .005657	.558 .006198	.607 .006739	.705 .007838	.803 .008920
0.028	.068 .000759	.119 .001318	.167 .001859	.216 .002400	.265 .002941	.315 .003499	.364 .004040	.412 .004581	.461 .005122	.511 .005680	.560 .006221	.609 .006762	.708 .007862	.805 .008944
0.032	.071 .000787	.121 .001345	.170 .001886	.218 .002427	.267 .002968	.317 .003526	.366 .004067	.415 .004608	.463 .005149	.514 .005708	.562 .006249	.611 .006789	.710 .007889	.807 .008971
0.038	.075 .000837	.126 .001396	.174 .001937	.223 .002478	.272 .003019	.322 .003577	.371 .004118	.419 .004659	.468 .005200	.518 .005758	.567 .006299	.616 .006840	.715 .007940	.812 .009021
0.040	.077 .000853	.127 .001411	.176 .001952	.224 .002493	.273 .003034	.323 .003593	.372 .004134	.421 .004675	.469 .005215	.520 .005774	.568 .006315	.617 .006856	.716 .007955	.813 .009037
0.051		.134 .001413	.183 .002034	.232 .002575	.280 .003116	.331 .003675	.379 .004215	.428 .004756	.477 .005297	.527 .005855	.576 .006397	.624 .006934	.723 .008037	.821 .009119
0.064		.144 .001595	.192 .002136	.241 .002676	.290 .003218	.340 .003776	.389 .004317	.437 .004858	.486 .005399	.536 .005957	.585 .006498	.634 .007039	.732 .008138	.830 .009220
0.072			.198 .002202	.247 .002743	.296 .003284	.346 .003842	.394 .004283	.443 .004924	.492 .005465	.542 .006023	.591 .006564	.639 .007105	.738 .008205	.836 .009287
0.078			.202 .002249	.251 .002790	.300 .003331	.350 .003889	.399 .004430	.447 .004963	.496 .005512	.546 .006070	.595 .006611	.644 .007152	.743 .008252	.840 .009333
0.081			.204 .002272	.253 .002813	.302 .003354	.352 .003912	.401 .004453	.449 .004969	.498 .005535	.548 .006094	.598 .006635	.646 .007176	.745 .008275	.842 .009357
0.091			.212 .002350	.260 .002891	.309 .003432	.359 .003990	.408 .004531	.456 .005072	.505 .005613	.555 .006172	.604 .006713	.653 .007254	.752 .008353	.849 .009435
0.094			.214 .002374	.262 .002914	.311 .003455	.361 .004014	.410 .004555	.459 .005096	.507 .005637	.558 .006195	.606 .006736	.655 .007277	.754 .008376	.851 .009458
0.102				.268 .002977	.317 .003518	.367 .004076	.416 .004617	.464 .005158	.513 .005699	.563 .006257	.612 .006798	.661 .007339	.760 .008439	.857 .009521
0.109				.273 .003031	.321 .003572	.372 .004131	.420 .004672	.469 .005213	.518 .005754	.568 .006312	.617 .006853	.665 .007394	.764 .008493	.862 .009575
0.125				.284 .003156	.333 .003697	.383 .004256	.432 .004797	.480 .005338	.529 .005878	.579 .006437	.628 .006978	.677 .007519	.776 .008618	.873 .009700
0.156					.355 .003939	.405 .004497	.453 .005038	.502 .005579	.551 .006120	.601 .006679	.650 .007220	.698 .007761	.797 .008860	.895 .009942
0.188						.417 .004747	.476 .005288	.525 .005829	.573 .006370	.624 .006928	.672 .007469	.721 .008010	.820 .009109	.917 .010191
0.250								.568 .006313	.617 .006853	.667 .007412	.716 .007953	.764 .008494	.863 .009593	.961 .010675

Figure 2-67. *Bend allowance chart showing the amount of material used in a 90° bend and in each degree of bend*

If a bend allowance chart is not available, use this formula:

$$\text{Bend Allowance} = (0.01743\ R) + (0.0078\ T) \cdot \text{degree of bend}$$

R = Bend radius
T = Metal thickness

Layout of a Sheet-Metal Channel

In order to best understand the technique of sheet-metal layout, consider a channel such as that seen in Figure 2-68. This channel is made of 0.040-inch-thick 2024T4 aluminum alloy. The dimension across the bottom of the channel is 2 inches and each side of the channel is 1 inch high.

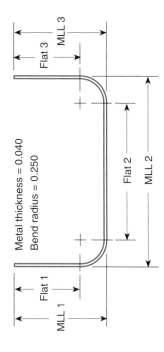

Metal thickness = 0.040
Bend radius = 0.250

Flat 1 · MLL 1 · Flat 2 · MLL 2 · Flat 3 · MLL 3

Mold Line Length 1 = 1 inch
MLL 2 = 2 inches
MLL 3 = 1 inch

Figure 2-68. *Sheet-metal channel used for explanation of layout*

To lay out this channel, follow these steps:

1. Choose the correct bend radius.
2. Find the setback.
3. Find the length of each of the flats.
4. Find the bend allowance.
5. Lay out the flat pattern.
6. Draw the sight lines on the flat pattern.

Choose the Correct Bend Radius

Use the chart in Figure 2-64 (Page 105) to choose the correct bend radius for the alloy and temper and the metal thickness. For 0.040, 2024T4 the minimum allowable radius is $\frac{3}{32}$ inch (0.094 inch). Since this is a practical problem, choose a radius of $\frac{1}{4}$ inch (0.250 inch).

bend allowance. The amount of material actually used to make a bend in a piece of sheet metal. Bend allowance depends upon the thickness of the metal and the radius of the bend and is normally found in a bend allowance chart.

mold line. A line used in the development of a flat pattern for a formed piece of sheet metal. The mold line is an extension of the flat side of a part beyond the radius. The mold line dimensions of a part is the dimension made to the intersection of mold lines and is the dimension the part would have if its corners had no radius.

Find the Setback

Since all of the angles in this channel are 90° angles, the setback is simply the bend radius of 0.250 plus the metal thickness of 0.040, or 0.290 inch. Move the radius bar of the brake back so the bend tangent is 0.290 inch back from the brake leaf hinge. *See* Figure 2-65, Page 106.

Find the Length of Each of the Flats

The flats, or flat portions of the channel, are equal to the mold line length minus the setback for each of the sides, and the mold line length minus two setbacks for the bottom.

Flat 1 = 1.00 − 0.29 = 0.71 inch
Flat 2 = 2.00 − (2 · 0.29) = 1.42 inch
Flat 3 = 1.00 − 0.29 = 0.71 inch

Find the Bend Allowance

Use the bend allowance chart in Figure 2-67, Page 107, by following a row of figures for 0.040-inch-thick material to the column for $\frac{1}{4}$ inch (0.250) bend radius. The bend allowance is 0.421 inch, which rounds off to the practical dimension of 0.42 inch.

Just to prove that the bend allowance formula on Page 108 works:

Bend Allowance = $(0.01743\ R) + (0.0078\ T) \cdot$ degree of bend
= $[(0.01743 \cdot 0.25) + (0.0078 \cdot 0.040)] \cdot 90$
= 0.420 inch

Lay Out the Flat Pattern

When you know the lengths of the flats and the bend allowances, you can lay out the flat pattern. Note that the metal needed to make the channel is less than the dimensions of the outside of the channel. This is because the metal follows the radius of the bend rather than going from mold line to mold line. The larger the bend radius, the less the material used for the channel. *See* Figure 2-69.

flat pattern layout. The pattern for a sheet metal part that has the material used for each flat surface, and for all of the bends marked out with bend-tangent lines drawn between the flats and bend allowances.

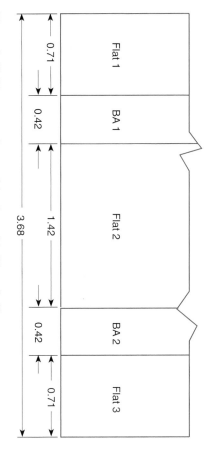

Figure 2-69. *Flat pattern layout of the channel in Figure 2-68*

Draw the Sight Lines on the Flat Pattern

The pattern laid out in Figure 2-69 is complete, except for a very handy line you can draw to help position the bend tangent line directly at the point the bend should start. Draw a line inside the bend allowance that is one bend radius away from the bend tangent line for the sides of the channel. Put the metal in the brake with the flat for one side of the channel under the clamp and adjust the position of the metal until the sight line is directly below the edge of the radius bar, as is shown in Figure 2-71. Now clamp the brake on the metal and you can raise the leaf to make the bend. The bend will begin exactly on the bend tangent line.

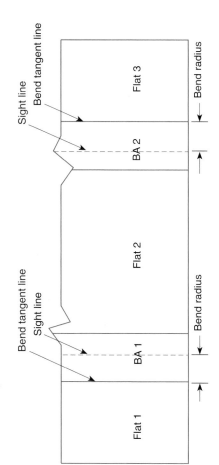

Figure 2-70. *Draw a sight line inside of the bend allowance area that is one bend radius from the bend tangent line that will be under the radius bar.*

Folding a Box

You can form a box the same way as the channel just described, but you must also drill relief holes at the intersection of the inside bend tangent lines, and bend it in a box brake. The relief holes, whose diameter is approximately twice the bend radius, relieve stresses in the metal as it is bent and prevent the metal tearing. Two opposite sides of the box are bent first, and then the fingers of the brake adjusted so the folded-up sides will ride up in the cracks between the fingers when the leaf is raised to bend the other two sides. *See* Figure 2-72.

sight line. A line drawn on a sheet metal layout that is one bend radius from the bend-tangent line. The sight line is lined up directly below the nose of the radius bar in a cornice brake. When the metal is clamped in this position, the bend tangent line is in the correct position for the start of the bend.

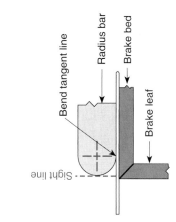

Figure 2-71. *Sight down over the edge of the radius bar and adjust the metal in the brake until the sight line is directly below the tip of the radius bar. Clamp the brake and make the bend.*

relief hole. A hole drilled at the point at which two bend lines meet in a piece of sheet metal. This hole spreads the stresses caused by the bends and prevents the metal cracking.

Forming Compound Curves

Large compound curves are formed in sheets of metal in the aircraft factories with drop hammers. The metal to be formed is placed over a heavy metal female die, and a matching male die is dropped onto the sheet metal. It drives the metal down into the female die and forms the compound curves with a minimum of work hardening of the material.

Smaller parts with more drastic curves are formed in hydropresses. The metal to be formed is cut to shape and all of the burrs are removed from its edges. This piece, called a blank, is then placed over a hard steel male die and is held in place by locator pins on the die fitting through index holes in the blank. The die with the blank is placed on the bed of the hydropress and a rubber pad in the ram of the press is forced down over the die with several thousand tons of pressure. The sheet metal is forced down into all of the recesses of the die and down along its sides.

Forming Small Compound-Curved Parts in the Maintenance Shop

It is often necessary to fabricate small compound-curved parts in the maintenance shop, for example, a reinforcing doubler to go inside a fuselage ring when splicing in a replacement section.

compound curve. A curve formed in more than one plane. The surface of a sphere is a compound curve.

doubler. A piece of sheet metal used to strengthen and stiffen a repair in a sheet metal structure.

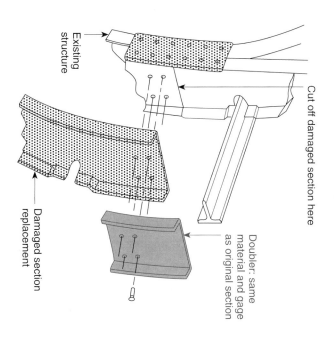

Cut off damaged section here

Existing structure

Doubler: same material and gage as original section

Damaged section replacement

Figure 2-73. *A formed reinforcing doubler is used when splicing a new section of a fuselage ring in place. This doubler has compound curves.*

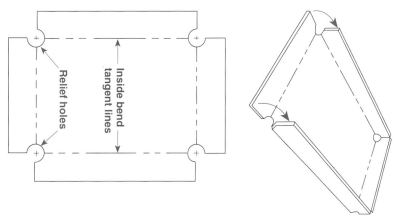

Inside bend tangent lines

Relief holes

Figure 2-72. *When laying out a box, drill relief holes at the intersections of the inside bend tangent lines. These relief holes relieve stresses that could cause the box to crack in the corners.*

To form this reinforcement, first make a forming block of hardwood, such as birch or maple, that fits into the fuselage ring with enough clearance for the thickness of the doubler metal. The radius on the edges of the forming block should be the same as that inside the fuselage ring. The edges should taper back about three degrees so the metal will be bent more than 90° and will spring back to an exact right angle. Make a backup plate of hardwood, the same shape as the forming block, but just enough smaller that it comes to the edge of the radius on the forming block. Drill holes for bolts that are used as alignment pins. These bolts are not used to clamp the blocks together, but rather to keep them from shifting.

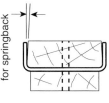

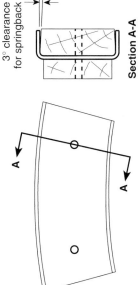

3° clearance for springback

A

A

Section A-A

Figure 2-74. *A forming block and backup block used for forming compound curves in a piece of aluminum alloy.*

Cut the sheet metal blank from the same alloy and thickness as is used in the fuselage ring, and drill holes to fit over the alignment pins. Make the blank slightly larger than needed, as it can be trimmed to the exact dimensions when the forming is complete, but do not make it excessively large because one side has to stretch while the other side must shrink. Remove all burrs from the edges of the material, especially in the side that must stretch because a nick or burr could cause the material to crack.

Place the metal between the forming block and backup block and clamp them tightly in a large vise with the concave curve up. Use a soft-face mallet and begin working the metal down from near the ends, working toward the center. Hold a tapered wedge of hardwood behind the metal as is shown in Figure 2-75 and strike the metal as near the edge of the radius as you can. Fold the metal down against the forming block by bending it just a little with each blow of the mallet. As you fold it down, the metal will buckle, but keep these buckles small and they can be worked out by shrinking the metal. Make the bend using as few blows as possible to keep from work-hardening the material, while at the same time use enough blows to keep the buckles down to a size that can be worked out completely.

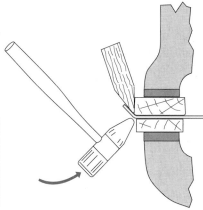

Figure 2-75. *Back the metal up with a piece of tapered hardwood to control the amount of bending done by each blow of the mallet.*

concave surface. A surface that is curved inward. The outer edges are higher than the center.

extruded angle. A structural angle formed by passing metal heated to its plastic state through specially shaped dies.

convex surface. A surface that is curved outward. The outer edges are lower than the center.

lightening hole. A hole cut in a piece of structural material to get rid of weight without losing any strength. A hole several inches in diameter may be cut in a piece of metal at a point where the metal is not needed for strength, and the edges of the hole are flanged to give it rigidity. A piece of metal with properly flanged lightening holes is more rigid than the metal before the holes were cut.

arbor press. A press with either a mechanically or hydraulically operated ram used in a maintenance shop for a variety of pressing functions.

joggle. A small offset near the edge of a piece of sheet metal. It allows one sheet of metal to overlap another sheet while maintaining a flush surface.

When you've finished the concave side of the reinforcement, turn the block over so the convex side is up and clamp it tightly in the vise. Begin working this side in the center of the bend and work toward the ends. The metal on this side must be stretched. Use the hardwood wedge behind the metal and form the curve with as few blows as possible, but with enough blows that the metal is stretched gradually so it does not crack and split.

It is often necessary to curve an extruded angle so it will conform to the shape of the structure. Gentle curves can be formed by shrinking or stretching one of the sides. To form a convex curve, stretch the side by hammering it with a soft-face mallet while holding it flat against a piece of steel. This thins and stretches the side and bends the angle. *See* Figure 2-76.

Form a concave curve in an extruded angle by shrinking one of the sides. Place the angle over a piece of hardwood that has had a V-shaped notch cut in it. Hammer on the standing side of the angle. The standing side of the angle must be shrunk to form the curve, and special care must be taken to prevent the material from buckling. It takes practice and skill to know exactly how hard to strike the material to form it without either excessively strain-hardening it or causing it to buckle. *See* Figure 2-77.

Flanging Lightening Holes

Thin sheet metal used for aircraft components usually has plenty of strength, but it often lacks stiffness or rigidity. To increase the stiffness of a part, the metal is often corrugated, and the edges of holes are flanged.

The web of a stamped metal wing rib does not carry an excessive amount of load, and the rib can be made much lighter by cutting large lightening holes that remove a considerable amount of metal. With these holes cut, the rib is still strong enough, but it lacks rigidity. If the edges of these lightening holes are flanged, the rib will be made stiff.

A set of flanging dies is used to flange the lightening holes. The hole is cut in the rib with a hole saw, a punch, or a fly cutter, and the edges are smoothed to prevent their cracking or tearing. The hole is placed over the tapered male die, which is placed in the female die. Pressure is applied with an arbor press that forces the dies together and flanges the edges of the lightening holes. *See* Figure 2-78.

Joggling

It is often necessary to install a doubler inside an aircraft structure and tie it to an extruded angle. In order for the doubler to lie flat against both the skin and the angle, its edges must be joggled, as in Figure 2-79.

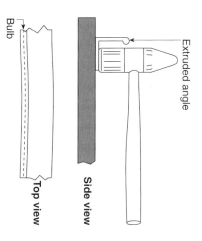

Extruded angle

Bulb

Side view

Top view

Figure 2-76. *A convex curve can be formed in an extruded angle by stretching one side of the angle.*

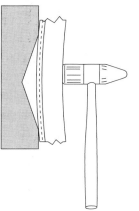

Figure 2-77. *A concave curve can be formed in an extruded angle by shrinking one side of the angle.*

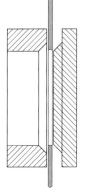

Figure 2-78. *A set of flanging dies is used to flange the edges of a lightening hole to give stiffness to thin sheet metal parts.*

Bulb angle

Figure 2-79. *A joggle allows a doubler to fit flat against the skin and also flat against the bulb angle.*

Answers begin on Page 167. Page numbers refer to chapter text.

66. The minimum bend radius for a piece of 0.040 2024T4 aluminum alloy is _____ inch. *Page 105*

67. The bend radius specified for a piece of aircraft sheet metal is the radius of the _____ (inside or outside) of the bend. *Page 105*

68. The metal on the inside of a bend is under a _____ (compressive or tensile) stress. *Page 105*

69. When making a bend in a piece of sheet metal, the metal will be the strongest if the bend is made _____ (with or across) the grain of the metal. *Page 105*

70. The minimum bend radius that should be used on a piece of 0.051-inch 7075-T6 sheet metal is _____ inch. *Page 105*

71. The setback required for making a 45° bend is _____ (more or less) than the setback for a 90° angle. *Page 106*

72. The correct setback for a 135° bend in a piece of 0.040 sheet metal with a ⅛-inch bend radius is _____ inch. *Page 106*

73. The bend allowance for a 90° bend in a piece of 0.051 aluminum alloy bent around a ⅛-inch radius is _____ inch. *Page 107*

74. The bend allowance for a 45° bend in a piece of 0.040 aluminum alloy bent around a ⅛-inch radius is _____ inch. *Page 107*

75. A channel using a ¼-inch bend radius will require _____ (more or less) material than one using a ⅛-inch bend radius. *Page 109*

76. Relief holes drilled in the corner of a pattern for a box should be drilled at the intersection of the _____ lines. *Page 111*

77. A sight line is drawn inside the bend allowance portion of a flat pattern a distance of one _____ from the bend tangent line that is clamped under the radius bar. *Page 110*

78. When forming a concave curve in a piece of sheet metal using a forming block, the forming should begin at the _____ (center or ends) of the curve. *Page 112*

79. When forming a convex curve in a piece of sheet metal using a forming block, the forming should begin at the _____ (center or ends) of the curve. *Page 113*

80. Flanging the edges of a lightening hole in a stamped sheet metal wing rib gives the rib added _____ (strength or stiffness). *Page 113*

Sheet-Metal Joints Using Solid Rivets

Riveted joints are an important part of an aircraft structure, and an aviation maintenance technician must know how to design a joint that will properly carry the stresses from one piece of material to the other. He or she must also know the proper way to install and remove rivets and know how to evaluate rivets.

Rivet Selection

When selecting rivets for a seam in an aircraft skin or for joining other pieces of aircraft sheet metal, take several things into consideration:

• If possible the rivet should not require heat treatment before it is driven. This means that if the required size is not excessive, AD (2117T) alloy rivets should be used rather than D (2017T) or DD (2024T) rivets.

• If magnesium sheets are to be joined, B (5056T) rivets should be used.

• Countersunk head rivets should be used in locations where smooth airflow is important. This essentially means at least on the forward half of the upper surface of the wing.

• Universal head rivets may be used for any location in which a protruding head rivet is required.

• The rivet size and material must be chosen so that the shear strength of the rivet is slightly less than the bearing strength of the sheets of material being joined. This allows the joint to fail by the rivets shearing rather than the metal tearing.

• Rivet size is chosen so the diameter of the rivet is approximately three times the thickness of the thickest sheet being joined.

Rivet Layout

When laying out the rows of rivets, the rivets should be close enough together to get maximum strength in the joint, but should not be so close that the holes weaken the material. The rivets must be placed far enough away from the edge of the metal that it does not tear. *See* Figure 2-80 on the next page.

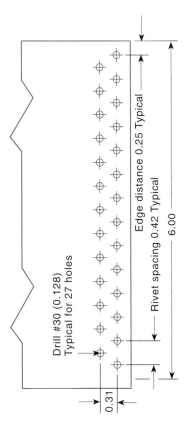

Figure 2-80. *Rivet layout for a two-row splice designed to carry 50% of the metal strength.*

Drill #30 (0.128)
Typical for 27 holes

0.31

Edge distance 0.25 Typical

6.00

Rivet spacing 0.42 Typical

Rivet Pitch

Rivet pitch is the distance between the center of adjacent rivet holes in a row. This should not be less than 3 rivet shank diameters, or more than 10 to 12 diameters.

Transverse Pitch

Transverse pitch, also called rivet gage, is the distance between rows of rivets in a multirow seam. Transverse pitch should be 75% of the rivet pitch.

Edge Distance

To prevent the rivets tearing the sheet at the edge, the center of the rivet holes should be no closer to the edge of the sheet than two diameters of the rivet shank for protruding head rivets, or two-and-one-half diameters for flush rivets.

Layout Practice

Consider this problem. We want to rivet together two pieces of 0.040 2024T3 material that are 6 inches wide so that the strength of the riveted joint will carry at least 50% of the strength of the metal. Protruding head rivets are to be used. Take these steps:

• Find the strength needed by the joint.

• Select the rivet.

• Lay out the rivet pattern.

pitch (rivet). The distance between the centers of adjacent rivets installed in the same row.

transverse pitch. *See* gage.

gage (rivet). The distance between rows of rivets in a multirow seam. Gage is also called transverse pitch.

edge distance. The distance between the center of a rivet hole and the edge of the sheet of metal.

Find the Strength Needed by the Joint

Refer to the chart in Figure 2-14 on Page 75 and find that the minimum tensile strength of 2024-T3 aluminum alloy is 70,000 psi. The sheets we are to join are 0.040 inch thick and 6 inches wide. This gives a cross-sectional area of 0.24 square inch.

6 · 0.040 = 0.24 square inch

Find the full strength of this material by multiplying this area by the strength of the material in pounds per square inch.

70,000 psi · 0.24 sq. in. = 16,800 pounds

This joint is required to carry 50% of this strength, so it must carry 8,400 pounds.

16,800 · 0.50 = 8,400 pounds

Select the Rivet

Protruding head rivets are to be used, so we will use universal head (MS20470) rivets. The thickest sheet to be joined is 0.040 inches thick, so the rivet diameter should be three times this, or 0.12 inch. The nearest standard diameter to this is $\frac{1}{8}$-inch (0.125). To prevent having to heat-treat the rivets before driving them, choose AD (2117T) rivets.

Refer to the chart in Figure 2-15 on Page 76 to find that each $\frac{1}{8}$-inch 2117T rivet has a shear strength of 331 pounds. The joint should fail in shear rather than in bearing, so check the bearing strength chart of Figure 2-17 on Page 76 and see that the bearing strength for 0.040 sheet with $\frac{1}{8}$-inch rivets is 410 pounds. This shows that the bearing strength and shear strength are reasonably close together, but the bearing strength is greater than the shear strength, so this is a good choice.

The joint must carry 8,400 pounds, so 25.4, or actually 26 rivets, are needed.

You can also select the rivet by using a chart similar to the one in Figure 2-81, which is excerpted from the Advisory Circular 43.13-1A. According to this chart, we will need 7.7 rivets per inch for 100% strength. But since we are only designing for 50% strength, we will need only 3.85 rivets per inch, or for the six-inch width, will need 23.1, or 24 rivets. The two-rivet difference found by the two methods is caused by the use of different sources of information for the strength of the aluminum alloy sheet. When a manufacturer's engineering data disagrees with the general information in AC 43.13-1A, always use the manufacturer's information.

Notice the line below the 4.9 in the $\frac{1}{8}$-inch rivet column in the chart in Figure 2-81. When a $\frac{1}{8}$-inch AD rivet is used in any sheet thicker than 0.025 inch, the rivet will shear. When used in 0.025 or thinner sheet, the metal will tear. *See* Figure 2-81 on the next page.

| Thickness of Metal (inches) | Number of AD Protruding-Head Rivets Needed Per Inch Width of Damage | | | | | Number of Bolts Needed |
	3/32	1/8	5/32	3/16	1/4	AN-3
0.016	6.5	4.9				
0.020	6.9	4.9				
0.025	8.6	4.9	3.9			
0.032	11.1	6.2	3.9	3.3		
0.036	12.5	7.0	3.9	3.3	2.4	3.3
0.040	13.8	7.7	4.5	3.5	2.4	3.3
0.051		9.8	5.0	4.5	2.5	3.3
0.064		12.3	6.4	5.6	3.1	3.3
0.081			8.1	7.1	3.9	3.3
0.091			10.2	7.9	4.4	3.3
0.102			11.4	8.9	4.9	3.4
0.128			12.8	11.2	6.2	3.4

Number of Rivets or Bolts Required for Structural Repair of Bare 2024-T3 Aluminum Alloy

Notes:
1. For stringers in the upper surface of a wing, or in a fuselage, 80% of the number of rivets shown may be used.
2. For intermediate frames, 60% of the number of rivets shown may be used.
3. For single-lap sheet joints, 75% of the number shown may be used.
4. Combinations of sheet thickness and rivet size *above the line* in each column will fail in bearing (the sheet will tear). Combinations *below the line* will fail in shear (the rivet will shear).

Figure 2-81. *Chart for determining correct number of rivets for a repair*

Lay Out the Rivet Pattern

You can make a good joint by using two rows of rivets. To stagger them, we must have an odd number of rivets, so use 27 rivets with 14 in one row and 13 in the other row. Figure 2-80, Page 116, shows the way this layout is made. The minimum edge distance is 2D, or $\frac{1}{4}$ inch. This leaves 5.5 inches between the two end rivets and we want 14 rivets in this row, so the rivet pitch will be 0.42 inch. This is greater than the minimum pitch, which is 3D or 0.375. The transverse pitch is 75% of the pitch, or 0.31 inch.

Spray the metal very lightly with zinc chromate primer and draw a line 0.25 inch from the end with a sharp soft lead pencil. This line is the center of the rivets in the first row and is the proper edge distance from the end of the metal. Make a mark across this line 0.25 inch from each edge of the metal. These mark the centers of the end rivet holes. Divide the distance between the end rivets into 13 equal spaces. This is 0.42 inch, and to be sure the spaces are equal, set a pair of dividers to this distance and make a very small mark across your pencil line for the center of each rivet hole.

Draw a line 0.31 inch from the first row of rivets. This is the center line for the second row of rivets. Place a mark across this line midway between each rivet hole in the first row.

Mark the second sheet of metal with a line across its end 0.25 inch from the edge. This assures that the rivet holes in the bottom sheet will have the proper edge distance.

Hole Preparation for Protruding Head Rivets

After laying out the rivet pattern, you are ready to drill the holes and get the material ready to rivet together. Make a slight depression with a prick punch at each location at which a rivet hole is to be drilled. The prick punch has a sharper point than a center punch, and it can be more accurately positioned at the center of the marks you have just made. Tap the prick punch lightly with a small hammer.

When you've marked all of the rivet holes with a prick punch, use a center punch and make each prick punch mark slightly larger to enable a drill to start cutting without walking over the metal. Do not hit the center punch hard enough to distort the metal, but just hard enough to make a depression large enough for the drill point.

Choose the correct size drill for the rivet. The rivet hole must be large enough for the rivet to enter without scraping the sides, and it must not be too large for the rivet to completely fill when its shank is swelled by driving. Figure 2-82 shows the correct drill size to use for each of the most commonly used rivets.

Drilling the Holes

With the correct-size drill installed in the drill chuck of an air or electric drill motor, drill a pilot hole, usually one rivet-size smaller than the one you will use for joining the metal. In this case, choose a number 40 drill.

Place the metal sheet on a piece of scrap wood so your work bench will not be damaged by the drill. If you are right-handed, hold the drill motor in your right hand and support it away from the metal with your left hand in such a way that your two hands are working against each other. The right hand is trying to force the drill into the metal and the left hand is forcing it back. This allows good control of the drill motor and allows you to drill holes that are straight and true.

When all of the pilot holes are drilled in one of the sheets, use two small C-clamps with their jaws padded with masking tape to clamp the two sheets together. The edge-distance line you have drawn on the bottom sheet should be visible through the center of the holes in the second row, and the edges of the two sheets should be aligned. Drill through the end holes in the second row and install silver-colored (³⁄₃₂-inch) Cleco fasteners. Now the C-clamps can be removed and all of the other holes drilled with a number 30 drill. Install two copper-colored (¹⁄₈-inch) Clecos and remove the ones through the pilot holes and drill these holes through with the number 30 drill.

Remove the Clecos and deburr all of the holes by twisting a large drill, one about ¹⁄₄ inch in diameter, in the hole by hand, just enough to remove the burrs from the edges. The holes are now ready for the installation of protruding head rivets.

Rivet Size (inch)	Drill Size
3/32	40 (0.098)
1/8	30 (0.128)
5/32	21 (0.159)
3/16	11 (0.191)
1/4	F (0.257)
5/16	O (0.316)
3/8	V (0.377)

Figure 2-82. *Drill size for solid rivet installation*

drill motor. An electric or pneumatic motor that drives a chuck that holds a twist drill. The best drill motors produce high torque, and their speed can be controlled.

pilot hole. A small hole punched or drilled in a piece of sheet metal to locate a rivet hole.

Hole Preparation for Flush Rivets

If flush rivets are to be installed, the hole must be either countersunk or dimpled, depending upon the thickness of the metal.

Countersinking

The determination to countersink or dimple depends upon the thickness of the top sheet of metal. The metal must be thicker than the head of the rivet. *See* Figure 2-83.

Use a 100° countersink cutter with a ⅛-inch pilot, such as the one in Figure 2-84. Use a piece of scrap metal of the same thickness as is being riveted and drill several number 30 holes in it. Use these holes to set the depth of the countersink tool. Adjust the countersink stop until it cuts a depression that allows the rivet head to be flush with the surface of the metal.

Dimpling

If the metal to be joined is too thin to be countersunk, you can dimple it. This is a process in which you press the edges of the rivet hole into a cone shape that allows the rivet head to be flush with the surface of the metal. There are two methods of dimpling a piece of metal: radius dimpling and coin dimpling.

Radius Dimpling

Radius dimpling is done by pressing a male die through the rivet hole and into a female die. The male die is struck a blow with a hammer that forms the metal into the recess that allows the rivet head to be flush with the metal. The edges of a radius-dimpled hole curve smoothly into the hole without any sharp edges. *See* Figure 2-85.

---

countersinking. Preparation of a rivet hole for a flush rivet by beveling the edges of the holes with a cutter of the correct angle.

Desired: top skin thicker than head of rivet.

Acceptable: top skin as thick as head of rivet

Not acceptable: top skin thinner than head of rivet.

Figure 2-83. *Countersinking*

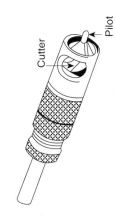

Pilot

Cutter

Figure 2-84. *A countersinking tool has a threaded cutter with a pilot surrounded with an adjustable skirt. The amount the cutter protrudes from the skirt determines the depth the countersink will cut.*

radius dimpling. A process of preparing a hole in sheet metal for flush riveting. A cone-shaped male die forces the edges of the rivet hole into the depression in a female die. Radius dimpling forms a round-edged depression into which the rivet head fits.

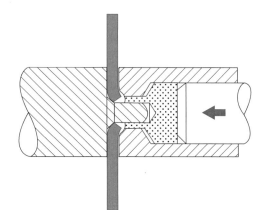

Figure 2-85. *Radius dimpling of a rivet hole*

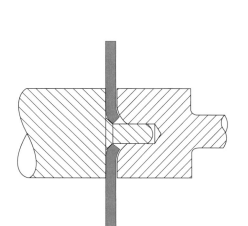

Figure 2-86. *Coin dimpling of a rivet hole*

Coin Dimpling

Coin dimpling is normally done with some type of pneumatic squeezer that exerts enough pressure to properly coin the material. The female die used for coin dimpling is considerably different than that used for radius dimpling. Figure 2-86 shows the dies used for coin dimpling.

To coin-dimple a hole, stick the male die through the hole to be dimpled and press it into the female die. Then force the coining ram up against the edge of the hole. This ram forces the metal tightly between the two dies and forms a dimple with sharp edges.

Coin dimpling can be done with the metal cold, or when dimpling hard metals such as 7075-T6 aluminum alloy, magnesium alloys, or titanium alloys, the dies may be heated with a built-in heater. This heat softens the metal enough that it can be dimpled without cracking. When the metal is heated for dimpling, it is said to be hot dimpled, or thermal dimpled.

When metals of different thicknesses are flush riveted together, a combination of countersinking and dimpling must be used. Figure 2-87 shows the procedure for three conditions.

Rivet Installation

Two methods of driving rivets are commonly used in aircraft construction and maintenance: compression riveting and gun riveting. Compression, or squeeze, riveting is often used when a large number of rivets must be installed in a location where both sides of the material are accessible to a clamp-type riveter. Gun riveting is used for all other locations.

Compression Riveting

When both sides of the material to be riveted are accessible to a rivet squeezer such as those seen in Figure 2-60 on Page 102, use compression riveting.

Set up the riveter for the chosen rivet and the thickness of material by installing the correct cupped set in the stationary jaw and a flat set in the movable jaw. Install washers between the jaws and the dollies, or sets, to adjust the distance they will be separated when the jaws are fully closed. This distance is equal to the total thickness of the materials being joined plus one half of the rivet shank diameter. This will allow the rivet to be upset with the proper size shop head. Squeeze a few rivets in a piece of scrap material of the correct thickness to check the adjustment of the sets. To use this type of riveter, just install the rivet in the hole, place the rivet head in the cupped dolly in the stationary jaw, and pull the trigger. Air pressure on a piston inside the squeezer forces the movable jaw toward the stationary jaw and squeezes the rivet, forming the shop head. *See* Figure 2-88 on the next page.

coin dimpling. A process of preparing a hole in sheet metal for flush riveting. A coining die is pressed into the rivet hole to form a sharp-edged depression into which the rivet head fits.

hot dimpling. A process used to dimple, or indent, the hole into which a flush rivet is to be installed. Hot dimpling is done by clamping the metal between heating elements and forcing the dies through the holes in the softened metal. Hot dimpling prevents hard metal from cracking when it is dimpled.

When top sheet is thick enough; it is countersunk and bottom sheet is left flat.

When top sheet is thin and bottom sheet thick, bottom sheet is countersunk and top sheet coin-dimpled.

When both sheets are too thin for countersinking, both are coin- or radius-dimpled.

Figure 2-87. *Hole preparation for flush riveting*

Gun Riveting

The greatest majority of rivets used in aircraft maintenance and repair are driven with rivet guns and bucking bars. Figure 2-89 shows the steps involved in properly driving a solid rivet. These steps are:

1. Install the correct rivet set.

2. Adjust the hitting force of the gun.

3. Install the rivet in the hole and position the rivet set against the rivet head.

4. Select the correct bucking bar and position it against the rivet shank.

5. Drive the rivet.

6. Evaluate the rivet.

   See Figure 2-89.

Install the Correct Rivet Set

Install the correct set for the rivet being driven in the rivet gun. The radius of the correct set is slightly larger than the radius of the rivet head, which allows the blows from the rivet gun to concentrate at the center of the rivet head. When the correct set is installed, screw a beehive spring onto the rivet gun to prevent the set dropping out of the gun.

Adjust the Hitting Force of the Gun

Hold the rivet set against a piece of scrap wood and pull the trigger. The set should hit the wood with a good solid blow, but not split it. Experience will give you the feel of the proper force the gun should have. If you are not sure of the adjustment, drive a few rivets in scrap material to get the feel of the proper adjustment.

Install the Rivet and Position the Set

The shank of the rivet chosen for installation should stick through the material by one-and-one-half diameters of the shank. Position the set so that it is exactly square with the material being riveted.

Select the Bucking Bar and Position It Against the Rivet Shank

Choose a bucking bar that is the proper weight for the rivet being driven and hold it absolutely flat against the end of the rivet shank. Figure 2-59 on Page 101 lists the correct weight of bucking bar for the rivet size.

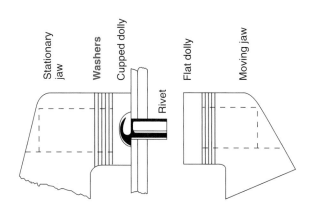

Figure 2-88. *Adjustment of the sets of a squeeze riveter is done by adding or removing washers between the jaws and the dollies.*

Stationary jaw

Washers

Cupped dolly

Rivet

Flat dolly

Moving jaw

A Select and install correct rivet set in gun.

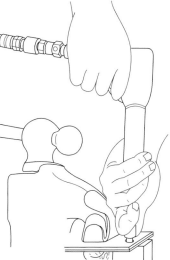

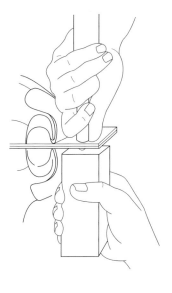

B Adjust hitting force of gun.

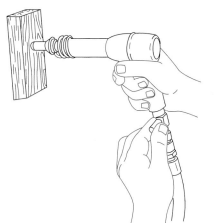

C Hold rivet set against rivet head.

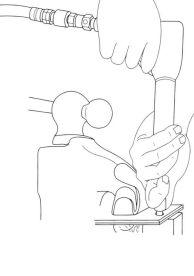

D Rivet set must be perfectly square with material being riveted.

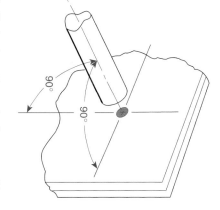

90°

90°

E Position bucking bar against end of rivet shank and drive rivet.

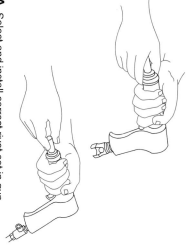

Figure 2-89. *Correct procedures for driving a solid rivet*

Drive the Rivet

Press the rivet set against the rivet head and the bucking bar against the rivet shank. Hold enough pressure on the bucking bar to try to force the rivet out of the hole, and just enough more pressure on the rivet gun that holds the rivet head against the metal. Holding this balance of pressure, pull the trigger of the gun, and drive the rivet with as few blows as possible.

Evaluate the Rivet

A properly driven rivet should have a shop head that is round with slightly bowed sides. The head is flat and parallel with the material, and the diameter of the head is one and one-half times the diameter of the rivet shank, and its thickness is one-half the shank diameter.

Some of the more common problems with their causes and suggested remedies are listed in Figure 2-90.

shop head. The head of a rivet which is formed when the shank is upset against a bucking bar.

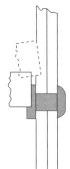

Open head. Set not held straight on head, or hole drilled at angle. "D" rivet remove; "AD" rivet drive more.

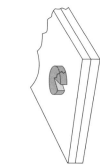

High head. Too long a shank, or not driven enough. "D" rivet remove; "AD" rivet drive more.

Cut formed head. Bucking bar did not cover entire end of rivet. Remove rivet.

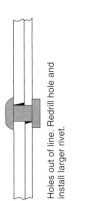

Cracked head. Hard rivet or hit too long. Remove rivet.

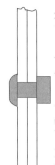

Correctly-driven 100°-countersunk rivet.

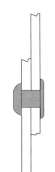

Thin head. Rivet too short or hit too hard. Remove rivet.

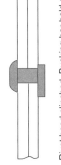

Rivet head clinched. Bucking bar held at angle when rivet was driven. Remove rivet.

Holes out of line. Redrill hole and install larger rivet.

Countersink too deep. Wrong rivet or wrong countersink. Remove rivet and replace with next larger size.

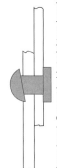

Correctly-driven universal head rivet.

Skin marked by rivet set. Set not centered on head. Remove rivet and burnish skin.

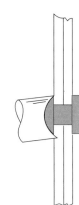

Rivet swelled between sheets. Parts not properly held together, or chips between sheets. Remove rivet, correct condition.

Formed head high on one side. Bucking bar held at angle when riveting. Remove rivet if head too thin on one side.

Figure 2-90. *Rivet evaluation*

Removal of Bad Rivets

To remove a rivet, follow the procedure in Figure 2-91.

1. Use a center punch to make a drill-starting indentation in the center of the manufactured head. AD rivets have a small dimple in the center of their head that makes this step easy.
2. Drill a straight hole in the center of the head with a drill that is one drill size smaller than the one used for the rivet. Drill this hole only through the head.
3. Knock the drilled head off the rivet shank with a cape chisel or pry it off with a pin punch.
4. Use a bucking bar to back up the skin around the rivet and punch the shank out of the skin with a pin punch.

NACA Method of Flush Riveting

The NACA (National Advisory Committe for Aeronautics) method of flush riveting uses a universal head or flush head rivet on the inside of the structure with the shop head formed in a countersunk hole in the outside skin.

Team Riveting

Manufacturing and repairing an airplane often requires two people to drive rivets. The operator of the rivet gun is usually on the outside and the rivet bucker is on the inside. When the two cannot communicate directly, a code of taps may be used.

Drill the rivet hole and countersink the outside skin. Insert the rivet from the inside. The shop head is formed in the countersunk depression. Use either a squeeze riveter or a gun. After driving the rivet, mill off the excess portion of the shop's head flush with the skin with an air-driven microshaver. See Figure 2-93.

When the bucker is in position and ready for the rivet to be driven, he or she taps on the shank of the rivet one time. The riveter feels this tap through the rivet gun and knows to drive the rivet. If the rivet is driven correctly the bucker taps twice before the rivet set is removed. This is a signal that the rivet

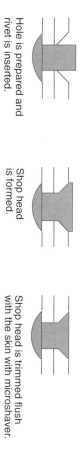

Hole is prepared and rivet is inserted.

Shop head is formed.

Shop head is trimmed flush with the skin with microshaver.

Figure 2-92. *NACA method of flush riveting*

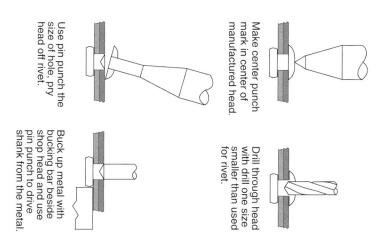

Make center punch mark in center of manufactured head.

Drill through head with drill one size smaller than used for rivet.

Use pin punch the size of hole, pry head off rivet.

Buck up metal with bucking bar beside shop head and use pin punch to drive shank from the metal.

Figure 2-91. *Procedure for removing a solid rivet*

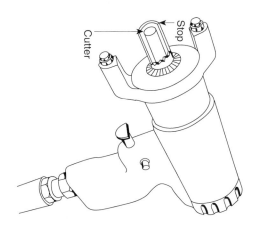

Stop

Cutter

Figure 2-93. *An air-driven microshaver*

is good and they should proceed to the next rivet. Three taps on the rivet means that the rivet is bad and will have to be removed. The riveter marks the rivet for removal and goes on to the next one.

STUDY QUESTIONS: SHEET-METAL JOINTS USING SOLID RIVETS

Answers begin on Page 167. Page numbers refer to chapter text.

81. The solid aluminum alloy rivet recommended for magnesium skin is made of alloy _____ . *Page 115*

82. The rivet to use for joining two sheets of metal should have a diameter at least _____ times the thickness of the thickest sheet being joined. *Page 115*

83. The distance between the center of the rivet holes in a single row of rivets is called the rivet _____ . *Page 116*

84. When a single row of MS 20470AD-4 rivets is laid out, the center of the holes should be no closer than _____ inch and no farther apart than _____ inches. *Page 116*

85. When laying out a two-row riveted seam, the rivet pitch is ½ inch, and the transverse pitch, or gage, should be _____ inch. *Page 116*

86. When making a rivet seam using MS20470AD-3 rivets, make sure that the center of the rivet holes is no closer to the edge of the sheet than _____ inch. *Page 116*

87. A riveted joint should be designed so it will fail in _____ (bearing or shear). *Page 117*

88. When a rivet pattern is laid out on a piece of aluminum alloy, the marks can be made easy to see if the metal is first sprayed with a light coat of _____ . *Page 118*

89. The correct size drill to use for a ⅛-inch rivet is a number _____ . *Page 119*

90. Pilot holes for ⅛-inch rivets should be made with a number _____ drill. *Page 119*

91. The determination to countersink or dimple a skin in preparation for flush riveting is determined by the _____ of the skin. *Page 120*

92. Two methods of dimpling are:
   a. _____
   b. _____
   Page 120

93. Hot, or thermal, dimpling is a form of _____ dimpling using heated dies. *Page 121*

94. The inside radius of a rivet set should be slightly _____ (larger or smaller) than the radius of the head of the rivet. *Page 122*

95. The shank of a rivet should stick out of the sheet by _____ times the rivet shank diameter. *Page 122*

96. A properly formed shop head on a rivet should have a diameter of _____ times the diameter of the rivet shank. *Page 124*

97. A properly formed shop head on a rivet should have a thickness of _____ of the rivet shank diameter. *Page 124*

98. The shop head of a rivet driven by the NACA flush rivet procedure is shaved flush with the skin with a _____. *Page 125*

99. When riveting by the team method when it is impossible to see the person holding the rivet gun, the bucker indicates a good rivet by tapping on the rivet _____ time/times. *Page 125*

Repair of Sheet-Metal Structure

Aviation Maintenance Technicians repair damaged sheet-metal aircraft structures. All repairs must meet certain basic requirements:

- The repair must restore the structure to its original or equivalent condition of strength and rigidity.

- The repair must be as lightweight as possible, consistent with strength.

- The repair must not distort the aerodynamic shape of the aircraft.

- The repair must not change the weight of a component in such a way that it can cause flutter or vibration.

- The repair must be approved by the FAA.

Appraisal of the Damage

The first and perhaps the most essential step in repairing an aircraft structure is to carefully and accurately appraise the damage. Decide whether to repair or replace the damaged component, and if you decide to repair it, you must decide whether to repair it yourself or to remove it and have a repair station that specializes in this type of repair do the work.

Obvious damage is easy to appraise, but it is often the hidden damage that makes the difference between a profitable repair and one that loses money for the shop. You must consider the possibility that any visible damage may extend into the structure where it is not visible. Stresses that caused the damage may have deformed or broken structural components not visible from the surface.

Carefully examine all rivets adjacent to areas that have been strained. If you can slip a thin feeler gage between either rivet head and the skin, it's possible the rivet has been stretched. Remove the rivet and examine the hole for indication of elongation. Elongated rivet holes should be drilled out for the next larger size rivet if the edge distance and rivet spacing allows.

Sometimes a damaged aircraft has been allowed to sit in the open and collect water and dirt inside the structure or, even worse, to rest on bare concrete for a period of time. In these cases it is extremely important to examine carefully for evidence of corrosion. Corrosion can require replacement of skins or structural members that were not damaged in the original accident.

Modern aircraft are designed to have maximum strength and a minimum weight, and all repairs must be made so as not to compromise this strength. The manufacturers issue structural repair information for normal repairs, and their engineering departments are available to assist in designing repairs that are more complex than those shown in the repair manual.

Classification of Damage

Damage can be classified into three categories: negligible, repairable, and damage that requires replacement of the component.

Negligible damage is that which does not affect the airworthiness of the aircraft. Typical examples of negligible damage are smooth dents in the outside skin that are free of cracks and sharp corners, and that are not caused by stress wrinkles.

Repairable damage normally consists of the damage that can be repaired by the replacement of skins and repairs that are described in the structural repair manual.

Damage that requires replacement of a component is damage that involves extensive corrosion, or parts that are damaged beyond the limits specified in the structural repair manual.

Repair of Cracks in Noncritical Areas

Engine cowling and baffles are subjected to a great deal of vibration and often crack. If the crack is not stopped, it will grow until the component is seriously damaged and will require replacement or extensive repair.

When a crack is discovered, drill a small hole with a #40 or #30 drill slightly beyond the end of the visible crack. This hole distributes the stresses at the end of the crack so they will be less than the tensile strength of the metal. Install a patch over the crack to prevent vibration from causing further damage to the weakened component.

Surface Patch for Stressed Skin

One typical repair used as a practical project in many Aviation Maintenance Technician schools is a patch for a piece of stressed skin that carries all of the strength of the skin from one side of the damage into the patch, then from the patch into the skin on the other side.

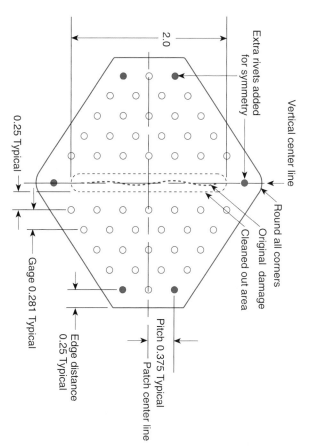

Figure 2-94. *Typical patch for a crack in a piece of stressed skin. This patch is designed to carry 100% of the strength of the skin across the patch.*

Assume the crack is in a piece of 0.032-inch 2024-T3 aluminum alloy skin, and can be cleaned out to a length of 2.0 inches with the ends rounded. The patch will be made of the same alloy and thickness as the original skin. For this repair determine the number of rivets by using the chart from Advisory Circular 43.13-1A that is shown in Figure 2-81 on Page 118.

Follow these steps:

1. Clean out the damage and round the ends of the cleaned-out area. Use a soft lead pencil and mark a horizontal and a vertical center line across the hole.

2. Cut a piece of 0.032-inch 2024-T3 aluminum alloy about 5 inches square. Clean the surface and spray on a very light coat of zinc chromate primer. Using a sharp lead pencil, draw a horizontal and vertical center line on the patch material. Hold the patch under the cleaned-out damage with the center lines crossing in the center of the hole. Trace the outline of the hole on the patch material.

3. Select the rivet. This repair does not require flush riveting, so an MS20470AD universal-head rivet will be used. For 0.032-inch skin use a $^3/_{32}$-inch rivet. Its diameter is approximately three times the thickness of the skin.

4. Find the number of rivets required. Use the chart in Figure 2-81. Follow the column for a $^3/_{32}$-inch rivet down to the row for 0.032-inch sheet. This shows that you will need 11.1 rivets per inch of cleaned-out damage. This will require at least 22.2, or actually, 23 rivets on each side of the damage.

5. Determine the rivet pitch. The minimum pitch for a $^3/_{32}$-inch rivet is 3D, or $^9/_{32}$ (0.28) inch, and the maximum pitch is 12D, or $1^1/_8$ (1.125) inch. A good choice is 4D, or $^3/_8$ (0.375) inch.

6. Decide on the edge distance. The recommended distance between the center of the rivet hole and the edge of the sheet is at least 2D. Using the minimum does not allow for ever having to use a larger rivet, such as would be needed if a hole were damaged. A good choice is $^1/_4$ (0.25) inch which is 2.7D, and it allows a $^1/_8$-inch rivet to be used if it is ever necessary. Draw a vertical line $^1/_4$ (0.25) inch from each edge of the damage outline on the patch.

7. Determine the number of rivets in each row. Twenty-three rivets are needed on each side of the patch, and the pitch is 0.375. This allows 7 rivets in the first row. To stagger the rivets, there should be 6 rivets in the second, 5 in the third, and 4 in the fourth row. This leaves 1 rivet for the fifth row.

8. Lay out the first row of rivets. Mark the center of one rivet at the intersection of the center line and the edge distance line. Mark the center of the other 6 rivets in this row. Space them at $^3/_8$ (0.375) inch intervals on both sides of the center rivet.

9. Choose the gage, or transverse pitch. This is 75% of the rivet pitch, or $^9/_{32}$ (0.281) inch. Draw 4 lines parallel to the first row of rivets on each side of the damage. The rows are separated by 0.281 inch.

10. Mark the location of the 6 rivets in the second row. These rivets are centered between the rivets in the first row and are on the first rivet gage line.

11. Mark the location of the 5 rivets in the third row. These rivets are in horizontal alignment with the rivets in the first row.

12. Mark the location of the 4 rivets in the fourth row. These are aligned with the rivets in the second row.

13. Mark the location of the single rivet in the center of the fifth row. This is all of the rivets needed to carry the load into the patch on one side

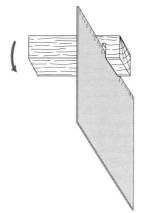

Figure 2-95. *Slightly crimp the edges of the patch by using a small hardwood stick with a saw cut across it at one end. There should be just enough crimp to prevent the edges of the sheet rising up.*

of the damage and out on the other side, but to make the patch symmetrical, place 2 more rivets in the fifth row.

Symmetry is important, not just to make the patch look good, but to avoid abrupt changes in the cross-sectional area and prevent stress risers that could cause structural failure.

14. Draw lines through the end rivets in each row and mark the location of a rivet at the intersection of these lines and the vertical center line. These two rivets do not carry any stress across the patch, but they prevent the edges of the patch curling up.

15. Draw lines for the outside of the patch 0.25 inch from the center line of all the outside rivets. Cut the patch along the outside lines, round all of the corners, and deburr the edges of the patch.

16. Mark the center of each rivet hole with a prick punch, and then make a drill-starting indentation at each mark with a center punch.

17. Drill all of the rivet holes with a #40 drill, and deburr the edges of the holes.

18. Mark the location of a rivet hole on the damaged skin 0.25 inch from the edge of the cleaned-out damage along the horizontal center line. Make a center punch mark at this location and drill a #40 hole.

19. Put the patch over the damaged area and hold it in place with a silver-colored Cleco fastener. Align the center line on the patch with the center line on the skin and drill a #40 hole through the patch along the center line on the opposite side of the damage. Secure this with a Cleco fastener.

20. With the patch in place, drill the rest of the rivet holes.

21. Remove the patch, deburr all the holes, and slightly crimp the edges of the patch as shown in Figure 2-96. Spray the skin where the patch is to be installed, and the inside of the patch with a light coat of zinc chromate primer.

22. Rivet the patch in place.

Flush Patch

When you must patch an aircraft skin in a location where a smooth surface is needed, a flush patch such as the one in Figure 2-96 is installed. The damage in this example is in a piece of 0.025-inch 2024-T3 aluminum alloy skin, and it is cleaned out to a 1.5-inch-diameter hole. The repair must be flush, so MS20426AD rivets will be used.

symmetrical. The same on either side of the center line.

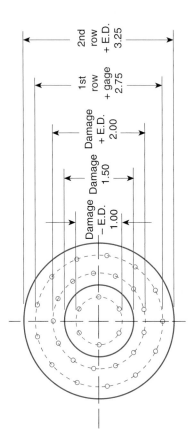

Figure 2-96. *Flush patch for stressed skin structure carrying 100% of the skin strength.*

Prepare the patch material of the same alloy and thickness as the original skin, and follow these steps:

1. Draw a horizontal and vertical center line across the damage, and clean it out to a circular hole.

2. Determine the number of rivets needed. Use the chart in Figure 2-81 on Page 124. For 0.025-inch skin and $^3/_{32}$-inch rivets, 8.6 rivets per inch are needed on both sides of the cleaned-out damage. The cleaned-out area is 1.5 inches in diameter, which requires 12.9, or 13 rivets on each side.

3. Plan the layout of the rivets. A total of 26 rivets is needed to carry 100% of the skin strength, and the layout can use the same minimums used in the previous repair:

   Edge distance — 0.25 inch

   Pitch — 0.375 inch

   Gage — 0.281 inch

4. Prepare the patch material using the same alloy and thickness as the damaged skin. Spray it with a mist coat of zinc chromate primer, and draw a horizontal and a vertical center line and a 1.5-inch-diameter circle representing the cleaned-out damage.

5. Lay out the first row of rivets. This row is laid out on a circle drawn one edge distance, or 0.25 inch, from the edge of the hole. The diameter of this circle is 2.0 inches and its circumference is $\pi \cdot D$, or $3.14 \cdot 2 = 6.28$ inches.

   In order to have 13 rivets in each row, the spacing of the inner row is $6.28 \div 13 = 0.48$ inch. This is slightly more than 5D which is well within the 3D to 12D range. Make a mark for the center of each rivet in this row.

6. Lay out the second row of rivets. The row is laid out on a circle that is 75% of the pitch from the first row. This circle has a diameter of 2.75 inches and a circumference of $3.14 \cdot 2.75 = 8.64$ inches. The 13 rivets in this row

therefore have a spacing of 0.66 inch, which is 7D, and is within the recommended range. Make a mark for each rivet in this row, placing it between the rivets in the first row.

7. Determine the outside diameter of the patch. An edge distance of 0.25 inch outside the second row of rivets gives the patch an outside diameter of 3.25 inches.

8. Lay out the rivets for the insert. Draw a circle one edge distance, or 0.25 inch, inside the circle that represents the cleaned-out damage. This circle has a diameter of 1.0 inch. Six rivets laid out around this circle will have a pitch of approximately 5.6D which is a good choice. Mark a rivet location every 60° around this circle.

9. Cut the patch along the outside diameter line and smooth its edges. Use a prick punch to mark each rivet hole and follow this with a center punch. Drill all of the holes with a #40 drill, and deburr their edges.

10. Drill a #40 hole one edge distance, or 0.25 inch, from the edge of the cleaned out damage on the skin along the vertical center line. Fasten the patch over the damage with a silver-colored Cleco fastener. Align the center line on the patch with that on the skin, and drill a hole through the skin across the patch from the first hole. Insert another Cleco fastener and drill all of the rest of the holes.

11. Mark, and cut out the insert from a piece of metal the same thickness as the original skin. Draw a circle one edge distance, or 0.25 inch, inside of the insert and drill six #40 holes to match the holes in the patch.

12. Dimple all of the holes in the original skin, the patch, and the insert with a 100° radius-dimpling tool.

13. Spray the skin, the patch, and the insert with zinc chromate primer and install the patch on the inside of the skin and hold it in place with Cleco fasteners. Install all of the rivets in the holes in the skin. Place the insert in the hole in the skin and rivet it to the patch.

Stringer Repair

Repair damaged bulb-angle stringers by removing the damaged section and inserting a filler, then reinforcing both sides with the same alloy and thickness of metal as the damaged stringer. *See* Figure 2-97 on the next page.

Follow these steps:

1. Remove the damaged portion of the stringer.

2. Cut a strip of aluminum of the same thickness and alloy as the bulb angle that is as wide as the distance between the bulb and the flat leg of the angle.

3. Cut and form an angle of this same material that has the same dimensions as the bulb angle.

bulb angle. An L-shaped metal extrusion having an enlarged, rounded edge that resembles a bulb on one of its legs.

4. Lay out a single line of rivets along the center line of the standing leg of the bulb angle and the filler. There should be at least 5 rivets on each side of the damage. Observe the minimum edge distance and the recommended pitch distance for these rivets.

5. Drill rivet holes through the stringer, the reinforcing angle, the filler, and the strip, and rivet the three sections of the repair together, using MS20470AD rivets.

6. Rivet the filler to the skin through the original rivet holes.

7. Rivet the reinforcing angle to the skin with the same rivet spacing as is used for the bulb angle stringer. Stagger these holes between those in the stringer.

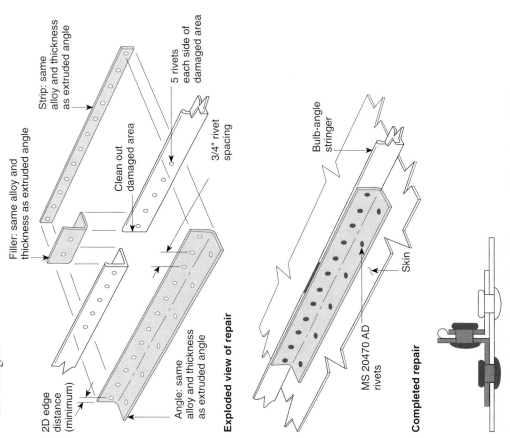

Strip: same alloy and thickness as extruded angle

5 rivets each side of damaged area

Clean out damaged area

3/4" rivet spacing

Filler: same alloy and thickness as extruded angle

2D edge distance (minimum)

Angle: same alloy and thickness as extruded angle

Exploded view of repair

Bulb-angle stringer

MS 20470 AD rivets

Skin

Completed repair

Cross-sectional view of repair. Shaded components have been added.

Figure 2-97. *A typical stringer repair*

Repairs to Pressure Vessels

When the skin of a pressurized aircraft is damaged, it must be repaired in such a way that the pressurizing air does not leak through the repair. Figure 2-98 shows a typical flush patch to a pressure vessel skin. The damage is cleaned out and all the corners are given an ample radius to prevent cracks.

Make the doubler and patch of the same alloy and thickness as the damaged skin, and observe the minimums for the rivet spacing and edge distances. Apply a coating of sealant to the doubler, and rivet it in place. Then rivet the patch to the doubler.

pressure vessel. The portion of a pressurized aircraft structure that is sealed and pressurized.

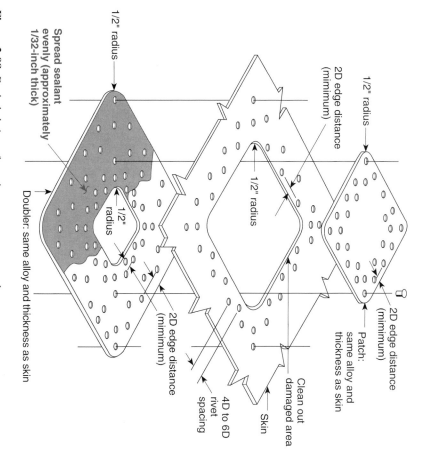

Figure 2-98. *Exploded view of repair to a pressure vessel*

Labels on figure:
1/2" radius
Spread sealant evenly (approximately 1/32-inch thick)
Doubler: same alloy and thickness as skin
1/2" radius
2D edge distance (mimimum)
1/2" radius
1/2" radius
2D edge distance (mimimum)
2D edge distance (mimimum)
Patch: same alloy and thickness as skin
4D to 6D rivet spacing
Clean out damaged area
Skin

Repairs to Floats and Seaplane Hulls

Floats and seaplane hulls are repaired in much the same way as pressure vessels. The patch is designed in the same way as one for any other structure exposed to similar loads, but before the patch is riveted in place, it is coated with a resilient sealant, and the rivets are dipped in the sealant before they are driven.

Replacement of a Section of the Aircraft Skin

It is sometimes advisable to replace an entire section of skin rather than patching it. When doing this, be sure to support the structure so the skin being replaced is not under any kind of load. Carefully drill out all the rivets holding the old skin, and cut the new skin of the same thickness and alloy as the one you are replacing. Mark the rivet holes with a transfer punch. Drill enough rivet holes to secure the new skin with Cleco fasteners and secure it in place. Locate the remaining holes with a hole finder. The manufacturer of the aircraft can often furnish replacement skins that have all of the rivet holes located with pilot holes. It is especially important to get a new skin from the manufacturer when replacing a skin with compound curves or corrugations, as these are very difficult to fabricate.

If you are not replacing an entire skin, but making a new seam, determine the number of rivets by duplicating the number of rivets in the nearest seam that is inboard or forward of this new seam.

Approval of the Repair

Before aircraft progressed to their present state of complexity, repairs and alterations were relatively simple. Information included in Advisory Circular 43.13-1A *Acceptable Methods, Techniques, and Practices — Aircraft Inspection and Repair* and Advisory Circular 43.13-2A *Acceptable Methods, Techniques, and Practices — Aircraft Alteration* was used as authority for the work. Now that aircraft fly so fast and carry such great loads, and the structure is so light, this generalized information is no longer adequate for use as authority.

To get a repaired or altered aircraft approved for return to service, you must complete an FAA Form 337 *Major Repair and Alteration (Airframe, Powerplant, Propeller, or Appliance).* This form requires two types of approval: approval of the data, and approval of the work. The specific design of the repair or the data used for the repair must be approved by the FAA, then an authorized person or agency must examine the repair and sign a statement that the repair conforms in all respects to the data that has been approved.

Before performing a major repair or major alteration, carefully research the project and consult the aircraft manufacturer if necessary. Make a sketch or drawing of the work and identify all pertinent materials and components. Include or reference all approved data. Submit this outline of the work to be done to the local FAA Maintenance Inspector for his or her approval. If there is any reason that this repair might not be approved, it is far better to learn of it before the work is begun.

Answers begin on Page 167. Page numbers refer to chapter text.

100. The minimum recommended edge distance for a rivet in a repair is _____ times the rivet shank diameter. *Page 130*

101. If it is possible to slip a thin feeler gage under the head of a rivet that is beyond the area of visible damage, it is possible that the rivet has been _____. *Page 128*

102. Aluminum alloy structure that has been allowed to rest on a bare concrete floor for some time is likely to be damaged by _____. *Page 128*

103. A small crack in a piece of aircraft sheet metal can be stopped from growing by drilling a hole with a number _____ or _____ drill at its end. *Page 128*

104. The limits for the distance between the centers of adjacent rivets in a stressed skin patch are between _____ D and _____ D. *Page 130*

105. When patching an aircraft structural component, the material used for the patch should be of the same alloy and _____ as the damaged material. *Page 129*

106. When making a new seam in a piece of aircraft skin, you can duplicate the number of rivets in the nearest seam that is _____ or _____ of the seam. *Page 136*

107. Information included in Advisory Circular 43.13-1A _____ (may or may not) be used as approved data for making a major repair on an aircraft. *Page 136*

108. Two types of approval must be made for all major repairs and major alterations. These are approval of the

a. _____

b. _____

Page 136

Aircraft Welding

A major technical breakthrough in the early days of aviation history was the replacement of the wood-and-wire-truss fuselage structure with a welded-steel tubing structure. The steel tubular structure is stronger, easier to build and maintain, and much safer in the event of a crash.

Most welding of early-day aircraft structure was done with oxyacetylene torches because the available electric arc equipment did not allow sufficient control for the thin-wall tubing used in aircraft structure.

World War II saw the development of the shielded arc process of welding, which used electronically controlled equipment making arc-welding of aircraft structure practical. This equipment has been developed and perfected to the extent that it is now an accepted method of constructing and repairing aircraft tubular steel structure.

The high-strength alloys used in modern aircraft construction are more difficult to weld than simple steel tubing, so much welding is done in specially equipped shops by technicians who specialize in welding. All technicians, however, should be well aware of the different types of welding and know their advantages and limitations.

Types of Welding

Three basic types of welding are used in aircraft construction and maintenance, and each has applications for which it is best suited. Gas welding is generally best suited for welding thin sheets and tubes made of steel, aluminum, and magnesium. Electric arc welding is best suited for heavy sheets and castings. Electric resistance welding is mainly used for welding thin sheets of aluminum alloy and stainless steel for such applications as fuel tanks.

Gas Welding

Gas welding is a fusion process in which heat is supplied by burning a mixture of oxygen and a fuel gas such as acetylene or hydrogen. A welding torch is used to mix the gases in the proper proportions and to direct the flame against the parts to be welded. The molten edges of the parts then flow together, and after cooling form a single solid piece. Usually a welding rod is dipped into the molten pool to add additional material to the joint to increase its strength.

Acetylene is the most widely used fuel gas because of its high flame temperature when it is mixed with oxygen. The temperature of an oxyacetylene flame ranges from about 5,700°F to 6,300°F, which is far above the melting temperature of all commercially used metals.

Hydrogen is often used as a fuel gas for welding aluminum and magnesium because it produces a very clean flame. The temperature of an oxyhydrogen flame is slightly lower than that of an oxyacetylene flame, and it is hot enough for welding aluminum.

Gas Welding Equipment

Gas welding equipment may be either portable or stationary. Stationary equipment usually consists of an oxygen and an acetylene manifold that supplies several welding stations. Portable welding equipment is normally mounted on a hand truck so it can be moved to any location in the shop.

The typical equipment needed for gas welding consists of:

- Oxygen and acetylene cylinders
- Oxygen and acetylene regulators with pressure gages
- Welding hoses
- Welding torch with extra tips and connectors
- Welding goggles, torch lighter, special wrench, and fire extinguisher

Fuel Gases

Most gas welding for aircraft maintenance is oxyacetylene welding, and in this introduction, we will consider only the two gases oxygen and acetylene.

Oxygen

Oxygen is a colorless, odorless gas that does not burn by itself. It supports combustion and combines with other fuel gases to cause them to release a great amount of heat when they are burned.

Oxygen makes up about 21% of the volume of the earth's atmosphere, and is one of the major components of water. Commercial oxygen is produced by cooling air to such a low temperature that it changes into a liquid. Then, at a carefully controlled temperature, the liquid air is allowed to boil and release its oxygen. Another way of producing commercial oxygen is to break water into its two components, hydrogen and oxygen, electrolytically. Both gases are collected and compressed for use in welding. Welding oxygen is called "technical" oxygen, and differs from aviators' breathing oxygen because stringent controls are used to remove all traces of water from breathing oxygen. Aviators' breathing oxygen can be used for welding, but technical oxygen must never be used to charge the breathing oxygen system in an aircraft.

Acetylene

Acetylene is a colorless, flammable gas that has a distinctive unpleasant odor detectable even when it is greatly diluted with air. Acetylene is not a natural gas, but is produced by the reaction of calcium carbide with water.

Acetylene is stable when stored under a pressure of less than 15 psi, but at pressures above this, it becomes dangerously unstable. Because of this instability, it is stored in steel cylinders filled with a porous material such as a mixture of asbestos and charcoal. The mixture is then saturated with

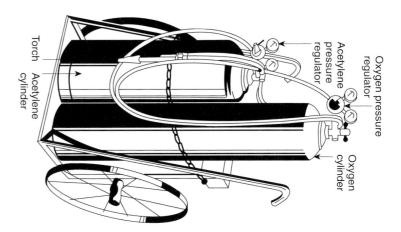

Figure 2-99. *Portable oxyacetylene welding equipment*

Oxygen pressure regulator

Acetylene pressure regulator

Torch

Acetylene cylinder

Oxygen cylinder

acetone. The acetone absorbs approximately 25 times its own volume of acetylene, and allows the cylinder to be charged to a pressure of 250 psi without the acetylene becoming unstable.

Gas Storage Cylinders

Oxygen is stored in seamless steel cylinders under a pressure of 2,200 psi at 70°F. The cylinders for technical oxygen are painted solid green, but those used for aviators' breathing oxygen are green with a white band around the top. Oxygen cylinders are fitted with a cylinder valve that has a safety disk that will burst and release the gas if the cylinder pressure builds up to a dangerous level. The valve has a handwheel and a stem seal that seals when the valve is fully open. For this reason, when a regulator is attached to the cylinder, the valve must be fully open to prevent loss of oxygen around the stem. The outlet nipple on an oxygen cylinder has male threads to prevent the possibility of installing an acetylene regulator.

A steel cap must be screwed onto an oxygen cylinder to cover the valve any time the regulator is not attached. This prevents damage if the cylinder is knocked over. If a valve is ever knocked off an oxygen cylinder, the escaping high-pressure gas will convert the cylinder into a jet-propelled missile that can do extensive damage to anyone or anything it hits.

Acetylene gas is stored in a seamless steel cylinder that has a recessed ring around both ends. The head ring protects the valve from damage, and the foot ring protects the cylinder from moisture and corrosion. The stem of the cylinder valve has a square shank on which a special wrench fits, and the regulator screws into female threads. Special safety fuse plugs screw into both the top and bottom of the cylinder. In case of a fire, a low-melting-point alloy in a small passage in these plugs melts and allows the gas to escape without building up its pressure to a dangerous level. The holes in these plugs are too small for the flame to burn back into the cylinder and cause an explosion.

Pressure Regulators

Pressure regulators attach to the cylinder valves of both the oxygen and acetylene cylinders. These are normally two-stage regulators. The first stage reduces the pressure to a constant intermediate value, and the second stage reduces this pressure to a much lower level that is appropriate for the torch being used.

Oxygen Regulator

Oxygen regulators have a sealing nipple and a nut to attach the regulator to the cylinder valve. The hose connection on the oxygen regulator has right-hand threads, while the hose connection on the acetylene regulator has left-hand threads. The cylinder-pressure gage shows the pressure inside the oxygen cylinder when the cylinder valve is turned on. It is graduated to a maximum pressure of 3,000 psi. The low, or torch, pressure gage has a top reading of 200 psi. The adjusting handle in the center of the regulator controls the pressure of the oxygen delivered to the torch. When the handle is screwed to the left until it turns freely with no opposition, the regulator is shut off and no oxygen can flow to the torch.

If the regulator should leak, a safety disk in the low-pressure side will rupture and release the oxygen out the back of the regulator before the pressure can build up enough to damage the regulator diaphragm.

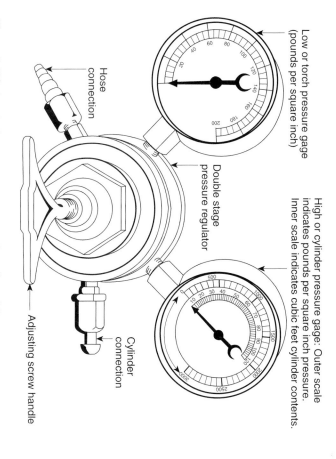

Low or torch pressure gage
(pounds per square inch)

Hose
connection

Double stage
pressure regulator

High or cylinder pressure gage: Outer scale
indicates pounds per square inch pressure.
Inner scale indicates cubic feet cylinder contents.

Adjusting screw handle

Cylinder
connection

Figure 2-100. *A typical two-stage oxygen regulator for welding*

Acetylene Regulator

The acetylene regulator has a sealing nipple and male threads that screw into the nut on the acetylene cylinder valve. The hose connection has left-hand threads. The high-pressure gage that reads the cylinder pressure when the cylinder valve is open has a range up to about 400 psi, and the torch gage has a range of up to about 30 or 40 psi. The regulator has a safety disk similar to that in the oxygen regulator that will rupture if the regulator should leak. The handle in the center of the regulator adjusts the acetylene pressure delivered to the torch, and when it is turned to the left until no opposition is felt, the valve is shut off and no acetylene can flow to the torch.

Hoses

The hoses used to connect the regulators to the torch are typically made of a high-quality rubber surrounded with two layers of rubber-impregnated fabric. An outer layer of tough rubber protects the hose from abrasion. The oxygen and acetylene hoses, called twin hoses, are joined side-by-side so they are less prone to tangle when in use. The acetylene hose is red, its fittings have left-hand threads, and the coupling nuts have a groove around the center of the hexes. The oxygen hose is green, its fittings have right-hand threads, and the coupling nuts do not have a groove.

Torches

Welding torches mix the gases in correct proportion and control the amount of gas delivered to the tip to regulate the size and type of flame. Almost all torches have two valves, one for the oxygen and one for the acetylene. Torches designed for welding heavy materials usually have the valves at the hose end of the mixing chamber, while those designed for welding lightweight metals have the valves at the tip end. There are two basic types of torches in use; balanced-pressure torches and injector torches. The choice of torch type depends upon the source of the acetylene.

Balanced-Pressure Torches

Use balanced-pressure torches when the acetylene is supplied from a cylinder and can be delivered to the torch under the required pressure. The pressures generally used are between one and five psi for both the oxygen and the acetylene, with the actual pressure depending upon the thickness of the metal being welded.

Oxygen and acetylene flow from the regulators into the torch handle, through oxygen and acetylene tubes to the needle valves. From the needle valves, the gases flow into the mixing head where they are mixed and then delivered to the tip.

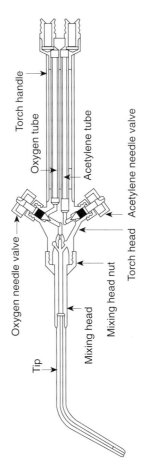

Torch handle

Oxygen tube

Acetylene tube

Acetylene needle valve

Oxygen needle valve

Torch head

Mixing head nut

Mixing head

Tip

Figure 2-101. *A balanced-pressure welding torch for aircraft use*

Injector Torches

When the acetylene is supplied from an acetylene generator, its pressure is usually very low. To get the proper amount to the tip to produce the required heat, oxygen under a much higher pressure, usually 10 to 40 times as high as that of the acetylene, flows through a small orifice. The resulting high velocity produces a low pressure which draws the acetylene into the mixing chamber.

Torch Tips

Welding torch tips are generally made of hard copper, and the size of the orifice in the tip determines the velocity of the gases leaving the torch. The temperature of the welding flame is determined by the gases used, but the amount of heat delivered to the work is determined by the amount of gas burned.

The size tip to use is determined by not only the thickness of the material being welded, but also by the nature of the weld, the experience of the welder, and the position in which the weld is to be made. There is no uniform system for numbering the tips that relate to the amount of heat they will produce, but Figure 2-102 gives a starting point for determining the size orifice in the tip to use with various thicknesses of steel.

Keep the orifice in the tip clean and undistorted. When the tip is used it often becomes clogged with carbon and the flame is distorted. Any time the flame splits or becomes misshapen, shut the torch down and clean the tip with tip cleaners made for the purpose. Never use a drill or any other hard metal to clean a tip, as it will distort the hole.

Torch Lighters

Never light welding torches with a match or a cigarette lighter. They offer no protection for your hand when the gasses ignite. Use a flint-type lighter that has a flame cup for preventing the flame from reaching out.

Welding Goggles

Wear welding goggles that fit close to the face at all times when welding or cutting. The dark lenses protect your eyes from the ultraviolet and infrared rays that are produced, and clear glass lenses that are inexpensive to replace protect the colored glass from damage caused by molten metal splattering against them.

The color of the lens is determined by the type of welding: Green or brown lenses are typically used for welding steel, but blue lenses are often used for welding aluminum because it is easier to detect the condition of the surface of the metal. The shade of the lens is identified by a number, with the lower numbers indicating the lighter shades.

Filler Rod

When two pieces of metal are welded, their edges melt and they flow together to form a single piece. To strengthen the weld, filler metal is added to the molten pool so it becomes part of the weld. This filler metal comes in the form of welding rods. Standard welding rods are 36-inches long, copper plated to keep them from rusting, and available in diameters from $1/16$ to $1/4$ inch.

When selecting the rod for a particular job, follow the recommendations of the rod manufacturer to assure that the alloy of the rod is correct for the type of metal you are welding.

Tip Orifice Drill Size	Approximate Steel Thickness (inch)
76-70	0.031 (1/32)
69-60	0.062 (1/16)
57-54	0.125 (1/8)
53-48	0.250 (1/4)

Figure 2-102. *Relationship between tip orifice size and the thickness of the metal to be welded*

Setting Up the Equipment

The gas welding equipment for most maintenance shops is mounted on a cart and ready for operation as soon as it is wheeled into position. There are some precautions and procedures that should be observed for maximum safety.

Compressed Gas Safety

The oxygen's high pressure makes special precautions necessary when the cylinders are replaced. As soon as you remove the regulator from the cylinder, screw a steel cap in place to protect the valve. When you've installed the new cylinder on the cart, secure it with the chain or clamp so it cannot accidentally fall over. Be sure that no greasy rags or tools are used around the oxygen cylinder. Oxygen does not burn, but it supports combustion so violently that an oily or greasy rag can catch fire.

It is permissible to store oxygen cylinders on their side, but acetylene cylinders should always be stored upright. If one has been stored on its side, place it in an upright position for at least 2 hours before connecting it into the welding rig. This allows the acetone to settle to the bottom of the cylinder so it will not be drawn out with the gas. Be sure the regulator reduces the pressure below 15 psi, because acetylene is unstable above this pressure.

Connecting the Equipment

It is important that oxyacetylene equipment be properly set up and adjusted. This is the procedure to follow:

- Before attaching the regulators to the cylinders, momentarily open the cylinder valves and allow any dirt or contamination that may be in the valve to be blown out.

- After installing the regulators, connect the hoses to the regulators and tighten the nuts with the correct-size open-end wrench.

- Screw the adjusting handles of the regulators all of the way to the left until you meet no resistance. This shuts the gas off to the hose fitting.

- Open the oxygen cylinder valve by turning the handwheel all the way to the left. This valve seats in its fully open position and prevents the oxygen leaking past the valve stem.

- Open the acetylene valve a quarter of a turn and leave the wrench on the valve stem. This allows the acetylene to be turned off in a hurry if a fire should ever start.

- Before connecting the torch to the hoses, screw in the adjusting screw handles enough to cause gas to flow and purge the lines of air and any contaminants that may have collected in the hose. After purging the hoses, screw the adjusting screw handles back out.

- After connecting the torch to the hoses, turn the torch valves off and screw in the adjusting screw handles until about 20 psi is indicated on the oxygen gage and 5 psi is shown on the acetylene gage.

- Screw the adjusting screw handles to the left to shut off all flow to the torch and watch the torch gages for any indication of leakage. If the hoses and torch do not hold the pressure, there is probably a leak. Cover the suspected area with a soap and water solution and watch for bubbles. Do not check for a leak with a flame or with any type of oil. If you find a leak, correct it before proceeding.

Lighting and Adjusting the Torch

With the torch connected and the correct size tip for the work being welded installed, the torch can be lit and adjusted.

Open the oxygen valve on the torch and turn the adjusting screw on the regulator in until the torch gage indicates the correct pressure for the size orifice in the tip. The correct pressures are shown in Figure 2-103. When the pressure is adjusted, turn off the oxygen valve on the torch.

Turn on the torch acetylene valve and adjust the acetylene pressure in the same way as you did the oxygen. Then shut off the torch valve for the acetylene until you are ready to light the torch.

When the torch is to be lit, slightly open the torch acetylene valve for about a quarter to half of a turn. Use the torch lighter to ignite the acetylene, and then open the acetylene valve until the flame leaves the tip for about 1/16 inch. Open the torch oxygen valve until the flame returns to the face of the tip and changes to a bluish-white color, and an inner cone forms.

The relationship between the acetylene and oxygen is indicated by the type of flame. *See* Figure 2-104.

Generally a neutral flame is used, because it does not alter the composition of the base metal to any extent, and can be used for most metals. The temperature of a neutral flame is approximately 5,900°F. To get a neutral flame, control the torch oxygen valve until there is a definite white feather around the inner cone, and then increase the oxygen until the feather just disappears. The end of the inner cone should be rounded, and the outer flame should be blue with a tinge of purple around its outer edges and at the point.

A reducing flame, sometimes called a carburizing flame, is cooler and its temperature is about 5,700°F. A reducing flame should be used only for very special purposes, as the extra acetylene causes carbon to be deposited in the molten metal. A reducing flame is identified by a very distinctive white feather around the inner cone, and the outer flame will be whiter than it is around a neutral flame.

An oxidizing flame is one in which there is more oxygen than in a neutral flame. The inner cone is pointed rather than rounded, and the outer flame is smaller than that around a neutral flame. A hissing sound is often heard when the torch is adjusted to produce an oxidizing flame. The temperature of an oxidizing flame is around 6,300°F.

neutral flame. An oxyacetylene flame produced when the ratio of oxygen and acetylene is correct and there is no excess of oxygen or carbon. A neutral flame has a rounded inner cone and no feather around it.

Figure 2-103. *Recommended torch pressures for various size tip orifices*

Tip Orifice (Drill Size)	Torch Pressure (psi)	
	Oxygen	Acetylene
60 – 69	4	4
54 – 57	5	5
44 – 52	8	8
40 – 50	9	9

carburizing flame. An oxyacetylene flame produced by an excess of acetylene. This flame is identified by a feather around the inner cone. A carburizing flame is also called a reducing flame.

oxidizing flame. An oxyacetylene flame in which there is an excess of oxygen. The inner cone is pointed and often a hissing sound is heard.

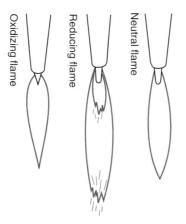

Neutral flame

Reducing flame

Oxidizing flame

Figure 2-104. *Oxyacetylene flames*

Welding flames may be classified as soft or harsh. The temperature of the flame is a function of the welding gases, and the amount of heat put into a weld is a function of the amount of gas being burned. The softness or harshness of a flame is a function of the velocity of the gases flowing from the tip. A soft flame is one in which the velocity of the gases is low, and a harsh flame is one in which the velocity is high.

When a soft flame is required to put a lot of heat into the metal, use a tip with a larger orifice than usual.

Shutting Down the Equipment

After the welding is completed, the equipment must be properly shut down. Extinguish the flame by turning off the torch acetylene valve and then the torch oxygen valve. If the torch remains unlit for any period of time, both of the cylinder valves should be turned off. Open the torch acetylene valve to allow the gas in the line to escape. Close the acetylene valve and open the torch oxygen valve until the oxygen all bleeds out. Close the oxygen valve and then turn the adjustment screws in both regulators to the left until no opposition is felt and the gases are shut off to the torch. Coil the hoses up neatly to protect them from damage.

Gas Welding Techniques

Most gas welding by aviation maintenance technicians is to relatively thin-gage steel, and so the techniques involved in this type of welding are the ones discussed here.

Holding the Torch

For the best control when welding thin-gage material, hold the torch as is seen in Figure 2-105. The tip should be in line with the joint being welded, and inclined between 30° and 60° from the perpendicular, with the actual angle depending upon the amount of penetration needed. The thicker the material, the more nearly vertical the torch is held.

If the inner cone of the flame is held about ⅛ inch from the surface of the metal, a puddle of molten metal will form. This puddle should be composed of equal parts of the two pieces of metal being joined. As soon as the puddle appears, begin moving the tip in a circular pattern around the outer edge of the puddle, moving it slightly in the direction you want the weld to progress, melting just a little bit of the forward edge on each circle. This pattern assures an even distribution of heat between the two pieces of metal. *See* Figure 2-106.

For thin-gage tubing and sheet metal, point the torch in the direction the weld is progressing. Add the filler rod to the puddle as the edges of the joint melt before the flame. This is called forehand welding. *See* Figure 2-107.

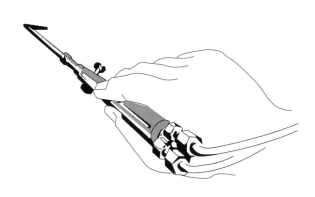

Figure 2-105. *Correct method of holding an oxyacetylene torch*

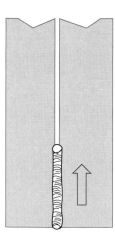

Figure 2-106. *The tip of the torch should form a series of circles, with each one moving slightly in the direction the weld is to progress.*

forehand welding. *Welding in which the torch is pointed in the direction the weld is progressing.*

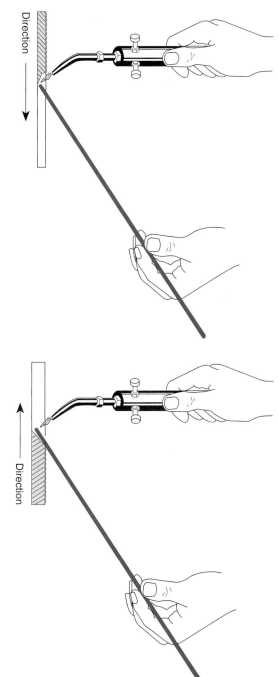

Figure 2-107. *Forehand welding is used for thin-gage tubing and sheet.*

Figure 2-108. *Backhand welding is used for heavy-gage sheet steel.*

The preferred method for welding heavy-gage metal is the backhand method, shown in Figure 2-108. Point the torch away from the direction the weld is progressing. Add the rod to the puddle between the flame and the finished weld. Backhand welding is not used on thin-gage metal because the greater amount of heat produced in the metal is likely to overheat and burn it.

Welding Positions

The ideal position for welding is the flat position, in which the material is flat and the welding is all done from the top with the torch pointed down on the work. But this is not always possible in the real world of aircraft repair. When welding on tubular structure, some of the weld is flat, some is horizontal, some is vertical, and some is overhead.

When welding in the overhead position point the torch upward toward the work and prevent the puddle from sagging by keeping it small and not allowing a drop to form. Use the rod to control the puddle and keep the volume of flame to the minimum needed to assure good fusion of the base metal and the filler rod.

Horizontal welding is done by holding the torch in such a way that the flame is inclined upward at an angle between 45° and 60°. Dip the rod in the top of the puddle and do not allow the weld to get too hot.

Vertical welds are started at the bottom with the flame inclined upward between 45° and 60°. It is important that a vertical weld not be allowed to become overheated. To prevent overheating, you may have to periodically remove the flame from the weld for an instant and then return it to the puddle. Add the rod at the top of the puddle in front of the flame.

backhand welding. Welding in which the torch is pointed away from the direction the weld is progressing.

Welded Joints

Three types of welded joints find common use in aircraft construction and repair: the butt joint; lap joint; and T, or fillet, joint.

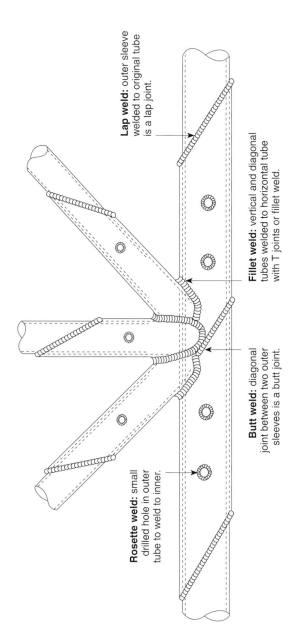

Lap weld: outer sleeve welded to original tube is a lap joint.

Fillet weld: vertical and diagonal tubes welded to horizontal tube with T joints or fillet weld.

Butt weld: diagonal joint between two outer sleeves is a butt joint.

Rosette weld: small drilled hole in outer tube to weld to inner.

Figure 2-109. *Types of welded joints*

rosette weld. A method of securing one metal tube inside another by welding. Small holes are drilled in the outer tube and the inner tube is welded to it around the circumference of the holes.

A butt joint is made when two pieces of material are placed edge to edge so there is no overlapping. Use filler rod in a butt joint to give the metal the strength it needs.

Lap joints are the most common type of joint in tubular structure repair. When one tube is placed over another, the edges of the outside tube are welded to the inner tube with a lap joint.

T joints, or fillet welds, are often used in tubular structure to join one tube to another at an angle, or to attach lugs to the tubing. A single fillet is satisfactory for thin-gage metal, but heavier materials should be welded on both sides. A proper fillet weld should penetrate the base metal by 25% to 50% of its thickness.

Control of Expansion and Contraction

Metal heated for welding expands, and when it cools it contracts. These dimensional changes cause the metal to buckle. When the weld is completed, the contraction may cause the metal to crack.

An easy way to see the effect of expansion and contraction is to watch what happens when two pieces of steel sheet are butt-welded together. If the two sheets are placed side by side and welded, one sheet will overlap the other before the weld is completed. To prevent overlapping, separate the sheets by their thickness at one end, and by approximately $1/8$ to $1/4$ inch per foot of length at their other end. The actual separation depends upon the thickness and type of the metal. Begin the weld, and watch the sheets draw together. If they have been separated by the correct distance, they will draw together without overlapping by the time the weld is completed. *See* Figure 2-110.

Another way to prevent excessive warping when making a straight butt weld is to use the process of skip welding, as seen in Figure 2-111. Place the sheets beside each other with about the thickness of the metal separating them. Tack weld them together by forming small puddles at the ends and about every 1 1/4- to 1 1/2-inch along the length of the sheets. Begin the welding at point A and weld back to the edge of the sheet. Then start at point B and weld back to point A, next weld from C to B, and finally from the edge to point C. You can prevent large welded structures from warping by first clamping all the parts in a heavy jig or fixture and then performing the welding. After the welding is completed the entire structure is normalized to relieve the strains caused by the concentrations of heat during the welding process. With the structure still clamped in the jig, it is heated uniformly to a red heat and allowed to cool slowly in still air.

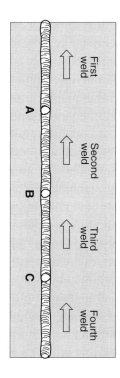

Figure 2-111. *Distortion can be minimized in a long butt weld by skip welding. Tack weld the pieces together and then complete the welds as is shown by the arrows.*

Characteristics of a Good Weld

In a good weld:

- The seam should be smooth with the bead ripples evenly spaced and of a uniform thickness.
- The weld should be built up, providing extra thickness at the joint.
- The weld should taper off smoothly into the base metal.
- No oxide should be formed on the base metal close to the weld.
- The weld should show no signs of blow holes, porosity, projecting globules, or undercutting of the base metal.
- The base metal should show no signs of burns, pits, cracks, or distortion.

Never file welds to improve their appearance, and never fill them with solder, brazing material, or filler of any sort. If it is necessary to reweld a joint, remove all the old weld before rewelding.

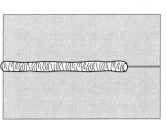

The gap closes as the weld progresses.

Figure 2-110. *Allowance for expansion in a straight butt weld*

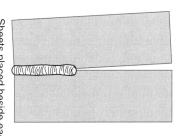

Sheets placed beside each other with more space at one end.

tack weld. A method of holding parts together before they are permanently welded. The parts are assembled, and small spots of weld are placed at strategic locations to hold them in position.

normalizing. A process of strain-relieving steel that has been welded and left in a strained condition. The steel is heated to a specified temperature, usually red hot, and allowed to cool in still air to room temperature.

Oxyacetylene Cutting

Oxyacetylene cutting rapidly oxidizes the metal. Ferrous metals combine with oxygen in the air to form iron oxide, or rust. Heat accelerates the combining action, and if pure oxygen is substituted for the air, the combination is extremely rapid.

A cutting torch, such as the one in Figure 2-112, is typical of those used in aviation maintenance shops. The torch is attached to the same hoses used for welding and lit in the same way as a welding torch. Typical regulator pressures for cutting steel up to about $\frac{1}{4}$-inch thick are 4 psi for the acetylene and 15 psi for the oxygen. The oxygen needle valve is adjusted to get a neutral flame from the preheating orifices, and the cutting oxygen lever is depressed to produce a flow of high-velocity oxygen through the flame.

To cut the steel, mark the cut with soapstone or chalk, and begin at the edge of the material. Hold the tip perpendicular to the surface until a spot in the metal turns red hot, then gradually depress the oxygen control lever. As soon as the cutting starts and a stream of sparks appears on the bottom of the material, depress the oxygen lever fully. Continue to move the torch across the work at a speed just fast enough for the cut to continue to penetrate the material completely.

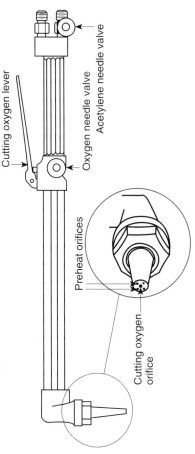

Cutting oxygen lever

Oxygen needle valve
Acetylene needle valve

Preheat orifices

Cutting oxygen orifice

Figure 2-112. *A typical oxyacetylene cutting torch*

Gas Welding of Aluminum

Aluminum welding presents a special problem in that aluminum does not change color as steel does before it melts. It is very easy to melt a hole through the metal rather than correctly fuse its edges. Thin aluminum sheet and tubing may be gas welded, but arc welding is preferred for thick aluminum sheet and castings.

Not all aluminum alloys are suitable for welding. Alloys 2014, 2017, 2024, and 7075 should not be welded, as the strength in the area of the weld is drastically reduced and the corrosion resistance is seriously impaired. Alloys 1100, 3003, 5052, 5056, 6061 and 6063 are suitable for welding.

When the welding torch is held vertically over a piece of sheet aluminum and the flame brought down until the tip of the inner cone nearly touches the metal, it will very suddenly, and without warning, melt and a hole will appear. But if the torch is held at an angle of about 30° to the plane of the surface, you will be able to melt the surface without forming a hole. As you slowly move the flame across the surface, a small puddle will form, and it will solidify as quickly as the flame is lifted.

Practice welding aluminum by forming a flange along the edges of two pieces that sticks up about the thickness of the metal. Place the two flanges next to each other, as shown in Figure 2-113, and practice welding them together without using any filler rod.

Two alloys are used for aluminum welding rods. Alloy 1100 rods are used for welding 1100 and 3003 aluminum because they give good ductility and good corrosion resistance. Rods made of 4043 alloy are used for all other wrought alloys and for castings because of their superior strength.

Because oxides form rapidly on the surface of aluminum, the use of flux is very important. The oxides chemically combine with the flux and are kept away from the molten metal.

Most fluxes are available as a powder that is mixed with water to form a paste. Apply this flux generously to both the top and bottom of the material to be welded, and to the flange, if one is used. After completing the welding, it is extremely important to scrub away all traces of the flux with a stiff bristle brush and hot water, as flux is corrosive to metal.

When using a filler rod to weld aluminum, cover the area to be welded with flux, and hold the torch at a low angle over its surface. Move the torch with a small circular motion over the starting point until the flux melts, and then scrape the rod across the surface, lifting it after each pass to prevent it melting before the parent metal. As soon as the surface of the metal is sufficiently hot, the rod will penetrate the surface. When the rod penetrates, hold it in the flame just long enough to melt some of it to reinforce the weld.

Forehand welding is preferred, because the flame preheats the metal before it is welded and keeps the flame away from the completed weld. The amount of heat put into the weld is actually controlled by the angle between the torch and the surface of the metal.

Brazing and Soldering

In the process of thermally joining metals, there are three procedures: welding, brazing, and soldering. In welding, the edges of two pieces of metal are melted and allowed to flow together to form one piece. Filler rod is usually added to the molten metal to increase the strength of the joint.

Brazing and soldering are methods of joining metals by heating them enough to melt a relatively low-melting-point nonferrous alloy. When the alloy melts, it flows out and wets the parent metal. When it cools it holds the metal parts together. The difference between brazing and soldering is

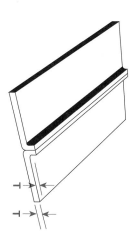

Figure 2-113. *Aluminum sheets flanged for practice welding*

brazing. A method of thermally joining metal parts by wetting the surface with a molten nonferrous alloy. When the molten material cools and solidifies, it holds the pieces together.

Brazing materials melt at a temperature higher than 800°F, but lower than the melting temperature of the metal on which they are used.

soldering. A method of thermally joining metal parts with a molten nonferrous alloy that melts at a temperature below 800°F. The molten alloy is pulled up between close-fitting parts by capillary action. When the alloy cools and hardens, it forms a strong, leak-proof connection.

parent metal. The metal being welded. This term is used to distinguish the metal being welded from the metal of the welding rod.

basically the temperature of the alloy. Brazing materials melt at temperatures higher than 800°F, but lower than the melting temperature of the metals being joined. Solder melts at a temperature lower than 800°F.

Brazing

Brazing is the process of joining metal parts by melting a brazing alloy on the surface. These alloys generally have a bronze base and they melt at about 1,600°F. (Steel melts at around 2,600°F.)

Thoroughly clean the surface to be brazed and heat it, in the case of steel, to a dull red. Heat the brazing rod and dip it in a flux made of borax and boric acid. The flux adheres to the rod so none need be applied to the metal. Move the torch with a neutral flame in a semicircular pattern over the seam to be brazed and hold the brazing rod in the flame near the tip. When the rod melts and flows over the base metal that is hotter than the melting point of the rod, the bronze alloy flows into the joint by capillary attraction. Continue to add rod until the joint is built up to the smooth seam you want. After the seam is completed, allow it to cool slowly.

A brazed joint is not strong enough for most aircraft structural applications, and it can be used as a repair procedure only in applications in which brazing was originally approved. A brazed joint should never be repaired by welding, as the brazing material gets into the structure of the metal and prevents a proper weld.

Silver Soldering

Silver soldering is a form of brazing used for attaching the fittings to high-pressure oxygen lines. Its chief characteristics are its ability to withstand vibration and high temperature.

Clean and assemble the end of the tube and the inside of the fitting. The fitting must fit tightly over the end of the tube as the solder is drawn into the joint by capillary attraction. Prepare borax and boric acid paste flux and wipe it on the tube to cover the area where the fitting is installed. Use a soft, neutral flame to heat the fitting and tube until the flux turns liquid. Shortly after the flux liquefies, touch the joint with the silver solder. It will melt and be drawn into the fitting around the tubing. Only an extremely small film of solder is needed to give the joint the integrity it needs.

Soft Soldering

Soft soldering is done with an alloy of tin and lead, and its melting temperature is determined by the ratio of these two components. An alloy of 50% tin and 50% lead is commonly used for general soldering. Its melting point is 414°F. Solder used for electronic components is usually 63% tin and 37% lead, and it melts at 361°F.

Metal parts that can be washed after soldering may be soldered using an acid flux to clean the metal, but electrical components must never be soldered with an acid flux. Most solder is available in the form of a hollow wire with the flux on the inside. The solder used for electrical components has its hollow core filled with a synthetic resin that melts and flows out ahead of the solder to exclude air from the hot metal and prevent the formation of oxides.

Soft solder should never be depended upon for strength. The joint must be designed to have all of the needed mechanical strength, and then solder is melted and flowed over the joint to make it air- and liquid-tight and to give it good electrical conductivity.

STUDY QUESTIONS: GAS WELDING, CUTTING, BRAZING AND SOLDERING

Answers begin on Page 167. Page numbers refer to chapter text.

109. The most widely used fuel gas for aircraft gas welding is _____. *Page 138*

110. It _____ (is or is not) permissible to use technical oxygen for charging a breathing oxygen system in an aircraft. *Page 139*

111. Acetylene gas is produced when _____ reacts with water. *Page 139*

112. The acetylene in a storage cylinder is absorbed in _____ which makes it safe to store under pressure. *Page 140*

113. The hose connection on an oxygen regulator has _____ (right-hand or left-hand) threads. *Page 140*

114. The hose connection on an acetylene regulator has _____ (right-hand or left-hand) threads. *Page 141*

115. The temperature of the flame used for gas welding is determined by the _____. *Page 143*

116. A twist drill _____ (is or is not) the correct tool to use to clean the orifice in a welding torch tip. *Page 143*

117. The valve on the oxygen cylinder should be opened _____ (all the way or part way). *Page 144*

118. The valve on the acetylene cylinder should be opened _____ (all the way or part way). *Page 144*

Continued

119. Welding hoses and connections should be checked for leaks with _____ . *Page 145*

120. The oxyacetylene flame that is the hottest is a/an _____ (reducing, neutral, or oxidizing) flame. *Page 145*

121. A flame that has a rounded inner cone and no feather around it is a/an _____ (reducing, neutral, or oxidizing) flame. *Page 145*

122. Thin steel tube and sheet is best welded by the _____ (backhand or forehand) method. *Page 147*

123. A flame that has a definite feather around its inner cone is a/an _____ (reducing, neutral, or oxidizing) flame. *Page 145*

124. Another name for a reducing flame is a /an _____ flame. *Page 145*

125. When making a vertical weld, the weld should be started at the _____ (top or bottom). *Page 147*

126. When welding aluminum, flux should be applied to _____ (both sides or top side only) of the metal. *Page 151*

127. After welding aluminum, all traces of the flux should be removed by scrubbing the area with a bristle brush and _____ . *Page 151*

128. The amount of heat put into the metal when gas welding aluminum is controlled by varying the _____ between the torch and the metal. *Page 151*

129. Brazing flux is applied to the heated brazing _____ . *Page 152*

130. The recommended oxyacetylene flame for brazing is _____ (neutral, oxidizing, or reducing). *Page 152*

Electric Welding

There are two basic types of electric welding: electric arc welding and electrical resistance welding. Electric arc welding is typically used for rather heavy material. The metal is melted in the extreme heat of an electric arc between the work and a hand-held electrode. Electrical resistance welding is used for thin sheets of metal. Thin sheets of metal are clamped between two electrodes or rollers and high-amperage, low-voltage current flows through the metal. The resistance of the metal to the flow of current causes enough heat to melt the metal and fuse the pieces together.

This section discusses several types of electric arc welding.

Electric Arc Welding

Electric arc welding has been used for many years as the primary method of joining heavy steel. Developments in the last few decades allow electric arc welding to be used in aircraft manufacture and maintenance for welding thin-wall tubing.

Shielded Metal Arc Welding (SMAW)

Electric arc welding that uses a flux-covered rod is called shielded metal arc welding. This type of welding has been used for many years for heavy steel construction, but it finds little use in aircraft maintenance except for building shop equipment. The welding machine that produces the low-voltage and high-current power for this welding may be either a motor-driven DC generator or an AC transformer-type machine. Each type of machine has advantages and disadvantages.

Gas Shielded Arc Welding

One of the problems encountered with welding is the contamination of the molten metal with oxides caused by oxygen in the air. This problem is often handled by using flux that dissolves the oxides that have formed and covers the molten metal to exclude the oxygen and prevent further oxide formation.

Aluminum and magnesium are difficult to weld by conventional methods, and in 1942 when the Northrop company received a contract from the U. S. Army Air Corps to build an all-magnesium, all-welded, tailless fighter, the XP-56, the welding process known as Heliarc® welding was developed. The welding arc is shielded by a flow of helium gas that excludes oxygen from the molten metal. The results are a neat, sound weld with a minimum of splatter and distortion.

Gas shielded arc welding has become extremely important in modern technology and there are two versions of it in use; one that uses a consumable wire rod as the electrode and the other that uses a nonconsumable tungsten electrode. The first was originally called metal inert gas, or MIG, welding, and the second was called tungsten inert gas, or TIG, welding. As the technologies

MIG welding. Metal inert gas welding is a form of electric arc welding in which the electrode is a consumable wire. MIG welding is now called GMA (Gas Metal Arc) welding.

TIG welding. Tungsten inert gas welding is a form of electric arc welding in which the electrode is a nonconsumable tungsten wire. TIG welding is now called GTA (Gas Tungsten Arc) Welding.

developed, other gases, some not inert, were used as shielding gases, and the names for these types of welding were changed to gas metal arc welding (GMAW) and gas tungsten arc welding (GTAW). In this introduction to gas shielded arc welding, we will discuss the more generally used GTAW.

Gas Tungsten Arc Welding (GTAW)

In GTA welding, the electrode is a fine nonconsumable tungsten wire used to create the arc, and filler rod is used to reinforce the weld as in oxyacetylene welding. Figure 2-114 shows the typical setup for GTA welding. The gas supply with a regulator and flowmeter provides a constant flow of shielding gas to the torch and the electrical current for welding is supplied by a power unit. A ground wire attached to the work from the power unit completes the setup.

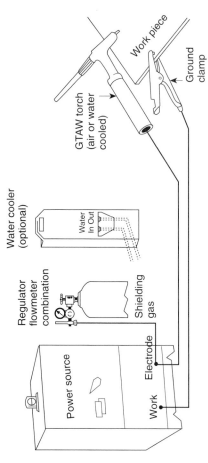

Figure 2-114. *Typical setup for GTA welding*

Shielding Gases

The gases used to shield the arc in GTA welding are either argon or helium. An arc shielded with helium is hotter than one shielded with argon and it produces a deeper penetration, but there is a greater tendency to splatter. Because of argon's greater density, it produces a cleaner weld and is used almost exclusively for welding very thin material. Helium and argon are stored in steel cylinders similar to those used for oxygen. Both helium and argon cylinders are painted gray, but helium cylinders have an orange band at the top and argon cylinders have a white band.

Regulator and Flowmeter

A regulator, similar to a single-stage oxygen regulator, is used on the shielding gas cylinder, and a flowmeter is installed between the regulator and the torch to give the technician an indication of the amount of shielding gas flowing over the weld. The amount of flow is controlled by the regulator, and should be kept at the value recommended for the particular type of welding being done.

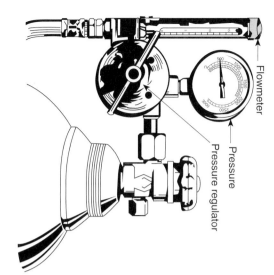

Figure 2-115. *A typical regulator and flowmeter for the shielding gas used in GTA welding*

Power Unit

The power unit used for GTA welding can supply DC-straight polarity (the electrode is negative), DC-reverse polarity, (the electrode is positive), and AC. DC-straight polarity produces the most heat and deepest penetration, but DC-reverse polarity has an advantage in welding aluminum and magnesium that, as the electrons flow from the work into the electrode, they blast off the surface oxides that have formed on the metal.

AC welding is similar to a combination of straight polarity and reverse polarity DC, but if the oxide coating on the surface of the metal is strong enough, it acts as a rectifier and no current flows during the half cycle when the electrode is positive, and the welding is similar to DC-straight polarity.

reverse polarity welding. DC-electric arc welding in which the electrode is positive with respect to the work.

straight polarity welding. DC-electric arc welding in which the electrode is negative with respect to the work.

rectification. A condition in AC-electric arc welding in which oxides on the surface of the metal act as a rectifier and prevent electrons flowing from the metal to the electrode during the half cycle when the electrode is positive.

To overcome this problem of rectification, a high-voltage, high-frequency, low-amperage AC signal is superimposed on the AC welding current. This high voltage penetrates the oxide film and allows the weld to have the good characteristics of both types of DC welding. This superimposed high-frequency AC gives these advantages:

- The arc can be started without touching the electrode to the work.
- The arc has better stability.
- A longer arc is possible.
- The tungsten electrodes have a longer life.
- A wider range of current can be used for a specific diameter of electrode.

Figure 2-116. *This truck-mounted GTA welding equipment has a power supply that provides AC and DC with high frequency AC for arc starting and stabilizing. This entire equipment can be taken to the aircraft for on-the-spot repairs.*

Hand-Held Torches

Torches for GTA welding are available in both air-cooled and water-cooled versions with air cooling used for the lower current welding applications. Both an air-cooled torch and a water-cooled torch are shown in Figure 2-117. Gas and cooling water are brought into the water-cooled torch through appropriate hoses, and after cooling the torch, the water drains back through the tube which encases the power cable.

The electrode is held in the torch with a split collet that allows it to be extended as it is consumed. The gas flows out around the electrode and is directed against the work by a ceramic gas shielding cup that screws onto the torch.

Electrodes

The electrodes for GTA welding are made of tungsten wire and are available in diameters from 0.010 inch to 0.250 inch and in lengths from 3 inches to 24 inches. Pure tungsten electrodes are used for most general welding of steel, but its current-carrying ability is limited. Tungsten alloyed with thorium emits electrons more readily than pure tungsten, it resists contamination better, and makes the arc easier to start and more stable. But, thorium alloyed rods are much more expensive than pure tungsten electrodes. Tungsten

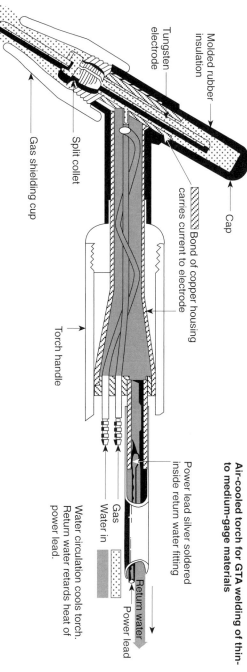

Molded rubber insulation

Tungsten electrode

Cap

▨ Bond of copper housing carries current to electrode

Split collet

Torch handle

Gas shielding cup

Gas
Water in

Power lead silver soldered inside return water fitting

Water circulation cools torch. Return water retards heat of power lead.

Return water

Power lead

Typical water-cooled GTA torch

Figure 2-117. *GTAW hand-held torches*

Air-cooled torch for GTA welding of thin- to medium-gage materials

electrodes alloyed with zirconium fall between the characteristics of pure tungsten and tungsten alloyed with thorium, but they are superior in some instances when used for some types of AC welding.

Electrodes used for DC-straight polarity welding should have its end pointed and may be smaller than that used for DC-reverse polarity and AC welding. For the latter two types of welding, the end of the electrode is normally rounded.

Welding Techniques and Procedures

GTA welding is specially suited for aluminum and most of the aluminum alloys, as there is no need to use corrosive flux. Some alloys, specifically 2024 and 7075, should not be fusion-welded because of hot cracking and impairment of their corrosion resistance, but most others can be welded. The corrosion resistance and heat treatment of some alloys such as 2014 and 2017 are affected by welding, and when a heat-treatable alloy is welded, it should be re-heat-treated after the welding is completed.

The steps to follow in GTA welding are:

- Choose the correct electrode size and gas cup for the thickness of the material being welded and, after polishing the electrode with steel wool, install it in the torch so that it protrudes about $1/8$ to $1/4$ inch from the end of the gas cup for butt welding or $1/4$– to $3/8$-inch for fillet welding.

- Select the correct filler rod for the material being welded. Typically 1100 rod can be used for 1100 or 3003 alloys and 4043, 5154, 6356, or 5456 should be used for the other alloys. Clean the rod and the metal to be welded to remove all traces of oil or grease.

Almost all aluminum welding will be done using AC with superimposed high-frequency AC. With this type of current, the arc can be started without actually touching the metal with the electrode tip.

- Hold the torch horizontally about 2 inches above the work and swing the tip down until it is about $1/8$ inch from the work with a smooth wrist movement. This should start the arc.

- The downward motion of the torch should be rapid so there will be a maximum amount of gas protection in the weld zone.

- When making the first start while AC welding, the electrode will have to be moved closer to the work before the arc starts than it is when the electrode is hot.

    To stop the arc, snap the electrode back to the horizontal position.

After starting the arc, preheat the work by moving the torch in a small circular motion until a molten puddle 3 to 5 times the thickness of the material is developed, then hold the torch at an angle of approximately 75° to the surface of the work with the end of the electrode about $1/8$ inch above the work.

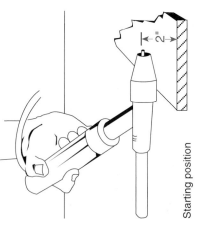

Starting position

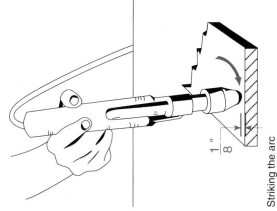

Striking the arc

Figure 2-118. *Starting the arc*

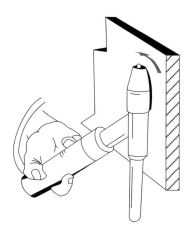

Figure 2-119. *Breaking the arc*

When the puddle becomes bright and fluid, move the torch slowly and steadily along the joint at a speed which will produce a bead of uniform penetration or width. No oscillating or other movement of the torch except for a steady forward motion is required.

When filler rod is required, hold the rod at an angle of approximately 15° to the work, and just clear of the arc stream. Once the puddle has formed, move the torch to the rear of the puddle and add filler rod by quickly touching it in the leading edge of the puddle. Add only a small amount of rod, then remove the rod and bring the torch back up to the leading edge. When the puddle is again bright, repeat these steps.

The arc speed is governed by the amount of current and the thickness of the material. The speed should be adjusted to obtain a bead that has uniform height and width. Good penetration is indicated by a very small, smooth bead, and the penetration should be uniform on the underside of the work.

Some precautions to be observed when running a bead are:

- Do not add filler rod until the puddle is well established.

- Do not insert the filer rod in the arc stream. This will cause considerable spatter and will melt an excessive amount of the rod.

- Do not attempt to hold the filler rod in the molten puddle. The amount of filler rod determines the buildup of the bead, and little or no buildup is necessary.

Inspection of the Weld

After completing a weld, inspect it carefully to determine that it is completely adequate for the purpose for which it was made. Some possible defects and their most probable causes are:

- Bead too narrow. This usually indicates that the weld was made at an excessive speed.

- Bead too wide. This usually indicates that the weld was made with too slow a speed.

- Weld is contaminated. This is indicated by a black deposit on the weld and is caused by the electrode coming in contact with the weld metal.

- Weld is oxidized. This is caused by an insufficient supply of shielding gas.

Electrical Resistance Welding

Electrical resistance welding is a special type of welding used for joining very thin sheets of metal, and it replaces riveting in many instances. There are two types of resistance welding, spot welding and seam welding. One of the widely used aviation applications for spot and seam welding is that of welding fuel tanks for aircraft.

Spot and Seam Welding

The heat required for spot welding is generated when current flows through the metal being welded, while considerable pressure is exerted on the electrodes that carry the current into and out of the metal.

Figure 2-120 shows the principle of spot welding. Two copper electrodes are forced together with the metal being welded between them. A pulse of high-current electricity flows through the metal and heats it to near its melting point. As it softens, the pressure on the electrodes forces the softened metal to form a spot between the sheets that joins them. The length of time the current flows is called the dwell time, and it is controlled by an electronic controller to assure that all of the spots will be uniform.

Seam welding is similar to spot welding except that copper wheels replace the rod-type electrodes. The controller sends pulses of current between the wheels so that spot welds are made close enough together to overlap and form a solid seam.

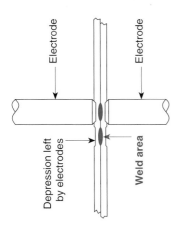

Figure 2-120. *The principle of spot welding*

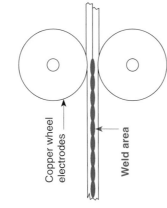

Figure 2-121. *The principle of seam welding*

STUDY QUESTIONS: ELECTRIC WELDING

Answers begin on Page 167. Page numbers refer to chapter text.

131. In straight polarity DC welding, the electrode is _____ (positive or negative).
    Page 157

132. The electrode used for DC reverse polarity GTA welding is _____ (larger or smaller) than that used for DC straight polarity. *Page 160*

133. The filler rod is dipped into the _____ front or back of the puddle when using GTA welding. *Page 161*

134. Too wide a bead indicates that the weld was made too _____ (fast or slow).
    Page 161

135. A black deposit on a weld bead is an indication that the weld is _____ .
    Page 161

136. Two methods of welding very thin aluminum alloy and stainless steel sheets are _____ and _____ . *Page 162*

Repair of Aircraft Structure by Welding

The welded steel tubular structure of low-performance aircraft is relatively easy to repair. Advisory Circular 43.13-1A *Acceptable Methods, Techniques, and Practices — Aircraft Inspection and Repair* illustrates many of the typical repairs that can be made. The repairs described in AC 43.13-1A are *acceptable*, not *approved*, and therefore cannot be used as authorization for a major repair, but they can be submitted to the local FAA maintenance inspector for his or her approval for a specific repair *before* the repair is made.

Any welded structure that needs repair on modern sheet metal aircraft, especially those that are part of the engine mount or landing gear, should be studied with caution, and only the repairs made that are specifically approved by the aircraft manufacturer. Some welded structural members that are heat-treated must not be repaired by welding.

Specific Welded Repairs

The repairs described here are taken from AC 43.13-1A and illustrate good practices. Before making any repair on a certificated aircraft, make a sketch of the desired repair and have it approved by the FAA.

Welded Patch Repair

If the damage to a tube does not extend to more than ¼ of its circumference, repair it by welding a tapered patch over the damaged area. The area to be covered must be free from cracks, abrasions, and sharp corners, and it must be substantially re-formed without cracking. The patch material should be the same type of steel and the one gage thicker than the damaged tube.

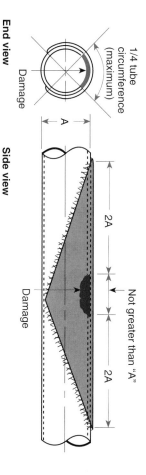

End view   Side view

1/4 tube circumference (maximum)

Damage

A

2A

2A

Not greater than "A"

Damage

Figure 2-122. *A welded patch repair*

repair. A maintenance procedure in which a damaged component is restored to its original condition, or at least to a condition that allows it to fulfill its design function.

Longeron Dented at a Cluster

If a fuselage longeron is dented at a cluster, re-form the dent as much as possible and weld a finger patch over it similar to the one in Figure 2-123. Make a pattern of lightweight cardboard and cut the patch from the same material and thickness as the longeron. Remove all of the finish from the tubing to be covered and tack-weld the patch to the longeron and heat it and form it around the tubes so that there is no gap of more than $^1/_{16}$ inch between the tubing and the patch. After the patch is formed and tack-welded in place, complete the welding.

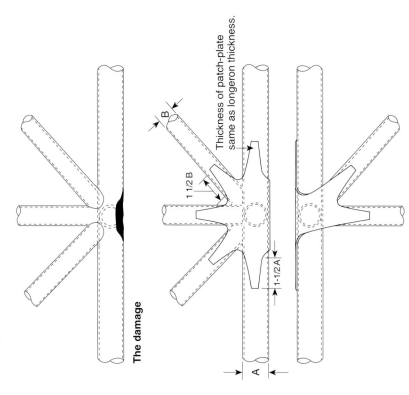

The damage

Patch plate before forming and welding

Patch plate formed and welded to the tubes

Thickness of patch-plate same as longeron thickness.

Figure 2-123. *Repair to a longeron dented at a cluster*

Tubing Spliced by the Inner-Sleeve Method

A new piece of tubing may be spliced into a structure by using an inner-sleeve splice, such as the one in Figure 2-124, by following these steps:

1. Remove the damaged section of tubing by making a 30° diagonal cut at each end.

2. Select the replacement tubing of the same material and wall thickness as the original and cut both of its ends with the same diagonal angle. This replacement tube should allow $\frac{1}{8}$ inch of space at each end so the outside tube can be welded to the inner sleeve.

3. Select tubing for the inner sleeve of the same material and wall thickness as the original, but with an outside diameter that just fits into the inside of the original tubing.

4. Drill holes for the rosette welds that have a diameter of $\frac{1}{4}$ of the outside diameter of the outside tube.

5. Put the inner sleeves inside the replacement tube and insert the replacement in the damaged area. Center the inner sleeves inside the diagonal cuts.

6. Weld the two outer tubes together, and to the inner sleeve at each end, and weld the inner sleeve to the outer tube through the rosette weld holes.

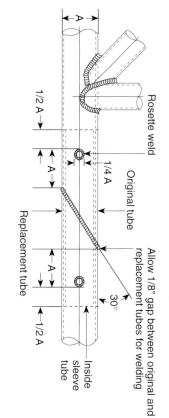

Rosette weld

Original tube

1/4 A

A

A

Replacement tube

30°

Inside sleeve tube

1/2 A

Allow 1/8" gap between original and replacement tubes for welding

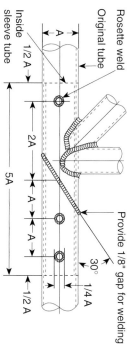

Rosette weld
Original tube

1/2 A

2A

A

A

A

5A

Inside sleeve tube

Provide 1/8" gap for welding

30°

1/4 A

1/2 A

Figure 2-124. *Tube splicing by the inner-sleeve method*

Tubing Spliced by the Outer-Sleeve Method

If the repair is in a location that it does not cause a bulge in the outside fabric, splice the tubing by the much easier outer-sleeve method shown in Figure 2-125. Follow these steps:

1. Remove the damaged section of tubing by making straight cuts across its ends.

2. Select the replacement tubing of the same material and wall thickness as the original that matches the length of the damaged material. This tube must bear against the stubs of the original tubing with a total tolerance not to exceed $\frac{1}{32}$-inch.

3. Select the outer-sleeve material that is the same material and at least the same wall thickness as the original tubes, and with an inside diameter that does not allow more than $\frac{1}{16}$-inch clearance between the outer sleeve and the original tubing.

4. Cut the outer tube with a fishmouth cut as is shown in Figure 2-125. Drill holes for the rosette welds that have a diameter of $\frac{1}{4}$ of the outside diameter of the original tubing.

5. Center the outer sleeves over each end of the repair and weld them to the original and the replacement tubes, and weld the outer sleeve to the tubing through the holes for the rosette welds.

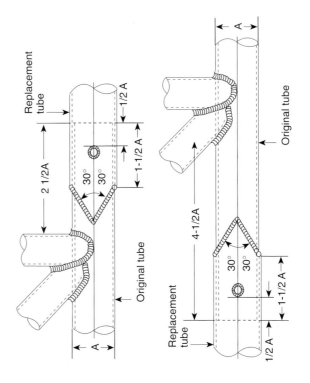

Figure 2-125. *Tube splicing by the outer-sleeve method*

Answers begin below. Page numbers refer to chapter text.

137. The welded structural repairs shown in Advisory Circular 43.13-1A _____ (may or may not) be used by themselves as authorization for making a similar repair to the structure of a certificated aircraft. *Page 163*

138. Heat-treated landing gear components _____ (may or may not) be repaired by welding. *Page 163*

139. The material used for a patch over a damaged longeron should be of the same material and the same wall thickness as the _____ . *Page 164*

140. When making an inner-sleeve repair, there should be a gap of _____ inch between the ends of the replacement tube and the original tubing to allow the outer tubing to be welded to the inner sleeve. *Page 165*

141. The diameter of the holes for a rosette weld is _____ of the diameter of the original tubing. *Page 165*

Answers to Metallic Aircraft Structures Study Questions

1. monocoque
2. semimonocoque
3. a. tension
   b. compression
   c. torsion
   d. bending
   e. shear
4. stress
5. strain
6. elastic limit
7. a. copper
   b. magnesium
   c. zinc
8. solution
9. intergranular
10. aging
11. precipitation
12. artificial aging
13. slowly
14. can

15. T3
16. T6
17. H14
18. O
19. is not
20. annealing
21. is not
22. clad
23. weaker
24. anodized
25. conversion
26. more
27. does
28. ferrous
29. carbon
30. chromium, nickel
31. ultimate
32. hardness
33. 186,000
34. does not

35. 70,000
36. shear
37. shear
38. 2117
39. 1100
40. 2017
41. 2024
42. 5056
43. AD, 2117, B, 5056
44. 2017, 2024
45. 5056
46. a. 100° countersunk,
       2117, ⅛, ¼
    b. Universal, 2024,
       ³⁄₁₆, ½
    c. Round, 2017, ⅛,
       ⅜
47. Monel
48. are not
49. are

50. locking collar
51. Rivnut
52. shear
53. soft lead pencil
54. thickness
55. 2
56. 70
57. numbers, letters, fractions
58. larger
59. cornice
60. slip roll former
61. sand bag
62. few
63. greater
64. 3, 4
65. silver
66. 3/32
67. inside
68. compressive
69. across
70. 1/4
71. less
72. 0.4
73. 0.232
74. 0.112
75. less
76. inside bend tangent
77. bend radius
78. ends
79. center
80. stiffness
81. 5056

82. 3
83. pitch
84. 3/8, 1 1/2
85. 3/8
86. 3/16
87. shear
88. zinc chromate primer
89. 30
90. 40
91. thickness
92. a. coin dimpling
    b. radius dimpling
93. coin
94. larger
95. 1 1/2
96. 1 1/2
97. 1/2
98. microshaver
99. 2
100. 2
101. stretched
102. corrosion
103. 40, 30
104. 3, 12
105. thickness
106. inboard, forward
107. may not
108. a. data
     b. work
109. acetylene
110. is not
111. calcium carbide

112. acetone
113. right-hand
114. left-hand
115. gases used
116. is not
117. all of the way
118. part way
119. soap and water
120. oxidizing
121. neutral
122. forehand
123. reducing
124. carburizing
125. bottom
126. both sides
127. hot water
128. angle
129. rod
130. neutral
131. negative
132. larger
133. front
134. slow
135. contaminated
136. spot welding, seam welding
137. may not
138. may not
139. longeron
140. 1/8
141. 1/4

NONMETALLIC
AIRCRAFT STRUCTURES

3

Continued

Aircraft Wood Structure

Wood is a highly desirable material for aircraft construction. It is lightweight, strong, and has long life when it is properly preserved. It was used extensively in the early days of aircraft construction, but is out of favor for modern commercial aircraft because it does not lend itself to automated high-volume production. This role has been filled by all-metal aircraft and is currently being challenged by composite structures.

Aircraft Wood

There are two basic classifications of wood, hardwood and softwood. These classifications are not based on the actual hardness of the wood, but on its cell structure.

Hardwoods come from deciduous, broadleaf, trees, whose leaves fall each year. The wood has visible pores and is usually (but not always) heavier and denser than softwoods. Softwoods come from evergreen trees that have needles and cones and are typified by their fiber-like cells.

The properties of the various woods that are used in aircraft construction are seen in Figure 3-1.

composite. Something made up of different materials combined in such a way that the characteristics of the resulting material are different from those of any of the components.

deciduous. A type of tree that sheds its foliage at the end of the growing season. Hardwoods come from deciduous trees.

hardwood. Wood from a broadleaf tree that sheds its leaves each year.

softwood. Wood from a tree that bears cones and has needles rather than leaves.

Species of wood	Strength compared with spruce	Remarks
Sitka spruce	100%	Reference wood
Douglas fir	Exceeds spruce	Difficult to work, some tendency to split.
Noble fir	Slightly exceeds spruce except in shear	Satisfactory for direct replacement for spruce.
Western hemlock	Slightly exceeds spruce	Less uniform than spruce.
Northern white pine	85% to 96% of spruce	Must use increased size to compensate for lower strength.
White cedar	Exceeds spruce	May be used as a substitute for spruce.
Yellow poplar	Slightly less than spruce	Must use increased size to compensate for lower strength.

Figure 3-1. *Properties of aircraft structural wood*

Types of Wood

Solid wood is often used for aircraft wing spars, but the difficulty in getting a single piece of wood large enough for a spar that meets all of the specifications for aircraft structural wood often makes laminated spars less expensive and thus preferable to solid spars.

Laminated wood is made of strips of wood glued together in such a way that the grain of all strips run in the same direction. Wing spars made of strips of Sitka spruce glued together are acceptable as a direct replacement for solid spars, provided both spars are of the same high-quality material.

Wooden propellers are made of laminations of birch glued together so that the propeller has more uniformity and strength than it would have if it were made of a single piece of birch.

Plywood is made of sheets of wood veneer glued together with the grains of adjacent layers crossing each other at either 45° or 90°. Aircraft plywood with surface plies of mahogany, birch, or spruce often has a core of poplar or basswood to provide the strongest glue bond between the plies. Plywood up through $3/16$-inch in thickness normally has three plies, and $1/4$-inch or thicker plywood has five plies.

Evaluating Wood for Aircraft Use

When you look at the end of a piece of wood, you will notice that it has concentric rings that are alternately light and dark. These are called annual rings because each dark and light pair represents one growth cycle. The light ring is called springwood and it marks the rapid growth of the tree during the early spring of the year. The dark ring is called summerwood and shows the amount the tree grew during the summer when growth is slower. Summerwood is denser and heavier than springwood.

Wood fibers swell as they absorb moisture and shrink as they lose it. These dimensional changes are greatest along the annual rings and much less across the rings.

laminated wood. A type of wood made by gluing several pieces of thin wood together. The grain of all pieces runs in the same direction.

plywood. A wood product made by gluing several pieces of thin wood veneer together. The grain of the wood in each layer runs at 90° or 45° to the grain of the layer next to it.

veneer. Thin sheets of wood "peeled" from a log. A wide-blade knife held against the surface of the log peels away the veneer as the log is rotated in the cutter.

Veneer is used for making plywood. Several sheets of veneer are glued together, with the grain of each sheet placed at 45° or 90° to the grain of the sheets next to it.

annual rings. The rings that appear in the end of a log cut from a tree. The number of annual rings per inch gives an indication of the strength of the wood. The more rings there are and the closer they are together, the stronger the wood.

The pattern of alternating light and dark rings is caused by the season variations in the growth rate of the tree. A tree grows quickly in the spring and produces the light-colored, less dense rings. The slower growth during the summer, or latter part of the growing season, produces the dark colored, denser rings.

springwood. The portion of an annual ring that is formed principally during the first part of the growing season, the spring of the year. Springwood is softer, more porous, and lighter than the summerwood.

summerwood. The less porous, usually harder portion of an annual ring that forms in the latter part of the growing season, the summer of the year.

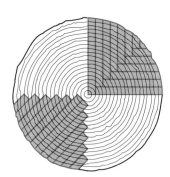

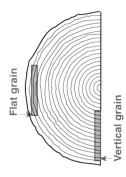

Flat grain

Vertical grain

Figure 3-2. *Planks cut tangent to the annual rings (flat grain) distort, or warp, as their moisture content changes. Planks cut across the annual rings (vertical grain) change their dimensions very little as moisture content changes.*

Figure 3-3. *A log is quartersawed to produce the maximum number of planks with vertical grain. Two methods of quartersawing are illustrated.*

Aircraft structural wood is cut from the tree in such a way that most of the grain lies at 45° or more to the wide dimension of the wood plank. Wood cut in this way is said to have vertical grain.

Logs are quartersawed to produce planks with vertical grain.

Sitka spruce is the reference wood for aircraft structure, and it must meet certain requirements to be used for this purpose. Typical requirements for aircraft spruce are included in the FAA Advisory Circular 43.13-1A *Acceptable Methods, Techniques, and Practices—Aircraft Inspection and Repair.* These requirements are shown in Figure 3-4.

quartersawed wood. Wood sawed from a tree in such a way that the annual rings cross the plank at an angle greater than 45°.

Moisture content—12%
Minimum annual rings per inch—6
Maximum slope of the grain—1 inch in 15 inches

Defects permitted:

Cross grain—Spiral grain, diagonal grain, or a combination of the two is acceptable providing the grain does not diverge from the longitudinal more than 1 in 15. A check of all four faces of the board is necessary to determine the amount of divergence. The direction of free-flowing ink will frequently assist in determining grain direction.

Wavy, curly and interlocked grain—Acceptable, if local irregularities do not exceed limitations specified for spiral and directional grain.

Knots—Sound hard knots up to ³⁄₈-inch in maximum diameter are acceptable providing: (1) They are not in the projecting portions of I-beams, along the edges of rectangular or beveled unrouted beams, or along the edges of flanges of box beams (except in low-stressed portions) (2) They do not cause grain divergence at the edges of the board or in the flanges of a beam of more than 1:15. (3) They are not in the center third of the beam and are not closer than 20 inches to another knot or other defect (pertains to ³⁄₈-inch knots—smaller knots may be proportionally closer). Knots greater than ¼-inch must be used with caution.

Pin knot clusters—Small clusters are acceptable providing they produce only a small effect on grain direction.

Pitch pockets—Acceptable, in center portion of a beam providing they are at least 14 inches apart when they lie in the same growth ring and do not exceed 1-¹⁄₂ inch length by ¹⁄₈ inch width by ¹⁄₈ inch depth, and providing they are not along the projecting portions of I-beams, along the edges of rectangular or beveled unrouted beams, or along the edges of the flanges of box beams.

Mineral streaks—Acceptable, providing careful inspection fails to reveal any decay.

Defects not permitted:

Cross grain—Not acceptable, except as noted above.

Wavy, curly, and interlocked grain—Not acceptable, except as noted above.

Hard knots—Not acceptable, except as noted above.

Pin knot clusters—Not acceptable if they produce large effect on grain direction.

Spike knots—These are knots running completely through the depth of a beam, perpendicular to the annual rings and appear most frequently in quarter sawed lumber. Reject wood containing this defect.

Pitch pockets—Not acceptable, except as noted above.

Mineral streaks—Not acceptable if accompanied by decay.

Checks, shakes, and splits—Checks are longitudinal cracks extending, in general, across the annual rings. Shakes are longitudinal cracks usually between two annual rings. Splits are longitudinal cracks induced by artificially induced stress. Reject wood containing these defects.

Compression wood—This defect is very detrimental to strength and is difficult to recognize readily. It is characterized by high specific gravity; has the appearance of an excessive growth of summerwood; and in most species shows but little contrast in color between springwood and summerwood. In doubtful cases, reject the material, or subject samples to a toughness machine test to establish the quality of the wood. Reject all material containing compression wood.

Compression failures—This defect is caused from the wood being overstressed in compression due to natural forces during the growth of the tree, felling trees on rough or irregular ground, or rough handling of logs or lumber. Compression failures are characterized by a buckling of the fibers that appear as streaks on the surface of the piece substantially at right angles to the grain, and vary from pronounced failures to very fine hairlines that require close inspection to detect. Reject wood containing obvious failures. In doubtful cases reject the wood, or make a closer inspection in the form of microscopic examination or toughness test; the latter means being the more reliable.

Decay—Examine all stains and discolorations carefully to determine whether or not they are harmless, or in a stage of preliminary or advanced decay. All pieces must be free from rot, dote, red heart, purple heart, and all other forms of decay.

Figure 3-4. *Typical requirements for aircraft spruce*

Glues and Gluing

Wood aircraft depend entirely on glued joints for their strength. Tiny nails are often used in joints securing a plywood gusset to a wing rib cap strip and cross member, but the nails do not supply any strength to the joint; they only provide the pressure needed to allow the glued joint to develop its maximum strength.

Types of Glue

Today there are a number of high-strength glues on the market. Plastic resin and resorcinol are generally FAA-approved for use on certificated airplanes. Other glues, such as epoxies, also produce extremely strong glued joints, but they should be specifically approved by the local FAA inspector before they are used on certificated aircraft.

Surface Preparation for Gluing

A good glued joint in a wood aircraft structure should be stronger than the wood itself. When a glued joint is broken, the wood fibers should tear before the glue separates.

The surfaces to be glued should be perfectly flat and smooth to provide intimate contact. Apply the glue according to the recommendations of the glue manufacturer, and clamp the parts together to provide the proper amount of pressure. The glue penetrates into the surface of the parts and bonds them together.

The design of a glued joint is important. The joint must be loaded in shear only, and the grain of the two pieces must be parallel. Proper and improper grain orientation is illustrated in Figure 3-5.

The moisture content of the wood is important. Twelve percent is ideal, but it is very important that both pieces have the same content. Ensure this by keeping both pieces in the same room at least overnight. Do not give the surfaces the final preparation more than eight hours before the glue is applied.

Cut the wood with a fine-tooth saw and smooth it with a planer or jointer. Since the strength of the glued joint is provided by the glue entering the fibers of the wood of both pieces, the pieces should be in intimate contact. Tooth planing or other means of roughening the surface are not recommended because this prevents intimate contact.

Don't sand the surfaces, because sanding dust will get into the fibers and prevent the entry of the glue. Scrape the surfaces with a piece of window glass that has been scored with a glass cutter and broken so that it is perfectly straight, if you want to ensure perfect contact.

cap strip. The main top and bottom members of a wing rib. The cap strips give the rib its aerodynamic shape.

Incorrect:
Joint has end grains of both pieces in contact.

Incorrect:
Joint has end grain of one piece in contact with edge grain of the other.

Correct:
Both pieces are cut parallel to grain. This grain orientation produces the strongest joint.

Figure 3-5. *Grain orientation for a scarfed glue joint*

planer. A woodworking power tool used to smooth the surfaces of a piece of wood.

jointer. A woodworking power tool used to smooth the edges of a piece of wood.

Proper Gluing Procedures

Once the wood has been prepared for gluing, mix the glue according to the manufacturer's recommendations and apply it to either one surface or both surfaces. One technique that assures excellent adhesion is to apply one coat of glue to each of the surfaces and force it into the pores of the wood with a putty knife, then brush on a second coat and assemble the parts.

When the parts have been assembled and properly aligned, apply the correct amount of pressure, using cabinetmaker's parallel clamps to assure that the pressure is evenly applied. Softwoods used for wing spars and ribs should have a pressure of between 125 and 150 pounds per square inch. For hardwoods, the pressure should be between 150 and 200 pounds per square inch.

Truss-type wing ribs have a large number of end-grain joints that do not produce the full strength of the wood. To increase the strength of these joints, glue a gusset made of thin plywood over the joints as shown in Figure 3-6. The pressure needed when gluing a gusset to the rib is provided by brass-plated, cement-coated aircraft nails. The brass plating prevents the nails from rusting and the cement improves their holding power. There should be at least four nails per square inch, and in no instance should the nails be more than 3/4-inch apart.

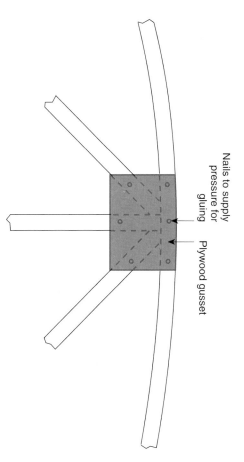

Nails to supply pressure for gluing

Plywood gusset

Figure 3-6. *A plywood gusset glued over the joints in a truss-type wing rib provides the strength needed for an end-grain joint. The pressure needed for the gluing is provided by aircraft nails.*

gusset. A small plate attached to two or more members of a truss structure. A gusset strengthens the truss.

Construction and Repair of Wood Structures

Amateur-built aircraft are often made of wood because the materials are less expensive than those for metal aircraft, and less special tooling is required. Commercial aircraft manufacturers have just about completely phased out wood construction because of the high cost of the labor they require.

There are still quite a few smaller general aviation airplanes flying that have wooden wing spars and wooden ribs, and a few have some plywood covering. Some of the repairs these aircraft are most likely to need are described here.

Wing Spar Repair

The spars are the main stress-carrying members of a truss-type aircraft wing. They are typically made of aircraft-grade Sitka spruce and may be solid, laminated, or built up.

Most of the loads carried by a wing spar are carried in its upper and lower caps. The web, or center portion, of the spar carries a much smaller load than the caps, and it is possible to decrease the weight of the spar by removing some of the web thickness.

If part of the web is removed, there must be solid wood of full thickness at each point where the wing attaches to the fuselage and where the struts attach to the wing. These locations are typically reinforced with birch plywood to provide a good bearing surface for the attachment bolts.

Elongated bolt holes or cracks near the bolt holes in a wood spar usually require the replacement of the spar or the removal of the damaged area. A new section of spar can be spliced in. The splice or its reinforcing plates must not be under any fitting.

Figure 3-7 shows a typical method for splicing a solid or laminated spar. Before any actual spar splice is made, make a sketch of the repair including all the pertinent details and submit it to the FAA maintenance inspector for his or her approval.

amateur-built aircraft. Aircraft built by individuals as a hobby rather than by factories as commercial products. Although amateur-built, or homebuilt, aircraft are subject to some FAA regulations, they are not required to meet the stringent requirements imposed upon FAA-certificated aircraft.

web of a spar. The part of a spar between the caps.

fitting. An attachment device that is used to connect components to an aircraft structure.

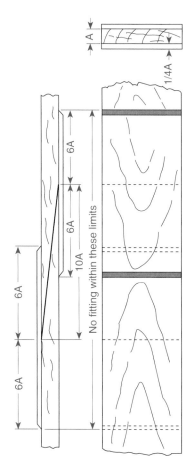

Figure 3-7. *Acceptable method for splicing a solid or laminated wood wing spar*

Remove the damaged area by cutting the spar at a 12-to-1 scarf angle (10:1 is the minimum allowable angle) and cutting a piece of new aircraft-grade wood of the same dimensions, and with the same scarf angle.

Spread the glue on the two prepared ends and place a pressure block on each side. Clamp the spar and pressure blocks together with cabinetmaker's parallel clamps. Check to be sure that the joint is perfectly straight, then tighten the clamps until a uniform bead of glue is squeezed from the joint. Wipe this glue off and allow the pressure to remain for at least the time specified for the particular glue at the existing ambient temperature.

Once you remove the clamps, cut the solid spruce or birch plywood reinforcing plates as wide as the spar, 12 times as long as the spar is thick, and one-fourth as thick as the spar. Taper the ends of these plates with a slope of about 5 to 1 to prevent an abrupt change in the cross-sectional area, and prepare the plates to be glued in place. The center of the reinforcing plates should be in line with the end of the cut in the spar, and they must overlap by twice the thickness of the spar. Scrape the surface of the spar and the reinforcing plates with the edge of a piece of glass to remove all surface contamination or roughness, and glue the reinforcing plates in position. *See* Figure 3-7.

Rib Repairs

The most common damage to a wing rib is a broken cap strip. This may be repaired by removing the damaged area by cutting the cap strip with a 12:1 taper (10:1 minimum). Cut the replacement material with the same taper and glue the pieces together. When cutting the taper in both pieces of wood, be sure that the cuts are parallel to the grain of the wood so there will be no end-grain glue joints. *See* Figure 3-5 on Page 178.

Glue the pieces together and when the glue is completely dry, cut reinforcing plates of aircraft-grade plywood as shown in Figure 3-8, and glue them in place using aircraft nails to supply the pressure. The face grain of the plywood must be parallel to the cap strip.

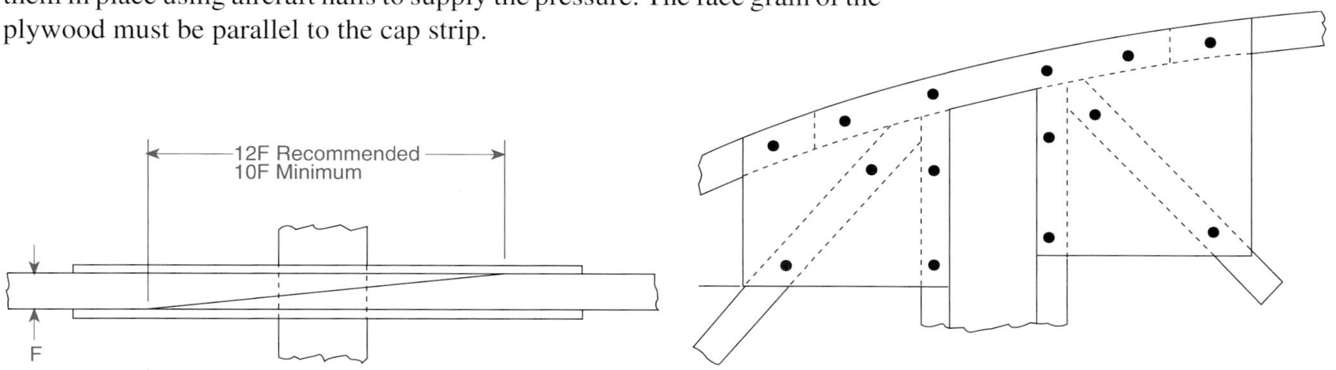

scarf joint. A joint in a wood structure in which the ends to be joined are cut in a long taper, normally about 12:1, and fastened together by gluing. A glued scarf joint makes a strong splice because the joint is made along the side of the wood fibers rather than along their ends.

12F Recommended
10F Minimum

F

Figure 3-8. *Wing rib cap strip splice at a spar*

Repair to Damaged Plywood Structures

You can repair small holes in a plywood skin if they can be cleaned out to a diameter of less than one inch. Repair them by doping a fabric patch over them, unless the damage is in the leading edge of a wing. The fabric should extend at least one inch beyond the edges of the hole.

You can repair plywood skins 1/8-inch thick or less that are damaged between or along framing members with surface, or overlay, patches. Bevel the edges of all these patches back for a distance of four thicknesses of the wood to prevent an abrupt change in cross-sectional area.

Repair small holes in plywood skins not more than 1/10-inch thick whose largest dimensions are not over 15 times the skin thickness with a splayed patch.

Trim the damage to a circular hole with a maximum dimension of 15 times the skin thickness, and taper the edges of the hole back five times the skin thickness. Cut a patch that exactly fills the cleaned-out and tapered hole and orient the face ply in the same direction as that of the damaged skin.

Glue the patch in place, and when the glue is thoroughly dry, sand the surface and refinish it to match the rest of the skin.

A properly prepared and inserted scarf patch is the best repair for damaged plywood skins and is preferred for most skin repairs. Clean out the damaged area and taper back the edges of the hole at least 12 times the thickness of the skin. Cut the patch and taper its edges to match those of the prepared hole and glue it in place. Apply pressure with a nailing strip that is nailed in place over a piece of cellophane or vinyl sheeting to prevent the strip sticking to the skin. After the glue is completely dry, break away the nailing strip and remove the nails with a pair of diagonal cutters. Sand the surface and refinish it to match the rest of the skin.

Protection and Inspection of Wooden Aircraft Structures

Decay and dry rot (caused by a certain species of fungus) are major problems associated with wood aircraft. This fungus gets its nourishment from the cellulose of the wood and reproduces by forming microscopic spores, or seed. These spores are carried by the air currents and when they settle on an unprotected piece of wood in the presence of moisture, they multiply and cause the wood to disintegrate.

The low points of the aircraft must have an adequate number of drain holes, so moisture that accumulates inside the structure will drain out. These holes also ventilate the structure to prevent water from condensing inside it.

Decay first shows up as a discoloration of the wood, usually black, gray, or brown. Discoloration is not always caused by decay, but you should check any discolored area. Stick a sharp-pointed knife blade into the discolored area

splayed patch. A type of patch made in an aircraft plywood structure in which the edges of the patch are tapered for approximately five times the thickness of the plywood. A splayed patch is not recommended for use on plywood less than 1/10 inch thick.

nailing strip. A method of applying pressure to the glue in a scarf joint repair in a plywood skin. A strip of thin plywood is nailed over the glued scarf joint with the nails extending into a supporting structure beneath the skin. The strip is installed over vinyl sheeting to prevent it sticking to the skin. When the glue is thoroughly dry, the nailing strip is broken away and the nails removed.

decay. Decomposition. The breakdown of the structure of wood fibers. Wood that shows any indication of decay must be rejected for use in aircraft structure.

dry rot. Decomposition of wood fibers caused by fungi. Dry rot destroys all strength in the wood.

fungus (*plural* fungi). Any of several types of plant life that include yeasts, molds, and mildew.

and pry the wood up. If it comes up as a long splinter, the wood is good, and no decay is present. But if it comes up as a chunk about the size of the knife blade tip, the wood has decayed and must be replaced.

You can protect aircraft structure against decay by keeping air and moisture from the wood. Wood whose moisture content is kept below about 20% will not decay.

After you've completed all of the cutting, drilling, and gluing in an aircraft repair, saturate the wood with a wood preservative (typically a non-oil-base vehicle with copper naphthonate or pentachlorophenol). After the preservative is dry, give the structure several coats of varnish to seal the surface.

STUDY QUESTIONS: AIRCRAFT WOOD CONSTRUCTION

Answers begin on Page 263. Page numbers refer to chapter text.

1. Wood that comes from a cone-bearing tree is a ———— (softwood or hardwood). *Page 175*

2. Hardwoods ———— (are or are not) always more dense than softwoods. *Page 175*

3. The standard for comparing all aircraft structural wood is ————. *Page 175*

4. A wood product made of strips of wood glued together in such a way that all of the grains run in the same direction is called ———— wood. *Page 176*

5. Wood propellers are made of laminations of ———— (what kind of wood). *Page 176*

6. The grains in the plies of a sheet of aircraft plywood cross each other at either ———— or ———— degrees. *Page 176*

7. Aircraft plywood with mahogany or birch faces often have cores made of ———— or ————. *Page 176*

8. The light bands seen in the end of a piece of wood are called ———— (springwood or summerwood). *Page 176*

9. The desirable moisture content of aircraft spruce is ———— percent. *Page 177*

10. The maximum allowable grain divergence in aircraft spruce is 1: ————. *Page 177*

Continued

11. A sound hard knot that is ³⁄₈ inch in diameter in the web of a solid wood wing spar _____ (is or is not) an acceptable defect. *Page 177*

12. A pitch pocket 1 inch long, ⅛ inch wide and ³⁄₃₂ inch deep in the center of a solid wood wing spar _____ (is or is not) an acceptable defect. *Page 177*

13. A wood wing spar blank containing some compression wood _____ (is or is not) acceptable for use. *Page 177*

14. Nails in a glued joint _____ (do or do not) increase the strength of the joint. *Page 178*

15. A properly designed glued joint should be loaded in _____ (shear or tension). *Page 178*

16. There should be a time lapse of no more than _____ hours between the final surfacing of the wood and the application of the glue. *Page 178*

17. When preparing solid wood for a glued joint, the surface _____ (should or should not) be roughened to help the glue adhere. *Page 178*

18. Final smoothing of the wood surfaces to be joined _____ (should or should not) be done with fine sandpaper. *Page 178*

19. When using aircraft nails to apply pressure for gluing gussets to a wing rib, the maximum distance between nails is _____ inch. *Page 179*

20. A laminated wood spar _____ (may or may not) be used to replace a solid wood spar if they are both made of the same quality wood. *Page 180*

21. The majority of the flight loads applied to a wing spar are carried in the _____ (caps or web) of the spar. *Page 180*

22. Locations where bolts pass through a wooden spar are reinforced with plywood made of _____. *Page 180*

23. Elongated bolt holes in a wing spar _____ (should or should not) be repaired by drilling the hole oversize and using the next larger size bolt. *Page 180*

24. The minimum taper to use when splicing a solid or laminated wood wing spar is _____ to 1. *Page 181*

25. The reinforcing plate over a splice in a wing spar _____ (may or may not) be in a location through which the wing strut bolts pass. *Page 180*

26. A small hole in the leading edge of a plywood wing that cleans out to less than one inch in diameter _____ (can or cannot) be repaired with a fabric patch. *Page 182*

27. The choice repair for all types of plywood skin damage is a _____ (splayed or scarf) patch. *Page 182*

28. Aircraft wood with a moisture content of less than _____ % is not susceptible to decay or dry rot. *Page 183*

29. When a sharp knife point stuck into a piece of aircraft wood pries up a chunk of wood instead of a hard splinter, the wood _____ (is or is not) likely infected with decay. *Page 183*

Aircraft Fabric Covering

Fabric Covering Systems

Fabric-covered aircraft were at one time the most popular type, but today, all-metal construction is standard. Aviation maintenance technicians are likely to encounter fabric covering only on some of the special-purpose aircraft, such as those used for agricultural applications, or when restoring antique airplanes. Many amateur-built aircraft are fabric-covered, and the newly initiated primary category for aircraft will likely bring about new FAA-certificated fabric-covered aircraft.

In this *Aviation Maintenance Technician Series*, we are concerned with aircraft fabric covering as it applies to FAA-certificated aircraft. While these principles also apply to amateur-built aircraft, the freedom from restrictive Federal Aviation Regulations allows an amateur builder to use some materials and procedures that are not approved for certificated aircraft.

Organic Fabrics

Cotton and linen are two popular natural, or organic, covering fabrics. Cotton is still used, but linen is not readily available in the United States.

For many years, mercerized long-staple Grade-A cotton has been the standard covering material for aircraft. This fabric weighs approximately 4.5 ounces per square yard, has between 80 and 84 threads per inch (tpi), and a minimum strength of 80 pounds per inch in both the warp and fill directions.

V_{NE}. Never-exceed speed. The maximum speed the aircraft is allowed to attain in any conditions of flight.

polyester fibers. A synthetic fiber made by the polymerization process in which tiny molecules are united to form a long chain of molecules.

Polyester fibers are woven into fabrics that are known by their trade names of Dacron, Fortrel, and Kodel. Polyester film and sheet are known as Mylar and Celenar.

greige (pronounced "gray"). The unshrunk condition of a polyester fabric as it is removed from the loom.

Grade-A cotton fabric meets Aeronautical Material Specification AMS 3806 and Military Specifications MIL-C-5646, and it is manufactured under Technical Standard Order TSO-C15. Grade-A fabric is approved for use on aircraft that have wing loadings greater than 9 pounds per square foot (psf) and with never-exceed speeds (V_{NE}) in excess of 160 miles per hour.

Inorganic Fabrics

There are two inorganic fabrics used for covering FAA-certificated aircraft; fabric made from polyester fibers and fabric made of glass filaments.

Fabric made from polyester fibers is sold under such trade names as Ceconite®, Superflite®, and Poly-Fiber® and is the most widely used covering material today. Polyester fibers used in aircraft covering are heated and stretched during manufacturing. This hot stretching orients the molecules and increases the strength and toughness of the fibers. Once the fibers are made into threads and woven into the fabric, they will return to their original unstretched length when reheated. Polyester used for aircraft covering is applied in its greige condition. It has not been passed through shrinking rollers, and it still contains some sizing, which is the lubricant required on the warp threads when the fabric is woven in the high-speed dry looms.

Fiberglass cloth is a loose weave of glass filaments treated with tinted butyrate dope to hold the filaments together for ease of installation. Install this fabric according to the instructions in the STC that is sold with the material.

Covering System Approvals

Appendix A of Federal Aviation Regulations Part 43, *Maintenance, Preventive Maintenance, Rebuilding, and Alteration*, classifies the re-covering of an aircraft as a major repair. As any major repair, it must meet specific criteria, and an FAA Form 337, *Major Repair and Alteration* must be completed and properly filed to accompany the repair.

Original Equipment Manufacturer

When an aircraft is designed and the prototype is built, the FAA approves all the materials and methods used for the covering. When the aircraft is re-covered, the same type of materials must be used and they must be installed in the same way as was approved by the FAA. Re-covering an aircraft in this way is considered to be a major repair.

Supplemental Type Certificates

Most fabric-covered aircraft were certificated before synthetic fabrics became popular, and their certification calls for cotton fabric covering. The lower cost, additional strength, weight saving, and increased service life make re-covering these aircraft with one of the polyester fabrics a very practical alteration.

Since changing the type of fabric on the aircraft is a major alteration and prevents the aircraft conforming to its Approved Type Certificate (ATC), it must be issued a Supplemental Type Certificate (STC).

The holder of the STC authorizes its use as approved data when all of the materials specified in the STC are used, and when all of its procedures are followed.

FAA Field Approval

If for some reason you do not want to use the same materials used by the original manufacturer, nor the materials specified in an STC, consider getting FAA field approval. A field approval is time-consuming and not typically cost-effective, but it does allow for use of new or different materials or procedures.

To get a field approval, submit an FAA Form 337 to the FAA Flight Standards District Office describing in detail the procedure you want to follow. The FAA maintenance inspector may approve the data, or he or she may require more data to prove that this new procedure will allow the aircraft to meet or exceed the requirements for its original certification. When this data is approved, you may make the alteration. Then an IA must inspect the work for conformity to the approved data. If it conforms, the aircraft is approved for return to service and the Form 337 is completed and returned to the FAA FSDO.

Aircraft Re-Covering

Re-covering an aircraft is an expensive and time-consuming project. Do not undertake it until it is definitely necessary. The structure to be re-covered must be thoroughly inspected, and all measures must be taken to preserve the structure, since it will will not be visible for another inspection for several years.

Is Re-Covering Necessary?

The fabric on an aircraft is allowed to deteriorate until its strength is 70% of that required for the original fabric. New Grade-A cotton fabric has a strength of 80 pounds per inch, and it is allowed to deteriorate until its strength is 56 pounds per inch.

FAA FSDO. Federal Aviation Administration Flight Standards District Office. An FAA field office serving an assigned geographical area staffed with Flight Standards personnel who serve the aviation industry and the general public on matters relating to certification and operation of air carrier and general aviation aircraft.

An airplane whose V_{NE} is less than 160 mph and whose wing loading is less than 9 psf may be covered with intermediate fabric whose new strength is 65 pounds per inch. Any fabric installed on this type of aircraft is allowed to deteriorate to 46 pounds per inch (70% of 65 pounds per inch) before it must be replaced.

Often the finish on aircraft fabric dries out and cracks, giving the appearance that the aircraft needs re-covering, when what has actually happened is that the plasticizers have dried out of the dope and it is brittle. If the fabric is still good, the finish can be rejuvenated. Rejuvenation does nothing to improve the strength of the fabric, however. When the fabric deteriorates to 70% of the strength required for new fabric, it must be replaced.

Fabric Testing

The technician is required on each 100-hour or annual inspection to determine that the fabric meets at least its minimum strength requirements. Two commonly used methods of determining the strength of the fabric are the Maule test and the Seyboth test.

The Maule tester, Figure 3-9, is a precision spring-loaded instrument with a blunt pin on its end and a scale calibrated in pounds per inch. Hold the tester squarely against the fabric and press until the scale indicates the minimum allowable strength of the fabric. If the tester penetrates the fabric, it indicates that the fabric strength is below the minimum allowable. If both the fabric and the finish are good, the tester will make a small depression that will return to its original smooth surface with no permanent damage.

The Seyboth tester has a specially shaped, spring-loaded sharp point and an indicator pin that is marked with green, yellow, and red-colored bands. To use this tester, hold it straight against the fabric and press it down until the point penetrates the fabric enough to allow the wide shoulder to rest on the surface of the fabric. The amount of force required to penetrate the fabric is indicated by the color of the band on the indicator pin that protrudes from the body of the tester. If the fabric is very weak, only a small amount of force is needed, and the red band will show. If the fabric is somewhat stronger, more force is needed and the yellow band will be exposed. If the fabric is airworthy, enough force will be needed to cause one of the green bands to show. When the test is completed, place a small circular patch over the hole left by the tester. *See* Figure 3-10.

The indications given by these two testers are adequate to identify good fabric, but since both of them test fabric that is covered by the dope film, they do not indicate the actual strength of the undoped fabric. To determine the actual strength of the fabric by itself, remove a strip of fabric about $1\frac{1}{4}$ inch wide and 6 inches long from the upper surface of the wing or fuselage. Take it from an area that is finished with a dark color, because dark colors absorb heat and in these locations the fabric is most likely to be weakened. Soak the

Figure 3-9. *The Maule fabric tester indicates the strength of the fabric in pounds per inch without making a hole in the fabric.*

plasticizer. A constituent in dope or lacquer that gives its film flexibility and resilience.

rejuvenate. Restore the resilience to an aircraft finishing material. This is done by the use of a rejuvenator.

fabric strip in dope thinner to remove all the dope, then pull the threads from the edges until you have a strip that is exactly one inch wide. Clamp the strip in a fabric pull tester and pull it until the strip breaks. The indication on the tester when the strip breaks is the tensile strength of the fabric.

Preparation for Re-Covering

If the fabric is too weak to be airworthy, you should begin to prepare the aircraft for re-covering. In this portion of our text, we follow the procedure used for covering the popular Piper Super Cub, as this procedure is typical for most fabric-covered aircraft.

First remove the wings and tail surfaces and carefully store them in the proper type of cradle so they will not be damaged while the aircraft is disassembled.

Remove the Old Fabric

Carefully remove the fabric by cutting it along one of the fuselage longerons or the trailing edges of the wings and tail surfaces. Cut all the lacing cord used to hold the fabric to the structure. If the fabric is held to the wing with screws or clips, cut the surface tape and remove them.

Roll up the old covering and keep it until the re-covering job is complete, because you will probably need it to locate the positions for inspection rings and the holes through which control cables must pass.

Inspect the Structure

When the structure is completely uncovered, inspect the parts that are not visible when the covering is in place.

The lower longerons in the tail end of the fuselage are exposed to moisture and dirt and are likely to be rusted. Carefully sand off any rust and probe the entire tubing with a sharp-pointed awl to determine whether or not rust has weakened the metal.

Inspect the controls under the floorboards and replace any components that are worn or damaged, and lubricate those joints that will be difficult to reach when the covering is in place.

Inspect the tail surfaces for any indication of rust or damage. Check the hinges to be sure that they have not worn excessively and check for cracks. Carefully inspect the stabilizer adjustment mechanism or trim tabs if any are installed.

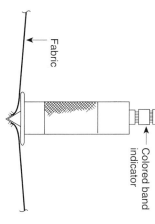

Fabric

Colored band indicator

Figure 3-10. *The Seyboth fabric tester indicates the relative strength of the fabric with colored bands around the indicator pin. This pin protrudes from the top of the tester when it is pushed in until the wide face of the plunger rests on the fabric.*

The wings demand the most attention. Check the spars for condition, especially at the root end and at the locations where the wing struts attach. Check wooden spars to be sure that none of the varnish has cracked. Revarnish any areas that show bare wood.

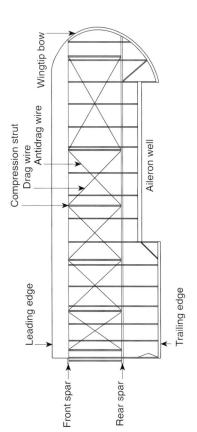

Figure 3-11. *Truss-type airplane wing*

compression strut. A heavy structural member, often in the form of a steel tube, used to hold the spars of a Pratt truss airplane wing apart. A compression strut opposes the compressive loads between the spars arising from the tensile loads produced by the drag and antidrag wires.

drag wire. A structural wire inside a Pratt truss airplane wing between the spars. Drag wires run from the front spar inboard, to the rear spar at the next bay outboard. Drag wires oppose the forces that try to drag the wing backward.

antidrag wire. A structural wire inside a Pratt truss airplane wing between the spars. Antidrag wires run from the rear spar inboard, to the front spar at the next bay outboard. Antidrag wires oppose the forces that try to pull the wing forward.

Inspect the leading and trailing edges for corrosion or cracks. The leading edges of these wings are covered with thin aluminum alloy sheet back to the front spar, and this metal is easily dented. Repair any dents or replace sections of the metal that are dented beyond repair.

Check the control cables and pulleys. Replace any pulleys that are stuck or that show wear from the cables. Check the electrical wiring and replace any whose insulation is cracked. Secure the wire to the structure by the method used by the manufacturer. Check the pitot-static plumbing to be sure there are no leaks in the lines to be covered.

Check the wing truss for squareness. Use a wood or metal trammel bar and a pair of trammel points. Place a mark in the center of the top of both the front and rear spars aligned with the center of each of the compression struts. Set the trammel points to measure distance A, Figure 3-12, then measure distance B. If these distances are not exactly the same, adjust the drag and antidrag wires until they are.

After all the adjustments are made, look down each of the spars to determine that they are perfectly straight. If they are not, repeat the trammel process.

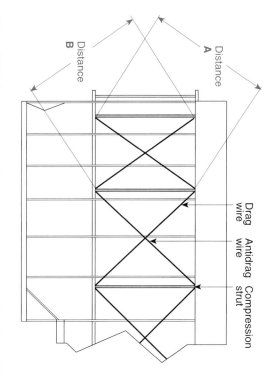

Figure 3-12. *A truss-type wing is squared up by measuring the diagonal distance across each of the bays with a trammel bar and trammel points. If distances A and B are not identical, adjust the drag and antidrag wires.*

Prepare the Structure

Once the structural inspection is complete and the repairs made, prepare the structure to receive the covering.

Remove all the dried dope that was used to attach the original fabric to the steel tubing, and prime the tubing with a good primer, such as one of the epoxies.

When preparing the wing, cover all the overlapping edges of the leading edge metal with cloth tape to protect the fabric.

Use reinforcing tape to brace all the ribs so they will remain in position until the fabric is stitched in place. This tape is applied across the middle of the ribs in the manner shown in Figure 3-13. Start at the root rib, work out to the tip, and loop the tape around the tip bow and back to the root rib. At the root rib, tie the ends together.

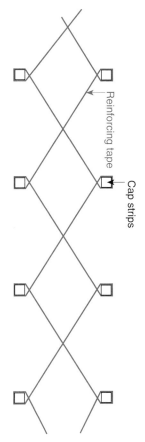

Figure 3-13. *Wing ribs are braced with reinforcing tape wrapped around the middle of the cap strips in this fashion.*

trammel (*verb*). The procedure used to square up the Pratt truss in an airplane wing. Trammel points are set on the trammel bar so they measure the distance between the center of the front spar, at the inboard compression strut, and the center of the rear spar at the next compression strut outboard. The drag and antidrag wires are adjusted until the distance between the center of the rear spar at the inboard compression strut and the center of the front spar at the next outboard compression strut is exactly the same as that between the first points measured.

trammel bar. A wood or metal bar on which trammel points are mounted to compare distances.

trammel points. A set of sharp-pointed pins that protrude from the sides of a trammel bar.

In the figure: Distance A, Distance B, Drag wire, Antidrag wire, Compression strut

In Figure 3-13: Reinforcing tape, Cap strips

Cotton Fabric Covering

In this section we consider the procedure for covering an aircraft with Grade-A cotton, and then in the following section we will emphasize the differences when using polyester.

Textiles

Purchase the fabric from a legitimate supplier of aircraft materials. Grade-A fabric should be stamped TSO-C15 or AMS 3806 along the selvage edge. This fabric is usually available either by the yard in widths of 50 or 64 inches, or in pre-sewn envelopes tailored for specific aircraft.

Thread for sewing the fabric must meet VT-276 specifications, and the fabric is attached to the aircraft structure with waxed linen rib-lacing cord which meets MIL-T-6779 specifications.

Reinforcing tape is a narrow tape made of heavy cotton thread. It is placed over all of the ribs and any part of the structure to which the fabric is to be laced. It is normally available in widths from 1/4 to 1/2 inch, and wider for special applications. Reinforcing tape is also used to support the wing ribs before the fabric is installed, as shown in Figure 3-13 on Page 191.

Surface tape is made of Grade-A cotton and cut with pinked, or notched, edges to prevent its raveling. This tape is doped over all of the ribs after the rib lacing is completed, around the leading and trailing edges, and around the tips of all of the surfaces.

The length of most surface tape is parallel to the warp threads, but there is a bias-cut tape whose threads cross its length at a 45° angle. Bias-cut tape is used around the tips of some wings and tail surfaces where straight-cut tape will not lie down smoothly.

bias-cut surface tape. A fabric tape in which the threads run at an angle of 45° to the length of the tape. Bias-cut tape may be stretched around a compound curve such as a wing tip bow without wrinkling.

Chemicals

Fabric-covered aircraft use a number of highly specialized chemicals such as cements, dopes, thinners, solvents, retarders, and rejuvenators. It is extremely important when buying these chemicals that they are all fresh and compatible. The best way of assuring this is to use materials from the same manufacturer and purchase them from a reputable supplier of aircraft materials.

There are many places where the fabric is glued to the structure rather than sewn. The adhesive used to attach the fabric is similar to a heavy nitrate dope, but it contains different plasticizers. It can be thinned to the proper brushing consistency with nitrate thinner, but, because of its different components, it should not be mixed with dope.

Aircraft dope consists of a film base, solvents, plasticizers, and thinners. The film base is made of cellulose fibers dissolved in an acid. It wets and encloses, or encapsulates, the fibers of the fabric, and when it dries it shrinks the fibers and pulls them tightly together. Solvents dissolve the film base material, and plasticizers are mixed with the dissolved film base to control its characteristics and give it resilience to prevent its cracking when it dries.

Thinners adjust the viscosity of dope, giving it the correct consistency for brushing or spraying. Two basic types of dopes are used on fabric-covered aircraft: nitrate and butyrate.

Nitrate dope is the oldest type of aircraft fabric dope. It has excellent encapsulating properties, which make it the best material for attaching the fabric to the structure and for the initial coats of dope, but it has the serious drawback of being highly flammable.

Butyrate dope has better tautening characteristics than nitrate dope, and while it will burn, it does not ignite as easily as nitrate. Its main drawback is that it does not encapsulate the fibers as well as nitrate.

The solvents used in butyrate dope are more potent than those used in nitrate dope, and butyrate dope will soften the nitrate film base and may be applied over it. The solvents used in nitrate dope will not adequately soften the butyrate film, and nitrate dope should not be applied over butyrate dope.

Clear dope is an organic product and the fabrics to which it is applied are weakened by the ultraviolet rays of the sun. To prevent this damage, extremely tiny flakes of aluminum metal are mixed with clear dope and sprayed over the coats of clear dope. The aluminum flakes spread out and form a light-tight covering that prevents the ultraviolet rays reaching the clear dope and the fabric.

The aluminum flakes are available as a powder and also in the more convenient form of a ready-mixed paste. To prepare the dope, first mix about three and a half ounces of paste with dope thinner and then pour a gallon of unthinned butyrate dope into the thinned paste.

Colored dopes are used to give an aircraft an attractive finish and to protect it from the elements. For many years, aircraft were finished only with aluminum-pigmented dope. This provided the needed ultraviolet protection and added a minimum of weight. Modern aircraft are finished with many different colors, although lighter colors predominate because they absorb the least heat from the sun, so fabric finished with light-colored dope lasts longer.

Some pigments, especially some of the reds, are soluble in the solvents used in their application and they will bleed up through any of the finishing coats that are applied over them. Bleeding dopes must be applied after all the other coats have dried.

Aircraft dope is a complex mixture of film base, solvents, and plasticizers. Its viscosity must be adjusted by the addition of thinner before it is brushed or sprayed on the fabric. Because of its complex composition, only thinners that are made especially for the particular dope should be used.

The dope dries when the solvents and thinner evaporate and leave the resilient film attached to the fabric. If the solvents evaporate too rapidly, they will absorb enough heat to drop the temperature of the air, allowing moisture to condense and deposit on the surface of the wet dope. The moisture causes the cellulose to precipitate from the dope film and form a white porous deposit called blush. A blushed doped surface is weak, porous, and unattractive.

bleeding dope. Dope whose pigments are soluble in the solvents or thinners used in the finishing system. The color will bleed up through the finish coats.

blush. A defect in a lacquer or dope finish caused by moisture condensing on the surface before the finish dries.

If the humidity of the air is high, the evaporation of the solvents cools the air enough to cause the moisture to condense. The water condensed from the air mixes with the lacquer or dope and forms a dull, porous, chalky-looking finish called blush. A blushed finish is neither attractive nor protective.

If the humidity of the air in the paint room is high enough for the dope to blush, you can use retarder in place of some of the thinner. Retarder is a thinner that has certain additives that slow its rate of evaporation.

Cotton and linen fabrics are susceptible to destruction by mildew and fungus, which can weaken the fabric in a relatively short time unless you mix fungicidal paste, including a small amount of nonbleeding dye, with thinned clear dope for the first coat. This dope must thoroughly penetrate and encapsulate the fabric for the fungicidal agent to be effective.

Installing the Fabric

When the structure has been inspected and repaired as necessary, and the covering system has been chosen, you are ready for the most important steps in re-covering, installing the fabric.

The Envelope Method

If you are using a pre-sewn envelope, you are ready to install the fabric. Begin with the simplest structures first and then, as you gain experience, progress to the more complex components. Install in this order: flaps, ailerons, tail surfaces, landing gear legs, wings, and fuselage.

When covering the small components, slip the envelope over the structure and straighten the seam so that it runs straight down the trailing edge. Close the open end by cementing the fabric to the structure. First brush a coat of full-bodied nitrate cement on the structure where the fabric will attach and allow it to dry. Then cover the dried cement with a second coat thinned to a good brushing consistency and place the fabric in position. Don't pull it tight, just smooth. Work the fabric down into the wet cement with your fingers to get all of the air bubbles out of it.

When covering the wings, slip the envelope over the tip and straighten the seam around the center of the tip bow and along the trailing edge. Any chordwise seams should all be parallel to the line of flight and should not lie over a wing rib.

When the covering is in place with all the seams straight, begin cementing the fabric at the tip end of the aileron well. Give the metal a full-bodied coat of nitrate cement. When it is thoroughly dry, brush on a coat of thinned cement. Place the fabric in position, and pull it smooth. Press it down into the wet cement and work out the air bubbles.

Turn the wing over and coat the fabric you have just cemented in the aileron well with a coat of thinned cement. Pull the fabric smooth and work its edges down into the wet dope.

full-bodied. Not thinned.

Close out the aileron well and then the root end of the wing. When doing this work it is very important to continually check that the seams are not pulled away from the center of the trailing edge.

Slip the fuselage envelope over the structure from the tail. Be sure that the tubing to which the fabric is to attach is absolutely clean and primed with epoxy primer, then coat the tubing with full-bodied nitrate cement. When it is dry, apply a thinned coat of cement and press the edges of the fabric into it, working out all the air bubbles. Trim the fabric so it will wrap around the tubing but not lap up onto the fabric on the inside.

If the fuselage has an integral vertical fin, slip the fin cover in place with the seams straight along the leading edge, and cement the fabric from the fin to the fabric from the fuselage.

The Blanket Method

When pre-sewn envelopes are unavailable, use the blanket method. Choose the width of fabric that will let you sew up a blanket with at least one foot of fabric at the tip and at the root, and will not cause chordwise seams to lie over a wing rib.

Sew the blanket using an FAA-approved machine-sewing thread and any of the seams shown in Figure 3-14. Apply a full-bodied coat of cement to both sides of the trailing edge and the wingtip bow. When this is dry, cover it with a coat of thinned cement and press the fabric from one side of the wing down into it, working out all of the air bubbles. After the cement is dry, trim the fabric, and turn the wing over. Pull the fabric smooth but not tight, and brush a coat of thinned nitrate cement over the fabric that has just been cemented down. Press the fabric down into the wet cement and work out all the air bubbles. Continue all around the trailing edge and the wingtip bow.

When the cement is dry, trim the fabric with pinking shears to leave at least a one-inch overlap around the wing tip and the trailing edge. Cement the overlap and close out the aileron well as described in the envelope method section.

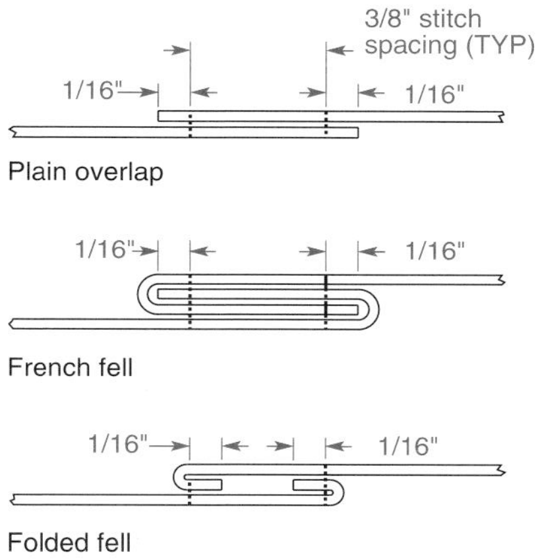

Removing the Wrinkles

You can remove wrinkles from installed fabric by wetting the fabric with distilled or demineralized water. Wet the fabric thoroughly but do not use so much water that it runs down the inside of the structure.

The wet fabric will pull up to a drumhead tightness and all of the wrinkles will pull out. It will lose some of its tightness when it dries, but the wrinkles will be gone.

Plain overlap

1/16"

1/16"

3/8" stitch
spacing (TYP)

French fell

1/16"

1/16"

Folded fell

1/16"

1/16"

Figure 3-14. *Machine-sewed seams used to join aircraft cotton fabric*

It is important not to cut the fabric around any fittings while it is wet. It moves about considerably while it is shrinking, so the hole would end up too large and in the wrong location.

The First Coat of Dope

Allow the water to dry completely, but do not allow more than 48 hours to elapse between the time the fabric is installed and the fungicidal dope is applied. If the fabric is left untreated for longer than this, airborne fungus spores will settle on the fabric.

Pour unthinned nitrate dope into fungicidal paste at the ratio of one gallon of dope for four ounces of paste. Stir until the paste is mixed evenly throughout the dope and then thin the dope with equal parts of nitrate dope thinner.

Use a good quality animal-bristle brush and work the thinned fungicidal dope well into the fabric so that the threads in the fabric are completely surrounded, but none of the dope runs down inside the fabric. The dye in the fungicidal paste helps you see when the fabric is completely treated and gives an indication of the uniformity of the application.

When you apply the first coat of dope, the fabric becomes stiff and baggy, but it will shrink when you apply additional coats of dope.

Attaching the Fabric

The fabric must be attached to the wing ribs in such a way that the aerodynamic force caused by the low pressure above the wing is transmitted into the structure, lifting the entire aircraft.

Many aircraft have the fabric laced to the ribs with waxed linen rib-lacing cord. This is a time-consuming operation, and much time is saved by attaching the fabric with metal clips or sheet metal screws. The fabric must be attached by the method used by the manufacturer unless a Supplemental Type Certificate is used.

The rib-stitch spacing is based on the never-exceed speed (V_{NE}) of the aircraft. Be sure to copy the spacing used by the manufacturer, or use the chart in Figure 3-15, and submit this rib-stitch spacing to the FAA when having your data for the re-covering approved before starting the work.

If the aircraft has a V_{NE} of 250 mph or more, apply antitear strips (made of the same fabric used for the covering and wide enough that the rib stitching will pass through them) to the upper surface of the wing and also the bottom surface inside the slipstream. The antitear strips are doped over each rib cap strip so they will be between the fabric and the reinforcing tape.

antitear strip. Strips of aircraft fabric laid under the reinforcing tape before the fabric is stitched to an aircraft wing.

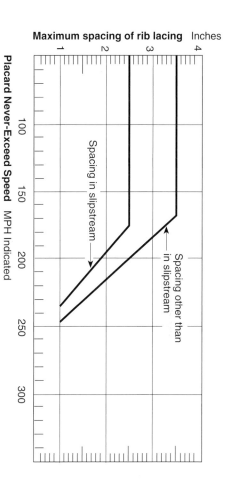

Maximum spacing of rib lacing Inches

Placard Never-Exceed Speed MPH Indicated

Spacing in slipstream

Spacing other than in slipstream

Figure 3-15. *Rib-stitch spacing chart*

Mark each rib with a lead pencil where the rib stitches will be placed. The spacing between the first and last stitches is one half of the spacing for all of the other stitches. Notice that the stitch spacing inside the slipstream is much closer than the spacing outside. For this purpose, the slipstream is considered to be the diameter of the propeller plus an additional rib on each side.

Soak strips of reinforcing tape in nitrate dope and squeeze the dope through the tape with your fingers to completely saturate it, with no air in the fibers. Place the tape over each rib with about a half-inch extending beyond the first and last stitches. Pull the tape smooth and press it down over the rib with your fingers.

Use a rib-stitch needle and punch holes on each side of each rib at the location marked for the stitches. Make the holes as close to the cap strips as you can get them. Place the knots on the side of the wing where they will be least visible. On a high-wing aircraft, place them on the top and on a low-wing aircraft, place them on the bottom.

For the typical wing, begin with lengths of rib-stitch cord about four times the length of the wing chord. Follow the procedure in Figure 3-16. Begin at the holes nearest the trailing edge and, using a long rib-stitch needle, make a double loop of the cord around the rib and tie a square knot in the center of the reinforcing tape on the side of the rib and tie a square knot in the center of the reinforcing tape on the side of the wing opposite that on which the regular stitches will be made.

Bring both ends of the cord back through the same holes and tie them with another square knot, this one placed on the side of the reinforcing tape. Lock this knot on both sides with half hitches around the loop, and cut off the excess cord on the short end. *See* Figure 3-16 on the next page.

reinforcing tape. A narrow strip of woven fabric material placed over the fabric as it is being attached to the aircraft structure with rib lacing cord. This tape carries a large amount of the load and prevents the fabric tearing at the stitches.

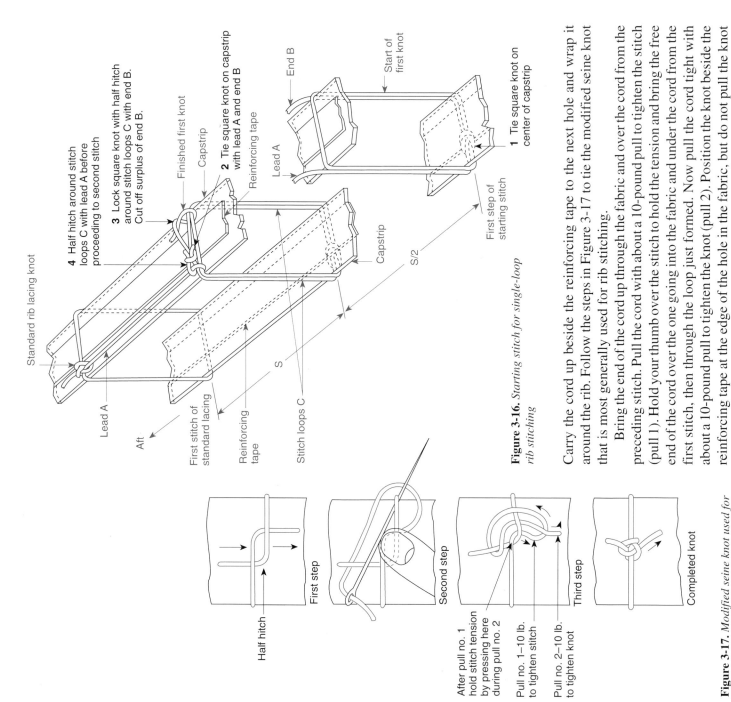

Figure 3-16. *Starting stitch for single-loop rib stitching*

Carry the cord up beside the reinforcing tape to the next hole and wrap it around the rib. Follow the steps in Figure 3-17 to tie the modified seine knot that is most generally used for rib stitching.

Bring the end of the cord up through the fabric and over the cord from the preceding stitch. Pull the cord with about a 10-pound pull to tighten the stitch (pull 1). Hold your thumb over the stitch to hold the tension and bring the free end of the cord over the one going into the fabric and under the cord from the first stitch, then through the loop just formed. Now pull the cord tight with about a 10-pound pull to tighten the knot (pull 2). Position the knot beside the reinforcing tape at the edge of the hole in the fabric, but do not pull the knot down inside the fabric.

Figure 3-17. *Modified seine knot used for rib stitching*

Make the final stitch at one-half the normal spacing, and use a double loop similar to that used for the first stitch. If the rib stitching cord is not long enough to completely lace a rib, it may be spliced using the splice knot shown in Figure 3-18. Do not use a square knot for splicing the cord because it will slip.

Pull to tighten

Knot formed but not tightened

Load

Knot completed

Load

Pull to tighten

Figure 3-18. *Use this splice knot to join lengths of waxed rib lacing cord.*

Because rib stitching is such a labor intensive operation, several manufacturers use metal wire clips to attach the fabric to metal wing ribs. Two types of clips commonly used are the Martin-type clip and the Cessna-type clip seen in Figure 3-19.

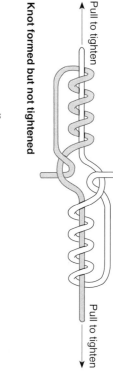

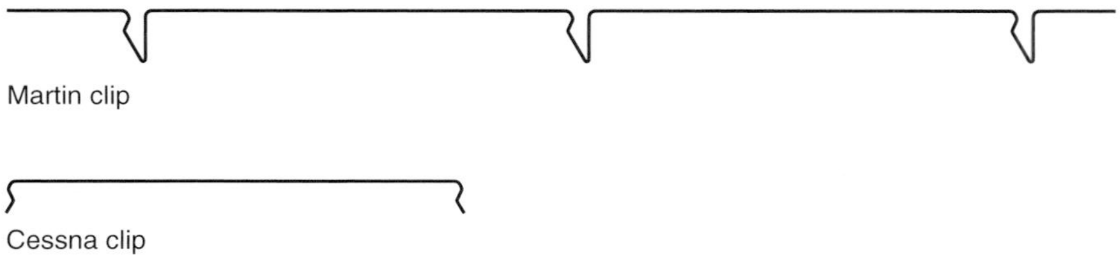

Martin clip

Cessna clip

Figure 3-19. *Fabric clips used to secure fabric to the wings of some aircraft*

Using a clip to attach the fabric to a wing that originally used rib stitching constitutes a major alteration to the airframe, and should be approved by the FAA before the work is started.

Another method of attaching the fabric to the wing ribs is by using very short sheet metal screws and a plastic or thin aluminum washer like that in Figure 3-20. Before drilling screw holes in a wing rib to which the fabric was originally stitched, have the alteration approved by the FAA.

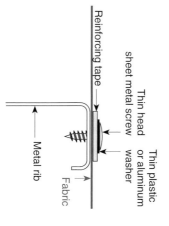

Reinforcing tape

Thin head sheet metal screw

Thin plastic or aluminum washer

Metal rib

Fabric

Figure 3-20. *Attachment of fabric to metal wing rib cap strips with sheet metal screws and a plastic or thin aluminum washer*

Drain Grommets and Inspection Rings

Drain grommets are attached to the fabric at all of the low points in the structure to ventilate the aircraft and prevent condensed moisture from rotting the fabric. These grommets are small doughnut-shaped pieces of acetate plastic with an outside diameter of about $3/4$-inch and with a $5/16$-inch hole in the center. Seaplane grommets are made with a small scoop formed in the plastic. They are installed with the opening to the rear to prevent water from spraying into the structure when the aircraft operates on the water. After completing the re-covering job, open the drain grommets by cutting the fabric from the inside of the grommet with a sharp-pointed knife blade.

Inspection rings are also made of acetate plastic and have an outside diameter of $4 5/8$ inches and an inside diameter of $3 1/2$ inches. They are installed at the locations chosen by the aircraft manufacturer to allow access to the inside of the structure for inspection and servicing. After re-covering the aircraft, cut the center from those inspection rings where access is required to the structure for the assembly. Do not open any inspection holes until they are needed. When the holes are cut, an inspection plate can be slipped into place to make a neat cover for the inspection hole.

Application of Surface Tape

After the fabric has been attached to the wings, brush on a coat of full-bodied butyrate dope.

Allow this coat of dope to dry completely and then lightly dry-sand it with 320-grit sandpaper. Sand it just enough to remove the rough nap of the fabric raised by the dope. Be extremely careful when sanding. It is terribly easy for the sharp sandpaper to cut completely through the doped fabric.

Before beginning to dry-sand any fabric-covered aircraft structure, ground it electrically by connecting some metal part of the structure to a cold water pipe or to some metal part of the shop building. Rubbing the dry fabric with sandpaper will generate enough static electricity to, unless the structure is adequately grounded, produce a spark that could cause the nitrate dope fumes to explode.

Cut lengths of 2-inch pinked-edge surface tape long enough to go from the trailing edge around the leading edge, and then back to the trailing edge. Saturate this tape with dope, and brush a coat of full-bodied dope over the rib. Place the tape in the dope, centered over the rib, and work it down into the dope with two fingers straddling the reinforcing tape. Press out all the air bubbles.

By this time the fabric has some stiffness, and will not move around any more, so you can cut it around all of the fittings that are to protrude. Use a very sharp knife to cut around the fittings, and then apply surface tape or a pinked-edge patch to reinforce the fabric at these points.

surface tape. Strips of aircraft fabric that are doped over all seams and places where the fabric is stitched to the aircraft structure. Surface tape is also doped over the wing leading edges where abrasive wear occurs.

The edges of surface tape are pinked, or notched, to keep them from raveling before the dope is applied.

nap of the fabric. The ends of the fibers in a fabric. The first coat of dope on cotton or linen fabric raises the nap, and the fiber ends stick up. These ends must be carefully removed by sanding to get a smooth finish.

pinked-edge tape. Cloth tape whose edges have small V-shaped notches cut along their length. The pinked edges prevent the tape from raveling.

Install all the drain grommets and inspection rings by soaking them in dope to soften them and then placing them in a heavy bed of dope. Work them down to the fabric with your fingers.

Cover all of the glued-down edges of the fabric in the aileron wells with 2-inch surface tape worked down into a coat of dope.

Cut a piece of 4-inch-wide surface tape long enough to go from the root of the wing along the leading edge and around the tip to the aileron well. Brush a coat of full-bodied dope along the leading edge and press the fabric down into it, working the air bubbles out of it with your fingers. Brush a coat of dope around the wing tip bow, and pull the tape tight. Center it around the tip, and clamp it at the aileron well with a spring clamp. Pulling the tape tight around the tip causes the edges to lie down on both sides of the tip. Lift the edges of the tape and work a small brush, wet with thinned dope, up underneath the tape to completely saturate it. Work the tape down on one side of the tip, and then on the other side rather than working down both sides at the same time.

Cover the trailing edge with 3-inch surface tape that has been notched along both edges at intervals not exceeding 6 inches. If the tape should separate from the trailing edge, it will tear at one of the notches rather than loosening the entire strip, which could seriously affect the controllability of the aircraft.

Application of the Finish System

The finishing system of a fabric-covered aircraft consists of the fill coats, the ultraviolet-blocking coat, and the finish coats. These are all discussed in the portion of this chapter dealing with "Fabric Finishing," beginning on Page 219.

Inorganic Fabric Covering

Organic fabrics are thought of as the "standard system" for fabric-covered aircraft, but inorganic fabrics have gained so much popularity that the vast majority of aircraft today are covered with some form of inorganic material, with polyester fabrics being the most important.

Polyester fabric approved for aircraft covering is stronger than Grade-A cotton, and has an exceptionally long life. Because it is so widely used, its price has decreased to well below that of Grade-A cotton.

In this portion of the text we will consider the major differences between the application of polyester and cotton.

Covering an aircraft with polyester fabric that was originally covered with cotton constitutes a major alteration and usually requires the use of a Supplemental Type Certificate (STC), obtained by the manufacturer or distributor of the materials.

ultraviolet-blocking dope. Dope that contains aluminum powder or some other pigment that blocks the passage of ultraviolet rays of the sun. This coat of dope protects the organic fabrics and clear dope from deterioration by these rays.

The STC requires that the person installing the fabric follow the instructions in the procedures manual furnished with the materials. There must be no substitution of materials and no deviation from the procedures described in the manual. When the aircraft is ready to be approved for return to service, an FAA Form 337 must be completed, listing the STC as approved data. A technician holding an Inspection Authorization must inspect the work for conformity to the instructions in the STC manual, and if it conforms, he or she can then approve the aircraft for return to service.

The Poly-Fiber System

One system for covering aircraft with polyester fabrics is that perfected by Poly-Fiber Aircraft Coatings of Riverside, California. Pertinent differences between the procedures for using cotton and Poly-Fiber have been condensed from the *Poly-Fiber Covering and Painting Manual*, and are included here with their permission.

Materials Used

Three weights of Poly-Fiber fabric are available, all three are lighter than Grade-A cotton, and two of them are considerably stronger. All three of the fabrics approved for use with this STC are identified with a stamp similar to the one in Figure 3-21 stamped along one edge at three-foot intervals.

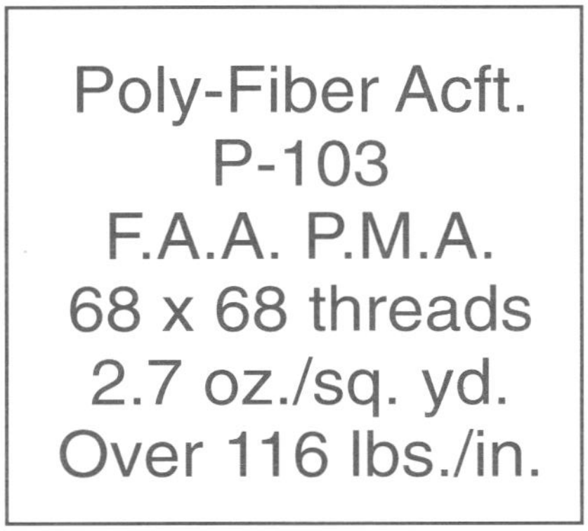

Both machine sewing and hand sewing require polyester thread, and there are two types of polyester rib-lacing cord used with this system. One is a round cord, and the other is a flat braided cord used where the minimum protrusion is desired.

A woven twill-type polyester reinforcing tape with an adhesive coating applied to one side is used over the wing ribs and is available in several widths. A tape made of the same material without the adhesive coating is available for inter-rib bracing.

Pinked-edge finishing tape is available in the various weights of fabric and widths. Linear tape is used for most of the required taping, and bias tape, with the threads oriented at 45° to the length, is available for use around wingtip bows and other severe compound curves.

The fabric is attached to the structure with a high-strength cement called Poly-Tak. When Poly-Tak is used with the recommended overlaps, there are no wing loading or V_{NE} restrictions.

The fabric is heat-shrunk on the structure, and Poly-Brush, which is a high-solids-content one-part air-drying adhesive coating, is used to seal the weave of the fabric.

Almost the only natural enemy of polyester fabric is the sun. The fill coats of Poly-Spray are aluminum pigmented to prevent the ultraviolet rays from reaching the fabric, and to provide a sanding base for a smooth finish.

For the finish coats, use Poly-Tone material. For a more chemical resistant finish, use Aero-Thane enamel, a flexible, two-part polyurethane enamel.

Poly-Fiber Acft.
P-103
F.A.A. P.M.A.
68 x 68 threads
2.7 oz./sq. yd.
Over 116 lbs./in.

Figure 3-21. *Markings such as this are used to identify fabric used when re-covering an aircraft by the Poly-Fiber system.*

enamel. A type of finishing material that flows out to form a smooth surface. Enamel is usually made of a pigment suspended in some form of resin. When the resin cures, it leaves a smooth, glossy protective surface.

Installing and Shrinking the Fabric

The fabric in the Poly-Fiber system is installed in basically the same way as cotton fabric, except that it is fixed to the structure with Poly-Tak cement.

Shrink the fabric by using a steam or dry iron adjusted to a temperature of 250°F. Move it lightly touching the fabric at a speed of about 4 to 7 inches per second. Go over the entire surface, and then go back and repeat the process, using several 250° passes. After the fabric has shrunk as much as it will at 250°F, increase the temperature to 350° and make several passes to give the fabric its final tautening and stabilizing.

When the fabric has reached its final tautness, scrub it with Poly-Fiber reducer or MEK on a clean rag to remove any lint or dust. Brush on the first coat of Poly-Brush to thoroughly saturate the fabric, but be careful that none of the liquid runs down on the inside of the fabric. This first coat of Poly-Brush should close the porosity of the fabric.

Attaching the Fabric

Attach the fabric to the structure with sheet metal screws (or with clips if they were originally used by the aircraft manufacturer). Rib lacing as described for the cotton covering system may be used with Poly-Fiber, but the STC procedure manual describes a rib lacing method for this system that produces a much cleaner (aerodynamically and esthetically) attachment.

Application of Surface Tape and Hole Reinforcements

Attach plastic inspection rings and drainage grommets to the fabric with Poly-Tak cement, and for longevity, cover them with fabric patches.

Apply surface tape by brushing thinned Poly-Brush on the structure where the tape is to go and then press the tape down into it with your fingers. Allow the Poly-Brush to dry, and then apply a second coat. When this coat dries, use a 225°F iron to smooth down the tape edges and form the tape around the corners.

The Finish

After completing the fabric installation and placing all of the tapes and hole reinforcements, apply the second coat of Poly-Brush.

When the Poly-Brush coats are dry, spray on three coats of Poly-Spray, wet-sanding after the second coat. When the third coat is applied, completely cover all the surface to block the ultraviolet rays of the sun from the fabric.

Light from a 60-watt bulb held near the surface of the fabric should not be visible from inside the structure.

Finish Poly-Fiber with either Poly-Tone or Aero-Thane.

tack rag. A clean, lintless rag, slightly damp with thinner. A tack rag is used to wipe a surface to prepare it to receive a coat of finishing material.

The Superflite System

Superflite is the registered trade name for a series of inorganic fabric covering and finishing materials produced by Superflite of Elk Grove Village, Illinois. Superflite fabrics are woven of polyester fibers on a loom that uses water rather than ethylene glycol as its lubricant. This is especially important for aircraft fabric, because of the tenacity with which dope adheres to fabric that has been woven on water-lubricated looms.

The following information has been excerpted from the Superflite Systems manuals and is used with their permission. When re-covering an aircraft with any material that requires a Supplemental Type Certificate, it is extremely important, and a legal requirement, that only the materials specified in the STC be used and all of the procedures described in the manual be followed in detail.

Superflite System I

Superflite System I uses Superflite 102 fabric that is attached to the structure with SuperBond cement. After the fabric is in place and all of the edges cemented to the structure, shrink it by ironing it with an accurately calibrated iron adjusted to 250°F. After shrinking the surface evenly at this temperature, increase the temperature to 350°F and further shrink it. This temperature should produce a fully tightened, wrinkle-free surface.

Once the fabric is uniformly tight, brush a full wet coat of reduced Dac-Proofer over the entire surface. When the first coat is dry, use a brush or a short-nap, bonnet-type paint roller to apply the second coat. This one is applied at right angles to the first coat. This second coat should be thinned with enough retarding thinner to allow it to dry slowly and not rope.

The Dac-Proofer acts as a foundation for the fill and topcoats. It penetrates the fabric and encapsulates the fibers, bonding to itself on the back side of the fabric. Since it is not used as a filler, use only enough to give the fabric an even blue appearance.

Attach the dried, Dac-Proofer coated fabric to the structure with screws, clips, or rib lacing, as it was originally attached by the manufacturer. You can follow the procedure for rib lacing described earlier in the organic fabrics section, but the applications manual also describes a hidden-knot method of lacing you can use with this system.

Apply the surface tapes, using either nitrate or butyrate dope. Use a roller and apply a swath of full-bodied dope slightly wider than the tape where the tape is to go. Lay the tape into the dope and smooth it in place with your fingers. Then roll on a second coat of dope, applying enough pressure to squeeze out all of the air bubbles. Extra passes of the roller will pick up the dope that has been squeezed out and will result in a smooth surface.

dope roping. Brushing aircraft dope onto a surface in such a way that it forms a stringy, uneven surface rather than flowing out smoothly.

Install the inspection rings and drainage grommets with SuperBond cement. When the dope and cement are dry, spray on three full-bodied cross coats of SpraFil. SpraFil is a high-solid, nonshrinking butyrate dope that contains aluminum pigment. It serves as the fill coats and also provides the ultraviolet protection for the fabric. After the SpraFil has dried overnight, sand the taped areas smooth and sand any spots that may have been caused by dust that settled on the surface while the SpraFil was wet. Remove all of the sanding dust with a damp cloth.

Do the final finish with three or more cross coats of Superflite pigmented gloss dope, waiting at least three hours between coats. An especially fine finish can be provided by spraying on a topcoat which consists of clear butyrate dope to which 10% colored dope has been added, and the combination thinned with an equal part of retarder.

Superflite System II

Superflite System II uses the same fabric and the same installation procedure as System I, but it uses special chemicals to allow a polyurethane enamel to be used for its famous wet look.

Attach the fabric to the structure using SuperFlite U-500 urethane adhesive. Use a mixture of primer base, catalyst, flexative, and reducer as both the primer and fill coats. Spray three coats of the mixture on the entire surface, waiting only until the surface is dry to touch between coats.

The final finish is provided by two coats of Superthane pigmented polyurethane, to which has been added the catalyst, a flexative, and the required reducer. Spray this on in a light tack coat and allow it to set for a few minutes, and then follow it with a full wet coat.

The Ceconite 7600 System

The Ceconite 7600 system is approved by the use of an STC for covering FAA-certificated aircraft. This system differs from other systems in the chemicals used and their unique method of application. The information given here has been condensed from the procedures manual furnished with the STC by the Blue River Aircraft Supply of Harvard, Nebraska, and used with their permission. When covering an aircraft with this system, follow the procedures manual in detail.

Materials Used

The Ceconite 7600 system uses a 3.8-, 2.8-, or 1.9-ounce-per-square-yard polyester fabric that has been precoated under controlled temperature and pressure with a thermoset water-borne epoxy-ester resin. This precoating makes the fabric easy to work with and ensures the proper bonding of its chemicals.

cross coat. A double coat of aircraft finishing material in which the second coat is sprayed at right angles to the first coat, before the solvents have evaporated from the first coat.

Surface tapes are available in the 2.8- and 1.9-ounce material, and with both plain and pinked edges and with linear and bias cuts. The reinforcing tape, rib-stitching cord, and both machine- and hand-sewing threads are also made of polyester fibers.

Installing the Fabric

When installing the fabric, pull it snug over the surface, and cut the holes for all protruding fittings so that the fabric will fit smoothly.

Attach the fabric to the structure with 7602 Cement and 7603 Cement Activator. Do not mix these two chemicals, but first apply a full brush coat of the cement and allow it to dry thoroughly in locations where the fabric is to be attached to the structure, then apply a second coat and allow it to dry. When the cement is completely dry, brush a coat of activator over it and press the fabric down into the activated cement. Apply a coat of activator over the fabric, and while it is still wet, wipe it off with a soft cloth or paper towel. This smoothes the cemented surface and assures complete penetration of the fabric. All cemented seams should lie over some structural member, and should have a 3-inch overlap. A correctly made cemented seam has a uniform dark green appearance with no visible voids.

Shrinking the Fabric

Use an electric iron that is accurately calibrated to 400°F to tauten the fabric. Begin over the ribs and cemented areas with a close-quarter iron set below the 400°F limit. When these areas have been shrunk initially, reduce the large iron's temperature to below 400°F and move it slowly over all of the open areas of the fabric, working out all the wrinkles. Don't try to do this with one pass, but use patience and several passes of the iron. When the wrinkles are out and the fabric is smooth, increase the temperature of the iron to a maximum of 400°F. Iron the entire surface at this temperature one time and allow the fabric to cool, then iron it a second time to give the fabric its final tautening and stabilizing.

Attaching the Fabric

The reinforcing tape used over the wing ribs and the other places where the fabric is stitched to the structure is a woven polyester tape with adhesive on one side. Press the tape down over each rib, allowing it to extend slightly beyond each rib stitch.

Attach the fabric to the structure in the same way it was when the aircraft was originally built. If it was attached by rib stitching, use the procedures described for the application of organic fabrics.

Apply the surface tape and hole reinforcements by applying a coat of 7602 cement to the areas where they should go and allow it to dry. Apply a coat of cement to one side of the tape and allow it to dry. When the cement is dry, apply

close-quarter iron. A small hand-held iron with an accurately calibrated thermostat. This iron is used for heat-shrinking polyester fabrics in areas that would be difficult to work with a large iron.

a coat of cement activator to the cement on the surface and press precut lengths of cement-covered surface tape into the activated cement.

Apply a second coat of activator to the top of the tape and wipe it off with a soft cloth, working it into the tape to remove any air bubbles or voids.

As soon as the activated cement becomes tacky, after about 10 to 15 minutes, press the tape down against the reinforcing tape and rib stitches with a very short bristle brush, working the tape down to eliminate all air bubbles.

Put cement around the leading edge, wing tip, and trailing edges of the surface. Activate it, and pull the surface tape tight so it will lie down around the curves. Severe curves should be taped with bias-cut tape. Heat the edges of the tape with the close-quarter iron to shrink the fabric so it will lie perfectly flat, then work cement activator under the tape, and finish it with more activator on top of the tape.

Attach inspection rings to the fabric by applying two coats of cement in a circular area slightly larger than the ring. When the cement is dry, apply activator and work the ring down into the activated cement with a twisting motion. Cover the ring with a circular patch of fabric worked down into more activated cement. Be sure the fabric is pressed down tightly against the edges of the ring.

Apply drain grommets in the same way, and when the fabric patches are in place and pressed down tight and the activated cement has dried, melt the holes through the fabric with a ¼-inch soldering iron tip whose end has been filed round rather than pointed.

The Finish

The 7601 Filler Coat used with this system contains many solids to provide a surface that blocks the ultraviolet rays of the sun and also fills the weave of the fabric. This material must be mixed thoroughly to completely suspend all the solids, and then strained to remove any clumps of pigment.

Clean the fabric area to remove all dust, then wipe it down with a cloth dampened in Flexi-Gloss Cleaner to remove all fingerprints and all traces of oil that may have gotten onto the fabric. Dampen the fabric thoroughly with distilled or demineralized water applied with a sponge, and while the fabric is still wet, apply the filler with a foam brush, paying special attention to get even coverage.

Apply subsequent coats of the filler with a spray gun. Use the material unthinned and with only enough air pressure on the gun to get thin, even coats. After enough filler has been sprayed on the surface to fill the weave, wet- or dry-sand the surface with 320 or 400 sandpaper, taking care not to cut through the fabric.

With the Ceconite 7600 system, use finish coats either of catalyzed polyurethanes or several coats of pigmented butyrate dope (applied by the methods described in the section on aircraft painting and finishing).

Repair of Aircraft Fabric

FAR 43, Appendix A gives examples of airframe major repairs as "Repair of fabric covering involving an area greater than that required to repair two adjacent ribs," and "Replacement of fabric on fabric-covered parts such as wings, fuselages, stabilizers, and control surfaces."

Advisory Circular 43.13-1A *Acceptable Methods, Techniques, and Practices—Aircraft Inspection and Repair* gives some examples of repairs to fabric. It is important to understand that this is *acceptable* data, not *approved* data, and any major repair to an aircraft must be based on approved data. Before beginning any major repair, describe exactly what you plan to do, and list the materials that will be used. Submit this data to the FAA FSDO. The procedure to follow is described in the General textbook of this *Aviation Maintenance Technician Series*. When the data is approved, follow it in detail, and have the work inspected for conformity to the data by a technician holding an Inspection Authorization.

The repairs described here are adequate to return the fabric covering to an airworthy condition and are used with utility-finished aircraft. Repairs to show-type finishes are much more complex, but they result in repairs that can hardly be detected.

Tear in the Fabric

Figure 3-22 shows a typical L-shaped tear in the fabric covering of an aircraft. Use a curved needle and well-waxed thread. Start at the apex of the tear and work back to the end of the tear. Use a baseball stitch and lock it every 8 to 10 stitches with a half hitch, and at each end with a modified seine knot like the one in Figure 3-17 on Page 198.

After sewing the edges of the tear together, soften the old dope with fresh dope, and using a putty knife, scrape away all of the finish down to the clear dope coats. Cut a patch of the same type of fabric as the kind you are repairing. Make it large enough to extend 1½ inches beyond the damage in all directions, and cut the edges with pinking shears to assist it in sticking down. Place the patch in a bed of full-bodied dope and press it down into the dope with your fingers to remove all of the air bubbles. Finish the repaired area to match the rest of the structure.

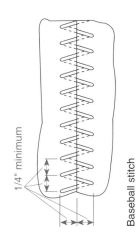

1/4" minimum

Baseball stitch

Lock stitching every 8 or 10 stitches, and at ends with modified seine knot

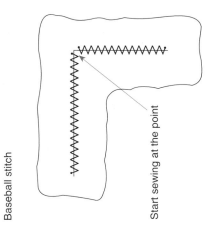

Start sewing at the point

Figure 3-22. *Repair to tears in aircraft fabric*

Doped-on Patch

You can make doped-on, or unsewed, repairs to all fabric-covered aircraft surfaces provided the never-exceed speed is not greater than 150 miles per hour and the damage does not exceed 16 inches in any direction.

Cut out the damaged fabric, making a round or oval-shaped opening. Clean the edges of the fabric to be covered, and remove the old dope down to the clear coats by sanding or using dope thinner.

For holes up to 8 inches in size, make the fabric patch of sufficient size to overlap the edges of the hole by at least 2 inches in all directions. On holes larger than 8 inches, size the patch so it will overlap the fabric around the hole by at least one quarter of the hole diameter with a maximum overlap of 4 inches. If the hole extends over a rib or closer than the required overlap to a rib or other laced member, extend the patch at least 3 inches beyond the rib. In this case, after the edges of the patch have been doped in place and the dope has dried, lace the patch to the rib over a new section of reinforcing tape in the usual manner. Do not remove the old rib lacing and reinforcing tape. All patches should have pinked edges, or if smooth, should be finished with pinked-edge surface tape.

STUDY QUESTIONS: FABRIC COVERING

Answers begin on Page 263. Page numbers refer to chapter text.

30. Grade-A cotton fabric is manufactured under Technical Standard Order TSO C-_____. *Page 186*

31. New Grade-A cotton fabric has a minimum strength of _____ pounds per inch in both warp and fill directions. *Page 185*

32. Three types of fabric that may be used to cover an aircraft structure are: _____, _____, and _____. *Pages 185 and 186*

33. Re-covering an aircraft with the same materials and the same methods used by the original manufacturer is classified as a _____. *Page 186*

34. Re-covering an aircraft with different materials from those used by the original manufacturer is classified as a _____. *Page 187*

35. When an aircraft is re-covered, the work must be inspected by an aviation maintenance technician who holds an Inspection Authorization, and an FAA Form _____ must be completed and filed with the FAA FSDO. *Page 187*

Continued

36. Aircraft fabric must be replaced when its strength has deteriorated to _____ % of the strength of the fabric required for the aircraft. *Page 187*

37. A fabric whose strength has deteriorated to 65% of that required for new fabric _____ (can or cannot) have some of its strength restored by rejuvenation. *Page 188*

38. Cracks in the finish of a fabric-covered structure _____ (are or are not) an indication that the fabric should be replaced. *Page 188*

39. When making a fabric test, check the fabric in an area that is finished with a _____ (dark or light) color. *Page 188*

40. The squareness of a wing truss is checked by making comparative diagonal distance checks across each bay with a _____ bar and points. *Page 190*

41. Grade-A cotton must have the identification marks _____ or _____ stamped along its selvage edge. *Page 192*

42. Pinked-edge surface tape has a series of V-shaped notches cut along its edges to prevent it _____ . *Page 192*

43. Surface tape that lies down most smoothly around wing tips and the tips of control surfaces is _____ (bias or straight) cut. *Page 192*

44. The two types of dopes are _____ and _____ . *Page 193*

45. The type of dope that is best for the initial attachment of the fabric to the structure is _____ (butyrate or nitrate). *Page 193*

46. It _____ (is or is not) proper to apply nitrate dope over butyrate dope. *Page 193*

47. Aircraft dope and fabric are protected from damage by ultraviolet rays of the sun by a layer of _____ -pigmented dope applied over the clear dope. *Page 193*

48. When mixing aluminum paste with clear dope you should pour the _____ (dope into the paste or paste into the dope). *Page 193*

49. If a bleeding dope is to be used for one of the colors on an aircraft structure, it should be applied _____ (first or last). *Page 193*

50. The two methods of applying fabric to an aircraft structure are the _____ and _____ methods. *Pages 194 and 195*

51. The openings for strut fittings _____ (should or should not) be cut while Grade-A cotton fabric is wet with water to remove the wrinkles. *Page 196*

52. When mixing fungicidal paste with clear dope you should pour the _____ (dope into the paste or paste into the dope). *Page 196*

53. Wrinkles are pulled out of cotton fabric by wetting the fabric with _____ (dope or water). *Page 195*

54. The first coat of dope applied to cotton fabric is typically _____ (nitrate or butyrate). *Page 196*

55. The first coat of dope applied to cotton fabric should be _____ (full bodied or thinned). *Page 196*

56. The rib stitch spacing for the end stitches is _____ that of the rest of the stitches. *Page 197*

57. Replacing rib stitching with metal clips constitutes a major _____ (repair or alteration). *Page 199*

58. The second coat of dope that is applied to cotton fabric should be _____ (nitrate or butyrate). *Page 200*

59. Before dry-sanding any doped surface, the aircraft structure should be _____ to prevent a spark caused by static electricity. *Page 200*

60. Surface tape, drain grommets, and inspection rings are applied with the _____ (first or second) coat of dope. *Page 200*

61. The description of a repair in AC 43.13-1A _____ (does or does not) constitute approved data for making a major repair to a fabric-covered aircraft. *Page 208*

62. When sewing an L-shaped tear in aircraft fabric covering, start sewing at the _____ (ends or apex) of the tear. *Page 208*

63. A doped-on patch repair may be made to a fabric-covered aircraft provided the V_{NE} is not greater than _____ mph and the damage does not exceed _____ inches in any direction. *Page 209*

64. When baseball stitching a patch into an aircraft structure, the stitches should be spaced approximately _____-inch apart and locked with a half hitch ever _____ or _____ stitches. *Page 208*

Aircraft Painting and Finishing

Painting and finishing is a highly specialized field. Just a glance at the beautiful finishes that are evident at air meets like Oshkosh show that aircraft finishing is a true art form. In this section we introduce the basic finishing systems for both metal and fabric aircraft.

Metal Finishing

An aircraft's finish is important for more than just cosmetic reasons. It preserves the metal, and its smoothness reduces air resistance, making the aircraft fly more efficiently.

The many hours transport aircraft fly today have brought about some serious problems, known as problems of the "aging fleet." These aircraft often have hidden corrosion that must be found and properly treated, then the aircraft refinished.

In this section of the *AMTS* we consider the preparation of the structure for receiving the finish and review the finishing systems.

Paint Removal

Begin preparing the metal to receive the finish by removing any old finish.

For years the only way to remove old finish was to use chemical stripper that loosened it and allowed it to be washed away. But today with the emphasis on environmental protection, the residue from chemical stripping is considered hazardous waste, and the cost of its disposal has made dry-stripping a viable alternative.

Before beginning any paint removal, prepare the aircraft by very carefully masking off all areas that should not be stripped. Protect windshields and windows with aluminum foil taped down tightly so no stripper can get under it, and cover all of the other parts with a good grade of polyethylene sheeting.

It is very important that any time you work with potent chemicals you have adequate physical protection. Follow the recommendations of the manufacturer of the chemicals for the type of respiratory and eye protection you will need.

Chemical Stripping

There are two basic types of finish on metal aircraft, enamels and lacquers, and each requires different procedures for its removal.

Enamel cures to a hard, impervious finish that bonds tightly to the primer on the surface of the metal. To remove it, apply a heavy coat of stripper with a bristle brush or a nonatomizing spray, and cover it with polyethylene sheeting to prevent it evaporating before it does its work. The potent solvents, principally methylene chloride, in the stripper enter the enamel film and swell it enough that it buckles, or wrinkles up, and pulls away from the primer.

Most strippers of this type contain wax that gets between the wrinkled-up film and the metal to prevent it resticking. Leave the stripper on the surface until all of the finish has swelled up and pulled away from the primer. If some areas dry out too soon, apply more stripper. After the entire surface has wrinkled up, wash the residue off with hot water or steam and dispose of it in a way that is compatible with the local environmental regulations.

There will be some residue left around the rivets and other fasteners as well as along the seams in the skin. Scrub these areas with a brass wire brush or aluminum wool. Do not use steel wool, as particles of the steel will become embedded in the softer aluminum and will cause severe corrosion.

Any wax left from the stripper will prevent subsequent coats of finish from adhering to the surface, so it must be completely removed. After removing all traces of the paint residue, scrub the entire surface with a solvent such as acetone or methyl-ethyl-ketone (MEK), toluol, or xylol, which will absorb the wax. Lacquer thinner will not absorb it but will just move it around and leave the surface contaminated.

Polyurethane enamels are gaining wide acceptance because of their chemical resistance and their shiny wet look. Polyurethanes are more difficult to remove than other enamels because their impervious film is not easily attacked by the solvents in the strippers. But, if you apply the stripper and cover it with polyethylene sheeting to slow its evaporation, the active agent in the stripper will wrinkle the finish and loosen its bond to the primer.

Acrylic lacquer does not expand and wrinkle up when it is attacked by the solvents in the stripper, rather it simply softens. Apply the stripper the same way you would for enamel, and cover it with polyethylene sheeting. When it has been on the surface for a sufficient length of time, roll the sheeting back to expose a small section of the softened finish. Remove the finish from the surface with a plexiglass or hard rubber scraper and scrub the cleaned off area with a rag wet with MEK or acetone, being very careful to get all traces of the wax from around the rivets and out of the seams in the skin. Roll back the sheeting and remove the finish from more of the surface.

Do not use chemical paint strippers on aircraft fabric or on fiberglass parts such as radomes or wheel speed fairings. The solvents in the stripper may attack the resins in these parts and weaken or distort them. Remove the finish by sanding or by plastic media blasting.

Dry Stripping

Aircraft refinishing shops that work on large aircraft have an expensive problem of disposing of the hazardous waste products left when paint is chemically stripped. These shops have done quite a bit of research into dry stripping or plastic media blasting (PMB), and this has proven to be an effective method of removing paint from heavy-skinned aircraft, especially

plastic media blasting (PMB). A method of removing paint from an aircraft surface by dry-blasting it with tiny plastic beads.

military aircraft. The finish is blasted from the surface with tiny sharp-edged plastic beads. The size, shape, and hardness of these beads and the air pressure used to propel them determine the amount of finish that will be removed.

PMB requires a high degree of skill, but it gives the operator far better control when removing the finish than chemical stripping. With proper choice of beads and air pressure, the finish can be removed without causing any damage to the underlying metal, even to the primer. The beads can be reused, and the residue from the old finish is much easier to dispose of than that left from chemical stripping. One of the limitations of the present PMB paint removal is that it can damage thin-skinned general aviation aircraft, but continued research may eliminate this problem.

Preparation for Painting

When the finish is removed from a metal aircraft, you have an opportunity to carefully inspect it for any indication of corrosion, to remove all traces you may find, and to protect it from further corrosion. Finally you have the opportunity to prepare it to receive the new finishing system.

Corrosion Detection

Review the section on Cleaning and Corrosion Control in the General textbook of the *Aviation Maintenance Technician Series* to get a good understanding of the appearance and causes of corrosion. Any traces of corrosion you find must be removed and the surface treated to prevent the formation of subsequent corrosion.

The form of corrosion that is most likely to be found under a paint film is filiform corrosion. This is a thread-like corrosion primarily caused by improperly cured wash primer that left some of the phosphoric acid trapped beneath the paint film. If there are any tracks left from the corrosion or gray powdery residue on the surface of the metal, scrub it all away with a nylon scrubber such as a Scotch-Brite pad.

Carefully examine the area around all fasteners for any indication of galvanic corrosion. Any blisters in the metal that could indicate intergranular corrosion should be probed with a sharp tool to determine whether or not they are actually pockets of corrosion deposits. If you find traces of intergranular corrosion, use an eddy current or ultrasonic tester to determine its extent. Intergranular corrosion is usually difficult to remove and often requires the replacement of the affected metal.

Conversion Coating

Three conditions must be met for a metal to corrode: there must be an electrode potential difference, there must be a conductive path between the areas of potential difference, and an electrolyte must cover these areas. A surface may be protected from corrosion by the elimination of any one or more of the three.

After removing all traces of corrosion from the metal and repairing any damages, you can treat the surface with a conversion coating, which is a chemical that forms an airtight film on the surface that prevents any electrolyte reaching the metal. Phosphoric acid can be used to form a phosphate film on the metal surface.

Another well-known treatment is the proprietary product Alodine. To apply Alodine, follow these steps:

1. Brush on a coat of aluminum cleaner such as Alumiprep or Metal Prep. This cleans and etches the metal and prepares it for further treatment.

2. Rinse the surface with water and check to be sure that it supports an unbroken film of water, indicating that there are no contaminants on the surface.

3. Brush or spray a liberal coat of Alodine on the surface. Allow it to remain on the surface for two to five minutes and then rinse it off. The film will be soft while it is wet, but as soon as it dries, it will become hard and protective.

Caution: Rags used to apply the Alodine coating must be kept wet until they can be thoroughly washed before discarding. Rags with dry Alodine chemical in them can constitute a fire hazard.

Primers

A primer provides a good bond between the surface being finished and the material used for the topcoats. There are several types of primers available, but the three discussed here are zinc chromate, wash primer, and epoxy primer.

Zinc Chromate

For decades zinc chromate has been the standard primer for use on aircraft. It is an inhibitive primer, meaning that its base of alkyd resin is somewhat porous and when water enters it, some of the chromate ions are released and held on the surface of the metal. This ionized surface prevents the electrolytic action necessary for corrosion to form.

Zinc chromate can be used on both ferrous and nonferrous metals and is compatible with most finishing materials, but there are some necessary precautions. It should not be applied over a wash primer unless the phosphoric acid has been completely converted into the phosphate film. The zinc chromate will tend to trap water and allow filiform corrosion to form. Also zinc chromate is not recommended for use under acrylic lacquers because the solvents used with acrylics tend to lift the zinc chromate.

Zinc chromate primer conforms to MIL-P-8585A and is available in both yellow and dark green colors. It is thinned with toluene or proprietary thinners to get it to the proper consistency for spraying. To increase the usefulness of this primer, it is also available in aerosol spray cans.

primer. A component in a finishing system that provides a good bond between the surface and the material used for the topcoats.

epoxy. A polyether resin that has wide application, as a matrix for composite materials, and as an adhesive that bonds many different types of materials.

There have been some studies that indicate that there may be a possible link between an excessive inhalation of zinc chromate dust and lung cancer.

Wash Primer

High-volume production of aircraft requires a primer that cures quickly and allows the topcoat to be sprayed on relatively soon after its application. A three-part wash primer that meets specification MIL-P-15328 satisfies this requirement and is widely used in aircraft factories.

Wash primer is prepared by mixing 4 parts of the primer with 1 part of its activator, an acid diluent, and adjusting its viscosity with between 4 and 8 parts of thinner. Allow it to stand for 20 minutes to begin its cure, stir it, and spray it on the surface. It should be sprayed on in a very thin coat, only about 0.000 3 inch (0.3 mil). A coat of this thickness does not hide the surface of the metal, but gives it a slightly greenish-amber tint.

The acid in the primer requires about 30 minutes to convert into the phosphate film, and you must not apply the topcoats until this has taken place. But you must apply them within 8 hours or the primer will harden to the extent that the topcoats will not adhere as they should. If the topcoat is not applied within this time limit, spray on another coat of the primer, this time without the activator. When the primer is dry to the touch it is ready for the topcoats.

It is important that there is enough moisture in the air to convert the acid in the primer into the phosphate film. Specific information is given with the primer, but, basically, if the relative humidity is less than 55% with a paint room temperature of 75°F, you should add about an ounce of distilled water to one gallon of the thinner to provide the needed water.

Epoxy Primer

Epoxy primer gives the best corrosion protection of any of the modern primers. This two-component primer produces a tough dope-proof finish, and it can be used over all metals as well as composite materials. When you need maximum corrosion protection, you can apply epoxy primer over wash primer.

To use epoxy primer, first wash the surface with a clean rag wet with MEK, toluol, or acrylic lacquer thinner. Then mix the epoxy primer with the amount of mixing liquid specified by the primer manufacturer. Stir these components separately and then stir them together. Add the required amount of thinner to adjust the viscosity for spraying and allow the mixture to sit for 30 minutes to begin its cure. Spray on a single, light, even coat of primer, just enough to slightly color the metal.

Epoxy primer must be allowed at least five hours, and preferably overnight, to develop enough hardness to prevent acrylic lacquer or synthetic enamel topcoats from sinking into it and losing their gloss. Polyurethanes are ideally suited for application over epoxy primer and can be applied after a wait of only one hour.

MEK. Methyl-ethyl-ketone, an organic chemical solvent that is soluble in water and is used as a solvent for vinyl and nitrocellulose films. MEK is an efficient cleaner for preparing surfaces for priming or painting.

If epoxy primer has been applied for more than 24 hours before the application of the topcoat, its surface must be scuffed with a Scotch-Brite pad or 600-grit sandpaper to break the glaze enough for the topcoats to bond.

Finishing Systems

Three popular finishing systems are used for all-metal aircraft. Most of the high-volume general aviation aircraft were finished at the factory with acrylic lacquer because of the speed with which the entire finishing system could be applied. Synthetic enamels have been used for many years because of the good finish they produce and their ease of application. But the most popular finishing system today is the polyurethane system because of its chemical resistance, durability, and its famous wet look.

Acrylic Lacquer

Apply acrylic lacquers over a wash primer or over an epoxy primer. After the primer has completely cured, rub it down with a handful of wadded-up kraft paper to provide enough surface roughness so the topcoats will bond properly.

The low solids content of acrylic lacquer requires careful attention to its application. The finished color is best applied over a white base coat, and it should be applied in several thin coats rather than fewer heavy coats. Thin 4 parts of lacquer with 5 parts of thinner, and spray on a very light tack coat. As soon as the solvents have evaporated, spray on at least three cross coats, allowing about a half-hour between the coats. The gloss of the final coat may be improved by adding about one-fourth as much retarder as there is thinner. When retarder is used, the finish should dry overnight before doing any taping or masking.

Synthetic Enamel

Synthetic enamels are made of pigments suspended in resins that cure by oxidization. These enamels have been used for years to finish automobiles and have been used to some extent for metal aircraft. They produce a glossy finish that does not require rubbing but their chemical and abrasive resistance is not nearly so good as that of polyurethanes.

Synthetic enamel can be applied over a zinc chromate primer and is thinned to the proper viscosity for spraying. Spray a light mist coat on the surface and as soon as the thinner evaporates out, in about 10 or 15 minutes, spray on a wet cross coat. After drying for about 48 hours the surface will be ready to tape and mask for trim coats.

lacquer. A finishing material made of a film base, solvents, plasticizers, and thinners. The film base forms a tough film over the surface when it dries. The solvents dissolve the film base so it can be applied as a liquid. The plasticizers give the film base the needed resilience, and the thinners dilute the lacquer so it can be applied with a spray gun. Lacquer is sprayed on the surface as a liquid and when the solvents and thinners evaporate, the film base remains as a tough decorative and protective coating.

kraft paper. A tough brown wrapping paper like that used for paper bags.

Polyurethane

Polyurethane is the most popular finish for modern metal aircraft because of its chemical and abrasive resistance and its wet look. It is a two-part, chemically cured finish that contains approximately twice the solids used in acrylic lacquer. Its exceptionally good finish is due to its slow-flowing resins which continue to flow after the thinners evaporate until they form a perfectly flat surface, and cure uniformly throughout. Light reflecting from this flat surface gives the finish its shiny appearance.

Polyurethane finishes resist most of the chemicals used in agricultural application as well as the acid and alkali fumes in the battery box areas. Solvents such as acetone have a minimal effect on it, and paint strippers must be held in contact with the finish for a considerable length of time before they penetrate the film and loosen it from the primer.

The primer used with polyurethanes is an important part of the complete system. For maximum corrosion protection, cover a well-cured wash primer with an epoxy primer and then apply the polyurethane finish.

Mix the polyurethane and its catalyst in the proportions specified on the can, and allow it to sit for an induction time of 20 to 30 minutes as directed by the manufacturer. Thin the mixed material by adding the proper reducer until its viscosity, as determined by a viscosity cup, is correct for spraying. Dip the cup into the thinned material and measure the time in seconds from the instant the cup is lifted from the liquid until the first break in the flow through the hole in the bottom of the cup. There is a definite pot life for the mixed material. This time is noted on the can, and if the material is not used within this time period, it must be discarded and a new batch mixed.

Spray a very light tack coat of the material on the surface, and when the thinner evaporates, spray on a full wet cross coat. Polyurethane is not as flexible as some of the other finishes, and it is important that the cross coat not be too thick. If the material builds up at the skin lap joints it could crack when it dries.

The low surface tension and slow drying time allow the material to flow out perfectly flat, and it takes several days before the finish attains its final hardness and smoothness. Its surface is usually dry enough to tape in about 5 hours, but if possible, delay taping until the finish has cured for at least 24 hours.

Polyurethanes are catalyzed materials whose catalysts are highly reactive to moisture. Cans of the materials should not be left open longer than is necessary, as moisture could enter and, when the can is closed, react with the material, causing it to expand and burst the can.

It is extremely important that the spray equipment be thoroughly cleaned before the polyurethane material hardens. If it cures in the spray guns and hoses, it is almost impossible to remove.

viscosity. The resistance of a fluid to flow. Viscosity refers to the "stiffness" of the fluid, or its internal friction.

viscosity cup. A specially shaped cup with an accurately sized hole in its bottom. The cup is submerged in the liquid to completely fill it. It is then lifted from the liquid and the time in seconds is measured from the beginning of the flow through the hole until the first break in this flow. The viscosity of the liquid relates to this time.

pot life. The length of time a resin will remain workable after the catalyst has been added. If a catalyzed material is not used within its usable pot life, it must be discarded and a new batch mixed.

tack coat. A coat of finishing material sprayed on the surface and allowed to dry until the solvents evaporate. As soon as the solvents evaporate, a wet full-bodied coat of material is sprayed over it.

Fabric Finishing

The finishes for fabric-covered aircraft are different from those used on metal or composite aircraft because of the amount of flexing that the fabric does. There are several new types of finishes used on amateur-built aircraft, but only the materials and systems approved for use on FAA-certificated aircraft are discussed here.

Organic Fabric Finishes

In the section of this text on Aircraft Fabric Covering, we discussed the way an aircraft structure is covered with Grade-A cotton. That discussion carried the process from the installation of the fabric through the initial shrinking. In this section we will discuss the finishing of the fabric and in a later section the application of the registration numbers and trim.

The Fill Coats

After the fabric has been shrunk initially, the rib stitching done, and the surface tape in place, apply the fill coats of dope. The number of coats of dope applied depends upon the type of finish you want. A utility finish uses the minimum number of coats needed to give satisfactory shrinkage and coverage. It usually consists of two coats of full-bodied clear butyrate dope brushed on, and two full, wet, cross coats of clear dope sprayed on. Wet-sand the surface with 400-grit sandpaper after the dope has fully dried. By this time, the weave of the fabric should be completely filled and the fabric ready to receive the ultraviolet-blocking coats.

Show-type finishes, with their deep, glass-like appearance, are achieved with fill provided by the clear dope and not by the aluminum dope. Spray on a wet cross coat of clear dope and wet-sand it with 400-grit and then 600-grit sandpaper. Wash all of the sanding residue off and dry the surface, then apply another cross coat of clear dope. Continue sanding and applying coats until the finish is as smooth as you desire.

The Ultraviolet-Blocking Coats

Use clear dope in which tiny flakes of aluminum metal are suspended to protect the clear dope fill coats and the fabrics by blocking the ultraviolet rays of the sun.

To properly prepare aluminum-pigmented dope, mix 1 pound of aluminum paste with 5 gallons clear dope. This is the same as 3½ ounces of paste per gallon of dope. When mixing it, mix some thinner into the paste and then pour the dope into the thinned paste. When the aluminum paste and dope are thoroughly mixed, prepare the dope for spraying by thinning it with equal parts of thinner and pouring it through a paint strainer to remove any clumps of the aluminum powder.

---

utility finish. The finish of an aircraft that gives the necessary tautness and fill to the fabric and the necessary protection to the metal, but does not have the glossy appearance of a show-type finish.

show-type finish. The type of finish put on aircraft intended for show. This finish is usually made up of many coats of dope with much sanding and rubbing of the surface between coats.

Too much aluminum powder in the dope or too many coats applied to the surface will cause the dope to delaminate. The finish coats will adhere to one layer of aluminum flakes, and the fill coats will adhere to another layer. The fill coats should provide the needed smoothness and the aluminum pigment should be used only to block the sun.

The Finish Coats

When rebuilding an aircraft, it is often the procedure to finish all of the components up through the aluminum-pigmented dope and apply the finish coats to all of the surfaces at the same time. This assures that the final finish will be uniform. However, the finish on some of the surfaces that were the first re-covered must be "opened up" so they will accept the finish coats. Spray a mixture of half thinner and half retarder over the old dope. The retarder prevents the thinner evaporating before it softens the dope surface. If the dope has been applied for a long time, it may be necessary to open it up by spraying on a mixture of equal parts of thinner and rejuvenator. Allow the doped surface to dry only until it is no longer tacky and immediately spray on the colored dope.

All colored dope is slightly transparent, and to get the truest color from the dope and to insure uniformity, all of the surfaces should be given a first coat of white dope. The richest color is produced when the maximum amount of light reflects from the smooth coat of white dope and shines through the semitransparent colored dope.

The white dope should dry for at least 24 hours before the colored coats are sprayed on. The best finish with butyrate dope is obtained by using extra thinner and some retarder to give the dope a longer time to flow out and smooth itself. The final coat may be made more glossy by mixing about 20% clear dope with the colored dope and replacing some of the thinner with retarder. Be sure when applying any dope to follow the instructions of the dope manufacturer in detail.

Inorganic Fabric Finishes

Some aircraft covered with polyester fabrics are finished with pigmented nontautening butyrate dope. These finishing systems are similar to those described for organic fabrics.

Other inorganic fabric systems use proprietary finishes and these are described in the section "Inorganic Fabric Covering," beginning on Page 201.

Finishing Problems

The function of a finishing system on an aircraft is to provide a surface that is both protective and decorative, and anything that prevents either of these qualities can be considered to be a finishing problem. The problems considered here are common with cellulose dope finishes.

Poor Adhesion

A topcoat of dope can actually peel off of the fill coats. This indicates the use of improper topcoat materials or too much aluminum powder in the fill coats.

The solvents in nitrate dope are not potent enough to open up a dried butyrate dope film, and if nitrate is sprayed over butyrate, it will not sink in to form the needed bond. When it dries, it can be peeled off.

If there is too much aluminum pigment in the fill coats of dope, the dope in the fill coats will bond to one layer of aluminum powder and the finish coats will bond to another layer. There is not a sufficient bond between the layers of aluminum powder to prevent the topcoat peeling away.

Blushing

Blushing is the most common problem with dope finishes. When the humidity is high, the drop in temperature that occurs when the solvents in the dope evaporate cause water to condense from the air. When this water mixes with the wet dope film, it causes the cellulose to precipitate out. This gives the film a chalky appearance which is neither strong nor attractive.

Prevent blushing by heating the air in the spray booth. Warm air can hold more water in its vapor state, and the temperature drop caused by the thinners evaporating will not cause water to condense out.

If the humidity is not too high, some retarder can be mixed with the dope in place of some of the thinner. The slower evaporation of the solvents in the retarder does not drop the temperature enough for water to condense from the air.

If the dope you have just sprayed blushes, spray over it a very light mist coat consisting of a mixture of one part retarder and two parts thinner. Allow it to dry and then spray on another coat. The blushed surface should melt down and re-form as a smooth glossy surface. If this does not remove the blush, sand the surface to remove the blushed area and reapply the finish when the humidity is lower.

Pinholes

Aircraft dope is composed of solids and solvents. The solids remain on the surface of the fabric and the solvents evaporate. If the dope film is exposed to too much heat or to a draft of air, the surface will harden enough to prevent the vapors escaping as the solvents evaporate. Tiny bubbles of vapors will unite beneath this hardened surface until they form a large bubble with enough pressure to force its way through the surface. Rather than the surface re-forming smoothly, pits or pinholes will remain where each bubble burst.

Excessive atomizing air on the spray gun will force enough air into the dope film that will also cause pinholes to form.

retarder. Dope thinner that has certain additives that slow its rate of evaporation to prevent the dope blushing.

Orange Peel

Dope should dry from the fabric outward, with the surface drying last. Dope shrinks as it dries, and if the surface dries first, the shrinkage of the body of the dope will cause the surface to wrinkle and resemble the skin, or peel, of an orange.

Improper spray techniques, a draft or air over the surface, or the use of thinners that evaporate too fast will give the surface an orange-peel appearance.

Fisheyes

Fisheyes are localized spots in the finish that do not dry. They are typically caused by surface contaminations such as wax, oil, or some of the silicone products. These contaminants mix with the dope and prevent its drying.

Fisheyes can be prevented by keeping the surface clean and free of the contaminants. Before spraying the dope on the surface, scrub it with a rag damp with toluol or MEK.

Runs and Sags

Runs and sags in a doped finish indicate too much finish. You can apply too much finish by moving the spray gun too slowly, holding the gun too close to the surface, or improperly thinning the dope.

It is always better to apply several thin coats of dope rather than a single heavy coat. The thin coats are far less likely to run or sag.

Dope Roping

Dope roping is the rough trail of dope that is left behind the brush when the dope is too heavy for properly application. This means you are not using enough thinner, or that the dope is too cold for proper brushing.

Ringworms and Rejuvenation

Plasticizers are used in cellulose dopes to give resilience to their film. In time these plasticizers migrate from the film and leave it brittle. When a blunt object is pressed against the brittle film, the film cracks in a series of concentric circles that resemble a ringworm. If these ringworms are not properly treated, they will allow sunlight and moisture to reach the fabric and cause it to deteriorate in a very short time. When the film dries and ringworms form, the fabric should be rejuvenated.

Rejuvenation is the process in which a dried dope film is softened with strong solvents and held in its softened state until new plasticizers in the rejuvenator combine with the film base.

Before rejuvenating a fabric surface, determine the condition of the fabric. Rejuvenation does nothing to restore the strength of the fabric, and if its strength has deteriorated to its allowed minimum, the fabric should be replaced rather than finish rejuvenated.

rejuvenate. Restore the resilience to an aircraft finishing material. This is done by the use of a rejuvenator.

rejuvenator. A finishing material used to restore resilience to an old dope film. Rejuvenator contains strong solvents to open the dried-out film and plasticizers to restore resilience to the old dope.

If the fabric is good, scrub it with clear water and a nylon scrubber such as a Scotch-Brite pad. If the surface has been waxed, scrub it with a rag damp with toluol or MEK. Spray the surface with a mixture of one part rejuvenator and one part butyrate thinner. Allow the rejuvenator to soften the dope film and reflow the dope into the cracks.

Paint and Dope Application

The application of dope was at one time a very common function of an aircraft mechanic, but today, aircraft finishing has pretty much been relegated to specialty shops, and few aviation maintenance technicians are seriously involved with it. But, as with other aspects of this profession, we should be familiar with its fundamentals.

Finishing Equipment

In this section, we consider the basic equipment necessary for setting up a paint shop in a facility that could do an occasional paint job. Fixed base operators that specialize in aircraft finishing have special buildings used solely for aircraft painting. These buildings have provisions for filtering the air and removing all paint fumes. Stringent OSHA (Occupational Safety and Health Act) requirements must be met in regard to paint storage, electrical outlets, personal protection, and fire safety, as well as the collection and disposition of the materials removed from the aircraft when the finish is stripped.

Spray Area

When aircraft finishing is occasional, the area in which it is done may be isolated from the rest of the shop in a temporary spray booth. Build it with a framework that can be covered with polyethylene sheeting to contain the fumes and paint overspray. An exhaust fan located near the floor should be able to move enough air that there is never more than just a slight odor of the finishing material. There should be no electrical extension cords or unprotected electrical outlets in the spray booth that could cause an electrical spark, and there should be adequate fire extinguishers inside the spray booth.

An ample supply of running water should be available to flush your eyes if you should get any finishing material in them. There should also be provisions for flushing the floor with water when sweeping up dried overspray from dope and lacquer. This overspray is highly flammable when it is dry, but can safely be swept when it has been wet with water.

Air Supply

There should be an air compressor available that can supply enough clean air to supply all of the spray guns you are likely to need at one time.

The air storage tank should have a water drain trap that can be drained daily, and there should an air transformer conveniently located in the booth. The air transformer, Figure 3-23, contains an air pressure regulator and pressure gages showing the inlet air pressure and the pressure being delivered to the spray gun. It also has an air filter and a container in which moisture which collects from the compressed air can be trapped and held until it can be drained out, at least daily.

Spray Equipment

Most of the smaller paint shops use air-atomized spray equipment exclusively. This equipment uses compressed air to atomize the material and propel it to the surface being finished. This is the only type of equipment that will be discussed beyond an introduction here.

Airless spray equipment atomizes the material and propels it by forcing it through a small atomizing nozzle at pressure often above 1,000 psi. Airless spraying is usually used only where large volumes of material must be deposited in a minimum amount of time.

Electrostatic spray equipment is another specialized system seldom used in small repair shops. This system places a high electrostatic potential on the atomized material leaving the spray gun. An opposite potential is placed on the object being painted, and it attracts the spray, even causing it to wrap around and coat the side of the object away from the spray gun.

Electrostatic spraying causes very little overspray, and produces a much more uniform coating than either air or airless spraying alone.

Air-Atomized Spray Equipment

The air-atomizing spray gun like the one in Figure 3-24 is typical of the gun used in aircraft maintenance shops. This gun can be used as either a suction cup gun or a pressure pot gun by changing the fluid tip.

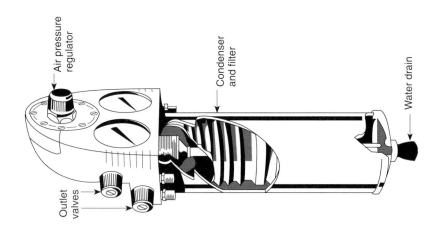

Air pressure regulator

Outlet valves

Condenser and filter

Water drain

Figure 3-23. *The air transformer contains a water drain trap, a filter element, a pressure regulator, and the necessary gages and connections for spray guns.*

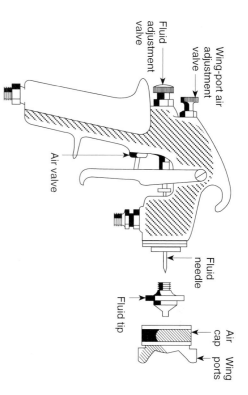

Figure 3-24. *An air-atomizing spray gun can be used as either a suction cup gun or a pressure pot gun by changing the fluid tip.*

Wing-port air adjustment valve

Fluid adjustment valve

Air valve

Fluid needle

Fluid tip

Air cap

Wing cap ports

This spray gun has three valves to give the operator control of the material that is being applied.

When the trigger is first pulled, it opens the air valve which sends atomizing air into the wing-port holes. Continued pulling of the trigger opens the fluid valve and allows the material to spray from the gun.

The wing-port air valve is adjusted by the upper knob, and it determines the shape of the spray pattern. When the valve is screwed in, very little air flows through the wing-port holes and the pattern is circular. Opening the valve flattens the spray pattern. The wide part of the spray pattern is always perpendicular to the wing ports.

The fluid adjustment valve, the lower knob, controls the amount of fluid that is allowed to flow from the gun. Screwing the knob out increases the amount of fluid that can be discharged.

The spray gun in Figure 3-24 can be used as either a suction cup gun or a pressure pot gun by changing the fluid tip. When it is used as a suction cup gun with a one-quart cup attached, the proper fluid tip extends beyond the air cap. When a pressure pot is connected to the gun, a fluid tip is used that is flush with the air cap. *See* Figure 3-25.

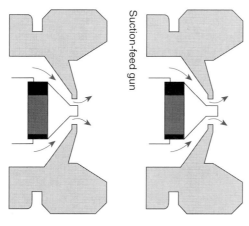

Suction-feed gun

Pressure-feed gun

Figure 3-25. *The fluid tip determines whether the spray gun is set up for a suction cup or a pressure pot.*

A tip that protrudes from the air cap produces enough suction to draw material from a cup attached to the gun.

A tip that is flush with the air cap is used when the material is forced by air pressure from the pressure pot to the gun.

Safety Equipment

Painting aircraft is a maintenance operation that requires unique safety precautions. Painting involves the application of combustible materials in an atomized form that can be easily ignited. Some chemicals are prone to spontaneous combustion, and many of them are toxic or at least irritating to the skin.

Fire Safety

All large aircraft paint shops are equipped with sprinkler systems that will deluge the entire shop with water if a fire should develop. Small shops should be protected by a sufficient number of carbon dioxide fire extinguishers of adequate size strategically located within the shop.

All solvents in the paint shop should be stored in safety cans of a type that is approved by the insurance company that carries the policy for the shop.

Rags that have been used for the application of conversion coating materials should be kept wet until they can be thoroughly washed out, and then they should be kept in closed containers until they are disposed of.

Dried dope and lacquer overspray should never be dry-swept from the paint shop. Flood the floor with water and sweep the overspray while it is wet.

Respiratory Safety

The exhaust fan should remove most of the vapors from the paint booth, but there are usually enough contaminants left in the air that they could cause respiratory problems.

Two types of protective devices that can be used when painting aircraft are: cartridge-type masks, and hoods that cover the entire head. Some cartridge masks filter out only solid particles, while others remove certain fumes. The hoods are slightly pressurized with compressed air, and they prevent any fumes reaching the wearer.

Always wear the type of mask that is recommended by the manufacturer of the finishing material, and on cartridge-type masks, change the cartridges at the recommended intervals.

Toxicity Safety

Some finishing materials are toxic and irritating to certain people. When using any toxic material, protect yourself with gloves, long polyethylene sleeves, and a face mask. If any toxic material gets on your skin, flush it off immediately. If any gets in your eyes, flush it out with plenty of fresh water and get medical aid without delay.

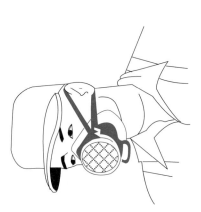

Cartridge-type mask

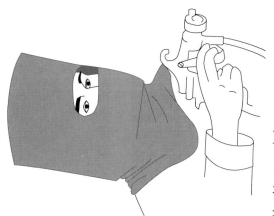

Hood-type respirator

Figure 3-26. *Respiratory protection devices for paint spray safety*

Application of the Finish

A finish that is both attractive and protective depends upon two very basic factors, the proper preparation of the surface and the proper application of the finish. We have discussed the preparation of the surface, and in this section we will discuss the proper application of the finish.

Spraying on the Finish

Finish for an entire aircraft is applied with a pressure pot similar to that in Figure 3-27. Suction cups like that in Figure 3-28 are used for applying trim and any time a small amount of finishing material is to be sprayed.

When using a pressure pot, mix the finishing material as recommended by the paint manufacturer and add the proper amount of thinner to give the finish the correct viscosity.

Dip a viscosity cup into the material to fill it. Lift the cup, and measure the time from the instant the bottom of the cup is raised above the fluid until the first break occurs in the flow from the hole in the bottom of the cup. Adjust the viscosity until this time is the same as that for a batch of the finish that you know had the proper viscosity.

Adjust the air pressure on the pot to the value that will deliver the correct amount of material. Do this by adjusting the air pressure on the gun to about 35 to 40 psi measured at the gun as shown in Figure 3-29, and then bring up the pressure on the pot until the correct amount of material is being sprayed. The pot pressure is normally around 6 to 8 psi, and never above 10 psi.

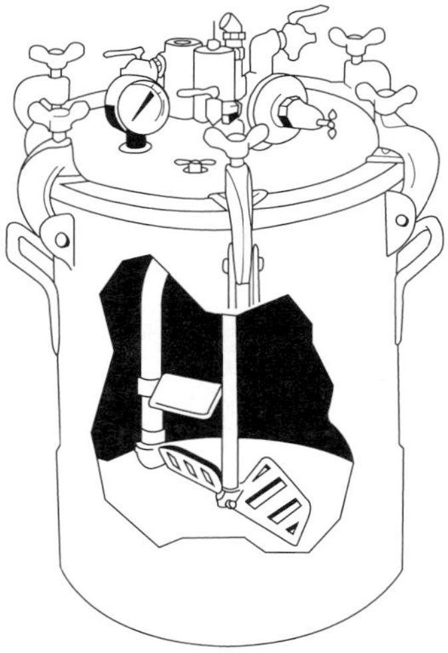

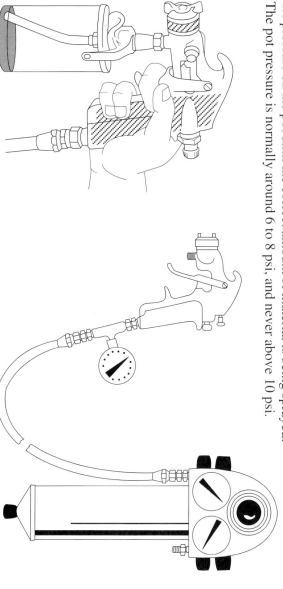

Figure 3-28. *A suction cup gun is used for applying the trim and for small paint jobs.*

Figure 3-29. *Measure the correct air pressure for spraying at the gun, not at the transformer. The difference in the two pressures arises from the pressure loss in the hose.*

Figure 3-27. *A pressure pot is used for painting an entire aircraft.*

Adjusting the Spray Pattern

With the air pressure on the gun and on the pressure pot correctly adjusted, adjust the valves on the spray gun to get the best spray pattern. Open the wing-port air valve completely and the fluid valve about 1½ turns for a starter. *See Figure 3-24 on Page 225.*

Turn the air cap until the wing ports are perpendicular to the direction you want the spray pattern and pull the trigger all the way. This opens both the air valve and the fluid valve, and the fluid will spray out of the gun. Adjust the wing-port air valve to get a properly flat pattern and the fluid valve to get the correct amount of material.

Hold the spray gun perpendicular to the surface and between 6 and 10 inches from the surface being sprayed. This distance should produce a good wet coat and yet not deliver enough material to cause runs or sags. Move the gun parallel to the surface. Begin the stroke and pull the trigger. Release the trigger before completing the stroke.

Do not move the spray gun in an arc, as this will make an uneven film, thick when the gun is near the surface and thin when the spray is arced away.

Sequence of Painting

When the spray gun is properly adjusted, you may begin to apply the material. Before spraying the flat portions of the aircraft, spray the edges and corners. By spraying along the corner, the thickest film will be along the edges, and it will blend out in the flat portion.

Each time you make a pass with a spray gun, you deposit a single layer of finishing material about 10 to 12 inches wide. This coat is slightly thicker in the center and tapers off at the edges. To get an even buildup of finish, spray the first pass across the surface, then come back and spray the second pass, overlapping all but about two or three inches of the finish left by the first pass. Continue overlapping most of the previous stroke with each new stroke until you have an even film of the correct thickness with no runs or sags.

When painting a complete aircraft, first paint the ends and leading edges of the ailerons and flaps, then the flap and aileron wells. Then paint the wing tips and the wing leading and trailing edges. Paint all the landing gear and wheel wells and all of the control horns and hinges. After all of these difficult areas have been sprayed, spray the flat surfaces.

Spray the tack coats crosswise on the fuselage and spanwise along the wing and tail surfaces. Spray the primer and finish coats lengthwise on the fuselage and chordwise on the wing and tail surfaces.

Paint Gun Problems

Professional paint spray guns are precision tools and when they are properly cared for they will produce a good finish, but they can have problems. Knowing the cause of the most common problems will help produce a smooth, even finish.

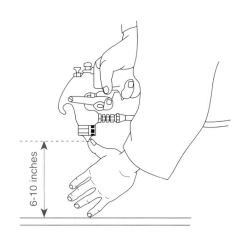

6-10 inches

Figure 3-30. *Hold the nozzle of the spray gun between 6 and 10 inches from the surface being sprayed.*

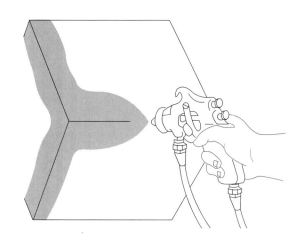

Figure 3-31. *When painting the corners of a surface, spray parallel to the corner first and then blend this in with the rest of the surface by spraying perpendicular to the corner.*

Distorted Spray Pattern

The correct and incorrect spray patterns are illustrated in Figure 3-32. A correct spray pattern is an ellipse, and a pattern that is more round than elliptical indicates an insufficient amount of atomizing air pressure. Excessive atomizing air pressure will cause the pattern to be dumbbell shaped. A pattern that is somewhat pear shaped is caused by a material buildup around one side of the fluid nozzle, cutting off the atomizing air to one side of the pattern. A banana-shaped pattern indicates that one of the wing-port holes is plugged and the pattern is being blown to one side by air through the opposite wing-port hole.

Spray Gun Spitting

Suction cup spray guns spit when air gets into the fluid as it is being sprayed. This can indicate too little material in the cup, or air leaking into the fluid line between the cup and the fluid nozzle.

Cleaning the Spray Equipment

Clean paint spray equipment immediately after you finish spraying. If you used a suction cup, dump all of the finishing material from it and put some thinner in it. Spray this thinner through the gun, triggering the gun repeatedly to flush out all of the passageways, and clean the tip of the needle. Continue this until there is no trace of the material leaving the gun with the thinner.

If you have been spraying with a pressure pot, empty the gun and hoses back into the pot. Loosen the lid on the pot and the air cap on the gun. Hold a rag over the air cap and pull the trigger. This will force air back through the gun and hose and push all of the material back into the pot. Empty and clean the pot and put thinner in it. Replace the lid and spray the thinner through the hose and gun until no trace of the material comes out with the thinner.

Soak the nozzle of the spray gun in a container of thinner, but do not soak the entire gun, as it will ruin the packings.

Application of Trim and Registration Numbers

Federal Aviation Regulations Part 45 gives the requirements for the color and placement of the registration numbers on FAA-certificated aircraft.

The registration numbers must be of a color that contrasts with that of the rest of the aircraft. Silver may be considered to be a contrasting color, but because of its reflective characteristics, its use should be approved by the local FAA maintenance inspector before it is used.

FAR Part 45 gives some exceptions to this rule, but generally the registration marks must consist of the Roman capital letter N followed by the registration number assigned to the particular aircraft. For a fixed-wing aircraft, these characters should be placed on the side of the fuselage so they are between the trailing edge of the wing and the leading edge of the

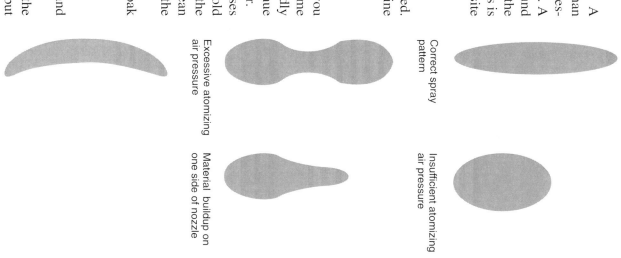

Correct spray
pattern

Insufficient atomizing
air pressure

Excessive atomizing
air pressure

Material buildup on
one side of nozzle

One wing-port hole is plugged up

Figure 3-32. *Paint spray patterns*

For rotorcraft, they must be displayed on both sides of the cabin, fuselage, boom, or tail.

The characters should be of equal height and at least 12 inches tall and two-thirds as wide as they are tall. The width of the letters M and W may be the same as their height. The stroke of the characters should be one-sixth as thick as the character is high, and the spacing between them should be at least one-fourth of the character width.

Figure 3-33 gives an example of all of the numerals and letters that are used in the registration numbers.

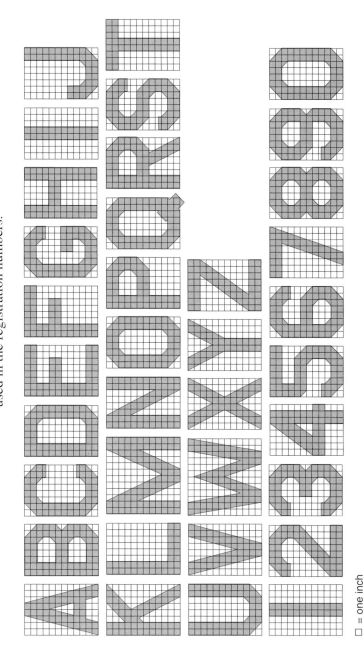

□ = one inch

Figure 3-33. *Letters and numerals used for aircraft registration numbers*

Ready-made masks, or stencils, are available that have the characters die-cut into an adhesive paper. You may apply the body color and stick the stencil in place. Remove the letter portion of the mask and spray on the color for the numbers. Or, you may spray on the color for the numbers and stick the stencil in place and remove all but the letter portion, then spray on the body color.

There is a typical universal template that will allow you to lay out the registration numbers. This template is shown in Figure 3-34, and it may be made from thin aluminum sheet.

After applying the base color to the fuselage and allowing it to dry for at least 24 hours, you may lay out and apply the registration numbers. It is very important when laying out the numbers that you use only the very best quality professional masking tape you can get. Poor quality tape does not seal the edges tight, and it causes rough edges of the letters.

Lay down two strips of half-inch tape, 12 inches apart, to form the top and bottom of the letters. Block out the letters as is seen in Figure 3-35 and then, using the template, outline the letter on the fabric, making very light marks with a soft lead pencil. Do not use a ball-point pen, as the ink will bleed up through the finish.

Mask the characters with thin tape pressed down firmly and smoothly along the edges. Do not cut the tape as there is a danger of cutting the fabric; rather tear it back against the edge of a knife blade or piece of thin aluminum sheet held flat against the surface. Fill in all parts of the characters that you do not want to paint, and mask beyond the top and bottom of the numbers with a good quality masking paper or aluminum foil. Do not use newspapers as they will allow some of the finishing material to bleed through. Ordinary kraft paper or polyethylene sheeting may be used to mask any portion of the structure where the overspray will be dry.

Spray a coat of the body color over the masked-off area first. If any paint bleeds under the masking tape it will be the body color and it will not produce ragged edges. When this is no longer tacky, spray on the color used for the numbers. The edges of the registration numbers will be smooth if the masking tape is removed as soon as the paint is no longer tacky to the touch. If the tape is allowed to remain until the paint is completely dry, the edges of the characters will likely be sharp and rough.

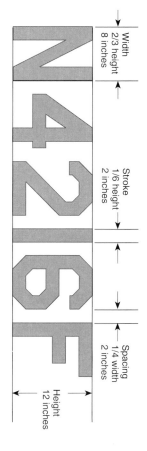

Figure 3-35. *Layout of registration numbers*

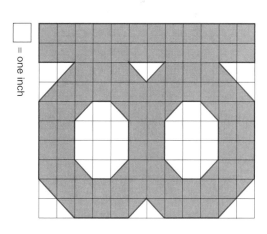

Figure 3-34. *Universal template for laying out registration numbers*

☐ = one inch

65. Paint strippers remove _____ (enamel or lacquer) by swelling the film and causing it to pull away from the primer. *Page 212*

66. Paint strippers remove acrylic lacquer by _____ (softening or swelling) the film. *Page 213*

67. The wax left on a surface after paint stripper has been used _____ (can or cannot) be removed with lacquer thinner. *Page 213*

68. The finish may be dry-stripped from an aircraft surface by blasting it with _____ . *Page 214*

69. Corrosion that occurs in the form of thread-like deposits under a paint film is called _____ corrosion. *Page 214*

70. If intergranular corrosion is suspected, the area should be inspected with a/an _____ or _____ instrument. *Page 214*

71. Acrylic lacquers should be applied in _____ (one heavy coat or several light coats). *Page 217*

72. Synthetic enamels _____ (may or may not) be applied over zinc chromate primer. *Page 217*

73. Synthetic enamel should dry for at least _____ hours before it is taped for the trim coats. *Page 217*

74. Polyurethane enamels should be applied over a/an _____ primer. *Page 218*

75. It is best if polyurethane enamel is allowed to dry for _____ hours before it is taped for the trim coats. *Page 218*

76. The fill coats of dope _____ (should or should not) completely fill the weave of cotton fabric. *Page 219*

77. The aluminum-pigmented dope _____ (is or is not) used primarily to provide a smooth surface for the finish coats of dope. *Page 220*

78. For the richest colors in a doped finish, all of the surfaces should be undercoated with _____ dope. *Page 220*

79. A doped surface is more likely to blush when the relative humidity is _____ (high or low). *Page 221*

80. A draft of air across the surface of freshly applied dope will cause _____ (pinholes or fisheyes). *Page 221*

81. A surface resembling the peel of an orange may be caused by the thinner in the dope evaporating too _____ (fast or slow). *Page 222*

82. Fisheyes can be prevented by scrubbing the surface to be sprayed with a rag damp with _____ or _____ . *Page 222*

83. A topcoat of nitrate dope _____ (will or will not) bond to butyrate fill coats. *Page 221*

84. Rejuvenation _____ (does or does not) restore strength to weakened fabric. *Page 222*

85. The shape of the spray pattern produced by a paint spray gun is determined by the amount of air flowing through the _____ holes. *Page 228*

86. The exhaust fan in a spray booth should be _____ (near the floor or high up on the wall). *Page 223*

87. To get the proper thickness of paint film, the spray gun should be held between _____ and _____ inches from the surface being sprayed. *Page 228*

88. Each pass of the spray gun should overlap all but about _____ or _____ inches of the previous pass. *Page 228*

89. The correct shape for the spray pattern of a paint gun is a/an _____ . *Page 229*

90. A dumbbell-shaped spray pattern is caused by too _____ (much or little) atomizing air pressure. *Page 229*

91. A paint spray gun _____ (should or should not) be cleaned by soaking the entire gun in a container of thinner. *Page 229*

92. The registration numbers of an aircraft certificated in the United States must be preceded by the letter _____ . *Page 229*

93. The minimum height of a registration number on a fixed-wing aircraft must be _____ inches. *Page 230*

Continued

94. A ball-point pen _____ (is or is not) a good instrument to use when laying out registration numbers on a doped fuselage. *Page 231*

95. The masking tape used to lay out the registration numbers _____ (should or should not) be removed as soon as the finish is no longer tacky to the touch. *Page 231*

Composite Structures

Aircraft structures have evolved fully as much as have their powerplants. The very first airframes were made of open trusses of either wood strips or bamboo. The aerodynamic surfaces were made of lightweight wood covered with cotton or linen fabric, shrunk and made air tight with a syrup-like collodion product that dried to a hard film.

The next major development came with the welded steel tube fuselage structure that replaced the wooden truss. This structure is strong, but it has the disadvantage that to give it a streamlined shape, a superstructure must be built around the load-bearing truss. This adds weight but is needed for aerodynamic smoothness and esthetics.

In the late 1920s, the Lockheed Company developed a streamlined wooden monocoque structure that carried virtually all of the stresses in its outer skin. This lightweight streamlined structure was used on some of the most efficient aircraft of the time. It, however, had the disadvantage of being extremely labor intensive in its construction.

The next logical step in the evolution of aircraft structure was to replace the wooden monocoque with a thin aluminum alloy monocoque. This decreased the dependence upon skilled craftsmen for its construction and made mass production of interchangeable parts practical and cost effective.

Metal stressed-skin aircraft structure has been the standard since the 1930s, but a new era is dawning, that of composites. Composite structure can be made stronger, lighter in weight, more rigid, and less costly than metal.

We have experienced what may be termed a plastics revolution. Early plastic materials such as celluloid and Beetleware gave promise of a low-cost, easy-to-manufacture material, but they did not have the strength needed for structural applications. One of the first plastic materials used in aviation was a thermosetting phenol-formaldehyde resin that was reinforced with paper or linen cloth. This phenolic material, called Micarta, pioneered in the early 1930s, is still used for control cable pulleys and fairleads and for electrical insulators.

collodion. Cellulose nitrate used as a film base for certain aircraft dopes.

monocoque. A single-shell type of aircraft structure in which all of the flight loads are carried in the outside skin of the structure.

plastics. The generic name for any of the organic materials produced by polymerization. Plastics can be shaped by molding or drawing.

Glass fibers, both woven into cloth and packed into loose mat and roving, have been reinforced with polyester resins and used for radomes, wing tips, and wheel pants since the early 1950s. This material is truly a composite, and may be thought of as being the ancestor of modern composite structural materials.

Modern composite materials use fibers of graphite and Kevlar as well as glass for most applications, with boron and ceramic used in some special applications. These fibers are primarily bonded into an epoxy resin matrix.

Composite structural components have the advantage over metal of being lighter in weight, stronger, more rigid, and better able to withstand the sonic vibrations that are commonly encountered in aircraft structure.

The military forces have been responsible for much of the development in advanced composite structure because performance and the successful accomplishment of military goals have always been more important than cost. The airlines have also contributed to its development because every pound of weight saved by replacing metal with composite materials adds a pound of payload capability for each flight and reduces the fuel burn.

Builders of amateur-built aircraft have made extensive use of some of the simpler composites because they can be used to produce beautiful, stream-lined, lightweight, and strong aircraft structure without requiring elaborate tooling. Construction is quite labor intensive, but, since homebuilt aircraft are usually labors of love, the long hours required for their construction are not a deterrent.

General aviation, held back by economic constraints, has made few uses of advanced composites, but aircraft such as the Beech Starship show that there are applications in this area.

Figure 3-36. *The Beech Starship is one of the first commercially produced general aviation aircraft to make extensive use of composite construction.*

Repairs to modern composite structure are complex. It requires special training and experience to produce a repair that restores the structure to its original strength, stiffness, rigidity, vibration characteristics, and aerodynamic smoothness.

In this text, we introduce the technology of composites to an extent that will allow you to profit from the specialized training offered by the aircraft manufacturers and by specialized composite repair training facilities. Most of the materials and procedures described are those used in the construction and repair of FAA-certificated aircraft rather than homebuilt or military aircraft.

Composite Materials

Modern composite structure consists of high-strength fibers oriented in the proper direction to withstand the stresses imposed upon them. These fibers are encapsulated in a matrix that bonds them together and carries the aerodynamic and structural loads into the fibers.

By their very nature, composite materials are divided into two basic categories: the reinforcing materials and the matrix.

Reinforcing Materials

Reinforcing materials consist of fibers that may be made into tapes, woven into a fabric, grouped together into a loosely compacted mat, or lightly twisted into a roll, or strand, called roving.

Fiberglass

Thin fibers are drawn from molten glass and spun together into threads and woven into a shiny, white cloth. There are two types of glass used for fibers, E-glass (electrical glass) and S-glass (structural glass). E-glass has high electrical strength and is used for most nonaviation and some aviation applications. S-glass is stronger, tougher, and stiffer than E-glass and is used in applications where its superior qualities outweigh its higher cost.

Kevlar

Kevlar® is the DuPont Company's registered trade name for its aramid fiber. It has a yellow color and is lightweight, strong, and extremely flexible and has excellent resistance to the chemicals normally associated with aircraft operations.

Kevlar is used to replace fiberglass in many applications. A properly designed Kevlar part has the strength of a similar metal part, but is much lighter in weight.

roving. A lightly twisted roll or strand of fibers.

Kevlar®. A patented synthetic aramid fiber noted for its flexibility and light weight. It is to a great extent replacing fiberglass as a reinforcing fabric for composite construction.

236

One of the major advantages of Kevlar is its flexibility under load and its ability to withstand impact, shock, and vibration. It is often used for helicopter rotor blades where twisting and vibration cause metal blades to fatigue and develop cracks. Blades made of Kevlar can absorb these stresses without damage.

Graphite

Graphite, or carbon, fibers are woven into a black fabric that is extremely strong for its weight and is very stiff. It is used for primary structure where high strength and rigidity are the prime considerations. The stiffness of graphite fibers has made it possible to explore the potential of the efficient forward-swept wing in the research airplane, the Grumman X-29.

graphite. A form of carbon. Structural graphite is used in composite structure because of its strength and stiffness.

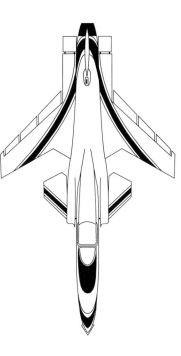

Figure 3-37. *The aerodynamic advantages of a forward-swept wing were not able to be exploited until graphite fibers were developed. The extreme stiffness of graphite made it possible to build a wing that does not twist under aerodynamic loads.*

Graphite may be bonded to aluminum alloy components, but take special care, because contact with the graphite is likely to cause the aluminum alloy to corrode.

Fiber Orientation

Wood is weak across its grain, but strong parallel to it, and when it is necessary for wood to have multidirectional strength, it is made into plywood whose thin veneers are glued together with their grains oriented at 45° or 90° to each other.

The same thing is true about composite materials whose major strength and stiffness is parallel to its fibers. Strength and stiffness can be tailored to the aerodynamic loads it must carry by the proper choice of the fabric weave and by the orientation of the fibers in the adjacent plies in the fabric layup.

Unidirectional Fabrics

Fabric made with all of the major fibers running in the same direction is called a unidirectional fabric. Unidirectional fabric is not woven, but the major fibers are laid in the warp direction and are held together with small cross threads.

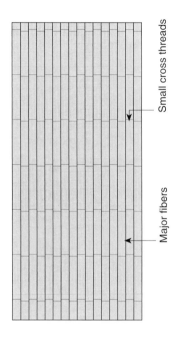

Figure 3-38. *All of the major fibers in a piece of unidirectional fabric run in the same direction.*

unidirectional fabric. Fabric in which all of the threads run in the same direction. These threads are often bound with a few fibers run at right angles, just enough to hold the yarns together and prevent their bunching.

aeroelastic tailoring. The design of an aerodynamic surface whose strength and stiffness are matched to the aerodynamic loads that will be imposed upon it.

warp threads. Threads that run the length of the roll of fabric, parallel to the selvage edge. Warp threads are often stronger than fill threads.

plain-weave fabric. Fabric in which each warp thread passes over one fill thread and under the next. Plain-weave fabric typically has the same strength in both warp and fill directions.

satin-weave fabric. Fabric in which the warp threads pass under one fill thread and over several more. Satin-weave fabrics are used when the lay-up must be made over complex shapes.

When the maximum amount of strength and rigidity are needed in a structure, several layers of unidirectional fabric can be laid up with the fibers of each of the layers running in the direction required to furnish the required strength. The stiffness required in the Grumman X-29 forward-swept wing is furnished by a wing box whose covers are made up of criss-crossed tapes of unidirectional graphite, crossing each other at 45° angles to oppose the aerodynamic stresses. There are 156 layers of material at the point of maximum thickness. This type of design in which the characteristics of the material are matched to the aerodynamic loads is called aeroelastic tailoring.

Bidirectional Fabrics

Woven fabrics are made by interlacing fill threads with the warp threads as the fabric is being woven on the looms. The particular weave is chosen to give the fabric the desired characteristics. Some of the most generally used weaves are the plain weave and various types of satin weaves.

In the plain weave fabric, Figure 3-39, each warp thread passes over one fill thread and under the next. Plain-weave fabrics are the most stable for lay-ups because the threads slip less than other weaves.

Satin weaves are those in which one warp thread passes over several fill threads and under just one. Satin weaves are used when the fabric must be draped into complex shapes with a high degree of smoothness.

In crowfoot satin, each warp thread passes under one fill thread and over three. In five-harness satin weave, each warp thread passes under one fill thread and over four. In eight-harness satin weave, each warp thread passes over one fill thread and under seven.

fill threads. Threads in a piece of fabric that run across the width of the fabric, interweaving with the warp threads. Fill threads are often called woof, or weft, threads.

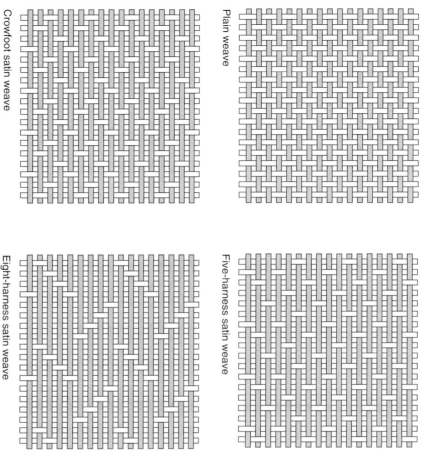

Plain weave

Five-harness satin weave

Crowfoot satin weave

Eight-harness satin weave

Figure 3-39. *Fabric weaves*

Hybrids

A hybrid fabric is composed of different types of fibers woven together to obtain special characteristics. One of the more popular hybrid composites is Kevlar and graphite. Fibers of each material are woven together to produce a fabric that has some of the better characteristics of both of the fibers.

Matrix Materials

The two components of a composite material are the reinforcing materials and the matrix that binds these materials together and transfers stresses into them. The matrix materials used for most composite materials are in the form of resins, but some of the ceramic composites use a metallic matrix.

Two basic types of resins are used in aircraft construction: thermoplastic and thermosetting. A thermoplastic resin is one that may be softened with heat. The transparent acrylic plastic material that is used for windshields and side windows of most of the small general aviation aircraft is a familiar type of thermoplastic material. When a piece of acrylic plastic is heated to a specified temperature, it may be formed into almost any shape that is needed. When it cools, it retains its shape. It may be reshaped by again heating it.

Thermosetting resins are used to reinforce glass, Kevlar, and graphite fibers. These resins are cured by heat and once cured, they do not change their shape, even when they are reheated. The two basic thermosetting resins used in aircraft construction are polyester and epoxy.

Polyester Resins

Polyester resins were the first developed, and have been used primarily with fiberglass. Polyesters do not provide the strength needed for most of the modern applications, but because of their low cost and relative ease of use, they are used for some nonstructural applications such as fairings.

Polyester resins are two-part materials: a resin and a catalyst. Typically about one ounce of catalyst is used with one gallon of resin.

Epoxy Resins

A number of epoxy resins are used as a matrix material. Each of them have different characteristics. Some are liquids as thin as water, and others are thick syrups. Some have good high-temperature characteristics, others are better suited for low-temperature applications. Some are very rigid, while others are quite flexible. Some cure quickly, and others allow for a longer working time before they cure.

Almost all aircraft structural epoxy is a two-part material, resin and catalyst, that is quite different from polyester resins. Rather than using a small amount of catalyst to initiate the resin's cure as is done with polyester, epoxy resins use a different type of catalyst, or hardener, and use much more of it.

It is extremely important to follow the approved instructions when mixing epoxy resins. The material must be fresh; that is, it must be used within its allowable shelf life which is stamped on the container. You must use the correct resin and the correct hardener, and the two materials must be accurately weighed and mixed for the recommended length of time. After mixing the materials, you must use them within the usable pot life, which is given in terms of minutes, and which is stamped on the container.

matrix. The material used in composite construction to bond the fibers together and to transmit the forces into the fibers. Resins are the most widely used matrix materials.

thermoplastic resin. A type of plastic material that becomes soft when heated and hardens when cooled.

thermosetting resin. A type of plastic material that, when once hardened by heat, cannot be softened by being heated again.

polyester resin. A thermosetting resin used as a matrix for much of the fiberglass used in composite construction.

Preimpregnated Materials

It is critical to ensure that all of the fibers are uniformly wet with the matrix material. In order to properly transfer stresses into the reinforcing material, all of the fibers must be completely encapsulated. Some of the epoxy resins are rather viscous and it is difficult to thoroughly saturate the material.

When absolute uniformity is required for volume production of composite structure, manufacturers often use preimpregnated materials called prepregs. Prepregs are made by immersing graphite, fiberglass, or Kevlar fabric in a resin solution that contains the correct amount of catalyst. The excess resin is removed and the material is dried. A sheet of parting film is placed on one side of the material and it is rolled up and placed in a refrigerator to prevent its curing until it is used.

Adhesives

An adhesive is a resin that is used to bond parts together. Some adhesives are available as two-part liquids that are mixed when they are needed. Another form of adhesive that is extremely handy for certain types of construction and repair is film-type adhesive. This adhesive is made up of catalyzed resin that is formed into a thin film. A plastic backing sheet is put on one side and stored in a refrigerator. To use it, cut a piece of the film to the proper size and put it into place between the prepared surface and a prepreg patch. Heat and pressure cure the adhesive and securely bond the patch in place.

Foaming adhesives are used to bond sections of honeycomb core. This adhesive is in the form of a thick tape or sheet which is wrapped around the replacement core plug. When heat is applied, the adhesive foams up and expands to fill all of the crevices and hardens to insure a good joint.

Core Materials

Aluminum alloy has a high enough tensile strength that a very thin sheet may be strong enough for a given application, but this thin sheet does not have enough stiffness to make it a totally adequate structural material. One of the early incursions into the field of composite materials was done by bonding end-grain balsa wood between two thin sheets of aluminum alloy. The metal provided the strength, and the balsa wood provided the thickness and thus the stiffness without adding too much weight. This type of composite is called sandwich construction.

Sandwich construction in which a lightweight core material is bonded between face plies of metal or resin-reinforced fabric is used today for all types of aircraft from homebuilt machines to high-speed, state-of-the-art military aircraft.

prepreg. Preimpregnated fabric. A type of composite material in which the reinforcing fibers are encapsulated in an uncured resin. Prepreg materials must be kept refrigerated to prevent them from curing before they are used.

sandwich material. A type of composite structural material in which a core material is bonded between face sheets of metal or resin-impregnated fabric.

Foam

Many of the composite-construction homebuilt aircraft are made by laying resin-impregnated fiberglass or Kevlar fabric over a foam form. There are two basic types of foam used for this purpose, Styrofoam and urethane foam.

The Styrofoam used for aircraft construction is not the same material used for coffee cups and picnic ice chests. It is closed-cell foam whose cell size and density are carefully controlled. Styrofoam is cut with a hot wire, and it must be used with epoxy resin, as polyester resin will dissolve it.

Urethane foam has an advantage over Styrofoam in that, unlike Styrofoam, it is fuel proof. It must not be cut with a hot wire as it gives off noxious fumes, but it can be cut and shaped with a sharp knife. Either epoxy or polyester resins can be used with urethane foam.

Honeycomb

While foam finds most of its applications in lightweight aircraft construction, honeycomb is used as the sandwich core for most of the high-performance applications.

Honeycomb for aircraft structural applications is made of aluminum, paper, fiberglass, stainless steel, and Nomex®, which is gaining a high degree of popularity. Honeycomb is made by forming the core material into a ribbon which contains a series of crimps, then joining them together as seen in Figure 3-40. Honeycomb core material is normally loaded in such a way that compressive stresses are imposed perpendicular to the cells, in the thickness direction. The core has little strength in its width direction, and it is important when replacing a piece of honeycomb core to be sure that the cells are properly oriented so that the length, or the ribbon, of the new piece runs in the same direction as the length of the core in the damaged area.

hot-wire cutter. A cutter used to shape blocks of Styrofoam. The wire is stretched tight between the arms of a frame and heated by electrical current. The hot wire melts its way through the foam.

Nomex®. A patented nylon material used to make the honeycomb core for certain types of sandwich materials.

ribbon direction. The direction in a piece of honeycomb material that is parallel to the length of the strips of material that make up the core.

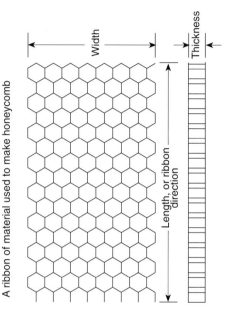

A ribbon of material used to make honeycomb

Width

Length, or ribbon direction

Thickness

Figure 3-40. *Honeycomb core material is made of strips, or ribbons, of material formed into crimps and joined into the familiar hexagonal pattern. It is best suited for compressive loads along its thickness. It has strength along its length, but little along its width.*

Fillers

Often the resins used in composite construction do not have the consistency needed for the application. When this is the case, fillers can be added to change the thin liquid into a syrup or a paste. The most widely used filler is microballoons, or microspheres. This product is made up of tiny hollow glass spheres that are mixed with the resin. The spheres displace four to six times their weight in most resins, and the cured resin forms a low-density product that can be sanded or filed.

The consistency of the finished product is determined by the amount of filler mixed with the resin. The resin is mixed with the correct amount of hardener and then the microballoons are folded into it. Approximately equal volumes of resin and microballoons produce a wet slurry mix. Two to four times as much filler as resin produces a syrupy mixture and a greater amount of microballoons results in a dry paste.

Manufacturing Methods

The manufacturing of a composite structure requires entirely different procedures from those used with sheet metal. The basic principle of much composite construction involves the process of laying up the reinforcing material in such a way that the maximum strength of each ply is oriented in the correct direction. The engineers who designed the part have computed all of the stresses to which the part will be subjected and have specified the orientation of the fibers. As was mentioned earlier, the top and bottom skins of the wing box of the forward-swept wing of the Grumman X-29 are made up of unidirectional graphite tapes. The plies of these tapes are oriented at 45° increments to give the wing its unique ability to withstand the twisting loads without the divergence that has prevented the use of the efficient forward-swept configuration in the past.

After the correct number of plies of material have been laid up with the proper orientation, the complete assembly must be cured. This is typically done with pressure and heat. There are three ways to apply heat and pressure: by matched dies, by a vacuum bag, and in an autoclave.

Matched Dies

When a large number of identical parts are to be made, manufacturers use a set of heated matched dies similar to the ones in Figure 3-41. Prepreg material is placed over the female die, or unimpregnated fibers are laid in a bed of resin in the female die. The male die is then forced down into the female die to give the finished product the desired shape and to ensure that all of the fibers are completely encapsulated with the resin. Pressure and heat are applied for a specific length of time to cure the resin.

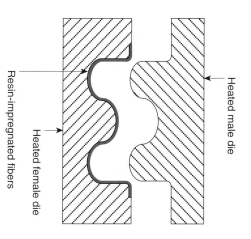

Figure 3-41. *Heated matched dies are used for making a large number of identical parts.*

Heated male die

Heated female die

Resin-impregnated fibers

microballoons. Tiny, hollow spheres of glass or phenolic material used to add body to a resin.

autoclave. A pressure vessel inside of which air can be heated to a high temperature and pressure raised to a high value.

Autoclaves are used in the composite manufacturing industry to apply heat and pressure for curing the resins.

lay-up. The placement of the various layers of resin-impregnated fabric in the mold for a piece of laminated composite material.

Vacuum Bag

You can use a female mold, if not enough identical parts are being manufactured to justify the expense of a set of matched dies. Lay out the resin-impregnated fabric according to the specifications of the engineers, and place a vacuum bag over the lay-up, as shown in Figure 3-42. Connect the bag to a vacuum pump and evacuate it to the specified low pressure. The pressure of the atmosphere forces the plies tightly together and ensures complete encapsulation of all of the fibers. If the mold is not heated, you can place a heating pad inside the vacuum bag, or place the mold, lay-up, and vacuum bag in an oven with accurate temperature control and held at the specified temperature for the length of time specified for the particular component.

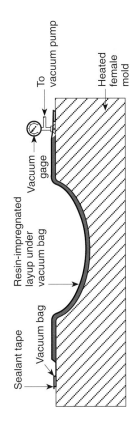

Figure 3-42. *A vacuum bag may be used to apply the pressure to a composite lay-up to assure that it takes the shape of the female die and to ensure that all of the individual fibers are completely encapsulated.*

Autoclaves

An autoclave is a pressure vessel in which air can be heated to a high temperature and pressure raised to a high value. Many manufacturers of composite structures use autoclaves to apply the heat and pressure needed to cure resins.

Filament Winding

When a component such as a helicopter rotor blade or a propeller blade must have the most strength possible, it may be filament-wound as illustrated in Figure 3-43. A mandrel in the shape of the component is mounted in a fixture that rotates it. Preimpregnated filaments are fed off spools and wrapped around the mandrel. The head through which the filaments pass is computer-controlled so the different layers of the filaments can be oriented at the angle specified by the engineers. When the wrapping is completed, the component is placed in an autoclave and heated and held under the required pressure for the specified length of time.

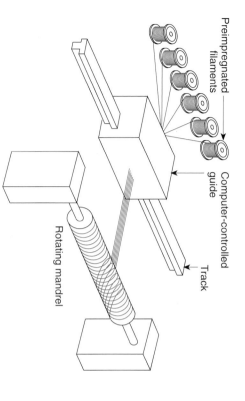

Figure 3-43. *When the maximum strength is required, the part may be filament-wound and cured in an autoclave.*

Preimpregnated filaments

Computer-controlled guide

Rotating mandrel

Track

Composite Structure Inspection and Repair

Composite construction of aircraft is a new technology, and its inspection and repair have not yet been standardized. Each damaged area must be individually assessed and the repair designed so that it will meet the requirements specified by the manufacturer's engineering department and described in the structural repair manual (SRM). No general text can describe all types of repairs, but some fundamental considerations are common to most repairs, and these are described here.

Inspection

Before any repair is considered, you must determine the extent of the damage and choose a method of repair.

Delamination is one of the most common types of damage found in composite structure. If the face plies separate from the core material, or if some of the plies separate from each other, the material loses its strength and must be repaired. One of the simplest methods of inspecting a structure for delaminations is to tap the suspected area with the edge of a coin. If there is no delamination, the coin will produce a clear ringing sound, but if there is delamination, the sound will be a dull thud. The coin tap procedure is not a quantitative test, but it gives an indication when further investigation is needed.

Cracks in the surface may be indications of serious damage, or they may be superficial and require no repair other than touching up the paint. It is important to be able to determine which is the case. Ultrasonic inspection may be used to determine if a part is actually damaged. Pulses of high-frequency vibrations are fed into the part and reflected back into a pickup. The results are displayed on the screen of a cathode-ray tube.

SRM. Structural Repair Manual. An SRM, issued by the aircraft manufacturer, details various typical repairs applicable to a specific aircraft.

delamination. The separation of the layers of a laminated material.

Radiograpic inspection, such as X-ray and gamma-ray, can be used to examine the inside of a piece of composite structure. This method is about the only way water inside a honeycomb core can be detected.

Repair

Assume that a careful inspection has found damage in a piece of honeycomb-core composite material that has three plies of fabric on each side. The damage extends through the surface skin into the core material. Two typical repairs are described in this section to show the room-temperature cure and the hot curing method.

Room-Temperature Cure

First, outline the damaged area. In this example, no part of the damage extends beyond a two-inch circle. The edges of the cleaned-out hole will taper back so that one inch of each ply is exposed on each side of the damage. For this repair in a three-ply face sheet, an area 10 inches in diameter must be cleaned up and prepared.

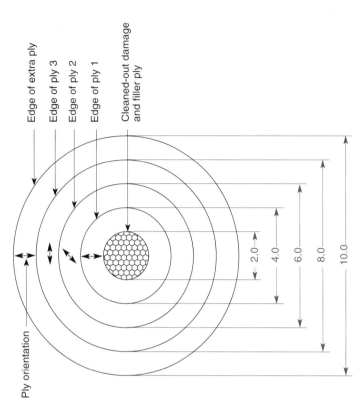

Figure 3-44. *Typical dimensions for a room-temperature repair to the face plies of a honeycomb core composite panel*

Draw a circle with a diameter of 11 inches, centered on the damage. Carefully mask the area to be repaired so the adjacent finish will not be damaged. Remove all the finish from this area by sanding carefully with 80- to 150-grit sandpaper. During this sanding, be careful that you do not allow heat to build up that could cause delamination. Never use any type of paint stripper on composite structure, because some of the fibers may absorb the chemicals from the stripper, which would prevent proper bonding of the patch. Do not sand into the fibers in this top layer of fabric.

Remove the damage with a high-speed router. First cut through the top skin and remove it. Then, using a flush cutter, remove the honeycomb down to within about $\frac{1}{16}$-inch from the bottom skin. This last bit of core material can be removed by careful hand sanding.

Draw a circle with an eight-inch diameter, centered on the damage. This will be the outer edge of the original material. Use a small right-angle pneumatic sander, and carefully sand through the first ply of material. Taper the sanding so you get through this ply in one inch. You can tell when you are through a layer by watching the direction of the threads, as each layer of fabric is oriented in a different direction. Sand through the next ply in such a way that you are through it in another inch. Continue through the third ply, and be extremely careful as you approach the edge of the hole that you do not expose the core.

After removing the damage and scarfing back the area to receive the repair, remove all the sanding residue with a vacuum cleaner. Don't use compressed air, because you might delaminate the plies that are now exposed. Clean the surface with a rag damp with a solvent such as methyl-ethyl-ketone (MEK) or acetone to remove any of the oils that may have been left by your fingers as you were feeling to determine the progress in the sanding. Oils from a fingerprint will prevent the patches from bonding properly.

Cut a plug of honeycomb of the same material and density as that removed from the damaged area. When inserting it into the hole, be sure to orient it so that the ribbon direction is the same as that in the structure being repaired. Secure the plug with the type of adhesive that is specified in the structural repair manual. Plugs are often installed by wrapping them with foaming adhesive. When the repair is cured, the adhesive foams and bonds the core to the surrounding honeycomb.

Lay out the repair ply inserts by tracing circles the actual size of each insert onto pieces of clear plastic. Mark an arrow on each circle to show the orientation of the warp threads.

Place the fabric for the replacement plies on a sheet of clean plastic. Be sure that the fabric is the type of material, weight, and weave specified in the structural repair manual (SRM). When handling the material, use clean lint-free or latex gloves to prevent getting oils from your hand on the material.

Mix the resin as directed in the SRM. Be sure that the resin is the one specified for the repair and that it is within its usable shelf life. Mix it according to the instructions furnished by the resin manufacturer. Pour enough of the mixed resin over the fabric to provide between a 50-to-55%-by-weight fabric-to-resin combination, and very carefully work it into the weave. Each thread must be thoroughly encapsulated, but the weave must not be distorted.

Place the plastic patterns for each of the ply inserts over the resin-impregnated material, observing the direction of the warp threads. Cut the inserts from the material, following the outline you have made.

The structural repair manual shows the orientation of the plies of the fabric by the use of a warp clock such as the one in Figure 3-45. The 0° (or reference direction) is shown and the orientation of each ply is noted in degrees positive or negative from the reference direction.

Be sure that the structure is ready to receive the patch. Spread a thin layer of resin on the repair area before laying any of the plies in place. Remove the plastic from the filler ply which is the same diameter as the exposed core, and carefully lay it in place, observing the direction of the warp threads. Remove the plastic from the first repair ply insert and lay it in place. Follow this with the second ply and the third ply, and finally put the extra ply in place. Put a thin sanding ply over the extra ply. This ply is to give aerodynamic smooth-ness to the repair.

Lay a piece of perforated parting film over the repair, and place a sheet of bleeder material over it. This bleeder is a porous material that holds the resin that is squeezed from the material as the pressure is put on it.

Lay down four strips of sealing tape around the repair area and place the vacuum bagging material that has the fitting for the vacuum pump over the tape. Press it down into the tape to produce a seal. Connect the vacuum pump and check for the presence of leaks, which will be indicated by a hissing sound. Hold the vacuum on the repair for the time specified by the structural repair manual. *See* Figure 3-46.

Hot-Bond Repair

You can make a stronger repair using the hot-bond process, in which the laid-up repair is cured with both heat and pressure. For the two-inch damage, the repair is smaller, because each ply is cut back less than is necessary for the room-temperature cure.

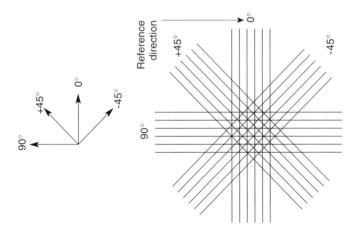

Figure 3-45. *A warp clock is included in a structural repair manual to show the correct orientation of the warp threads in each ply of the material.*

warp clock. An alignment indicator included in a structural repair manual to show the orientation of the plies of a composite material. The ply direction is shown in relation to a reference direction.

parting film. A layer of thin plastic material placed between a composite lay-up and the heating blanket. It prevents the blanket from sticking to the fabric.

bleeder. A material such as glass cloth or mat that is placed over a composite lay-up to absorb the excess resin forced out of the ply fibers when pressure is applied.

Prepare the area as described above, using the dimensions shown in Figure 3-47. In a hot-bond repair, cut back each layer half an inch on each side.

Remove the damaged material and draw a circle with a five-inch diameter, centered on the damage. This will be the outer edge of the original material. Carefully sand through each ply of material, tapering the sanding so you expose half an inch of each ply, but do not expose the core. Clean the surface with a rag damp with methyl-ethyl-ketone (MEK) or acetone.

Cut a plug of honeycomb as described in the room-temperature-cured repair section, and wrap it with a foaming adhesive. When the repair is cured, the heat causes the adhesive to foam and bond the core to the surrounding honeycomb.

Lay out the repair ply inserts by tracing the actual size of each insert onto pieces of clear plastic. Mark an arrow on each circle to show the orientation of the warp threads.

Use prepreg and the adhesive specified in the SRM to make this repair. Lay the plastic patterns for each of the ply inserts over the prepreg, orienting the arrow on the plastic with the warp threads, and cut the inserts, following the pattern.

Be sure that the structure is ready to receive the patch. Lay a piece of film adhesive in place, and remove the plastic from the filler ply that is the same size as the exposed core. Carefully put it in place, observing the direction of the warp threads as specified in the SRM. Then remove the plastic from each of the repair plies and the extra ply, and lay them in place, again paying attention to the ply orientation.

Figure 3-46. *Typical lay-up for vacuum-bagging of a room-temperature cured repair*

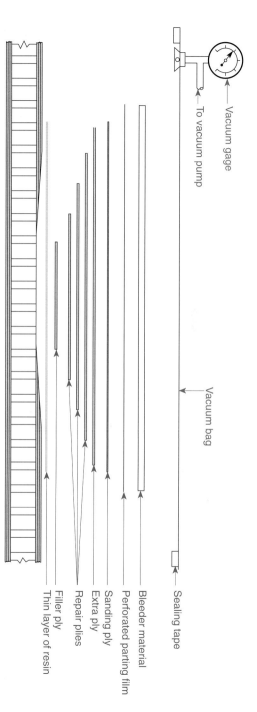

Vacuum gage

To vacuum pump

Vacuum bag

Bleeder material

Perforated parting film

Sanding ply

Extra ply

Repair plies

Filler ply

Thin layer of resin

Sealing tape

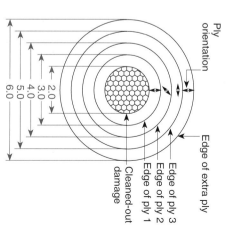

Figure 3-47. *Typical dimensions for a hot-bond repair to the face plies and core of a honeycomb composite panel*

Ply orientation

Edge of ply 3
Edge of ply 2
Edge of ply 1

Edge of extra ply

Cleaned-out damage

2.0
3.0
4.0
5.0
6.0

Place a thin sanding ply and then a piece of perforated parting film over the repair, and you are ready to vacuum bag the repair to apply heat and pressure. *See* Figure 3-48.

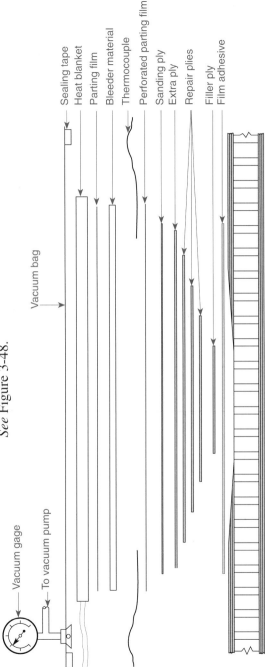

Sealing tape
Heat blanket
Parting film
Bleeder material
Thermocouple
Perforated parting film
Sanding ply
Extra ply
Repair plies
Filler ply
Film adhesive

Vacuum bag

Vacuum gage
To vacuum pump

Figure 3-48. *Typical lay-up for a hot bond repair*

Place the thermocouples from the heater on top of the parting film and lay a sheet of bleeder material over the film. This bleeder is a porous material that holds the resin squeezed from the material as it is placed under pressure to cure the repair. Place a piece of nonperforated parting film over the bleeder and the heat blanket on top of it.

Lay the sealing tape around the repair area, and then carefully seal around the wires for the heat blanket and the thermocouple. Place the vacuum bagging material that has the fitting for the vacuum pump over the tape. Press it down into the tape to produce a seal. Connect the vacuum pump and check for leaks.

Curing the Repair

Some of the lower-strength resins cure at room temperature, but almost all of the stronger matrix systems require heat, and the structural repair manuals specify the rate of heat rise, curing temperature and time, and the rate of cooling. You can only maintain this curing program by using some type of programmed controller.

The controller in Figure 3-49 is ideally suited for curing a patch like the one in our example. The vacuum line, the thermocouples, and the heat blanket are connected, and the controller is programmed to apply the vacuum and to increase the temperature at the rate specified in the SRM to the required cure temperature.

When this temperature is reached, it will hold it for the required length of time and then will decrease the temperature at the recommended rate to allow the resin to achieve its maximum strength without becoming brittle.

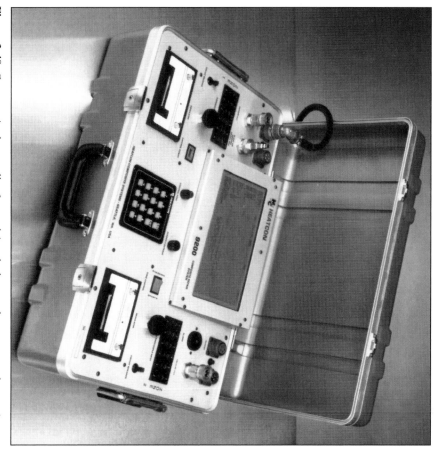

Figure 3-49. *Computerized controller for applying the heat and pressure to the repair at a carefully programmed rate.*

Cutting and Sanding Composite Materials

You can cut uncured reinforcing materials with conventional heavy-duty industrial fabric shears, but there are special ceramic-blade shears with serrated edges that are better for cutting Kevlar. The serrations hold the fibers, allowing the cut to be made with a minimum of pulling and fraying.

Cured composite materials may be cut, drilled, and otherwise machined. Some of the tools used for working with composites are different from those used with metal.

Kevlar generates special problems during drilling because of the fibers' tendency to pull and stretch. This leaves the fuzzy ends of the fabric inside the hole. Special drills are available for Kevlar, including the brad-point drill in Figure 3-50. When drilling, use a high speed and little pressure, especially as the drill cuts through the back of the material. *See* Figure 3-50.

Side view

End view

Figure 3-50. *Brad-point drills are used to drill Kevlar without leaving fuzz inside the hole.*

Side view

End view

Figure 3-51. *Spade drill for drilling graphite material*

Hole cutters designed to cut fuzz-free holes in Kevlar are available. They have carbide cutting edges and diameters from $7/16$-inch up to 3 inches.

Drill graphite with a spade drill like the one in Figure 3-51. This drill has ample space for the drill dust to leave the hole, so it will not enlarge the hole. Graphite, like Kevlar, should be drilled at a high speed with only a little pressure on the drill.

Glass and graphite fibers will dull ordinary steel saw blades, so be sure to use carbide-tipped saws or saws with diamond dust for their cutting edges when you are cutting cured composite materials.

The best way to scarf laminated materials is to sand with a small, high-speed, right-angle sander. These sanders can be fitted with one-inch, two-inch, or three-inch-diameter disks, and they turn at about 20,000 rpm. Aluminum oxide disks are suitable for sanding glass or Kevlar, but you should use silicon carbide for sanding graphite.

You *must* wear a dust respirator when sanding composite materials because the tiny airborne particles can be extremely hazardous to your lungs.

Safety Around Composites

Certain chemicals used with composite construction cause allergic reactions for some people, so take precautions when working with them. Take special care when handling chemicals classified as hazardous materials, and be sure to dispose of their residue in a manner that complies with local environmental requirements.

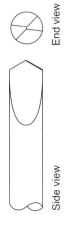

The Material Safety Data Sheets (MSDS) that come with the chemicals contain information about their flammability, ventilation requirements, and health precautions. Learn and heed this information. Keep a copy of the MSDS to give to medical personnel in the event of a chemical medical emergency, so they can take the appropriate action.

Skin Care

Take special care to keep the chemicals used in composite construction and repair from direct contact with the skin. If any of them do, wash them off immediately. Wear latex or butyl gloves when working with these chemicals, and wear a shop coat to prevent the chemicals from contaminating your clothing and holding the vapors in contact with your skin.

There are protective hand gels that can be used on your hands before working with the resins. These gels leave a thin, invisible, flexible film on your hands that prevent the chemicals getting to your skin. The gel is easy to wash off when the work is finished. Typically this protective gel must not be used when wearing gloves.

Eye Care

Take all precautions to protect your eyes. It is extremely important to wear goggles that provide complete eye protection when working with composite materials. Be sure that the goggles you wear protect your eyes from splashed chemicals as well as from sanding dust and particles that fly when you cut or drill the cured materials.

If you should get any chemicals in your eyes, rinse them immediately with plenty of fresh water and get medical assistance at once.

Respiratory Care

Particles of glass and graphite produced by sanding can be extremely hazardous to your lungs, and you should not sand without wearing a respirator that protects against these particles.

When working with resins such as epoxies in a poorly ventilated area, you should wear a respirator mask designed to protect against these vapors.

MSDS. Material Safety Data Sheets. MSDS are required by the Federal Government to be available in workplaces to inform workers of the dangers that may exist from contact with certain materials.

STUDY QUESTIONS: COMPOSITE STRUCTURES

Answers begin on Page 263. Page numbers refer to chapter text.

96. An aircraft structure that carries most of the aerodynamic stresses in its outer skin is called a/an _____ structure. *Page 234*

97. The glass fibers that produce the stronger structure are made of _____ (E or S)-glass. *Page 236*

98. Kevlar fabric is noted for being _____ (flexible or stiff). *Page 236*

99. Graphite fabric is noted for being _____ (flexible or stiff). *Page 237*

100. Corrosion can be a problem with aluminum alloys when they are bonded to _____ (fiberglass or graphite). *Page 237*

101. The type of plastic material that is softened by heat and that regains its hardness when it is cooled is a _____ (thermoplastic or thermosetting) material. *Page 240*

102. Polyester resins _____ (are or are not) used as a matrix material for modern high-strength composite structures. *Page 240*

103. There _____ (is or is not) more than one type of epoxy resin. *Page 240*

104. Prepregs are prevented from curing before they are used by storage in a/an _____. *Page 241*

105. Film-type adhesives _____ (do or do not) need to be stored in a refrigerator to extend their shelf life. *Page 241*

106. The adhesive recommended to bond a plug of honeycomb material into a honeycomb panel is a/an _____ adhesive. *Page 241*

107. A block of Styrofoam to be used as the form for an aircraft component _____ (can or cannot) be cut with a hot-wire cutter. *Page 242*

108. Urethane foam _____ (can or cannot) be used with a polyester resin. *Page 242*

109. Three ways heat and pressure can be applied to composite component are:

a. _____

b. _____

c. _____

Page 243

Continued

110. The simplest method to check a piece of composite structure for possible delamination damage is to tap the suspected area with the edge of a/an _____ . *Page 245*

111. A method of nondestructive inspection used to check a piece of composite structure for crack damage is a/an _____ inspection. *Page 245*

112. Water inside a honeycomb core can be detected by using _____ inspection. *Page 246*

113. The finish on a piece of composite structure to be repaired may be properly removed with _____ (paint stripper or sandpaper). *Page 247*

114. After the damage has been removed from a piece of honeycomb-core composite material, all of the sanding dust should be removed with _____ (vacuum or compressed air). *Page 247*

115. When installing the replacement plug in a piece of honeycomb core, it is important that the length or direction of the plug be the same as that of the structure. *Page 247*

116. When drilling cured composite materials, the drill should be turned _____ (fast or slow). *Page 252*

Transparent Plastics

Acrylic plastics have been used for windshields and side windows of the smaller general aviation aircraft for many years. Acrylics are of the thermoplastic family of resins, which means that they can be softened by heat, and when they are cooled they will regain their original hardness and rigidity. They are not damaged by repeated heating and cooling, so long as they are not overheated. Acrylic plastics are known by their trade names of Plexiglas and Lucite in the United States, and in the United Kingdom as Perspex.

It is possible that acetate plastics may be encountered in some older aircraft. These are also thermoplastic, but since they yellow and become brittle with age, they have almost all been replaced with the superior acrylic. Determine whether the material is acetate or acrylic by rubbing a bit of acetone on the surface. If it softens, it is probably acetate, but if the surface turns white and does not soften, it is acrylic.

Storing and Handling Transparent Plastic Materials

Transparent acrylics are strong, but their surface is soft and easily damaged if they are mishandled or improperly stored. Sheets of the material from the manufacturer are covered with sheets of paper. Leave this paper on the surface while storing the material, and as much as possible when the material is being worked. Formed components such as windshields are usually covered with a plastic protector sprayed on the finished component. It forms a tough film you can easily strip off when the windshield is installed.

If at all possible, store flat sheets in a bin in which they are tilted approximately 10° from the vertical. If they must be stored horizontally, be sure there are no chips or dirt between the sheets, and do not make the stacks more than 18 inches high. Put the smaller sheets on top so no sheets will overhang.

Working with Transparent Plastic Materials

Acrylic plastics are soft and can be sawed and drilled in much the same way as aluminum alloys. The basic difference between working with metal and acrylic is acrylic's poor heat conduction. It tends to get hot and melt if proper provisions are not made for cooling.

Cutting

A band saw is the favored tool for cutting acrylics. Mark the outline of the part on the protecting paper and cut to within about $1/16$-inch of the line. Do the final trimming with a disk or belt sander.

Use a circular saw for straight cuts if the blades are hollow ground, or have enough set to the teeth to prevent binding. When cutting thick material, take care not to feed it into the saw too fast. This will cause overheating and the material will begin to melt at the edges of the cut. If the material smokes, or starts to soften, slow the cutting.

Drilling

The poor heat conductivity of acrylics requires the use of a coolant when drilling deep holes. Use a water-soluble cutting oil, which will provide adequate cooling and not attack the plastic.

The drill used for acrylic should have smooth flutes and a 0° rake angle, and the included angle should be greater than that used for drilling aluminum. Turn the drill at a high speed and use a light to moderate pressure. Back up thin material with a piece of wood so the drill will not break or chip the edges of the hole when it comes through the back side.

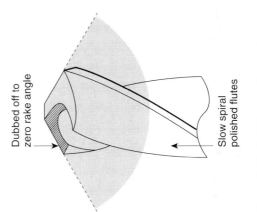

Dubbed off to zero rake angle

Slow spiral polished flutes

Figure 3-52. *Drill for acrylic plastics*

Forming Acrylic Plastics

Acrylic plastics can be heated until they are soft, and then formed either by draping them or stretching them over a male die or by pulling them into a female die with vacuum. Acrylics should not be cold formed except for very large-radius simple curves, neither should they be pulled into shape in a curved frame without heating. Either of these two forming methods places the plastic under a severe strain and can cause crazing.

Soften small pieces of acrylic by placing them in an oil bath and heating them. Hold them at a specified temperature for the recommended time and then allow them to cool slowly. You can't use water because it boils at a temperature below that required for softening the acrylic.

For example, you can form a landing light cover from 0.125-inch acrylic by following these steps:

1. Make a wooden form with the exact curvature of the wing leading edge, and cover it with outing flannel.

2. Make a paper pattern of the cover and transfer it to the acrylic. Trim the acrylic to a size slightly larger than the finished dimensions and polish the edges so there will be no stress risers. Remove the protective paper.

3. Heat the acrylic in an oil bath to approximately 230°F and hold it for two hours. Remove it from the oil and drape it over the form. Use cotton gloves to smooth it down over the form, and allow it to cool slowly. Remove it from the form and trim it to the final dimensions with a file. Polish the edges and drill the holes for attachment.

Form complex compound-curved parts like bubble canopies by using a female mold and a vacuum pump. Heat the sheet of plastic and place it over the female mold. Clamp the edges tightly enough so it will not buckle, but loose enough to allow slippage. Apply the suction to the mold and the plastic will pull down to form the part. Allow the molded component to cool slowly, and then remove it from the mold and trim the edges.

Cementing Transparent Plastic Materials

A properly made joint in a piece of acrylic plastic is almost as strong as the material itself. The joint is made by actually melting the edges of the part and forcing them to flow together as seen in Figure 3-53 on the following page.

crazing. A form of stress-caused damage that occurs in a transparent thermoplastic material. Crazing appears as a series of tiny, hair-like cracks just below the surface of the plastic.

The cements used with acrylics are usually clear thin liquids such as methylene chloride or ethylene dichloride. To make a good joint with the soak method, follow these steps:

1. Mask off the parts of the plastic that are not to be affected by the solvent.

2. Soak the edge of one of the pieces in the solvent until a soft cushion forms.

3. Press the pieces together so the cushion will diffuse into the other piece and form a cushion on it.

4. Allow the pressure to remain until the solvent has evaporated from the cushions and they become hard. Remove the excess material and dress the repair to conform to the original material.

You can also cement plastics with the glue method. Dissolve some acrylic shavings in the liquid solvent to make it into a viscous syrup. Apply the syrup to either one or both of the parts and allow the cushion to form. Assemble the parts and apply pressure. Allow the pressure to remain until the solvents evaporate and the cushions harden.

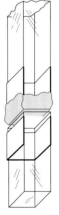

Edge of one piece is soaked in solvent.

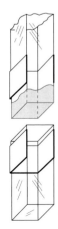

Solvent forms a cushion on edge of the plastic.

Press two pieces together and hold pressure until solvents evaporate.

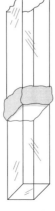

When solvents evaporate, joint is almost as strong as rest of material.

Figure 3-53. *Cementing acrylic plastics by the soak method*

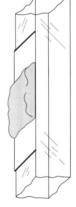

Apply viscous syrup to area where joint is to be made; allow cushion to form.

Press pieces together and apply steady pressure.

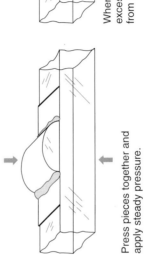

Assemble parts.

When solvents have evaporated, trim excess material that has extruded from between parts.

Figure 3-54. *Cementing acrylic plastics by the glue method*

Methods of Applying Pressure

Pressure must be applied to the plastic in some way that will maintain a constant force as the plastic shrinks when the solvents evaporate. The best way of applying pressure to small areas is with spring clamps. Weights can also be used effectively. (C-clamps or parallel clamps are not usable.)

Curing Transparent Plastic Materials

The solvents in a cemented joint never completely evaporate, and since the cushion has expanded, the joint is slightly weaker than the original material. These joints can be strengthened by forcing the solvents to diffuse into more of the material. Figure 3-55 shows the way the solvents concentrate in the joint. If the plastic is heated to about 120°F and held at this temperature for about 48 hours, the cushions will expand and the solvents in them will diffuse into a larger volume. The solvent content and the strength of the cured material is nearly the same as that of the original material.

Cleaning Transparent Plastic Materials

Acrylic plastics are soft and their surfaces are easily scratched. When cleaning a plastic windshield or window, flush it with plenty of fresh water and use your bare hand to dislodge any dirt particles. Do not use a rag, because particles remain in cloth and will scratch the plastic. For particularly stubborn areas, or areas that have oil or grease on them, use a mild soap and water solution to clean the area.

Polishing and Protection

There are several good commercial polishes on the market that clean and polish plastic windshields. These cleaners typically contain an antistatic material that prevents the windshield from attracting dust, and wax that fills the minute surface scratches. When applying these waxes, use only a clean, soft cloth or a lint-free wiper. Do not use ordinary shop rags, because they collect tiny particles of metal and abrasives that are not removed in their normal laundering.

A good grade of paste wax will protect the plastic and cause rain to ball up and blow off rather than spreading out and distorting vision.

Installing Plastic Windshields and Windows

Replacing a windshield in an airplane requires patience and attention to detail. You can obtain new windshields from the aircraft manufacturer or from component manufacturers whose products are made under a Parts Manufacturer Approval (FAA-PMA). New windshields are formed to fit generally, but there is usually an excess of material that you must trim away for a perfect fit.

Remove the old windshield and clean out all the old sealant from the channels. Using the old windshield as a pattern, file or grind away the excess plastic from the edges of the new one. Install the type of sealer specified in the aircraft structural repair manual and put the new windshield in place.

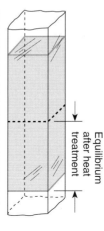 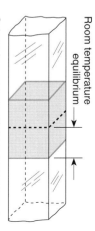

Room temperature equilibrium

Solvent in a cemented joint is concentrated in the cushions.

By heating repaired area and holding it at elevated temperature, solvents disburse and joint becomes stronger.

Equilibrium after heat treatment

Figure 3-55. *Curing of an acrylic plastic cemented joint*

The new windshield should fit into the retainer for the full depth specified by the manufacturer, and there should be at least ⅛-inch clearance between the edges of the plastic and the structure to allow for dimensional changes as the temperature changes. Replace all the screws in the retainers.

Some windshields are held in place with machine screws and self-locking nuts. When the screws pass through holes in the plastic, special care must be taken. The holes in the plastic should be ⅛-inch oversize to allow the plastic to shift with temperature changes. Some installations use spacers to prevent the screws being overtightened, but in the absence of spacers, tighten each nut to a firm fit, then back it off for one full turn.

Repairing Transparent Plastic Materials

Inspection and repair of windshields and side windows in pressurized aircraft are important jobs for the aviation maintenance technician. These transparencies are part of the pressure vessel and you must take special care when inspecting and maintaining them to find and repair all damage.

Crazing

The most common types of damage are crazing and cuts. Crazing, or tiny, hair-like cracks that may or may not extend all of the way to the surface, may be caused by stresses or by chemical fumes. These tiny cracks cannot be felt, but must be removed with abrasives. It is extremely important, after removing all of the damage, to ensure that the window still has the required thickness, and that the removal has not caused visual distortion. Because of the high cost of the windows and the disasterous consequences if they were to blow out, any damage to windows of pressurized aircraft should be assessed and repaired by specialists. Repair stations who specialize in window repair can measure thickness of the repaired window accurately with ultrasonic thickness measuring instruments, and use grid patterns to check for optical distortion.

An AMT can usually repair minor damage to windshields and side windows for small unpressurized general aviation aircraft by using progressively finer sandpapers and finishing the repair by polishing it with Micro-Mesh®, the registered trademark of Micro Surface Finishing Products of Wilton, Iowa.

Remove a scratch in a window by beginning the sanding with 320 wet-or-dry sandpaper wrapped around a foam sanding block, sanding with straight strokes, and using firm, but not hard pressure. Do not use circular strokes, and periodically change the direction of the strokes by 90°. Remove the damage with the 320-grit paper, then remove the pattern it left with 400-grit paper. Next remove the pattern of this paper with 600-grit.

After you remove the damage, the surface retains the pattern left by the 600-grit paper. Restore the full transparency by polishing it with Micro-Mesh.

Micro-Mesh®. A patented graduated series of cloth-backed cushioned sheets that contain abrasive crystals. Micro-Mesh is used for polishing and restoring transparency to acrylic plastic windows and windshields.

Micro-Mesh comes with a graduated series of cloth-backed cushioned sheets, containing abrasive crystals. As you rub the Micro-Mesh across the surface, the soft cushion lets the crystals seek a common level with their broader facets oriented along the surfaces. This produces a planing action which cuts the surface smooth and level, rather than gouging it the way the sharp edges of sandpaper grit do.

First apply a mist spray of water on the window. Use the coarsest abrasive (the lowest number in the kit) wrapped around a foam block to remove all of the pattern left by the 600-grit sandpaper. When this pattern is removed, clean the surface thoroughly and use the sheet with the next finer abrasive. Remove the scratches left by the preceding sheet and clean the surface and go to the next finer sheet. Continue through to the sheet with the finest abrasive in the kit, and then clean the surface and apply a very thin film of antistatic cream/wax with a flannel cloth. Rinse out the Micro-Mesh sheets, dry them, and store them in their plastic envelopes for future use.

Micro-Mesh is also available in disc form for use with a random orbital sander. Orbital sanders, however, should be used on transparent plastics only by technicians with skill and training in this application.

Holes

Holes and cracks in transparent plastic materials can be repaired if they are not in the line of the pilot's vision. If they are in the line of vision, the entire windshield or window should be replaced.

Clean out the damage and round all of the edges to prevent stress concentrations. Cut a patch of the same type and thickness of material as the original that is large enough to extend at least 3/4-inch beyond the edges of the cleaned-out damage. Bevel the edges of the patch, and if the original material is curved, form the patch to match. Soften it by placing it in a pan of oil that is heated to between 250°F and 300°F. When it is soft, form it to match the damaged area. Thoroughly clean the patch and soften the side that is to contact the original part with a viscous cement. Put it in place and apply pressure for at least three hours. Allow the patch to cure for at least 24 hours before doing any further polishing.

Cracks

Vibration causes cracks to develop along the edges of plastic material. These cracks usually begin at nicks or scratches on the edge of the material and progress across the sheet.

All the stresses that caused the original crack are concentrated at the point, and the stresses acting on this extremely small area can cause the crack to continue. To stop it, drill a hole about 1/8-inch in diameter at the end of the crack. Now the stresses have a much larger area to act on and the crack cannot continue.

Surface patch for a round hole

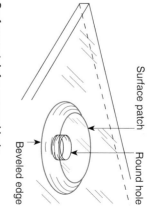

Surface patch   Round hole

Beveled edge

Surface patch for irregularly-shaped damage

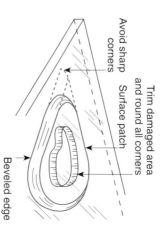

Avoid sharp corners

Trim damaged area and round all corners   Surface patch

Beveled edge

Figure 3-56. *Repair of a hole in a piece of transparent acrylic plastic*

After stop-drilling the crack, cut a patch of the same type and thickness of material as the original that is large enough to extend at least ¾-inch beyond the edges of the cleaned-out damage. Form the patch and cement it in place in the same way as described for repairing a hole.

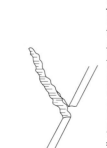

All stresses concentrate at end of crack.

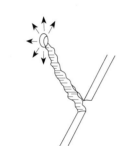

Stop-drilling end of crack spreads stresses around entire circumference and stops crack.

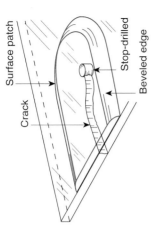

Surface patch

Crack

Stop-drilled

Beveled edge

Finished repair has piece of acrylic cemented over damage.

Figure 3-57. *Repair of a crack in a piece of transparent acrylic plastic*

STUDY QUESTIONS: TRANSPARENT PLASTICS

Answers begin on Page 263. Page numbers refer to chapter text.

117. One of the biggest differences in working aluminum and acrylic plastics lies in the _____ (better or poorer) heat conduction of the acrylic. *Page 256*

118. Acetone _____ (does or does not) soften acrylic plastic. *Page 255*

119. The preferable way to store flat sheets of acrylic plastic is _____ (horizontal or vertical). *Page 256*

120. When a piece of acrylic plastic is cut on a band saw to the approximate outline of the part, the final trim can be made with a/an _____. *Page 256*

121. When drilling acrylic plastics, the drill should be turned _____ (fast or slow). *Page 256*

122. Small pieces of acrylic plastic can be heated for forming in a/an _____ (oil or water) bath. *Page 257*

123. Two chemicals that can be used as a solvent for acrylic plastic are:

a.

b.
Page 258

124. A C-clamp _____ (is or is not) recommended for holding pressure on an acrylic plastic material while it is being cemented. *Page 258*

125. The best type of clamp to use to apply pressure when cementing two pieces of acrylic plastic together is a/an _____ clamp. *Page 258*

126. The best method of removing dirt from a plastic windshield is by flushing it with _____ . *Page 259*

127. Oil and grease can be removed from acrylic plastic with a _____ solution. *Page 259*

128. After cleaning a windshield, it should be coated with a good grade of _____ . *Page 259*

129. The window of a pressurized aircraft can be checked for thickness with a/an _____ thickness measuring instrument. *Page 260*

130. Crazing can be removed from an acrylic windshield. *Page 260*

131. When removing scratches from a windshield with sandpaper, the paper should be moved in a _____ (straight or circular) motion. *Page 260*

132. A patch cemented over a hole or crack should extend for _____ inch beyond the damage. *Page 262*

Answers to Nonmetallic Aircraft Structures Study Questions

1. softwood
2. are not
3. Sitka spruce
4. laminated
5. birch
6. 45, 90
7. poplar, basswood
8. springwood
9. 12
10. 15
11. is
12. is
13. is not
14. is not
15. shear
16. 8
17. should not
18. should not
19. ¾
20. may
21. caps
22. birch
23. should not
24. 10
25. should not
26. cannot
27. scarf

Continued

28. 20
29. is
30. 15
31. 80
32. cotton, polyester, fiberglass
33. major repair
34. major alteration
35. 337
36. 70
37. cannot
38. are not
39. dark
40. trammel
41. TSO-C-15, AMS 3806
42. raveling
43. bias
44. nitrate, butyrate
45. nitrate
46. is not
47. aluminum
48. dope into the paste
49. last
50. envelope, blanket
51. should not
52. dope into the paste
53. water
54. nitrate
55. thinned
56. ½
57. alteration
58. butyrate
59. grounded
60. second
61. does not
62. apex
63. 150, 16

64. ¼, 8, 10
65. enamel
66. softening
67. cannot
68. plastic beads
69. filiform
70. eddy currents
71. several light coats
72. may
73. 48
74. epoxy
75. 24
76. should
77. is not
78. white
79. high
80. pinholes
81. fast
82. toluol, MEK
83. will not
84. does not
85. wing port
86. near the floor
87. 6, 10
88. 2, 3
89. ellipse
90. much
91. should not
92. N
93. 12
94. is not
95. should
96. aeroelastic tailoring
97. S
98. flexible
99. stiff

100. graphite
101. thermoplastic
102. are not
103. is
104. refrigerator
105. do
106. foaming
107. can
108. can
109. a. matched dies
    b. vacuum bag
    c. autoclave
110. coin
111. ultrasonic
112. radiographic
113. sandpaper
114. vacuum
115. ribbon
116. fast
117. poorer
118. does not
119. vertical
120. sander
121. fast
122. oil
123. a. methylene chloride
    b. ethylene dichloride
124. is not
125. spring
126. fresh water
127. soap and water
128. wax
129. ultrasonic
130. abrasives
131. straight
132. ¾

ASSEMBLY AND RIGGING

4

Continued

ASSEMBLY AND RIGGING

Airplane Controls

This chapter considers the hardware used to control aircraft, and the way aircraft are assembled and rigged for the most efficient flight.

Airplane Primary Flight Controls

An airplane is controlled by rotating it about one or more of its three axes. The ailerons rotate it about its longitudinal axis to produce roll, elevators or their equivalent rotate it about its lateral axis to produce pitch, and the rudder rotates the airplane about its vertical axis to produce yaw.

Controls for Roll

Ailerons and spoilers are used to roll, or rotate an aircraft about its longitudinal axis by varying the amount of lift produced by the two wings. Ailerons increase the lift on one wing while decreasing lift on the opposite wing. Spoilers are used on some airplanes to aid the ailerons by spoiling the lift on one wing to make it move downward.

Ailerons

Ailerons are the primary roll control. To roll an airplane to the left, turn the control wheel to the left. The aileron on the left wing moves up, decreasing the camber, or curvature, of the left wing and decreasing the lift it produces. A carry-through, or balance, cable pulls the right aileron down, increasing its camber and lift. The airplane rolls to the left about its longitudinal axis. *See* Figure 4-1 on the next page.

An airplane is turned to the left by banking, or rolling, it to the left. When the right aileron moves down to increase the lift on the right wing and start the roll, it also increases the induced drag, which pulls the nose to the *right*. As soon as the wing rises, the lift tilts and its horizontal component pulls the nose around to the left as it should.

The movement of the nose in the wrong direction at the beginning of a turn is called adverse yaw, and is minimized by using differential aileron travel. The aileron moving upward travels a greater distance than the aileron moving

roll. Rotation of an aircraft about its longitudinal axis.

spoilers. Flight controls that are raised up from the upper surface of a wing to destroy, or spoil, lift. Flight spoilers are used in conjunction with the ailerons to decrease lift and increase drag on the descending wing. Ground spoilers are used to produce a great amount of drag to slow the airplane on its landing roll.

longitudinal axis. An imaginary line, passing through the center of gravity of an airplane, and extending lengthwise through it from nose to tail.

banking. The act of rotating an aircraft about its longitudinal axis.

balance cable. When the control wheel is rotated, a cable from the cockpit pulls one aileron down and relaxes the cable going to the other aileron. The balance cable pulls the other aileron up.

differential aileron travel. Aileron movement in which the upward-moving aileron deflects a greater distance than the one moving downward. The up aileron produces parasite drag to counteract the induced drag caused by the down aileron. Differential aileron travel is used to counteract adverse yaw.

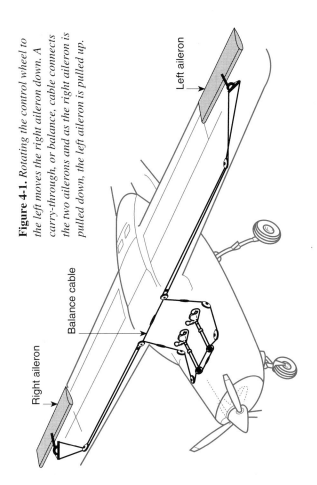

Figure 4-1. *Rotating the control wheel to the left moves the right aileron down. A carry-through, or balance, cable connects the two ailerons and as the right aileron is pulled down, the left aileron is pulled up.*

Right aileron

Balance cable

Left aileron

downward. The extra upward travel creates just about enough parasite drag to counteract the induced drag caused by the lowered aileron. The aileron shown in Figure 4-2 is a Frise aileron. Part of its nose extends below the bottom wing surface as an additional aid in preventing adverse yaw.

At the beginning of a turn, the pilot uses the rudder to overcome adverse yaw by rotating the airplane about its vertical, or yaw, axis. This starts the nose moving in the correct direction. As soon as the bank is established, the adverse yaw force disappears and the rudder is neutralized. The rudder controls of some airplanes, such as the one in Figure 4-3, are interconnected with the aileron controls through a spring in such a way that rotating the control wheel pulls the rudder cable.

Many large jet transport airplanes have two ailerons on each wing and flight spoilers to assist in roll control. The flight spoiler deflects on the wing with the upward moving aileron. *See* Figure 4-34 on Page 286. The outboard ailerons are locked in their faired, or streamline, position when the trailing edge flaps are up. The inboard ailerons and the flight spoilers provide enough roll control for high-speed flight, but when the flaps are lowered, the inboard and outboard ailerons work together to provide the additional roll control needed for low-speed flight. All the flight spoilers can be raised together to act as speed brakes.

The ailerons are hydraulically powered, but they have internal balance panels and servo tabs to help move them in case of hydraulic system failure.

Frise aileron. An aileron with its hinge line set back from the leading edge so that when it is deflected upward, part of the leading edge projects below the wing and produces parasite drag to help overcome adverse yaw.

vertical axis. An imaginary line, passing vertically through the center of gravity of an airplane.

yaw. Rotation of an aircraft about its vertical axis.

speed brakes. A secondary control of an airplane that produces drag without causing a change in the pitch attitude of the airplane. Speed brakes allow an airplane to make a steep descent without building up excessive forward airspeed.

balance panel. A flat panel that is hinged to the leading edge of some ailerons that produces a force which assists the pilot in holding them deflected. The balance panel divides a chamber ahead of the aileron in such a way that when the aileron is deflected downward, for example, air flowing over its top surface produces a low pressure that acts on the balance panel and causes it to apply an upward force to the leading edge as long as it is deflected.

servo tab. A small movable tab built into the trailing edge of a primary control surface of an airplane. The cockpit controls move the tab in such a direction that it produces an aerodynamic force that moves the surface on which it is mounted.

Elevons

Delta airplanes, and airplanes with highly swept wings that do not have a conventional empennage to provide pitch control, use elevons. These are movable control surfaces on the wings' trailing edge. The elevons operate together for pitch control, and differentially for aileron control.

Controls for Pitch

When an airplane is trimmed for straight and level flight at a fixed airspeed, the downward force on the horizontal stabilizer balances the nose-down tendency caused by the center of gravity's position ahead of the center of lift. All of the aerodynamic forces are balanced and no control forces are needed. But the airplane can be rotated about its lateral axis by increasing or decreasing the downward tail load.

Elevator

The most generally used pitch control for an airplane is the fixed horizontal stabilizer with a movable elevator hinged to its trailing edge, as is illustrated in Figure 4-4 on the next page. When the pilot pulls back the control yoke, the trailing edge of the elevator moves up and increases the down load caused by the horizontal tail surface. The tail moves down and rotates the airplane nose-up about its lateral axis.

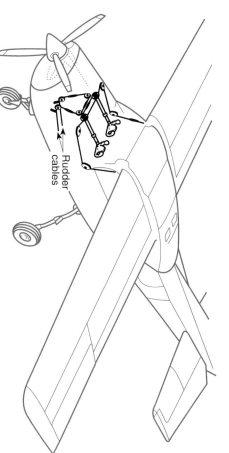

Rudder cables

Figure 4-3. *The rudder of this airplane is connected to the aileron controls through springs. This starts the nose moving in the correct direction without the pilot having to use the rudder pedals.*

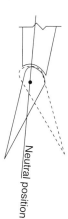

Neutral position

Figure 4-2. *Differential aileron movement is used to minimize adverse yaw when a turn is begun. The aileron moving upward travels a greater distance than the one moving downward. This produces additional parasite drag to oppose the induced drag on the opposite wing caused by the downward deflected aileron.*

delta airplane. an airplane with a triangular-shaped wing. This wing has an extreme amount of sweepback on its leading edge and a trailing edge that is almost perpendicular to the longitudinal axis of the airplane.

elevons. Movable control surfaces on the trailing edge of a delta wing or a flying wing airplane. These surfaces operate together to serve as elevators, and differentially to act as ailerons.

pitch. Rotation of an aircraft about its lateral axis.

lateral axis. An imaginary line, passing through the center of gravity of an airplane, and extending across it from wing tip to wing tip.

control yoke. The movable column on which an airplane control wheel is mounted. The yoke may be moved in or out to actuate the elevators, and the control wheel may be rotated to actuate the ailerons.

271

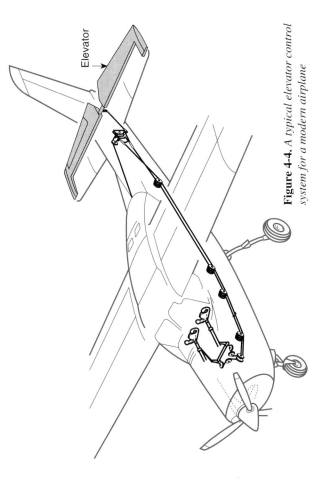

Elevator

Figure 4-4. *A typical elevator control system for a modern airplane*

stabilator. A single-piece horizontal tail surface that serves the functions of both the horizontal stabilizer and the elevators. The stabilator pivots about its front spar.

Stabilator

Some airplanes use a stabilator for pitch control. This is a single-piece horizontal surface that pivots about a point approximately one third of the way back from the leading edge. When the control wheel is pulled back, the leading edge of the stabilator moves down and increases the downward force produced by the tail. This rotates the nose up. When the wheel is pushed in, the nose of the stabilator moves up, decreasing the tail load, and the airplane rotates nose down.

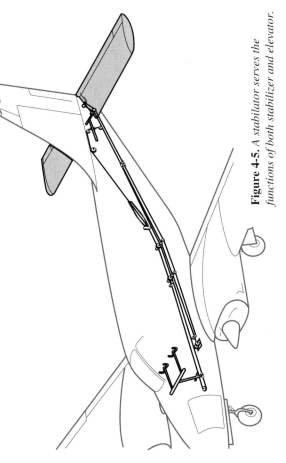

Figure 4-5. *A stabilator serves the functions of both stabilizer and elevator.*

Ruddervators

Some airplanes, most notably V-tail Beech Bonanzas, have two fixed stabilizers and two movable ruddervators arranged in a V. *See* Figure 1-33 on Page 29. The control system is such that moving the control wheel in and out actuates the movable surfaces together so they act as elevators and rotate the airplane about its lateral axis. When the rudder pedals are depressed, the surfaces move differentially, acting as a rudder to rotate the airplane about its vertical axis.

Canard

Conventional aircraft achieve longitudinal stability and control through horizontal stabilizers on the tail that produce a downward aerodynamic force. This downward force acts as part of the flight load, and the wing must produce lift to overcome it.

A canard is a horizontal stabilizing surface located ahead of the main wing that makes the airplane inherently stall-proof. The center of gravity is located ahead of the main wing, and the angle of incidence of the canard is greater than that of the main wing, so it will stall first. *See* Figure 4-6. When the canard stalls, the nose drops and the smooth airflow over the canard is restored, and its lift is increased to bring the airplane back to straight and level flight.

Some canards have movable surfaces on their trailing edge for pitch control and others pivot the entire surface for control. The angle of sweep of canards mounted on some high-performance airplanes may be varied in flight to optimize the flight characteristics.

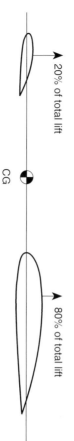

20% of total lift

CG

80% of total lift

Figure 4-6. *The angle of incidence of the canard is greater than that of the main wing and it will stall first. When it stalls, the nose of the airplane drops and flying speed is restored.*

Controls for Yaw

An airplane is turned by tilting the lift vector with the ailerons. The rudder is used only at the beginning of the turn to overcome adverse yaw and for such flight conditions as crosswind takeoffs and landings.

Figure 4-7 on the next page shows a typical rudder control system. When the pilot presses the left rudder pedal, the trailing edge of the rudder moves to the left and produces an aerodynamic load on the vertical tail which moves the tail to the right and the nose to the left.

Some airplanes have eliminated the movable rudder entirely, and others have connected it to the aileron controls through springs so that when a turn is started, the rudder moves in the correct direction automatically.

ruddervators. Movable control surfaces on a V-tail airplane that are controlled by both the rudder pedals and the control yoke. When the yoke is moved in and out, the ruddervators move together and act as the elevators. When the rudder pedals are depressed the ruddervators move differentially and act as a rudder.

canard. A horizontal control surface mounted ahead of the wing to provide longitudinal stability and control.

center of gravity. The location on an aircraft about which the force of gravity is concentrated.

angle of incidence. The acute angle formed between the chord line of an airfoil and the longitudinal axis of the airplane.

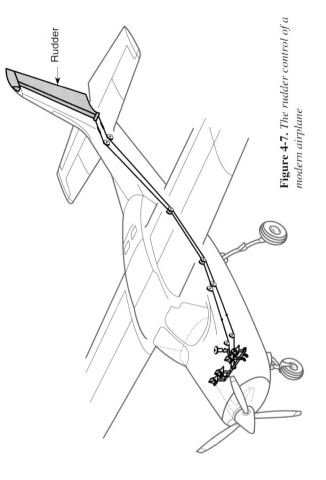

Rudder

Figure 4-7. *The rudder control of a modern airplane*

Airplane Secondary Flight Controls

Primary flight controls rotate the airplane about its three axes, but secondary controls are used to assist or to modify the effect of the primary controls. There are two basic types of secondary flight controls: those that modify the amount of lift the primary controls produce, and those that change the amount of force needed to operate the primary controls.

Surfaces That Modify the Lift

Aerodynamic lift is determined by the shape and size of the airfoil section, and can be changed by modifying either or both of these factors. A more recent approach to modifying lift is by controlling the flow of air over the surface.

Flaps

Flaps are the most widely used method for modifying lift. Most flaps are on the trailing edge of the wing inboard of the ailerons, but some are located on the wings' leading edges.

Plain Flaps

The simplest type of flap is the plain flap, illustrated in Figure 4-8. This flap is simply a hinged portion of the trailing edge of the wing inboard of the ailerons. It can be lowered to increase the camber. Lowering plain flaps increases the maximum coefficient of lift and produces a great deal of drag.

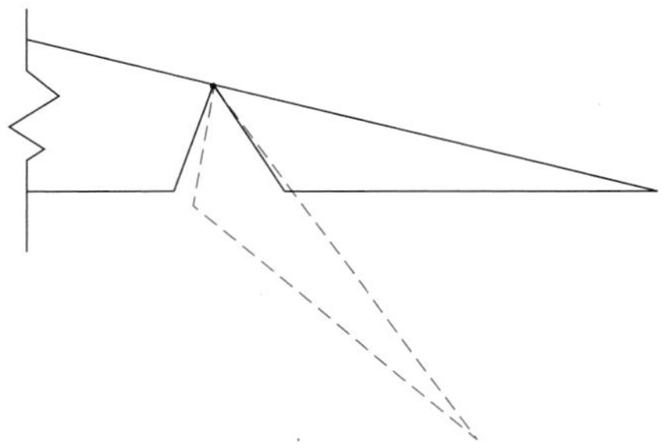

Figure 4-8. *Plain flaps are a hinged portion of the trailing edge of a wing inboard of the ailerons.*

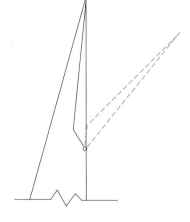

Figure 4-9. *A split flap is a plate that extends below the wing's lower surface. It increases both the lift and the drag.*

Split Flaps

A split flap, such as the one in Figure 4-9, consists of a plate that is deflected from the lower surface of the wing. Lowering a split flap increases the maximum coefficient of lift slightly more than a plain flap, but it produces a turbulent wake and therefore increases the drag much more than a plain flap. Some airplanes use a narrow-chord split flap mounted on the rear wing spar that does not extend to the wing trailing edge.

Slotted Flaps

A slotted flap, similar to the one in Figure 4-10, acts like a simple flap, except that there is a slot between the leading edge of the flap and the inner surface of the flap well. High-energy air from below the wing flows through the slot and speeds up the air over the upper surface of the flap. This delays airflow separation to a higher coefficient of lift. Slotted flaps produce a much greater increase in the coefficient of lift than either the plain or split flap.

Fowler Flaps

Fowler flaps are similar to slotted flaps, except that they move aft along a set of tracks to increase the chord of the wing (and thus its area) when they are lowered. A Fowler flap produces a greater increase in lift with the least change in drag than any other type of flap. *See* Figure 4-11.

Triple-Slotted Flaps

Many large jet transport airplanes use triple-slotted flaps like the one in Figure 4-12. As this flap is lowered, it slides out of the wing on tracks and increases the camber and wing area in the same way as a Fowler flap, but it separates and forms slots between its segments. The air flowing through these slots is forced down against the flap upper surface, which delays airflow separation and produces additional lift.

Leading Edge Flaps

Some high-performance airplanes have flaps on the leading edges as well as on the trailing edges. Figure 4-13 on the next page shows a drooped leading edge that is lowered at the same time as the trailing edge flaps to increase the camber of the wing and allow it to attain a higher angle of attack before the airflow breaks away over the upper surface.

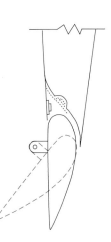

Figure 4-10. *A slotted flap forms a slot between the flap and the flap well that ducts high-energy air back over the top of the flap to delay airflow separation.*

Figure 4-11. *Fowler flaps move aft along a set of tracks to increase the wing chord when they are lowered. They produce a large increase in lift and a minimum increase in drag.*

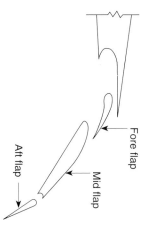

Fore flap

Mid flap

Aft flap

Figure 4-12. *A triple-slotted flap forms slots between the flap segments when it is lowered. Air flowing through these slots energizes the air above the flap surface and delays airflow separation while increasing the lift the flap produces.*

A Kruger flap, as seen in Figure 4-14, is a special type of leading edge flap that effectively increases the camber of the wing when it is lowered. The leading edge flaps shown on the wing of the Boeing 727 airliner in Figure 4-34 on Page 286 are Kruger flaps. These flaps are controlled by movement of the trailing edge flaps.

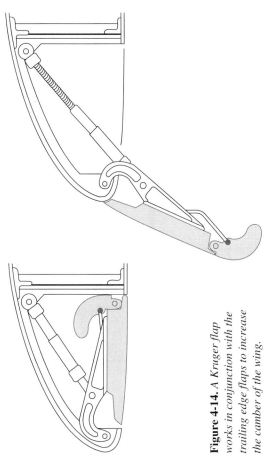

Figure 4-14. *A Kruger flap works in conjunction with the trailing edge flaps to increase the camber of the wing.*

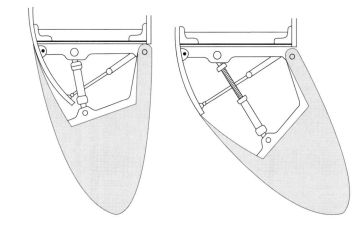

Figure 4-13. *A drooped leading edge that folds down when the trailing edge flaps are lowered allows the wing to reach a higher angle of attack before the airflow breaks away from its upper surface.*

Slats

A slat forms the leading edge of the wing when it is retracted, and when it is extended it forms a duct that forces high-energy air across the surface of the wing to delay airflow separation. *See* Figure 4-15. The Boeing 727 wing shown in Figure 4-34 on Page 286 has four slats and three leading edge flaps. When the outboard trailing edge flaps are extended 2°, two slats on each side extend, and when they are lowered more than 5°, all the slats and leading edge flaps are extended.

Many high-performance military fighter airplanes have retractable leading edge slats fitted into the wing with curved support rails that ride between bearings. When the wing has a low angle of attack, the air forces the slat tightly against the leading edge of the wing where it produces a minimum of interference. At a high angle of attack, aerodynamic forces pull the slat out from the leading edge, and it forms a duct that forces high-energy air down over the upper surface of the wing and delays airflow separation to a higher angle of attack.

Spoilers

Flight spoilers are hinged surfaces located ahead of the flaps. They are used in conjunction with the ailerons to assist in roll control. When the ailerons are deflected, the flight spoilers on the wing with the up aileron automatically

When slat is retracted, it forms
leading edge of wing.

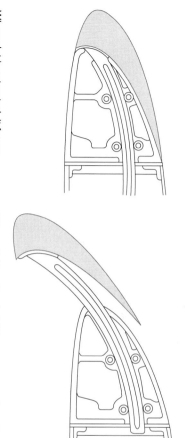

When slat is extended, it increases camber of
wing and forms duct that directs high-energy air
back over upper surface of wing.

Figure 4-15. *Automatic slat used on high-performance fighter aircraft*

deploy to a maximum of 30° to decrease the lift on the wing that is moving down. They also produce additional parasite drag to overcome adverse yaw. When a large amount of aileron is used, the spoilers account for about 80% of the roll rate.

Flight spoilers move differentially when they are used for roll control, but they may be deployed symmetrically and used as speed brakes by actuating the speed brake control. When used as speed brakes they may be extended between 0° and 45° depending on the position of the speed brake control. Ground spoilers deploy to their full 45° opening when the airplane is on the ground with weight on the landing gear and the speed brake lever is moved through its 10° position.

Some high-performance general aviation airplanes have spoilers, or speed brakes, installed on the front wing spar in such a way that they may be raised above the upper wing surface in flight to allow the airplane to make a steep descent without gaining an excess of speed, and without having to decrease the engine power to the extent that the cylinders will be damaged by too rapid cooling.

Devices That Change the Operating Forces

Stability is an important function of an airplane, but controllability is equally important. As airplanes have become larger and faster and have higher performance, the control system loads have become extremely high and the pilot must have some kind of assistance to move them. The controls on most large airplanes are moved by electrical or hydraulic servos. This section, however, discusses only the devices that change the forces aerodynamically.

stability. The characteristic of an aircraft that causes it to return to its original flight condition after it has been disturbed.

controllability. The characteristic of an aircraft that allows it to change its flight attitude in response to the pilot's movement of the cockpit controls.

Balance Surfaces

Some controls have a portion of the surface extending out ahead of the hinge line, like the rudder in Figure 4-16. When the rudder is deflected, air strikes the portion ahead of the hinge line and assists in deflecting it and holding it deflected. Some aerodynamic balance surfaces are also weighted to give them static balance.

Tabs

Small auxiliary devices on the trailing edges of the various primary control surfaces are used to produce aerodynamic forces to trim the aircraft or to aid the pilot in moving the controls. Some tabs are fixed to the surface and are adjustable only on the ground. These tabs are used to produce a fixed air load on the control surface to trim the airplane against a permanent out-of-balance condition. The tabs discussed in this section are adjustable to compensate for varying flight conditions.

Trim Tabs

Trim tabs such as those in Figure 4-17 may be installed on the rudder, aileron, and elevator. They are controllable from the cockpit and allow the pilot to deflect them in such a direction that they produce an aerodynamic force on the control surface that holds it deflected to correct for an out-of-balance condition. This allows the airplane to be adjusted to fly straight and level with hands and feet off of the controls. Once a trim tab is adjusted, it maintains a fixed relationship with the control surface as it is moved.

Balance Tabs

A balance tab, like that in Figure 4-18, works automatically to produce an air load on the control surface that assists the pilot in moving the surface. When the cockpit control is moved to raise the trailing edge of the control surface, the linkage pulls the balance tab so that it moves in the opposite direction. This opposite deflection produces an aerodynamic force that assists the pilot in moving the surface. The linkage for many balance tabs is adjustable to allow the position of the tab to be changed in flight so the tab can serve as a trim tab as well as a balance tab.

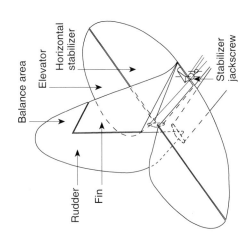

Balance area

Elevator

Horizontal stabilizer

Rudder

Fin

Stabilizer jackscrew

Figure 4-16. *This empennage has an aerodynamically balanced rudder. The top portion of the rudder extends ahead of the hinge line to provide an aerodynamic assist in deflecting it.*

trim tab. A small control tab mounted on the trailing edge of a movable control surface. The tab may be adjusted to provide an aerodynamic force to hold the surface on which it is mounted deflected to trim the airplane for hands-off flight at a specified airspeed.

balance tab. An adjustable tab mounted on the trailing edge of a control surface to produce a force that aids the pilot in moving the surface. The tab is automatically actuated in such a way as it moves in the direction opposite to the direction the control surface on which it is mounted moves.

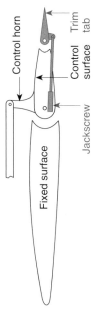

Control horn

Control surface

Trim tab

Jackscrew

Fixed surface

Figure 4-17. *A trim tab is adjustable from the cockpit to allow the pilot to trim the airplane so it will fly straight and level with hands and feet off of the controls.*

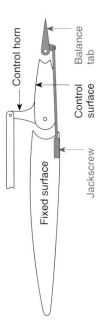

Control horn

Control surface

Balance tab

Jackscrew

Fixed surface

Figure 4-18. *A balance tab moves in the direction opposite to that of the control surface on which it is mounted. This opposite deflection produces an aerodynamic force that aids the pilot in moving the surface. This balance tab may be adjusted in flight so that it also acts as a trim tab.*

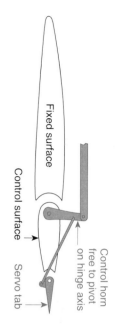

Figure 4-19. *A servo tab is controlled from the cockpit to produce an aerodynamic force which moves the primary control surface.*

Fixed surface

Control surface

Servo tab

Control horn free to pivot on hinge axis

Servo Tabs

A servo tab, also called a control tab, is installed on the control surfaces of airplanes requiring such high control forces that it is impractical to move the primary control surface itself. The cockpit control is attached to the servo tab so that it moves in the direction opposite that desired for the primary surface. Deflection of the servo tab produces an aerodynamic force that deflects the primary surface, which in turn rotates the airplane about the desired axis. *See* Figure 4-19.

Spring Tabs

A spring tab is used on high-performance airplanes that, under high-speed conditions, develop aerodynamic forces so great that assistance is needed to help the pilot move the controls. Figure 4-20 shows that the control horn is attached to the control surface through a torsion rod. For normal flight the horn moves the control surface and the spring tab does not deflect. But at high speeds when the control force becomes excessive, the torsion rod twists and allows the horn to move relative to the surface. The linkage deflects the spring tab in such a direction that it produces an aerodynamic force that aids the pilot in moving the primary surface.

Antiservo Tabs

An antiservo tab is installed on the trailing edge of a stabilator to decrease its sensitivity. The tab is attached to the aircraft structure through a linkage rod and a jackscrew to allow it to be used as a trim tab.

When the stabilator is deflected, air strikes the portion ahead of the pivot point and tries to increase its deflection. This makes the stabilator too sensitive. To decrease this sensitivity, the antiservo tab on its trailing edge moves in the same direction as the stabilator. When the trailing edge of the stabilator moves up, the antiservo tab moves up and produces a downward load that tries to move the stabilator back to its streamline position. When the trailing edge of the stabilator moves down, the antiservo tab moves down, producing an upward force that tries to streamline the stabilator. *See* Figure 4-21.

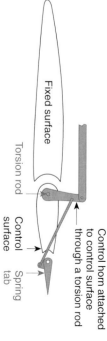

Figure 4-20. *A spring tab deflects only when control forces become so high that the pilot needs assistance in moving the primary control surface.*

Fixed surface

Torsion rod

Control surface

Spring tab

Control horn attached to control surface through a torsion rod

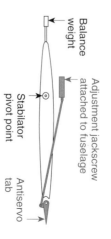

Balance weight

Adjustment jackscrew attached to fuselage

Stabilator pivot point

Antiservo tab

Antiservo tab is connected to adjustable jackscrew to allow pilot to position it to produce correct tail-down load for hands-off straight and level flight.

When control wheel is pulled back, stabilator nose moves down, increasing down load on tail and rotating airplane nose up about its lateral axis. Antiservo tab moves up to produce stabilizing force on stabilator.

When control wheel is moved forward, stabilator nose moves up, decreasing downward tail load and allowing airplane to rotate nose down about its lateral axis. Antiservo tab moves down.

Figure 4-21. *Antiservo tab*

ASSEMBLY AND RIGGING

279

torsion rod. A device in a spring tab to which the control horn is attached. For normal operation, the torsion rod acts as a fixed attachment point, but when the control surface loads are high, the torsion rod twists and allows the control horn to deflect the spring tab.

antiservo tab. A tab installed on the trailing edge of a stabilator to make it less sensitive. The tab automatically moves in the same direction as the stabilator to produce an aerodynamic force that tries to bring the surface back to a streamline position. This tab is also called an antibalance tab.

jackscrew. A hardened steel rod with strong threads cut into it. A jackscrew is rotated by hand or with a motor to apply a force or to lift an object.

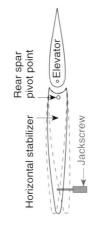

Figure 4-22. *Some airplanes provide longitudinal trim by pivoting the horizontal stabilizer about its rear spar and raising or lowering the leading edge by means of a jackscrew.*

Adjustable Stabilizer

Rather than using tabs on the trailing edge of the primary control surface, some airplanes are trimmed longitudinally by adjusting the position of the leading edge of the horizontal stabilizer. These stabilizers pivot about the rear spar, and a jackscrew controlled from the cockpit raises or lowers the leading edge. Raising the leading edge gives the airplane nose-down trim, and lowering the leading edge trims the airplane in a nose-up direction. *See* Figure 4-22.

Balance Panel

A balance panel, such as the one in Figure 4-23, is used on some large airplanes to assist the pilot in moving the ailerons. The hinged balance panel forms a movable partition for the sealed space ahead of the aileron. When the aileron is deflected upward, as seen here, the air over its bottom surface speeds up and produces a low pressure below the balance panel. This low pressure pulls the balance panel down and puts a force on the leading edge of the aileron in such a direction that it assists the pilot in holding the aileron deflected upward.

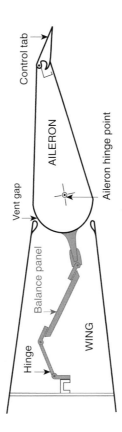

Figure 4-23. *A balance panel uses the low pressure caused by the deflected aileron to create a force that helps hold the aileron deflected.*

Bungee Spring

Some airplanes have a spring whose tension may be controlled by the pilot. The spring holds a mechanical force on the control system to trim the airplane for hands-off flight at the desired airspeed. Such a bungee system is shown in Figure 4-24.

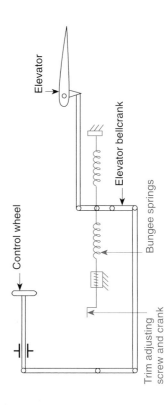

Figure 4-24. *The force provided by the bungee spring may be adjusted in flight by the pilot to provide the correct force on the control wheel to trim the airplane for hands-off flight at any desired airspeed.*

Elevator Downspring

To increase the aft CG limit, the manufacturers of some airplanes install elevator downsprings like the one in Figure 4-25.

When an airplane is operating with its CG at its aft limit, the elevator trim tab is adjusted to move the elevator so it will decrease the aerodynamic down load produced by the tail. Under some loading conditions, the elevator will actually be deflected downward to produce an upward tail load. If the airplane in this unstable condition encounters turbulence when it is slowed for its landing approach, the elevator will momentarily streamline, and at this slow speed the trim tab does not have enough power to force it back down to lower the nose. The airplane is likely to stall, which at this low altitude can be fatal. The elevator downspring produces a mechanical force that tries to move the elevator down and lower the nose. In normal flight conditions, this force is overcome by the elevator trim tab which adjusts the stabilizing down load. But under the conditions just noted, when the trim tab loses its effectiveness and is unable to move the elevator down, the downspring exerts its force and moves the elevator down, lowering the nose and preventing a stall.

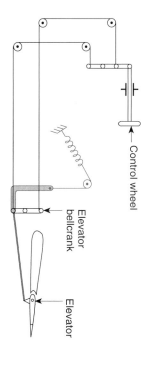

Figure 4-25. *The elevator downspring produces a mechanical force on the elevator that lowers the nose and prevents a stall when an aft CG location causes the tail load to be ineffective at low airspeed.*

Control wheel

Elevator bellcrank

Elevator

Control System Operating Methods

There are a number of methods of actuating the control surfaces from the cockpit. The time-honored method is to connect the surface to the cockpit control with a steel cable, but there are other mechanical methods discussed here, as well as electrically and hydraulically operated controls.

Cable Operated Systems

In the cable-operated control system, the cockpit controls are connected to the control surfaces with high-strength steel cable. In this section, we will examine the types of cables and the components used in this popular system.

elevator downspring. A spring in the elevator control system that produces a mechanical force that tries to lower the elevator. In normal flight this spring force is overcome by the aerodynamic force from the elevator trim tab. But in slow flight with an aft CG position, the trim tab loses its effectiveness and the downspring lowers the nose to prevent a stall.

Control Cables

Steel cables used in aircraft control systems may be of any of the four types shown in Figure 4-26. These cables are available in sizes from 1/32-inch through 1/4-inch diameter and may be made of either corrosion-resistant steel or galvanized steel.

Nonflexible cable is used for straight runs where the cable does not pass over any pulley. Flexible cable can be used where it passes over a pulley, but should not be used where the flexing requirements are extreme, as they are in most primary flight control systems. The extra-flexible, or 7 x 19, cable is the one most widely used for primary control systems.

The strengths of 7 x 7 and 7 x 19 cable are shown in Figure 4-27. These strengths are for straight runs of cable and do not include the effect of wrapped ends.

The smallest cable that can be used in the primary control system of an aircraft is 1/8-inch, but smaller cables may be used to actuate trim tabs if the manufacturer has approved it.

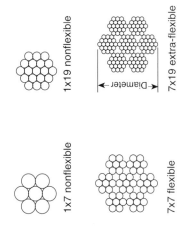

1x7 nonflexible   1x19 nonflexible

7x7 flexible   7x19 extra-flexible

Figure 4-26. *Steel control cables used in aircraft control systems*

Cable Diameter (inch)	Breaking Strength (pounds)	
	Carbon Steel	Corrosion Resistant Steel
1/16	480	480
1/8	2,000	1,760
3/16	4,200	3,700
1/4	7,000	6,400

Figure 4-27. *Breaking strength of 7x7 and 7x19 aircraft steel control cable*

Most modern cable installations use swaged terminals such as those in Figure 4-28. When properly swaged, these terminals have 100% of the strength of the cable itself.

Some of the older and smaller aircraft use a Nicopress thimble-eye terminal shown in Figure 4-29. In this type of terminal the end of the cable is passed through a heavy copper sleeve, wrapped around a steel thimble and passed back into the sleeve. The sleeve is then crimped with a special crimping tool. This type of terminal has 100% of the strength of the cable on which it is installed.

There is more information on cable terminals in the General textbook of this *Aviation Maintenance Technician Series.*

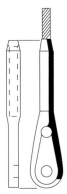

Threaded cable terminal

Fork-end cable terminal

Eye-end cable terminal

Figure 4-28. *Swaged control cable terminals*

Fairleads and Pulleys

Anytime a cable passes through a bulkhead or near one, a fairlead should be used to protect both the cable and the structure. A fairlead should never be used to change the direction of a control cable, and it should never deflect a control cable more than 3°. *See* Figure 4-30.

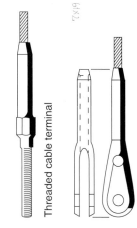

Figure 4-29. *Nicopress thimble-eye cable terminals have 100% of the strength of the cable on which they are installed.*

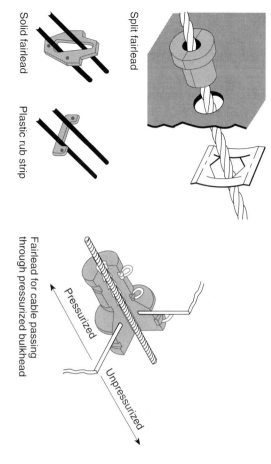

Split fairlead

Solid fairlead   Plastic rub strip

Figure 4-30. *Fairleads are used to guide control cables where they pass through a structural member.*

Fairlead for cable passing through pressurized bulkhead

Pressurized   Unpressurized

fairlead. A plastic or wooden guide used to prevent a steel control cable rubbing against an aircraft structure.

Pulleys are used where a control cable must make a change in direction. Most pulleys are made of a phenolic plastic-reinforced fabric or aluminum, and they may have either a sealed ball bearing or a bronze bushing. Each pulley installed in the aircraft must have a cable guard installed to prevent the cable from slipping out of the pulley groove when it is slacked off. *See* Figure 4-31.

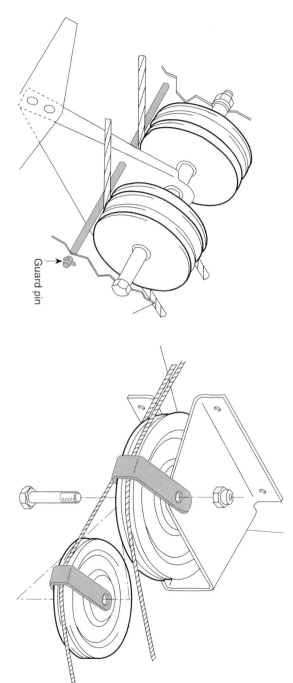

Guard pin

Figure 4-31. *Two types of guards used with a pulley to prevent the cable from slipping out of the groove*

Push-Pull Rod Systems

Another popular type of control actuation system is the push-pull rod system, which is used extensively in helicopter controls. In this system the cockpit control is connected to the device to be operated with a hollow aluminum tube whose ends are fitted with threaded inserts and a clevis, or more frequently, a rod-end bearing. Figure 4-32 shows such a push-pull rod.

Both the cockpit control and the device to be actuated are locked in the correct rigging position, and the rod ends are screwed in or out on the threaded end of the inserts to get the rod to the correct length and the rod end in correct alignment, then the check nuts are screwed tightly against the rod-end fittings to lock them in place.

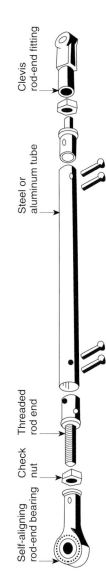

Self-aligning rod-end bearing

Check nut

Threaded rod end

Steel or aluminum tube

Clevis rod-end fitting

Figure 4-32. *A typical push-pull control rod*

Rod-End Fittings

The rod-end bearing shown in Figure 4-33 is typical of the terminal used on a push-pull rod. When installing this type of fitting be sure that the threaded portion of the rod extends into the fitting far enough that the inspection hole is covered. This ensures that there are enough threads engaged to give full strength to the joint. On an inspection, try to insert a piece of safety wire into the inspection hole. The threaded end of the rod should prevent the wire from going through the hole.

The antifriction bearing installed in a rod-end fitting is covered with a disc of thin sheet metal held in place by the edges of the fitting peened over the disc. When you install the bearing, you must be sure that the closed side of the fitting is next to the device to which the rod is attached, as illustrated in Figure 4-33. The rod will still remain attached to the device even if the bearing should fail.

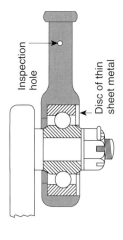

Inspection hole

Disc of thin sheet metal

Figure 4-33. *The correct installation of an antifriction rod-end bearing*

torque tube. A tube in an aircraft control system that transmits a torsional force from the operating control to the control surface.

Torque Tube Systems

A torque tube is a hollow metal tube used to transmit a torsional, or twisting, force between the actuating control and the device being controlled. The flaps and ailerons of small airplanes are often actuated from the cockpit by means of torque tubes.

Large airplane control systems often use torque tubes between an electric or hydraulic motor and a jackscrew to actuate flaps, slats, and other control surfaces.

Fly-By-Wire Systems

Some state-of-the art modern airplane designs use fly-by-wire systems to connect the flight control surfaces to the cockpit controls with electrical wires, rather than with steel cables, push-pull tubes, torque tubes, or other mechanical methods. The cockpit controls are devices that convert the movements or pressures exerted by the pilot into electrical signals which are sent into a computer programmed with all of the flight characteristics of the airplane.

The computer output is directed through more wires to electrohydraulic valves that convert the electrical signal into hydraulic fluid flow. This flow changes the position of a main control valve, which directs hydraulic fluid to the appropriate control actuators. Within the actuators, linear variable displacement transducers complete the loop and send feedback signals to the computer, informing it of the amount and speed of actuator movement.

Rather than using a control wheel or stick that actually moves, some fly-by-wire-equipped airplanes have sidestick controllers to fly the airplane. Pressures exerted on the controller mounted on the cockpit side console are converted into electrical signals, just as are movements of conventional controls. The General Dynamics F-16 uses a sidestick controller.

Fly-By-Light Systems

While fly-by-wire systems offer the significant benefits of reduced aircraft weight, simplified control routing, and improved control consistency, they do have one significant drawback — they are susceptible to electromagnetic interference (EMI). Fly-by-light systems use fiber optic cables rather than wires to transmit the control signals. Digital electrical signals from the computer are converted into light signals and sent through the aircraft via fiber optic cables to electro-optic converters. Here the light signals are changed back to electrical signals for the actuation of the hydraulic control valves.

The weight saving, freedom from EMI, and capability of high-speed data transmission ensure that fly-by-light systems will be found on an increasing number of aircraft in the future.

Control Actuation Systems for Large Airplanes

The control forces required by large transport airplanes are too great for a pilot to fly them manually, so the control surfaces are actually moved by hydraulic servos, or actuators. Figure 4-34 on the next page identifies the flight control surfaces on a Boeing 727 airplane. We will consider each of these surfaces and the way they are actuated.

The primary flight controls of this airplane consist of inboard and outboard ailerons, elevators, and upper and lower rudders. These controls are operated hydraulically from two independent hydraulic systems, the A system and the B system.

fly-by-wire. A method of control used by some modern aircraft in which control movement or pressures exerted by the pilot are directed into a digital computer where they are input into a program tailored to the flight characteristics of the aircraft. The computer output signal is sent to actuators at the control surfaces to move them the optimum amount for the desired maneuver.

sidestick controller. A cockpit flight control used on some of the fly-by-wire equipped airplanes. The stick is mounted rigidly on the side console of the cockpit, and pressures exerted on the stick by the pilot produce electrical signals that are sent to the computer that flies the airplane.

The ailerons and elevators typically are powered from both A and B systems, but either system can operate the controls, which also can be operated manually.

The upper rudder is operated by B system. The lower rudder is operated by A system, and also can be operated by the standby hydraulic system.

There are five flight spoilers on each wing to assist the ailerons in roll control. The three inboard spoilers are operated by B system and the two outboard spoilers are operated by A system. All the flight spoilers plus two ground spoilers on each wing may be operated when the airplane is on the ground and weight is on the landing gear.

The leading edge of the horizontal stabilizer may be raised or lowered with an electrically operated jackscrew. If the electrical actuator should fail, the stabilizer may be positioned manually with a trim wheel.

Hydraulic actuators supplied from A system actuate the leading edge flaps and slats, but if A system should fail, these devices may be extended by the standby hydraulic system.

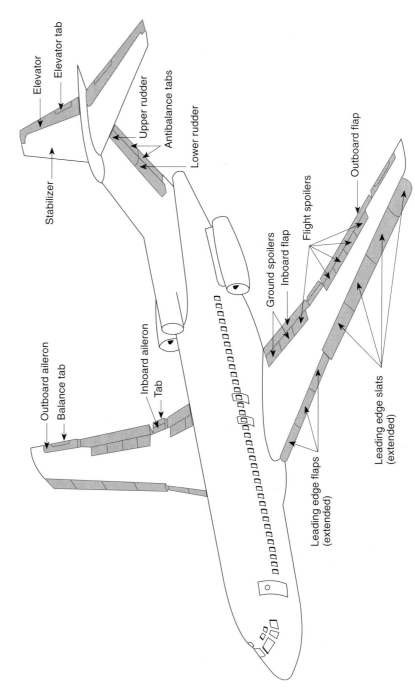

Figure 4-34. *Flight controls for a Boeing 727 jet transport airplane*

Roll Control

Each wing has two ailerons that are powered by a dual power unit supplied from both A and B systems. Either system can give full actuation of the ailerons. Movement of the ailerons is assisted by internal balance panels and balance tabs.

When the flaps are up, the outboard ailerons are locked in their faired position, but as the flaps extend, the outboard ailerons become progressively effective, and by the time the outboard flaps have extended 5°, 80% of the outboard aileron travel is available.

If all hydraulic pressure is lost, the tab on the inboard aileron is mechanically linked to the control wheel. This allows the pilot to move the tab to produce aerodynamic forces on the aileron, which deflects it to provide roll control.

The aileron trim control allows the pilots to center the hydraulic power units, which can provide aileron trim when the hydraulic systems are functioning.

The flight spoilers actuate with the ailerons in normal flight to provide roll control by deflecting to a maximum of 30°. They can also be actuated by movement of the speed brake control for deflections between 0° and 45°, depending upon the position of the speed brake handle. When the airplane is on the ground, the ground spoilers extend to their full 45° when the speed brake lever is moved through 10°.

The hydraulic pressure that actuates the flight spoilers will be relieved if the air loads on the spoilers become great enough to stall the actuator. This allows the spoilers to blow down until the airspeed is decreased.

Pitch Control

The elevators are controlled by two dual hydraulic power units that are supplied by both A and B systems and controlled by fore-and-aft movement of the control column. The elevator tabs act as balance tabs for normal flight when hydraulic pressure is available, but if hydraulic pressure should fail, the tabs can be moved from the cockpit so that they act as control tabs to produce aerodynamic forces that move the elevators.

A feel computer is incorporated in the elevator system. It senses airspeed, which gives the pilot a progressive restraint on the control column, and indicates the amount of control forces being used.

Pitch trim is provided by varying the angle of incidence of the horizontal stabilizer with a jackscrew that can be actuated electrically or manually.

Yaw Control

The Boeing 727 has two separate, independent rudders. The upper rudder power unit is supplied from B system and the lower rudder is operated from A system, or from the standby system. Both rudders have antibalance tabs.

The rudder system is protected against structural damage in high-speed flight by automatically limiting the hydraulic pressure to the rudder power systems when the trailing edge flaps are retracted.

The rudder pedals, in addition to controlling the rudder, also steer the nose wheel through 8° of travel, but this control may be overridden by the nose wheel steering wheel.

A yaw damper controls the rudder power systems all the time pressure is available from the main hydraulic systems. Yaw is sensed by the rate gyros in the two turn and slip indicators, and they provide rudder displacement proportional to, but opposite in direction to, the amount of yaw. One rate gyro controls the yaw damper for the upper rudder, and the other controls the yaw damper for the lower rudder. There is no yaw damper action for the lower rudder when it is being operated by the standby system.

Wing Flaps

The two triple-slotted Fowler flaps on each wing's trailing edge are operated by torque tubes and jackscrews which are powered by separate hydraulic motors for the inboard and outboard flaps. The hydraulic motors are supplied by A system. When the outboard flaps extend 2° the leading edge flaps and slats extend.

In the event of loss of all hydraulic pressure, the flaps may be operated by electric motors which drive the torque tubes, while the hydraulic fluid circulates in the hydraulic motors without causing opposition.

yaw damper. An automatic control of an airplane that senses yaw with a rate gyro and moves the rudder an amount proportional to the rate of yaw, but in the opposite direction.

STUDY QUESTIONS: AIRPLANE CONTROLS

Answers begin on Page 317. Page numbers refer to chapter text.

1. The aileron that moves upward travels a _____ (greater or lesser) distance than the aileron that moves downward. *Page 269*

2. Large transport aircraft have two ailerons on each wing. For high-speed flight the _____ (inner or outer) aileron is locked in place and does not move. *Page 270*

3. When the ailerons of a large transport airplane are deflected, the flight spoilers on the wing with the _____ (up or down) aileron extend automatically. *Page 270*

4. Flight spoilers may be extended the same amount on each wing to act as _____ . *Page 270*

5. Delta-wing airplanes have movable control surfaces on the trailing edge of the wings that act as both elevators and ailerons. These surfaces are called _____ . *Page 271*

6. The movable control surfaces on a V-tail airplane act as both elevators and rudders. These surfaces are called _____ . *Page 273*

7. In a conventional airplane using a horizontal stabilator and elevators mounted on the tail, the normal aerodynamic force acts _____ (upward or downward). *Page 271*

8. A canard surface has an angle of incidence that causes it to stall _____ (before or after) the main wing stalls. *Page 273*

9. The type of wing flap that produces the greatest amount of increase in lift with the minimum change in drag is the _____ flap. *Page 275*

10. A leading edge flap _____ (increases or decreases) the camber of a wing. *Page 275*

11. Slats extend from the leading edge of the wing to _____ (increase or decrease) the wing camber. *Page 277*

12. A trim tab _____ (does or does not) move relative to the control surface on which it is installed as the surface is moved in flight. *Page 278*

13. A balance tab moves in the _____ (same or opposite) direction as the control surface on which it is mounted. *Page 278*

14. The type of tab that is controlled from the cockpit to produce an aerodynamic force that moves the primary control surface is called a/an _____ tab. *Page 279*

15. A servo tab moves in the _____ (same or opposite) direction as the control surface on which it is mounted. *Page 279*

16. A spring tab automatically deflects when the control forces are _____ (high or low). *Page 279*

17. An antiservo tab moves in the _____ (same or opposite) direction as the control surface on which it is mounted. *Page 279*

18. Adjusting the leading edge of a movable stabilizer upward gives the airplane a nose-_____ (up or down) trim. *Page 280*

19. An elevator downspring is effective in slow flight when the CG position is at or beyond its _____ (forward or aft) limit. *Page 281*

Continued

20. The strength of a swaged cable terminal is _____ percent of the cable strength. *Page 282*

21. The smallest size cable that can be used in a primary control system is _____ inch diameter. *Page 282*

22. The strength of a Nicopress thimble-eye cable terminal is _____ percent of the cable strength. *Page 282*

23. A fairlead should not deflect a control cable more than _____ degrees. *Page 282*

24. To determine that a rod-end bearing is properly installed on a push-pull rod, the threads of the rod end _____ (should or should not) cover the inspection hole. *Page 284*

25. When installing an antifriction rod-end bearing, the _____ (open or closed) side of the bearing should be against the device being actuated. *Page 284*

26. A tube that is used to apply a torsional force to a control surface is called a _____ tube. *Page 284*

27. The Boeing 727 airplane uses _____ (electrical or hydraulic) actuators to move the primary flight control surfaces. *Page 285*

Airplane Assembly and Rigging

Airplanes must be assembled and rigged in strict accordance with the airplane manufacturer's instructions. Improper assembly procedures can damage the aircraft, and if it is not rigged properly, it cannot fly as the manufacturer designed it to do.

Manufacturer's maintenance manuals provide information on the assembly of the aircraft and the Type Certificate Data Sheets issued by the FAA list pertinent rigging information that must be adhered to.

Airplane Assembly

Airplane assembly, like almost all other aspects of aviation maintenance, has grown in complexity as airplanes become more efficient and complex. No step-by-step assembly procedure can be described that would apply to all airplanes or all situations, but several pointers do apply in most instances.

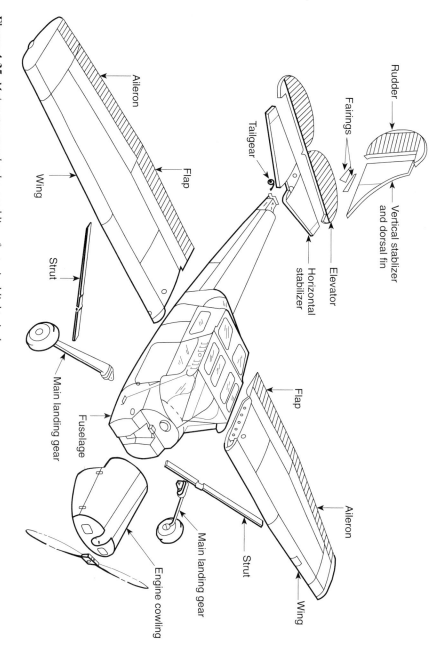

Figure 4-35. *Major structural subassemblies of a typical light airplane*

Installing the Wings and Landing Gear

Before installing the landing gear, support the fuselage by the method recommended by the manufacturer. This sometimes involves constructing a heavy wooden cradle with supports cut to conform to the fuselage frame that the manufacturer recommends. These supports should be well padded to prevent damage to the aircraft skin. The landing gear of most low-wing airplanes is in the wing, so the wing must be installed first. The wing assembly is usually quite heavy and either it must be raised in place to meet the fuselage, or the fuselage must be lowered into the wing. With either method, proper equipment must be used to support the wing or fuselage so they can be slowly and carefully mated. Be sure that all the needed new attachment hardware is available and all the needed alignment punches and drifts are within easy reach. When assembling high-wing airplanes, the landing gear is usually installed first and then the wing.

spirit level. A curved glass tube partially filled with a liquid, but with a bubble in it. When the device in which the tube is mounted is level, the bubble will be in the center of the tube.

surveyor's transit. An instrument consisting of a telescope mounted on a flat, graduated, circular plate on a tripod. The plate can be adjusted so it is level, and its graduations oriented to magnetic north. When an object is viewed through the telescope, its azimuth and elevation may be determined.

dihedral. The positive angle formed between the lateral axis of an airplane and a line which passes through the center of the wing or the horizontal stabilizer.

cantilever wing. A wing that is supported by its internal structure and requires no external supports.

Leveling the Airplane

With the wings and landing gear installed, the next step is to level the airplane so there will be the proper reference from which all alignment can be done. The Type Certificate Data Sheets for the particular airplane specifies the method the manufacturer used for leveling the airplane, and you should use this same method. Some manufacturers require you to drop a plumb bob from some point on the structure, which must align with another point below it. Other manufacturers call for the use of a spirit level placed at a specified location. Many of the large airplanes are leveled by using a surveyor's transit to align marks at the front and rear of the fuselage for longitudinal leveling, and objects on the wings for lateral leveling.

Aligning the Wings

Two very important alignments must be made for the wings of an airplane: the dihedral and the angle of incidence must be correct.

Dihedral

Cantilever wings are constructed in such a way that the dihedral cannot be changed. The main wing spar is generally bolted to the center section with special high-strength bolts or high-strength dowel pins held in place with bolts. Figure 4-36 shows the way the front spar of both a low-wing and a high-wing cantilever airplane are attached to the center section.

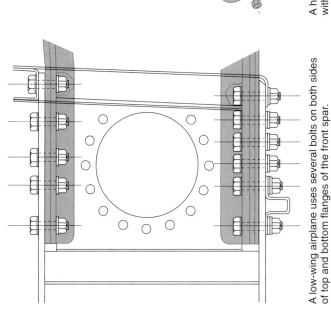

A low-wing airplane uses several bolts on both sides of top and bottom flanges of the front spar.

A high-wing airplane attaches the front-wing spar to the center section with high-strength dowel pins held in place by bolts and nuts.

Figure 4-36. *Front spar attachment for cantilever-wing airplanes*

The dihedral of strut-braced airplanes can be adjusted by changing the length of the strut that attaches to the front wing spar. The amount of dihedral is measured using a dihedral board, which is a tapered board made with the angle specified in the airplane service manual. It is held against the lower surface of the wing under the front spar. When the dihedral angle is correctly adjusted, a spirit level held against the bottom of the board will be level.

Angle of Incidence

The angle of incidence of some cantilever wings may be adjusted at the rear spar. One popular way of doing this is by the use of eccentric bushings. This is illustrated in Figure 4-38. The hole in the wing rear spar fitting is larger than that in the fuselage rear spar carry-through fitting. An eccentric bushing is installed in both sides of the wing spar fitting and the bolt and nut are installed but not tightened. The angle of incidence is checked at the point specified by the manufacturer using a protractor or an incidence board and a spirit level. The bushings on both sides of the wing spar are turned to raise or lower the rear spar until the incidence angle is correct, then the nut is torqued to the recommended value.

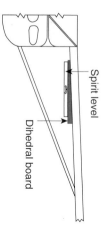

Figure 4-37. *The dihedral angle is checked with a dihedral board and a spirit level.*

Spirit level

Dihedral board

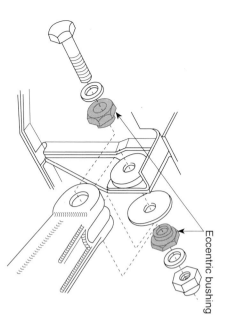

Eccentric bushing

Figure 4-38. *The angle of incidence of some cantilever airplanes is adjusted by rotating eccentric bushings in the rear wing spar fitting.*

Wash In and Wash Out

Wing-heavy flight conditions are often corrected on strut-braced airplanes by adjusting the length of the rear struts. A wing may be washed in by shortening the rear strut. This twists the wing and increases the angle of incidence, increasing the lift and the induced drag on that wing. This typically decreases the airspeed slightly. Lengthening the rear strut decreases the angle of incidence and washes the wing out. If very much correction is needed, one wing is washed in and the opposite wing is washed out.

eccentric bushing. A special bushing used between the rear spar of certain cantilever airplane wings and the wing attachment fitting on the fuselage. The portion of the bushing that fits through the hole in the spar is slightly offset from that which passes through the holes in the fitting. By rotating the bushing, the rear spar may be moved up or down to adjust the root incidence of the wing.

wash in. A twist in an airplane wing that increases its angle of incidence near the tip.

wash out. A twist in an airplane wing that decreases its angle of incidence near the tip.

wing heavy. An out-of-trim flight condition in which an airplane flies hands off, with one wing low.

Installing and Aligning the Empennage

The fixed horizontal and vertical tail surfaces are installed according to the manufacturer's recommendations, and a symmetry check is performed to ensure that the wings and tail are all symmetrical with the fuselage.

Symmetry Check

The manufacturer's maintenance manual lists the points to be measured on a symmetry check. These usually include measuring from a point near the tip of the vertical fin to a point near the tip of both sides of the horizontal stabilizer, and from the point on the vertical fin to points on each wing near the tip. Another measurement is made from the point near each wing tip to a point on the nose of the fuselage. All of the measurements on the right and left sides should be the same within the tolerances allowed by the manufacturer. Any difference in these measurements is an indication of structural deformation. A careful investigation must be made to find the reason for the difference and appropriate action taken to correct the problem.

Control Surface Installation and Rigging

When the airplane has been assembled and its alignment checked, all of the attachment bolts are tightened to the manufacturer's recommendations and marked with a spot of paint to signify that they have been properly torqued. Then the control surfaces should be installed and rigged.

Control Surface Balancing

Most modern airplanes are so aerodynamically clean and they fly at such high speeds that it is extremely important that all movable control surfaces be statically balanced. If the balance is improper, it is very likely that the surfaces will flutter in some condition of high-speed flight. When flutter develops, the surface can be damaged or destroyed, and this can cause loss of the aircraft.

The manufacturer recommends the method of checking the surfaces for static balance and gives the tolerances in the maintenance manual for the aircraft. Figure 4-39 shows a typical control surface balancing fixture.

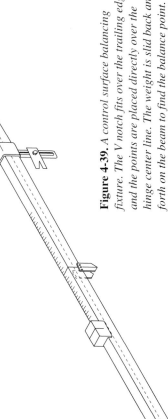

Figure 4-39. *A control surface balancing fixture. The V notch fits over the trailing edge and the points are placed directly over the hinge center line. The weight is slid back and forth on the beam to find the balance point.*

Check an aileron for static balance by mounting it upside down with a bolt through its hinge bearings resting on the knife edges of two balancing mandrels. Place the balancing fixture on the aileron, as directed in the manufacturer's maintenance manual, with the points over the hinge line. Move the weight until the assembly balances, and note the location at which the balance is attained. This gives the inch-pounds of overbalance or underbalance. If the surface does not balance within the tolerance specified by the manufacturer, change the balance weight in the leading edge of the surface as indicated in the maintenance manual.

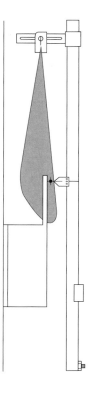

Figure 4-40. *Checking aileron balance*

When all the surfaces are balanced within the tolerances allowed by the manufacturer, they are ready for installation and rigging. Install the surface according to the directions in the appropriate maintenance manual and use only the hardware specified in the illustrated parts list.

Rigging the Ailerons

Lock the control yoke in position. One way to do this is to use a special rigging pin that fits in holes the manufacturer has provided in the control column and the support where it passes through the instrument panel. Such a device is shown in Figure 4-41.

Put a control lock between the aileron and the flap to hold the aileron in its neutral position and then connect the control cables. Adjust the cable tension to the value specified in the maintenance manual.

Adjusting Cable Tension

If cable tension is too light, the cables might slip out of the pulley grooves, and if it is too heavy, the controls will be difficult to move and there will be excessive wear in the control system. To complicate this problem, an all-metal airplane changes its dimensions considerably as its temperature changes, and the cable tension varies a great deal because of these changes. If the cables are rigged with the correct tension when the airplane is sitting on a hot ramp, the airplane will contract when it gets cold at high altitude and the cables will become extremely loose. Large airplanes typically have automatic cable tension regulators that compensate for dimensional changes in the airframe and maintain a relatively constant cable tension.

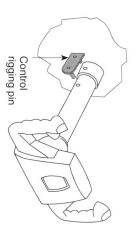

Control
rigging pin

Figure 4-41. *The control yoke of some airplanes may be held in position for rigging by using a special rigging pin that fits in holes the manufacturer has provided in the control yoke and its support.*

A control cable rigging chart typical of those furnished for a specific airplane is shown in Figure 4-42. For example, to find the tension that is required for a ⅛-inch 7 x 19 cable when the airplane temperature is 100°F, follow the vertical line for 100°F upward until it intersects the curve for ⅛-inch, 7 x 19 cable. From this point, draw a line horizontally to the right to the rigging load index. This cable at this temperature should be rigged to a tension of 79 pounds.

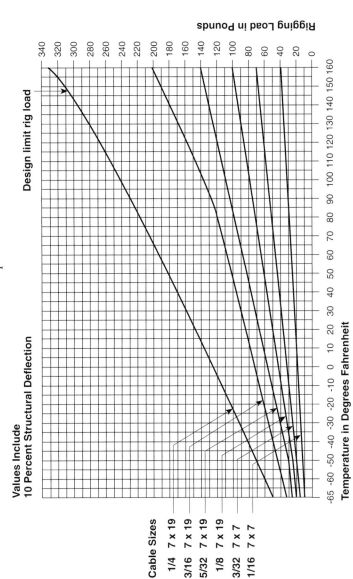

**Values Include
10 Percent Structural Deflection**

Design limit rig load

Rigging Load in Pounds

Temperature in Degrees Fahrenheit

Cable Sizes

1/4	7 x 19
3/16	7 x 19
5/32	7 x 19
1/8	7 x 19
3/32	7 x 7
1/16	7 x 7

Figure 4-42. *A typical rigging load chart for aircraft steel control cables*

Check the cable tension with a tensiometer like the one in Figure 4-43. Release the trigger of the tensiometer and pass the cable between the anvils and the riser. Then clamp the trigger against the housing, to cause the riser to press against the cable. Push the pointer lock in to lock the pointer, and then remove the tensiometer and read the indication. Use the chart furnished with the tensiometer to convert the dial indication to the cable tension. The chart in Figure 4-44 is similar to the chart furnished with the tensiometer.

To find the tensiometer indication that shows the cable is adjusted to 79 pounds, use the chart in Figure 4-44 and interpolate. Seventy-nine pounds is 90% of the way between 70 and 80, so the tensiometer indication will be 90% of the way between 50 and 57, or 56.

Install riser No. 1 in the tensiometer, and adjust the turnbuckles until the tensiometer reads 56. The cable tension will then be 79 pounds, which is correct for 100°F.

Checking Control Travel

The Type Certificate Data Sheets for the airplane specifies the travel for each of the primary controls. Once you've adjusted the cable tension, you are ready to check for the correct travel.

One type of tool you can use for this is the protractor shown in Figure 4-45. Attach it to the upper surface of the aileron with its rubber suction cup, and with the aileron locked in its streamline position, rotate the circular dial until zero is below the tip of the weighted pointer. Remove the rigging tool from the control column and unlock the aileron. Move it to its full up position and read the protractor to find the number of degrees the aileron has traveled. Without changing the protractor, move the aileron to its full down position and read the degrees of downward deflection. If the travel is not correct, follow the instructions in the maintenance manual to adjust it so that it is within the tolerance allowed by the manufacturer.

A precision measuring instrument you can use for measuring control surface deflection is the universal propeller protractor in Figure 4-46. This instrument can measure deflection to a tenth of a degree and is primarily used for measuring propeller pitch. Flight control travel is not usually measured to the fraction of a degree. This instrument has a movable ring and a movable disk with a spirit level in the center of the disk. To use it, follow these steps:

1. Align the zeroes on the ring and the disk scales.

2. Place the bottom of the protractor on top of the aileron.

3. Unlock the ring from the frame and rotate the ring until the bubble centers in the spirit level.

4. Lock the ring to the frame and deflect the aileron fully up. Unlock the disk from the ring and turn the disk adjuster until the bubble centers in the spirit level.

5. Read the up deflection on the disk scale against the zero mark on the ring. See Figure 4-46 on the next page.

Use Riser No. 1 with 1/16, 3/32, and 1/8 inch cable
Use Riser No. 2 with 5/32 and 3/16 inch cable

Tensiometer Indication Cable Diameter (inch)					Cable Tension (pounds)
1/16	3/32	1/8	5/32	3/16	
12	16	21	12	20	30
19	23	29	17	26	40
25	30	36	22	32	50
31	36	43	26	37	60
36	42	50	30	42	70
41	48	57	34	47	80
46	54	63	38	52	90
46	60	69	42	56	100
51			46	60	110
			50	64	120

Figure 4-44. *Typical chart relating control cable tension to a given tensiometer reading*

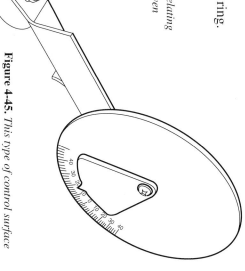

Figure 4-45. *This type of control surface protractor is held on the surface with its rubber suction cup when measuring control surface travel.*

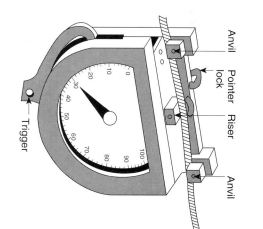

Figure 4-43. *A tensiometer determines control cable tension by measuring the force required to deflect the cable a specific amount.*

Anvil
lock — Pointer — Riser — Anvil
Trigger

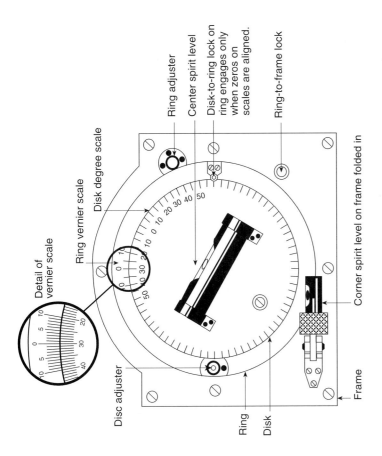

Figure 4-46. *A universal propeller protractor can be used to measure control surface deflection*

Checking and Safetying the System

After adjusting the cable tension and checking to be sure the controls have their proper up and down travel, check and safety the entire system.

Since many of the bolts in the control system are subject to rotation, they should not have self-locking nuts unless the manufacturer has used them and they are specified in the illustrated parts list. The bolts should all be installed in the direction that is shown in the illustrated parts list.

Be sure that every pulley has the proper cable guard installed and that with full travel of the controls no cable fitting comes within 2 inches of any fairlead or pulley, and check to see that no fairlead deflects the cable more than 3°. If a turnbuckle should come closer than is allowed to any pulley, readjust the cable to prevent it, and if it cannot be kept from coming this close, replace the cable assembly.

Safety the turnbuckles using one of the methods shown in Figure 4-47 or with a special clip such as that in Figure 4-49 on Page 299. Be sure that no more than 3 threads are exposed on either side of the turnbuckle barrel, and that both ends of all safety wires are ended with at least 4 full turns around the turnbuckle fitting. *See Figure 4-47.*

turnbuckle. A component in an aircraft control system used to adjust cable tension. A turnbuckle consists of a brass tubular barrel with right-hand threads in one end and left-hand in the other end. Control cable terminals screw into the two ends of the barrel and turning the barrel pulls the terminals together, shortening the cable.

Four turns minimum
This applies to all turnbuckle wrapping.

Double-wrap spiral

Double-wrap

Single-wrap spiral

Single-wrap

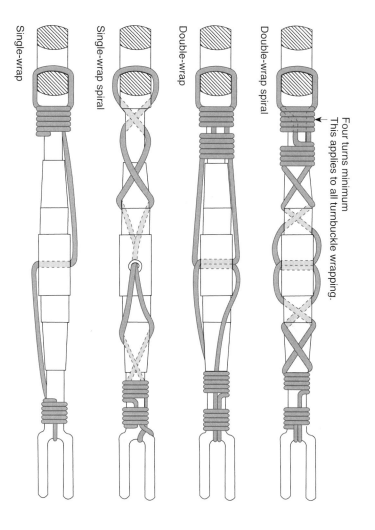

Figure 4-47. *Methods of safety wiring turnbuckles*

The size and type of safety wire for each cable size is shown in Figure 4-48.

Cable Diameter	Type of Wrap	Diameter of Wire	Material of Wire
1/16	Single	0.040	Brass
3/32	Single	0.040	Brass
1/8	Single	0.040	Stainless Steel
1/8	Double	0.040	Brass
1/8	Single	0.057 (min)	Brass

Figure 4-48. *Turnbuckle safetying guide*

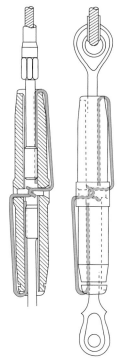

Figure 4-49. *MS Clip-type locking device for turnbuckles.*

Rigging the Elevator

The elevators are rigged in essentially the same way as the ailerons. The control yoke is locked in the same way, and the elevators are streamlined with the horizontal stabilizer with a control surface lock. The cable tension is adjusted in the same way, the travel is measured in the same way, and the system is inspected and safetied in the same way.

Rigging the Rudder

Before adjusting the control cable tension, lock the controls in their neutral position using the method specified in the airplane manufacturer's service manual. A common method for holding the rudder pedals in place is to clamp a piece of wood across the pedals with C-clamps, as shown in Figure 4-50.

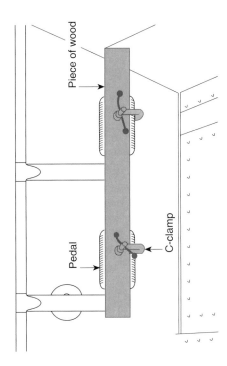

Figure 4-50. *Rudder pedals may be held in place for rigging by clamping a piece of wood across the pedals with C-clamps.*

Hold the rudder centered by clamping straightedges on both sides, and centering the rudder midway between them as shown in Figure 4-51. Adjust the turnbuckles to get the recommended cable tension.

After adjusting the cable tension, remove the straightedges and the lock from the rudder pedals, and check for full travel in both directions. Two common ways of checking this travel are illustrated in Figure 4-52. You can make a wire pointer of a welding rod taped to the aft end of the fuselage and bending it until it touches the trailing edge of the rudder. Deflect the rudder each way, and measure the distance between the pointer and the rudder trailing edge. The manufacturer's service manual specifies the distance tolerance for this type of measurement.

When the cable tension and the rudder travel are correct, check the entire system for freedom of operation, and safety all of the nuts and turnbuckles.

Control Movement Check

It seems almost unnecessary to mention this, but controls have been known to be rigged backward. The final check in any rigging procedure is to be sure all the control surfaces move in the correct direction when the cockpit control is moved.

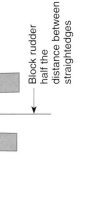

Figure 4-51. *Hold the rudder centered for adjusting cable tension by clamping straightedges on either side and centering the rudder trailing edge between them.*

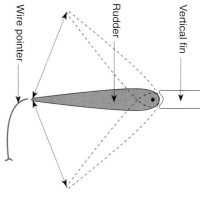

Vertical fin

Rudder

Wire pointer

A wire taped to aft end of fuselage can be bent until it touches rudder trailing edge when rudder is locked in place. Deflect rudder and measure distance between end of wire and rudder trailing edge.

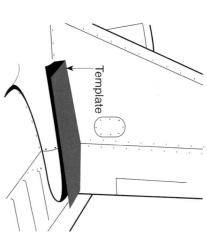

Template

A template made according to plans in aircraft maintenance manual can be held against vertical fin to measure amount of rudder deflection.

Figure 4-52. *Methods of measuring rudder deflection*

When the control wheel is pushed in to rotate the airplane nose down about its lateral axis, the trailing edge of the elevators should move down. When it is pulled back to rotate the airplane nose up, the elevator trailing edge should move up.

When the control wheel is rotated to the right to rotate the airplane to the right about its longitudinal axis, the trailing edge of the right aileron should move upward and the trailing edge of the left aileron should move down. Rotating the wheel to the left moves the controls in the opposite direction.

Moving the right rudder pedal forward deflects the trailing edge of the rudder to the right, and moving the left pedal forward moves the rudder trailing edge to the left.

Rotating the elevator trim tab to trim the airplane for nose-down flight raises the trailing edge of the tab. This creates an aerodynamic load on the elevator that moves it down and deflects the airplane nose down.

STUDY QUESTIONS: AIRPLANE ASSEMBLY AND RIGGING

Answers begin on Page 317. Page numbers refer to chapter text.

28. The method that should be used for leveling an aircraft for proper assembly and rigging may be found in the _____ for the aircraft. *Page 292*

29. The dihedral on a strut-braced airplane is adjusted by changing the length of the _____ (front or rear) strut. *Page 293*

Continued

30. Twisting a wing in such a way that its angle of incidence at the tip is increased is called washing the wing _____ (in or out). *Page 293*

31. A check to determine that the major components of an airplane are in their proper basic alignment is called a/an _____ check. *Page 294*

32. If a bolt in the control system is subject to rotation, a self-locking nut _____ (should or should not) be used. *Page 298*

33. Use the rigging load chart in Figure 4-42 and find the proper rigging load for a ⅛-inch 7 x 19 extra flexible cable when the temperature is 85°F. The cable should be rigged to a tension of _____ pounds. *Page 296*

34. Use the tensiometer chart of Figure 4-44. For a ⅛-inch 7 x 19 cable to have a tension of 73 pounds, the tensiometer should read _____. *Page 297*

35. A turnbuckle in a control system must not come closer to a pulley or fairlead than _____ inch/es. *Page 298*

36. To assure that the turnbuckle ends have sufficient threads inside the barrel to develop their full strength, no more than _____ threads are allowed to be outside of a turnbuckle barrel. *Page 298*

37. When safetying a turnbuckle with safety wire, the safetying must terminate with at least _____ turns of wire around the turnbuckle end. *Page 299*

38. When the control wheel is pulled back, the trailing edge of the elevators should move _____ (up or down). *Page 301*

39. When the control wheel is moved forward, the trailing edge of the elevators should move _____ (up or down). *Page 301*

40. When the control wheel is rotated to the right, the trailing edge of the right aileron should move _____ (up or down). *Page 301*

41. When the control wheel is rotated to the left, the trailing edge of the left aileron should move _____ (up or down). *Page 301*

42. When the right rudder pedal is pushed in, the trailing edge of the rudder should move to the
——— (right or left). *Page 301*

43. When the elevator trim tab is adjusted for a nose-down condition, the trailing edge of the tab should move
——— (up or down). *Page 301*

Helicopter Assembly and Rigging

Helicopter Controls

Successful rotor-wing development started with the autogiro, which uses aerodynamic forces rather than an engine to turn the rotor. The more simple autogiros were controlled by tilting the rotor mast to tilt the plane of the rotor. But the success of rotor-wing flight has been made possible by the development of the control systems that compensate for torque of the main rotor, and systems that rotate the helicopter about its three axes while overcoming the problems of dissymmetry of lift.

The pilot of a helicopter has three basic controls; the collective pitch control, the cyclic pitch control, and the antitorque pedals.

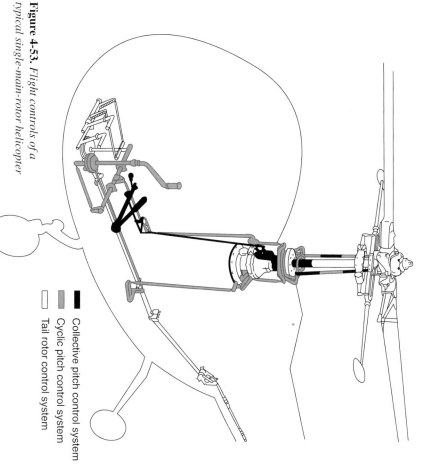

■	Collective pitch control system
▨	Cyclic pitch control system
□	Tail rotor control system

Figure 4-53. *Flight controls of a typical single-main-rotor helicopter*

The Swashplate

The heart of the typical helicopter control system is the swashplate assembly shown in Figure 4-54. This unit mounts around the rotor mast near its base, and it contains a nonrotating bearing race and a rotating race. The nonrotating race has two control arms 90° apart that are connected to the cyclic control so the swashplate can be tilted fore and aft or sideways. Running through the center of the swashplate assembly and rotating with the rotor shaft is a collective pitch sleeve that can be raised or lowered by the collective pitch control.

swashplate. The component in a helicopter control system that consists basically of two bearing races with ball bearings between them.

The lower, or nonrotating, race is tilted by the cyclic control, and the upper, or rotating, race has arms which connect to the control horns on the rotor blades.

Movement of the cyclic pitch control is transmitted to the rotating blades through the swashplate. Movement of the collective pitch control raises or lowers the entire swashplate assembly to change the pitch of all of the blades at the same time.

The Collective Pitch Control

The collective pitch control adjusts the pitch of all of the blades at the same time. This changes the lift of the entire rotor disc and allows the helicopter to go up or down. The engine throttle is coordinated with the collective pitch control in such a way that when the collective control is pulled up to increase the rotor blade pitch, the engine is automatically given more fuel so that the additional drag produced by the increased pitch does not slow the rotor. A motorcycle-type twist-grip throttle control is mounted on the collective pitch control. If the engine speed does not remain constant when the collective pitch is increased, the throttle grip can be rotated to get the correct RPM.

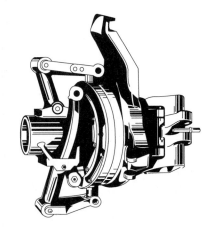

Figure 4-54. *A typical swashplate assembly that mounts around the base of the rotor mast.*

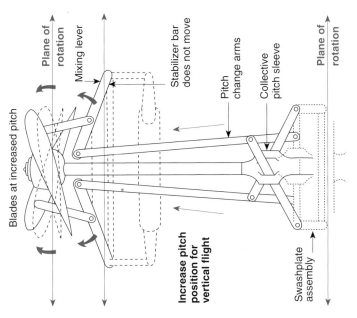

Plane of rotation

Mixing lever

Blades at increased pitch

Stabilizer bar does not move

Pitch change arms

Collective pitch sleeve

Increase pitch position for vertical flight

Plane of rotation

Swashplate assembly

Figure 4-55. *Raising the collective pitch control raises the collective pitch sleeve which causes the pitch of all of the rotor blades to increase at the same time.*

The operation of the collective pitch control is illustrated in Figure 4-55. When the pilot raises the collective pitch control, the collective pitch sleeve is raised, forcing the pitch change arms upward. This raises the inner end of the mixing lever, which causes the pitch control links to increase the pitch of all of the rotor blades at the same time.

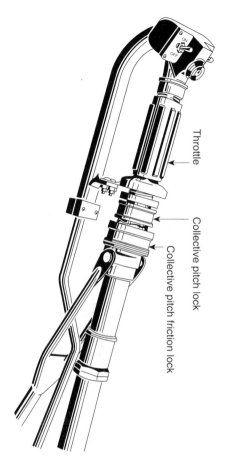

Throttle

Collective pitch lock

Collective pitch friction lock

Figure 4-56. *The collective pitch control lever has a twist-grip throttle control to allow the pilot to trim the RPM to the exact value needed.*

The Cyclic Pitch Control

The cyclic pitch control operated by the pilot's right hand tilts the swash plate to change the pitch of the rotor blades at a particular point in their rotation. This pitch change tilts the plane of rotation of the rotor disk. The lift always acts along the bisector of the coning angle, and when the rotor disc is tilted the lift develops a horizontal vector that moves the helicopter in the direction the disc is tilted.

The cyclic control operates the two pitch arms on the swash plate. When the pilot moves the cyclic control forward, the swash plate tilts forward. When Figure 4-58 on the next page. When the swash plate tilts forward, the pitch of the advancing blade is decreased and the pitch of the retreating blade is increased. Because of gyroscopic precession, the effect of the pitch change will be felt 90° after the point the pitch change is made, and the rotor disc will tilt forward.

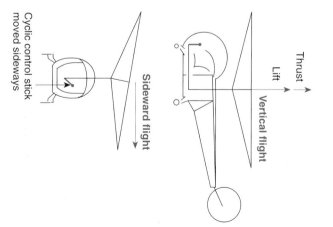

Thrust

Lift

Vertical flight

Cyclic control stick moved sideways

Sideward flight

Figure 4-57. *The lift produced by a helicopter rotor always acts along the bisector of the coning angle of the rotor blades. This produces a horizontal vector that moves the helicopter in the direction the rotor is tilted.*

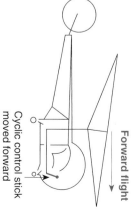

Cyclic control stick moved forward

Forward flight

coning angle. The angle formed between the plane of rotation of a helicopter rotor blade when it is producing lift and a line perpendicular to the rotor shaft.

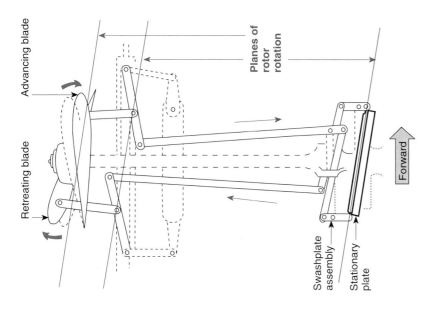

Advancing blade

Retreating blade

Planes of rotor rotation

Swashplate assembly

Stationary plate

Forward

Figure 4-58. *When the cyclic control is moved forward, the swashplate tilts forward. This decreases the pitch of advancing blade and increases the pitch of the retreating blade. Because of gyroscopic precession, the rotor disc will tilt forward.*

Horizontal Stabilizers

The rotor disc must be tilted forward in order for a helicopter to fly forwards. This results in a nose-low attitude for the fuselage, which is an inefficient flight attitude. To allow the fuselage to achieve a more level attitude in forward flight, most helicopters have some form of horizontal stabilizer mounted near the rear of the fuselage. Some of these stabilizers are synchronized with the cyclic control, so their downward force increases as the pilot moves the cyclic stick forward to increase the forward airspeed. Other helicopters have fixed stabilizers with a deeply cambered airfoil that produces a large aerodynamic download.

Torque Compensation

When the engine mounted in the fuselage of a helicopter turns the rotor, a force is produced that tries to rotate the fuselage in the opposite direction. This force, called torque, must be compensated for in order to allow the fuselage to remain pointed in the direction of desired flight. A number of methods have been tried, many unsuccessful, but three have been most successful: dual rotors mounted on coaxial shafts, dual rotors with one ahead of the other or one on either side of the fuselage, and a single main rotor with a torque-compensating tail rotor spinning in a vertical plane. The latter approach is by far the most common.

One of the latest approaches to torque compensation is NOTAR, or No Tail Rotor, developed by McDonnell-Douglas Helicopters. See Figure 4-59. This system does away with the dangers, complexities and noise of a tail rotor. A controllable-pitch fan, driven by the transmission, blows air down the hollow tail boom to a nozzle at the end of the shaft that is fitted with a set of 90° turning vanes. Both the pitch of the fan and the size of the nozzle openings are varied by the pilot's pedals to control the antitorque force the jet of air produces.

Two slots in the bottom of the tail boom direct air out in a tangential fashion, blowing to the left side. This air mixes with the downwash from the main rotor and accelerates it on the right side and deflects it to the left. The resulting low pressure on the right side and deflection of air to the left provide most of the antitorque force in a hover. In forward flight, when the downwashed air does not strike the tail boom, the antitorque force is provided by the tail jet and by a vertical stabilizer.

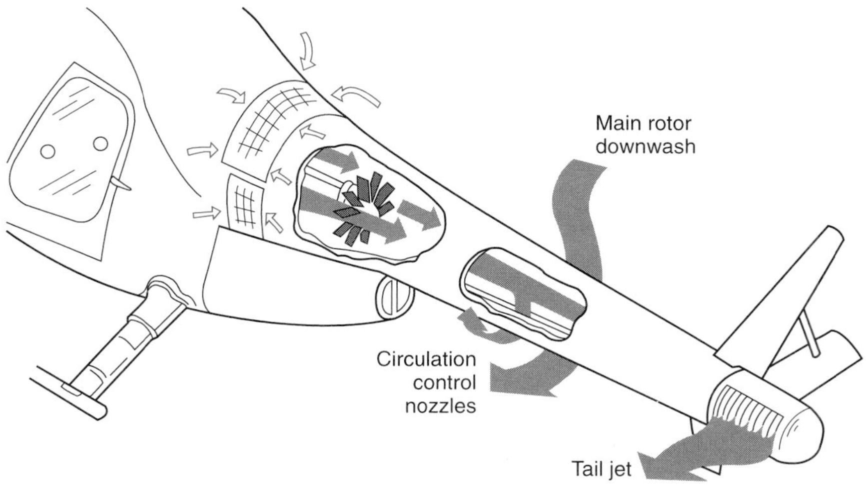

torque. A force that produces, or tries to produce rotation.

coaxial. Rotating about the same axis. Coaxial rotors of a helicopter are mounted on concentric shafts in such a way that they turn in opposite directions to cancel torque.

Circulation control nozzles

Main rotor downwash

Tail jet

Figure 4-59. *The NOTAR or No Tail Rotor system developed by McDonnell-Douglas Helicopters controls the circulation of the main rotor downwash to compensate for torque in a hover. The thrust from the air leaving the tail boom compensates for torque in forward flight.*

The single main rotor with a vertical auxiliary tail rotor is by far the most popular configuration. The engine drives the main rotor through a transmission that reduces the engine RPM to a speed proper for the rotor. A takeoff from the transmission drives a long shaft to a tail rotor gear box on whose output shaft the tail rotor mounts.

Figure 4-61 illustrates a typical tail rotor control system. The main rotor of most helicopters rotates to the left, as viewed from above, and the torque tries to rotate the fuselage to the right. When the antitorque pedals are even, the tail rotor produces enough thrust to the right to counter the torque rotational force to the left. When the pilot moves the left pedal forward, the pitch of the tail rotor blades increases, and the thrust increases enough to overcome the torque effect and rotate the fuselage to the left. When the pilot moves the right pedal forward, the tail rotor pitch is decreased. This decreases the thrust and allows the torque to pull the nose to the right.

The side thrust caused by the tail rotor causes a helicopter to drift to the right, and to compensate for this, the main rotor mast is often rigged so that it is offset to the left a few degrees to produce a thrust component to the left.

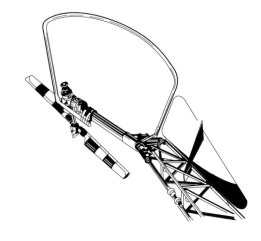

Figure 4-60. *The tail rotor supplies sideways thrust to prevent torque from the engine rotating the fuselage. The pitch of the tail rotor is controlled by the pilot's antitorque pedals.*

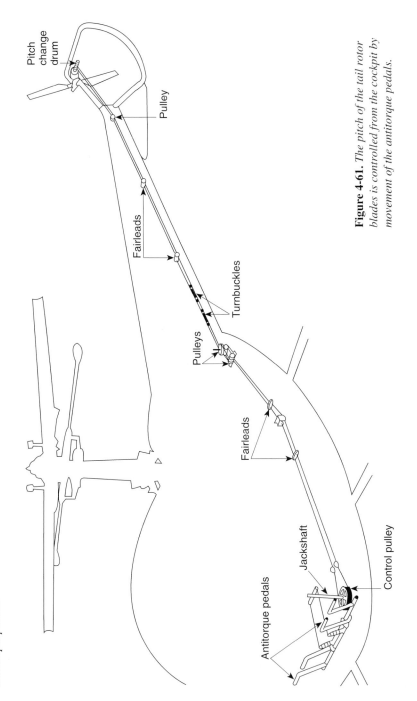

Figure 4-61. *The pitch of the tail rotor blades is controlled from the cockpit by movement of the antitorque pedals.*

308

Stabilizer Systems

A helicopter is statically stable but dynamically unstable, and because of this, requires some form of stabilization. One system that has been used very successfully is the stabilizer bar system, illustrated in Figure 4-62.

The bar with weighted ends is mounted on the rotor mast so that it turns with the rotor and is free to pivot about the mast. The stabilizer bar acts as a gyroscope and possesses the characteristic of rigidity in space. It will try to remain in the same plane as the helicopter pitches and rolls.

Look at Figure 4-62 and follow this explanation. The drawing is made with the helicopter in level flight. Now, suppose the nose of the helicopter drops. The mast tilts forward, but the stabilizer bar continues to rotate in the same plane. The pitch control links increase the pitch of the advancing blade (the one toward you in the illustration), and decrease the pitch of the retreating blade. Gyroscopic precession causes the pitch change to be effective 90° of rotation ahead of the point of application. This will cause the nose to rise back to level flight attitude.

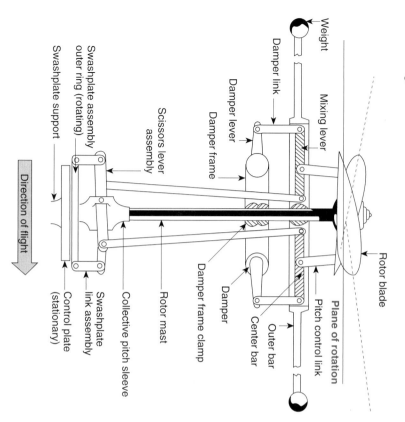

Figure 4-62. *A stabilizer bar and flight control linkage*

Weight

Damper link

Damper lever

Damper frame

Scissors lever assembly

Damper lever

Mixing lever

Damper

Damper frame clamp

Rotor mast

Collective pitch sleeve

Swashplate assembly outer ring (rotating)

Swashplate support

Control plate (stationary)

Swashplate link assembly

Center bar

Outer bar

Pitch control link

Plane of rotation

Rotor blade

Direction of flight

Rotor Systems

Three basic types of rotor systems are used in modern helicopters: fully articulated, semirigid, and rigid. Each system has advantages and disadvantages. *See* Figure 4-63.

Fully Articulated Rotors

Rotors with more than two blades are typically of the fully articulated type. The blades of a fully articulated rotor are free to move up and down (flap), move back and forth in their plane of rotation (drag), and rotate about their longitudinal axis (feather). *See* Figure 4-64.

As the helicopter moves horizontally, the increased speed of the advancing blade gives it more lift, and since this blade is mounted to the hub through a flapping hinge, it is free to rise. As it flaps upward, its angle of attack decreases and the lift is decreased. Flapping reduces the asymmetrical lift caused by horizontal movement of the helicopter.

The coriolis effect causes a rotor blade to try to move back and forth in its plane of rotation as it flaps up and down. To prevent the vibration and the strain on the blades this would cause, the blade is hinged to the hub through the drag, or lead-lag, hinge.

The pitch of the rotor blades is controlled by pitch change arms rotating the blade about its feather axis. The collective pitch control changes the blade angle of all blades at the same time, and the cyclic control changes the blade angle of each blade at a certain location in its rotation.

Semirigid Rotor

Most two-blade rotors are of the semirigid type. These have the blades attached to the hub through a feathering bearing that allows their pitch to be changed, but there are no flapping or drag hinges. The hub of a semirigid rotor is mounted on the mast with a seesaw, or teetering, hinge that allows the entire rotor to rock as a unit. The advancing blade rises and the retreating blade descends to compensate for dissymmetry of lift.

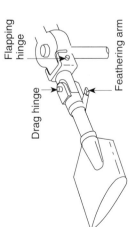

Flapping hinge

Feathering arm

Drag hinge

Fully articulated rotor blades are free to flap, drag, and feather.

Teetering hinge

Blades of semirigid rotor are free to feather, and blades flap as rotor rocks back and forth as a unit.

Blades of rigid rotor are free to feather, but are not hinged to flap or drag.

Figure 4-63. *Helicopter rotor systems*

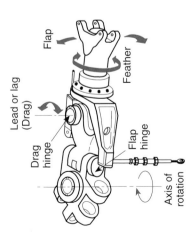

Lead or lag (Drag)

Drag hinge

Flap

Feather

Flap hinge

Axis of rotation

Figure 4-64. *The blade of a fully articulated rotor is free to flap, drag, and feather.*

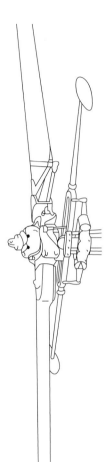

Figure 4-65. *A semirigid rotor attaches to the mast with a teetering hinge that allows it to flap as a unit. Pitch change arms control each blade about its feather axis.*

Rigid Rotor

A relatively recent type of rotor is the rigid rotor, which is attached to the mast in such a way that its only freedom of motion is around its feather axis. The blades are made of a material that allows them to flex enough to provide the necessary flapping and dragging.

Helicopter Powerplants

The lack of suitable powerplants slowed the development of the helicopter. Some helicopters use reciprocating engines similar to those used in airplanes, but the ideal powerplant is a turbine engine, and almost all modern helicopters except the small trainers are turbine powered.

Reciprocating Engines

Some reciprocating engines are mounted with their crankshaft vertical, and these engines must have dry sump lubrication systems which carry their oil supply in tanks outside of the engine. The engines in some of the smaller helicopters are mounted horizontally and drive the transmission through a series of V belts.

A helicopter has two engine problems that are not shared with airplanes. Helicopters have no propeller to act as a flywheel and to supply cooling air to the cylinders. The engine is coupled through the transmission to the rotor, and so must be operated with a higher idling speed than a comparable airplane engine. The engine is cooled by belt-driven blowers that force air through the engine cooling fins.

The engine of a helicopter is controlled differently from the engine of an airplane. The power output is controlled by a linkage to the collective pitch control that supplies the fuel needed to maintain the desired engine and rotor RPM. When the collective pitch is increased, the rotor loads the engine, and additional fuel is supplied to bring the engine speed back up to the desired RPM. The relationship between the indications of the tachometer and manifold pressure gage gives the pilot an indication of the power the engine is supplying to the rotor.

Turbine Engines

The requirement for relatively constant engine speed, small size, and light weight makes the turbine engine ideal for helicopters. For this reason, almost all helicopters except the small trainers are powered by turboshaft engines.

Turboshaft engines used in helicopters may be of either the direct-shaft or the free-turbine type. Direct-shaft engines have a single rotating element and are similar to turbojet engines except that they have additional turbine stages. These extra turbine stages extract additional energy from the expanding gases and use it to drive the rotor through the transmission. A free-turbine engine has one or more turbine stages that drive an output shaft that is entirely independent of the rotating element in the gas-generator portion of the engine. Free-turbine engines may be designed so that the output shaft extends from either the hot end or the cold end.

Transmission

The engine drives the rotor through a transmission that reduces the engine output shaft speed to the much lower speed needed to drive the rotor. Some transmissions are mounted directly on the engine and others are driven by a splined shaft. The transmission on some of the smaller helicopters is driven from the engine with a series of rubber V belts.

The tail rotor is usually driven from the transmission, so its speed is directly proportional to the speed of the main rotor.

Clutch

Reciprocating engines and direct-shaft turbine engines must have some form of clutch between the engine and the transmission to remove the load of the rotor from the engine when the engine is being started. These clutches are often automatic, so that they are disengaged when the engine is being started, but as soon as the engine reaches a predetermined speed, they automatically engage and couple the engine to the rotor. Helicopters normally have a dual tachometer with one needle indicating the engine speed and the other the rotor speed. When the clutch is only partially engaged, the needles are split, but when it is fully engaged, the needles are superimposed and are said to be "married."

Free-turbine engines do not need a clutch, as the engine is not connected to the gas-generator portion of the engine and therefore does not place any load on the starter.

Some of the smaller helicopters that drive the transmission through V belts use a manual belt tightener as a clutch. The belts are loosened for starting the engine, and when the rotors are to be engaged, the belt tightener is engaged by the pilot and the transmission is gradually connected to the engine.

Freewheeling Unit

All helicopters must have some means of disconnecting the engine from the rotor in case of engine failure. These units are always automatically operated and are often of the sprag type seen in Figure 4-66.

When the engine is driving the rotor, the rollers bind between the sprocket and the cam, and the sprocket drives the cam. Any time the engine slows and the drive sprocket speed drops below that of the output shaft, the cam allows the rollers to move back away from the sprocket and disengage the rotor from the engine. As part of the pretakeoff check, the throttle is rolled back enough for the engine speed to drop below the rotor speed. This allows the pilot to determine that the rotor disengages. When the throttle is opened, the engine speed increases and the freewheeling unit re-engages.

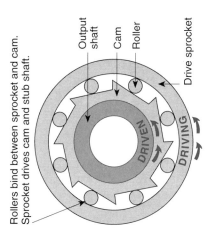

Rollers bind between sprocket and cam. Sprocket drives cam and stub shaft.

Freewheeling unit engaged, with engine driving rotor

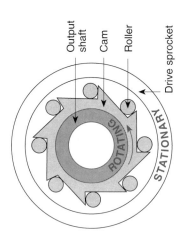

Freewheeling unit disengaged, in autorotation position

Figure 4-66. *Sprag-type freewheeling unit*

Helicopter Vibrations

Any device with the rotating mass a helicopter has is bound to have vibrations, and to complicate these vibrations, aerodynamic forces produce additional vibrations. As a result, vibration is a major problem with helicopters.

Before you can correct abnormal vibrations, you should understand them. There are two basic types of vibration, lateral and vertical, and two basic frequency ranges: low frequency and high frequency.

Low-frequency vibrations are those that are related to the main rotor and are usually classified as 1:1 or 2:1. This means that the vibration frequency is the same as the rotor RPM (1:1) or twice the rotor speed (2:1).

Low-frequency vertical vibration is usually caused by one rotor blade producing more lift than the other. This is usually caused by the blades having the wrong pitch angle or not being adjusted for proper track. Low-frequency lateral vibration is caused by the main rotor blades being out of static balance.

High-frequency vibrations are felt as a buzz rather than a beat and are usually associated with the engine, cooling fan, or the tail rotor.

The first step in minimizing the vibration is to be sure that the rotors are in static balance, both spanwise and chordwise. Chordwise balance of a semirigid rotor is obtained by changing the length of the drag braces at the root of the rotor blade. Articulated rotors are balanced by balancing the hub without any blades installed, and balancing each of the blades against a master blade. The final balancing is done in flight.

When the main rotor has been statically balanced and installed on the helicopter, you must check it for track.

An early method of blade tracking was to have the blade tips leave colored marks on the cloth curtain of a tracking flag. The blade tips were marked with colored wax crayons, a different color on each tip. The engine was started and the helicopter lifted, almost to a hover, and a tracking flag, like the one in Figure 4-67, was very carefully tilted in toward the rotor until the tips just touched the flag curtain.

When the tips touched the curtain, they left marks on the cloth. The colors of these marks showed which blade was flying high and which was flying low. Pitch adjustments were made so the blades followed in the same track.

A much better way to track a rotor is by using strobe lights, as shown in Figure 4-68 on the next page. The advantage of strobe tracking is that it can be done in flight, and much more can be determined about the true track of the rotor than can be done with the older flag method.

For this method, distinctive reflectors are installed on the tips of each of the rotor blades, and the helicopter is flown. Shine a strobe light on the rotor blade tips and observe the reflections. If the blades are in track, the reflections will form a straight line, and if they do not, you will be able to determine which blade is riding high or low by the identity of its reflection.

The state-of-the-art method of checking helicopter vibration involves using an electronic balancer/analyzer such as the Chadwick-Helmuth Model 8500C shown in Figure 4-69. This instrument eliminates the need for separate

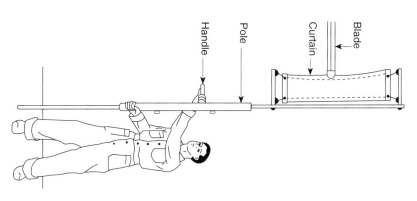

Figure 4-67. *Checking the track of the blades of a helicopter rotor using a cloth tracking flag*

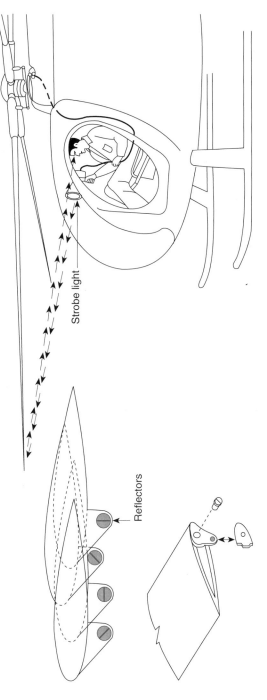

Strobe light

Reflectors

Figure 4-68. *Checking helicopter rotor blade track with a strobe light*

track and balance calculations, and it eliminates the need for costly flight tests to determine whether or not the adjustments were correct.

Complete vibration information on the specific helicopter or airplane is stored in a personal computer (PC), and when a vibration check is to be made, this information is downloaded to a disc which is inserted into the balancer/analyzer and is taken to the aircraft. Here it shows where to install sensors, connect cables, and the correct location for the balancing weights.

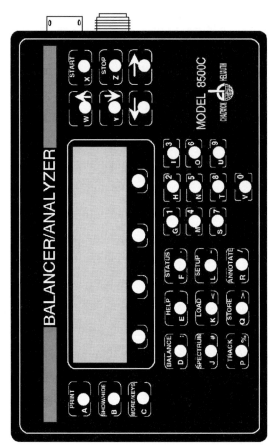

Figure 4-69. *The Chadwick-Helmuth Model 8500C is a state-of-the-art balancer/analyzer that allows you to take the correct action to minimize vibrations in a helicopter.*

A typical track and balancing test flight consists of a hover, then a forward flight at 130 knots, and the return to land. During this flight, the balancer/analyzer gathers data, determines corrective action, and displays the solution. Changes to weight, sweep, pitch link, and tab are made as indicated, and a second flight is made to verify the results. The vibration was measured in two flight regimes, but the corrections that were chosen by the balancer/analyzer minimize vibration for all speeds from hover to the never-exceed speed V_{NE}.

blade track. The condition of a helicopter rotor in which each blade follows in exactly the same path as the blade ahead of it.

STUDY QUESTIONS: HELICOPTER ASSEMBLY AND RIGGING

Answers begin on Page 317. Page numbers refer to chapter text.

44. The throttle of a helicopter is automatically controlled by movement of the _____ (collective or cyclic) pitch control. *Page 304*

45. The twist-grip throttle control is mounted on the _____ (collective or cyclic) pitch control. *Page 305*

46. When the cyclic control is moved backward, the pitch of the advancing blade is _____ (increased or decreased). *Page 305*

47. The direction a helicopter moves in flight is determined by the direction the _____ is tilted. *Page 305*

48. The main rotor of most single-rotor helicopters rotates to the _____ (right or left) as viewed from above. *Page 308*

49. Torque on a single-rotor helicopter is compensated by varying the _____ (pitch or speed) of the tail rotor. *Page 308*

50. To compensate for drift caused by thrust of the tail rotor, the main rotor mast is offset a few degrees to the _____ (right or left). *Page 308*

51. The horizontal stabilizer on a helicopter is designed to hold the fuselage relatively level in _____ (high or low) speed flight. *Page 306*

52. When the pitch of the advancing blade is increased, the helicopter will rotate nose _____ (up or down). *Page 305*

53. Another name for the drag hinge in a helicopter rotor is the _____ hinge. *Page 310*

Continued

54. The blades of a rigid rotor are allowed to rotate about their _____ (flap, drag, or feather) axis. *Page 311*

55. Fully articulated rotor blades typically have _____ (two or more than two) blades. *Page 310*

56. Cooling air for a helicopter reciprocating engine is normally provided by an engine-driven _____. *Page 311*

57. A helicopter with a free-turbine engine _____ (does or does not) require a clutch between the engine and the transmission. *Page 312*

58. A helicopter with a free-turbine engine _____ (does or does not) require a freewheeling system between the rotor and the transmission. *Page 312*

59. Low frequency vibrations in a helicopter are normally related to the _____. *Page 313*

60. A 1:1 vertical vibration is usually caused by a main rotor blade being out of _____ (balance or track). *Page 313*

61. A 1:1 lateral vibration is usually caused by a main rotor blade being out of _____ (balance or track). *Page 313*

62. A strobe light check of blade track _____ (can or cannot) be made in flight. *Page 313*

Answers to Assembly and Rigging Study Questions

1. greater
2. outer
3. up
4. speed brakes
5. elevons
6. ruddervators
7. downward
8. before
9. Fowler
10. increases
11. increase
12. does not
13. opposite
14. servo
15. opposite
16. high
17. same
18. down
19. aft
20. 100
21. ⅛

22. 100
23. 3
24. should
25. closed
26. torque
27. hydraulic
28. Type Certificate Data Sheets
29. front
30. in
31. symmetry
32. should not
33. 73
34. 52
35. 2
36. 3
37. 4
38. up
39. down
40. up
41. up
42. right

43. up
44. collective
45. collective
46. increased
47. rotor disc
48. left
49. pitch
50. left
51. high
52. up
53. lead-lag
54. feather
55. more than two
56. blower
57. does not
58. does
59. main rotor
60. track
61. balance
62. can

HYDRAULIC AND PNEUMATIC POWER SYSTEMS

Continued

HYDRAULIC AND PNEUMATIC POWER SYSTEMS

5

An Introduction to Fluid Power Systems

Fluid power systems are mechanical systems in which a moving fluid performs work. This fluid may be either a compressible gas or an incompressible liquid. Systems that use compressible fluids are called pneumatic systems, and those that use incompressible fluids are called hydraulic systems.

Historical Overview

With the free and almost unlimited power available in flowing water, much early human industry was located along rivers. People used water for transportation, and diverted water to flow over large wooden waterwheels that turned shafts inside factory buildings. Pulleys and belts drove the lathes and drill presses from these water-driven shafts.

As civilization moved westward and farming and cattle raising became important industries, the all-essential water was taken from wells by pumps driven by windmills, a pneumatic device.

Today we still use waterwheels and windmills, although the form has changed. Instead of using slow-turning waterwheels to drive the machine tools, we use high-speed turbines, driven by water collected behind huge dams, to generate the electricity that drives our industrial tools. Modern windmills also use the inexhaustible power in moving air to drive electrical generators.

Modern aircraft would not be nearly as efficient as they are if it were not for fluid power systems. Hydraulic brakes allow the pilot to control the aircraft on the ground without using complex mechanical linkage. Hydraulic retraction systems pull the heavy landing gear up into the wheel wells to reduce wind resistance, and hydraulically boosted controls make it possible for human and automatic pilots to fly heavy, high-speed jet transport aircraft. High-pressure pneumatic systems are used as backups for hydraulic systems, and low-pressure pneumatic systems drive many of the gyro-operated flight instruments. Pneumatic deicer systems break off ice that has formed on the leading edges of the flight surfaces.

---

fluid power. The transmission of force by the movement of a fluid.

The most familiar examples of fluid power systems are hydraulic and pneumatic systems.

fluid. A substance, either a liquid or a gas, that flows and tends to conform to the shape of its container.

turbine. A rotary device actuated by impulse or reaction of a fluid flowing through vanes or blades that are arranged around a central shaft.

hydraulics. The system of fluid power which transmits force through an incompressible fluid.

pneumatics. The system of fluid power which transmits force by the use of a compressible fluid.

Basic Laws of Physics

Fluid power systems are essentially systems for gaining a mechanical advantage. The law of conservation of energy does not allow us to create nor destroy energy, but we have a wide latitude of things we can do with the energy we have. Most of the energy we use is involved in doing work for us.

Review of Terms and Relationships

Here, we will review some of the terms and the principles of basic physics used in this study. There is a comprehensive discussion of Basic Physics in the *Aviation Maintenance Technician Series, General* textbook.

Area

area. The number of square units in a surface.

Area is measured in square inches or square feet in the English system, and in square centimeters and square meters in the metric system.

To find the area of a plane rectangular surface, multiply the surface's length by its width.

$$\text{Area} = \text{Length} \cdot \text{Width}$$

Find the area of a square by squaring the length of one of its sides.

$$\text{Area} = \text{Side}^2$$

The area of a plane triangular figure is exactly one half of the area of a rectangle whose sides are the same length as the base and the altitude of the triangle.

$$\text{Area} = (\text{Base} \cdot \text{Altitude}) \div 2$$

In most hydraulic and pneumatic actuators, the fluid acts on a piston that has a circular head. To find the area of a circle, use the formula:

$$\text{Area} = \pi \cdot R^2$$
$$\pi = 3.1416$$
$$R = \text{radius of the piston head}$$

A simpler formula uses the diameter of the piston rather than its radius:

$$\text{Area} = 0.7854 \times D^2$$
$$0.7854 = \text{a constant (or, } \pi \div 4)$$
$$D = \text{diameter of the piston head}$$

The constant 0.7854 is near enough to ¾ (75%) to allow you to quickly estimate the area of a circle by squaring its diameter and taking three quarters of this value. To find the approximate area of a circle with a 10-inch diameter, square its diameter ($10^2 = 100$) and multiply this by 0.75. The approximate area is 75 square inches. The actual area is 78.54 square inches.

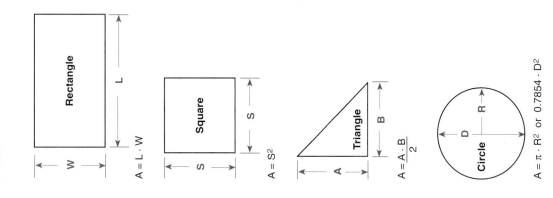

Rectangle
W
L
$A = L \cdot W$

Square
S
S
$A = S^2$

Triangle
A
B
$A = \dfrac{A \cdot B}{2}$

Circle
D
R
$A = \pi \cdot R^2$ or $0.7854 \cdot D^2$

Figure 5-1. *Formulas for finding area*

Distance

Practical mechanics is concerned with movement. The distance an object is moved enters into many computations.

Distance is measured in inches or feet in the English system, and in centimeters or meters in the metric system.

Volume

Many fluid power computations find or use the amount of fluid available or the amount of fluid moved.

Fluid volume is measured in cubic units. The English system uses cubic inches or cubic feet; the metric system uses cubic centimeters or cubic meters.

Find the volume of a square or rectangular container by multiplying the length, width, and height of the container.

Volume = Length · Width · Height

Find the volume of a cylinder by multiplying the area of its end by its height.

Volume = 0.7854 · Diameter^2 · Height

Find the volume of a spherical container (such as an accumulator), with this formula:

Volume = $(\pi \div 6) \cdot D^3$

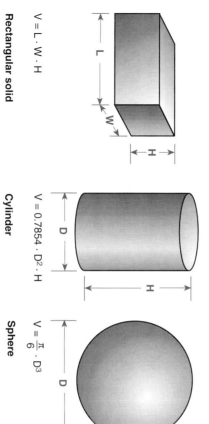

V = L · W · H

Rectangular solid

V = 0.7854 · D^2 · H

Cylinder

$V = \dfrac{\pi}{6} \cdot D^3$

Sphere

Figure 5-2. *Formulas for finding volume*

circle. A closed plane figure with every point an equal distance from the center. A circle has the greatest area for its circumference of any enclosed shape.

rectangle. A plane surface with four sides whose opposite sides are parallel and whose angles are all right angles.

square. A four-sided plane figure whose sides are all the same length, whose opposite sides are parallel, and whose angles are all right angles.

triangle. A three-sided, closed plane figure. The sum of the three angles in a triangle is always equal to 180°.

constant. A value used in a mathematical computation that is the same every time it is used.

For example, the relationship between the length of the circumference of a circle and the length of its diameter is a constant, 3.1416. This constant is called by the Greek name of pi (π).

Work

Work is the product of a force multiplied by the distance over which the force acts.

When you lift a 10-pound weight 4 feet, you are doing 40 foot-pounds of work. And, if a 10-pound force pushes a 200-pound handcart across the hangar floor for a distance of 4 feet, it is doing 40 foot-pounds of work.

It requires the same amount of work to carry a case of oil up a flight of stairs in one trip with all of the cans in a box as to carry the same amount of oil up the same stairs in many trips, carrying one can at a time. Work is simply force times distance, and does not consider time.

In the English system of measurement, work is expressed in such units as foot-pounds, inch-pounds, or inch-ounces. In the metric system, work is measured in meter-kilograms or centimeter-grams.

Power

Power is a measure of the amount of work done in a given period of time. If you lift a 10-pound weight 4 feet in 1 second, you use 40 foot-pounds per second. Find power by dividing the amount of work by the amount of time used to do it.

$$\text{Power} = (\text{Force} \cdot \text{Distance}) \div \text{Time}$$

The horsepower is the standard unit of mechanical power. One horsepower is 33,000 foot-pounds of work done in 1 minute, or 550 foot-pounds of work done in 1 second. One horsepower is also equal to 746 watts of electrical power.

In the metric system, 1 metric horsepower is 4,500 meter-kilograms of work done in 1 minute, or 75 meter-kilograms of work done in 1 second. One metric horsepower is equal to 0.986 horsepower.

Compute power in a hydraulic system by multiplying the flow rate in gallons per minute by the pressure of the fluid in pounds per square inch. This gives the force-distance-time relationship. One gallon is equal to 231 cubic inches, and a flow of 1 gallon per minute (gpm) under a pressure of 1 pound per square inch (psi) will produce 0.000 583 horsepower.

$$\text{Horsepower} = \text{gpm} \cdot \text{psi} \cdot 0.000\ 583$$

Relationship Between Force, Pressure and Area

In the English system of measurement, force is measured in pounds, area in square inches, and pressure in pounds per square inch.

The amount of force a fluid power system can produce is determined by the amount of pressure used and the area on which the pressure is acting. The relationship between pressure, force, and area is illustrated in the circle in Figure 5-3. The value of the upper half of the circle is equal to the product of the two lower quarters of the circle.

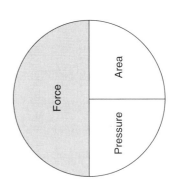

Figure 5-3. *Relationship between force, pressure, and area*

---

work. The product of force times distance.

force. Energy brought to bear on an object that tends to cause motion or to change motion.

foot-pound. A measure of work accomplished when a force of 1 pound moves an object a distance of 1 foot.

inch-pound. A measure of work accomplished when a force of 1 pound moves an object a distance of 1 inch.

kilogram. One thousand grams.

gram. The basic unit of weight or mass in the metric system. One gram equals about 0.035 ounce.

horsepower. A unit of mechanical power that is equal to 33,000 foot-pounds of work done in 1 minute, or 550 foot-pounds of work done in 1 second.

A 1,000-psi hydraulic system, acting on a piston with an area of 0.5 square inch, will produce a force of 500 pounds.

$$F = P \cdot A$$
$$= 1,000 \cdot 0.5$$
$$= 500 \text{ pounds}$$

The area needed for a 1,000-psi hydraulic system to produce a force of 5,000 pounds is 5 square inches.

$$A = F \div P$$
$$= 5,000 \div 1,000$$
$$= 5 \text{ square inches}$$

A pressure of 2,500 psi is needed to act on a piston with an area of 2 square inches to produce 5,000 pounds of force.

$$P = F \div A$$
$$= 5,000 \div 2$$
$$= 2,500 \text{ psi}$$

Relationship Between Volume, Area and Distance

Find the amount of fluid needed to move an actuator using the relationship illustrated in Figure 5-4. With this relationship, you can find the amount of fluid needed to move a piston of a given size a given distance. Or, find the distance a given amount of fluid will move the piston, or the size piston needed for a given distance of movement when you know the volume of the fluid.

When a piston with an area of 20 square inches is moved into a cylinder for a distance of 5 inches, 100 cubic inches of fluid will be displaced.

$$V = A \cdot D$$
$$= 20 \cdot 5$$
$$= 100 \text{ cubic inches}$$

To move 100 cubic inches of fluid from a cylinder with a piston movement of 5 inches, the piston must have an area of 20 square inches.

$$A = V \div D$$
$$= 100 \div 5$$
$$= 20 \text{ square inches}$$

A piston with an area of 20 square inches will displace 100 cubic inches of fluid when it is moved 5 inches into a cylinder.

$$D = V \div A$$
$$= 100 \div 20$$
$$= 5 \text{ inches}$$

power. The time rate of doing work. Power is force multiplied by distance (work), divided by time.

pressure. Force per unit area. Hydraulic and pneumatic pressure are normally given in units of pounds per square inch (psi).

watt. The basic unit of electrical power. One watt is equal to 1/746 horsepower.

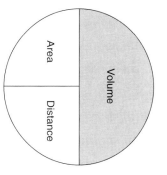

Figure 5-4. *Relationship between volume, area, and distance*

potential energy. Energy that is possessed by an object because of its position, configuration, or by the chemical arrangement of its constituents.

kinetic energy. Energy that is possessed by an object because of its motion.

The Law of Conservation of Energy

We can neither create nor destroy energy, but we can change the form of the energy in order to use it. When the form is changed, we have exactly the same amount of energy we started with.

Most mechanical devices produce less useful work than is put into them. This is because of friction or inefficiency, but the total energy output is the same as the total energy input.

Energy in a fluid power system may be in one of two forms: potential or kinetic. Potential energy in a fluid power system is expressed in the pressure of the fluid, and kinetic energy is expressed in the velocity of the moving fluid.

Relationship Between Height and Pressure

The pressure a static fluid exerts is determined by the height of the fluid, and has nothing to do with its volume. If the height of the liquid in a piece of half-inch tubing is exactly the same as the height of the liquid in a 100-gallon tank, the pressure at the bottom of the tube will be exactly the same as the pressure at the bottom of the tank. *See* Figure 5-5.

One gallon of pure water weighs 8.35 pounds and contains 231 cubic inches. Therefore a one-square inch column of water 231 inches high exerts a force on the bottom of the container of 8.35 pounds and produces a pressure of 8.35 pounds per square inch. If the water level in a 100 gallon tank is 231 inches above the bottom, every square inch of bottom area is acted on by 8.35 pounds of force, and the pressure is 8.35 psi. Neither the shape of the container nor the amount of water has any effect on the pressure. Pressure is determined only by the density of the fluid and by the height of the top of the fluid above the bottom of the container.

The densities of common liquids you as an aviation maintenance technician are likely to encounter are listed in Figure 5-6.

To find the pressure exerted by a column of fluid, use this formula:

Pressure = Density · Height

Find the pressure at the bottom of a tank of kerosine whose height is 60 inches. Use the formula:

Pressure = Density · Height
= 0.02961 · 60
= 1.78 psi

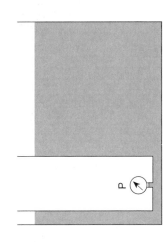

Figure 5-5. *The pressure exerted by a column of fluid is determined by the density of the fluid and by the height of the top of the fluid above the bottom of the container.*

Liquid	Density (pounds per cubic inch)
Gasoline	0.02602
JP-4	0.02857
Methyl alcohol	0.02926
Kerosine	0.02961
Oil (petroleum)	0.03178
Oil (synthetic)	0.03359
Water (fresh)	0.03615

Figure 5-6. *Density of various liquids*

Pascal's Law

Pascal's law explains the way power is transmitted in a closed hydraulic or pneumatic system. Stated in simple terms, **Pascal's law says that pressure in an enclosed container is transmitted equally and undiminished to all parts of the container, and it acts at right angles to the walls that enclose it.**

Figure 5-7 shows an open container that is filled with a liquid. Pressure gages show that the pressure is determined by the difference between the height of the gage and the top of the liquid.

In Figure 5-8, a piston is placed on the top of the liquid and the weight (W) presses down on it. This creates a pressure inside the container of liquid, and the pressure on each of the gages increases by the same amount.

Find the amount of pressure increase by multiplying the area of the piston by the force caused by the weight. It is the same on every one of the gages regardless of their position in the system, or of the shape of the container.

Pascal's law explains why automobile hydraulic brakes have equal braking action, for example. When the brake pedal is depressed, the pressure is transmitted equally to each of the wheels regardless of the distance between the brake master cylinder and the wheel cylinder.

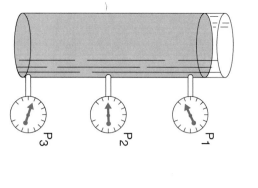

Figure 5-7. *The pressure produced by liquid in an open container is caused by the height of the liquid above the point at which the pressure is measured. The higher the liquid above the gage, the greater the pressure.*

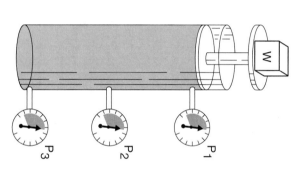

Figure 5-8. *When pressure is applied to a liquid in a closed container, the pressure rises to the same amount in all parts of the container.*

Mechanical Advantage

An application of Pascal's law shows the mechanical advantage in a hydraulic system. To briefly review the principle of mechanical advantage, look at the balance in Figure 5-9.

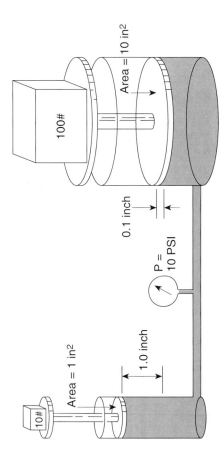

Figure 5-9. *Hydraulic cylinders produce a mechanical advantage. The work done by the small piston is exactly the same as that done by the large piston. A small force on the small piston will produce a large force on the large piston, but the small piston must travel farther than the large one.*

Figure 5-9 is a simple hydraulic jack. The small piston has an area of 1 square inch, and the large piston has an area of 10 square inches. When a force of 10 pounds is applied to the small piston, a pressure of 10 psi is built up in the fluid. According to Pascal's law, this pressure is the same throughout the system, and 10 pounds of force acts on each square inch of the large piston. This pressure produces a force of 100 pounds on the large piston that lifts the weight.

When the small piston moves down 1 inch, 1 cubic inch of fluid is forced out of the small cylinder into the large cylinder. This fluid spreads out over the entire large piston and it raises it only 0.1 inch. The small piston must move down 10 inches to raise the large piston 1 inch.

The work done by the small piston is 10 inches times 10 pounds, or 100 inch-pounds. The work done by the large piston is also 100 inch-pounds (1 inch x 100 pounds).

Hydraulic systems are quite efficient, and we do not usually consider system losses in the study of practical hydraulic systems.

Bernoulli's Principle

Pascal's law deals with the static, or still, condition of the fluid. When fluid is in motion, other things happen, and these are best explained by Bernoulli's principle.

When considering fluid in motion, start with the premise that the total amount of energy in the fluid remains constant. No energy is added to the fluid, nor is any lost from it.

Bernoulli's principle explains the relationship between pressure and velocity in a stream of moving fluid. The total energy in the fluid is made up of potential energy and kinetic energy. The potential energy relates to the pressure of the fluid, and the kinetic energy relates to its velocity. *See* Figure 5-10.

An incompressible fluid flowing through a tube with a constant cross-sectional area has a specific velocity. This fluid exerts a given amount of pressure on the wall of the tube. When the fluid flows through the restriction, it speeds up and its kinetic energy increases. Since the total energy remains constant, the increase in kinetic energy results in an accompanying decrease in potential energy, its pressure.

When the fluid leaves the restricted area and returns to the original size tube, its velocity decreases to its original value and its pressure rises back to its original value.

Bernoulli's principle tells us that as long as the total energy in a flow of fluid remains constant, any increase in the velocity of the fluid will result in a decrease in the pressure that is exerted by the fluid.

Bernoulli's principle. The basic principle that explains the relation between kinetic energy and potential energy in fluids that are in motion.

When the total energy in a column of moving fluid remains constant, any increase in the kinetic energy of the fluid (its velocity) results in a decrease in its potential energy (its pressure).

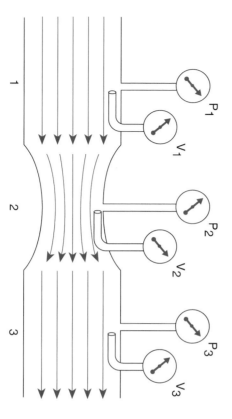

Figure 5-10. *The total energy in the fluid flowing through this venturi tube remains constant at all points.*

Pressure Drop in Moving Fluid

There are many similarities between the flow of electrons in an electrical system and the flow of fluid in a fluid power system. One of these similarities is the drop in pressure as the flow of fluid encounters an opposition. This is the same as the drop in voltage caused by current flowing through a resistance.

Figure 5-11 shows the way the pressure drops along a tube through which fluid is flowing. The pressure in the reservoir is shown by the height of the liquid. The pressure decreases along the line leaving the reservoir as is indicated by the height of the fluid in each of the vertical tubes. The friction encountered by the fluid causes the pressure drop in the same way resistance in an electrical system causes a pressure drop.

The pressure drop in a moving fluid can be used in fluid control devices like hydraulic fuses. When fluid flowing through a tube encounters a restrictor, pressure is dropped across it. The amount of this pressure drop is proportional to the rate of flow of the fluid. In a hydraulic fuse, an excessive rate of flow will cause enough pressure drop to shut off all flow.

Advantages and Disadvantages of Fluid Power Systems

There are three primary systems for actuating landing gear, flaps, control surfaces, airstair doors, and other devices on an aircraft; these are hydraulic, pneumatic, and electrical. Each of these systems has advantages and disadvantages.

A number of aircraft use electric motors to raise and lower the landing gear and to operate the wing flaps. Some aircraft use high-pressure compressed air to actuate these devices as well as the brakes. In a majority of aircraft, however, these devices are actuated by hydraulic power.

Some of the simplest airplanes use hydraulic brakes, and many use hydraulic actuators to raise and lower the landing gear. Large airplanes also use hydraulic power to operate the primary flight controls.

Hydraulic systems are highly efficient, and experience very little loss due to fluid friction. They are lightweight and easy to maintain and can produce almost any force needed. Hydraulic systems can operate with a stalled actuator without causing any fire danger. Backup systems are simple, with electrically operated pumps or hand pumps to take over in the event of failure of an engine-driven pump, and in case of the loss of all hydraulic fluid, emergency backup pneumatic systems can use stored high-pressure compressed air to lower the landing gear and actuate the brakes.

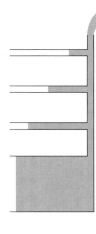

Figure 5-11. *The friction encountered as fluid flows through a tube causes a pressure drop.*

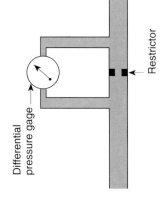

Differential pressure gage

Restrictor

Figure 5-12. *When fluid flows through a restrictor, pressure is dropped across it that is proportional to the rate of flow.*

restrictor. A fluid power system component that controls the rate of actuator movement by restricting the flow of fluid into or out of the actuator.

hydraulic fuse. A type of flow control valve that allows a normal flow of fluid in the system but, if the flow rate is excessive, or if too much fluid flows for normal operation, the fuse will shut off all further flow.

Pneumatic systems have an additional advantage in that they use air as their operating fluid, and since there is an unlimited supply of air, no return system is needed. The air is compressed, directed to the actuator, and used, and then it is exhausted overboard.

Fluid power systems do have disadvantages. All of the actuators must be connected to the system with tubing that carries high-pressure fluid. These lines and fittings have considerably more weight than wires used in electrical systems, and fluid is prone to leak, especially when it is required to pass through fittings that allow movement. The high-pressure air that is used in pneumatic systems requires special care in its operation, as it can be quite dangerous if improperly handled.

STUDY QUESTIONS: AN INTRODUCTION TO FLUID POWER SYSTEMS

Answers begin on Page 415. Page numbers refer to chapter text.

1. A fluid power system that uses a noncompressible fluid is called a _____ (hydraulic or pneumatic) system. *Page 323*

2. A fluid power system that uses a compressible fluid is called a _____ (hydraulic or pneumatic) system. *Page 323*

3. A hydraulic piston that has a diameter of 3.0 inches has an area of _____ square inches. *Page 324*

4. A cylindrical hydraulic reservoir that has a diameter of 6.0 inches and a height of 8.0 inches has a volume of _____ cubic inches. *Page 325*

5. A spherical container whose diameter is 12 inches has a volume of _____ cubic inches.

6. A 395-pound drum of oil is rolled 40 feet across the hangar floor. It requires a force of 15 pounds to roll the drum. The work done in rolling this drum is _____ foot-pounds. *Page 326*

7. The amount of power needed to raise a weight is increased when the time used to raise it is _____ (increased or decreased). *Page 326*

8. One horsepower is the equivalent of _____ foot-pounds of work done in one minute. *Page 326*

9. One horsepower is the equivalent of _____ foot-pounds of work done in one second. *Page 326*

Continued

10. One horsepower is equivalent to _____ watts of electrical power. *Page 326*

11. A 700-pound engine is raised with a hoist for a distance of 5 feet in 30 seconds. This requires _____ horsepower. *Page 326*

12. One U.S. gallon is equal to _____ cubic inches. *Page 326*

13. A flow of 3 gallons per minute of hydraulic fluid under a pressure of 1,000 psi produces _____ horsepower. *Page 326*

14. A 3,000-psi hydraulic system acts on a piston having an area of 2 square inches. The piston produces _____ pounds of force. *Page 327*

15. A force of 4,000 pounds is required by a 1,000-psi hydraulic system. This force will require a piston having an area of _____ square inches. *Page 327*

16. For a piston with an area of 2.0 square inch to produce a force of 500 pounds, a hydraulic hand pump must furnish _____ psi of pressure. *Page 327*

17. When a piston with an area of 3.0 square inches is moved 6.0 inches, _____ cubic inches of fluid will be moved. *Page 327*

18. For a piston with an area of 6.0 square inches to move 36 cubic inches of fluid, it must be moved _____ inches. *Page 327*

19. A piston must move 100 cubic inches of fluid when it is moved 5.0 inches. In order to do this, the piston must have an area of _____ square inches. *Page 327*

20. Kinetic energy in a fluid power system is in the form of the _____ (pressure or velocity) of the fluid. *Page 331*

21. Potential energy in a fluid power system is in the form of the _____ (pressure or velocity) of the fluid. *Page 331*

22. The pressure on the bottom of a reservoir caused by kerosine that has a level of 18 inches above the bottom is _____ psi. *Page 328*

23. A hydraulic jack requires a force on the handle of 30 pounds to exert a force of 600 pounds on the object being raised. The jack has a mechanical advantage of _____. *Page 330*

24. According to Bernoulli's principle, when the total energy in a column of moving fluid remains constant, an increase in the velocity of the fluid results in a corresponding _____ (increase or decrease) in the pressure. *Page 331*

25. The pressure drop caused by an obstruction in a line carrying a flow of fluid is directly proportional to the _____ (rate or volume) of flow. *Page 332*

Basic Aircraft Hydraulic Systems

All hydraulic systems must have several basic components, a fluid to transmit the force, a reservoir to hold the fluid, a pump to move the fluid, an actuator to change the flow of fluid into mechanical work, lines to carry the fluid, and valves to control the flow and pressure of the fluid. Other components increase the efficiency of the systems.

The hydraulic systems in a modern airplane can be quite complex, but they become less difficult to understand when we look at the way the systems have evolved from the most simple to the complete modern system.

When flying was less complex than it is today, there was little need for hydraulic systems. Airplanes flew so slowly that drag was no great concern, so the landing gear did not need to be retracted. Landing speeds were so slow that there was no need for wing flaps, and once the airplane was on the ground, the tail skid served as a very effective brake. Paved runways, however, brought about the need for brakes, and the first simple hydraulic system came into being.

Sealed Brake System

A diaphragm-type master cylinder and an expander tube brake such as the one in Figure 5-13 is a complete hydraulic system in its simplest form.

The entire system is sealed, and when the brake pedal is depressed, it moves a diaphragm which forces fluid into a synthetic rubber expander tube mounted around a frame on the wheel. When fluid expands the tube, it pushes against asbestos-type brake blocks, and they produce friction with the brake drum that rotates with the wheel. When the brake pedal is released, the return spring moves the diaphragm back and releases the brake. This type of system is so small that expansion of the fluid caused by heat is taken up by the flexibility of the diaphragm in the master cylinders.

actuator. A fluid power device that changes fluid pressure into mechanical movement.

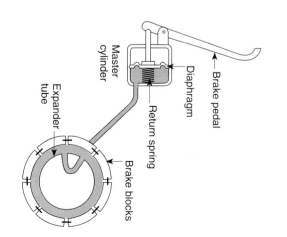

Brake pedal

Master cylinder

Diaphragm

Return spring

Expander tube

Brake blocks

Figure 5-13. *The expander-tube brake and diaphragm-type master cylinder is the simplest type of hydraulic system.*

Hydraulic and Pneumatic Power Systems

335

Reservoir-Type Brake System

Heavier and faster airplanes require more pressure and a greater volume of fluid to operate the brakes. This requirement brought about the vented brake system similar to the one used in automobiles.

The master cylinder is a single-acting pump. The piston is moved inward by the pilot's foot, and it is returned by a spring when foot pressure is released.

Figure 5-14 illustrates this system. The first movement of the piston closes the compensator port in the master cylinder, and the piston forces fluid into the wheel cylinder. This moves the wheel pistons outward, which forces the brake linings against the inside of the rotating brake drum to create the friction that slows the airplane. When the pedal is released, a spring forces the master cylinder piston back beyond the compensator port, and the entire system is vented to the atmosphere through the reservoir. When heat expands the fluid, it backs up into the reservoir and does not create any pressure in the system that could cause the brakes to drag. When there is a small leak in the brake lines or wheel cylinders, the master cylinder replaces the fluid lost each time the piston is moved back beyond the compensator port.

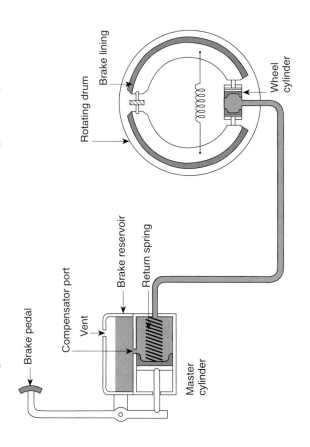

Figure 5-14. *A reservoir-type master cylinder vents the lines and wheel cylinders to the atmosphere through the compensator port to prevent heat expansion of the fluid from causing the brakes to drag. It also replenishes fluid lost in the system.*

Single-Acting Actuator System

As airplane weight and speed increased, flaps were installed that allowed the pilot to slow the airplane for landing. Many of the flaps on the small airplanes were mechanically operated, but some used single-acting hydraulic cylinders. The selector valve was rotated to the FLAPS-DOWN position and the hand pump was pumped. Fluid forced the piston in the flap actuator to move the flaps down. When the pilot rotated the selector valve to the FLAPS-UP position, a spring inside the flap actuator moved the piston back, raising the flaps and returning the fluid to the reservoir. Two check valves inside the pump allow as much fluid to be pumped as is needed to lower the flaps.

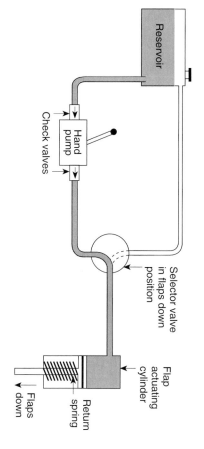

Figure 5-15. *A selector valve allows fluid from the hand pump to go to the actuator cylinder, or to return from the actuator to the reservoir.*

Double-Acting Actuator System

A single-acting actuator is satisfactory for hydraulic brakes and for very simple wing flaps, but when airplanes began to fly fast enough that parasite drag became a major problem, retractable landing gear was installed that required double-acting actuators. These actuators use hydraulic pressure to move the actuator piston in both directions.

Figure 5-16 on the next page illustrates a very simple system using a reservoir, a hand pump, a selector valve, and a double-acting actuator. To lower the landing gear, turn the selector valve to the GEAR-DOWN position and actuate the hand pump. Fluid under pressure enters the top of the cylinder and moves the piston down, forcing the landing gear down. The fluid that had been on the bottom of the piston returns to the reservoir through the selector valve. To raise the landing gear, turn the selector valve to the GEAR-UP position and actuate the hand pump. Fluid under pressure now enters the bottom of the actuator and moves the piston up. The fluid that had been in the top of the actuator returns to the reservoir through the selector valve.

single-acting actuator. A linear hydraulic or pneumatic actuator that uses fluid power for movement in one direction and a spring force for its return.

selector valve. A flow control valve used in hydraulic systems that directs pressurized fluid into one side of an actuator, and at the same time directs return fluid from the other side of the actuator back to the reservoir.

There are two basic types of selector valves: open-center valves and closed-center valves. The four-port closed-center valve is the most frequently used type.

check valve. A hydraulic component that allows full flow of fluid in one direction but blocks all flow in the opposite direction.

double-acting actuator. A linear actuator moved in both directions by fluid power.

HYDRAULIC AND PNEUMATIC POWER SYSTEMS

337

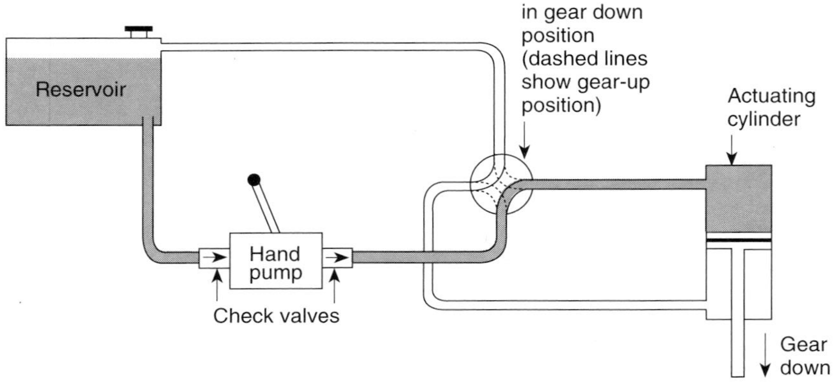

Figure 5-16. *The selector valve allows fluid from the hand pump to go to one side of the actuator cylinder to lower the landing gear. Fluid on the other side of the actuator piston returns through the selector valve to the reservoir.*

Power Pump Systems

As airplanes continued to evolve into heavier and faster machines with greater demands for their hydraulic systems, an engine-driven pump became the prime fluid mover. A hand pump was used as an emergency backup source of pressure and to actuate the system when the engine was not running.

Most engine-driven pumps are constant-displacement pumps that move a specific volume of fluid each time they rotate. This type of pump requires some means of relieving the pump of its load when system actuation is not needed, and some means must be provided to relieve any pressure in excess of a safe level.

Manual Pump Control Valve System

In this basic system, an engine-driven pump receives its fluid from the reservoir and moves it continually. When no unit is actuated, the fluid flows through the pump control valve back to the reservoir through the filter. The fluid circulates continually, but since it encounters very little restriction, almost no power is taken from the engine to drive the pump.

To lower the landing gear, the pilot places the selector valve in the GEAR-DOWN position and then closes the pump control valve (turns it ON). This shuts off the return of fluid to the reservoir, and the pump forces fluid into the landing gear actuating cylinders and lowers the landing gear.

When the landing gear is down and locked, the pressure builds up, but it cannot damage the system because it is relieved by the pressure relief valve until the pilot opens the pump control valve and unloads the pump. Some pump control valves are automatic and open when the pressure builds up after the actuation is completed. *See* Figure 5-17.

constant-displacement pump. A pump which displaces, or moves, a constant amount of fluid each time it turns.

The faster a constant-displacement pump turns, the more fluid it moves.

pump control valve. A control valve in a hydraulic system that allows the pilot to manually direct the output of the hydraulic pump back to the reservoir when no unit is being actuated.

relief valve. A pressure-control valve that relieves any pressure over the amount for which it is set. They are damage-preventing units used in both hydraulic and pneumatic systems.

Pressure relief valves prevent damaging high pressures that could be caused by a malfunctioning pressure regulator, or by thermal expansion of fluid trapped in portions of the system.

power control valve. A hand-operated hydraulic pump unloading valve.

When the valve is open, fluid flows from the pump to the reservoir with little opposition. To actuate the unit, turn the selector valve, and manually close the power control valve. Pressurized fluid flows to the unit, and when it is completely actuated, the power control valve automatically opens.

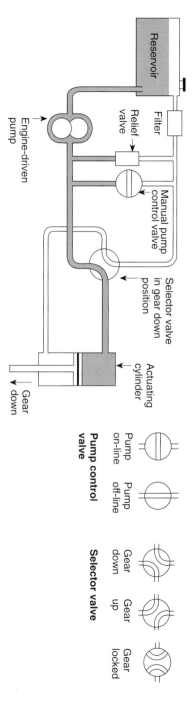

Figure 5-17. *A manual pump control valve keeps the pump unloaded when no unit is actuated.*

Reservoir

Filter

Relief
valve

Engine-driven
pump

Manual pump
control valve

Selector valve
in gear down
position

Actuating
cylinder

Gear
down

**Pump control
valve**

Pump
on-line

Pump
off-line

Selector valve

Gear
down

Gear
up

Gear
locked

unloading valve. This is another name for system pressure regulator. *See* system pressure regulator.

system-pressure regulator. An automatic hydraulic-system pressure control valve. When the system pressure is low, the output of the constant-delivery pump is directed into the system. When the pressure builds up to a specified kick-out pressure, the regulator shifts and unloads the pump so its output is directed back into the reservoir with very little opposition. The pump remains unloaded until the system pressure drops to the regulator kick-in pressure.

Power Control Valve System

A power control valve is similar in its function to a pump control valve. It is closed manually, but opens automatically. When no unit is actuated, the valve remains in its OPEN position and fluid circulates freely between the pump and the reservoir.

To actuate a unit, move the selector valve to the correct position and push the power control valve in to its CLOSED position. As soon as actuation is complete and the pressure builds up, the power control valve will automatically open and relieve the pump.

Because the power control valve opens automatically, pressure never rises high enough to operate the system pressure relief valve. To check its operation, push the power control valve in to its CLOSED position and hold it there until the pressure builds up high enough for the relief valve to function.

Automatic Unloading Valve System

The final stage in the evolution of the basic hydraulic system includes an automatic pump control valve called an unloading valve, or system pressure regulator, and an accumulator to maintain system pressure when the pump is unloaded. *See* Figure 5-18 on the next page.

The engine-driven pump receives its fluid from the reservoir, and moves it through the unloading valve into the system pressure manifold, where the accumulator holds it under pressure. When the system pressure rises to a specified value, called the kick-out pressure, the unloading valve shifts and directs the pump outlet into the return manifold. A check valve inside the unloading valve traps the fluid in the pressure manifold, where it is kept pressurized by the accumulator. The pump circulates the fluid through the unloading valve and the system filter back into the reservoir all the time the system pressure is above the unloading valve kick-in pressure. This circulation has almost no opposition, and very little engine power is used to drive the pump.

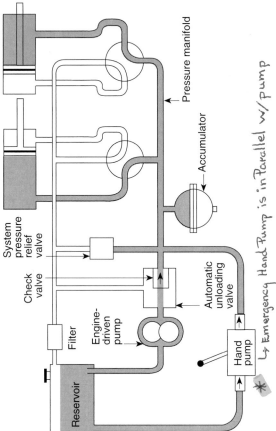

Figure 5-18. *The accumulator holds pressure on the system, and the automatic unloading valve keeps the pump unloaded as long as the operating range of pressure is maintained.*

↳ Emergency Hand Pump is in Parallel w/ pump

accumulator. A hydraulic component that consists of two compartments separated by a movable component such as a piston, diaphragm, or bladder. One compartment is filled with compressed air or nitrogen, and the other is filled with hydraulic fluid and is connected into the system pressure manifold.

pressure manifold. The portion of a fluid power system from which the selector valves receive their pressurized fluid.

kick-in pressure. The pressure at which an unloading valve causes a hydraulic pump to direct its fluid into the system manifold.

return manifold. The portion of a fluid power system through which the fluid is returned to the reservoir.

kick-out pressure. The pressure at which an unloading valve shuts off the flow of fluid into the system pressure manifold and directs it back to the reservoir under a much reduced pressure.

standpipe. A pipe sticking up in a tank or reservoir that allows part of the tank to be used as a reserve, or standby, source of fluid.

hydraulic powerpack. A small, self-contained hydraulic system that consists of a reservoir, pump, selector valves, and relief valves. The powerpack is removable from the aircraft as a unit to facilitate maintenance and service.

When some component in the system is actuated, the system pressure drops to the unloading valve kick-in pressure, and the unloading valve shifts to shut off the flow to the reservoir and direct the pump output into the system pressure manifold. The pump supplies all of the fluid needed for the actuation. A hand pump draws its fluid from the bottom of the reservoir, and may be used to produce pressure or actuate the system when the engine is not operating. If a leak in the system should allow all the fluid available to the engine-driven pump to be pumped overboard, the hand pump still has access to enough fluid below the standpipe in the reservoir to lower the landing gear and actuate the brakes. The system pressure relief valve in this system serves the same function as that in the simpler system.

Open-Center System

To minimize the complexity of hydraulic systems, some small and medium-sized aircraft use an open-center hydraulic system.

An open-center system such as the one in Figure 5-19 does not use a system pressure regulator, but rather uses special open-center selector valves installed in series with each other. When no unit is being actuated, the fluid flows from the reservoir through the open center of all of the valves, back into the reservoir. When either the landing gear or flaps is actuated, the selector valve for that system is shifted so that fluid flows into one side of the actuator. Fluid from the opposite side of the actuator returns to the reservoir through the other selector valves.

When the actuation is complete, the pressure builds up and automatically shifts the valve back into its open-center position. This allows the fluid to circulate through the system with almost no load on the pump.

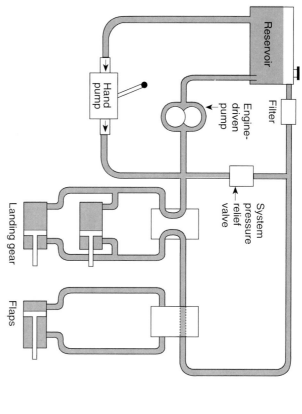

Figure 5-19. *An open-center system requires no separate unloading valve, but returns fluid to the reservoir through the open center of the selector valves when no unit is actuated.*

open-center selector valve. A type of selector valve that functions as an unloading valve as well as a selector valve.

Power Pack System

The hydraulic power pack was developed to make hydraulic systems easy to service and lightweight. The system shown in Figures 6-18 and 6-19 of Chapter 6 uses a power pack that contains the reservoir, pump, high-pressure relief valve, low-pressure control valve, and a shuttle valve all in one unit. *See* Figures 6-18 and 6-19 on Pages 434 and 435.

STUDY QUESTIONS: BASIC AIRCRAFT HYDRAULIC SYSTEMS

Answers begin on Page 415. Page numbers refer to chapter text.

26. The master cylinder in a simple brake system is a _____ (single or double)-action pump. *Page 336*

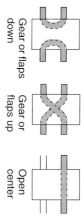

27. In a reservoir-type brake system, the brake line and wheel cylinders are vented to the atmosphere through the _____ port in the master cylinder. *Page 336*

Continued

28. Fluid is returned from a single-acting actuator by the action of a _____ pushing on the piston. *Page 336*

29. Hydraulic fluid from the return side of a double-acting actuator returns to the reservoir through the _____ . *Page 337*

30. An engine-driven hydraulic pump that moves a specific amount of fluid each time it rotates is called a _____-displacement pump. *Page 338*

31. An engine-driven constant-displacement pump _____ (does or does not) require some type of valve to unload the pump when no component in the system is actuated. *Page 338*

32. When lowering the landing gear in an airplane equipped with a hydraulic system using a manual pump control valve, the gear selector valve is placed in the DOWN position _____ (before or after) the pump control valve is closed. *Page 338*

33. The hydraulic pump is unloaded when the manual pump control valve is _____ (opened or closed). *Page 339*

34. A power control valve is similar to a pump control valve. Both are turned ON manually, but the power control valve opens, or turns OFF, _____ (automatically or manually). *Page 339*

35. A valve that prevents pressure rising to a dangerous level in a hydraulic system is called an _____ valve. *Page 338*

36. Another name for an automatic unloading valve is a/an _____ . *Page 339*

37. When an automatic unloading valve is used in a hydraulic system, the pressure is held on the system when the pump is unloaded by a/an _____ . *Page 339*

38. The selector valves in an open-center hydraulic system are arranged in _____ (series or parallel). *Page 340*

39. An open-center hydraulic system _____ (does or does not) need a pump unloading valve. *Page 341*

Hydraulic System Components

This section describes the purpose and operation of a number of hydraulic system components.

Hydraulic Fluids

Aircraft reciprocating engines use hydraulic valve lifters to open the intake and exhaust valves, and these lifters use engine lubricating oil as their fluid. Turbine engines are often equipped with variable inlet guide vanes and compressor bleed valves that are moved by hydraulic actuators that use fuel as the fluid. A pneumatic system uses air as its fluid. Almost any fluid, either liquid or gaseous, can be used to transmit a force, but in an aircraft hydraulic system, more requirements must be met than just those of transmitting a force.

Fluid that is used in an aircraft hydraulic system must be as incompressible as practical, and it must have a low viscosity so it will flow through the lines with a minimum of friction. It must be chemically stable, have good lubricating properties so the pump and system components will not wear excessively, and it must not foam in operation. It must be compatible with the metal in the components and with the elastic materials of which the seals are made, and it must have a high flash point and a high fire point.

The technical bulletins furnished by the fluid manufacturer provides information about the compatibility of the hydraulic fluids with the various aircraft materials.

Types of Hydraulic Fluids

Three basic types of hydraulic fluids are used in aircraft hydraulic systems: vegetable base, mineral base, and synthetic base. These fluids are not compatible with each other, and you must be able to identify each of them and understand their advantages and limitations. If a system is inadvertently serviced with the wrong type of fluid, all the fluid must be drained, the system flushed with the proper solvent, and all of the seals in the system changed.

Vegetable-Base Hydraulic Fluid

MIL-H-7644, vegetable-base fluid, was used in the past when aircraft hydraulic system requirements were not nearly so severe as they are today. Vegetable-base hydraulic fluid is essentially castor oil and alcohol, and it is dyed blue for identification. Natural rubber seals can be used with vegetable-base fluid, and a system using this fluid can be flushed with alcohol.

You are unlikely to find vegetable-base hydraulic fluid when servicing modern aircraft, but you may encounter it in some of the independent brake systems of older aircraft.

Mineral-Base Hydraulic Fluid

MIL-H-5606 mineral-base hydraulic fluid is still widely used for aircraft hydraulic systems. A kerosine-type petroleum product that has good lubricating characteristics, it contains additives that inhibit foaming and keep it from reacting with metal to form corrosion. MIL-H-5606 fluid is chemically stable, and it has a very small change in its viscosity as its temperature changes. Its main disadvantage is that it is flammable.

Mineral-base hydraulic fluid is dyed red for identification, and systems that use this fluid may be flushed with naphtha, varsol, or Stoddard solvent. Neoprene seals and hoses may be used with mineral-base hydraulic fluid. If you spill mineral-base hydraulic fluid on an aircraft tire, remove it by washing the tire with soap and water.

Synthetic-Hydrocarbon-Base Hydraulic Fluid

The familiar "red oil," as MIL-H-5606 is commonly known, is being replaced in some military aircraft with MIL-H-83282 fluid. This is also dyed red, but it has a synthetic hydrocarbon base. It is compatible with all of the materials used with 5606 fluid. The main advantage of 83282 fluid is that it is fire resistant.

Another fluid that is compatible with MIL-H-5606 fluid is MIL-H-81019 fluid, which is used in extremely low temperatures. It is operational at a temperature as low as -90°F. This fluid is also dyed red to prevent it being inadvertently used with systems that should use fluids that have other than a mineral base.

Phosphate Ester Hydraulic Fluid

MIL-H-5606 hydraulic fluid can create a fire hazard if a line breaks and sprays the fluid out under high pressure into an area near a hot engine. In 1948, the Monsanto Company, in cooperation with the Douglas Aircraft Company, developed a fire-resistant phosphate ester hydraulic fluid named Skydrol 7000. As jet aircraft became the standard for the transportation industry, Skydrol 500A was developed to meet its needs. As aircraft hydraulic systems became more demanding, newer fluid specifications were developed, and since 1978 Skydrol LD-4 and Skydrol 500B-4 have been created to meet the demands for commercial aircraft hydraulic fluid.

Skydrol LD-4 and 500B-4 are colored light purple, and they are only slightly heavier than water. (Specific gravity 1.009 and 1.057.) One of the main advantages of this type of hydraulic fluid is its wide range of operating temperatures. Skydrol hydraulic fluid can operate when its temperature is as low as -65°F to a temperature greater than 225°F.

For all of its advantages, Skydrol is not without its limitations. Skydrol is quite susceptible to contamination by water from the atmosphere, so containers of Skydrol must be kept tightly sealed. Skydrol will attack polyvinyl chlorides, and it must not be allowed to drip onto electrical wiring, as it will damage the insulation. It will also act as a paint remover and lift most types of finishing materials other than epoxy or polyurethane from an aircraft. If you spill Skydrol on aircraft tires, remove it with soap and water.

Skydrol fluid will not damage the metals commonly used in aircraft construction, and it is compatible with natural fibers and with such synthetics as nylon and some polyesters. Butyl, silicone rubber, or Teflon seals may be used with Skydrol. When servicing a system that uses Skydrol, be very sure to use only the seals that have the part numbers specified by the aircraft manufacturer, because seals that are compatible with other types of hydraulic fluid will be ruined if they are installed in a system that uses Skydrol.

Systems using Skydrol fluid should be flushed with trichlorethylene. Components containing Skydrol fluid can be cleaned with Stoddard solvent, methyl ethyl ketone (MEK), or isopropyl alcohol.

Contamination and Protection of Hydraulic Fluids

Hydraulic systems operate with high pressures, and the components used in these systems have such close fitting parts that any contamination in the fluid will cause the components to fail.

When servicing a hydraulic system, be sure to use only the correct fluid. The service manual for the aircraft specifies the type of fluid, and the reservoir should have the required type of fluid plainly marked with a placard near the filler opening.

Use the patch test to determine whether or not hydraulic fluid is contaminated. Pass a measured volume of fluid through a special patch-type filter in a test kit. After all of the fluid has passed through, analyze the filter and observe the type and amount of contaminants. The instructions that accompany the test kit explain the procedures used to evaluate the test patch.

To give an idea of the importance of using perfectly clean and uncontaminated fluid, Figure 5-20 on the next page shows a comparison of contaminant size. One micron is one millionth of a meter, or approximately 0.000039 inch. (One inch is equal to 25,400 microns.) The unaided human eye can see contaminants as small as 40 microns, and modern hydraulic filters can filter out contaminants larger than 3 microns. This high degree of filtration is important because some of the clearances in new hydraulic components are as small as 2 microns (0.000 080 inch).

polyvinyl chloride. A thermoplastic resin that is used in the manufacture of transparent tubing for electrical insulation and fluid lines which are subject to low pressures.

Butyl. The trade name for a synthetic rubber product that is made by the polymerization of isobutylene.

Butyl withstands such potent chemicals as phosphate ester-base (Skydrol) hydraulic fluids.

silicone rubber. An elastomeric material made from silicone elastomers. Silicone rubber is compatible with fluids that attack other natural or synthetic rubbers.

Teflon. The registered trade name for a fluorocarbon resin used to make hydraulic and pneumatic seals, hoses, and backup rings.

micron. One millionth of a meter. The micron is a unit of measurement that is often used to measure the effectiveness of a hydraulic filter.

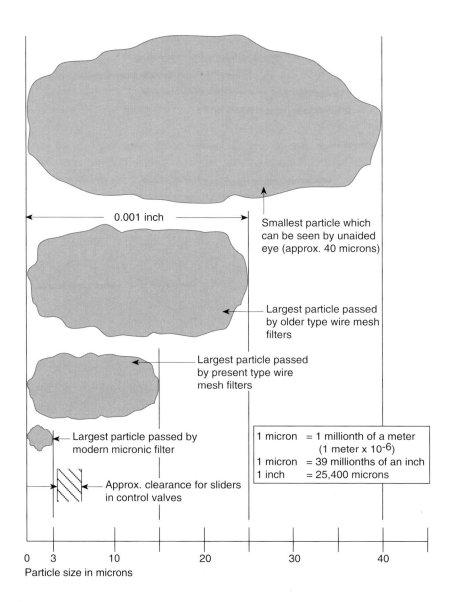

Figure 5-20. *Relative sizes of hydraulic system contaminants*

The following labels appear in the figure:

0.001 inch

Smallest particle which can be seen by unaided eye (approx. 40 microns)

Largest particle passed by older type wire mesh filters

Largest particle passed by present type wire mesh filters

Largest particle passed by modern micronic filter

Approx. clearance for sliders in control valves

1 micron	= 1 millionth of a meter (1 meter x 10⁻⁶)
1 micron	= 39 millionths of an inch
1 inch	= 25,400 microns

Particle size in microns
0 3 10 20 30 40

STUDY QUESTIONS: HYDRAULIC FLUIDS

Answers begin on Page 415. Page numbers refer to chapter text.

40. Vegetable-base hydraulic fluid is dyed _____ for identification. *Page 343*

41. Hydraulic systems using vegetable-base fluid can be flushed out with _____ . *Page 343*

42. Hydraulic systems using vegetable-base fluid have seals made of _____ rubber. *Page 343*

43. Mineral-base hydraulic fluid is dyed _____ for identification. *Page 344*

44. Hydraulic systems using mineral-base fluid can be flushed out with _____ . *Page 344*

45. Hydraulic systems using mineral-base fluid have seals made of _____ . *Page 344*

46. Mineral-base hydraulic fluid can be removed from an aircraft tire by washing the tire with _____ . *Page 344*

47. A popular synthetic hydraulic fluid with a phosphate ester base is popularly known as _____ . *Page 344*

48. Skydrol 500B-4 fluid is dyed _____ for identification. *Page 344*

49. Hydraulic systems using phosphate ester-base fluid can be flushed out with _____ . *Page 345*

50. Hydraulic systems using phosphate ester-base fluid have seals made of _____ . *Page 345*

51. Skydrol hydraulic fluid that has been spilled on aircraft tires should be removed with _____ . *Page 345*

Hydraulic Reservoirs

The reservoir is the component that stores the fluid and serves as an expansion chamber to provide a space for the fluid when its volume increases because of temperature. The reservoir also serves as a point at which the fluid can purge itself of any air it accumulates in its operational cycle.

Reservoirs must have enough capacity to hold all of the fluid that can be returned to the system with any configuration of the landing gear, flaps, and all other hydraulically actuated units. It is important when servicing a reservoir to decrease the system pressure to zero, as this will return the maximum amount of fluid to the reservoir. If the reservoir is filled when the accumulator is charged with fluid, it will be overfull when the accumulator is discharged.

Nonpressurized Reservoirs

Airplanes that fly at relatively low altitudes are usually equipped with nonpressurized reservoirs such as the one in Figure 5-21 on the next page. The fluid-return fitting in the reservoir is usually directed in such a way as to minimize foaming, and any air that is in the fluid will be swirled out, or extracted. Some reservoirs have filters built into their return line to filter all of the fluid that is returned from the system.

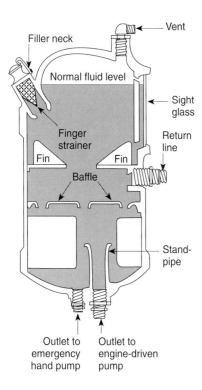

Figure 5-21. *A typical nonpressurized hydraulic reservoir*

The reservoirs for all but the simplest hydraulic systems have two outlets. One outlet is located either partially up the side of the reservoir or is connected to a standpipe inside the reservoir. This outlet supplies fluid to the engine-driven hydraulic pump. The other outlet is located at the bottom of the reservoir, and connects to the emergency hand pump. If a leak develops in the system that causes a loss of all of the fluid that can be moved by the engine-driven pump, there will still be enough fluid left in the bottom of the reservoir for emergency extension of the landing gear and for emergency application of the brakes.

There is a trend in many of the smaller aircraft with limited hydraulic systems to incorporate all of the hydraulic power system into a power pack which contains the reservoir, valves, and electric pump all in one easy-to-service unit. Such a system is illustrated in Figures 6-18 and 6-19 on Pages 434 and 435.

Pressurized Reservoirs

When airplanes fly at high altitudes, where the outside air pressure is low, there is not enough air pressure to force the hydraulic fluid from the reservoir into the inlet of the pump, so the pump tends to cavitate. Also, the hydraulic fluid that is returned to the reservoir develops a tendency to foam at high altitudes. To prevent pump cavitation and foaming of the return fluid, reservoirs in high-flying aircraft are pressurized. It is important to relieve the pressure in the reservoir before opening it for servicing.

One method of pressurizing a reservoir is to inject air into the returning fluid through an aspirator, or venturi tee fitting as shown in Figure 5-22. The fluid flowing back into the reservoir passes through the venturi, where it creates a low pressure and draws air from outside the reservoir into the venturi throat. The hydraulic fluid with air in it is swirled as it enters the top of the reservoir, and the air is expelled from the fluid. A relief valve in the reservoir maintains an air pressure of about 12 psi on the fluid.

Some turbine-engine-powered aircraft use a small amount of filtered compressor bleed air to pressurize the reservoir. These systems have an air pressure regulator between the engine and the reservoir to reduce the pressure to the proper value.

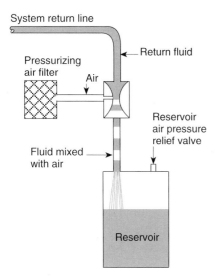

Figure 5-22. *A venturi tee fitting in the fluid return line to the reservoir pulls outside air into the hydraulic fluid to produce an air pressure above the fluid in the reservoir.*

Another way to pressurize the hydraulic reservoirs in turbine-engine-powered airplanes is to use the hydraulic system pressure acting on a small piston inside the reservoir. This small piston applies a force to a much larger piston that pressurizes the fluid. *See* Figure 5-23.

The fluid in this reservoir is pressurized to approximately 30 psi when the 3,000-psi system hydraulic pressure acts on a small piston inside the reservoir. This small piston moves a larger piston that has 100 times its area. The larger piston applies a force to the fluid inside the reservoir and builds up its pressure to 30 psi.

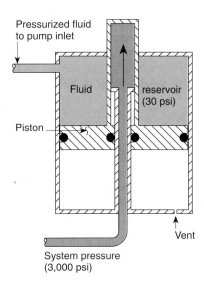

Figure 5-23. *The principle of a pressurized hydraulic reservoir, using hydraulic system pressure*

cavitation. A condition that exists in a hydraulic pump when there is not enough pressure in the reservoir to force fluid to the inlet of the pump. The pump picks up air instead of fluid.

STUDY QUESTIONS: HYDRAULIC RESERVOIRS

Answers begin on Page 415. Page numbers refer to chapter text.

52. Fluid taken from the standpipe in a hydraulic reservoir goes to the _____ (engine-driven pump or emergency hand pump). *Page 348*

53. A hydraulic unit that contains the reservoir, pump, and all of the valves is called a/an _____ . *Page 348*

54. Some hydraulic reservoirs are pressurized to prevent the pump _____ . *Page 348*

55. Three methods of pressurizing a hydraulic reservoir are:
    a. _____
    b. _____
    c. _____
    Pages 348 and 349

Hydraulic Pumps

Fluid power is produced when fluid is moved under pressure. The pumps used in a hydraulic system are simply fluid movers rather than pressure generators. Pressure is produced only when the flow of fluid from the pump is restricted.

The two basic types of hydraulic pumps are those operated by hand, and those driven by some source of mechanical power (such as an electric motor, or an aircraft engine).

Hand Pumps

Single-acting hand pumps move fluid only on one stroke of the piston, while double-acting pumps move fluid with both strokes. Double-acting pumps are commonly used in aircraft hydraulic systems because of their greater efficiency. Figure 5-24 shows a diagram of a piston-rod displacement, double-acting hydraulic hand pump.

On the stroke of the handle that pulls the piston outward, fluid is drawn into the pump through the inlet check valve. The outlet check valve inside the piston is seated, and the fluid on the back side of the piston is forced out of the pump outlet.

On the return stroke of the pump handle, the piston is forced into the cylinder. The pump inlet check valve seats, and the outlet check valve opens, allowing fluid to flow into the chamber that has the piston rod. The piston rod causes the volume of this side of the pump to be less than the volume of the fluid that was taken in, and approximately one half of the fluid that has just been taken into the pump is forced out the pump outlet.

To better understand the way this pump works, assume some values. The large end of the piston has an area of two square inches. The area of the piston rod is one square inch. The piston moves one inch each time the handle is moved through its full travel.

When the piston moves all the way to the left, two cubic inches of fluid are pulled into the cylinder through the inlet check valve, and the check valve closes. Now, when the piston is moved all of the way to the right, this two cubic inches of fluid passes through the outlet check valve. The volume of the chamber on the left side of the piston is only one cubic inch because the piston rod takes up the other cubic inch. Therefore one cubic inch of fluid leaves the pump through the outlet port, and the other cubic inch of fluid remains in the chamber on the left side of the piston. Each time the piston moves to the right, one cubic inch of fluid leaves the pump and no fluid is taken in. Each time the piston moves to the left, two cubic inches of fluid is taken into the pump and one cubic inch of fluid leaves the pump.

Hand pumps are simple devices and give little trouble, but their simplicity does not prevent some problems. For example, if the handle of a rebuilt hand pump cannot be moved in the normal pumping direction, there is a good probability that the outlet check valve is stuck closed or incorrectly installed.

If the outlet check valve is stuck in the open position, the handle will kick back during the normal intake stroke. Pressure from the accumulator will push back on the piston.

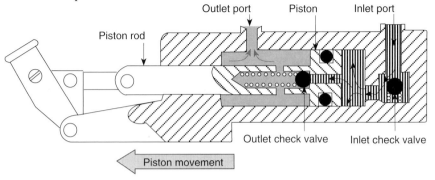

Piston is moved to the left, pulling 2 cubic inches of fluid into inlet port and forcing 1 cubic inch of fluid out the outlet port.

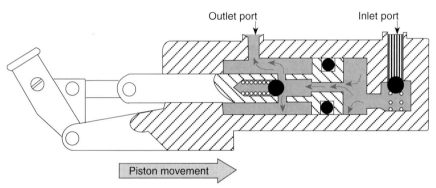

Piston is moved to the right, taking in no fluid and forcing 1 cubic inch of fluid out the outlet port.

Figure 5-24. *A double-acting, piston-rod displacement hydraulic hand pump*

Power Pumps

Power pumps are classified as either constant-displacement or variable-displacement. A constant-displacement pump moves a specific amount of fluid each time it rotates. A pump of this type must have some sort of relief valve or unloading device to prevent its building up so much pressure that it will rupture a line or perhaps damage itself. The drive shaft of almost all power pumps has a necked-down portion, called a shear section, that will break if the pressure-relief device fails. When this breaks, the pump will no longer operate, but the system will not be damaged.

shear section. A necked-down section of the drive shaft of a constant-displacement hydraulic pump. If the pump should seize, the shear section will break and prevent the pump being destroyed.

Some pumps use a shear pin rather than a shear section.

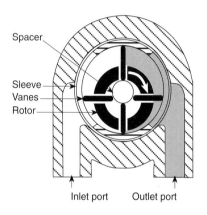

Figure 5-25. *A vane-type pump moves a relatively large volume of fluid under a low pressure.*

Variable-displacement pumps move a volume of fluid that is determined by the demands of the system. Variable-displacement pumps are often of the piston type, and the volume of their output is varied by changing either the actual or the effective stroke of the pistons.

Constant-Displacement Pumps

Constant-displacement pumps that produce a high volume of flow with a low pressure, a medium volume with medium pressure, and low volume with high pressure are available. In this section we will look at each of these.

Vane-Type Pumps

The vane pump is one of the simpler types of constant-displacement pumps used to move a large volume of fluid with a pressure of up to about 300 psi. *See* Figure 5-25.

The four steel vanes are free-floating in slots cut in the rotor. They are held against the wall of the steel sleeve by a steel pin spacer. As the rotor turns in the direction shown by the arrow, the volume between the vanes on the inlet side of the pump increases, and the volume between the vanes on the discharge side of the pump decreases. This change of volume pulls fluid into the pump through the inlet port and forces it out through the discharge port.

Vane-type pumps are used in some aircraft hydraulic systems, but they are more often used as fuel pumps and as air pumps to supply air for gyroscopic instruments and pneumatic deicer boots.

Gear-Type Pumps

Gear-type pumps move a medium volume of fluid under a pressure of between 300 and 1,500 psi. Two types of gear pumps are used in aircraft hydraulic systems, the simple spur-gear pump and the gerotor pump.

The spur-gear pump illustrated in Figure 5-26 uses two meshing external-tooth gears that fit closely into a figure-eight-shaped housing. One of the gears is driven by an engine accessory drive, and this gear drives the other one. As the gears rotate in the direction shown by the arrows, the space between the teeth on the inlet side of the pump becomes larger. Fluid is pulled into this space, trapped between the teeth and the housing, and carried around to the discharge side of the pump. Here the teeth of the two gears come into mesh and decrease the volume. As the volume is decreased, fluid is forced from the pump outlet.

A small amount of fluid leaks past the gears and around the shaft to help lubricate, cool, and seal the pump. This fluid drains back into the hollow shafts of the gears, where it is picked up by the low pressure at the inlet side of the pump. A case-pressure relief valve holds the fluid inside the hollow shafts of the gears, until it builds up a pressure of about 15 psi. This pressure is maintained to prevent air being taken into the pump in the event the shaft or the shaft seal becomes damaged. Fluid will be forced out of the pump rather than allowing air to be drawn into it. If air leaked into the pump, it would take the place of the fluid needed for lubrication and the pump would be damaged.

An overboard drain line connects to the base of the pump, and any hydraulic fluid dripping from this line indicates a damaged pump shaft seal. Engine oil dripping from this line indicates a damaged engine accessory drive oil seal.

As the output pressure of a gear-type pump builds up, there is a tendency for the case to distort which would allow fluid to leak past the ends of the gears. To prevent this leakage, some pumps direct high-pressure fluid from the discharge side of the pump back through a check valve into a cavity behind the bushing flanges. This high-pressure fluid forces the bushings tightly against the sides of the gears to decrease the side clearance of the gears and minimize leakage. It also compensates for wear of the bushings.

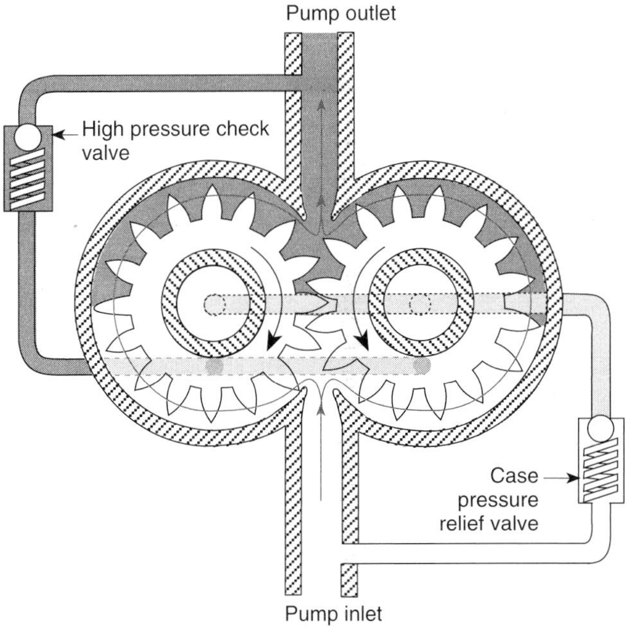

case pressure. A low pressure that is maintained inside the case of a hydraulic pump.

If a seal becomes damaged, hydraulic fluid will be forced out of the pump rather than allowing air to be drawn into the pump.

Figure 5-26. *A spur-gear-type pump moves a medium amount of fluid under a medium pressure.*

If the reservoir should become emptied, or if for any reason air gets into the pump inlet line, the pump intermittently picks up air and fluid, which causes the pump to chatter or cavitate. The lack of continuous lubrication causes the pump to overheat, which will cause its damage or destruction.

Gerotor Pumps

A gerotor pump, illustrated in Figure 5-27, is a combination internal and external gear pump.

The four-tooth spur gear is driven by an engine accessory drive, and as it turns, it rotates a five-tooth internal-gear rotor. As the gear and the rotor turn in the direction shown by the arrows, the space between the teeth gets larger on one side and smaller on the other. A plate with two crescent-shaped openings covers the gear and the rotor and forms the inlet and the outlet ports of the pump.

The opening located above the space that gets larger as the gear and the rotor turn is the inlet side of the pump, and the opening above the space that gets smaller as the teeth come into mesh is the outlet of the pump.

Piston Pumps

Aircraft hydraulic systems that require a relatively ~~small volume of fluid~~ under a pressure of 2,500 psi or more often use fixed-angle, multiple-piston pumps, such as the one in Figure 5-28.

There are usually seven or nine axially-drilled holes in the rotating cylinder block of this type of pump, and each hole contains a close-fitting piston attached to a drive plate by a ball-jointed rod. The cylinder block and the pistons are rotated as a unit by a shaft that is driven from an engine accessory drive.

The housing is angled so that the pistons on one side of the cylinder block are at the bottom of their stroke while the pistons on the other side of the block are at the top of their stroke. As the pump rotates one half of a turn, half of the pistons move from the top of their stroke to the bottom, and the pistons on the other side of the block move from the bottom of their stroke to the top.

A valve plate that has two crescent-shaped openings covers the ends of the cylinders. The pump outlet port is above the pistons that are moving up, and the inlet port is above the pistons that are moving down.

As the pistons move down in the cylinder block, they pull fluid into the pump, and as they move up, they force this fluid out of the pump into the system.

Variable-Displacement Pumps

An unloading valve of some sort must be used with a constant-displacement pump, but the same force used to control the unloading valve may be used to control the output of a variable-displacement pump, so there is no need for a separate control.

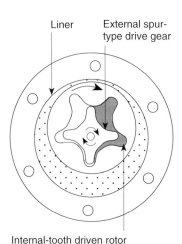

Figure 5-27. *A gerotor pump uses an external spur-type drive gear inside an internal-tooth driven gear.*

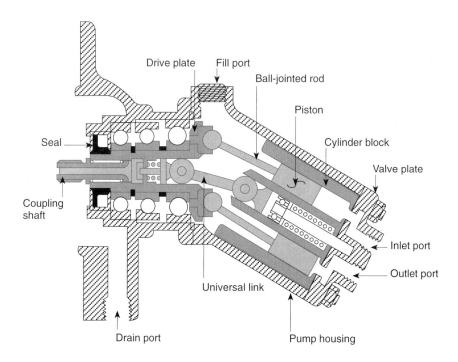

Figure 5-28. *Fixed-angle, multiple-piston pump*

gerotor pump. A form of constant-displacement gear pump. A gerotor pump uses an external-tooth spur gear that rides inside of and drives an internal-tooth rotor gear. There is one more tooth space inside the rotor than there are teeth on the drive gear.

As the gears rotate, the volume of the space between two of the teeth on the inlet side of the pump increases, while the volume of the space between two teeth on the opposite side of the pump decreases.

One of the more popular types of variable-displacement pumps is the Stratopower demand-type pump, shown in Figure 5-29 on the next page. This pump uses nine axially oriented cylinders and pistons. The pistons are driven up and down inside the cylinders by a wedge-shaped drive cam, and the pistons press against the cam with ball joint slippers.

When the slipper is against the thick part of the cam, the piston is at the top of its stroke, and, as the cam rotates, the piston moves down in the cylinder until the slipper is riding on the thin part of the cam. When the slipper is in this position, the piston is at the bottom of its stroke.

The physical stroke of the piston is the same regardless of the amount of fluid demanded by the system, but the effective length of the stroke controls the amount of fluid moved by this pump.

A balance between the fixed compensator spring force and the variable force caused by pump output pressure acting on an enlarged portion of the compensator stem moves the sleeves up or down over the outside of the pistons. This varies the position of the piston when the pressure is relieved, and thus varies the effective stroke of the piston.

Notice in the simplified diagram of the control system in Figure 5-30 that a passage from the discharge side of the pump directs output fluid pressure around the compensator stem. This stem is cut with a shoulder which serves as a piston. As the system pressure rises, this stem is pushed to the right,

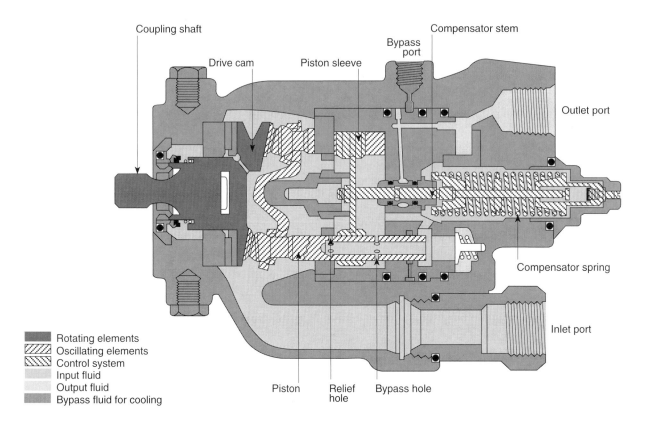

Coupling shaft · Drive cam · Piston sleeve · Bypass port · Compensator stem · Outlet port · Compensator spring · Inlet port · Piston · Relief hole · Bypass hole

Rotating elements
Oscillating elements
Control system
Input fluid
Output fluid
Bypass fluid for cooling

Figure 5-29. *Cutaway view of the Stratopower variable-displacement hydraulic pump*

compressing the compensator spring. The spider that moves the sleeves over the outside of the pistons is attached to the stem to vary the effective length of the piston stroke.

When the system pressure is low, as it is in Figure 5-30, the compensator spring forces the spider to move the sleeves to the left, or down on the pistons. The sleeves keep the relief holes covered for the full stroke of the piston, and the pistons move fluid out through the check valves into the pump discharge line during their entire stroke.

When the system pressure is high, as it is in Figure 5-31, it acts on the compensator-stem piston and compresses the compensator spring. This pulls the sleeves to the right, or up on the pistons so the relief holes are uncovered during most of their stroke. The pistons move through their full stroke, but since the fluid passes out the relief holes, no fluid is forced from the pump.

Any time the system pressure is at an intermediate value, the sleeves close the relief holes at some point along the stroke of the piston. In this way, just enough fluid is pumped to maintain the system pressure at the level for which the compensator spring is set.

When the pistons are at the extreme top of their stroke, the bypass hole in the piston aligns with a passage in the housing that connects to the outside bypass port. *See* Figure 5-29. A small amount of fluid flows though the bypass port back to the reservoir on each pressure stroke. This fluid picks up heat from the pump, and after it leaves the pump it passes through a case drain filter and a check valve and into a finned tubing heat exchanger inside one of the fuel tanks. *See* Figure 5-32 on the next page. From the heat exchanger it flows back into the reservoir. This flow of bypass fluid cools the pump by keeping fresh fluid flowing through it during the time in which there is no flow from the output port.

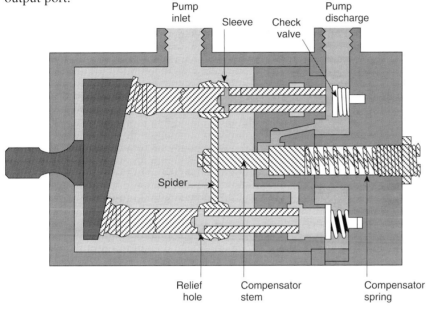

Figure 5-30. *The system pressure is low, the compensator spring has moved the spider and the sleeves to the left so that the relief holes are covered for most of the piston stroke, and fluid is moved out of the pump through the check valve.*

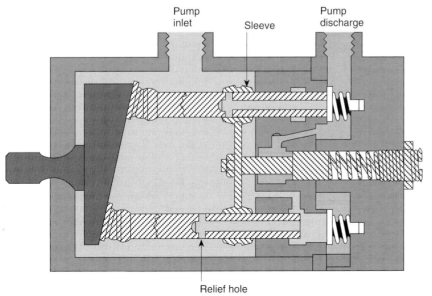

Figure 5-31. *The system pressure is high. Fluid pressing on the step cut in the compensator stem has compressed the compensator spring and moved the sleeves to the right so the relief holes are uncovered for almost all of the piston stroke. No fluid is moved out of the pump.*

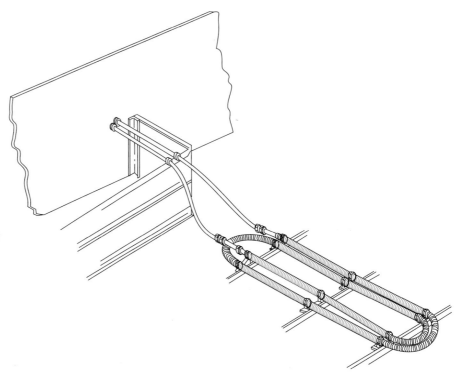

Figure 5-32. *Bypass fluid from the hydraulic pump flows through finned tubing submerged in fuel inside a fuel tank to remove heat from the fluid.*

STUDY QUESTIONS: HYDRAULIC PUMPS

Answers begin on Page 415. Page numbers refer to chapter text.

56. A hydraulic hand pump that moves some fluid every time the pump handle is moved is called a
_____ -acting pump. *Page 350*

57. A piston-rod displacement hand pump is a _____ (single or double)-acting pump. *Page 350*

58. If the handle of a rebuilt hydraulic hand pump cannot be moved in the direction of normal pumping, the
probable cause is an improperly installed _____ (inlet or outlet) check valve. *Page 350*

59. A pressure regulator, or unloading valve, must be used with a _____ (constant or variable)-
displacement hydraulic pump. *Page 351*

60. An engine-driven hydraulic pump is prevented from building up damagingly high pressure if the pressure
regulator and relief valve fail by a/an _____ in the drive shaft. *Page 351*

61. A vane-type engine-driven fluid pump is usually used for applications that must move a _____
(large or small) volume of fluid. *Page 352*

62. Hydraulic fluid flowing through a spur-gear-type pump moves _____ (between or around)
the gears. *Page 352*

63. Hydraulic fluid dripping from the overboard drain line connected to an engine-driven pump base indicates a damaged pump shaft _____ . *Page 353*

64. An air leak in the inlet line to an engine-driven hydraulic pump will cause the pump to _____ and _____ . *Page 354*

65. A piston-type engine-driven fluid pump is usually used for applications that require a _____ (high or low) pressure. *Page 354*

66. A variable-displacement hydraulic pump _____ (does or does not) require a pressure regulator or unloading valve. *Page 354*

67. A Stratopower variable-displacement hydraulic pump varies the discharge flow by altering the _____ (actual or effective) stroke of the pistons. *Page 355*

68. The hydraulic fluid that flows through the heat exchanger in the fuel tank is fluid that flows from the _____ port of the Stratopower variable-displacement pump. *Page 357*

Hydraulic Valves

Fluid power systems are much like electrical systems in that the object of the system is to control a flow so it can perform work. In hydraulic systems there are two types of valves, those that control flow and those that control pressure.

Ball-type check valve

Flow Control Valves

Flow control valves are much like switches in an electrical system. Some allow fluid to flow or prevent it from flowing. Others direct flow from one device to another, and still others regulate the rate of flow.

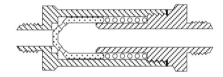

Cone-type check valve

Check Valves

Aircraft hydraulic systems include many situations where the fluid must flow in one direction and not flow in the opposite direction. Reverse flow can be prevented by the use of check valves.

The most common check valves are the ball-type, the cone-type, and the flapper, or swing-type, check valve.

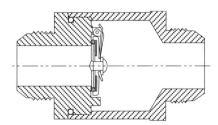

Flapper-type check valve

Figure 5-33. *Typical check valves. All of these valves allow a full flow from the left to right, but prevent any flow from right to left.*

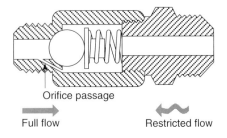

Orifice passage

Full flow   Restricted flow

Figure 5-34. *An orifice check valve allows full flow of fluid in one direction but a restricted flow in the opposite direction.*

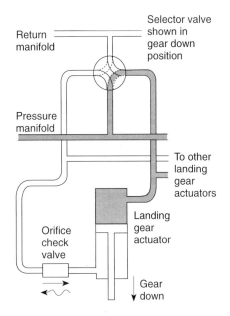

Return manifold

Selector valve shown in gear down position

Pressure manifold

To other landing gear actuators

Orifice check valve

Landing gear actuator

Gear down

Figure 5-35. *Installation of an orifice check valve in a landing gear actuating cylinder to slow the fluid flow during lowering the gear but allowing full flow for raising it.*

Fluid enters the ball-type check valve from the left side, forces the ball off of its seat, and flows through the valve. Fluid cannot flow through the valve in the opposite direction because the ball is held tightly against its seat by the spring force and by the fluid.

A cone-type check valve works in the same way as the ball-type valve, except the ball is replaced with a hollow cone. Fluid flows through the valve from left to right, forcing the cone off of its seat and passing through the holes in the surface of the cone. Reverse flow is prevented by the fluid and the spring holding the cone tight in its seat.

Large volumes of low-pressure fluid are often controlled by a flapper, or swing-type, check valve. Fluid flows through this valve from left to right, forcing the flapper off of its seat. Fluid flow in the reverse direction is prevented by the spring and the fluid hold the flapper tight against its seat.

Orifice Check Valve

Certain applications require full flow of fluid in one direction, but rather than blocking all of the fluid flowing in the opposite direction, these allow fluid to flow through the valve at a restricted rate. For these applications, an orifice check valve is used.

An orifice check valve may be used in a landing gear system to slow the extension of the gear and yet allow it to retract as quickly as possible. When used for this application, it is installed in the landing gear actuator gear-up line illustrated in Figure 5-35. When the landing gear selector valve is placed in the GEAR-DOWN position, the up locks release the landing gear and it falls out of the wheel well. The weight of the gear and the force of air blowing against the wheel as it drops down try to speed up the extension. The check valve restricts the flow of the fluid coming out of the actuator and prevents the landing gear from dropping too quickly. When the selector valve is placed in the GEAR-UP position, the fluid flows into the actuator gear-up line through the check valve in its unrestricted direction, and full flow raises the landing gear.

Selector Valves

One common type of flow control valve is the selector valve, which controls the direction of flow of the fluid used to actuate some hydraulic component.

Two types of selector valves are open-center valves and closed-center valves. An open-center valve directs fluid through the center of the valve back to the reservoir when no units are being actuated. A closed-center valve stops the flow of fluid when it is in its neutral position.

Both types of selector valves direct fluid under pressure to one side of the actuator, and vent the opposite side of the actuator to the reservoir.

Plug-Type, Closed-Center Selector Valve

Systems that use a relatively low pressure for actuation may use a simple plug-type selector valve such as the one in Figure 5-36. In one position of the selector handle, the pressure port and the side of the actuator that extends the piston are connected. The side of the actuator that retracts the piston is connected to the return line. When the selector handle is rotated 90°, the actuator ports are reversed; the retract port is connected to the pressure line, and the extend port is connected to the return line. Some selector valves have a neutral position in which the actuator is isolated from both the pressure and return manifolds.

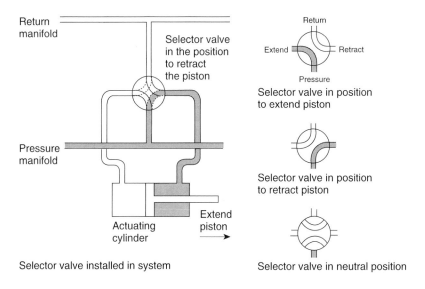

Selector valve installed in system

Figure 5-36. *Simplified diagram of a plug-type, closed-center, four-port selector valve*

Poppet-Type Closed-Center Selector Valve

Selector valves used in high-pressure hydraulic systems must have a much more positive shutoff of the fluid than provided by a plug-type valve, and often use poppet-type selector valves.

In the valve in Figure 5-37A on the next page, the selector valve control handle has been turned so that the cam lobes have lifted poppets 2 and 4 off of their seats, and fluid flows from the pressure manifold through the open valve 2 to the actuator extend line that moves the piston rod out of the cylinder. Return fluid from the right side of the actuating cylinder flows through the actuator retract line and through valve 4, back to the return manifold.

When the selector valve handle is rotated 90°, the cam allows valves 2 and 4 to close and opens valves 1 and 3. This is shown in Figure 5-37B. Fluid flows from the pressure manifold through valve 3 to the actuator retract line, and the piston rod moves into the cylinder. Fluid forced from the actuator flows

orifice check valve. A component in a hydraulic or pneumatic system that allows unrestricted flow in one direction, and restricted flow in the opposite direction.

closed-center selector valve. A type of flow-control valve used to direct pressurized fluid into one side of an actuator, and at the same time, direct the return fluid from the other side of the actuator to the fluid reservoir.

Closed-center selector valves are connected in parallel between the pressure manifold and the return manifold.

open-center hydraulic system. A fluid power system in which the selector valves are arranged in series with each other. Fluid flows from the pump through the center of the selector valves, back into the reservoir when no unit is being actuated.

through valve 1 to the return manifold. Another 90° of the selector valve handle closes all of the valves, as shown in Figure 5-37C. This shuts off all of the flow to and from the actuator.

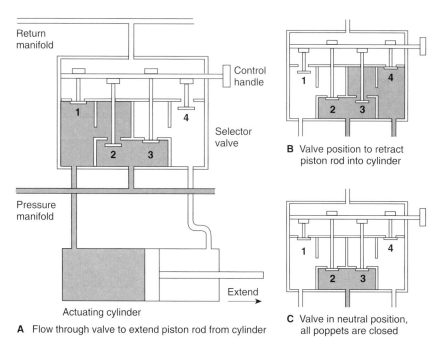

B Valve position to retract piston rod into cylinder

C Valve in neutral position, all poppets are closed

A Flow through valve to extend piston rod from cylinder

Figure 5-37. *Poppet-type closed-center selector valve*

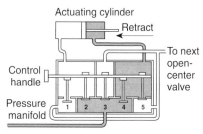

A Flow through valve to extend piston rod from cylinder

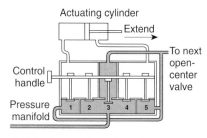

B Valve position to retract piston rod into cylinder.

C Valve in neutral position. All poppets are closed except poppet 3, which allows fluid to flow directly from pressure manifold to the next open-center valve.

Figure 5-38. *Poppet-type open-center selector valve*

Poppet-Type Open-Center Selector Valve

The open-center selector valve in Figure 5-38 is much like the closed-center valve, except for poppet number 3, which allows fluid to flow straight through the valve when nothing is actuated. Open-center selector valves are connected in series, rather than in parallel, as are closed-center valves.

Figure 5-38A shows the valve in the position to extend the actuator rod. Poppets 2 and 5 are off their seats, and fluid flows from the pressure manifold around poppet 2 to the actuator. The return fluid flows from the actuator around poppet 5 to the next open-center selector valve and then to the reservoir. *See* Figure 5-38A.

To retract the actuator rod, Figure 5-38B shows poppets 1 and 4 are off their seats. Fluid flows from the pressure manifold around poppet 4 to the actuator, and from the actuator around poppet 1 the next selector valve.

When nothing is being actuated, the selector valve is turned to its neutral position shown in Figure 5-38C. Poppet 3 is off its seat and all of the others are seated. Fluid flows from the pressure manifold around poppet 3, through the next selector valve, and then back to the reservoir.

Spool-Type Closed-Center Selector Valve

Some applications have only a small amount of force to actuate a control valve that directs fluid into and out of an actuator. These applications often use a spool-type selector valve.

Figure 5-39A shows the way the spool-type selector valve is installed in the system. View B shows the position of the spool that directs fluid into the actuator extending the piston. View C shows the position of the spool that retracts the piston, and view D shows the spool in the neutral position with all flow to the actuator cutoff.

Sequence Valves

Some modern aircraft with retractable landing gear have doors that close in-flight to cover the wheel-wells and make the airplane more streamlined.

Sequence valves are often used to assure that the landing gear does not extend or retract while the doors are closed. Sequence valves are check valves that allow fluid to flow in one direction but prevent it from flowing in the opposite direction until the valve is opened manually, so the fluid can flow in either direction.

Figure 5-40 shows the location of the sequence valves in a landing gear retraction system. When the landing gear selector handle is placed in the GEAR-DOWN position, fluid flows to the wheel-well door actuator, but cannot flow to the landing gear actuator because it is blocked by the sequence valve. When the wheel-well doors are fully open, a part of the door depresses the plunger in the sequence valve, and fluid flows into the landing gear actuator cylinder to lower the landing gear.

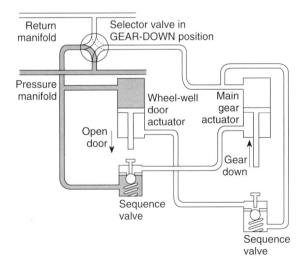

Figure 5-40. *A landing gear retraction system using a sequence valve to assure that the wheel well doors are fully open before the landing gear extends.*

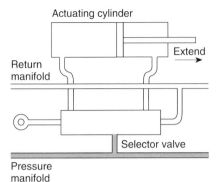

A Installation of valve in system

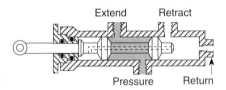

B Position of spool to extend piston

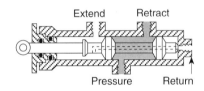

C Position of spool to retract piston

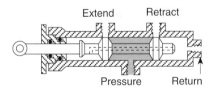

D Neutral position of spool

Figure 5-39. *Spool-type closed-center selector valve*

sequence valve. A valve in a hydraulic system that requires a certain action to be completed before another action can begin.

Sequence valves are used to assure that the hydraulically actuated wheel-well doors are completely open before pressure can be directed to the landing gear to lower it.

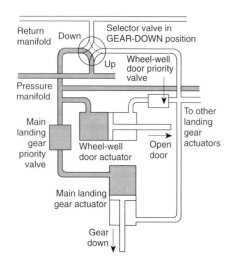

Figure 5-41. *Installation of priority valves in a landing gear actuating system to assure that the wheel well doors are fully open before the main landing gear is extended, and that the wheels are fully retracted before the wheel well doors close.*

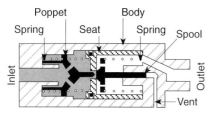

A Insufficient pressure, wheel-well doors are being actuated.

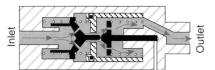

B Full pressure, landing gear is being lowered.

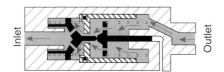

C Return fluid flow when gear is being retracted.

Figure 5-42. *Principle of operation of a priority valve*

When the landing gear selector valve is placed in the GEAR-UP position, fluid flows into the landing gear actuator to raise the landing gear, but the sequence valve prevents it flowing into the wheel-well door actuator. As soon as the landing gear is fully retracted, a part of the landing gear depresses the plunger in the wheel-well door sequence valve and opens it so fluid can flow into the wheel-well door actuator and close the wheel-well doors.

Priority Valve

A priority valve is similar to a sequence valve except that it is opened by hydraulic pressure rather than by mechanical contact.

Priority valves get their name from the fact that they control the sequence of operation of landing gear retraction and wheel-well door actuation by allowing the units that require the least pressure to have priority, or to actuate first.

Figure 5-41 shows the landing gear selector valve in the GEAR-DOWN position. Fluid flows to the wheel-well door actuator to open the doors, but it cannot flow to the main landing gear actuator, because it is shut off by the main landing gear priority valve.

Figure 5-42 shows the principle on which the priority valve operates. Figure 5-42A shows the valve in the position it is in before the wheel-well doors are fully open.

As soon as the doors are fully open, pressure builds up in the gear-down line and moves the poppet inside the priority valve to the right, as seen in Figure 5-42B. A pin on the poppet forces the spool valve off its seat and allows fluid to flow to the main landing gear actuator.

When the landing gear selector valve is placed in the GEAR-UP position, return fluid from the main landing gear actuator flows through the priority valve in the reverse direction as seen in Figure 5-42C. The fluid moves the seat to the left so that it opens the spool valve and allows fluid to flow through the selector valve to the reservoir.

Figure 5-41 shows a wheel-well door priority valve in the close-door line to the wheel-well door actuator. When the landing gear selector is placed in the GEAR-UP position, fluid flows into the main landing gear actuator to raise the gear. When the gear is up, the pressure builds up high enough to shift the poppet inside the wheel-well door priority valve. The poppet opens the spool valve and fluid flows into the wheel-well door cylinder to close it.

Flap Overload Valve

It is very important that wing flaps not be lowered when the airspeed is too high, and if the airspeed becomes too high when they are lowered, they must be raised. An excessive airload on the flaps can cause structural damage or unwanted pitching forces.

A flap overload valve can be installed in the wing flap hydraulic system to prevent the flaps from being lowered at too high an airspeed. If they are down when the airspeed increases, the valve allows them to raise automatically until the air load is within safe limits. *See* Figure 5-43.

When the flap selector valve is placed in the FLAPS-DOWN position, fluid flows through the overload valve from ports P to F and into the flaps-down side of the actuator. If they are being lowered when the airspeed is too high, the air loads on the flaps will require more pressure than the overload valve will allow. The valve shifts, holding the pressure in the flap actuator but returning fluid from the overload valve back to the reservoir through port R, the check valve, and the selector valve. As soon as the air load decreases to an allowable level the overload valve allows fluid to flow into the actuator to continue lowering the flaps.

flap overload valve. A valve in the flap system of an airplane that prevents the flaps being lowered at an airspeed which could cause structural damage. If the pilot tries to extend the flaps when the airspeed is too high, the opposition caused by the airflow will open the overload valve and return the fluid to the reservoir.

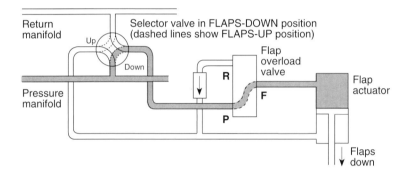

Figure 5-43. *The flap overload valve prevents the flaps from being lowered at too high an airspeed. If the flaps are down and the airspeed increases to too high a value, the flaps will raise automatically .*

If the airspeed increases to such an extent that the air load on the flaps becomes dangerously high when the flaps are down with the selector valve in the NEUTRAL position, the pressure on the down side of the actuator will increase and shift the overload valve so fluid flows through it from ports F to R and through the check valve to the up side of the actuator, allowing the flaps to retract until the air load is no longer excessive.

Flow Equalizer Valve

Some airplanes use a flow equalizer between the main landing gear actuating cylinders to cause the two landing gears to extend and retract evenly. *See* Figure 5-44 on the next page.

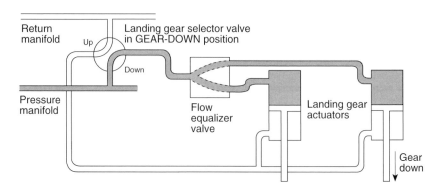

Figure 5-44. *A flow equalizer in the gear-down lines of a landing gear retraction system causes the two landing gears to move at the same speed as they retract and extend.*

crossflow valve. An automatic flow-control valve installed between the gear-up and gear-down lines of the landing gear of some large airplanes.

When the landing gear is released from its uplocks, its weight causes it to fall faster than the hydraulic system can supply fluid to the gear-down side of the actuation cylinder. The crossflow valve opens and directs fluid from the gear-up side into the gear-down side. This allows the gear to move down with a smooth motion.

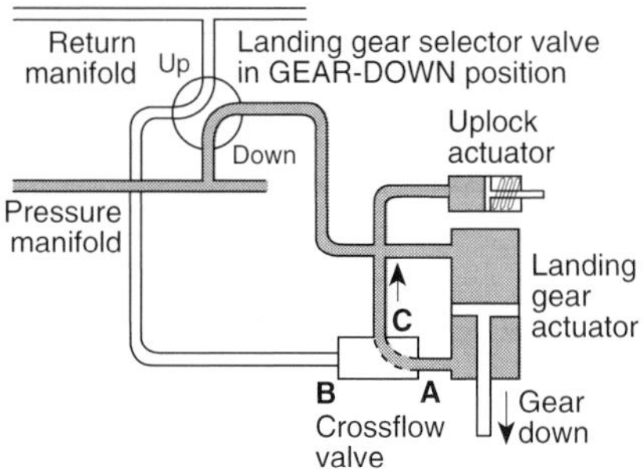

Figure 5-45. *When a heavy landing gear is released from its uplocks, its weight causes the piston to move faster than fluid from the selector valve can fill the gear-down side of the cylinder. Fluid flows through the crossflow valve and allows the gear to fall with a smooth and even motion.*

When the landing gear handle is placed in the GEAR-DOWN position, fluid flows through the selector valve and the flow equalizer valve on its way to the gear-down side of the two main-gear actuator cylinders. The fluid divides inside the flow equalizer and flows through two internal passages that are connected by a free-floating metering piston. If the right gear binds slightly, more fluid flows into the left actuator than to the right, and the metering piston moves over and restricts the flow to the left cylinder, forcing more fluid to flow into the right cylinder, keeping the flow to the two cylinders the same.

When the selector valve is moved to the GEAR-UP position, return fluid from the two actuators flows through the flow equalizer. The metering piston moves to whichever side is necessary to restrict the flow from the actuator that is moving fastest, and forces them to retract at the same speed.

Landing Gear Crossflow Valve

When a heavy landing gear is released from its uplocks, it pulls the actuator piston out faster than fluid from the selector valve can fill the down-side of the cylinder. A crossflow valve allows fluid to flow directly from the up-side of the actuator to the down-side until the system fluid can catch up with the demands of the actuator. *See* Figure 5-45.

When the landing gear selector is placed in the GEAR-DOWN position, fluid releases the uplock and the landing gear drops down. The weight of the gear pulls the piston out of the cylinder, and fluid from the up-side of the actuator flows through the crossflow valve from port A, out through port C directly to the down-side of the actuator. This allows the gear to fall smoothly and evenly. As soon as the pump catches up with the demands for fluid in the down-side of the actuator, the crossflow valve shuts off port C and fluid returns to the reservoir through port B and the selector valve.

When the gear selector is placed in the GEAR-UP position, fluid flows through the crossflow valve from port B to A with no appreciable restriction.

Hydraulic Fuses

Hydraulic systems on modern jet aircraft are extremely important, not only for raising and lowering the landing gear, but also for operating boosted control systems, thrust reversers, flaps, brakes, and many of the auxiliary systems. Most aircraft have more than one independent hydraulic system, and hydraulic fuses are used in these systems to block a line and shut off the flow of fluid if a serious leak should develop.

There are two types of hydraulic fuses; one shuts off the flow after a specific amount of fluid has flowed through it, and the other shuts off the flow if the pressure drop across the fuse indicates a broken line.

Figure 5-46 shows a pressure-drop-type fuse. Fluid flows through the fuse from left to right. When the flow rate is within the normal operating range, there is not enough pressure drop across the fuse to move the piston over against the force of the spring, and fluid flows through the fuse to the actuator. But if a line should break, the pressure at the break will be so low that the piston will be forced to the right and will shut off the flow of fluid to the actuator.

The fuse has no effect on the return flow of fluid from the actuator in normal action. The return fluid flowing through the fuse forces the piston to the left and uncovers the ports so fluid can flow through the fuse with no restriction.

The second type of fuse is shown in Figure 5-47 on the next page. This fuse shuts off the flow of fluid any time a specific amount of fluid flows through it, and prevents a loss of fluid even though the leak is not severe enough to cause the large pressure drop required to operate the other type of fuse.

In normal operation, (view A), fluid has forced the sleeve valve over to the right and fluid flows through the valve with a minimum of opposition. As the fluid flows through the fuse, some of it flows through the metering orifice and pushes the piston to the right.

By the time a specified amount of fluid passes through the fuse, the piston is forced all the way to the right, where it covers the ports and shuts off the flow of fluid through the fuse (view B).

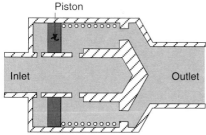

Flow of fluid though fuse for normal operation

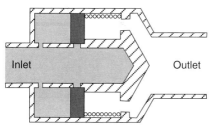

An excessive pressure drop has occurred and piston has been forced to the right, shutting off flow of fluid.

Figure 5-46. *Hydraulic fuse that operates on the principle of an excessive pressure drop.*

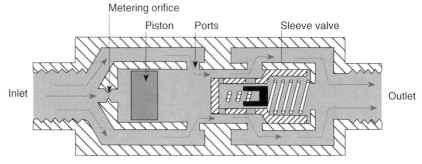

A Normal flow through fuse. The piston is moving over an amount proportional to amount of fluid that has passed through fuse.

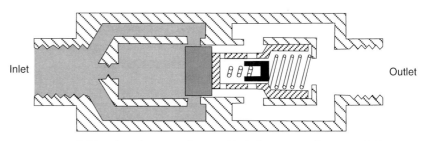

B The piston has moved over to block the ports, and no more fluid can flow through the fuse.

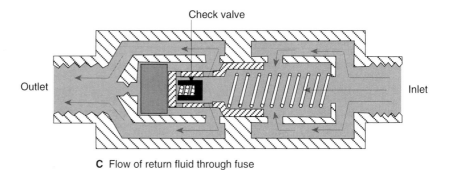

C Flow of return fluid through fuse

Figure 5-47. *Hydraulic fuse that shuts off the flow of fluid after a specific amount of fluid flows through*

When fluid flows through the fuse in the reverse direction, the sleeve valve and the piston are both moved to the left and fluid can flow through the fuse unrestricted (view C). *See* Figure 5-47.

Pressure Control Valves

There are two basic types of pressure control valves used in fluid power systems: pressure regulators and pressure relief valves. Pressure regulators relieve the fluid pump of its load while circulating fluid back to the reservoir. Relief valves do not relieve the pump of its load, but return just enough fluid to the reservoir to prevent pressure from becoming excessive.

Relief Valves

The simplest type of pressure control valve is the relief valve. In practical systems, however, a relief valve is used primarily as a backup device to prevent high pressure from damaging the system rather than as a pressure control device. When a relief valve relieves pressure, heat is generated and power is lost.

The system pressure relief valve opens and relieves any pressure above that which is maintained by the system pressure regulator. Only in the event of a malfunction of the regulator will the relief valve be required to function.

There are typically a number of pressure control valves in a hydraulic system with a wide range of relief pressures. To adjust any of the relief valves, you must temporarily adjust the pressure regulator to a pressure above that of the highest relief valve. Adjust the relief valve with the highest setting first, and then adjust the other valves in descending order of their relief pressure. When you have adjusted all of the relief valves, adjust the system pressure regulator to its correct pressure.

Thermal Relief Valves

Pressure can build up in parts of a hydraulic system where fluid is trapped in a line between the actuator and its selector valve. The trapped fluid gets hot and expands, and if there is no way to relieve the pressure, it can rupture a line or damage some of the components.

A thermal relief valve is a pressure relief valve that is installed between the portion of the system in which the pressure is trapped and the system return manifold. Thermal relief valves relieve pressure above the setting of the normal system pressure relief valve before it builds up high enough to do any damage. They do not interfere with normal system operation.

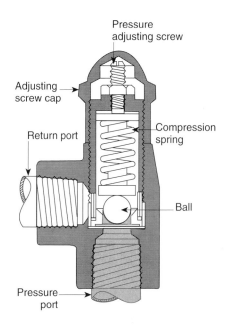

Figure 5-48. *Typical two-port pressure relief valve*

thermal relief valve. A relief valve in a hydraulic system that relieves pressure that builds up in an isolated part of the system because of heat. Thermal relief valves are set at a higher pressure than the system pressure relief valve.

Automatic Pressure Regulators or Unloading Valves

Closed-center hydraulic systems require an automatic regulator to maintain the pressure within a specified range and to keep the pump unloaded when no unit in the system is actuated. There are two basic types of automatic pressure regulators, the spool type and the balanced type. Both regulators accomplish the same purpose, and the principle of operation of the simpler balanced type regulator is illustrated in Figure 5-49.

Starting with a discharged system in which there is no fluid pressure in the accumulator, the pump pushes fluid through the check valve into the system and into the accumulator. The accumulator fills with fluid, and when no fluid is needed for actuation, the pressure builds up. This pressure enters both the top and bottom of the regulator. It pushes up on the piston and down on the ball.

The upward and downward forces reach a balance. The fluid pressure on the ball and the spring force on the piston are both downward forces, and the hydraulic pressure on the piston is an upward force. When the hydraulic pressure is 1,500 psi, these forces are balanced.

To understand the operation of this regulator, assume that the piston has an area of 1 square inch and the ball seat has an area of $\frac{1}{3}$ square inch. When the system pressure is 1,500 psi, there is a force of 1,500 pounds pushing up on the piston. To balance this upward force, there is a downward force of 1,000 pounds applied by the spring, and 500 pounds of force applied when the 1,500-psi hydraulic pressure pushes down on the $\frac{1}{3}$-square inch ball seat area.

Upward force
    Piston area = 1 square inch
    Pressure = 1,500 psi
    Total upward force = 1,500 · 1 = 1,500 pounds

Downward force
    Spring = 1,000 pounds
    Ball area = 0.333 square inch
    Force on ball = 1,500 · 0.333 = 500 pounds
    Total downward force = 1,000 + 500 = 1,500 pounds

When the pressure produced by the hydraulic pump rises above 1,500 psi, the force pushing up on the piston and the force pushing down on the ball both increase, but the spring force remains constant. The increased pressure pushing up on the large area of the piston moves the piston upward until the pin forces the ball off its seat and pump output flows through the valve to the return manifold.

As soon as the ball moves off its seat, the pressure on the pump side of the check valve drops to almost zero and the check valve seats, trapping pressure in the system where it is held by the accumulator. The pump is unloaded, and it circulates fluid through the system with very little opposition.

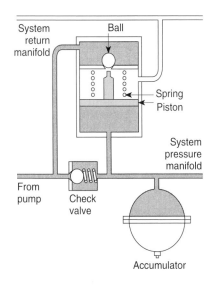

Figure 5-49. *Balanced-type system pressure regulator installed in a hydraulic system*

The system will continue to operate with the pump unloaded until the pressure held by the accumulator drops to slightly below 1,000 psi. As soon as the pressure below the piston drops to a value that produces an upward force is less than the downward force of the spring (1,000 pounds), the spring pushes the piston down and the ball seats. When the ball is seated, flow to the reservoir is shut off and the pressure builds back up to 1,500 psi. The pressure at which the pump unloads, 1,500 psi, is called the kick-out pressure and the pressure at which the ball seats to load the pump, 1,000 psi, is called the kick-in pressure.

Pressure Reducer

Some automatic pilots require less than system pressure for their actuation. These may use a simple pressure reducer like the one in Figure 5-50. This valve operates on the principle of a balance between hydraulic and spring forces.

Assume that the piston has an area of 1 square inch, and it is held against its seat by a spring that pushes down with a force of 100 pounds. The piston has a shoulder area of 0.5 square inch, and this area is acted on by the full system pressure, 1,500 psi. The cone-shaped seat of this valve has an area of 0.5 square inch, and it is acted on by the reduced pressure of 200 psi.

A tiny hole in the piston bleeds fluid into the chamber inside the piston, and a relief valve maintains the pressure of this fluid at 750 psi.

When the automatic pilot uses some of the fluid, the reduced pressure drops. The relief valve unseats, and the pressure above the piston decreases. System pressure raises the valve off of its seat and the reduced pressure rises back to its desired 200 psi value. As soon as the pressure rises to this value, the relief valve again seats, the pressure behind the piston builds back up to 750 psi, and the piston moves down to hold the reduced pressure constant.

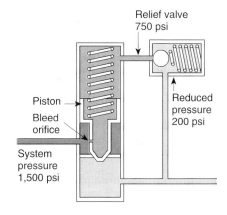

Figure 5-50. *Pressure reducer valve*

STUDY QUESTIONS: HYDRAULIC VALVES

Answers begin on Page 415. Page numbers refer to chapter text.

69. A flow control valve that allows full flow in one direction but no flow in the opposite direction is called a/ an _____ valve. *Page 359*

70. A flow control valve that allows a full flow in one direction but a restricted flow in the opposite direction is called a/an _____ . *Page 360*

71. A mechanically operated flow control valve that prevents fluid flowing to one unit before some other unit has actuated completely is called a/an _____ valve. *Page 363*

Continued

72. A pressure-operated flow control valve that prevents fluid flowing to one unit until another unit has actuated and hydraulic pressure has built up to a value high enough to shift the valve is called a/an _____ valve. *Page 364*

73. A flap overload valve is placed in the _____ (flaps-up or flaps-down) line. *Page 365*

74. Heavy landing gears are assisted in falling smoothly and evenly from the wheel wells by allowing fluid to flow from the up-side of the actuator to the down side through a _____ valve. *Page 366*

75. Two types of selector valves are _____ and _____. *Page 360*

76. Plug-type selector valves are used in _____ (high or low)-pressure fluid power systems. *Page 361*

77. One characteristic of a spool-type selector valve is that it requires a _____ (large or small) force to operate the control. *Page 363*

78. A flow equalizer valve installed in the landing gear gear-down line _____ (does or does not) equalize the flow for both extension and retraction of the landing gear. *Page 366*

79. A component that shuts off the flow of hydraulic fluid if a line should rupture is called a hydraulic _____ . *Page 367*

80. A pressure relief valve is usually used as a _____ (primary or backup) pressure regulating valve. *Page 369*

81. A thermal relief valve is adjusted to relieve at a pressure _____ (lower or higher) than that for which the main system pressure relief valve is adjusted. *Page 369*

82. Another name for a system pressure regulator is a/an _____ valve. *Page 370*

83. When one subsystem requires a lower pressure than the normal system operating pressure, a/an _____ valve is used. *Page 371*

Hydraulic Accumulators

Hydraulic fluid is not compressible, and in order to keep it under pressure, it must be stored against something compressible, such as the air or nitrogen in an accumulator.

Three basic types of accumulators are: the bladder-type, the diaphragm-type and the piston-type. The bladder and diaphragm accumulators are both steel spheres, and the piston-type is in the form of a strong cylinder.

Bladder-type accumulators have a heavy neoprene bladder, or bag, inside the steel sphere. The bladder is filled with a compressed gas such as air or nitrogen, and the hydraulic fluid is pumped into the sphere on the outside of the bladder. As the hydraulic fluid is pumped into the accumulator, it takes up some of the space the bladder had originally taken up, and the gas inside the bladder is further compressed.

The bladder presses against the hydraulic fluid inside the accumulator with a force that causes the pressure of the liquid on the outside of the bladder to be the same as the pressure of the gas inside the bladder. A metal plate is fitted into the bladder to cover the fluid entry port so that the bladder will not be extruded out into this opening. *See* Figure 5-51.

The diaphragm-type accumulator is made of two steel hemispheres fastened together with a folded neoprene diaphragm between the two halves. One side of the diaphragm is the air chamber and the other side is the fluid chamber.

When the hydraulic pump is not operating, the compressed gas forces the diaphragm over until the air chamber fills the entire sphere. As hydraulic fluid is pumped into the accumulator, the diaphragm is moved down, further compressing the gas and storing the hydraulic fluid under pressure. *See* Figure 5-52.

The piston-type accumulator is made of a steel or aluminum alloy cylinder divided into two compartments by a floating piston. Compressed air or nitrogen is put into one end of the cylinder and the hydraulic fluid is put into the other end. As more fluid is forced into the accumulator, the piston is moved over, further compressing the gas and storing the hydraulic fluid under pressure. *See* Figure 5-53 on the next page.

Accumulators are charged with compressed air or nitrogen to a pressure of approximately one third of the hydraulic system pressure. As the pump forces hydraulic fluid into the accumulator, the gas is further compressed, and it exerts a force on the hydraulic fluid, holding it under pressure after the system pressure regulator has unloaded the pump.

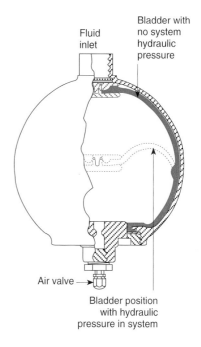

Figure 5-51. *Bladder-type accumulator*

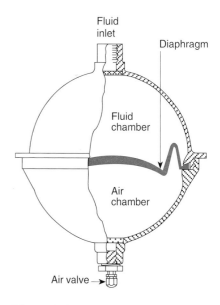

Figure 5-52. *Diaphragm-type accumulator*

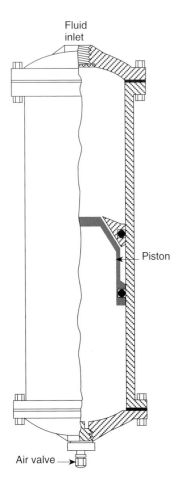

Figure 5-53. *Piston-type accumulator*

Air valves used in accumulators may be one of three types. The most simple is the AN812 valve in Figure 5-54. This valve seals the air inside the accumulator with a high-pressure core that is similar in appearance, but different in construction from the valve core that is used in tires. The valve core used in an accumulator air valve is identified by the letter H embossed on the end of the stem.

To deflate an accumulator equipped with an AN812 valve, do not depress the valve stem, but loosen the valve body in the accumulator. The bleed hole in the side of the valve allows the air to leak past the loosened threads.

Both AN6287-1 and MS28889 valves seal the air inside the accumulator with a steel-against-steel seal. The AN6287-1 valve has a valve core similar to the one used in the AN812 valve, but it has a swivel nut around the stem. To charge an accumulator equipped with an AN6287-1 valve, remove the protective cap from the valve, attach the charging hose to the valve, and loosen the swivel nut for one turn. Loosening the swivel nut backs the valve body off enough to allow air to pass into the accumulator. To deflate an accumulator fitted with this valve, remove the protective cap, loosen the swivel nut one turn, and depress the stem of the valve core. *See* Figure 5-55.

The MS28889 valve does not use a valve core. It depends entirely on the metal-to-metal seal to hold air in the accumulator. To charge an accumulator equipped with this valve, remove the protective cap, install the charging hose on the valve, loosen the swivel nut, and allow air to flow into the accumulator. To discharge the accumulator, remove the protective cap and loosen the swivel nut. *See* Figure 5-56.

The MS28889 and AN6287-1 valves are similar in appearance, except that there is no valve core in the MS28889 valve, and its swivel nut is the same size as the body of the valve. (The swivel nut on the AN6287-1 valve is smaller than the valve body). Another difference is that the MS28889 valve has a roll pin in its body that prevents the stem of the valve being screwed too far into the body.

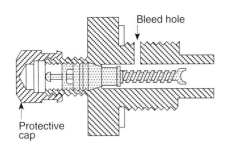

Figure 5-54. *AN812 high-pressure air valve*

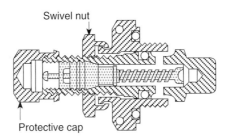

Figure 5-55. *AN6287-1 high-pressure air valve*

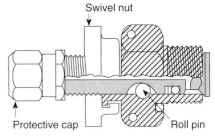

Figure 5-56. *MS28889 high-pressure air valve*

When an accumulator is installed in an aircraft it must be given an air preload charge. The amount of this charge is specified in the aircraft maintenance manual, and it is usually about one third of the normal system operating pressure. Some accumulators have an air pressure gage and an air filler valve that is accessible for line servicing. Other accumulators do not have any way of directly measuring the air preload pressure. If the accumulator does not have an air pressure gage, you may determine the preload pressure by following these steps:

1. Build up hydraulic system pressure with the hand pump until the system pressure gage indicates the rated pressure.

2. Very slowly bleed the pressure off by operating some component such as the flaps. Watch the pressure gage carefully while the pressure is bleeding down. The indication will decrease slowly until the preload pressure is reached, and then it will drop instantly to zero. The pressure indicated on the gage just before its sudden drop is the accumulator preload air pressure.

The system pressure gage in some hydraulic systems actually measures the air pressure in the accumulator rather than hydraulic fluid pressure. When there is no fluid pressure in the system, this type of gage will read the accumulator air preload charge, and as soon as fluid is pumped into the accumulator the fluid and air pressure will be the same and the gage will indicate the pressure on the hydraulic fluid. If the air preload pressure is 1,000 psi, and fluid is pumped into the accumulator until the gage reads 2,000 psi, the air and fluid pressure are both 2,000 psi. If the gage ever reads 0 psi, there is no accumulator preload air.

Before removing any component from the pressure manifold on which an accumulator is holding pressure, all of the system pressure must be bled off. Do this by actuating any unit whose movement will not cause any damage. Actuate the unit until the system pressure drops to zero, then it is safe to remove components from the pressure manifold.

accumulator air preload. Compressed air or nitrogen in one side of an accumulator. The air preload is usually about one third of the system hydraulic pressure. When fluid is pumped into the oil side of the accumulator the air is further compressed, and the air pressure and the fluid pressure will be the same.

STUDY QUESTIONS: HYDRAULIC ACCUMULATORS

Answers begin on Page 415. Page numbers refer to chapter text.

84. In order to store an incompressible fluid under pressure in a hydraulic system, a/an
_____ must be used. *Page 373*

85. The initial pressure of compressed air or nitrogen used to preload in an accumulator is approximately
_____ of the system pressure. *Page 373*

Continued

86. The air valve core used in an accumulator is identified as a high-pressure core by the letter _____ embossed on the stem. *Page 374*

87. An accumulator fitted with an AN812 air valve _____ (should or should not) be deflated by depressing the valve stem. *Page 374*

88. When hydraulic fluid is pumped into an accumulator, the preload air pressure will _____ (increase, decrease, or remain the same). *Page 375*

Hydraulic Filters

Hydraulic fluid must be kept clean. As many of the solid contaminants as possible must be removed from the fluid. These contaminants can damage the pumps, valves, and actuators in a hydraulic system.

The filtering capability of a hydraulic filter is measured in microns. One micron is one millionth of a meter, or 39 millionths of an inch (0.000 039 inch). The unaided human eye can see contaminants as small as 40 microns, and an effective filter should be able to remove contaminants larger than 5 microns. *See* Figure 5-20 on Page 346.

Two basic types of filters are used in aircraft hydraulic systems: surface filters and edge filters.

Surface filters trap the contaminants on the surface of the element, which may be made of sintered metal or a specially treated cellulose material. These filters usually have a bypass valve built into them that opens to allow the fluid to bypass the element if it should become clogged. Wire mesh and some sintered metal filter elements may be cleaned and reused, but others are noncleanable and are discarded on a regular scheduled basis.

Some of the latest filter elements are known as 5-micron noncleanable elements. These elements are made of a combination of organic and inorganic fibers integrally bonded with epoxy resin and faced with metallic mesh on both sides for protection and added mechanical strength. These elements should never be cleaned, but are replaced on a regular maintenance schedule.

Another new type of 5-micron filtering element is made of layers of very fine stainless steel fibers drawn into a random but controlled matrix. The matrix is then processed by compressing it and bonding all of the wires at their crossing points into a very thin layer. This type of filtering element is made in both cleanable and noncleanable forms.

The filter assembly in Figure 5-57 is typical of modern system filters. The filter head is installed in the hydraulic system either in the pressure side of the pump or in the return line to the reservoir. The filter bowl can be unscrewed from the head to remove the filter element. When the bowl is removed, the

sintered metal. A porous material made by fusing powdered metal under heat and pressure.

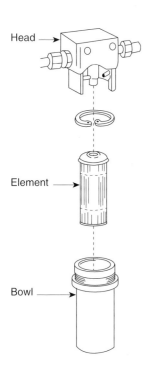

Figure 5-57. *External view of a hydraulic filter assembly*

Head →

Element →

Bowl →

shut-off diaphragm closes to prevent the loss of any fluid that is in the system downstream of the filter.

A bypass poppet valve is installed in this filter assembly to allow fluid to flow through the system in the event the filter element clogs. If the element clogs, there will be a large pressure drop across it, and the inlet fluid will force the valve off its seat. Unfiltered fluid will flow through the system. When enough pressure builds up across the filter to unseat the bypass valve, the red differential-pressure indicator button pops up to inform the maintenance technician that the filter element is clogged and has bypassed fluid. *See* Figure 5-58.

Edge filters, often called Cuno filters, are made up of stacks of thin metal disks with scrapers between them. All of the fluid flows between the disks, and contaminants are stopped on the edges of the disks. The degree of filtration is determined by the thickness of the separators between the disks.

Cuno filters are cleaned by turning the shaft that rotates the disks and scrapes the contaminants from between them into the outer housing, where they can be removed by draining the filter bowl.

epoxy. A flexible, thermosetting resin made by polymerization of an epoxide.

Epoxy is noted for its durability and its chemical resistance.

Cuno filter. The registered trade name for a particular style of edge-type fluid filter.

Cuno filters are made up of a stack of thin metal disks that are separated by thin scraper blades. Contaminants collect on the edge of the disks, and they are periodically scraped out and allowed to collect in the bottom of the filter case for future removal.

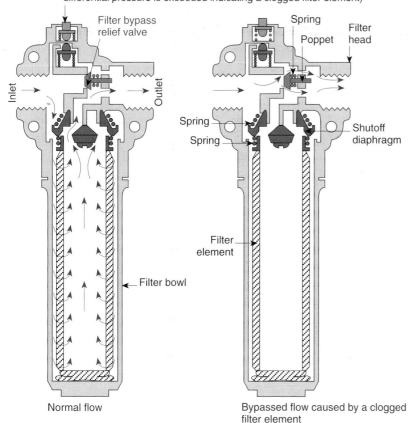

Red differential pressure indicator button (raises 3/16 inch when differential pressure is exceeded indicating a clogged filter element)

Filter bypass relief valve

Inlet

Outlet

Filter bowl

Normal flow

Spring

Poppet

Filter head

Spring

Spring

Shutoff diaphragm

Filter element

Bypassed flow caused by a clogged filter element

Figure 5-58. *Hydraulic filter assembly incorporating a differential pressure indicator*

Answers begin on Page 415. Page numbers refer to chapter text.

89. An efficient hydraulic filter should be able to remove contaminants larger than _____ microns. *Page 376*

90. A red indicator button sticking up on the top of a hydraulic filter is an indication that the filter element is _____ . *Page 377*

91. If a hydraulic filter clogs, unfiltered fluid flows to the system through a _____ valve in the filter. *Page 377*

92. The degree of filtration of a Cuno filter is determined by the thickness of the _____ (disks or separators). *Page 377*

Hydraulic Actuators

hydraulic actuator. The component in a hydraulic system that converts hydraulic pressure into mechanical force. The two main types of hydraulic actuators are linear actuators (cylinders and pistons) and rotary actuators (hydraulic motors).

The ultimate function of a hydraulic or pneumatic system is to convert the pressure in the fluid into work. In order to do this, there must be some form of movement, and this movement takes place in the actuator. Linear and rotary actuators are the most widely used. This section of the text discusses both types.

Linear Actuators

linear actuator. A fluid power actuator that uses a piston moving inside a cylinder to change pressure into linear, or straight-line, motion.

Linear actuators are made up of a cylinder and a piston. The cylinder is usually attached to the aircraft structure, and the piston is connected to the component that is being moved.

If two linear actuating cylinders with pistons having the same cross-sectional area but different lengths of stroke are connected to the same source of hydraulic pressure, they will exert equal amounts of force, and move at the same rate of speed. But it will take them a different length of time to reach the end of their stroke. If the cylinders have different areas, but are connected to the same source of pressure, they will produce different amounts of force.

The rate of movement of the piston in a linear actuator can be controlled by restricting the fluid flowing into or out of the cylinder.

Figure 5-59 shows three basic types of linear actuators. A single-acting actuator has a piston that is moved in one direction by hydraulic fluid, and is returned by a spring. A double-acting actuator uses hydraulic fluid to move the piston in both directions. An unbalanced, double-acting actuator has a piston rod extending from only one side of the piston, and a double-acting balanced actuator has piston rods extending from both sides of the piston.

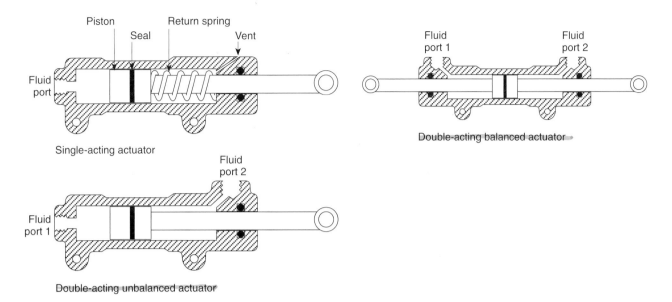

Figure 5-59. *Linear hydraulic actuators*

Unbalanced actuators have more area on one side of the piston than on the other because of the area that is taken up by the piston rod. As much force as possible is needed to raise the landing gear, so the fluid pushes against the full area of the piston. Not as much force is needed to lower the landing gear because of the weight of the struts and wheels, so the fluid is directed into the end of the actuator that has the piston rod. The fluid pushes on only the portion of the piston that is not taken up by the rod.

A balanced actuator has a shaft on both sides of the piston, so the area is the same on each side, and the same amount of force is developed in each direction. Balanced actuators are commonly used for hydraulic servos used with automatic pilots.

Linear actuators may have features that adapt them to special jobs. Figure 5-60 (Page 380) illustrates a landing gear actuator that has internal locks to hold the landing gear down. The actuator is locked with the piston retracted all the way into the cylinder until hydraulic pressure releases it. In Figure 5-60A, the piston is retracted, and the landing gear is down and locked by the locking balls that are forced into the groove in the end of the piston by the locking pin.

balanced actuator. A hydraulic or pneumatic actuator that has the same area on both sides of the piston.

When the landing gear selector is placed in the GEAR-UP position, fluid flows into the cylinder and forces the locking pin to the right, which allows the balls to drop down and release the piston. The spring forces the collar to the left to hold the balls against the locking pin. Movement of the locking pin pulls the check valve back and allows fluid to flow into the cylinder, extending the piston and raising the gear. *See* Figure 5-60B.

When the landing gear selector is placed in the GEAR-DOWN position, fluid moves the actuator piston into the cylinder, and the fluid on the gear-up side of the piston forces the check valve back. The fluid leaves the actuator. As the piston reaches its fully retracted position, it forces the collar back, and the spring behind the locking pin pushes it to the left and forces the balls into the groove at the end of the piston, locking it in place.

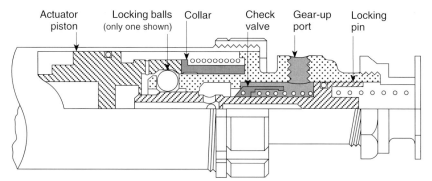

A Landing gear is down and locked with actuator piston fully retracted into cylinder and locked in place.

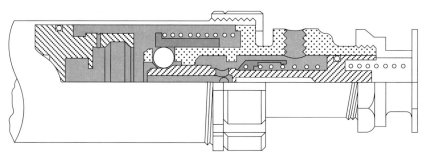

B Fluid has pushed locking pin back to release locking balls and allow fluid to force piston to extend, raising landing gear.

Figure 5-60. *Landing gear actuating cylinder with internal down lock*

Rotary Actuators

The efficient rack-and-pinion actuator is used on the single-engine Cessna airplanes to retract their landing gear. A piston with rack teeth cut onto its shaft rotates the pinion as the piston moves in or out of the cylinder. Rotation of the pinion gear raises or lowers the landing gear. *See* Figure 5-61.

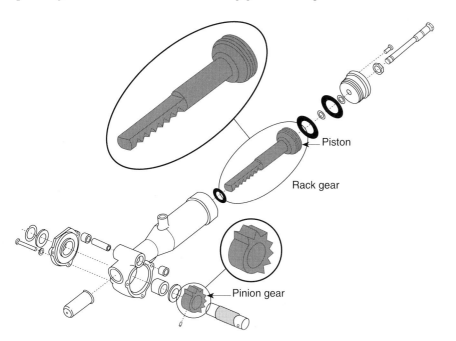

rotary actuator. A fluid power actuator whose output is rotational. A hydraulic motor is a rotary actuator.

rack-and-pinion actuator. A form of rotary actuator where the fluid acts on a piston on which a rack of gear teeth is cut. As the piston moves, it rotates a pinion gear which is mated with the teeth cut in the rack.

Figure 5-61. *Rack-and-pinion linear hydraulic actuator with a rotary output.*

Hydraulic motors are used to maintain continued rotation. Hydraulic motors are similar to hydraulic pumps except for certain design detail differences. Piston motors have many applications on larger aircraft where a considerable amount of power with good control is needed. The advantages of hydraulic motors over electric motors are its ability to instantaneously reverse the direction of rotation and its lack of fire hazard in the event of a stalled rotor.

Vane-type hydraulic motors that have provisions for balancing the load on the shaft are also used. Some of the pressure is directed to both sides of the motor, as is seen in the balanced-vane-type motor in Figure 5-62.

hydraulic motor. A hydraulic actuator that converts fluid pressure into rotary motion.

Hydraulic motors have an advantage in aircraft installations over electric motors, because they can operate in a stalled condition without the danger of a fire.

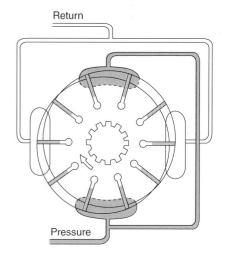

Figure 5-62. *Balanced-vane-type hydraulic motor*

Servo Actuators

Heavy, high-performance airplanes require so much force to move the control surfaces that the pilot is assisted by hydraulically boosted controls. Rather than moving the control surface itself, the cockpit controls move flow control valves connected to servo actuators that move the surfaces.

Movement of the pilot's control causes the flow control valve to direct hydraulic fluid to the proper side of the actuating piston to move the flight control surface in the correct direction. As the actuator piston moves to the position called for by the pilot's control, the internal linkage moves the flow control valve back to a neutral position and stops the flow of hydraulic fluid, and thus the movement of the piston.

STUDY QUESTIONS: HYDRAULIC SYSTEM ACTUATORS

Answers begin on Page 415. Page numbers refer to chapter text.

93. Two types of hydraulic actuators are _____ and _____ actuators. *Page 378*

94. A linear hydraulic actuator that has the same area on both sides of its piston is called a/an _____ actuator. *Page 379*

95. If two linear actuators with pistons having the same cross sectional area but different piston strokes are connected to the same source of hydraulic pressure, the pistons will move at _____ (the same or different) rates of speed. *Page 378*

96. If two linear actuators with pistons of different cross sectional area are connected to the same source of hydraulic pressure, the pistons will produce _____ (the same or different) forces. *Page 378*

97. The rate of movement of the piston in a linear actuator may be controlled by installing a/an _____ in the inlet or outlet port of the actuator. *Page 378*

98. A hydraulic actuator whose piston is moved in both directions by hydraulic fluid under pressure is called a/an _____ actuator. *Page 378*

99. A rack-and-pinion linear hydraulic actuator has an output that is _____ (linear or rotary). *Page 381*

100. On an aircraft having boosted controls, the pilot actually moves a _____ valve which directs fluid to the proper side of an actuator that moves the control surface. *Page 382*

High-Pressure Seals

Seals are used throughout hydraulic and pneumatic systems to minimize leakage and the loss of system pressure. There are two types of seals in use, gaskets and packings. Gaskets are used when there is no relative motion between the parts that are being sealed, and packings are used where relative motion does exist between the parts.

Chevron Seals

There are many different kinds of seals used in aircraft applications. These seals range all of the way from flat paper gaskets up through complex, multicomponent packings.

V-ring packings, or chevron seals, like the ones in Figure 5-63, are found in many high-pressure actuators. Chevron seals are single-direction seals with the pressure applied to their open sides. They are usually installed either in pairs, or in larger stacks with metal backup rings and spreaders used to force the lip of the seal tightly against the surfaces being sealed. The amount the chevron seal spreads is determined by the tightness of the adjusting nut that holds the seal on the shaft.

gasket. A seal between two parts where there is no relative motion.

packing. A seal between two parts where there is relative motion.

chevron seal. A form of one-way seal used on the piston of some fluid-power actuators. A chevron seal is made of a resilient material in the shape of the letter V. The pressure being sealed must be applied to the open side of the V.

Cross section of a chevron seal

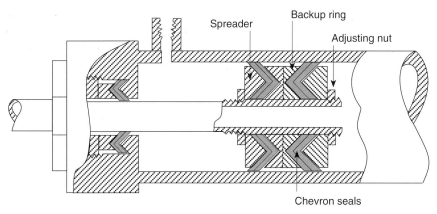

Proper installation of chevron seals

Figure 5-63. *Chevron seals, or V-ring packings*

O-ring. A widely used type of seal made in the form of a rubber ring with a round cross section. An O-ring seals in both directions, and it can be used as a packing or a gasket.

O-ring Seals

Many modern hydraulic and pneumatic systems use O-rings for both packings and gaskets. O-rings are fitted into grooves that are usually about 10% wider than the width of the O-ring, and deep enough that the distance between the bottom of the groove and the other mating surface is a little less than the cross-sectional diameter of the O-ring. This provides the squeeze needed for the O-ring to seal under conditions of zero pressure. If the O-ring is not squeezed, fluid will leak past it.

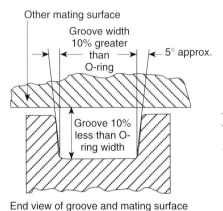

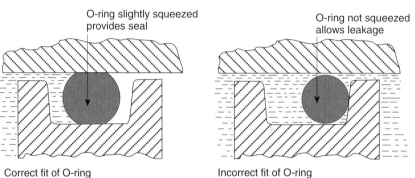

End view of groove and mating surface

Correct fit of O-ring

Incorrect fit of O-ring

Figure 5-64. *O-ring seals*

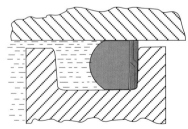

Without a backup ring, high pressure squeezes O-ring between surfaces being sealed.

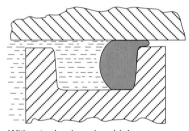

Backup ring installed on side of O-ring away from pressure prevents ring from being extruded.

Figure 5-65. *The use of a backup ring to prevent extrusion of the O-ring*

An O-ring seal of the correct size can withstand pressures of up to about 1,500 psi without distortion, but beyond this, there is a tendency for the ring to extrude into the groove between the two mating surfaces. Figure 5-65 shows that as the pressure of the fluid increases, the O-ring begins to wedge in tight between the wall of the groove and the inside of the cylinder. To prevent this, an anti-extrusion, or backup, ring is used. There are two types of anti-extrusion rings in use. One is made of leather, and the other is made of Teflon. Leather rings are installed in such a way that the hair side of the ring, the smooth side, is against the O-ring. Before installing a leather backup ring, soften it by soaking it in the fluid the ring will be used with.

Spiraled Teflon backup rings are used for pressures higher than 1,500 psi. The ends of the Teflon ring are scarfed, and it is possible for the ring to spiral in such a direction that the scarfs will be on the wrong side, and the ring will be damaged. Figure 5-66A shows the improper spiral of the ring. Figure 5-66B shows the proper spiral, and Figure 5-66C shows the way the ring looks after pressure has been applied and the ring has taken its set.

T-Seals

Another type of two-way seal is the T-seal shown in Figure 5-67. This seal can fit in the standard O-ring grooves, and is backed up with two Teflon backup rings. T-seals are most often installed in high-pressure (3,000 psi) systems.

Seal Identification

The material of which a seal is made is dictated by the fluid used in the system. Seals are identified by colored marks. *See* Figure 5-68.

There is perhaps no other component as small as a hydraulic seal upon which so much importance is placed. The correct seal and a wrong seal may look alike, and it is highly probable that if the wrong seal is installed, it may appear to work. The material of which the seal is made, its age, and its hardness are all important when making the proper replacement.

When replacing seals in a hydraulic system, use only the specific part number of the seal specified by the aircraft manufacturer. Purchase seals from the equipment manufacturer or a reputable aircraft parts supplier, and they should be sealed in individual packages marked with the part number, the composition of the seal, the name of the manufacturer, and the cure date.

The cure date is the date the seal was manufactured, and it is given in quarters. For example, 2Q94 indicates that the seal was manufactured in the second quarter, during the months of April, May, or June, of 1994. Rubber goods are not considered fresh if they are more than 24 months old.

Hydraulic seals must be bought only from a reputable supplier, because out-of-date seals can be repackaged and stamped with a fresh date. The old seal could be installed in good faith by an aviation maintenance technician and still fail because of deterioration. Yet, the technician is liable for the failure because installing an improper part in an aircraft is a violation of Federal Aviation Regulations.

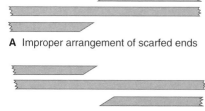

A Improper arrangement of scarfed ends

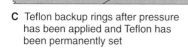

B Proper arrangement of scarfed ends

C Teflon backup rings after pressure has been applied and Teflon has been permanently set

Figure 5-66. *The proper installation of a Teflon backup ring*

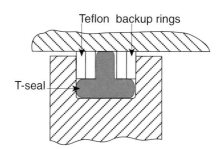

Figure 5-67. *The T-seal fits in an O-ring groove and is installed with Teflon backup rings on both sides.*

Color	Use
Blue dot or stripe	Air or MIL-H-5606 fluid
Red dot or stripe	Fuel
Yellow Dot	Synthetic engine oil
White Stripe	Petroleum-base engine oil
Green dash	Phosphate ester hydraulic fluid

Figure 5-68. *The colored marks on an O-ring seal show the fluid type with which the seal should be used .*

Seal Installation

When installing O-rings, take extreme care that the ring is not twisted, nicked, or damaged by either sharp edges of the threads over which the ring is installed or by the installation tool. Figure 5-69 shows some of the special O-ring installation and removal tools that can be used. These tools are usually made of brass and are polished so that there are no sharp edges that could nick the seal.

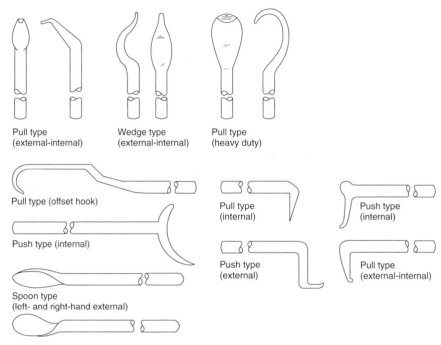

Pull type
(external-internal)

Wedge type
(external-internal)

Pull type
(heavy duty)

Pull type (offset hook)

Push type (internal)

Spoon type
(left- and right-hand external)

Pull type
(internal)

Push type
(external)

Push type
(internal)

Pull type
(external-internal)

Figure 5-69. *Typical tools for installation and removal of O-ring seals*

Figure 5-70 shows how to use these O-ring installation tools, and the proper method of installing and removing O-rings in both internal and external grooves.

When installing an O-ring over a sharp edge, cover the edge with paper, aluminum foil, brass shim stock, or a piece of plastic, as in Figure 5-71. *See* Figure 5-71 on Page 388.

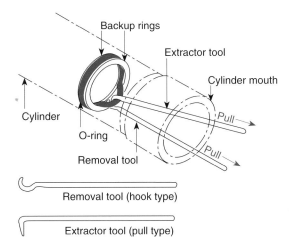

Internal O-ring removal using pull-type extractor
and hook type removal tools

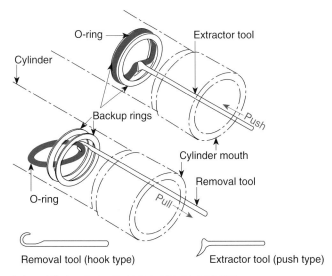

Internal O-ring removal using push type extractor
and hook type removal tools

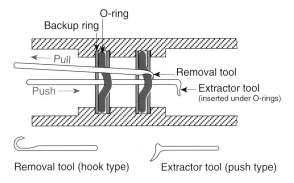

Dual internal O-ring removal using push type extractor
and hook type removal tools

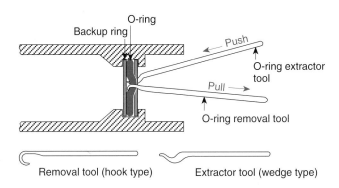

Internal O-ring removal using wedge type extractor
and hook type removal tools

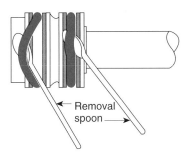

External O-ring removal using spoon type
extractor and removal tools

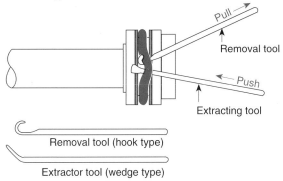

External O-ring removal using wedge type extractor
and hook type removal tools

Figure 5-70. *Proper procedure for removing O-ring seals*

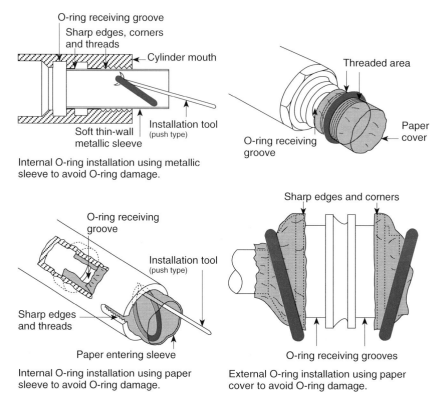

O-ring receiving groove

Sharp edges, corners and threads

Cylinder mouth

Installation tool (push type)

Soft thin-wall metallic sleeve

Internal O-ring installation using metallic sleeve to avoid O-ring damage.

Threaded area

O-ring receiving groove

Paper cover

O-ring receiving groove

Installation tool (push type)

Sharp edges and threads

Paper entering sleeve

Internal O-ring installation using paper sleeve to avoid O-ring damage.

Sharp edges and corners

O-ring receiving grooves

External O-ring installation using paper cover to avoid O-ring damage.

Figure 5-71. *Proper methods of protecting O-ring seals from damage when installing them over threads and sharp edges*

Wipers

O-rings and chevron seals do not seal around the shaft completely. Enough fluid is allowed to leak to lubricate the shaft, and this lubricant attracts dust. A felt wiper is usually installed in a counterbore around the shaft to keep the seals from being damaged when the shaft is retracted into the cylinder. This wiper removes any dirt or dust without restricting the movement of the shaft.

STUDY QUESTIONS: HIGH PRESSURE SEALS

Answers begin on Page 415. Page numbers refer to chapter text.

101. A high-pressure seal used to seal between two fixed surfaces is called a _____ (gasket or packing). *Page 383*

102. A high-pressure seal used to seal between a fixed and a movable surface is called a _____ (gasket or packing). *Page 383*

103. A chevron seal is a _____ (one-way or two-way) seal. *Page 383*

---

104. A chevron seal must be installed in such a way that the pressure is on the side of the _____ (apex or open end). *Page 383*

105. An O-ring seal is a _____ (one-way or two-way) seal. *Page 384*

106. An O-ring of the correct size can withstand pressures of up to about _____ psi without distortion. *Page 384*

107. When leather backup rings are used with an O-ring seal, the smooth, or hair, side of the ring should be _____ (toward or away from) the O-ring. *Page 384*

108. A backup ring is installed on the side of an O-ring _____ (toward or away from) the pressure. *Page 384*

109. An O-ring seal used with MIL-H-5606 hydraulic fluid will be identified with a _____ (what color) mark. *Page 385*

110. Four important bits of information that should be on the sealed envelope containing an O-ring seal are:
    a. _____
    b. _____
    c. _____
    d. _____
       Page 385

111. A felt ring is often installed around an actuator shaft to prevent dust and dirt entering the actuator and damaging the seals. This ring is called a/an _____ . *Page 388*

Fluid Power System Lines and Fittings

Any fluid power system, either a hydraulic or a pneumatic system, requires a source of fluid under pressure, actuators to change the pressure into force, valves to control the flow, and fluid lines to carry the fluid to and from the actuators. This section discusses fluid lines and their fittings. See Chapter 9 of the General textbook of this *Aviation Maintenance Technician Series* for a more in-depth discussion of these components.

Fluid Lines

There are two kinds of fluid lines used in aircraft systems, rigid and flexible. Rigid tubing is used where there is no relative movement within the system, and flexible hoses are used when a piece of rigid tubing connects to an actuator or other device with relative movement between the two.

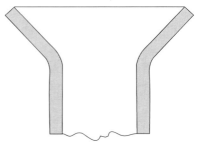

Single flare

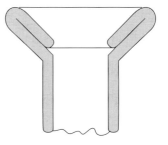

Double flare

Figure 5-72. *Flared fittings used on aircraft rigid tubing*

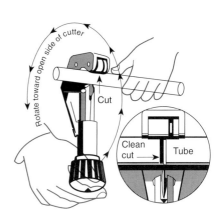

Figure 5-73. *Rigid tubing should be cut with a wheel-type tubing cutter to ensure a clean, square cut.*

Rigid Tubing

Most rigid fluid lines used in low-pressure hydraulic or pneumatic systems are made of 5052-O aluminum alloy. This metal is easy to form, and it has enough strength for most of the hydraulic systems used in smaller aircraft. High-pressure hydraulic systems often use 2024-T aluminum alloy, or annealed stainless steel tubing. High-pressure oxygen systems are required to use stainless steel tubing.

Rigid tubing must not have any dents in the heel of a bend, but dents are allowed in the straight part of the tubing if they are less than 20% of the outside diameter of the tube. Scratches or nicks that are less than 10% of the tubing wall thickness are allowed in aluminum alloy tubing provided they are not in the heel of a bend, and can be burnished so they will have no sharp edges.

There are two methods of attaching fittings to rigid tubing, flaring the tubing or using flareless fittings.

Preparation for Flared-Tube Fittings

Aircraft flared-tube fittings have a 37°-flare cone to distinguish them from automotive fittings, which have a 45°-flare cone. A double flare is recommended for use on soft aluminum alloy tubing of ⅜-inch diameter or smaller, and a single flare may be used on tubing of all sizes.

It is extremely important to use the correct procedure when making a flare in a piece of tubing.

Cut the end of the tube perfectly square, using either a tubing cutter or a fine-tooth hacksaw. If you use a tubing cutter such as the one in Figure 5-73, feed the cutting blade into the tube as it is rotated around the tube. After you cut the end of the tube, burr the inside edge with a special burring tool or with a sharp scraper. Smooth the ends and the outside edge of the tube with a fine file or with abrasive cloth, working around rather than across the end.

A number of flaring tools are available. The one shown in Figure 5-74 will single-flare tubing from ³⁄₁₆-inch through ¾-inch outside diameter. To flare a tube using this tool, first prepare the end of the tube by polishing out all nicks and scratches to prevent the flare splitting, then slide the nut and sleeve over the end of the tube. Rotate the dies to get the correct size for the tubing beneath the flare cone, and insert the end of the tube between the dies and adjust it so its end rests against the built-in stop. Then clamp the dies tightly against the tube.

Lubricate the flaring cone and screw it into the tube until the flare is the correct size. The outside edge of the flare should stick up above the top of the sleeve, but its outside diameter must not be larger than that of the sleeve. *See* Figures 5-74 and 5-75.

Preparation for Flareless Fittings

Install flareless fittings for rigid tubing, such as those in Figure 5-76, by first cutting and polishing the end of the tube (as described for the flaring process). Slip a nut and a sleeve over the end of the tube and insert the end into a presetting tool like the one in Figure 5-77. Be sure that the end of the tube bottoms out on the shoulder of the tool.

Lubricate the sleeve and the threads, and screw the nut down finger-tight. Hold the tube against the shoulder of the tool and screw the nut down $1\frac{3}{4}$ turn. This presets, or crimps, the sleeve onto the tube. There should be a uniform ridge of metal raised above the surface of the tube that is 50% as high as of the thickness of the front edge of the sleeve, and the sleeve should be slightly bowed. The sleeve may be rotated on the tube, but there must be no back and forth movement along the tube.

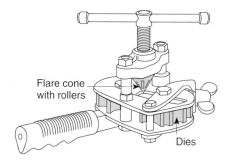

Flare cone with rollers

Dies

Figure 5-74. *Roller-type flaring tool*

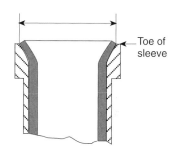

Toe of sleeve

Minimum diameter of flare

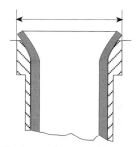

Maximum diameter of flare

Figure 5-75. *Proper flare dimensions*

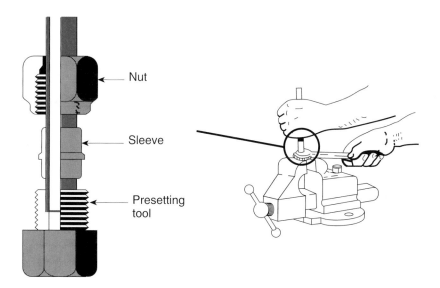

Nut

Sleeve

Presetting tool

Figure 5-77. *Presetting a flareless fitting on a rigid fluid line*

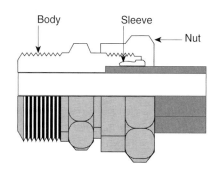

Body

Sleeve

Nut

Figure 5-76. *MS Flareless fitting for rigid fluid lines*

Tubing OD inches	Minimum Bend Radius (inches)	
	Aluminum Alloy	Steel
1/8	3/8	
3/16	7/16	21/32
1/4	9/16	7/8
5/16	3/4	1 1/8
3/8	15/16	1 5/16
1/2	1 1/4	1 3/4
5/8	1 1/2	2 3/16
3/4	1 3/4	2 5/8
1	3	3 1/2

Figure 5-78. *Minimum bend radius for aluminum alloy tubing*

Bending Rigid Tubing

Almost all tubing used for aircraft hydraulic systems has thin walls, and you must take special care when bending it. Observe the minimum bend radius shown in Figure 5-78.

Figure 5-79 illustrates both good and bad bends in a piece of thin-wall tubing. Good operating practices do not allow the outside diameter of a piece of tubing to be decreased in the flattest part of the bend to less than 75% of its original diameter.

Because it is so difficult to keep the tubing from flattening or wrinkling, you must almost always bend it using some form of tubing bender, such as the hand bender, shown in Figure 5-80.

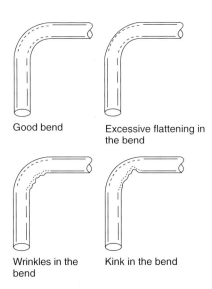

Good bend   Excessive flattening in the bend

Wrinkles in the bend   Kink in the bend

Figure 5-79. *Correct and incorrect tubing bends*

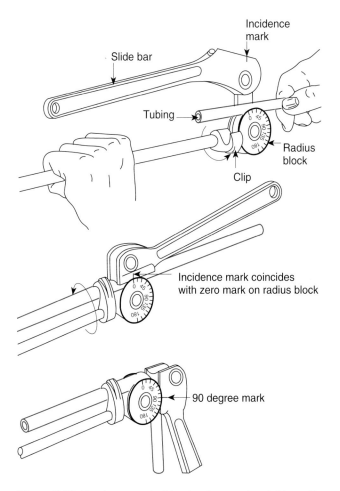

Slide bar

Incidence mark

Tubing

Radius block

Clip

Incidence mark coincides with zero mark on radius block

90 degree mark

Figure 5-80. *Hand-operated tubing benders can bend thin-wall tubing up to 3/4-inch diameter without the walls collapsing.*

Flexible Fluid Lines

Any time there is relative movement between the aircraft and the fluid power component, flexible fluid lines must be used to connect the device into the system. These fluid lines are available in three basic types: low-pressure hose, medium-pressure hose, and high-pressure hose.

The size of a rigid fluid line is its outside diameter measured in $\frac{1}{16}$-inch increments, but the size of a flexible line is approximately its inside diameter, also given in $\frac{1}{16}$-inch increments.

Low-Pressure Hose

Low-pressure flexible fluid lines are seldom used for hydraulic systems, but they are used in low-pressure pneumatic systems and in aircraft instrument installations. The maximum pressure allowed for low-pressure hose is typically less than 250 psi.

Low-pressure hose, MIL-H-5593, has a seamless synthetic rubber inner liner covered with a single cotton braid reinforcement. All low-pressure hose is covered with either a layer of smooth or ribbed synthetic rubber.

Figure 5-81. *Low-pressure hose has an inner liner and one layer of fabric-braid reinforcement.*

Medium-Pressure Hose

MIL-H-8794 hose has a smooth synthetic rubber inner liner covered with a cotton braid, and this braid is in turn covered with a single layer of steel wire braid. Over all of this is a rough, oil-resistant outer layer of cotton braid.

The operating pressure allowed for medium-pressure hose varies with its size. The smaller the diameter of the hose, the higher the allowable operating pressure. Generally MIL-H-8794 hose is used in hydraulic systems that operate with pressures of about 1,500 psi.

All of the flexible hose used in aircraft fluid power systems have a lay-line, a yellow-painted stripe that runs along the length of the hose. This stripe allows you to tell at a glance whether or not the hose is twisted. When installing flexible hose, be sure that the lay-line does not spiral around the hose. *See* Figure 5-82 on the next page.

Figure 5-82. *Medium-pressure hose has an inner liner and one layer of cotton braid and one layer of steel wire braid. It has a rough outer cover.*

High-Pressure Hose

MIL-H-8788 hose has a smooth synthetic inner liner, two high-tensile carbon steel braid reinforcements, a fabric braid, and a smooth black synthetic rubber outer cover.

Another high-pressure flexible hose is similar to MIL-H-8788, but it has a butyl inner liner and a smooth synthetic rubber outer cover that is colored green instead of black. The lay-line and the markings on this hose are white instead of yellow.

This green hose is to be used only with phosphate ester hydraulic fluid (Skydrol), and it is suitable for pressures of up to 3,000 psi, the same as MIL-H-8788 hose.

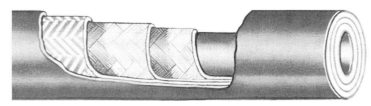

Figure 5-83. *High-pressure hose has an inner liner and two or three layers of steel wire braid. It has a smooth outer cover.*

Teflon Hose

The liner of Teflon hose is made of tetrafluorethylene, or Teflon, resin and covered with a stainless steel braid. Medium-pressure Teflon hose is covered with one stainless steel braid, and high-pressure hose has two layers of stainless steel braid.

Teflon hose has some very desirable operating characteristics and it may be used in fuel, lubricating oil, hydraulic, and pneumatic systems in aircraft. It has one characteristic, however, that you must be aware of in order to get the best service from it. The inner liner of Teflon hose is extruded, and it will take a set, or will become somewhat rigid, after it has been used with high-temperature or high-pressure fluids. After Teflon hose has been used, it should not be bent or have any of its bends straightened out. When Teflon hose is removed from an aircraft, it should be supported in the shape it had when it was installed.

Medium-pressure Teflon hose is covered with one layer of stainless steel braid.

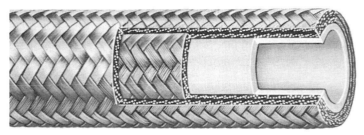

High-pressure Teflon hose is covered with two layers of stainless steel braid.

Figure 5-84

Fluid Line Fittings

It is important when installing or servicing a fluid power system in an aircraft to install only the correct fittings and to use correct installation procedures.

Pipe Fittings

Some components in aircraft hydraulic systems use National Pipe Taper (NPT) fittings to attach fluid lines to castings. Figure 5-85 shows a typical fitting.

The end of these fittings that screws into the casting is tapered about $\frac{1}{16}$-inch to the inch, and when it is installed in a casting, the first thread should be inserted into the hole and an approved thread lubricant applied sparingly to the second thread. When the fitting is screwed into the casting, the lubricant will squeeze out between the threads and prevent the threads from galling, and yet none of the lubricant will squeeze out and contaminate the system.

The way a tapered pipe fitting is measured is somewhat confusing. For example, the commonly used $\frac{1}{8}$-inch pipe fitting to which a $\frac{1}{4}$-inch rigid tube attaches does not measure $\frac{1}{8}$-inch either inside or outside. Its outside diameter and its threads are the same as those of a piece of standard iron pipe that has an inside diameter of $\frac{1}{8}$ inch. The hole into which a $\frac{1}{8}$-inch NPT fitting screws has a diameter of about $\frac{3}{8}$ inch.

galling. Fretting or pulling out chunks of a surface by sliding contact with another surface or body.

Figure 5-85. *An AN816 nipple has tapered pipe threads on one end and fittings for an AN flare fitting on the other end.*

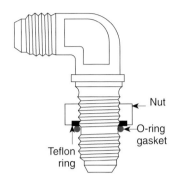

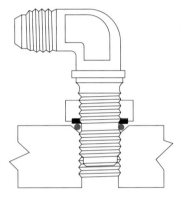

Screw nut onto upper threads and slip a Teflon ring and an O-ring gasket over lower threads into groove.

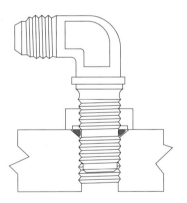

Screw fitting into casting until O-ring contacts housing.

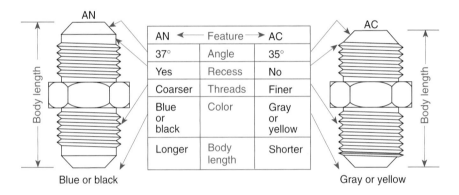

Align fitting with connecting lines and screw nut down until it contacts housing. The compressed O-ring forms fluid-tight seal.

Figure 5-87. *Proper installation of a bulkhead fitting*

AN and AC Flare Fittings

Flare fittings do not depend on any type of sealant to effect a good seal. They depend, rather, on a good fit between the flare cone and the flare in the end of the tube.

One word of caution regarding flare fittings: There are two types of flared tube fittings that look much alike, but they are definitely not interchangeable.

Figure 5-86 illustrates an AN fitting and an AC fitting. At first glance, these two fittings are similar, but a close inspection shows the differences. The AN fitting has a short shoulder between the first thread and the base of the flare cone, while the threads on the AC fitting start right at the flare cone. The threads on the AC fitting are generally finer (this is not the case with the smaller size fittings), and the aluminum alloy AN fittings are dyed blue, while the aluminum alloy AC fittings are dyed gray or yellow.

The dash number of these fittings designates the outside diameter of the rigid tube they fit. For example, an AN815-6D union is used to connect two $\frac{3}{8}$-inch ($\frac{6}{16}$-inch) outside diameter tubes.

AN	Feature	AC
37°	Angle	35°
Yes	Recess	No
Coarser	Threads	Finer
Blue or black	Color	Gray or yellow
Longer	Body length	Shorter

Figure 5-86. *Comparison between AN and AC fittings*

Universal or Bulkhead Fittings

Fittings such as the AN833 elbow are used to screw into castings or to carry fluid lines through a bulkhead. Figure 5-87 shows the correct way to install this fitting in a casting. Screw an AN6289 nut onto the top threads with the counterbored side of the nut toward the end of the fitting. Work a Teflon ring up into the counterbore of the nut, and then carefully slip the proper O-ring over the threads and up into the groove between the two sets of threads. Screw the nut down until the Teflon ring touches the O-ring and the O-ring rests against the inner end of the lower set of threads. Screw the fitting into the casting until the O-ring contacts the chamfered edges of the hole. Hold the nut with a wrench and screw the fitting into the hole for 1 to 1½ turns to position the fitting so that it points in the proper direction. Hold the fitting in proper alignment and torque the nut to the value that is specified in the aircraft service manual.

MS Flareless Fittings

There is a full line of flareless-type tube fittings available for use with the crimped-on sleeve and nut. The inside of the fitting has a smooth counterbore into which the end of the tube fits. The taper at the mouth of the fitting provides the seal between the fitting and the sleeve, and the seal between the sleeve and the tube is provided by the bite of the sleeve into the tube.

You must not overtorque flareless-type fittings. When assembling a fitting of this type, be sure that the sleeve is properly preset on the tube, and the tube inserted straight into the fitting. Screw the nut down finger-tight and then tighten it with a wrench for one sixth of a turn, one hex, or at the very most, one third of a turn, two hexes.

If the fitting leaks, rather than attempting to fix it by applying more torque, disassemble the fitting and find out what the trouble is. It is usually a damaged fitting or contamination between the sleeve and the fitting.

Quick-Disconnect Fittings

It is often necessary to actuate a hydraulic system without running the aircraft engine. This is usually done with pressure supplied by a ground-power unit also called a GPU, or hydraulic "mule." The inlet and outlet lines are disconnected from the engine-driven pump and connected to the pump in the mule. To prevent loss of fluid when making this change, the lines to the pump are fitted with quick-disconnect fittings such as the ones shown in Figure 5-88.

When the lines are disconnected the springs inside both halves of the fitting pull the poppet valves tightly into their seats and seal off the lines. When the lines are connected, plungers in each fitting meet and force the poppets off of their seats allowing fluid to flow freely through the fittings.

quick-disconnect fitting. A hydraulic line fitting that seals the line when the fitting is disconnected. Quick-disconnect fittings are used on the lines connected to the engine-driven hydraulic pump. They allow the pump to be disconnected and an auxiliary hydraulic power system connected to perform checks requiring hydraulic power while the aircraft is in the hangar.

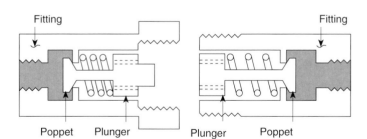

When fittings are disconnected, the springs hold poppet valves tightly on their seats.

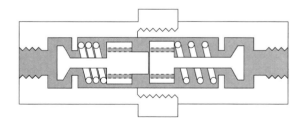

When fittings are connected, the plungers force poppets off their seats and fluid flows freely through the fittings.

Figure 5-88. *Quick-disconnect fittings*

Fluid Line Installation

Not only must the correct fluid lines be installed in an aircraft, but they must be installed properly. Here are a few basic rules regarding their installation:

Rigid Lines

When manufacturing a replacement rigid fluid line, be sure that all of the angles are correct, and inspect all of the bends to be sure that none of them are collapsed, kinked, or wrinkled. Fit the line in place to ensure that the tube aligns with the fittings at each end. The line should be straight with the fitting and should apply a slight pressure against it.

1. No tube, regardless of how short, should be installed unless there is at least one bend in it. This bend provides for vibration, and for the inevitable expansion and contraction that are caused by temperature changes and by the line being pressurized.

2. Never attempt to pull a tube up to the fitting with the nut. This will place a strain on the flare or the preset bite, and vibration can easily cause the tube to fail.

3. Where a fluid line is brought through a bulkhead, if it is not carried through with a bulkhead fitting, it must be supported with bonded cushion clamps and centered in the hole in such a way that there is protection against chafing.

4. All fluid lines should be run below electrical wire bundles so that there is no possibility of fluid dripping onto the wire.

5. All fluid lines should be identified at each end, and at least once in each compartment with color-coded tape to identify the type of fluid it carries.

6. Support clamps should be placed no farther apart than:

   $\frac{1}{8}$" tubing every 9 inches
   $\frac{1}{4}$" tubing every 12 inches
   $\frac{3}{8}$" tubing every 16 inches

   These clamps should be placed as near the bend as possible so the tubing will have a minimum amount of overhang.

Flexible Lines

Any time there is relative movement between the two ends of a fluid line, there should be a section of flexible hose installed.

1. The lay line along a flexible hose should never spiral. This would indicate the hose has twisted and had a built-in strain. Pressure surges in a twisted line can cause failure.

2. Always use a fitting that allows the hose to approach it without any bends near its end. Elbows are available in both 90° and 45° angles.

3. Never attempt to pull a hose up to its fitting with the nut. When pressure is applied to a hose, it will tend to expand its diameter and shorten its length. Allow the line to have slack of about 5 to 8 percent of its length.

4. Use the proper size cushion clamp to support the hose any time it goes through a bulkhead, or any place where vibration may place a twisting force on the fitting.

5. The liner of Teflon hose is extruded, and it has ample strength for applications in which there is no twist, but it is susceptible to failure if it is twisted or if it is bent with too small a bend radius.

6. Be sure to observe the minimum bend radius for all flexible hose. For MIL-H-8788 hose, the following are the minimum acceptable bend radii:

   -4 hose   3.0 inch minimum bend radius
   -6 hose   5.0 inch minimum bend radius
   -8 hose   5.75 inch minimum bend radius
   -10 hose   6.5 inch minimum bend radius

   If the hose is subjected to flexing, this radius must be increased.

7. It is possible to make up high-pressure hose if your shop is equipped with the proper tools. But, because of the extremely critical nature of high-pressure fluid lines, it is generally advisable to buy the replacement high-pressure fluid lines from the aircraft manufacturer, or from an approved supplier that makes them according to the manufacturer's specifications. By installing only fluid lines that carry the correct manufacturer's part number, you will be assured that the line is constructed of the proper material, and that it has been tested according to the procedure required by the manufacturer.

8. Before installing any fluid line, be sure to blow it out with compressed air to remove any obstructions or particles that may have been left in the process of manufacture, or which may have been allowed to enter the hose while it was in storage. Before a line is stored, cap both ends to prevent the entry of any contaminants.

Answers begin on Page 415. Page numbers refer to chapter text.

112. Rigid tubing used in low-pressure hydraulic systems is usually made of _____ aluminum alloy. *Page 390*

113. Rigid tubing used for high-pressure hydraulic systems is usually made of _____ aluminum alloy or annealed _____ . *Page 390*

114. A dent that is 10% of the diameter of a piece of aluminum alloy tubing _____ (is or is not) permissible if it is in the heel of a bend. *Page 390*

115. A scratch in a piece of aluminum alloy tubing is permissible if its depth is less than _____ percent of the tubing wall thickness, and it is not in the heel of a bend. *Page 390*

116. The flare cone angle used for aircraft flared tubing fittings has an angle of _____ degrees. *Page 390*

117. Soft aluminum alloy tubing should be double flared if its diameter is _____ inch or less. *Page 390*

118. A properly preset MS flareless fitting _____ (is or is not) allowed to rotate on the tube. *Page 391*

119. The minimum bend radius for a piece of ⅜-inch aluminum alloy tubing is _____ inch/es. *Page 392*

120. The maximum flattening allowed in the bend in a piece of rigid fluid line reduces the outside diameter of the tube in the bend to _____ percent of the original tube diameter. *Page 392*

121. A piece of flexible hose that has a ribbed outer covering is a _____ (low, medium, or high)-pressure hose. *Page 393*

122. A piece of flexible hose that has a rough outer covering is a _____ (low, medium, or high)-pressure hose. *Page 393*

123. A piece of flexible hose that has a smooth outer covering is a _____ (low, medium, or high)-pressure hose. *Page 394*

124. A piece of flexible hose that has a smooth green outer covering is designed to carry _____ (mineral or phosphate ester)-base fluid. *Page 394*

125. The highest pressure that can be carried in a low-pressure flexible hose is normally considered to be _____ psi. *Page 393*

126. Medium-pressure flexible hose is used in hydraulic systems with pressures up to _____ psi. *Page 393*

127. High-pressure flexible hose is used in hydraulic systems with pressures up to _____ psi. *Page 394*

128. A flexible hose with a stainless steel braid outer covering has a liner made of _____ . *Page 394*

129. When installing a tapered pipe thread in a casting, thread lubricant should be applied to the _____ (first or second) thread. *Page 395*

130. The nut of an MS flareless fitting should be screwed down finger tight on the fitting and then it should be tightened with a wrench for _____ or at the most _____ of a turn. *Page 397*

131. When a fluid line is routed through a section of an aircraft structure parallel with an electrical wire bundle, the fluid line should be _____ (above or below) the wire bundle. *Page 398*

132. A run of 3/8-inch rigid fluid line should be supported with a cushioned clamp at least every _____ inches. *Page 398*

133. The colored line that extends the length of a piece of flexible hose that is used to tell whether or not the hose was twisted during installation is called a/an _____ line. *Page 399*

134. Flexible hose changes its dimensions when it is pressurized. A piece of flexible hose should be between _____ and _____ percent longer than the distance between the fittings to which it attaches. *Page 399*

135. The minimum recommended bend radius for a piece of 1/2-inch MIL-H-8788 hose is _____ inches. *Page 399*

Pneumatic Systems

Pneumatic systems are fluid power systems that use a compressible fluid, air. These systems are dependable and lightweight, and because the fluid is air, there is no need for a return system.

Some aircraft have only a low-pressure pneumatic system to operate the gyro instruments; others use compressed air as an emergency backup for lowering the landing gear and operating the brakes in the event of a hydraulic system failure. Still others have a complete pneumatic system that actuates the landing gear retraction, nose wheel steering, passenger doors, and propeller brakes. Each of these types of systems is discussed in this section.

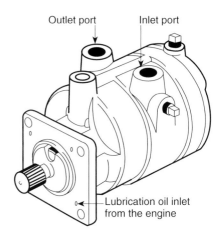

Figure 5-89. *This wet-type air pump is lubricated by engine oil taken into the pump through holes in the mounting flange.*

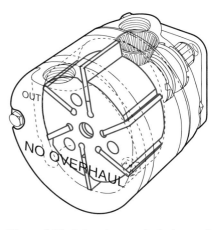

Figure 5-90. *A dry air pump is the heart of the low-pressure pneumatic system installed in most modern aircraft.*

deicer system. A system that removes ice after it has formed.

Low-Pressure Pneumatic Systems

The need for modern aircraft to fly anywhere any time has increased the importance of low-pressure pneumatic systems. These systems provide air for gyroscopic attitude and direction indicators and air to inflate the pneumatic deicer boots. This compressed air is usually provided by a vane-type engine-driven air pump.

This section of text covers a basic introduction to low-pressure pneumatic systems. A more comprehensive discussion is included in the sections on ice control and flight instruments.

Engine-Driven Air Pumps

For many years, engine-driven air pumps were used primarily to evacuate the case of air-driven gyroscopic instruments, so they were commonly called vacuum pumps. Later, the discharge air from these pumps was used to inflate deicer boots, and these pumps are now more correctly called air pumps. There are two types of air pumps that may be used: "wet" pumps and "dry" pumps.

Wet pumps have steel vanes that are lubricated and sealed with engine oil drawn in through the pump mounting pad and exhausted with the discharge air. This oil must be removed with an air-oil separator before the air can be used to inflate the deicer boots and drive the instrument gyros.

Dry pumps, such as the one in Figure 5-90, were developed so there would be no oil in the pump discharge air. The vanes in these pumps are made of carbon, and they need no lubrication. The basic problem with dry pumps is that the carbon vanes are breakable, and can easily be damaged by any contaminants entering the pump. It is extremely important that all air taken into these pumps be filtered, and when servicing the system that no contaminants be allowed to enter.

Pneumatic Deicer Systems

The compressed air system used for inflating deicer boots with a wet vacuum pump is shown in Figure 5-91. The oily air leaves the pump and passes through baffles in the oil separator. The oil collects on the baffles and drains down and is collected in the lower part of the separator and returned to the engine oil sump. Clean air leaves the separator and flows through the deicer on-off valve to a pressure relief valve that drops the pressure to the value needed for the boots. It then flows to the timer and distributor valve that distributes the air to the proper boots in the proper sequence. When the system is turned off, the air is directed overboard by the deicer on-off valve.

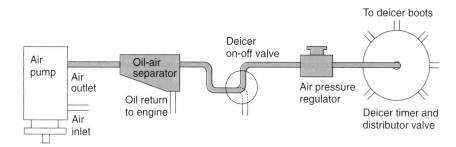

Figure 5-91. *Compressed air source for a pneumatic deicer system*

Pneumatic Gyro Power Systems

The gyroscope in pneumatic gyro instruments is driven by air impinging on buckets cut in the periphery of the wheel. There are two ways of obtaining this air. In some systems, like the one in Figure 5-92, the air pump evacuates the instrument case and air is drawn into the case through an air filter. The clean air is directed through a nozzle and it strikes the buckets and drives the gyro. A suction relief valve regulates the suction to the correct value for the instruments, and a suction gage reads the pressure drop across the instruments.

Since many modern airplanes fly at such high altitude that there is not enough atmospheric air pressure to drive the instruments when the case is evacuated, another method must be used. The pneumatic gyros installed in these airplanes are driven by the air from the pressure side of a dry air pump using a system such as that in Figure 5-93.

The air is filtered before it is taken into the air pump, and after it leaves, its pressure is regulated by an air pressure regulator. The air then flows through an in-line filter and into the instruments where it drives the gyros, and is then evacuated overboard.

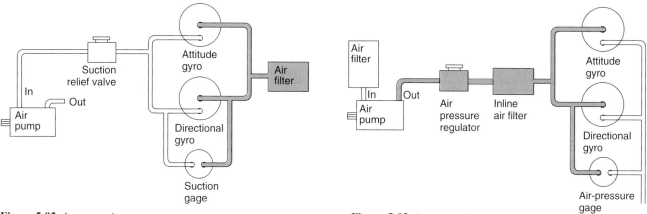

Figure 5-92. *A pneumatic gyroscopic instrument system using the suction side of the air pump*

Figure 5-93. *A pneumatic gyroscopic instrument system using the pressure side of a dry air pump*

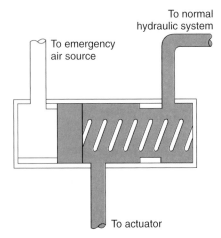

Figure 5-94. *A shuttle valve is used to direct either normal system hydraulic pressure or emergency compressed air into an actuator cylinder.*

shuttle valve. An automatic selector valve mounted on critical components such as landing gear actuation cylinders and brake cylinders.

For normal operation, system fluid flows into the actuator through the shuttle valve, but if normal system pressure is lost, emergency system pressure forces the shuttle over and emergency fluid flows into the actuator.

Backup High-Pressure Pneumatic Systems

In case the hydraulic systems in an aircraft fail, there must be provision for emergency extension of the landing gear and the application of the brakes.

The pneumatic backup system is simple and effective. A steel bottle, or cylinder, that contains approximately 3,000 psi of compressed air or nitrogen is installed in the aircraft, and a shuttle valve in the line to the actuator directs hydraulic fluid into the actuator for normal actuation, or compressed air for emergency actuation. If there is a failure in the hydraulic system and the landing gear must be lowered with the emergency air system, the landing gear selector is put in the GEAR-DOWN position to provide a return path for the hydraulic fluid in the actuators, and the emergency air valve is opened. High-pressure air shifts the shuttle valve and this air is directed into the actuator to lower the landing gear. This system is discussed in more detail in the chapter on landing gears.

Full Pneumatic Systems

The majority of airplanes built in the United States use hydraulic or electric power for such heavy-duty applications as landing gear retraction, but compressed air can also be used for these systems.

Some advantages of compressed air over other heavy-duty power systems are:

1. Air is universally available in an unlimited supply.

2. Pneumatic system components are reasonably simple and lightweight.

3. Weight is saved because compressed air is lightweight and no return system is needed.

4. There is no fire hazard, and the danger of explosion is slight.

5. Contamination is minimized by the use of proper filters.

Figure 5-95 shows a closed-center, high-pressure pneumatic system that uses two air compressors driven from the accessory gear boxes of the turboprop engines. Air is taken into the first stage of the compressor through an inlet air duct, and compressed. This compressed air then passes on successively to three other stages within the pumps. The discharge air from the fourth stage is routed through an intercooler and a bleed valve to the unloading valve. The bleed valve is held closed by oil pressure. In the event of oil pressure failure, the valve will open and relieve the pump of its load.

The unloading valve maintains air pressure in the system between 2,900 and 3,300 psi. When the pressure rises to 3,300 psi, a check valve traps it and unloads the pump by dumping its output overboard. When the system pressure drops to 2,900 psi, the pump is loaded and its output is directed back into the system.

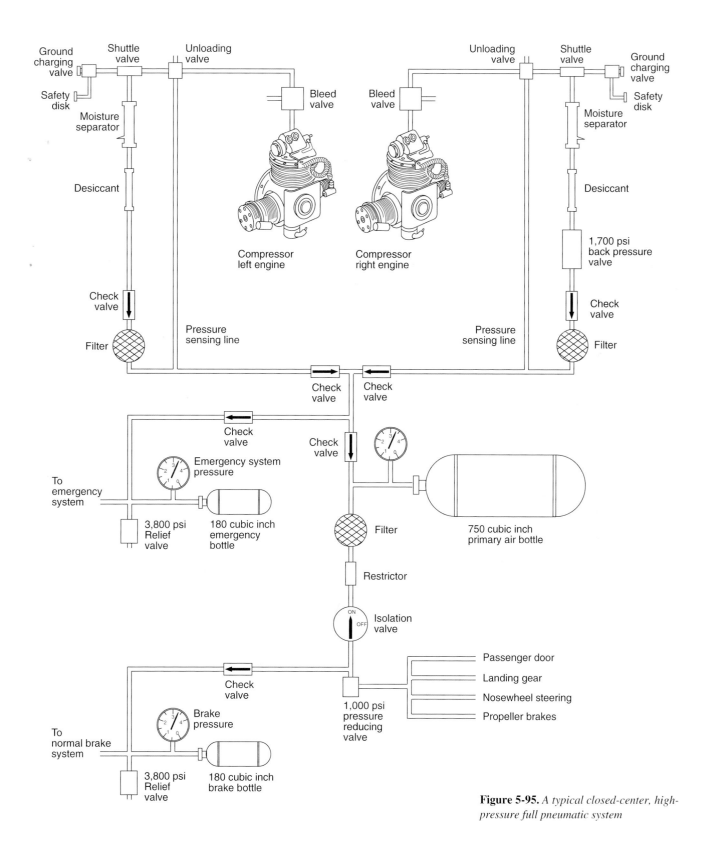

Figure 5-95. *A typical closed-center, high-pressure full pneumatic system*

A shuttle valve in the line between the compressor and the main system makes it possible to charge the system from a ground source. When the engine is not running and air pressure is supplied from the external source, the shuttle slides over and isolates the compressor.

Moisture in a compressed air system will freeze as the air pressure drops when a component is actuated. For this reason, every bit of water must be removed from the air. A separator collects moisture from the air and holds it on a baffle until the system is shut down. When the inlet pressure to the moisture separator drops below 450 psi, a drain valve opens and all of the accumulated moisture is discharged overboard. An electric heater prevents water that is trapped in the separator from freezing.

After the air leaves the moisture separator with about 98% of its moisture removed, it passes through a desiccant, or chemical dryer, to remove the last traces of moisture. Before the air enters the operating portion of the pneumatic system, it is filtered as it passes through a 10-micron, sintered-metal filter. (The smallest object we can usually see with our naked eye is about 40 microns.)

The system in the right engine nacelle has a back-pressure valve. This is essentially a pressure relief valve in the supply line. The back-pressure valve does not open until the pressure from the compressor or from the ground charging system is above 1,700 psi. This assures that the moisture separator will operate most efficiently. If it is necessary to operate the system from an external source whose pressure is less than 1,700 psi, the source can be connected into the left side of the system where there is no back-pressure valve.

There are three air storage bottles in this airplane, a 750-cubic-inch bottle for the main system, a 180-cubic-inch bottle for normal brake operation, and a second 180-cubic-inch bottle for emergency system operation.

A manually operated isolation valve allows the technician to close off the air supply so the system can be serviced and components changed without having to discharge the storage bottles.

The majority of the components in this system operate with a pressure of 1,000 psi, so a pressure-reducing valve is installed between the isolation valve and the supply manifold. This reduces the air pressure for normal operation of the landing gear, the passenger door, the propeller brake, and the nose wheel steering. This pressure-reducing valve not only lowers the pressure to 1,000 psi, but it also serves as a backup pressure relief valve.

An emergency system stores compressed air under the full system pressure of 3,300 psi and supplies it for the emergency extension of the landing gear and for emergency brake application.

moisture separator. A component in a high-pressure pneumatic system that removes most of the water vapor from the compressed air.

When the compressed air is used, its pressure drops, and this pressure drop causes a drop in temperature. If any moisture were allowed to remain in the air it would freeze and block the system.

desiccant. A chemical that absorbs moisture to remove it from the air.

Answers begin on Page 415. Page numbers refer to chapter text.

136. Oil from the discharge of a wet-type air pump is collected by a/an _____ and returned to the engine. *Page 402*

137. The vanes of a dry-type air pump are made of _____ . *Page 402*

138. The air pressure in a full pneumatic system is maintained in the correct range by the action of the _____ valve. *Page 404*

139. If the lubrication system for the high-pressure compressor fails, the _____ valve will relieve the pump of all of its load. *Page 404*

140. Water is removed from the compressed air in a full pneumatic system by the _____ . *Page 406*

141. The actuating components in a full pneumatic system may be serviced without discharging the air storage bottles by closing the _____ valve. *Page 406*

Large Aircraft Fluid Power Systems

Hydraulic power is so important for large aircraft that more than one main hydraulic system is installed, and in addition to these main systems, there are backup and emergency systems to supply power in case of main system failure.

Sources of Hydraulic Power

The main hydraulic power for large aircraft typically comes from engine-driven pumps, but there are also pumps driven by electric motors. These electric pumps, commonly driven by three-phase AC motors supply pressurized fluid to the system when the engines are not operating. Another source of hydraulic power is from pumps driven by compressed air from an auxiliary power unit (APU), a ground power unit (GPU), or from engine bleed air.

Power transfer units (PTUs) are used on some aircraft to pressurize one hydraulic system from another system without transferring any fluid between the systems. The PTU consists of a hydraulic motor driving a hydraulic pump. If, for example, pressure is needed in a system that is usually pressurized by an engine-driven pump without running the engine, pressure from another system that is powered by an electric pump can be used to drive the PTU. The pump in the PTU pressurizes the system.

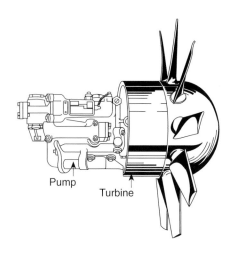

Figure 5-96. *A ram air turbine can be lowered into the air flowing around the aircraft to supply hydraulic pressure for emergency actuation of systems needed to get the aircraft safely on the ground.*

In the event that all hydraulic power is lost, some airplanes can extend a ram air turbine (RAT) into the airstream outside the aircraft and the air flowing through the turbine blades drives a hydraulic pump to produce enough hydraulic power to actuate the systems needed to get the aircraft safely on the ground.

Jet Transport Airplane Hydraulic System

Large jet transport airplanes such as the Boeing 727 have complex hydraulic systems that supply power to actuate the landing gear, flaps, spoilers, primary flight controls, and such auxiliary functions as the stairs. Figure 5-97 is a simplified diagram of a hydraulic system typical for these airplanes.

The Boeing 727 has three independent hydraulic systems: system A, system B, and a standby system. Follow these systems in Figure 5-97.

Pressure gages installed on the flight engineer's panel show the pressure of systems A and B, and a pressure gage on the first officer's instrument panel shows the pressure available to the brakes. Each of these gages measures the precharge air pressure in the accumulators. When the pumps are not operating, the gages show the precharge pressure, which is about 2,000 psi. If the air preload is ever lost, the gage for that accumulator will read zero regardless of the hydraulic pressure in the system.

System A

The fluid for system A, shown in Figure 5-97, is held in a reservoir that is pressurized by bleed air from engines 1 and 2. Fluid from the reservoir goes to engine-driven pumps on engines 1 and 2. These pumps pressurize the fluid to 3,000 psi, and this fluid flows through check valves into the system A pressure manifold and accumulator. After actuating the components in system A, the fluid returns to the reservoir through a filter.

System A provides power for the landing gear, nose wheel steering, nose wheel brakes, trailing edge flaps, leading edge flaps and slats, ground spoilers, outboard flight spoilers, ailerons, elevators, and lower rudder. *See* Figure 4-34 on Page 286 for a picture of the control surfaces.

Each of the engine-driven pumps has a solenoid-operated depressurization valve that allows the flight engineer to reduce the output pressure from 3,000 psi to approximately 0 psi. With the pump depressurized, fluid still flows through its case for lubrication and cooling. When the pilot pulls the fire-pull T handle, the pumps are automatically depressurized, and motor-operated fluid shutoff valves shut off the flow of fluid between the pump and the system.

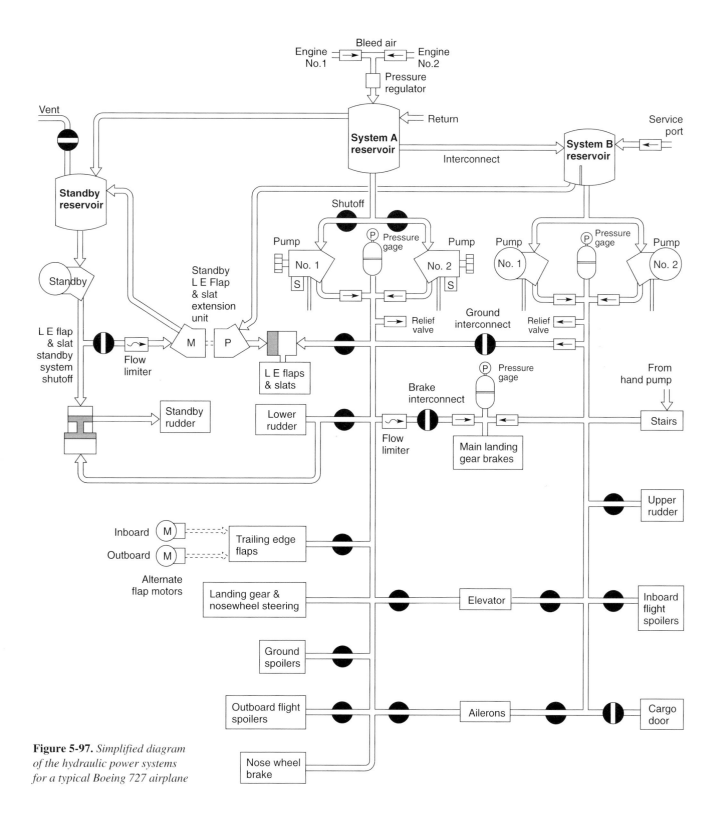

Figure 5-97. *Simplified diagram of the hydraulic power systems for a typical Boeing 727 airplane*

System B

System B is supplied by its own reservoir, and the system is pressurized by two electric-motor-driven pumps. System B operates the ailerons, elevators, inboard flight spoilers, upper rudder, aft stairs, and main landing gear brakes. System B can pressurize system A on the ground before engine starting by opening the ground interconnect valve.

System B reservoir has a baffle that divides its lower portion into two compartments. One supplies fluid to the two B system electric pumps, and the other supplies fluid to the standby leading edge flap and slat extension pump for emergency extension of the leading edge devices.

Standby System

The standby system is pressurized by a continuous-duty electric motor-driven pump supplied with power from the Essential AC bus through switches for either the alternate flap or the standby rudder. Pressure from the standby system is used to operate the standby rudder and extend the leading edge devices when system A pressure is lost.

Reservoir Servicing

The three reservoirs are serviced with a pressure unit or hand pump through system B reservoir. As soon as system B reservoir is full, fluid will flow into system A reservoir through the interconnect line, which is connected at the 2.5 gallon level. When the system A reservoir is full, the standby reservoir will fill. Fluid quantity indicators are installed on the flight engineer's panels for all three reservoirs.

STUDY QUESTIONS: LARGE AIRCRAFT FLUID POWER SYSTEMS

Answers begin on Page 415. Page numbers refer to chapter text.

142. Hydraulic pumps supplying pressure for large aircraft may be driven by five methods. These are:
    a. _____   d. _____
    b. _____   e. _____
    c. _____
        Page 407

143. When a power transfer unit is used to pressurize one hydraulic system in an aircraft from another system, fluid _____ (is or is not) transferred between the systems. *Page 407*

144. The hydraulic pumps used in a Boeing 727 system A are _____ (engine-driven or electric). *Page 408*

145. The hydraulic pumps used in a Boeing 727 system B are _____ (engine-driven or electric). *Page 410*

---

146. The hydraulic reservoirs used in a Boeing 727 are pressurized with _____ (hydraulic fluid or engine bleed air). *Page 408*

147. The hydraulic pressure gages on a Boeing 727 flight engineer's panels read _____ (accumulator air or hydraulic fluid) pressure. *Page 408*

148. Boeing 727 system A components may be actuated without the engine running by using system B pumps and opening the _____ valve. *Page 410*

149. Boeing 727 System A pump output pressure can be dropped to zero pressure by the flight engineer opening the solenoid-operated _____ valve. *Page 408*

150. All three hydraulic reservoirs in a Boeing 727 are serviced through the _____ reservoir. *Page 410*

Hydraulic System Maintenance and Troubleshooting

Hydraulic system maintenance consists of keeping the system filled with the proper fluid, maintaining all lines and fittings so there are no leaks, and cleaning or replacing system filters on the schedule recommended by the aircraft manufacturer.

If any system has been serviced with the wrong fluid, all of the fluid must be drained and the system flushed with the recommended solvent. The filter elements must be cleaned or replaced, and any seal that was touched by the wrong fluid must be replaced with a new seal bearing the correct part number, and a current cure date.

If any system component has failed, contaminants have probably gotten into the system, and the fluid must be drained and the filters replaced. Any components that operated with contaminated fluid should be carefully checked to be sure that there are no contaminants in the unit.

Hydraulic System Troubleshooting

Regardless of the system, the basic principle of troubleshooting is the same. Isolate the problem, and then eliminate everything in that area that is operating properly. Whatever is left is bound to contain the trouble.

You cannot isolate a problem unless you know the system thoroughly. Modern hydraulic systems are complex, and no troubleshooting can be done systematically without having the schematic diagram of the system before you.

Hydraulic systems are logically divided into power and actuation sections. The power section can be further divided into the main, the backup, and the emergency subsystems.

If some part of an actuation system does not work when running off the main power system, but does when running off the hand pump, the trouble could be a low supply of fluid in the reservoir (the fluid could be below the engine-driven pump supply port). Or, the pump itself could be at fault. Always check the more simple possibility first and eliminate it before moving on to the more difficult possibility.

If the system does not work properly with either the main power system or the backup system (the engine-driven pump or the hand pump), but it can be actuated by the emergency system, the actuation system is working but neither main nor the backup power systems are working. The systems could be out of fluid, or an unloading or a relief valve could be stuck in the open position.

If only one system fails to work, and there is pressure in the system, the trouble is in the actuation system. If, for instance, you cannot lower the landing gear, but the flaps actuate normally, the trouble is probably in the landing gear selector valve or between the gear selector valve and the gear actuators.

Troubleshooting Tips and Procedures

1. If no pressure is indicated on the system pressure gage, yet there is a return flow into the reservoir, the trouble probably does not lie with the pump, but in the pressure control valves for the system. Pumps are fluid movers, not pressure generators. A pressure regulator or a relief valve is probably stuck open.

2. If there is a restriction in the pump outlet or between the pump outlet and the system pressure regulator, the system pressure will drop when some unit is actuated. The pump is unable to provide the volume of fluid the system requires.

3. System pressure that is higher than normal could mean that the unloading valve is failing to unload the pump and a relief valve is maintaining the pressure. Knowing the setting of each relief valve will help determine which valve is doing the work. When a relief valve holds the system pressure, it usually makes a buzzing noise, and gets quite warm.

4. A loud hammering noise in a system that has an accumulator indicates an insufficient air preload in the accumulator. The pump goes on the line, or kicks in, and since there is no compressible fluid in the accumulator, the system pressure immediately builds up to the kick-out pressure and the pump goes off the line. This kicking in and out without any air to compress and cushion the shock causes the heavy hammering.

Continued

4. *(Continued)* Few hydraulic systems have air gages on the accumulators to show the amount of air preload, so, to find the amount of air pressure in the accumulator, pump the hand pump slowly, and watch the hydraulic pressure gage. The pressure will not rise at first, but when it does, it will jump up suddenly, and as you continue to pump, it will continue to rise, but slowly. The pressure jumped at the point fluid was first forced into the accumulator where it was opposed by the air. The amount of pressure shown on the gage after the first jump is the amount of air preload in the accumulator.

5. Pump chattering and subsequent overheating indicates air in the line. The most logical place for the air to enter is from a low reservoir. Another possibility is a leak in the suction line between the reservoir and the inlet to the pump.

6. Slow actuation of a unit is often caused by internal leakage in a valve or an actuator. This leakage also causes the pump to kick on and off the system more often than it should. If the system uses an electric pump, you will notice that the ammeter shows the pump to be operating quite often when nothing is actuated. The leaking component may be heated by the fluid leaking, and it can be identified by feeling all of the suspected units and checking the one that is unnaturally warm.

7. Spongy actuation is usually a sign of air in the system. Most double-acting systems are self-bleeding, so after a component has been replaced, it should be cycled a number of times to purge it of all of the air in the actuator and the lines back to the reservoir. If the actuating time decreases each time the system is cycled, the air is being worked out of the fluid.

    Some systems do not purge normally, and the manufacturer usually has special instructions in the service manual to explain the method that should be used to remove all of the trapped air.

8. Many hydraulic systems have several relief valves that are set to relieve at different pressures. To check these valves, screw the adjustment on all of the valves down so they will relieve at a pressure higher than the highest setting of any of the valves.

    Adjust the valve that requires the highest pressure first, and then adjust the rest of the valves, beginning at the valve that has the next highest setting and continue to the valve that has the lowest setting.

9. Sometimes a hydraulic pressure gage fluctuates rapidly, with the pointer forming a blur. This is an indication that a there is air in the gage line or that the gage is not adequately snubbed.

    Hold a shop rag around the back of the instrument and crack the fitting just enough to purge any air from the line, and then retighten it. If this does not cure the fluctuation, the gage snubber must be replaced.

snubber. A device in a hydraulic or pneumatic component that absorbs shock and/or vibration. A snubber is installed in the line to a hydraulic pressure gage to prevent the pointer fluctuating.

Troubleshooting hydraulic and pneumatic systems is usually a logical application of basic principles, and, as with all types of aircraft maintenance, the aircraft must be maintained in such a way that it continues to meet the conditions of its original airworthiness certification.

All of the work must be done according to the recommendations of the aircraft manufacturer. Whenever you have a particularly difficult problem, do not hesitate to contact the manufacturer's service representative for help. He or she has probably encountered the problem before and can save time and money in getting the aircraft back into productive service.

STUDY QUESTIONS: HYDRAULIC SYSTEM TROUBLESHOOTING

Answers begin on page 415. Page numbers refer to chapter text.

151. No systematic troubleshooting can be done without the use of a/an _____ diagram of the system. *Page 411*

152. The two basic sections of a hydraulic system are the _____ and the _____ sections. *Page 412*

153. There are three subdivisions of the power section of a hydraulic system. These are _____ , _____ , and _____ . *Page 412*

154. If only one system fails to operate as it should, and there is pressure in the system, the trouble is in the _____ (actuation or power) system. *Page 412*

155. If there is no pressure indicated on the system pressure gage, yet there is fluid flowing back into the reservoir, the problem is probably in the _____ (pump or pressure control valves). *Page 412*

156. If the system pressure drops when some unit is actuated, a probable cause could be a restriction in the line between the _____ (pump and the pressure regulator or selector valve and actuator). *Page 412*

157. A higher than normal system pressure is most likely to be caused by a malfunctioning _____ (unloading valve or relief valve). *Page 412*

158. A heavy chattering or banging in a hydraulic system is often caused by an insufficient air preload in the _____ . *Page 412*

159. Hydraulic pump chattering and overheating is usually caused by air in the pump _____ (inlet or discharge) line. *Page 413*

160. Spongy actuation of a hydraulic system is usually caused by _____ in the system. *Page 413*

161. When there are several relief valves in a hydraulic or pneumatic system, always begin adjusting with the valve that should be set to the _____ (highest or lowest) pressure first. *Page 413*

162. Rapid fluctuation of the pointer on a hydraulic pressure gage is usually an indication of _____ in the pressure gage line. *Page 413*

Answers to Hydraulic and Pneumatic Power Systems Study Questions

1. hydraulic
2. pneumatic
3. 7.07
4. 226.2
5. 904.8
6. 600
7. decreased
8. 33,000
9. 550
10. 746
11. 0.212
12. 231
13. 1.75
14. 6,000
15. 4
16. 250
17. 18
18. 6
19. 20.0
20. velocity
21. pressure
22. 0.53
23. 20
24. decrease
25. rate
26. single
27. compensator
28. spring
29. selector valve
30. constant
31. does
32. before

33. opened
34. automatically
35. pressure relief
36. system pressure regulator
37. accumulator
38. series
39. does not
40. blue
41. alcohol
42. natural
43. red
44. varsol
45. neoprene
46. soap and water
47. Skydrol
48. light purple
49. trichlorethylene
50. Butyl
51. soap and water
52. engine-driven pump
53. power pack
54. cavitating
55. a. aspirator
    b. engine compressor bleed air
    c. system hydraulic pressure
56. double
57. double
58. outlet
59. constant
60. shear section
61. large

62. around
63. seal
64. chatter, overheat
65. high
66. does not
67. effective
68. bypass
69. check
70. orifice check valve
71. sequence
72. priority
73. flaps-down
74. crossflow
75. open-center, closed-center
76. low
77. small
78. does
79. fuse
80. backup
81. higher
82. unloading
83. pressure reducing
84. accumulator
85. one third
86. H
87. should not
88. increase
89. 5
90. clogged
91. bypass
92. separators

Continued

93. linear, rotary
94. balanced
95. the same
96. different
97. restrictor
98. double-acting
99. rotary
100. flow control
101. gasket
102. packing
103. one way
104. open end
105. two way
106. 1,500
107. toward
108. away from
109. blue
110. a. part number
    b. composition of the seal
    c. name of the manufacturer
    d. cure date
111. wiper
112. 5052-O
113. 2024-T, stainless steel
114. is not
115. 10

116. 37
117. $\frac{3}{8}$
118. is
119. $\frac{15}{16}$
120. 75
121. low
122. medium
123. high
124. phosphate ester
125. 250
126. 1,500
127. 3,000
128. Teflon
129. second
130. $\frac{1}{6}$, $\frac{1}{3}$
131. below
132. 16
133. lay
134. 5, 8
135. 5.75
136. oil separator
137. carbon
138. unloading
139. bleed
140. moisture separator
141. isolation

142. a. engines
    b. electric motors
    c. air turbines
    d. hydraulic motors
    e. ram air turbines
143. is not
144. engine driven
145. electric
146. engine bleed air
147. accumulator air
148. ground interconnect
149. depressurization
150. system B
151. schematic
152. power, actuation
153. main, backup, emergency
154. actuation
155. pressure control valves
156. pump and pressure regulator
157. unloading valve
158. accumulator
159. inlet
160. air
161. highest
162. air

AIRCRAFT LANDING GEAR SYSTEMS

6

Continued

Continued

Aircraft Tires and Tubes *(Continued)*

Answers to Aircraft Landing Gear Systems Study Questions   *488*

AIRCRAFT LANDING GEAR SYSTEMS

6

No other single part of an aircraft structure takes the beating the landing gear is subjected to. A single hard landing can apply forces that are many times the weight of the aircraft to the tires, wheels, shock-absorbing system, and the entire structure. For this reason the landing gear system must be carefully inspected and maintained. This chapter examines the different types of landing gear, shock absorbers, retraction systems, wheels, brakes, antiskid systems, tires, and tubes.

Landing Gear Types

There are three basic types of landing surfaces: water, snow or ice, and hard or earthen surfaces. Each type of landing surface requires a different type of landing gear.

Operation from Water

Before the worldwide network of large airports was built, huge flying boats such as the 42-ton, four-engine Boeing 314A Clippers were used for carrying passengers and mail across both the Atlantic and Pacific oceans. But during World War II, large airports were built throughout the world, and the more efficient landplane took over for long distance flying, and large flying boats were no longer manufactured.

Small general aviation amphibians have been built with a flying boat hull and a retractable landing gear, but the large fuselage required by this basic design is aerodynamically inefficient. Almost all water operations today employ conventional land airplanes fitted with twin floats such as those in Figure 6-1. When aircraft must operate from land as well as water, amphibious floats with wheels are installed. The wheels retract into wells inside the float or fold over the top of the float, so they will not interfere with water operation.

amphibian. An aircraft with a landing gear that allows it to operate from both water and land surfaces.

Figure 6-1. *A conventional land airplane may be fitted with twin amphibious floats that allow operation from either land or water.*

Operation from Snow and Ice

An aircraft may safely operate from ice or snow when skis are installed. Some airplanes use wheel-replacement skis like the one in Figure 6-2. The wheel is removed and the ski is installed on the landing gear axle. A rubber shock cord keeps the nose of the ski pulled up in flight and steel cables limit the nose-up or nose-down movement of the ski.

Some airplanes use retractable skis. These skis fit around the wheels of the normal landing gear and are equipped with hydraulic cylinders that allow them to be moved up or down relative to the wheel. *See* Figure 6-3. For landing on a dry runway, the skis are pulled up so that the wheel protrudes below the ski, and for landing on ice or snow, the ski is lowered so that it is below the wheel.

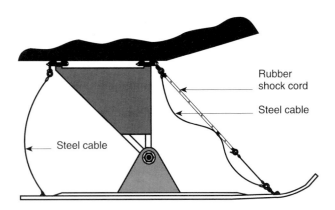

Rubber shock cord

Steel cable

Steel cable

Figure 6-2. *A wheel-replacement ski*

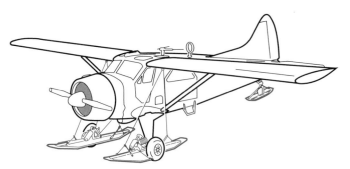

Figure 6-3. *Retractable skis allow the airplane to be operated from either dry runways or ice and snow without changing the landing gear.*

Operation from Hard Surfaces

Most flying is done from hard surfaces by landplanes equipped with wheels and tires. The landing gear for these airplanes has undergone quite an evolution.

Before hard-surfaced runways became abundant, most airplanes used a landing gear that allowed them to touch down on landing with a high angle of attack at the slowest possible landing speed. This landing gear had two main wheels located ahead of the airplane's center of gravity and a tail skid located at the very aft end of the fuselage. Early airplanes operated from grass fields and did not have any brakes. The tail skid acted as a brake to slow the airplane after landing. When wheel brakes were added to the main landing gear, the tail skid was replaced by a tail wheel.

The advent of hard-surfaced runways and the further development of airplanes replaced the tail wheel with a nose wheel. This so-called tricycle landing gear became the most popular configuration because it made airplanes easier to control during takeoff and landing as well as maneuvering on the ground.

When airplanes cruised at a slow airspeed, parasite drag was not a major consideration and light weight and ruggedness were the prime requirements for the landing gear. But when airplanes began to fly faster, streamlined covers were installed over the wheels to reduce the drag. These speed fairings, or wheel pants as they were originally called, added a small amount of weight, but appreciably reduced the drag. Finally, when speed became of major importance, retractable landing gear was developed.

The tail wheel landing gear is used for airplanes that primarily operate from unpaved areas.

Retractable landing gear minimizes parasite drag and is used on airplanes where speed is a primary consideration.

Tricycle landing gear is popular because of its good ground handling characteristics.

Figure 6-4. *Modern landing gear configurations.*

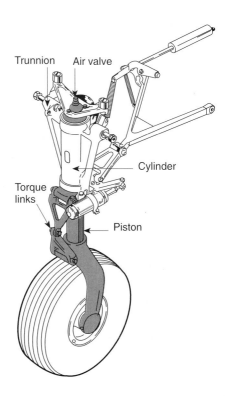

Figure 6-5. *Nose landing gear assembly*

Shock Absorbers

To absorb shock, the mechanical energy of the landing impact must be converted into some other form of energy. This is accomplished on most modern aircraft by using air-oil, or oleo, shock absorbers. Mechanical energy is converted into heat energy in the fluid. Taxi shocks are cushioned by air inside the strut. Some smaller aircraft use spring-oil shock absorbers that cushion the taxi shocks with a heavy steel coil spring.

Figure 6-5 shows a typical oleo shock absorber in the nose gear of a modern airplane. The wheel is attached to the piston of the oleo strut, and the piston is held in the cylinder by torque links, or scissors. The torque links allow the piston to move in and out of the cylinder, but they prevent its turning. The cylinder is attached to the structure of the aircraft through the trunnion that allows it to swing upward to retract.

Figure 6-6 shows the inside of an oleo shock absorber. The strut is made of two chambers that are separated by an orifice and a tapered metering pin which moves in and out of the orifice. The outer cylinder is attached to the aircraft structure, and the wheel assembly attaches to the piston.

When the aircraft takes off, the combined weight of the wheel and the air pressure inside the strut force the piston out to the limit allowed by the piston extension stop. Almost all the oil in the strut flows down into the hollow piston.

When the aircraft touches down on landing, the oil is forced into the upper chamber through the orifice, into the snubber tube, and out into the inner cylinder through the flapper valve, which is a one-way check valve. The small end of the metering pin is in the orifice at the beginning of the strut compression, and its tapered shape steadily decreases the area of the orifice as the strut collapses. The energy in the landing impact is absorbed by the oil as it is forced through the decreasing size orifice and by the air which compresses as the oil is forced into the upper chamber.

The momentum of the aircraft at touchdown compresses the strut to more than is required to support the aircraft weight, and when maximum compression is reached, the aircraft tries to rebound, or bounce. Fluid tries to flow back into the piston, but the flapper valve closes and the fluid must flow through the small holes in the snubber tube. This restriction of fluid flow prevents the rapid extension of the strut that would cause the airplane to bounce.

After the initial landing impact has been absorbed by the transfer of oil between the compartments, the taxi shocks are absorbed by the cushion supplied by the compressed air.

The combination of the snubber tube and the snubber knob on the top of the metering pin controls the rate of strut extension after takeoff. The combined forces of the compressed air in the top of the strut and the weight of the wheel, tire, and brake would cause the piston to extend very rapidly, and if the rate of extension were not controlled, damage would most likely result. The small holes in the snubber tube slow the extension by controlling the rate at which the oil in the cylinder is allowed to flow into the piston. Metering the oil through the snubber tube holes is effective until the strut is almost fully extended. Just before the piston reaches its full extension, the snubber knob on the end of the metering pin enters the orifice and greatly restricts the flow of oil through the orifice into the piston and almost completely stops the extension just before the piston extension stop reaches the extension stop sleeve.

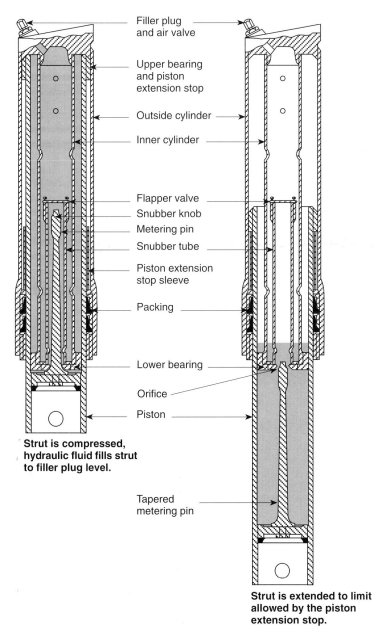

Filler plug and air valve

Upper bearing and piston extension stop

Outside cylinder

Inner cylinder

Flapper valve
Snubber knob
Metering pin
Snubber tube

Piston extension stop sleeve

Packing

Lower bearing

Orifice

Piston

Strut is compressed, hydraulic fluid fills strut to filler plug level.

Tapered metering pin

Strut is extended to limit allowed by the piston extension stop.

Figure 6-6. *Diagram of an oleo shock absorber*

Servicing Oleo Shock Struts

To service an oleo shock strut, jack the aircraft so there is no weight on the wheels. Deflate the strut through the high-pressure air valve, and then remove the filler plug. The strut can be moved in and out by hand on small aircraft, but an exerciser jack like that in Figure 6-7 is needed for large aircraft. Completely collapse the strut, and fill it with the proper fluid to the level of the filler plug. The proper fluid is specified in the aircraft maintenance manual and should also be noted on a placard attached to the shock strut. Remove the valve core from an AN812 high-pressure air valve (*see* Figure 5-56 on Page 374), and attach a bleeder hose; then screw the valve into the filler plug opening. Put the other end of the hose in a container of clean hydraulic fluid and work the piston up and down inside the cylinder until no air bubbles appear in the fluid. Completely collapse the strut and install the proper high-pressure air valve. Remove the aircraft from the jacks, and with the weight of the aircraft on the strut, put compressed air or nitrogen into the strut until it extends to the height specified in the aircraft maintenance manual.

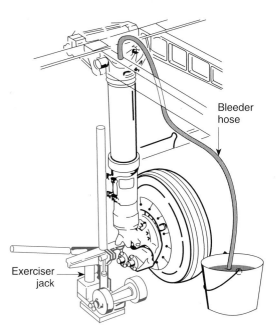

Figure 6-7. *Use an exerciser jack to move the piston in and out of the shock strut when servicing it with fluid.*

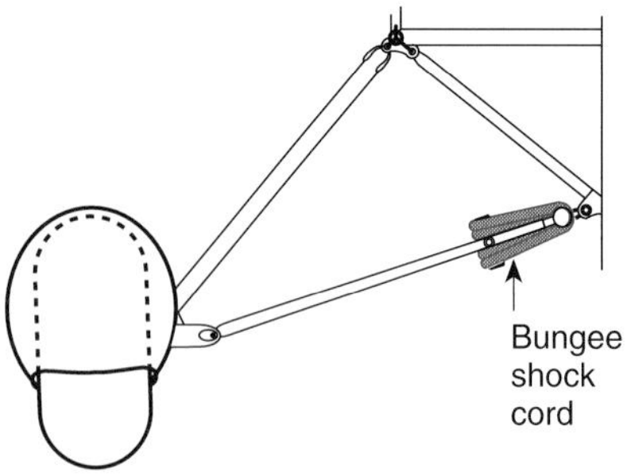

Figure 6-8. *This landing gear, typical of that used on many early Piper airplanes, softened the landing impact and taxi shocks with rings of rubber bands encased in a loose-weave cotton braid.*

Nonshock-Absorbing Landing Gears

Not all airplanes use shock absorbers. The popular single-engine series of Cessna airplanes uses a steel leaf or a tubular steel spring to accept the energy of the landing impact and return it to the aircraft. In a properly conducted landing, energy is returned in such a way that it does not cause any rebound. *See* Figure 6-4, Page 423.

Another type of landing gear that does not use a shock absorber was used on many of the early light airplanes. Elastic shock cord, called bungee cord, that is made up of many small strands of rubber encased in a loose-weave cotton braid, stretches with the landing impact and returns the energy to the airframe.

Wheel Alignment

It is important for the wheels of an airplane to be in proper alignment with the airframe. Two alignment checks are important: toe-in or toe-out and camber.

Toe-In or Toe-Out

A wheel is toed in when lines perpendicular to the axles of a main landing gear cross ahead of the aircraft. The front of the tires are closer together than the rear, and when the aircraft is rolled forward, the wheels try to move together.

Toe-out is the opposite condition; the front of the tires are farther apart than the rear, and when the aircraft rolls forward, the wheels try to move farther apart.

To check for wheel alignment, put two aluminum plates, about 18 inches square, with grease between them under each main wheel and rock the aircraft to relax the landing gear. Place a straightedge against the tires as seen in Figure 6-9, and hold a carpenter's square against the straightedge so it touches the tire just below the axle nut. Measure the distance between the square and the front and rear of the wheel rim. The wheel alignment should be within the tolerance specified in the aircraft maintenance manual.

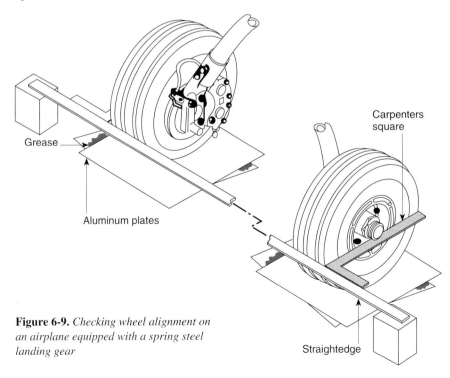

Figure 6-9. *Checking wheel alignment on an airplane equipped with a spring steel landing gear*

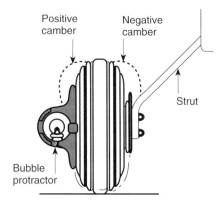

Figure 6-10. *Landing gear camber is measured with a bubble protractor.*

Camber

Camber is the amount the wheels of an aircraft are tilted, or inclined, from the vertical. If the top of the wheel tilts outward, the camber is positive, and if the top tilts inward, the camber is negative.

Wheel Alignment for Spring Steel Landing Gears

Align wheels of airplanes that use spring steel landing gears by adding or removing shims between the axle and the landing gear strut. The thickness of the shims necessary is determined by trial and measurement. The maximum thickness allowable is specified in the manufacturer's maintenance manual.

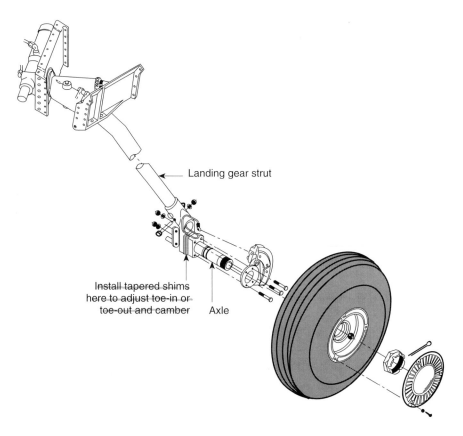

Figure 6-11. *Wheel alignment on spring steel landing gears is adjusted by adding or removing shims between the axle and the fitting on the end of the landing gear strut.*

Wheel Alignment for Landing Gears With Oleo Struts

Check the wheel alignment of aircraft that use oleo shock struts with a straightedge and a carpenter's square. Place the straightedge so that it touches the front or back of the two main gear tires and hold the square against the straightedge and the rim of the wheel as in Figure 6-12. Determine the amount of toe-in or toe-out by measuring between the square and the wheel rim. Correct any misalignment by inserting or removing shims between the arms of the torque links as in Figure 6-13.

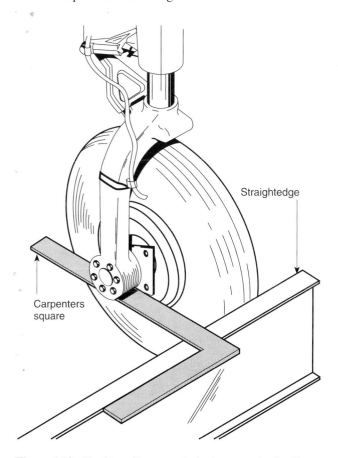

Figure 6-12. *Checking alignment of wheels on an oleo landing gear*

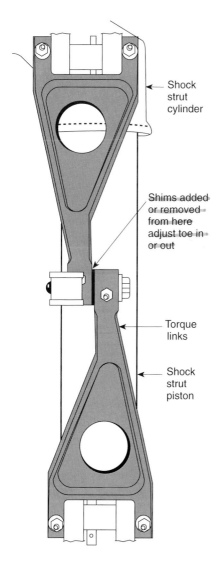

Figure 6-13. *Wheel alignment of an oleo landing gear is adjusted by adding or removing shims between the arms of the torque links.*

Ground Steering with a Tail Wheel

Most of the smaller tail wheel airplanes are steered on the ground with a steerable tail wheel that is connected to the rudder control horn through a spring and chain. This allows the pilot to steer the airplane when the tail is on the ground. The tail wheel automatically breaks into a full swiveling action when the wheel is forced more than about 45° from its trailing position for maneuvering in close quarters. When the airplane is moved straight ahead, the tail wheel returns to its steerable condition.

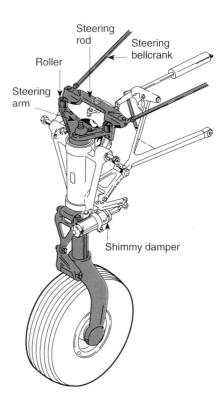

Figure 6-14. *Nose wheel steering for a retractable landing gear*

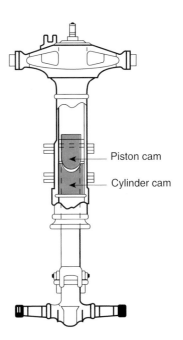

Figure 6-15. *Nose wheel centering cam*

The tail wheels of most of the larger airplanes are full-swiveling, but can be locked in alignment with the airplane's longitudinal axis. The wheel is locked for takeoff and landing to help hold the airplane straight down the runway when there is not enough airspeed for the rudder to be effective. When the airplane slows down, the tail wheel can be unlocked, allowing it to swivel freely. The airplane is then steered with differential use of the brakes.

Ground Steering with a Nose Wheel

The nose wheels of small airplanes may be either steerable or castering. A castering nose wheel is used on only the smallest airplanes, and steering is done by independent use of the brakes.

On some small airplanes, the nose wheels are steered by direct linkage to the rudder pedals. This results in a rather large turning radius, and to overcome this limitation other small airplanes have a cam arrangement that allows the nose wheel to be steered through a rather limited angular range, after which it breaks out and is free to caster until it reaches its built-in travel limits. When the airplane rolls straight ahead, its steering ability is restored.

One way of providing steering for the nose wheel of a retractable landing gear is seen in Figure 6-14. When the landing gear is down and locked, the steering bell crank presses against rollers on the steering arm which is a part of the oleo strut. When the landing gear is retracted, the wheel moves backward and the steering arm moves away from the steering bell crank.

It is very important when a nose wheel is being retracted that the wheel is centered so that it will fit into the wheel well. To accomplish this, a centering cam is installed inside the oleo strut in such a way that, as the strut extends, the cam forces the wheel straight ahead.

Large airplanes are steered by hydraulic pressure in the steering cylinders. These cylinders, shown in Figure 6-17 on Page 431, act as shimmy dampers for takeoff and landing but as steering cylinders for taxiing. Fluid is directed into and out of these cylinders by a steering control valve moved by the rudder pedals or a nose wheel steering wheel.

Shimmy Dampers

Nose wheels may shimmy at certain speeds. Shimmy dampers like the one in Figure 6-16 may be installed between the piston and the cylinder of the nose wheel oleo strut to prevent this.

The simple shimmy damper in Figure 6-16 has two compartments joined through a small bleed hole, or orifice. As the nose wheel fork rotates, hydraulic fluid is forced from one compartment into the other through the orifice. This restricted flow of fluid has no effect on normal nose wheel steering but opposes rapid movement of the piston and prevents shimmying.

Large aircraft typically combine shimmy damping and nose wheel steering. Hydraulic fluid under pressure is directed into one or the other of two steering cylinders mounted on the nose wheel strut as shown in Figure 6-17.

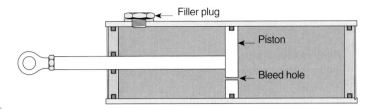

Figure 6-16. *A shimmy damper installed between the nose wheel cylinder and piston absorbs the shimmying vibrations by the transfer of hydraulic fluid from one side of the piston to the other through the bleed hole.*

A control wheel operated by the pilot directs pressure to one side of the nose wheel steering pistons, and fluid from the opposite side of the pistons is vented back into the reservoir through a pressure relief valve that holds a constant pressure on the system to snub shimmying. An accumulator in the line to the relief valve holds pressure on the system when the steering control valve is in its neutral position.

shimmy damper. A small hydraulic shock absorber installed between the nosewheel fork and the nosewheel cylinder attached to the aircraft structure.

shimmy. Abnormal, and often violent, vibration of the nose wheel of an airplane. Shimmying is usually caused by looseness of the nose wheel support mechanism, but may also be caused by tire imbalance.

centering cam. A cam in the nose-gear shock strut that causes the piston to center when the strut fully extends.

When the aircraft takes off and the strut extends, the wheel is straightened in its fore-and-aft position so it can be retracted into the wheel well.

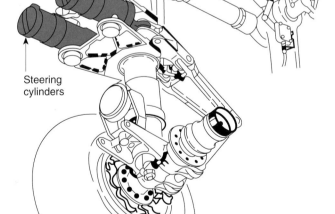

Figure 6-17. *Hydraulically operated nose gear steering cylinders allow the pilot to steer the airplane and also serve as shimmy dampers.*

Answers begin on Page 488. Page numbers refer to chapter text.

1. A spring steel landing gear _____ (does or does not) absorb shock. *Page 426*

2. An air-oil oleo shock strut absorbs the energy from the initial landing impact with the _____ (air or oil). *Page 424*

3. The opposition to the landing impact is gradually increased in an oleo shock strut by a tapered _____ decreasing the size of the orifice. *Page 424*

4. An air-oil oleo shock strut absorbs taxi shocks with the _____ (air or oil). *Page 424*

5. A spring-oil shock strut absorbs taxi shocks with the _____ (spring or oil). *Page 424*

6. Rebound is minimized with an oleo shock strut by restricting the flow of oil by the closing of the _____ valve. *Page 424*

7. Two places in which you can find the specification number for the proper fluid to use to service an oleo shock strut are:
    a. _____
    b. _____
       Page 426

8. An oleo shock strut can be charged with high-pressure compressed air or with _____ .
    Page 426

9. The correct amount of air in an oleo shock strut is measured by the _____ of the strut.
    Page 426

10. If the main wheels of an airplane are closer together at the front than at the rear, the landing gear is toed _____ (in or out). *Page 427*

11. If the top of the main wheel of an airplane tilts outward, the wheel has a _____ (positive or negative) camber. *Page 428*

12. The wheels of an airplane equipped with a spring steel landing gear are aligned by adding shims between the _____ and the _____ . *Page 428*

13. The wheels of an airplane equipped with an oleo shock absorber are aligned by adding shims between the _____ . *Page 429*

14. When a large transport category airplane is not being steered on the ground, the nose gear steering cylinders act as _____ . *Page 431*

15. An airplane with a castering nose wheel is steered by differential use of the _____ . *Page 430*

16. A retractable nose wheel is prevented from being retracted when it is not straight ahead by a/an _____ in the nose gear oleo strut. *Page 430*

Landing Gear Retraction Systems

As the speed of aircraft becomes high enough that the parasite drag of the landing gear is greater than the induced drag caused by the added weight of a retracting system, it becomes economically practical to retract the landing gear into the aircraft structure.

Small aircraft use simple mechanical retraction systems. Some use a hand crank to drive the retracting mechanism through a roller chain, and the most simple system of all uses a direct hand lever mechanism to raise and lower the wheels.

Many aircraft use electric motors to drive the gear-retracting mechanism, and some European-built aircraft use pneumatic systems. Most American-built aircraft use hydraulically retracted landing gears.

Power Pack System

The hydraulic power pack was developed to make hydraulic systems easy to service and lightweight. The system in Figure 6-18 (Page 434) uses a power pack that contains the reservoir, pump, thermal relief valve, high-pressure control valve, low-pressure control valve, and a shuttle valve all in one unit.

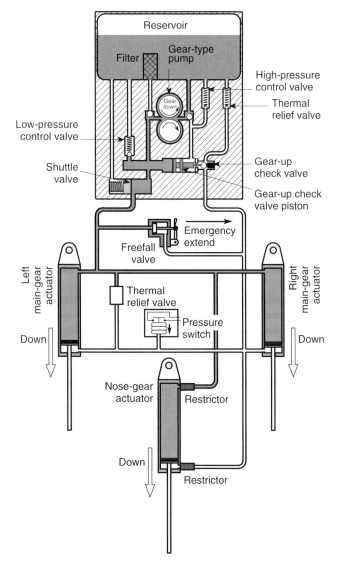

Reservoir

Filter

Gear-type pump

Gear down

High-pressure control valve

Thermal relief valve

Low-pressure control valve

Shuttle valve

Gear-up check valve

Gear-up check valve piston

Emergency extend

Freefall valve

Left main-gear actuator

Right main-gear actuator

Thermal relief valve

Pressure switch

Down

Down

Nose-gear actuator

Restrictor

Down

Restrictor

Figure 6-18. *Hydraulic power pack system while the landing gear is being lowered*

Lowering the Landing Gear

To lower the landing gear, the pilot moves the landing gear handle to the GEAR-DOWN position, and these events take place:

1. The landing gear handle actuates a switch that turns on the hydraulic pump motor in the power pack so that it turns in the direction shown by the arrows in Figure 6-18.

2. Fluid flows through the passage and check valve on the right side of the pump and around the outside of the gears.

3. The output from the pump moves the gear-up check valve piston to the right and unseats the gear-up check valve.

4. The pump output then flows down to the shuttle valve and forces it to the left, opening the passage to the gear-down side of the actuating cylinders.

5. Fluid flows into the down side of the three actuating cylinders and forces the pistons out. The nose gear is much easier to move than the main gears, so the fluid flows into and out of the nose-gear actuating cylinder through restrictors.

6. Return fluid from the up side of the actuators flows through the opened gear-up check valve back to the inlet side of the pump.

7. As each gear reaches its down-and-locked position, the pressure in the gear-down line builds up and fluid is bypassed back into the reservoir through the low-pressure control valve. When all three gears are down and locked, limit switches turn the pump motor off.

Raising the Landing Gear

When the airplane is in the air, the pilot can retract the landing gear by moving the landing gear handle to the GEAR-UP position. These events take place:

1. The landing gear handle actuates a switch that turns on the hydraulic pump motor in the power pack so that it turns in the direction shown in Figure 6-19.

2. Fluid flows through the filter and the check valve on the left side of the pump, around the gears, and out the right side, down to the gear-up check valve.

3. The fluid from the pump moves the gear-up check valve piston to the left, and the fluid unseats the ball and flows to the gear-up side of each of the gear actuating cylinders. The first movement of the piston releases the mechanical down locks and allows the gear to retract.

4. Fluid returns from the gear-down side of the actuators past the shuttle valve, which the spring has forced to the right, back into the reservoir.

5. This landing gear system does not have any mechanical up locks, but the gear is held retracted by hydraulic pressure. When all three gears are fully retracted, the pressure continues to build up until it reaches a value that opens the pressure switch and shuts the hydraulic pump motor off. If the pressure in the system leaks down to a specified value, the pressure switch will close and start the pump so it will restore the pressure to the cutout value.

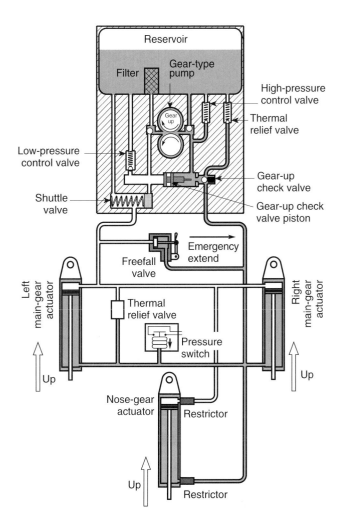

Figure 6-19. *Hydraulic power pack system while the landing gear is being raised*

Typical Landing Gear Retraction System

The landing gear retraction system shown in Figure 6-20 is for a tricycle landing gear airplane that has wheel-well doors that close when the landing gear is retracted. The schematic shows the system with the landing gear down and locked and the gear selector in the GEAR-UP position. Fluid flows to the three landing gear downlocks and releases them by moving their locking pins inward against the spring force so the landing gears can be retracted. Fluid flows into the up side of the three landing gear actuators and forces the pistons out. The oil flowing into the main-gear actuator passes through orifice check valves in the full-flow direction to retract the gears as soon as possible.

Both of the gear-door sequence valves are closed, and no fluid can flow through them until the main gears fully retract and the sequence valve plungers are depressed.

Return fluid from the main-gear actuators flows through the main-gear sequence valves which are held open by the gear-door actuators.

Emergency Extension of the Landing Gear

All aircraft with retractable landing gear are required to have some acceptable method of lowering the gear in flight if the normal actuating systems fail.

The landing gear shown in Figures 6-18 and 6-19 (Pages 434 and 435) has a free-fall valve between the gear-up and the gear-down lines of the power pack. If the power pack fails, the pilot can move the free-fall handle to the EMERGENCY EXTEND position, which opens the free-fall valve and allows fluid from the gear-up side of the actuating cylinders to flow directly to the gear-down side. The gear will then fall from the wheel wells with little opposition, and its weight combined with the air moving past it will force it to mechanically lock in place.

More complex landing gear systems use compressed air or nitrogen to provide the pressure for emergency extension of the gear. In such systems, a shuttle valve like the one shown in Figure 5-94 on Page 404 is installed at the actuator where the main hydraulic pressure and the emergency air pressure meet. During normal operation, fluid enters the actuator through one side of the shuttle valve. In the event of failure of the hydraulic system, the pilot can place the gear handle in the GEAR-DOWN position, which releases the emergency air supply into the system. The piston in the shuttle valve moves over to seal off the normal hydraulic system and direct compressed air into the actuator.

shuttle valve. A type of hydraulic valve mounted on the landing gear and brake actuator cylinders. A shuttle valve allows normal system fluid to flow into the actuators when the system pressure is in the correct operating range.

If normal system pressure is lost and the emergency system is actuated, the shuttle valve will automatically shift and allow emergency fluid to actuate the landing gear and apply the brakes.

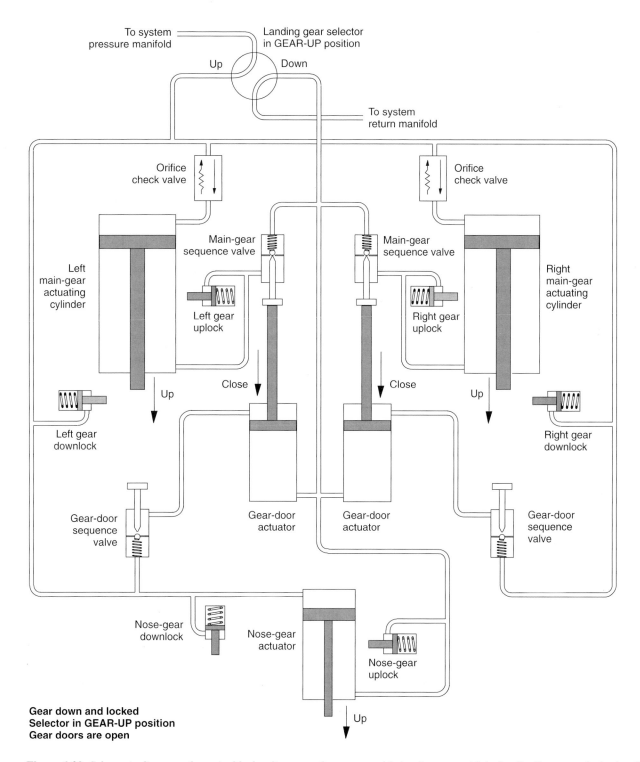

Figure 6-20. *Schematic diagram of a typical hydraulic system for a retractable landing gear with hydraulically actuated wheel-well doors*

Answers begin on Page 488. Page numbers refer to chapter text.

17. Four methods of actuating a retractable landing gear are:

   a. _____

   b. _____

   c. _____

   d. _____

   Page 433

18. A hydraulic system that has the reservoir, pump, and valves in a single easy-to-service unit is called a/an _____ system. *Page 433*

19. The mechanically operated valve that prevents the landing gear actuator from lowering the main gear before the wheel well doors are open is called a/an _____ valve. *Page 436*

20. Emergency actuation of the landing gear of some small airplanes consists of opening the free-fall valve between the landing gear _____ and the _____ and allowing the gear to free fall from the wheel wells. *Page 436*

21. Two gases that may be used for the emergency backup system for a hydraulically actuated landing gear are compressed _____ and _____ . *Page 436*

22. When a landing gear is extended by the emergency system, compressed air or nitrogen is directed into the actuating cylinder through a/an _____ valve. *Page 436*

Aircraft Brakes

In the study of aircraft brakes we first consider different types of brake actuating units and then the various methods of providing hydraulic pressure to them.

Brake Actuating Units

Aircraft brake systems slow the airplane down by changing kinetic energy from the motion of the aircraft into heat energy generated by the friction between the linings and the brake drum or disk.

Two basic types of brakes are in use, energizing and nonenergizing. Energizing brakes use the friction developed between the rotating and stationary parts to produce a wedging action that increases the braking force and reduces the pilot effort needed to obtain the desired braking action. Nonenergizing brakes do not use this wedging action.

Energizing Brakes

Drum-type brakes, similar to those used on automobiles, are a form of dual-servo brake. Movement of the aircraft either forward or backward causes the brake linings to wedge against the rotating drum when the brakes are applied.

Energizing brakes used on some of the smaller aircraft have a single-servo action. Only forward motion of the aircraft helps apply the brakes.

Energizing brakes have their shoes and linings mounted on a torque plate in such a way that they are free to move out against the rotating drum. When the brakes are applied, two pistons in the brake cylinder move out and push the linings against a cylindrical cast-iron drum that rotates with the wheel. Friction attempts to rotate the linings, but they are held in place by the cylinder assembly. Rotation of the brake drum wedges the linings tightly against it. When the hydraulic pressure is released, the retracting spring pulls the linings back from the drum and releases the brakes.

One of the limitations of this type of brake is fading. When the brake is used, the friction heats the drum and causes the open end to expand in a bell-mouthed fashion. The drum expands away from the linings and the friction area decreases.

Nonenergizing Brakes

Nonenergizing brakes are the most common type of brake on modern aircraft. These brakes are actuated by hydraulic pressure, and the amount of braking action depends upon the amount of pressure applied. Expander tube, single-disk, and multiple-disk brakes are all nonenergizing brakes.

---

energizing brake. A brake that uses the momentum of the aircraft to increase its effectiveness by wedging the shoe against the brake drum.

Energizing brakes are also called servo brakes. A single-servo brake is energizing only when moving in the forward direction, and a duo-servo brake is energizing when the aircraft is moving either forward or backward.

single-servo brake. A brake that uses the momentum of the aircraft rolling forward to help apply the brakes by wedging the brake shoe against the brake drum.

fading of brakes. The decrease in the amount of braking action that occurs with some types of brakes that are applied for a long period of time.

True fading occurs with overheated drum-type brakes. As the drum is heated, it expands in a bell-mouthed fashion. This decreases the amount of drum in contact with the brake shoes and decreases the braking action.

A condition similar to brake fading occurs when there is an internal leak in the brake master cylinder. The brakes are applied, but as the pedal is held down, fluid leaks past the piston, and the brakes slowly release.

nonenergizing brake. A brake that does not use the momentum of the aircraft to increase the friction.

expander-tube brake. A brake that uses hydraulic fluid inside a synthetic rubber tube around the brake hub to force rectangular blocks of brake-lining material against the rotating brake drum. Friction between the brake drum and the lining material slows the aircraft.

Expander Tube Brakes

Expander tube brakes use a heavy neoprene tube, such as the one in Figure 6-21, and have been used on airplanes as small as the Piper Cub, with a gross weight of 1,200 pounds, to the Boeing B-29 Superfortress bomber with a gross weight of 133,500 pounds.

In an expander tube brake, hydraulic fluid from the master cylinder is directed into the expander tube around the torque flange. When this tube is expanded by hydraulic fluid, it pushes the brake blocks out against the drum, and the friction between the blocks and the drum slows the aircraft. The heat generated in the lining is kept from damaging the expander tube by thin stainless steel heat shields placed between each of the lining blocks. As soon as the brake pedal is released, the return springs between the brake blocks collapse the expander tube and force the fluid back into the brake reservoir.

Some larger expander tube brakes have adjuster valves in the fluid line to the brake. This valve is a simple two-way relief valve that holds a given amount of pressure in the expander tube and keeps it from collapsing completely when the pedal is released. Brakes without adjuster valves cannot have their clearance adjusted. When the brake blocks have worn to the extent that the clearance between the block and the brake drum is greater than the aircraft service manual allows, the blocks must be replaced.

It is extremely important to avoid depressing the brake pedal when the brake drum is removed. Expanding the tube without the drum in place damages the brake blocks.

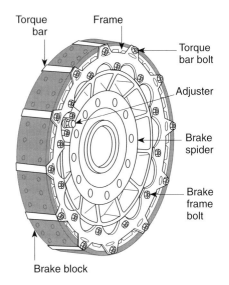

Assembled expander tube brake

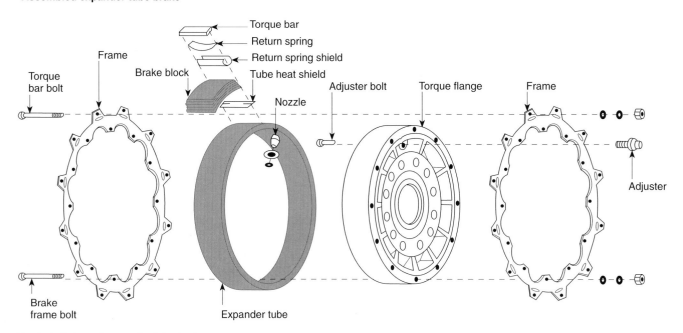

Exploded view of expander tube brake

Figure 6-21. *Expander tube brake*

Single-Disk Brakes

The most popular brake for modern light aircraft is the single-disk brake. This brake is actuated by hydraulic pressure from a master cylinder, and friction is produced when the rotating disk is squeezed between two brake linings in the caliper.

There are two types of single-disk brakes; one has the disk keyed into the wheel and it is free to move in and out as the brake is applied. This type of brake is called a floating-disk/fixed-caliper brake. The disk of the other type of brake is rigidly attached to the wheel, and the caliper moves in and out on two anchor bolts. This is called a fixed-disk/floating-caliper brake.

Figure 6-22 shows a typical Goodyear floating-disk/fixed-caliper single-disk brake. The disk is driven by hardened steel drive keys in the wheel so that it rotates with the wheel, but it is free to move in and out of the wheel on the keys. The disk is held centered in the wheel and kept from rattling by thin spring steel antirattle clips. The housing of the brake is bolted to the landing gear axle, and brake-lining pucks fit into cavities in the housing. One lining puck, the pressure-plate lining, fits into a recess against the piston in the caliper. The other puck, the backing-plate lining, fits into a recess in the backing plate. The disk rotates between the two linings and is clamped by them when hydraulic fluid under pressure forces the pressure-plate lining against the disk.

single-disk brakes. Aircraft brakes in which a single steel disk rotates with the wheel between two brake-lining blocks. When the brake is applied, the disk is clamped tightly between the lining blocks, and the friction slows the aircraft.

multiple-disk brakes. Aircraft brakes in which one set of disks is keyed to the axle and remains stationary. Between each stationary disk there is a rotating disk that is keyed to the inside of the wheel. When the brakes are applied, the stationary disks are forced together, clamping the rotating disks between them. The friction between the disks slows the aircraft.

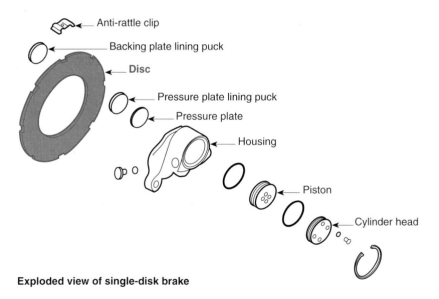

Anti-rattle clip
Backing plate lining puck
Disc
Pressure plate lining puck
Pressure plate
Housing
Piston
Cylinder head

Exploded view of single-disk brake

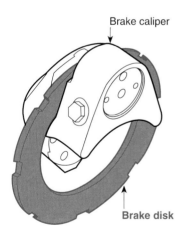

Brake caliper

Brake disk

Complete brake assembly for a light airplane

Figure 6-22. *Single-disk brake*

automatic adjuster. A subsystem in an aircraft disk brake that compensates for disk or lining wear. Each time the brakes are applied, the automatic adjuster is reset for zero clearance, and when the brakes are released, the clearance between the disks or the disk and lining is returned to a preset value.

backplate. A floating plate on which the wheel cylinder and the brake shoes attach on an energizing-type brake.

Some Goodyear single-disk brakes have automatic adjusters like the one in Figure 6-23. This feature automatically changes the amount the piston can return when the brakes are released, which compensates for the wear of the lining.

When the brake is applied, hydraulic fluid under pressure forces the piston over to the right and squeezes the disk between the two linings. The automatic adjusting pin is pulled through the grip so that when the brake is released, the piston and the lining move back only the amount allowed by the return spring.

As the lining wears, the adjusting pin is pulled into the grip and indicates the lining's wear. The aircraft service manual specifies the minimum amount the adjusting pin may protrude from the nut before the brake must be disassembled and the linings replaced.

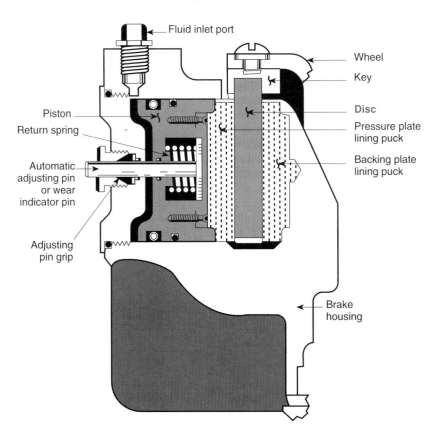

Figure 6-23. *Goodyear single-disk brake automatic adjuster*

To replace these linings, remove the antirattle clips and remove the wheel from the axle. The disk will remain between the linings. Carefully remove the disk, and lift out the lining pucks. Inspect the entire brake and install new lining pucks. Slip the disk between the pucks and re-install the wheel on the axle. Center the disk in the wheel with the antirattle clips, then adjust the axle nut and safety it with a cotter pin.

If the brake is not equipped with an automatic adjuster, measure lining wear by applying the brake and measuring the space between the disk and the inboard edge of the housing as shown in Figure 6-24. The aircraft service manual specifies the maximum distance before the brake must be disassembled and the linings replaced.

The Cleveland fixed-disk/floating-caliper brake uses a disk that is solidly bolted to the inner wheel half as shown in Figure 6-25. The brake assembly, Figure 6-26, is mounted on the aircraft by a torque plate that is bolted to the axle. One set of brake linings is riveted to the pressure plate and the other set is riveted to the backplate. The brake assembly, which consists of the brake cylinder, the pressure plate and its lining, and the backplate and its lining, attaches to the torque plate with two anchor bolts that slide back and forth through bushings in the torque plate. The disk that is bolted to the wheel rides between the two sets of linings. When the brakes are applied, hydraulic fluid under pressure forces the pistons out and squeezes the disk between the linings.

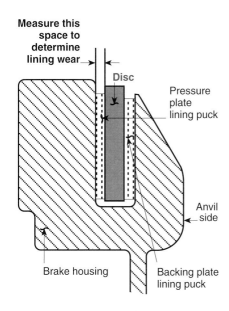

Figure 6-24. *Lining wear may be determined by measuring the space between the disk and the inboard side of the brake housing with the brakes applied.*

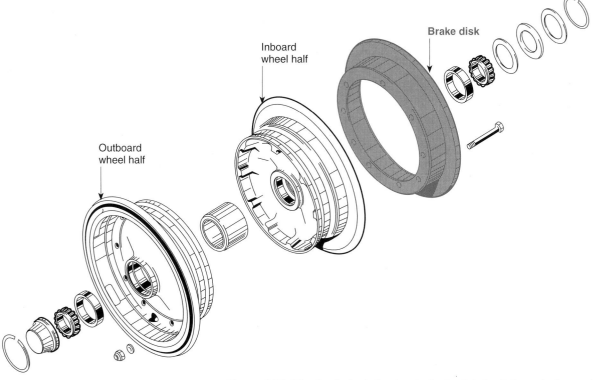

Figure 6-25. *Cleveland wheel showing the brake disk that bolts to the inner wheel half*

pressure plate. A strong, heavy plate used in a multiple-disk brake. The pressure plate receives the force from the brake cylinders and transmits this force to the disks.

You can replace the linings on Cleveland brakes without removing the wheel from the axle. Unbolt the cylinder assembly from the backplate, which will drop down and allow you to pull the entire assembly away from the torque plate, and then and slide the pressure plate off of the anchor bolts. One of the linings is riveted to the pressure plate and the other to the backplate. Replacement of the brake linings is made easy by using the brake relining kit available from the brake manufacturer. Remove the old rivets from the linings with the knockout punch. Inspect the entire brake and rivet new linings in place, using the rivet clinching tool and the rivets that are included in the kit.

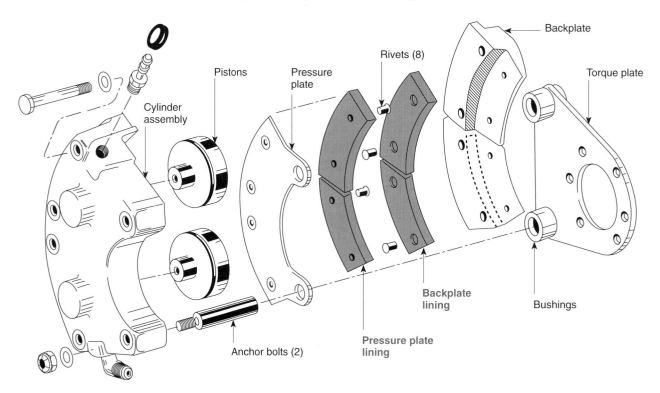

Figure 6-26. *Cleveland brake assembly. The disk that bolts to the wheel turns between the two sets of linings that are riveted to the pressure plate and the backplate. The entire brake assembly rides on the two anchor bolts which slide back and forth in bushings in the torque plate.*

Dual-Disk Brakes

Aircraft that need more braking action than a single-disk brake can supply, but not enough to justify the weight of a multiple-disk system, use the dual-disk brake.

The dual-disk brake is similar to a single-disk except that two disks rotate with the wheel, and there is a center carrier with brake lining pucks on both sides between these disks. The brake shown in Figure 6-27 has four cylinders, each with automatic adjusters. The housing assembly, center carrier, and backplate are all attached to the wheel axle with high-strength bolts. The disks mount inside the wheel and are driven by hardened steel keys that ride in the grooves around the periphery of the disks. When the brakes are applied, hydraulic fluid under pressure forces the pistons over and clamps the rotating disks between the linings which are backed up by the housing backplate.

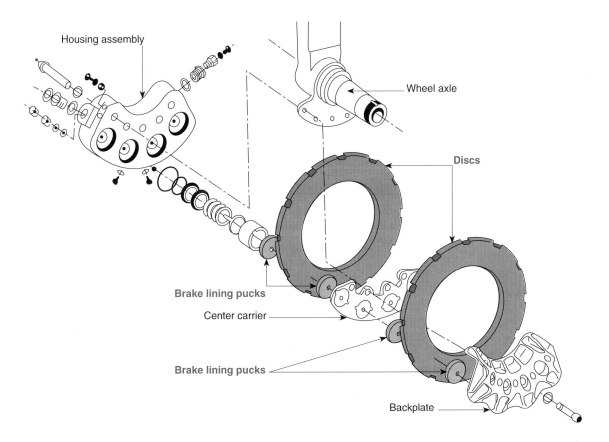

Figure 6-27. *A dual-disk brake works on the same principle as the single-disk brake, but has more disk area and more lining area.*

segmented-rotor brake. A heavy-duty, multiple-disk brake used on large, high-speed aircraft.

Stators that are surfaced with a material that retains its friction characteristics at high temperatures are keyed to the axle. Rotors which are keyed into the wheels mesh with the stators.

The rotors are made in segments to allow for cooling and for their large amounts of expansion.

Multiple-Disk Brakes

Simple physics determines the brake size for any given aircraft. The gross weight of the aircraft and the speed at the time of brake application determine the amount of heat generated when the brakes are applied. As the aircraft size, weight, and landing speed increase, the need for greater braking surface area and heat-dissipation capability also increases.

Thin-Disk Multiple-Disk Brake

The thin-disk multiple-disk brake was popular for heavy aircraft up through World War II. This brake provided maximum friction for minimum size and weight, and its action did not fade when the brake got hot. Two main disadvantages of this brake were the tendency of the disks to warp, causing the brakes to drag, and the need for manual adjustments as the disks wore.

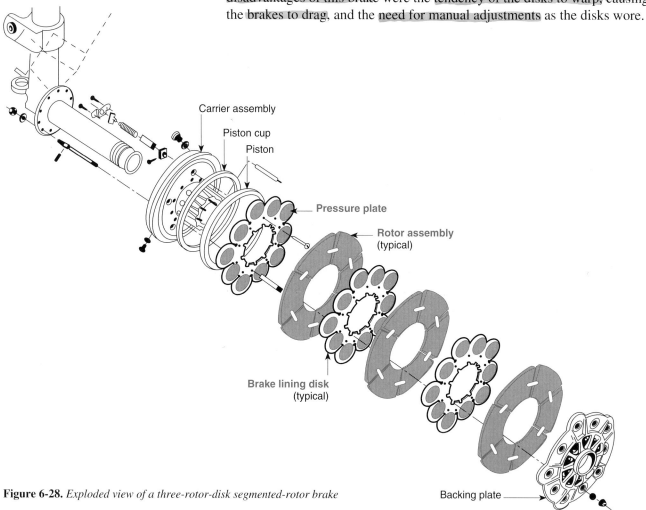

Carrier assembly

Piston cup

Piston

Pressure plate

Rotor assembly
(typical)

Brake lining disk
(typical)

Backing plate

Figure 6-28. *Exploded view of a three-rotor-disk segmented-rotor brake*

This brake has a series of steel disks, called stators, keyed to the axle. A rotor, or rotating disk, made of copper- or bronze-plated steel, rotates between each of them. These disks are approximately ⅛-inch thick, and they get very hot when the brake is used. The disks form such a solid mass of material that the heat has difficulty escaping. If the pilot sets the parking brake after using these brakes, the entrapped heat will warp the disks.

Segmented-Rotor Multiple-Disk Brake

Segmented-rotor multiple-disk brakes, which can dissipate the tremendous amount of heat produced by aborted takeoffs or emergency landings, are standard on most high-performance aircraft.

The segmented-rotor multiple-disk brake in Figure 6-28 has three rotating disks, or rotors, that are keyed into the wheel. Between each rotor is a stator plate, or brake lining disk, keyed to the axle. Riveted to each side of each stator plate are linings or wear pads that are made of a material that retains its friction characteristics under conditions of extremely high temperature. A pressure plate and a backing plate complete the brake.

The brake shown in Figures 6-28, 6-29, and 6-30 uses an annular cup-type actuator to apply the force to the pressure plate to squeeze the disks together.

Automatic adjusters attach to the pressure plate and push it back when the hydraulic pressure to the brakes is released. When pressure is applied to the brakes, the pressure plate compresses the return spring on the indicator pin, and as the lining wears, the pin is pulled through its friction collar. This is a pressed fit, so that as the brake is released, the grip of the friction collar pulls the pressure plate back as much as the adjuster housing will allow. Each time the brakes are applied, they automatically adjust for the wear of the linings. The amount the automatic adjuster pin sticks out of the retainer housing is an indication of the condition of the brake linings.

The brakes used on most of the large jet transport airplanes use a number of round brake cylinders rather than a single annular cylinder. Figure 6-31 on the next page shows the brake cylinder assembly of the multi-disk segmented-rotor brake used on a McDonnell-Douglas DC-9. This brake has 14 cylinders whose pistons press against the pressure plate. Seven of these cylinders are supplied with hydraulic fluid under pressure from System A. Seven other

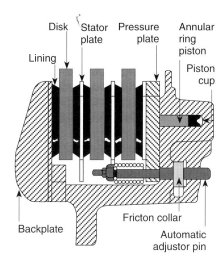

Figure 6-29. *Cutaway view of a three-rotor-disk segmented-rotor brake*

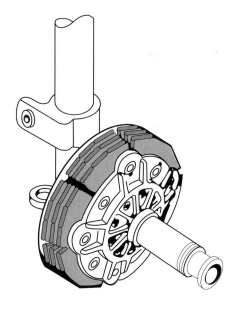

Figure 6-30. *View of an installed three-rotor-disk segmented-rotor brake.*

cylinders between those shown are supplied by fluid from System B. In this drawing, only the cylinders served by System A are shown. System B is identical to System A. System A fluid enters through the pressure port and is distributed to all of the cylinders through passages drilled in the brake housing. There are two bleeder valves at the highest point of the wheel in both systems.

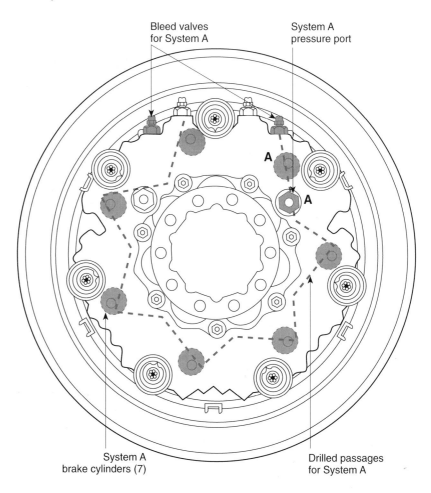

Figure 6-31. *Housing of the brake installed on a McDonnell-Douglas DC-9 showing the hydraulic ports and passages in System A. Identical cylinders, ports, and passages for System B are not shown.*

Carbon Disk Brakes

The latest development in aircraft brakes are multiple-disk brakes made of carbon composite material. These brakes, which have thick disks made of molded carbon fibers, are lighter in weight than a conventional brake with the same stopping power, and they can function at higher temperatures. Because of the greater cost of carbon brakes, they are currently used only on high-performance military aircraft and on certain transport airplanes where the weight they save makes them cost effective.

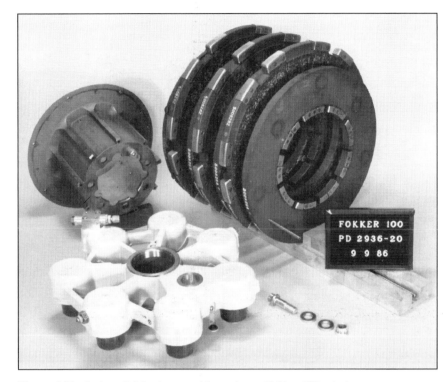

Figure 6-32. *Carbon disk brake assembly used on a Fokker 100 twin jet transport.*

Brake Actuation Systems

An aircraft brake system is composed of two subsystems: the friction producers and the actuating systems. The components in the wheels produce the friction that converts some of the aircraft's kinetic energy into heat energy. The hydraulic components in the aircraft allow the pilot to control the amount of friction the wheel units produce.

Independent Brake Master Cylinders

For years, independent master cylinders have been the most common pressure-generating systems for light aircraft brakes. The diaphragm-type master cylinder in Figure 6-33 on the next page is used for the simplest type of brakes.

The master cylinder and expander tube in the wheel are connected with the appropriate tubing, and the entire system is filled with hydraulic fluid from which all of the air has been purged. When the pilot pushes on the brake pedal, fluid is moved into the expander tube to apply the brake. This type of system is useful only on very small aircraft, and was used with success on the Piper Cub and Super Cub series of airplanes, which used one heel-operated master cylinder for each wheel. A single master cylinder of this type is turned around and operated by a cable from a pull handle under the instrument panel on Piper Tri-Pacers. This airplane has direct nosewheel steering, so independent braking is not needed, and one master cylinder supplies both brakes. For the parking brake, a shutoff valve is located between the master cylinder and the wheel unit. The brakes are applied and the shutoff valve traps pressure in the line.

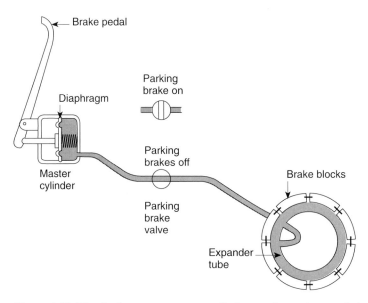

Figure 6-33. *The diaphragm-type master cylinder may be used to supply hydraulic fluid under pressure to the expander tube brakes of small aircraft.*

dragging brakes. Brakes that do not fully release when the brake pedal is released. The brakes are partially applied all the time, which causes excessive lining wear and heat.

compensator port. A small hole between a hydraulic brake master cylinder and the reservoir. When the brakes are released, this port is uncovered and the pressure on the fluid in the line to the brake master cylinder is the same as the atmospheric pressure.

When the brake is applied, the master-cylinder piston covers the compensator port and allows pressure in the line to the brake to build up and apply the brakes. When the brake is released, the piston uncovers the compensator port. If any fluid has been lost from the brake, the reservoir will refill the master cylinder.

Larger aircraft require more fluid for their brakes. This fluid must be vented to the atmosphere when the brakes are not applied. The vent for the brake system allows the fluid to expand when it is heated without causing the brakes to drag.

The many types of vented master cylinders all have the same basic components. The master cylinder in Figure 6-35 is typical of those used in modern light aircraft.

Each wheel cylinder is served by its own master cylinder, which is mounted on a pivot below the rudder pedals as in Figure 6-34. The pilot moves the entire rudder pedal forward for normal rudder actuation, but to actuate the brakes, the pilot applies pressure with his or her toes to lower the plunger into the cylinder.

The body of the master cylinder in Figure 6-35 serves as the reservoir for the fluid, and it is vented to the atmosphere. When the pedal is not depressed, the return spring forces the piston up so that the compensator sleeve holds the compensator port open to vent the fluid in the brake line and the wheel cylinder to the atmosphere.

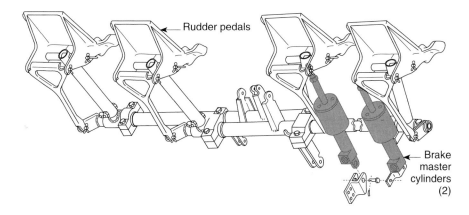

Rudder pedals

Brake
master
cylinders
(2)

Figure 6-34. *Individual brake master cylinders are installed below the rudder pedals. The brakes are applied by depressing the top of the pedal with the toe.*

Depressing the top of the rudder pedal pushes the piston away from the compensator sleeve, and a special O-ring and washer seals fluid in the line to the brake. The amount of pressure applied to the brakes is proportional to the amount of force the pilot applies to the brake pedal. When the pedal is released, the compensator sleeve contacts the piston and opens the compensator port. This vents the brake line into the reservoir.

The parking brake for this type of master cylinder is a simple spring-released ratchet mechanism that holds the piston down in the cylinder. To apply the parking brake, depress the brake pedal and pull the parking brake handle. This locks the piston down. To release the brake, depress the brake pedal more than was done for the initial application and the ratchet will release.

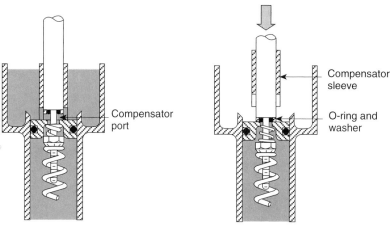

Compensator port

Compensator sleeve

O-ring and washer

Brake pedal is released and return spring has pushed piston rod to the top. Compensator sleeve holds the piston away from the seal and wheel cylinder is vented to the reservoir.

Brake pedal is depressed, piston rod pushes piston away from the compensator sleeve, and the O-ring seals piston to the piston rod.

Figure 6-35. *Individual vented brake master cylinder*

Servicing port

Vent

Piston rod

Compensator sleeve

Reservoir

Compensator port

Piston

Cylinder

Return spring

To wheel cylinder

Complete master cylinder assembly

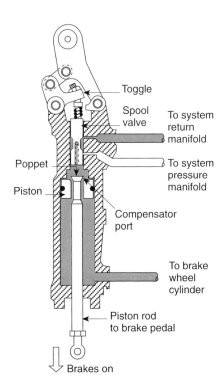

Figure 6-36. *Boosted brake master cylinder. Brakes are off.*

Labels in figure:
Toggle
Spool valve
To system return manifold
To system pressure manifold
Poppet
Piston
Compensator port
To brake wheel cylinder
Piston rod to brake pedal
Brakes on

Boosted Brakes

Some airplanes require more braking force than a manually applied independent master cylinder can produce, yet do not need the complexity of a power brake system. The boosted brake system is used for these airplanes.

In this system, the pilot applies pressure to the brake pedal as with any independent master cylinder. If more pressure is needed than the pilot can apply, continued pushing on the pedal allows some of the hydraulic system pressure to flow into the chamber behind the piston, and this pressure increases the force applied to the brakes.

The brake valve in Figure 6-36 attaches to the brake pedal in such a way that application of the brake pulls on the piston rod. The initial movement of the pedal closes the compensator port, the space between the poppet and the piston, and as the piston is pulled down, fluid is forced into the wheel cylinder to apply the brakes. If more pressure is needed at the wheel, the pilot pushes harder on the pedal. This additional movement causes the toggle to depress the spool valve which allows hydraulic system pressure to flow through the center of the spool valve and get behind the piston and help apply the brakes. The spring between the spool valve and the toggle acts as a regulator, preventing the pressure from continuing to build up when the brake pedal is held partially depressed.

As soon as the pilot releases the pedal, the spool valve moves back, shutting off the hydraulic system pressure. Fluid in the brake line is allowed to return to the reservoir through the system return manifold.

Power Brakes

Large aircraft brakes require more fluid and higher pressures than can be supplied by independent master cylinders, and brakes for these aircraft are actuated by pressure supplied from the main hydraulic power system of the aircraft. Power brake control valves operated by the pilot meter this pressure to give the pilot control of the braking action.

System Operation

To operate power brakes, the pilot depresses the brake pedal, which actuates the power brake control valve. Hydraulic fluid under pressure from the main hydraulic system is metered to the brake wheel cylinders proportionate to the amount of force the pilot applies to the brake pedal. The brake control valve is more of a regulator than a selector valve, because it must allow the pilot to hold the brakes partially applied without the pressure building up in the brake lines.

The brakes of these aircraft require a large volume of fluid, and its pressure must be considerably lower than that supplied by the main hydraulic system. The pressure supplied to the brake assembly by the brake control valve is lowered, and the volume increased, by deboosters installed near the wheels.

Since the brakes are in an area where damage can easily occur, hydraulic fuses are installed to prevent the loss of fluid in the event a hydraulic line is broken. There must also be an emergency brake system that can supply air or hydraulic pressure to the brake assemblies if the main hydraulic system should fail.

Figure 6-37 is a simplified schematic of a typical power brake system used in large jet aircraft. The brakes get their fluid from the main hydraulic system, and a check valve and an accumulator hold the pressure for the brakes in the event of a failure in the hydraulic system. The pilot and the copilot operate the power brake control valves through the appropriate linkages.

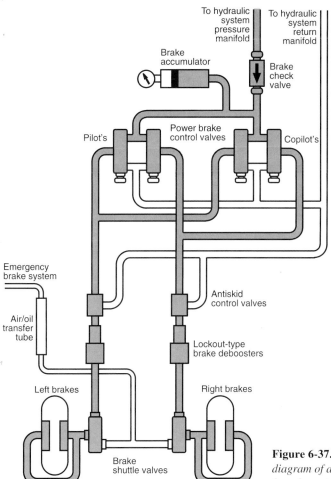

Figure 6-37. *A simplified schematic diagram of a power brake system for a large jet aircraft*

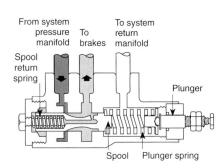

Brake pedal is depressed and fluid is flowing from system pressure manifold to brakes.

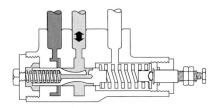

Brake pedal is held steady. Constant pressure is maintained in brake line.

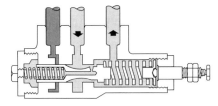

Brake pedal has been released and fluid is returned to system return manifold. Brake line is vented to the reservoir through brake control valve.

Figure 6-38. *Sliding-spool-type power brake control valve*

In large aircraft, the pilot has no feel for an impending skid of any of the tires, so an antiskid system is installed to sense the rate of deceleration of each wheel. This rate is compared with the maximum allowable deceleration rate, and if any wheel attempts to slow down too fast, as it does at the onset of a skid, the antiskid valve will direct fluid from the line to the affected brake assembly back into the system return manifold.

The pressure applied by the brake control valve is too high for proper brake application, so a debooster is installed in the line between the antiskid valve and the brake. This debooster lowers the pressure and increases the volume of fluid supplied to the wheel units.

In case of failure of the main hydraulic system, the pilot can actuate the emergency brake control valve that directs compressed nitrogen into an air/oil transfer tube. The resulting pressurized fluid shifts the shuttle valve on the brake assembly. This shuts off the main brake system and allows the brakes to be actuated by the emergency system.

Power Brake Control Valves

The diagrams in Figure 6-38 show the principle of the power brake control valve. Two types of these valves do the same thing, but they have a different physical appearance. One of the valves has its control spring mounted outside of the valve, and the other valve has the control spring inside, as shown in the figure.

In the top illustration, the pilot has applied the brake. The brake pedal acts on the plunger spring, which gives the pilot a feel of the amount of force he or she is applying to the brakes. This moves the spool to the left, shutting off the passage to the return manifold and connecting the pressure port to the brake line. Fluid under pressure goes to the brake and to the left end of the spool to move it back when the pressure called for by the pilot has been reached. This keeps the pressure supplied to the brake from increasing regardless of the length of time the brake pedal is depressed. If more pressure is needed at the brake, the pilot presses harder on the brake pedal. This further compresses the plunger spring and allows more fluid to flow to the brake.

When the brake pedal is held steady, the combined force of the spool-return spring and the fluid pressure on the spool moves the spool to the right just enough to shut off the passage to the pressure manifold, and fluid is trapped in the line to the brake actuating cylinders.

When the pilot releases the brakes, the force on the plunger spring is relaxed. The spool moves to the right, opening the passage between the brake line and the system return manifold. This allows fluid to flow from the brakes to the return line, releasing the brakes.

Antiskid System

Maximum braking is obtained when the wheel and tire rotate at about 80% of the speed of the aircraft. This rotational speed will produce the shortest stopping distance regardless of the runway surface conditions. Any increase or decrease in tire speed, including locking the brakes and sliding the tires on the runway, will increase the landing distance.

It is difficult to get effective braking on modern jet aircraft because of their small tires inflated to a high pressure and their high speed at touchdown. This problem is made increasingly difficult when the runway is covered with water. The surface friction is so low on a wet runway that the brakes tend to lock up, causing the tires to hydroplane on the surface of the water. When this happens, all braking action is lost for that wheel and directional control is difficult to maintain.

Airplanes that are so large that the pilot does not have a feel for each of the wheels must use an antiskid system to hold all of the tires in the slipping region without allowing a skid to develop. There are several methods of doing this, but the basics of the system described here illustrate the principle on which most antiskid systems operate.

When the pilot wants to stop the aircraft in the shortest distance, he or she depresses the brake pedals to produce maximum braking. Full braking pressure is sent to all of the brakes, but when any wheel begins to slow down fast enough to indicate that a tire is beginning to skid, the pressure in the brake of that wheel is dumped into the hydraulic system return manifold. The antiskid computer measures the amount of time needed for the wheel to spin back up, and then it shuts off the line to the return manifold. This allows a slightly lower pressure to build up in the brake, and if this lower pressure causes the tire to try to skid, the process is repeated, and a still lower pressure is held in the brake. As long as the brake pedals are held down, enough pressure is maintained in the brake cylinders to cause the tires to slip, but not skid. By continually sampling the deceleration rate of the wheel, just enough pressure is allowed into the brakes for maximum braking effectiveness.

If for any reason a wheel should lock up completely while another wheel is rotating, all of the pressure to that wheel is released. This feature of the anti-skid system is deactivated when the airplane speed is less than about 15 or 20 miles per hour. This allows normal braking for slow-speed turning and parking.

Antiskid System Components

There are two basic types of antiskid systems, those that use DC generators in the wheel-speed sensors and those that use AC generators. The typical antiskid system discussed here uses DC wheel-speed sensors.

antiskid system. An electrohydraulic system in an airplane's power brake system that senses the deceleration rate of every main landing gear wheel. If any wheel decelerates too rapidly, indicating an impending skid, pressure to that brake is released and the wheel stops decelerating. Pressure is then reapplied at a slightly lower value.

hydroplaning. A condition that exists when a high-speed airplane is landed on a water-covered runway. When the brakes are applied, the wheels lock up and the tires skid on the surface of the water in much the same way a water ski rides on the surface. Hydroplaning develops enough heat in a tire to ruin it.

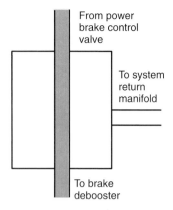

For normal operation, the valve serves only as passage between brake control valve and debooster.

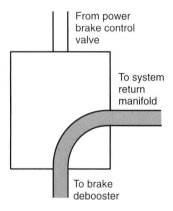

When wheel-speed sensor determines a skid is imminent, it directs antiskid control valve to shut off flow to debooster and vent debooster to system return manifold.

Figure 6-39. *Antiskid control valve*

Wheel-Speed Sensors

Wheel-speed sensors, or skid detectors, are small DC generators mounted in the axles of each of the main wheels. The armature of the detector generator is rotated by the wheel-hub dust cover so that it turns with the wheel and produces a voltage that is proportional to the speed of the wheel.

The voltage from the wheel-speed sensor is applied across a capacitor in an electronic control circuit in such a way that the faster the wheel turns, the greater the charge on the capacitor. As long as the wheel turns at a constant rate, or its speed is increasing or decreasing only slightly, the capacitor does not discharge appreciably. But if the wheel speed should decrease rapidly enough to exceed the limits programmed into the antiskid computer, there will be enough difference between the output voltage of the wheel-speed sensor and the voltage of the charge in the capacitor to signal an impending skid and actuate the antiskid control valve.

Antiskid Control Valves

The three-port electrohydraulic antiskid valve is installed in the pressure line between the brake control valve and the brake debooster. The third line connects the antiskid valve to the hydraulic system return manifold. *See* Figure 6-39.

For normal brake operation, the valve serves only as a passage and allows free flow of fluid to and from the debooster. When the wheel-speed sensor determines that one of the wheels is beginning to decelerate fast enough to cause a skid, the computer sends a signal to an electrical coil inside the antiskid valve that shuts off the pressure to the brake and opens the passage to the system return manifold.

Antiskid Control Box

The antiskid control box contains a computer and the electrical circuitry to interpret the signal from the wheel-speed sensors, compare them with a program tailored to the particular airplane, and send the appropriate signals to the antiskid control valves to hold the tires in a slip without allowing a skid to develop.

Figure 6-40 shows a block diagram of the antiskid system when the airplane is in the air before touchdown. The locked-wheel arming circuit is grounded through the airborne side of the landing-gear squat switch, and it causes the locked-wheel detector circuit to send a signal through the amplifier to the antiskid control valves to open the passages to the return manifold. This makes it impossible to land with the brakes applied.

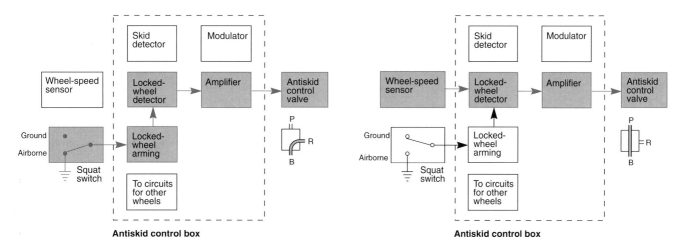

Figure 6-40. *Antiskid control box with the airplane in the air.* *The antiskid valve is held open so no pressure can be applied to the brake regardless of the position of the brake pedals.*

Figure 6-41. *Antiskid control box with the airplane on the ground.* *The wheels have built up a speed of 20 mph or more and the antiskid valve is open, allowing full pressure to be applied to the brakes.*

As soon as weight is on the landing gear, the squat switch changes position and opens the ground to the locked-wheel arming circuit. When the wheel speed builds up to about 20 miles per hour, the wheel-speed sensors produce enough voltage to cause the locked-wheel detector to send a signal to the antiskid valve allowing full pressure to go to the brake.

When the airplane is on the ground with all wheels turning at more than 20 mph, skid control is provided by the skid detectors and the modulator circuits. Any time a wheel decelerates at a rate higher than the programmed maximum, a signal is sent to the amplifier and then to the control valve to dump the brake pressure. At the same time, the skid detector sends a signal to the modulator which, by measuring the width of the skid detector signal, automatically establishes the amount of current that will continue to flow through the valve after the wheel has recovered from the skid. When the amplifier receives its signal from the modulator, it maintains this current, which is just enough to prevent the control valve from dumping all the pressure, but maintains a pressure slightly less than that which caused the skid.

squat switch. An electrical switch actuated by the landing gear scissors on the oleo strut. When no weight is on the landing gear, the oleo piston is extended and the switch is in one position, but when weight is on the gear, the oleo strut compresses and the switch changes its position.

Squat switches are used in antiskid brake systems, landing gear safety circuits, and cabin pressurization systems.

A timer circuit in the modulator then allows the pressure to increase slowly until another skid starts to occur and the cycle repeats itself. *See* Figure 6-42.

The antiskid system holds the tires in the slip area when the aircraft is operating on a wet or icy runway. If one tire begins to hydroplane or hits a patch of ice and slows down to less than 10 mph while its mated reference wheel is still rolling at more than 20 mph, the locked-wheel detector measures the width of the skid detector signal. If it is more than about $\frac{1}{10}$ second, it sends a FULL-DUMP signal to the control valve, which allows all of the fluid in the brakes to flow to the return manifold until the wheel spins back up to more than 10 mph.

When all of the wheels are turning at less than 20 mph, the locked-wheel arming circuit is inoperative. This gives the pilot full control of the brakes for low-speed taxiing and parking.

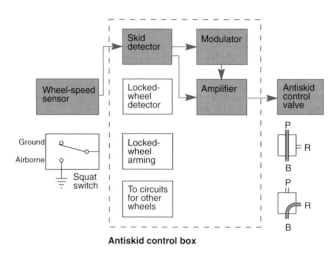

Figure 6-42. *Antiskid control box with the airplane on the ground. All wheels are turning at more than 20 mph. The skid detector is sensing the rate of change of wheel speed and sending the appropriate signal to the modulator. The signal from the modulator is amplified and sent to the antiskid control valve, which applies or releases the brakes to keep the tire in the slip area but prevents a skid from developing.*

System Tests

Antiskid braking systems include methods of checking system integrity before the brakes are needed. If the antiskid system does not function as it should, the pilot can disable it without affecting normal braking action.

Preflight Test

On a preflight inspection, the pilot can check the continuity of all of the wiring and the operation of the locked-wheel circuits, amplifiers, and control valves by depressing both brake pedals. Both brake indicator lights should illuminate. Since the wheel speed is zero and the locked-wheel arming circuit is not grounded through the squat switch, the locked-wheel detector cannot operate, and there is no signal to the control valve through the amplifier. The antiskid valve is fully open, directing all of the pressure from the brake valve to the brake.

With the brakes applied, pressing the antiskid test switch sends a signal through the speed sensors to the control boxes to simulate a wheel speed of more than 20 mph. This signal voltage is high enough to arm the locked-wheel detectors and high enough the keep them from sending a signal to the amplifier. Since there is no signal from the amplifier, the control valves are not energized and the brake indicator lights stay on. While the test switch is held down, the capacitor in the arming circuit is being charged.

When the test switch is released, the two brake indicator lights should go out, stay out for a few seconds, and then come back on. Releasing the switch drops the signal voltage to zero, which indicates a complete lockup of the wheels. The capacitor holds the voltage on the arming circuit, allowing the locked-wheel detectors to work. They detect the zero speed of the wheels and energize the amplifiers. Current is sent to the antiskid valves, causing them to dump all of the pressure into the return manifold and turn the brake indicator lights out.

The capacitor in the arming circuit soon discharges and prevents the locked-wheel detectors from working. This removes the signal from the amplifier and the control valve returns to its normal condition. The brakes are re-applied, and the brake indicator lights come back on.

Prelanding Check

With the airplane configured for landing and the landing gear down and locked, the pilot can determine that the antiskid system is operating properly by depressing the brake pedals. The brake indicator lights should remain off. The squat switch keeps the locked-wheel arming circuit energized, and the signal from the locked-wheel detectors causes the amplifier to send sufficient current into the control valves to hold the brakes fully released.

Depressing the brake test switch with the pedals depressed should cause the brake lights to turn on. This sends a signal through the wheel-speed sensors simulating a wheel speed of greater than 20 mph. If the system is operating properly, this voltage will override the signal from the squat switch and disable the locked-wheel arming circuit. This allows the locked-wheel detector to remove the signal from the amplifier so the control valve can restore normal action to the brakes. The brake indicator light should remain on as long as the test switch is held depressed.

When the test switch is released, the two brake lights should go out, indicating that the antiskid system is holding all of the pressure off of the brakes.

Disabling the System

If the antiskid system fails either the preflight or prelanding test, the system can be disabled without affecting normal braking in any way. Opening the antiskid switch removes all of the current from the control valve, allowing the valve to remain in the position for full flow of fluid between the brake valve and the brake.

Maintenance Checks

If an antiskid system has failed any of its tests, the source of the trouble is relatively simple to isolate. It is generally in one of three components: the wheel-speed sensor, the control box, or the control valve. Before blaming the antiskid system, however, be sure that the brakes are operating normally. There should be no warped disks or broken return springs, and there should be no air in the brake lines or cylinders.

The components of the antiskid system itself are quite complex and most of them must be repaired only by the manufacturer or an FAA-certificated repair station approved for the particular components.

Wheel-Speed Sensors

As in all systematic troubleshooting, first check the items that are easiest to reach or are most likely to fail. Remove the wheel hubcap and, with the brakes applied, flip the blade of the wheel-speed sensor to cause it to rotate in a clockwise direction. This blade will turn about 180° or less when it is flipped, but it is the rate, not the amount of movement, that is important. Watch the brake disk stack as the blade is flipped; the stack should relax and then retighten.

If the brakes do not release, remove the connector from the back of the sensor and check the resistance of the coil as the blade is rotated through a full revolution. The resistance should be that specified in the maintenance manual, and it should be smooth throughout the rotation of the blade. If the resistance is within the acceptable limits, place the multimeter on its lowest DC voltage scale and attach the leads to the pins, as indicated in the maintenance manual. Flip the blade in the clockwise direction and the voltmeter should indicate an upscale deflection. If a digital voltmeter is used, the voltage indication should be positive. If the wheel-speed sensor checks out electrically, check to be sure it is properly installed.

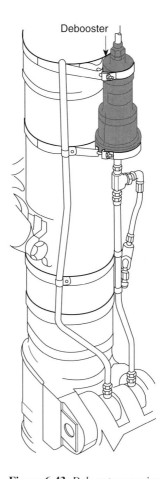

Debooster

Figure 6-43. *Deboosters are installed between the power brake control valve and the brake cylinders to decrease the pressure and increase the volume of fluid going to the brakes.*

Control Box

The control boxes for many antiskid installations have two identical channels. If the antiskid system on the right side of the aircraft is malfunctioning but the system on the other side is functioning properly, check the control box by temporarily swapping the electrical leads going into the control box. If the malfunctioning system moves to the left side and the right side clears up, the control box is at fault, but if the trouble does not change, the fault lies elsewhere. It is extremely important to re-install the electrical connectors on their correct plug before the aircraft is returned to service.

Antiskid Control Valve

The control valve is an electrohydraulic device, and if systematic troubleshooting identifies it as defective, return it to an appropriate facility to be repaired.

Deboosters

Hydraulic system pressure is normally too high for effective brake action, so deboosters are installed between the antiskid valve and the wheel cylinders to reduce the pressure and increase the volume of fluid going to the brakes. Deboosters used in some of the larger aircraft have a lockout feature that allows them to double as hydraulic fuses. *See* Figure 6-43.

The principle of deboosters is illustrated in Figure 6-44, where 1,500 psi pressure is applied to a piston that has an area of one square inch. This pressure produces 1,500 pounds of force. The other end of this piston has an area of five square inches, and the 1,500 pounds of force is spread out over the entire five square inches, so the pressure it produces in the fluid is only 300 psi.

The other function of the debooster is to increase the volume of the fluid that is sent to the brakes. One cubic inch of fluid at the system pressure moves the small piston down one inch. The larger piston also moves down one inch, but because of its larger area, it moves five cubic inches of fluid out to the brakes.

The debooster shown in Figure 6-44 has a pin-operated ball valve that allows fluid in the large end of the cylinder to be replenished if there should be a leak in the line to the brakes. If the debooster piston moves down enough to allow the pin to force the ball off its seat, fluid under system pressure will enter the lower chamber and replenish the lost fluid. As soon as enough fluid enters the chamber, it raises the piston so that the ball will reseat.

Lockout deboosters act as hydraulic fuses. They have a spring-loaded valve that prevents fluid from flowing into the large end of the cylinder to replace any that has leaked out. The piston can travel all the way to the bottom of the cylinder where the pin pushes the ball off its seat, but the spring-loaded valve keeps the fluid from entering the lower chamber. When the maintenance technician fixes the cause of the leak, the reset handle can be lifted, allowing fluid to flow into the large end, refilling the brakes.

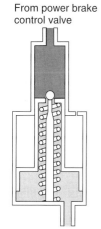

High-pressure fluid from power brake control valve presses down on small end of piston. Large end of piston forces fluid out to brake wheel cylinder.

If leakage in brake line should cause loss of fluid, pin will force the ball off its seat, and large end of debooster cylinder will be replenished with fluid.

Figure 6-44. *Brake debooster valve*

Emergency Brake System

In case of a total failure of the hydraulic system, the pilot can operate a pneumatic valve on the instrument panel and direct compressed nitrogen into the brake system to apply the brakes.

Rather than allowing compressed nitrogen to enter the wheel cylinders, which would require that the entire system be bled to remove it, the emergency nitrogen is directed into the air/oil transfer tube where it pressurizes hydraulic fluid. If the pressure of this fluid from the emergency system is greater than the pressure from the brake debooster, the brake shuttle valves will move over and fluid from the emergency system will actuate the brakes. To release the brakes, the pilot rotates the emergency brake handle to the left and the nitrogen pressure is vented overboard. This in turn relieves the pressure in the brake cylinders.

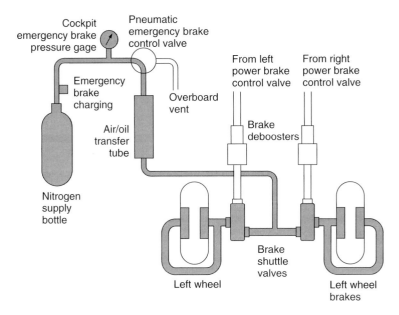

Figure 6-45. *Emergency brake system for a large jet transport airplane*

Dual Power Brake Actuating System

Many of the jet transport aircraft have dual power brakes that are operated by two independent hydraulic power systems. When the pilot or copilot depresses a brake pedal, the dual brake control valve directs fluid from each system into the brake actuating unit. Figure 6-31 on Page 448 shows the housing for one of the brakes installed on a McDonnell-Douglas DC-9. Seven of the brake-actuating cylinders are supplied with pressure from one hydraulic system through pressure port A, and the other seven cylinders are supplied with pressure from the other hydraulic system through pressure port B.

If either hydraulic system supplying pressure to the brakes should fail, the other system will supply enough pressure for adequate braking.

Auto Brake System

Some highly automated jet transport aircraft, such as the Boeing 757, have auto brake systems. A selector switch on the instrument panel allows the pilot to select a deceleration rate that will be controlled automatically after touchdown.

When the aircraft touches down with the auto brake system armed and the thrust levers at idle, the system will direct the correct amount of pressure to the brakes to achieve the desired rate of deceleration. The brake pressure will be decreased automatically to compensate for the deceleration caused by the thrust reversers and speed brakes.

The auto brake system will disengage if any of these things happen:

- The pilot moves the selector switch to the DISARM or OFF position.
- The pilot uses manual braking.
- The thrust levers are advanced.
- The speed brake lever is moved to the DOWN detent.

Brake Maintenance

The brakes of a modern aircraft take more abuse than almost any other component. The tremendous amount of kinetic energy caused by the weight and rolling speed of the aircraft must be transferred into the relatively small mass of the brake in order to stop the aircraft. Jet aircraft, for this reason, very often use thrust reversers to slow the aircraft after landing before the brakes are applied. An aborted takeoff is an emergency procedure that transfers far more heat into the brakes than they are designed to absorb, and the brakes, wheels, and tires are usually ruined.

If a brake shows any indication of overheating, or if it has been involved in an aborted takeoff, it should be removed from the aircraft, disassembled, and carefully inspected.

Carefully examine the housing for cracks or warping, and give it a hardness test at the points specified in the brake maintenance manual. Housings that have been overheated may have been softened and weakened to the extent that they are no longer airworthy. Seals that have been exposed to excessive heat must be replaced, as the heat destroys their ability to seal.

Disks in multiple-disk brakes often warp when they are overheated. Check all of the disks for warpage using the method specified in the brake maintenance manual.

aborted takeoff. A takeoff that is terminated prematurely when it is determined that some condition exists that makes takeoff or further flight dangerous.

Brakes that have sintered-metal friction material on the rotating disk often transfer some of this material to the stationary disk. Some transfer is allowed, but the disks must be carefully examined to ensure that the amount of allowable transfer has not been exceeded.

Glazed or warped disks cause the brake to apply and release many times a minute, which produces chattering or squealing. This is not only annoying, but the vibration it causes can damage the brake or the landing gear.

Warped disks can also cause the brakes to drag. They do not completely release when the pressure is relieved. This causes the brake to overheat and the disks to be further warped and damaged.

After thoroughly inspecting and reassembling the brake, you must pressure-test it according to the instructions in the maintenance manual. This test usually includes checking for proper application and release of the brakes and for any indication of leaks.

Installation of the Brake on the Aircraft

Brakes must be installed in exactly the way the manufacturer recommends in the aircraft maintenance manual. Use only the parts specified in the aircraft parts lists, and torque all of the bolts to the values specified in the maintenance manuals. Most bolt torque is specified for clean and dry threads, but some bolts on the brakes must be lubricated before they are torqued. Use only the lubricant specified by the manufacturer, and apply it only in the specified manner.

Bleeding the Brakes

Aircraft brakes are single-acting systems, and any air trapped in the fluid will give the brakes a spongy feel. They must be bled to remove all of the air from the fluid when they are first installed and any time the system is opened. There are two methods of removing air from brake systems: gravity bleeding and pressure bleeding.

Gravity Bleeding

Gravity bleeding, sometimes called top-down bleeding, is done by running the fluid from the master cylinder down through the brake cylinders. Power brakes can be bled only by this method.

Attach a clear plastic tube to the bleeder plug at the wheel cylinder, and immerse the end of the tube in a container of clean hydraulic fluid. Fill the reservoir, and slowly depress the brake pedal with the bleeder valve open. Watch the plastic tube as you continue to slowly pump the master cylinder. Continue to pump the brakes until fluid runs through the tube with no bubbles.

You may have to fill the reservoir a time or two in this process, as a large amount of fluid will have to be pumped through the system before all of the air is removed.

When the fluid runs clear of all traces of air, close the bleeder plug and remove the tube. Fill and cap the reservoir, making sure that the reservoir vent is open.

bleeding of brakes. The maintenance procedure of removing air entrapped in hydraulic fluid in the brakes. Fluid is bled from the brake system until fluid with no bubbles flows out.

spongy brakes. Hydraulic brakes whose pedal has a spongy feel because of air trapped in the fluid.

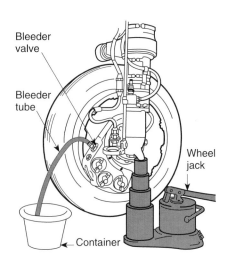

Figure 6-46. *Gravity bleeding of brakes*

Pressure Bleeding

Pressure bleeding is usually superior to gravity bleeding since it begins at a low point and drives the air out the top of the system, taking advantage of the natural tendency of air bubbles to rise in a liquid.

Connect a hose to the bleeder plug at the wheel cylinder, and attach a bleeder pot or hydraulic hand pump to the hose. Attach a clear plastic hose to a fitting in the top of the reservoir and immerse its free end in a container of clean hydraulic fluid. Open the bleeder plug and slowly force fluid through the brake, up through the reservoir, and out into the container of fluid. When the fluid flows out of the reservoir with no trace of air, close the bleeder plug and remove the hoses.

Some reservoirs may be overfilled in this process and fluid must be removed down to the "full" mark before replacing the reservoir cap. Do not reuse this removed fluid, but dispose of it in a manner approved by your local environmental laws. Be sure that the reservoir vent is open when the reservoir is capped.

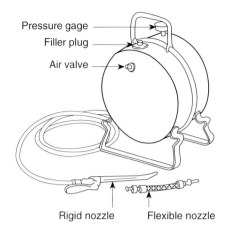

Figure 6-47. *Hydraulic brake pressure bleeder pot for pressure bleeding brakes*

STUDY QUESTIONS: AIRCRAFT BRAKES

Answers begin on Page 488. Page numbers refer to chapter text.

23. A brake that uses friction to help apply the brakes is called a/an _____ brake. *Page 439*

24. An expander tube brake is a/an _____ (energizing or nonenergizing) brake. *Page 439*

25. Clearance between the drum and the blocks of an expander tube brake is maintained constant by an automatic adjuster which traps a certain amount of hydraulic fluid in the _____ . *Page 440*

26. Fading of a drum-type brake is caused by uneven _____ of the drum caused by heat. *Page 439*

27. A single-disk brake _____ (is or is not) an energizing brake. *Page 439*

28. An automatic adjuster in a single-disk brake determines the amount the piston moves when the brakes are _____ (applied or released). *Page 442*

29. The amount of lining wear is indicated on a single-disk brake with automatic adjusters by the amount the adjusting pin protrudes from the nut. The more the linings are worn, the _____ (more or less) the pin protrudes. *Page 442*

30. Brake lining wear is measured on a single-disk brake without automatic adjusters by measuring the distance between the disk and the _____ (piston or anvil) side of the brake housing. *Page 443*

Continued

31. A dual-disk brake is similar to a single-disk except for the additional braking area furnished by the additional disk and _____ area. *Page 445*

32. One of the main limitations of a thin-disk multiple-disk brake is the tendency of the disks to _____ . *Page 446*

33. The brake linings in a segmented-rotor brake are part of the _____ (rotor or stator) *Page 447*

34. In a segmented-rotor brake, the disks are squeezed between the _____ and the _____ . *Page 447*

35. Carbon-disk brakes are _____ (heavier or lighter) than a metal-disk brake that has the same stopping capability. *Page 448*

36. The fluid in the brake wheel cylinder is vented to the atmosphere through the _____ port in the master cylinder. *Page 450*

37. If the compensator port were plugged, expansion of the fluid in the brake lines caused by heat would cause the brakes to _____ . *Page 450*

38. The brake system that uses the aircraft hydraulic system pressure to assist the pilot in applying force to the piston in the brake master cylinder is called a/an _____ brake. *Page 452*

39. A power brake control valve is a form of pressure _____ . *Page 452*

40. For maximum braking effectiveness, the wheels of an airplane should be allowed to _____ but not allowed to _____ . *Page 455*

41. When an airplane wheel locks up on a wet runway and the tire skids across the surface of the water, the tire is said to be _____ . *Page 455*

42. The three major components in an antiskid brake system are:
    a. _____
    b. _____
    c. _____
    Page 456

43. When the antiskid system is operating normally, it _____ (is or is not) possible to land with the brakes applied. *Page 456*

44. Pressure in the brake cylinders is maintained at a value just below that which would cause the tires to skid by the _____ circuit in the antiskid control box. *Page 457*

45. The wheel-speed sensor in an antiskid system is a small _____ . *Page 456*

46. A brake debooster valve _____ (increases or decreases) the volume of fluid flowing to the brake. *Page 460*

47. A lockout debooster acts as a hydraulic _____ . *Page 461*

48. The emergency brake system of a jet transport airplane uses _____ to actuate the brakes. *Page 462*

49. Two causes of disk brakes chattering or squealing are the disks being _____ or _____ . *Page 464*

50. Brake cylinder seals that have been overheated should be _____ . *Page 463*

51. Warped brake disks will cause a brake to drag. This will cause the brakes to _____ . *Page 464*

52. A brake housing can be checked for hidden damage from overheating by giving it a _____ test. *Page 463*

53. Two methods of bleeding aircraft brakes are:
    a. _____
    b. _____
    Page 464

54. Power brakes are bled by the _____ method. *Page 464*

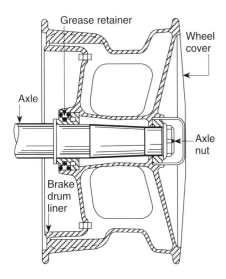

Figure 6-48. *Fixed-flange, drop-center wheel*

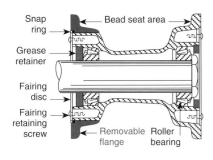

Figure 6-49. *Drop-center wheel with a removable outer flange*

Aircraft Wheels

Aircraft wheels have undergone as much evolutionary development as any aircraft part. Most aircraft up through the 1920s did not have any brakes, and the wheels were spoked, similar to those used on bicycles and motorcycles. The tires were relatively soft and could easily be pried over the rims. These wheels were streamlined with fabric or thin sheet metal to cover the spokes.

The next step in wheel development was the small diameter, fixed-flange, drop-center wheel which was intended to be used with a doughnut-type tire.

When stiffer tires were developed, wheels were designed that had one removable rim. The rim was removed and the tire and tube were assembled onto the wheel, and the rim was re-installed and held in place by a steel snap ring. Inflation of the tire locked the rim securely in place.

Tubeless tires prompted the development of the two-piece wheel, split in the center and sealed between the two halves with an O-ring. This is the most popular configuration of wheel in use today, and it is found on all types of aircraft from small trainers to large jet transport airplanes.

Wheel Nomenclature

Figure 6-50 is an exploded view of a typical two-piece aircraft wheel. These wheels are made of either aluminum or magnesium alloy, and depending upon their strength requirements, they may be either cast or forged.

Inboard Wheel Half

The inboard wheel half is fitted with steel-reinforced keys that fit into slots in the periphery of the brake disk to rotate the disk with the wheel. In the center of the wheel, there is a wheel-bearing boss into which is shrunk a polished steel bearing cup, or outer bearing race. A tapered roller bearing rides between this cup and a bearing race on the axle. A grease retainer covers the bearing and prevents dirt or water reaching the bearing surfaces.

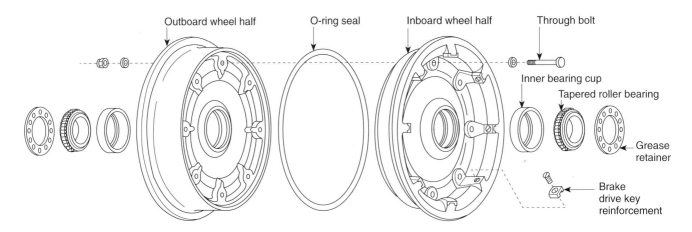

Figure 6-50. *Exploded view of a typical two-piece wheel for a light aircraft*

High-performance aircraft have one or more fusible plugs in the inboard wheel half. These plugs have a hole drilled through their center filled with a low-melting-point alloy. In the event of an aborted takeoff or other emergency braking, so much heat is produced in the brake that the air in the tire tries to expand, resulting in a pressure rise so high the wheel could explode. To prevent this, the center of the fusible plug melts and deflates the tire in a few seconds when the wheel reaches a dangerous temperature.

Some larger wheels also have an overinflation safety valve. When tires on these large wheels are inflated from a high-pressure air or nitrogen bottle, they can be overinflated to the extent that the tire could explode. If this happens, the overinflation safety valve will rupture and deflate the tire.

Outboard Wheel Half

The outboard wheel half also contains a shrunk-in outer race for a tapered roller bearing and a grease retainer similar to that used in the inner half of the wheel. A thin steel cap, held in place with a retaining ring, covers the end of the axle and the bearing. When the aircraft is equipped with an antiskid system, this cap has a built-in bracket that drives the blade of the wheel-speed sensor mounted in the landing gear axle.

If the wheel mounts a tubeless tire, there is an inflation valve in the outboard wheel half, and if a tube-type tire is used, there is a hole through which the tube valve stem protrudes.

Bead Seat Area

The bead seat area is the most critical part of an aircraft wheel. The metal in this area is under a high tensile load caused by the air pressure in the tire and intensified by hard landings. The bead seat area is rolled to prestress the surface with a compressive stress.

Wheel Maintenance

The abuse suffered by an aircraft wheel is directly related to the care given to the tire mounted on it. Tire care is discussed later in this chapter.

Wheel Removal

Aircraft wheels are lightweight and subjected to extremely heavy loads in hard landings. Some of the through bolts that hold the wheel halves together may have been weakened, and may break in the process of wheel disassembly. To preclude this possibility, always deflate the tire after the aircraft is on the jack and before loosening the axle nut. High-pressure tires should be deflated by screwing a deflator cap on the valve and allowing the air to escape through the hole in the cap. The high-pressure air in these tires can eject the valve core at a velocity high enough to cause personal injury. After all the air is out of the tire, remove the valve core.

fusible plugs. Plugs in the wheels of high-performance airplanes that use tubeless tires. The centers of the plugs are filled with a metal that melts at a relatively low temperature.

If a takeoff is aborted and the pilot uses the brakes excessively, the heat transferred into the wheel will melt the center of the fusible plugs and allow the air to escape from the tire before it builds up enough pressure to cause an explosion.

bead seat area. The flat surface on the inside of the rim of an aircraft wheel on which the bead of the tire seats.

deflator cap. A cap for a tire, strut, or accumulator air valve that, when screwed onto the valve, depresses the valve stem and allows the air to escape safely through a hole in the side of the cap.

Tire Removal

With the tire completely deflated, break the bead of the tire away from the wheel. Apply an even force as a straight push as near the rim as possible. Large wheels require a special tire-demounting tool, but you can break the smaller tires away from the wheel using an arbor press and a piece of wood to force the bead of the tire away from the wheel. Never use any kind of tire tool to pry the bead from the wheel, as the soft metal of which the wheel is made can easily be nicked or scratched. This will cause stress concentrations, or stress risers, that may ultimately cause the wheel to fail. When the bead is broken from both wheel halves, remove the nuts from the through bolts and remove the wheel halves and the O-ring seal from the tire.

Wheel Inspection

Clean the wheel with varsol or naphtha and scrub away all of the loosened deposits with a soft bristle brush. Dry the wheel with a flow of compressed air.

Inspect the entire wheel for indication of corrosion where moisture was trapped and held in contact with the metal. If you find any corrosion, you must dress it out by removing as little metal as is possible. After cleaning out all of the corrosion, treat the surface to prevent new corrosion from forming.

The rotor drive keys in the wheel are subjected to a great deal of stress, and absolutely no looseness is allowed between the drive keys and the slots in the rotor disks. Inspect the area around the slots with dye penetrant.

You can't inspect the bead seat area of the wheel with dye penetrant, because when the tire is removed, any cracks in this area will close up so tightly no penetrant can seep into them. When the tire is installed and inflated, the stresses will enlarge the cracks. Inspect these areas with eddy current equipment according to the instructions furnished by the wheel manufacturer.

Examine the fusible plugs carefully for any indication of softening of the core material that would indicate the wheel had been overheated. If there is any indication of deformation, replace all the plugs.

When aircraft wheels are manufactured, they are statically balanced. Balance weights are attached which must never be removed. The final balancing is done with the tire installed, and the weights used for final balancing are installed around the outside of the wheel rim or around the wheel bolt circle.

Bearing Maintenance

Remove the bearings from the wheel and soak them in a clean solvent such as varsol or naphtha to soften the dried grease. Remove all the residue with a soft bristle brush, and dry the bearing with a flow of low-pressure compressed air. Never spin the bearings with the air when drying them because the high-speed rotation of the dry metal-to-metal contact will overheat and damage the extremely smooth surfaces.

Carefully inspect the bearing races and rollers for any of the types of damage described in Figure 6-51. Any of these types of damage are cause for rejection of the bearing. Inspect the thin bearing cages that hold the rollers aligned on the races. Any damage or distortion to the cage is cause for replacing the bearing.

Galling	Damage caused by the rubbing of mating surfaces. When localized high spots rub against each other they become heated by friction enough to weld together. As they continue to move, the welded areas pull apart and destroy some of the surface.
Spalling	Damage in which chips are broken from the surface of a case-hardened material such as a bearing race. Spalling occurs when the bearing race is placed under a load great enough to distort the softer inner part of the metal and cause the hard, brittle surface to crack. Once a crack forms in the surface, chips break out.
Brinelling	Damage to the hardened surface of a bearing roller or race caused by excessive radial loads. When the bearing is overloaded, the rollers are forced into the race, and they leave small dips, or indentations, in the race on the surface of the roller.
Water stain	Black discolorations on bearing races and rollers where the surfaces were in contact in the presence of water. This discoloration is an indication of intergranular corrosion within the material.
Discoloration from overheating	Blue marks of the bearing rollers indicate that the bearing has been operated dry, or has been subjected to too high a rotational speed.
Rust	Rough red deposits on any of the rolling surfaces indicate that the bearing has been left unprotected from moisture in the air. Rust leaves pits that ruin the bearing surfaces.

Figure 6-51. *Types of damage that are cause for rejection of a wheel bearing*

Inspect the bearing cup that is shrunk into the wheel for any of the damages mentioned in Figure 6-51. If it is damaged, it must be replaced. Put the wheel half in an oven whose temperature can be carefully controlled. Heat it at the temperature specified in the wheel maintenance manual, generally no higher than 225°F for approximately 30 minutes. Remove the wheel from the oven and then tap the cup from its hole with a fiber drift.

To install a new cup, coat its outside surface with zinc chromate primer. Heat the wheel and chill the cup with dry ice, and then tap the cup into its hole with a plastic mallet or a fiber drift.

Pack the bearing with grease that meets the specification in the aircraft maintenance manual. Use a pressure packing tool if one is available. If you must pack them by hand, be sure to completely cover every roller and the inner cone. Wrap the greased bearing in clean waxed paper to protect it from dust and dirt until the wheel is ready to be reassembled and reinstalled.

Tire Installation

The installation of the tire on the wheel, final balancing, and installation of the wheel on the aircraft are discussed in the section, "Aircraft Tires and Tubes," beginning on Page 473.

Wheel Installation

Prepare the axle for receiving the wheel by removing any dirt or dried grease, inspecting it for any obvious damage, and checking the axle threads for their condition. Place the cleaned and greased bearings in the wheel and install the grease retainers. Slide the wheel on the axle and install the brake, following the instructions in the aircraft maintenance manual in detail.

One of the most critical items in the installation of a wheel is the torque on the axle nut. Some smaller aircraft only require that the axle nut be installed and tightened until a slight bearing drag is obvious when the wheel is rotated. Then back the nut off to the nearest castellation and install the cotter pin. The manufacturers of some of the larger aircraft specify two torque values, one to seat the bearing and the other for operational torque. First, while rotating the wheel, tighten the axle nut to the higher value to seat the bearing, then back the nut off and retighten it to the lower torque, then safety it.

STUDY QUESTIONS: AIRCRAFT WHEELS

Answers begin on Page 488. Page numbers refer to chapter text.

55. Most of the wheels used on modern aircraft are of the _____ (single-piece or two-piece) type. *Page 468*

56. Wheels on modern high-performance airplanes are prevented from exploding from heat generated in the brakes by _____ installed in the inboard wheel half. *Page 469*

57. The most highly stressed part of an aircraft wheel is the _____ . *Page 469*

58. The bead seat area of a wheel is strengthened against tensile loads by prestressing the surface with a _____ stress. *Page 469*

---

59. A wheel should be cleaned with _____ or _____ and dried with compressed air. *Page 470*

60. The dye penetrant method of inspection _____ (is or is not) an effective method of inspection for the bead seat area of a wheel. *Page 470*

61. The bead seat area of a wheel should be inspected by the _____ method. *Page 470*

Aircraft Tires and Tubes

Aircraft tires are different from any other type of tire because of their unique requirements. The total mileage an aircraft tire experiences over its lifetime is extremely low compared to tires on an automobile or truck. But the aircraft tire withstands far more beating from the landing impact than an automotive tire will ever experience. Therefore aircraft tires are allowed to deflect more than twice as much as automotive tires.

The abrasive surface of the runway causes extreme tread-wear on touchdown, because the tire accelerates from zero to more than one hundred miles per hour in only a few feet.

Evolution of Aircraft Tires

The first flying machines did not use any wheels or tires. The *Wright Flyer* had skids and was launched from a rail. The first wheeled landing gear used bicycle or motorcycle wheels and tires. It was not until around 1909 that the first tires were made specifically for the unusual requirements of an airplane.

As flight speeds increased and parasite drag became an important consideration, streamlined tires were made to reduce the drag caused by the exposed fixed landing gear. Most aircraft up to this time had no brakes; so tread pattern was of no concern.

Almost all aircraft were operated from grass surfaces, and the Airwheel, which was a low-pressure, high-flotation tire that looked much like a fat doughnut, was popular for many smaller airplanes. These tires had no tread pattern, but many airplanes that used them had brakes in the small wheels on which they were mounted. These brakes were effective only for maneuvering during low-speed taxiing and were not used for slowing the airplane on landing.

Tires with a patterned tread became important when airplanes got effective brakes that could be used to slow the landing roll. At first this tread was simply a diamond pattern that provided good braking on wet grass, but the rib tread proved be superior for operation on hard-surfaced runways. Today, almost all aircraft tires have a rib tread that consists of straight grooves molded into the tread material.

An interesting development in the tires for large aircraft was the change in their size. When developmental study was done on the first truly large aircraft in the late 1930s, the machines such as the Douglas XB-19 and the Boeing XB-15 had only a few wheels with very large, relatively low-pressure tires. As aircraft developed, so did their tires. Modern large aircraft use many wheels with much smaller high-pressure tires.

Tire Construction

Figure 6-52 is a cross-sectional drawing of a typical aircraft tire showing its major components. This section of the text discusses each of these components.

The Bead

bead (tire component). The high-strength carbon-steel wire bundles that give an aircraft tire its strength and stiffness where it mounts on the wheel.

The bead gives the tire the needed strength and stiffness to assure a firm mounting on the wheel. The bead is made of bundles of high-strength carbon-steel wire with two or three bead bundles on each side of the tire. Rubber apex strips streamline the round bead bundles to allow the fabric to fit smoothly around them without any voids. The bead bundles are enclosed in layers of rubberized fabric, called flippers, to insulate the carcass plies from the heat absorbed in the bead wires.

The Carcass

carcass (tire component). The layers of rubberized fabric that make up the body of an aircraft tire.

The carcass, or cord body, is the body of the tire that is made up of layers of rubberized fabric cut in strips with the threads running at an angle of about 45° to the length of the strip. These strips extend completely across the tire, around the bead, and partially up the side. Each ply is put on in such a way that the threads cross at an angle of about 90° to that of the adjacent plies. This type of construction is known as a bias ply tire. Radial tires, as used on most automobiles, have the threads in each layer of rubberized fabric running straight across the tire from one bead to the other.

The cords of the ply fabric were originally all cotton, then nylon became the most popular material. And now aramid fibers, which are stronger than nylon, polyester, or fiberglass, and even stronger, pound for pound, than steel, are used in some premium-quality tires.

The ply rating of a tire is not the actual number of plies of fabric used in the tire construction, but it indicates the number of plies of cotton fabric needed to produce the same strength as the actual plies.

Chafing strips, or chafers, are strips of rubberized fabric that wrap around the edges of the carcass plies and enclose the entire bead area. The chafing strips provide a smooth chafe-resisting surface between the tire and the bead seat area of the wheel.

The undertread is a layer of specially compounded rubber between the plies and the tread rubber that provides good adhesion between the tread and the carcass. Directly on top of the undertread are one or more plies of strong fabric that strengthen the tread and oppose centrifugal forces that try to pull the tread from the carcass during high-speed rotation. This tread reinforcement is not part of the ply rating, but it is used as a guide for retreaders to show when all of the tread rubber has been removed.

The inner liner of the carcass is a thin coating of rubber over the inside plies. For tubeless tires, this inner liner is made of a special rubber compound that is less permeable than the other rubber used in the tire. It seals the tire and minimizes the amount of air that can seep out, so the tire can act as an air container. For tube-type tires, the inner liner is specially smooth to prevent the tube from chafing against the inside of the tire.

ply rating. The rating of an aircraft tire that indicates its relative strength. The ply rating does not indicate the actual number of plies of fabric in the tire; rather it indicates the number of plies of cotton fabric needed to produce the same strength as the actual plies.

The Tread

The tread is the thick rubber around the periphery of the tire that serves as its wearing surface. The tread is made of specially compounded rubber and has a series of grooves molded into its surface to give the optimum traction with the runway surface.

A number of tread designs have been used on aircraft tires, but since the vast majority of aircraft operate from paved runways, the most popular tread is the rib tread, in which a series of straight grooves encircle the periphery of the tire as shown in Figure 6-52.

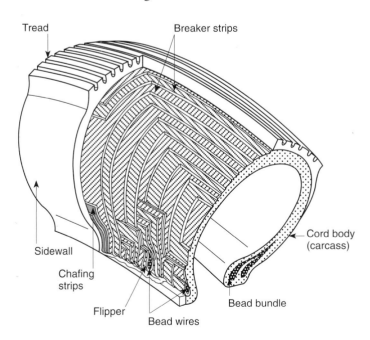

Figure 6-52. *The construction of an aircraft tire*

Figure 6-53. *Chines, or deflectors, are molded into the outer sidewall of nose wheel tires mounted on jet airplanes with engines mounted on the aft fuselage. These chines deflect water from the runway away from the engine inlets.*

The Sidewall

The side of a tire, from the tread to the bead, is covered with a special rubber compound that protects the ply fabric from cuts, bruises, and exposure to moisture and ozone.

The inner liner of tubeless tires is intended to hold air, but some will leak through. To prevent this air from expanding and causing the plies to separate when the tire gets hot, there are small vent holes in the sidewall near the bead. These vent holes are marked with paint and must be kept open at all times. The sidewalls of tube-type tires are vented to allow air trapped between the tube and the inner liner of the tire to escape.

Jet airplanes that have the engines mounted in pods on the rear of the fuselage ingest water that has been thrown up by the nose wheel tire when operating on wet runways. To prevent this problem, nose wheel tires for these airplanes have a chine, or deflector, molded into their outer sidewall that deflects the water outward so that it misses the rear engines.

The Inner Liner

The main difference between a tube-type tire and a tubeless tire is the inner liner. For tubeless tires, the inner liner is made of an impervious rubber compound, and no effort is made to keep it smooth. If a tube is used in a tubeless tire, it will be damaged by the rough surface. A tube-type tire has a smooth inner liner that will not chafe the tube in normal operation.

Tire Inspection

Modern aircraft tires so seldom give problems that they do not get the attention that they deserve. Tire inspection is simple, but it is extremely important.

Inflation

Heat is the greatest enemy of aircraft tires. Aircraft tires are designed to flex more than automobile tires, and the heat generated as the sidewalls flex can cause damage that is not likely to be detected until it causes the tire to fail.

The weight of the aircraft is supported by the air in the tires, and when the air pressure is correct, the tire flexes only within its design limits. But if the tire is operated with too low an inflation pressure, the sidewalls will flex enough to generate excessive heat.

If the tire is operated in an overinflated condition, the tread will not contact the runway as it should and the tire will have less resistance to skidding.

The proper inflation pressure for a tire is specified in the airframe service manual, and is the pressure of the tire when it is supporting the weight of the aircraft. Use this pressure rather than the inflation pressure specified in the tire manufacturer's manual. The same tire used on different airplanes will have different specified inflation pressures.

When a tire is loaded with the weight of the aircraft, it will deflect and its volume will decrease enough to increase the inflation pressure by approximately 4%. If the aircraft service manual specifies an inflation pressure of 190 psi, the tire should be inflated to 4% less than this or approximately 182 psi if it is inflated while the aircraft is on jacks or before the wheel and tire assembly is installed on the aircraft.

Inflation pressure should always be measured when the tire is cold, at least two to three hours after the last flight. Use a dial-type pressure gage that is periodically checked for accuracy.

The pressure of the air inside a tire varies with its temperature at the rate of about 1% for every 5°F. For example, a tire has an inflation pressure of 160 psi after it has stabilized at the hangar temperature of 60°F. If the airplane is moved outdoors where the temperature drops to 0°F, the pressure in the tire will drop by 12% to about 141 psi, and the tire is definitely underinflated.

Nylon tires stretch when they are first installed and inflated, and the pressure will drop by about 5 to 10% of the initial inflation pressure in the first 24 hours. Check newly mounted tires and adjust their pressure 24 hours after they are mounted.

Tread Condition

Notice the touchdown area of the runway of any modern airport and you will see that it is practically black. This is rubber left by the tires as they speed up from zero to the touchdown speed. The tread is worn away long before the carcass plies are dead of old age, and it is common practice to retread aircraft tires.

The tires should be operated with proper inflation pressure and removed for retreading while there is at least $\frac{1}{32}$-inch of tread at its shallowest point. If the tire is allowed to wear beyond this, there will not be enough tread for safe operation on a wet runway. A normally worn tread is shown in Figure 6-54A on the next page. When it is removed at this time it can safely be retreaded.

When a tire has been worn until the tread is completely gone over the carcass plies, scrap the tire. It is no longer safe to operate, and it is worn too much to be retreaded.

When the tire has been operated in an overinflated condition, the center of the tread will wear more than the tread on the shoulders of the tire. You can retread a tread worn to the extent of the one shown in Figure 6-54C.

Underinflation will cause the tread to wear away from the shoulders before it wears in the center. This is shown in Figure 6-54D. If the carcass of this tire has not been damaged, you can retread it.

Uneven tread wear is normally caused by the landing gear being out of alignment. At the first indication of this type of wear, check the alignment and correct it according to the instructions in the aircraft maintenance manual.

Any time a cut extends more than halfway across a rib, or if any of the carcass plies are exposed, take the tire out of service.

Hydroplaning causes a wheel to lock up and there will normally be an oval-shaped burned area on the tire. Remove any tire showing this type of damage from service.

Operation on grooved runways will often produce a series of chevron-shaped cuts across the tread. Any time these cuts extend across more than half of the rib, remove the tire.

Sidewall Condition

The sidewall rubber protects the carcass plies from damage, either from mechanical abrasion or from the action of chemicals or the sun. Weather checking or small snags or cuts in the sidewall rubber that do not expose the cords do not require removal of the tire, but if the ply cords are exposed, the cords have probably been weakened, and tire must be replaced.

The liner of a tubeless tire contains the air, but some of it seeps through the body plies, and so the sidewalls of these tires are vented to allow this air to escape. As much as 5% of the inflation pressure of the tire is allowed to diffuse through these vents in a 24-hour period. Sometimes these vents, which are located near the wheel rim, become clogged and do not adequately relieve this air. When they are obstructed, the pressure can build up between the plies, causing ply separation which will ruin the tire.

Tire Maintenance

The most important preventive maintenance for aircraft tires is keeping them properly inflated and free of grease and oil. If the aircraft is to remain out of service for an extended period of time, take the weight off the tires if possible, and if not, move the aircraft enough to rotate the tires periodically to minimize nylon flat-spotting that develops in all nylon tires.

Inspection

When the tire is off the wheel, you can carefully evaluate it to determine if it can be retreaded, or if it must be scrapped.

Replace any tire that has been involved in an aborted takeoff or excessive braking, or has been exposed to enough heat to melt the center of a fusible plug in the wheel. Even if the damage may not be obvious, the heat has probably caused enough damage to make the tire unsafe for further flight.

Replace any tire that has been used in a dual installation where its mating tire has failed, even if there is no obvious damage. The extra load placed on the tire that did not fail can cause enough stresses to weaken it and make it susceptible to future failure.

Spread the beads apart to examine the inside of the tire. Use an even force to spread them to avoid kinking the bead bundles, as a kinked bead is cause for rejecting the tire. Examine the inside of the tire for any indication of

A Normally worn tread. Tire should be removed and retreaded.

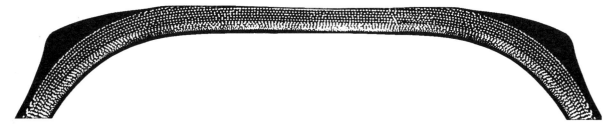

B Excessively worn tread. Worn down to the plies and too far gone for safe operation or retreading.

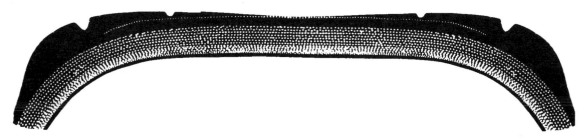

C Tire operated while overinflated. Center of tread worn more than on shoulders.

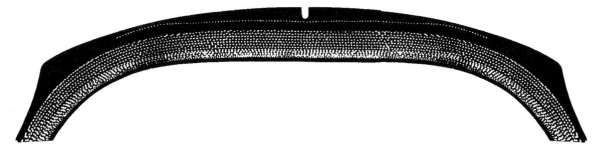

D Tire operated while underinflated. Shoulders of tread are worn more than in center.

Figure 6-54. *Tire tread wear patterns*

breakdown of the inner liner. Bulges or breaks in the inner liner may or may not be cause for rejection of the tire and should be evaluated by an approved facility which does aircraft tire retreading.

Inspect any bulges in the tread area that were marked when the tire was inflated. If the bulge indicates a separation of the plies, scrap the tire, but if it is a tread separation, you may be able to safely retread the tire.

Any cords that are exposed through cracks or other damage to the sidewall rubber are cause for rejecting the tire. These cords have probably been damaged, and the tire is weakened to the point that it cannot be safely retreaded.

Damage to the bead area is serious, and if the beads themselves have been damaged, scrap the tire. If the damage is restricted to the chafing strips, you can repair it when the tire is retreaded.

Retreading

retread. The replacement of the tread rubber on an aircraft tire.

Repairing aircraft tires is a special operation that requires a high degree of skill, experience, and equipment and should only be undertaken by an FAA-certificated repair station approved for this special work.

Advisory Circular 43.13-1A, *Acceptable Methods, Techniques, and Practices — Aircraft Inspection and Repair* lists a number of items that definitely render a tire unfit for retreading, and much time and expense can be saved by carefully inspecting the tire before sending it to a repair station for retreading. These damages render a tire irreparable:

- Breaks caused by flexing. Flexing damage is often the visible evidence of other damage that may not be visible.
- Any injury to the bead of a tubeless tire that would prevent the tire from sealing to the wheel
- Evidence of separation of the plies or around the bead wires
- Kinked or broken beads
- Weather cracks or radial cracks in the sidewall that extend into the cord body
- Evidence of blisters or heat damage
- Cracked, deteriorated, or damaged inner liner of tubeless tires

If there is no obvious damage that would prevent a tire from being retreaded, take it to a repair station for the work to be done.

When a tire is received, it is given a thorough inspection of its tread, sidewalls, and beads. The ply cords are checked for evidence of separation or fabric fatigue, and for any cords that have been damaged. If the tire passes this inspection, the old tread rubber is contour-buffed away to produce a smooth shoulder-to-shoulder surface. New tread rubber and reinforcement are applied to the buffed carcass, and the entire assembly is placed in a mold and is cured with heat. After the tire has cured and is removed from the mold, balance patches are bonded to the inside of the tire to give it the proper static balance. After this, the tire is given a final inspection and is approved for returned service.

A retreaded tire is identified by the letter "R" followed by a number showing the number of times it has been retreaded. The month and year the retread was applied and the name and location of the agency retreading the tire must also be marked on the tire.

The FAA does not specify the number of times a tire can be retreaded; this is determined by the condition of the carcass and by the policy of the user of the tire.

Storage

Aircraft tires and tubes are susceptible to damage from heat, sunlight, and ozone. They should be stored in an area that is not in the direct sunlight nor in the vicinity of fluorescent lights or such electric machinery as motors, generators, and battery chargers. All these devices convert oxygen into ozone, which is extremely harmful to rubber. The temperature in the storage area should be maintained between 32°F and 80°F (0°C and 27°C).

The storage area should be free from chemical fumes, and petroleum products such as oil, grease, and hydraulic fluid must not be allowed to come in contact with stored rubber products.

The tires should be stored vertically when possible in tire racks, with the tires supported on a flat surface which is at least three or four inches wide. If it is necessary to store them horizontally, do not stack them more than three to five tires high, depending on their size. When tubeless tires are stacked horizontally, the tires on the bottom of the stack may be distorted so much that a special bead-seating tool is needed to force the beads to seat on the wheel.

ozone. An unstable form of oxygen produced when an electric spark passes through the air. Ozone is harmful to rubber products.

Mounting

The wheels installed on most modern airplanes are of the two-piece, split type which makes tire mounting and demounting far easier than it is with a single-piece drop-center wheel. Wheels are highly stressed components and, like all critical maintenance, mounting tires requires that all of the aircraft manufacturer's instructions be followed in detail, especially those regarding lubrication, bolt torque, and balancing.

Tubeless Tires

Before mounting the tire on the wheel, carefully inspect the wheel for any indication of nicks, scratches, or other damage in the bead seat area and in the groove in which the O-ring seal between the halves is to fit. Examine the entire wheel for any indication of corrosion and be sure that all of the scratches and chips in the paint are touched up. Be sure that the wheel balance weights are properly and securely installed and check the condition of the fusible plugs. Carefully examine the O-ring seal for condition. There should be no nicks or breaks that could allow air to leak past. Clean the bead seat area of the wheel and the O-ring seating area with a cloth dampened with isopropyl alcohol, and place the inboard wheel half on a clean, flat surface where the wheel can be assembled.

Check the tire to assure that it is approved for the particular aircraft and that it is marked with the word TUBELESS on the sidewall. Check the inside of the tire for any foreign matter, and after checking the bead area, wipe it clean with a rag damp with isopropyl alcohol.

Lubricate the O-ring with the same kind of grease that is used on the wheel bearings. If the old O-ring is in good condition and is re-used, place it in as nearly the same position it was in when it was removed as is possible.

Carefully place the tire over the inboard wheel half with the red dot on the tire, which represents the light point of the tire, adjacent to the inflation valve, or adjacent to whatever mark is used to identify the heavy point of the wheel. Now the outboard wheel half can be slipped into the tire so that its bolt holes align with those in the inboard half.

Check with the service manual regarding the use of lubricant on the bolt threads. Some wheel manufacturers recommend that the threads, both sides of the washers, and the bearing side of the nuts be lightly lubricated with an antiseize compound. Install all the bolts, washers, and nuts and tighten all of the nuts in criss-cross fashion to one half of the recommended torque. Now, go back and torque all of the nuts to their final value, again tightening them in a criss-cross fashion across the wheel. It is important to use an accurately calibrated torque wrench. Impact wrenches are not recommended for use on aircraft wheels, because their torque is applied in a series of blows which applies more stress to the bolt than it is designed to take.

All large tires should be put into some type of safety cage for their initial inflation because of the danger of personal injury if the through bolts should fail. Regardless of the size tire, position the wheel in such a way that if the bolts should fail, none of the flying parts will hit any one. Use a clip-on air chuck and inflate the tire gradually, being sure that the bead seats firmly against the bead seat area of the wheel.

All nylon tires stretch, and the inflation pressure will decrease by between 5% and 10% within the first 12 to 24 hours the tire sits with no load applied. After the tire has stretched, adjust the air pressure, and the wheel is ready to install on the aircraft.

Tube-Type Tires

The preparation of the tire and the wheel for a tube-type tire are essentially the same as that for a tubeless tire. Wipe the inside of the tire to remove all traces of dirt or other foreign matter, and dust the inside with an approved tire talcum. Dust the deflated tube with talcum and insert it inside the tire with the valve sticking out on the side of the tire that has the serial number. Align the yellow mark on the tube, that identifies its heavy point, with the red dot on the tire that identifies its light point. If there is no yellow mark on the tube, the valve is considered to be the heavy point.

Inflate the tube just enough to round it out, but not enough to stretch the rubber, and install the tire and tube on the outboard wheel half with the valve centered in the hole in the wheel. Put the inboard wheel half in place, being careful that the tube is not pinched between the halves. Install the through bolts and torque them as was described for the tubeless tire installation.

Inflate the tire to its recommended pressure to seat the beads, and then deflate it completely. Finally, reinflate the tire to the recommended pressure.

This inflation, deflation, and reinflation sequence allows the tube to relax itself inside the tire and straighten out all of the wrinkles.

The inflation pressure of a tube-type tire will drop within the first 12- to 24-hour period after inflation because of the stretching of the tire and because any air that is trapped between the tube and the tire will escape and increase the volume of the tube slightly.

After installing a tube-type tire on the wheel, paint a slippage mark 1 inch wide and 2 inches long across the tire sidewall and wheel rim. This mark should be permanent and of a contrasting color such as white, red, or orange. If this mark is broken, it indicates that the tire has slipped on the wheel, and there is good reason to believe that the tube has been damaged.

slippage mark. A paint mark that extends across the edge of an aircraft wheel onto a tube-type tire. When this mark is broken, it indicates that the tire has slipped on the wheel, and there is good reason to believe that the tube has been damaged.

Balancing

Aircraft wheels are balanced when they are manufactured, and tires are marked with a red dot to identify their light point. The tire is assembled on the wheel with its light point opposite the valve or other mark identifying the heavy point of the wheel. This approximately balances the wheel and tire, but a balancing stand is needed to get the degree of balance that will prevent the wheel from vibrating.

Place the wheel on a balancing stand and identify its light point. Then mark two spots 45° from this light point and place balance weights on these points that will bring the wheel into balance.

Three types of weights are used on aircraft wheels; one type is installed on brackets held under the head of the wheel through bolts, another type mounts on steel straps and is held onto the wheel rim with cotter pins, and the other is in the form of a lead strip attached to the inside of the wheel rim with its adhesive backing. Be sure that only the type of weight that is approved for the wheel is used.

Aircraft Tubes

Aircraft tubes are made of a special compound of rubber, and when they are properly installed and maintained, they are virtually maintenance-free. There are only two reasons for the tube leaking air; one is a hole, and the other is a leaking valve.

The brakes of a modern airplane absorb a tremendous amount of kinetic energy converted into heat. This heat can damage aircraft tubes by causing the inner circumference of the tube to take a set, or develop square corners. Any tube that shows any indication of this type of deformation should be rejected.

Store tubes in their original boxes whenever possible, but if the box is not available, they should be dusted with tire talcum and wrapped in heavy paper. They may also be stored inflated by dusting the inside of the proper size tire and putting them in the tire and inflating them just enough to round them out. Store the tube and tire in a cool dry area away from any electrical equipment or chemical fumes.

A Summary of Aircraft Tires

Aircraft tires are designed to absorb a tremendous amount of energy on landing, but they are not designed to tolerate the heat that is generated by taxiing long distances. Aircraft tires flex much more than automobile tires and thus generate much more heat. This heat is increased if the tire is allowed to operate with inflation pressure lower than is recommended.

Improper piloting technique can shorten the life of a tire. If the pilot makes taxiing turns by locking one brake and pivoting the airplane about one wheel, the tread can be twisted so severely that it may separate from the carcass.

Hard landings can burst a tire or wrinkle the sidewall enough that the tire will have to be scrapped. After any exceptionally hard landing, the tires should be removed and carefully examined for broken cords, liners, or cuts in the tread. The wheels should also be inspected for indications of damage.

Proper inflation is one of the best ways of extending the life of a tire. Be sure to use an accurate pressure gage and check the pressure regularly. Compensate for temperature changes. Remember that the pressure inside a tire changes by approximately 1% for every 5°F temperature change.

If a tire is inflated when it is off the aircraft, allow for the change in pressure when the weight of the aircraft is on the wheels. The pressure will increase approximately 4% when the weight is placed on the wheels.

When tires are installed in a dual installation, they should be of the same size, manufacture, and tread pattern. If there is a difference of more than 5 psi between the pressure of the two tires it should be noted in the aircraft maintenance record, and this pressure difference should be checked daily to determine if it is changing. If the pressure varies on successive pressure checks, the cause should be determined.

Any time a retreaded tire is installed on an airplane having a retractable landing gear, a retraction check should be performed to be sure that the tire does not bind in the wheel well.

STUDY QUESTIONS: AIRCRAFT TIRES AND TUBES

Answers begin on Page 488. Page numbers refer to chapter text.

62. An aircraft tire is designed to flex, or deflect, _____ (more or less) than an automobile or truck tire. *Page 473*

63. The body of an aircraft tire is called the _____ . *Page 474*

64. A four-ply rating tire _____ (does or does not) necessarily have four plies of fabric. *Page 475*

65. The bundles of high-strength steel wires that are molded into a tire are called the _____ . *Page 474*

66. The threads in the plies of a tire cross the threads in adjacent plies at an angle of approximately _____ degrees. *Page 474*

67. The inner liner of a tubeless tire is _____ (smoother or rougher) than that used in a tube-type tire. *Page 476*

68. The tread design used on most modern aircraft tires is the _____ tread. *Page 475*

69. Nose wheel tires used on jet airplanes with engines mounted on the aft fuselage have a _____ or _____ molded into their outer sidewall. *Page 476*

70. Small holes in the sidewall of a tubeless tire are called _____ holes. *Page 476*

71. The correct tire inflation pressure to use is that which is recommended in the _____ (aircraft or tire) manufacturer's service manual. *Page 476*

72. The tire inflation pressure specified by the aircraft manufacturer is the pressure in the tire when the tire _____ (is or is not) supporting the weight of the aircraft. *Page 476*

73. The inflation pressure of a tire should not be measured until the tire has been able to cool down for _____ to _____ hours after flight. *Page 477*

Continued

74. The most accurate type of pressure gage to use for measuring tire inflation pressure is a _____ -type gage. *Page 477*

75. The air pressure inside a tire changes with the temperature. The pressure will increase approximately 1% for each _____ °F rise in temperature. *Page 477*

76. Inflation pressure will increase by approximately _____ -% when the weight of the aircraft is on the tire. *Page 477*

77. The inflation pressure of newly mounted nylon tires will decrease within the first day or so in service. This decrease is caused by the tire _____ . *Page 477*

78. Tires should be removed for retreading when the tread groove wears to a depth of _____ inch at the shallowest point. *Page 477*

79. A tire with the tread worn more in the middle than on the shoulders has been operated _____ (underinflated or overinflated). *Page 477*

80. A tire with the tread worn more on the shoulders than in the middle has been operated _____ (underinflated or overinflated). *Page 477*

81. Some air is allowed to seep through the inner lining of a tubeless tire and escape through vents in the sidewall rubber. As much as _____ % of the inflation pressure is allowed to seep out in a 24-hour period. *Page 478*

82. A burned area on a tire tread that indicates the tire has been hydroplaning _____ (is or is not) cause for removing the tire. *Page 478*

83. A tire should be removed from service if a cut extends across more than _____ of the width of a tread rib. *Page 478*

84. A shop tool that may be used to break a tire bead away from the wheel is a/an _____ . *Page 470*

85. A tire that has been involved in an aborted takeoff _____ (is or is not) safe for continued use. *Page 478*

86. A tire in a dual installation whose mate has failed should be _____ . *Page 478*

87. A kinked bead in a tire _____ (is or is not) a cause for rejecting the tire. *Page 480*

88. Exposed ply cords in the sidewall of an aircraft tire _____ (is or is not) cause for rejection of the tire. *Page 480*

89. The FAA _____ (does or does not) specify the number of times an aircraft tire can be retreaded. *Page 481*

90. Aircraft tires should be stored _____ (horizontally or vertically) whenever possible. *Page 481*

91. The red dot on an aircraft tire identifies the _____ (light or heavy) point of the tire. *Page 483*

92. The yellow mark on an aircraft tube identifies the _____ (light or heavy) point of the tube. *Page 483*

93. The valve of an aircraft tube should stick out on the side of the tire that _____ (does or does not) have the serial number. *Page 483*

94. The only lubricant approved for use between a tube and a tire is _____ . *Page 483*

95. When a retreaded tire is installed on an airplane with a retractable landing gear, a _____ test should be performed on the airplane. *Page 485*

Answers to Aircraft Landing Gear Systems Study Questions

1. does not
2. oil
3. metering pin
4. air
5. spring
6. flapper
7. a. aircraft maintenance manual
   b. placard attached to shock strut
8. nitrogen
9. extension
10. in
11. positive
12. landing gear strut, axle
13. torque link arms
14. shimmy dampers
15. brakes
16. centering cam
17. a. mechanical
    b. electric motors
    c. hydraulic actuators
    d. pneumatic actuators
18. power pack
19. sequence
20. up line, down line
21. air, nitrogen
22. shuttle
23. energizing
24. nonenergizing
25. expander tube
26. expansion
27. is not
28. released
29. less

30. piston
31. lining
32. warp
33. stator
34. pressure plate, backing plate
35. lighter
36. compensating
37. drag
38. boosted
39. regulator
40. slip, skid
41. hydroplaning
42. a. wheel-speed sensors
    b. control boxes
    c. antiskid control valves
43. is not
44. modulator
45. DC generator
46. increases
47. fuse
48. nitrogen
49. warped, glazed
50. replaced
51. overheat
52. hardness
53. a. gravity
    b. pressure
54. gravity
55. two-piece
56. fusible plugs
57. bead seat area
58. compressive
59. varsol, naphtha
60. is not
61. eddy current

62. more
63. carcass
64. does not
65. beads
66. 90
67. rougher
68. rib
69. deflector, chine
70. vent
71. aircraft
72. is
73. 2, 3
74. dial
75. 5
76. 4
77. stretching
78. $\frac{1}{32}$
79. overinflated
80. underinflated
81. 5
82. is
83. $\frac{1}{2}$
84. arbor press
85. is not
86. replaced
87. is
88. is
89. does not
90. vertically
91. light
92. heavy
93. does
94. tire talcum
95. retraction

AIRCRAFT ELECTRICAL SYSTEMS

7

Continued

AIRCRAFT ELECTRICAL SYSTEMS

7

An Introduction to Aircraft Electrical Systems

An aviation maintenance technician must have a solid foundation in basic electrical principles and a good working knowledge of the way these principles apply to complex systems. Electrical systems provide the muscle for retracting landing gears and starting engines and serve as the brains for electronic flight control and monitoring systems.

Basic electrical principles are covered in the *General* textbook of the *Aviation Maintenance Technician Series (AMTS)*. In the *General* text, electricity is discussed from a theoretical point of view, with emphasis on its laws. Circuit analysis considers the variables in both AC and DC circuits.

The *Airframe* textbook of the *AMTS* takes up where the *General* text leaves off, including a brief review of electrical terms and facts, followed by the practical application of basic electrical principles to aircraft electrical systems.

The *Powerplant* textbook of the *AMTS* covers practical aspects of the generation of electricity and some of the heavy-duty applications, such as engine starting systems.

Aircraft electrical systems covered here range from the simplest component schematics to logic flow charts used for systematic troubleshooting. The intent of this section is to present aircraft electrical systems in their most practical form.

No specific electrical schematics are used in this text, but the systems used have been adapted from actual aircraft. The procedures discussed are general in their nature, and this text must be considered as a reference document, not a service manual. Information issued by the aircraft manufacturer takes precedence over any procedure mentioned in this text.

One of the fundamental rules of aviation maintenance is that you must use the latest information furnished by the aircraft manufacturer when servicing any part of an aircraft. This is particularly true of electrical systems, as these systems and their components are far too expensive to risk damage as the result of improper servicing procedures.

To begin this study, we will examine the requirements for an aircraft electrical system and then review some terms and facts.

Electrical System Requirements

Federal Aviation Regulations Part 23—*Airworthiness Standards: Normal, Utility, Acrobatic, and Commuter Category Airplanes*—delineates the requirements for electrical systems in civilian nontransport category aircraft.

Basic requirements for these systems include the following:

- Each electrical system must be able to furnish the required power at the proper voltage to each load circuit essential for safe operation.
- Each electrical system must be free from hazards in itself, in its method of operation, and in its effects on other parts of the aircraft. It must be protected from damage and be so designed that it produces minimal possibility for electrical shock to crewmembers, passengers, or persons on the ground.
- Electrical power sources must function properly when connected in combination or independently, and no failure or malfunction of any electrical power source may impair the ability of the remaining source to supply load circuits essential to safe operation.
- Each system must be designed so that essential load circuits can be supplied in the event of reasonably probable faults or open circuits.
- There must be at least one generator if the electrical system supplies power to load circuits essential for safe operation. There must also be a means of giving immediate warning to the flight crew of a failure of the generator.
- There must be a master switch installed in the electrical system that allows the electrical power source to be disconnected from the main bus. The point of disconnection must be adjacent to the source controlled by the switch.

Review of Terms

Though by now you have a working knowledge of basic electricity, a brief review of some of the terms most commonly used in aircraft electrical systems should prove useful.

bus—A point in an aircraft electrical system supplied with power from the battery or the alternator and from which the various circuits get their power.

conductor—Any wire or other device through which current can flow.

current—The assumed flow of electricity that is considered to move through an electrical circuit from the positive side of a battery to its negative side. This is opposite to the flow, or movement, of electrons. Current is measured in amperes (amps) and its symbol is the letter I. Current follows the arrowheads in the diode and transistor symbols.

When current flows through a conductor, three things happen: heat is produced in the conductor, a magnetic field surrounds the conductor, and voltage is dropped across the conductor.

diode—A solid-state device that acts as an electron check valve. Electrons can flow through a diode in one direction, but cannot flow through it in the opposite direction.

electrons—Invisible negative electrical charges that actually move in an electrical circuit.

resistance—Opposition to the flow of current. The unit of resistance is the ohm, and its symbol is R.

voltage—Electrical pressure. The unit of voltage is the volt, and its symbol is either V (used in this text) or E (electromotive force).

voltage drop—The decrease in electrical pressure that occurs when current flows through a resistance.

Direction of Current Flow

One of the things that adds confusion to the study of electricity is the way electricity flows in a circuit.

Before much was known about electricity, its flow was compared to the flow of water in a river and was therefore called "current." As water currents flow from high to low, electrical current was considered to flow from positive (+) to negative (–). This was a reasonable conclusion, but was later determined to be wrong. Negatively charged electrons actually flow from negative to positive. This discovery was made only after countless textbooks about electricity had been written and symbols had been decided upon. Because of this, electrons in a circuit actually flow in the *opposite* direction to the way the arrowheads in the diode symbols point. This can be quite confusing.

In the *General* textbook, the term "electron flow" or "electrical current" was used to explain the basic principles of electricity. This *Airframe* textbook (and many other modern texts on practical electricity) uses "conventional current," or simply "current." This is an assumed flow rather than an actual flow, and it travels from positive to negative, which allows us to visualize the flow in the direction of the arrowheads in the diode and transistor symbols. Considering the flow in this direction makes aircraft electrical systems much easier to understand. *See* Figure 7-1.

Electrical System Components

The most important tool for understanding an aircraft electrical system is the schematic diagram. This road map of the electrical system uses standardized symbols to represent the various components, arranged in a logical sequence with regard to the circuit operation. However, their placement in the schematic tells nothing about their physical location in the aircraft.

This text uses standard symbols to show the way aircraft electrical circuits are built. Chapter 7's Appendix A, beginning on Page 576, show the most common symbols used in schematic diagrams of aircraft electrical systems.

electron current. The actual flow of electrons in a circuit. Electrons flow from the negative terminal of a power source through the external circuit to its positive terminal. The arrowheads in semiconductor symbols point in the direction opposite to the flow of electron current.

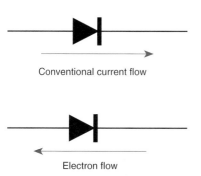

Figure 7-1. *Conventional current flows in the direction of the arrowheads of semiconductor diodes. Electron flow is in the opposite direction.*

conventional current. An imaginary flow of electricity that is said to flow from the positive terminal of a power source, through the external circuit to its negative terminal. The arrowheads in semiconductor symbols point in the direction of conventional current flow.

schematic diagram. A diagram of an electrical system in which the system components are represented by symbols rather than drawings or pictures of the actual devices.

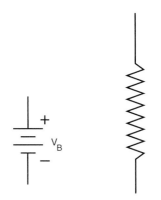

Figure 7-2. *Battery, or voltage source*   **Figure 7-3.** *Resistor, or an electrical load*

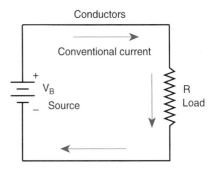

Figure 7-4. *A complete electrical circuit*

current. A general term used in this text for conventional current. *See* conventional current.

conductor. A material that allows electrons to move freely from one atom to another within the material.

electromotive force (EMF). The force that causes electrons to move from one atom to another within an electrical circuit. Electromotive force is an electrical pressure, and it is measured in volts.

DC Power Source

Figure 7-2 is the symbol for a battery. Conventional current leaves the positive (+) end and flows through the circuit to the negative (–) end. The long line is always the positive end of the battery.

Electrical Load

Figure 7-3 is the symbol for a resistor, or an electrical load. It may be an actual component, or it may be part of some other device. The filament in a light bulb and the heater element in a soldering iron are both resistances.

When current flows through a circuit, three things happen:
• A magnetic field surrounds the conductors that carry the current.
• Some of the energy used to push the current through the load is changed into heat, light, or mechanical energy.
• Some of the voltage is dropped across the load.

All conductors have some resistance, but in this study, the resistance of the system conductors is disregarded.

Basic Electrical Circuit

Figure 7-4 shows a complete electrical circuit. The battery (V_B) supplies an electrical pressure (voltage) that forces current through the resistor (R). The arrows in the diagram show the direction of conventional current.

Note: In the symbols used in electricity, voltage is normally represented by the letter E, for electromotive force, but modern practice is to use the symbol V for voltage. As stated earlier, this text uses V, so don't be disturbed when you see E used for voltage in other books. The subscript B denotes battery voltage.

The current furnished by the battery follows the arrows. The resistor gets hot, and all of the voltage, or electrical pressure, from the battery is used up (dropped) across the resistor.

All electrical circuits must have three things:

• A source of electrical energy—the battery
• A load to change the electrical energy into mechanical energy, heat, or light—the resistor
• Conductors, or wires, that join the source and the load

In addition to these components, switches and fuses may be added for current control and circuit protection.

Circuit Control Devices

Circuit control devices are those components which start or stop the flow of current, direct it to various parts of the circuit, or increase or decrease the amount of its flow. These components may be mechanical, or—more frequently the case—semiconductor devices.

Switches

Figure 7-5 shows the symbols for some of the more common switches used in aircraft electrical systems. When a switch is open, current cannot flow in the circuit, but when it is closed, current can flow.

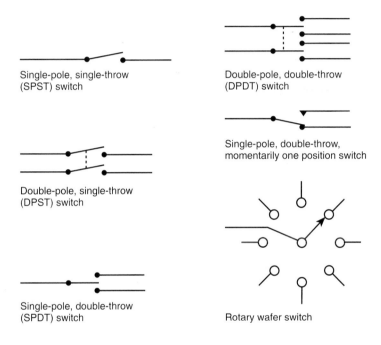

Figure 7-5. *Switch symbols*

In Figures 7-6 and 7-7, the symbol for a light bulb has replaced the resistor as the electrical load. Rays coming from the bulb show that current is flowing. When there are no rays, current is not flowing.

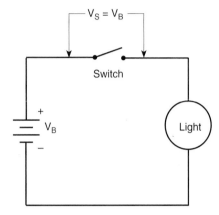

Figure 7-6. *This is an open circuit. No current is flowing and the light is off. All of the battery voltage is dropped across the open switch.*

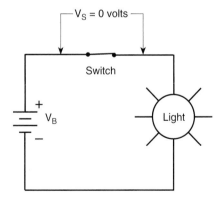

Figure 7-7. *This is a closed circuit. The circuit is complete, current is flowing, and the light is lit. No voltage is dropped across the closed switch. All of the voltage is dropped across the light.*

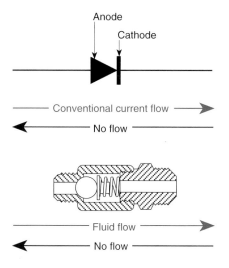

Figure 7-8. *A semiconductor diode controls current flow in an electrical circuit in the same way a check valve controls fluid flow in a hydraulic system. It allows flow in one direction but prevents its flow in the opposite direction. Conventional current flows through a diode in the direction shown by the arrowhead.*

Semiconductor Diodes

A semiconductor diode is an electron check valve that allows electrons to flow through it in one direction but blocks their flow in the opposite direction. Conventional current follows the direction of the arrowheads in the symbol. *See* Figure 7-8.

When a diode is installed in a circuit in such a way that its anode is more positive than its cathode, it is forward-biased and current can flow through it. A diode causes a voltage drop across it as current flows through it, but, unlike with a resistor, this voltage drop does not change with the amount of current. A silicon diode has a relatively constant voltage drop of approximately 0.7 volt across it when current flows through it. The voltage drop across a germanium diode is about 0.3 volt.

When a diode is installed in a circuit in such a way that its anode is more negative than its cathode, it is reverse-biased and current flow is blocked. No current can flow through it until the voltage across it reaches a value, called the "peak inverse voltage." At this voltage, the diode breaks down and conducts current in its reverse direction. When this happens, an ordinary diode is normally destroyed.

Zener Diodes

Though an ordinary diode can be destroyed when current flows through it in its reverse direction, a zener diode is designed to have a specific breakdown voltage and to operate with current flowing through it in its reverse direction.

A reverse-biased zener diode is used as the voltage sensing component in an electronic voltage regulator used with a DC alternator. In Figure 7-12, the zener diode holds a load voltage constant as the input voltage changes. A 5-volt zener diode is installed in a 12-volt DC circuit in series with a resistor so that its cathode is more positive than its anode.

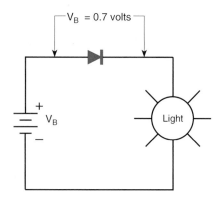

Figure 7-9. *A forward-biased diode acts as a closed switch, and current flows through it. There is a constant voltage drop of approximately 0.7 volt across a silicon diode.*

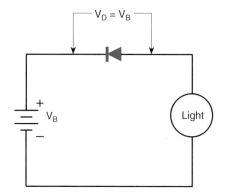

Figure 7-10. *A reverse-biased diode acts as an open switch. No current flows through it, and all of the battery voltage is dropped across the diode.*

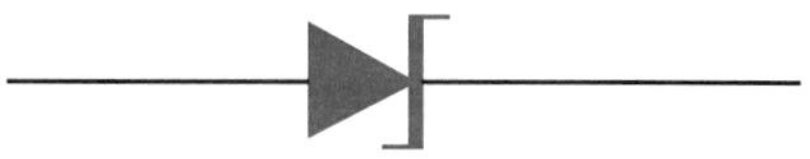

Figure 7-11. *A zener diode*

As soon as the voltage across the zener diode rises to 5 volts, it breaks down and conducts current to ground. Seven volts are dropped across the resistor, and the voltage across the zener diode and the electrical load remains constant at 5 volts. If the source voltage drops to 11 volts, the voltage drop across the zener diode remains at 5 volts and the resistor now drops 6 volts. If the input voltage rises to 13 volts, the voltage across the zener still remains at 5 volts, but the voltage across the resistor rises to 8 volts.

A zener diode must always have a resistor in series with it to limit the current allowed to flow through it when it is conducting in its reverse direction, since its resistance drops to an extremely low value when it breaks down.

Relays and Solenoids

A relay is a magnetically operated switch that is able to carry a large amount of current through its contacts. It takes only a small amount of current flowing through the coil to produce the magnetic pull needed to close the contacts.

Any time current flows in a wire, a magnetic field surrounds the wire. If the wire is formed into a coil of many turns wound around a core of soft iron, the magnetic field is concentrated enough that just a small amount of current produces a pull strong enough to close the contacts of the relay. As soon as the current stops flowing through the coil, a spring snaps the contacts open. *See* Figure 7-13.

A solenoid is similar to a relay, except that its core is movable. Solenoid switches, also called contactors, are used in circuits that carry large amounts of current. The main battery contactor and the starter solenoid are both solenoid switches. A heavy cable carries the current from the battery through the starter solenoid contacts to the starter motor, but only a small wire is needed between the solenoid coil and the starter switch in the cockpit to cause the solenoid contacts to close.

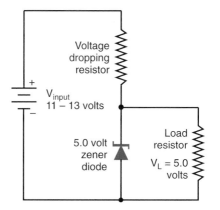

Figure 7-12. *A zener diode is used as a voltage-sensing unit.*

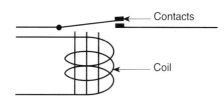

Figure 7-13. *An electromagnetic relay is a remotely operated switch that has a fixed core.*

semiconductor diode. A two-element electrical component that allows current to pass through it in one direction, but blocks its passage in the opposite direction. A diode acts in an electrical system in the same way a check valve acts in a hydraulic system.

reverse bias. A voltage placed across the PN junction in a semiconductor device with the positive voltage connected to the N-type material and the negative voltage to the P-type material

forward bias. A condition of operation of a semiconductor device such as a diode or transistor in which a positive voltage is connected to the P-type material and a negative voltage to the N-type material.

zener diode. A special type of solid-state diode designed to have a specific break-down voltage and to operate with current flowing through it in its reverse direction.

relay. An electrical component which uses a small amount of current flowing through a coil to produce a magnetic pull to close a set of contacts through which a large amount of current can flow. The core in a relay coil is fixed.

solenoid. An electrical component using a small amount of current flowing through a coil to produce a magnetic force that pulls an iron core into the center of the coil. The core may be attached to a set of heavy-duty electrical contacts, or it may be used to move a valve or other mechanical device.

Solenoid-operated valves are used in hydraulic and fuel systems. They can be opened or closed by a small switch located at some distance from the fluid lines themselves.

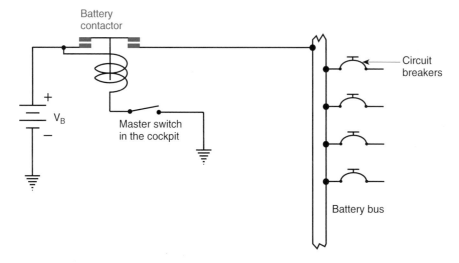

Figure 7-14. *A battery contactor is a remotely operated switch with a movable core. It connects the battery to the battery bus and is controlled by a very small flow of current through the master switch and the contactor coil.*

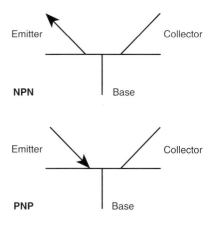

Figure 7-15. *Bipolar transistors*

Bipolar Transistors

One of the most important developments in the field of electricity and electronics is the transistor. Transistors take the place of vacuum tubes and electromechanical relays. They do the same job, but do it better, use much less power, are more rugged, have a longer life, and are far less expensive.

There are two types of bipolar transistors, NPN and PNP, which differ in their construction the way they are installed in electrical circuits. Figure 7-15 shows the symbols for these two types of transistors.

Transistors can be connected into a circuit so that they act much like a relay. Figure 7-16 shows a typical relay circuit, and the way an NPN transistor connected in a similar circuit performs the same functions as a relay.

The emitter of the NPN transistor in Figure 7-16 is connected to the negative terminal of the battery through the load, and the collector is connected to the positive terminal. When switch S_1 is closed, the base is connected to a voltage that is more positive than the emitter. A very small current flows into the base, and this causes a large current to flow through the collector and emitter and the load. When switch S_1 is open and no current is flowing through the base, there is no collector-emitter current to flow through the load.

It is easy to remember how a transistor acts as a switch: When the base and collector have the same polarity, the switch is ON; when there is no voltage on the base, or when its polarity is the same as that of the emitter, the switch is OFF.

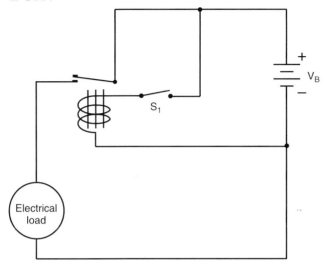

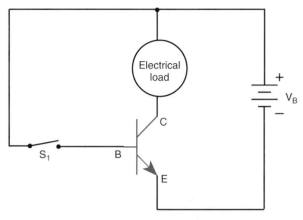

Very small amount of current flowing through base of a transistor controls a much larger flow of current through the load.

Small amount of current flowing through coil of a relay controls a much larger flow of current through the load.

Figure 7-16. *A transistor acts much like an electrical relay.*

A PNP transistor can be connected into the same kind of circuit as just seen, but the battery must be reversed so that the emitter is positive and the collector is negative. When the switch is closed, a small amount of current flows through the base, and a much larger current flows between the emitter and the collector. When the switch is opened, no base current flows, and no load current flows.

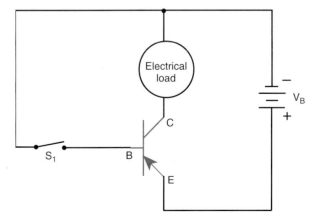

Figure 7-17. *A PNP transistor can work in the same way as the NPN transistor in Figure 7-16 if the battery polarity is reversed.*

bipolar transistor. A solid-state component in which the flow of current between its emitter and collector is controlled by a much smaller flow of current into or out of its base. Bipolar transistors may be of either the NPN or PNP type.

NPN transistor. A bipolar transistor made of a thin base of P-type silicon or germanium sandwiched between a collector and an emitter, both of which are made of N-type material.

PNP transistor. A bipolar transistor made of a thin base of N-type silicon or germanium sandwiched between a collector and an emitter, both of which are made of P-type material.

base. The electrode of a bipolar transistor between the emitter and the collector. Controlling a small flow of electrons moving into or out of the base controls a much larger flow of electrons between the emitter and the collector.

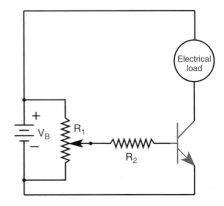

Figure 7-18. *A transistor varies the load current when its base current is varied. The greater the base-emitter current, the greater the collector-emitter, or load, current.*

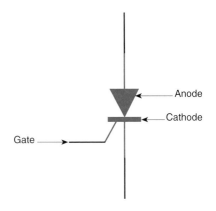

Figure 7-19. *A silicon controlled rectifier*

potentiometer. A variable resistor having connections to both ends of the resistance element and to the wiper that moves across the resistance.

amplifier. An electronic circuit in which a small change in voltage or current controls a much larger change in voltage or current.

silicon controlled rectifier (SCR). A semiconductor electron control device. An SCR blocks current flow in both directions until a pulse of positive voltage is applied to its gate. It then conducts in its forward direction, while continuing to block current in its reverse direction.

A transistor can be used not only as a switch, but also as a variable resistor. The switch circuit in Figure 7-16 can be replaced with a potentiometer across the voltage source, with the wiper connected to the base of the transistor, as shown in Figure 7-18.

This is an NPN transistor, and its base must be positive, the same as the collector, for it to conduct. When the wiper is at the bottom of the resistance element, the base of the transistor is negative, the same as the emitter. No current flows into the base, and no load current flows between the collector and the emitter.

When the wiper is moved to the top of the resistance, the base becomes positive, and the transistor conducts the maximum amount of load current. The amount of load current can be controlled by moving the wiper across the resistance. This kind of circuit is called an amplifier, because a very small change in base current can control a much larger change in load current.

Silicon Controlled Rectifier

A silicon controlled rectifier, or SCR, is a solid-state device that acts much like a diode that can be turned on with a short pulse of current.

The SCR has an anode, a cathode, and a gate. Current cannot flow through the SCR from the cathode to the anode or from the anode to the cathode until a pulse of positive current is sent into it through its gate. A positive pulse applied to the gate causes the SCR to conduct between its anode and its cathode. *See* Figure 7-19.

A holding coil, such as the one in Figure 7-20, requires only a pulse of current to close it. It remains closed until the main power circuit is momentarily opened.

When switch S_2 is closed, current flows through the relay coil to ground. This closes the contacts. As soon as the contacts are closed, current flows from the relay contact through the coil, and switch S_2 may be opened. The relay contacts remain closed with current flowing through the load until switch S_1 is momentarily opened. This breaks the ground to the relay coil and the relay contacts open, stopping all current through the load. *See* Figure 7-20.

An SCR does the same thing as a holding relay. Switch S_1 is normally closed, and voltage source V_B biases the SCR properly for it to conduct, but the SCR blocks all current until it is triggered by a momentary closing of switch S_2 in the gate circuit. When S_2 is closed, current flows through the gate resistor R_G into the gate of the SCR. Only a very small amount of current is needed to trigger the SCR into conducting. When the SCR conducts, current flows from the battery, through the SCR and the load, and back into the battery. Switch S_2 can be opened as soon as the SCR begins to conduct, and load current will continue to flow until switch S_1 is opened to stop it. Once the current is interrupted, no more can flow until S_2 is again closed.

An SCR can also act as a switch in an AC circuit. Figure 7-21 shows a simple circuit that allows a large amount of current to flow through the

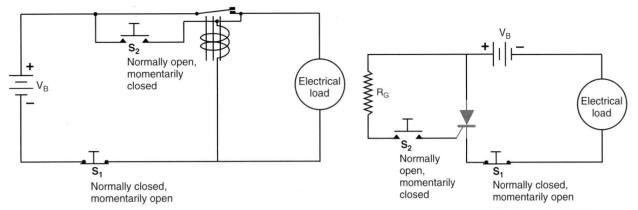

Contacts of a holding relay are closed by momentarily closing switch S_2. Current flows through load until switch S_1 is momentarily opened.

When switch S_2 is momentarily closed, the SCR is caused to conduct, and current flows through load until switch S_1 is momentarily opened.

Figure 7-20. *A silicon controlled rectifier acts as a holding relay.*

electrical load. This large load current can be controlled by a very small control current, which can be carried through a small wire and controlled with a small switch.

The waveform of the input AC in the circuit shows that it rises from zero to a peak value in the positive direction, and then it changes direction and goes through zero to a peak value in the negative direction. Since an SCR blocks current flow in both directions before it is triggered, no current flows through the SCR as long as switch S_1 is open.

When switch S_1 is closed, diode D_1 allows current to flow to the gate during the half of the AC cycle when the current is positive. This small pulse of positive current triggers the SCR into conducting, and load current flows during the entire positive half of the cycle. The SCR stops conducting as soon as the AC drops to zero. No current flows during the negative half-cycle, but it starts to conduct again at the beginning of the positive half-cycle.

holding relay. An electrical relay that is closed by sending a pulse of current through the coil. It remains closed until the current flowing through its contacts is interrupted.

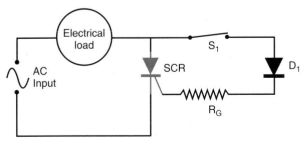

Small amount of current flows through switch S_1 and is rectified by diode D_1 to provide positive pulse on gate of SCR to trigger it into conduction.

Figure 7-21. *An SCR installed in an AC circuit acts as a high-current switch.*

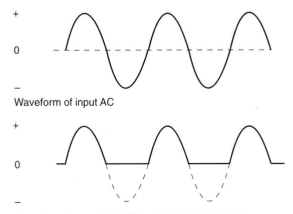

Waveform of input AC

Waveform of pulsating DC flowing through the load

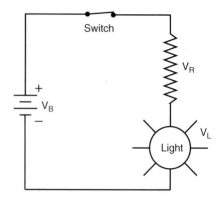

Figure 7-22. *In this closed series circuit, the sum of the voltage drops across the resistor and the light equals the voltage of the battery.*

series circuit. A method of connecting electrical components in such a way that all of the current flows through each of the components. There is only one path for current to flow.

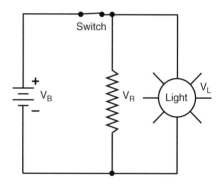

Figure 7-23. *In this closed parallel circuit, current from the battery divides, some flowing through the resistor and the rest flowing through the light.*

parallel circuit. A method of connecting electrical components so that each component forms a complete path from one terminal of the source of electrical energy to the other terminal.

Circuit Arrangement

There are three types of electrical circuits used in an aircraft and each has its own unique characteristics. A series circuit is one in which there is only one path for the current to flow in from one side of the battery to the other. A parallel circuit has several complete paths between the battery terminals. A complex circuit has some components in series and others in parallel.

Series Circuits

Figure 7-22 shows a series circuit. All of the components are connected in series, so all of the current must flow through each one of them. Voltage drops across each component until the sum of all of the voltage drops equals the voltage of the battery.

There is virtually no voltage drop across the closed switch S. The resistor changes some of the electrical energy from the battery into heat, and it drops some of the voltage. This voltage drop is called V_R.

The light changes energy from the battery into light and heat, and it drops voltage. This voltage drop is called V_L.

In a series circuit, the sum of all of the voltage drops is equal to the voltage of the battery.

$$V_R + V_L = V_B$$

Current is represented in an electrical formula with the letter I. In a series circuit, the current is the same everywhere in the circuit.

$$I_B = I_R = I_L$$

Parallel Circuits

In the parallel circuit in Figure 7-23, there are two complete paths for current to flow between terminals of the battery. When the current leaves the battery, it divides so that some flows through the resistor and some through the light. The voltage across the resistor (V_R) and the voltage across the light (V_L), are both the same as the voltage of the battery (V_B).

$$V_R = V_L = V_B$$

The current in a parallel circuit flowing through the battery (I_B) is equal to the sum of the currents flowing through the resistor (I_R) and the light (I_L).

$$I_B = I_R + I_L$$

Complex Circuits

Many circuits in an aircraft electrical system are complex rather than simple series or parallel circuits. These circuits have some components in series and some in parallel. In Figure 7-24, the switch and resistor R_1 are in series with the parallel circuit consisting of the light and resistor R_2.

To better understand the voltage, current, and resistance relationships that exist in a complex circuit, review the section on series-parallel circuits in the *General* textbook of the *AMTS*.

series-parallel circuit. An electrical circuit in which some of the components are connected in parallel and others are connected in series.

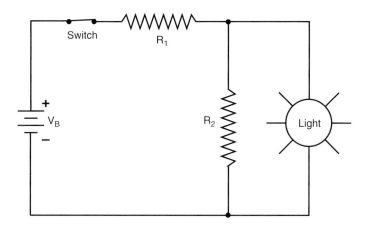

Figure 7-24. *In this complex circuit, the battery, switch, and resistor R₁ are in series with the parallel arrangement of resistor R₂ and the light.*

STUDY QUESTIONS: AN INTRODUCTION TO AIRCRAFT ELECTRICAL SYSTEMS

Answers begin on Page 580. Page numbers refer to chapter text.

1. The letter symbol used to represent electrical current is _____ . *Page 494*

2. The letter symbol used to represent electrical pressure is _____ or _____ . *Page 495*

3. The letter symbol used to represent electrical resistance is _____ . *Page 495*

4. The point in an aircraft electrical system from which the various circuits get their power is called a/an _____ . *Page 494*

5. Three things that happen in an electrical circuit when current flows through it are:
   a. _____
   b. _____
   c. _____
   Page 494

6. The longer line in the symbol for a battery indicates the _____ (positive or negative) terminal. *Page 496*

Continued

7. Electrons flowing in an electrical circuit flow in the _____ (same or opposite) direction as the arrowheads in a semiconductor diode symbol. *Page 495*

8. Conventional current in an electrical circuit is assumed to flow in the _____ (same or opposite) direction as the arrowheads in a semiconductor diode symbol. *Page 495*

9. Three things that must be included in all complete electrical circuits are:
   a. _____
   b. _____
   c. _____
   Page 496

10. If the bar in the symbol for a semiconductor diode is connected to the negative terminal of a battery, the diode is _____ (forward or reverse) biased. *Page 498*

11. A forward-biased diode act as a/an _____ (open or closed) switch. *Page 498*

12. The voltage drop across a forward-biased silicon diode is approximately _____ volt. *Page 498*

13. The voltage drop across a forward-biased silicon diode _____ (does or does not) vary with the current flowing through it. *Page 498*

14. A semiconductor device that can be used as a voltage sensor is a/an _____ . *Page 498*

15. A zener diode used as a voltage regulator is _____ (forward or reverse) biased. *Page 498*

16. An electrical relay has a _____ (fixed or movable) core. *Page 499*

17. A solenoid has a _____ (fixed or movable) core. *Page 499*

18. When the base of an NPN transistor has the same polarity as the collector, the transistor acts as a/an _____ (open or closed) switch. *Page 501*

19. When a transistor is connected in an amplifier circuit, bringing its base polarity closer to that of the collector _____ (increases or decreases) the collector-emitter current. *Page 502*

20. A semiconductor device that acts in the same way as a holding relay is a _____ . *Page 502*

21. In a complete series circuit, the sum of the voltage drops is the same as the applied voltage. This sentence is _____ (true or false). *Page 504*

22. The voltage drop across an open switch in a series circuit is _____ (zero volts or battery voltage). *Page 497*

23. The voltage drop across a closed switch in a series circuit is _____ (zero volts or battery voltage). *Page 497*

24. The amount of current that flows through each path of a parallel circuit is determined by the _____ of the path. *Page 504*

25. The voltage across each path of a parallel circuit is equal to the _____ voltage. *Page 504*

Aircraft Electrical Power Circuits

Aircraft electrical systems are divided into two main classifications of circuits: power circuits and load circuits. Power circuits consist of the battery circuits, ground-power circuits, generator and alternator circuits, and distribution circuits up to the power buses.

Battery Circuits

All aircraft electrical circuits must have a complete path from one side of the battery through the load to the other side of the battery. Airplanes use a single-wire electrical system. In this type of system, one side of the battery, almost always the negative side, is connected to the structure of the aircraft with a heavy cable. All of the components are connected to the positive side of the battery through the proper circuit breakers and switches, and the circuit is completed by connecting the negative connection of the component to the metal of the aircraft structure.

In electrical schematics, the symbol that shows several parallel lines forming an inverted pyramid like that in Figure 7-25, is used to show that this point is connected to the aircraft structure. In American English, this is called ground; the British call it earth. It is the reference from which all voltage measurements in the aircraft are made.

Figure 7-25. *The ground symbol indicates that the electrical component is connected to the metal structure of the aircraft so it will form a return path for the current to the battery. Ground is considered to have zero electrical potential, and voltage measurements, both positive and negative, are referenced from it.*

ground. The voltage reference point in an aircraft electrical system. Ground has zero electrical potential. Voltage values, both positive and negative, are measured from ground. In the United Kingdom, ground is spoken of as "earth."

In the circuit shown in Figure 7-26, the negative side of the battery is connected to ground and the positive side is connected to one of the contacts of the battery contactor and to one end of the contactor coil. The other end of the coil connects to ground through the master switch.

When the master switch is closed, current flows through the coil and produces a magnetic pull that closes the contacts. With the contacts closed, current flows to the battery bus, the point in the aircraft from which all other circuits get their power. The circuits are all connected to the bus through circuit breakers.

master switch. A switch in an aircraft electrical system that can disconnect the battery from the bus and open the generator or alternator field circuit.

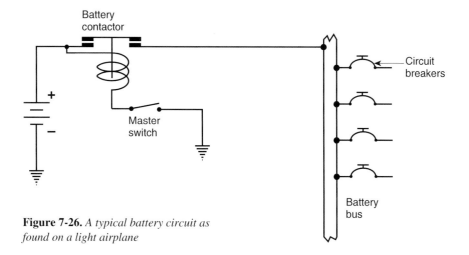

Figure 7-26. *A typical battery circuit as found on a light airplane*

Circuit Protection Devices

Federal Aviation Regulations Part 23—*Airworthiness Standards: Normal, Utility, Acrobatic, and Commuter Category Airplanes*—requires that all circuits other than the main circuit for the starter must be protected by a device that will open the circuit in the event of an excessive flow of current. This can be done with a current limiter, a fuse, or a circuit breaker. The primary function of a circuit protection device is to protect the wiring in the circuit. It should open the circuit before enough current flows to cause the insulation on the wire to smoke.

Figure 7-27 shows the symbols used for circuit protection devices. Any time too much current flows, these devices open the circuit and stop the current.

Some circuit breakers have an operating handle or button that allows them to be used as a switch to open or close a circuit manually. Other circuit breakers have only a button, which pops out when the circuit is overloaded but can be pushed back in to restore the circuit. These push-to-reset circuit breakers cannot be used to manually open a circuit. All circuit breakers have some means of showing when they have opened a circuit.

current limiter. An electrical component used to limit the amount of current a generator can produce. Some current limiters are a type of slow-blow fuse in the generator output. Other current limiters reduce the generator output voltage if the generator tries to put out more than its rated current.

circuit breaker. An electrical component that automatically opens a circuit any time excessive current flows through it.

A circuit breaker may be reset to restore the circuit after the fault causing the excessive current has been corrected.

Some commercial and industrial motors are protected by automatic-reset circuit breakers that are opened by heat when excessive current flows. When the motor windings and the circuit breaker cool down, the circuit breaker automatically resets and allows current to flow again. Automatic-reset circuit breakers are not permitted in aircraft electrical circuits.

Circuit breakers approved for use in aircraft electrical circuits must be of the "trip-free" type and must require a manual operation to restore service after tripping. Trip-free circuit breakers cannot be manually held closed if a fault exists in the circuit they are protecting. All fuses and circuit breakers that protect circuits that are essential to flight must be located and identified so that they are replaceable or resettable in flight.

Some circuits are protected by fuses instead of circuit breakers. A fuse is simply a strip of low-melting-point wire enclosed in a small glass tube with a metal terminal on each end. When too much current flows through the fuse, the heat caused by the current melts the fuse wire and opens the circuit. A new fuse must be installed before current can flow again.

If fuses are used, there must be one spare fuse of each rating or 50% spare fuses of each rating, whichever is greater.

Current limiters are high-current, slow-blow fuses that are installed as backup elements. They will open the circuit if the normal circuit protection devices fail.

Induced Current Protection

Fuses and circuit breakers are installed in a circuit to protect the wiring; many electrical components have built-in fuses to protect them from an excessive amount of current.

There is another type of circuit hazard in aircraft that carry a large amount of electronic equipment. Solid-state electronic equipment is extremely vulnerable to spikes of high voltage that are induced into a circuit when a current flow is interrupted.

Before going too much further, let's review some very important facts about the magnetic field that surrounds a wire when current flows through it.

- Any time current flows through a conductor, it causes a magnetic field to surround the conductor. The more current there is, the stronger the magnetic field.
- Any time a conductor is crossed by a changing magnetic field, or is moved through a stationary magnetic field, a voltage is induced in it that causes current to flow through it. This is called induced current.
- When the current flowing in a conductor changes, the magnetic field surrounding the conductor changes. As it builds up or collapses, it cuts across the conductor and generates a voltage that causes an induced current to flow.

Continued

Push-to-reset, pull-to-open circuit breaker

Switch-type circuit breaker

Push-to-reset circit breaker

Fuse

150-amp current limiter

Figure 7-27. *Electrical symbols used for circuit-protection devices*

slow-blow fuse. An electrical fuse that allows a large amount of current to flow for a short length of time but melts to open the circuit if more than its rated current flows for a longer period.

trip-free circuit breaker. A circuit breaker that opens a circuit any time an excessive amount of current flows regardless of the position of the circuit breaker's operating handle.

induced current. Electrical current produced in a conductor when it is moved through or crossed by a magnetic field.

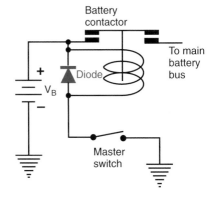

Figure 7-28. *A reverse-biased diode installed across the coil of the battery contactor allows the induced current that is produced when the master switch contacts open to be dissipated in the coil rather than arcing across the switch contacts.*

arcing. Sparking between a commutator and brush or between switch contacts that is caused by induced current when a circuit is broken.

ground-power unit (GPU). A service component used to supply electrical power to an aircraft when it is being operated on the ground.

• The amount of induced current is determined by the rate at which the magnetic field cuts across the conductor. The faster the current changes, the greater the induced current.

• Induced current always flows in the direction opposite to the flow of current that produced the magnetic field.

Consider the battery contactor shown in Figure 7-28. When current begins to flow through the contactor coil, a strong magnetic field builds up around the coil. This field surrounds the coil as long as current flows through it. But as soon as the switch between the coil and ground is opened, current stops flowing in the coil, and as it stops, the magnetic field collapses across all of the turns of wire in the coil. As the collapsing magnetic field cuts across the coil, it produces a short pulse, or spike, of very high voltage whose polarity is opposite to that of the battery. This voltage spike can damage any electronic equipment connected to the system when the master switch is opened. It can also damage the master switch by causing an arc to jump across the contacts as they are opening.

To prevent this kind of damage, a reverse-biased diode is connected across the contactor coil. During normal operation, no current can flow through it, but the high-voltage spike that is produced when the master switch is opened forward-biases the diode, and the induced current flows back through the contactor coil and is dissipated.

Ground-Power Circuit

The battery installed in an aircraft must be lightweight, and so it has a rather limited capacity. Because of this, it is often necessary to plug in a ground-power unit, or GPU, to provide electrical power for starting the engine and for operating some of the systems while the engine is not running.

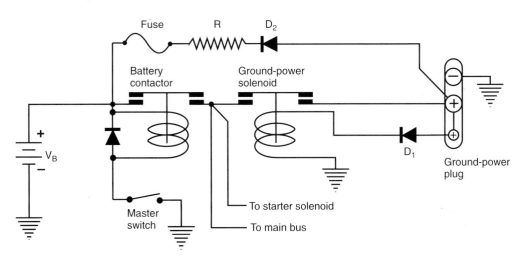

Figure 7-29. *A typical aircraft ground-power circuit*

It is extremely important that the polarity of the GPU be the same as that of the battery in the aircraft, as reversed polarity can damage much of the sensitive electronic equipment. The ground-power circuit shown in Figure 7-29 is made in such a way that no power can be connected to the aircraft if the polarities of the two sources are not correct.

The plug installed in the aircraft has three pins, with the two upper pins larger and longer than the bottom pin. The negative pin—the top pin in the diagram connects to the aircraft structure through a heavy cable. The middle pin is the positive pin, and it connects with a heavy cable to the contact of the ground-power solenoid. A small wire comes from this pin to diode D_2, resistor R, and a fuse connected in series. This wire then goes to the battery side of the battery contactor, to the same point where the coil of the battery contactor connects.

The GPU supplies power to the coil of the battery contactor so that it can be closed even if the battery in the aircraft is too low to close it. Closing this solenoid allows the GPU to charge the battery. It is important that the output voltage of the GPU be regulated so the battery will not be damaged by too high a voltage, which will cause an excessive charging rate.

Current flows from the positive pin of the ground-power plug to the battery coil through diode D_2, but this diode keeps the current from the battery from flowing back to the GPU plug. The resistor limits the current that can flow in this circuit to a value that is high enough to close the battery contactor, but not high enough to overcharge a fully charged battery. If there is a short circuit in the battery, the fuse will blow and open this circuit, preventing the battery relay from closing.

Sockets on the end of the ground-power cord make good contact with the two main pins in the ground-power plug. Then, as the sockets are pushed the rest of the way onto the plug, the short pin enters its socket and completes the circuit for the coil of the ground-power solenoid. Current from the GPU flows through diode D_1 to energize this coil. If the GPU has the wrong polarity, diode D_1 will block the current so that the GPU solenoid will not close.

Power Generating Systems

The battery is installed in an aircraft only to provide electrical power for starting the engine and to furnish current to assist the alternator (or generator) when an extra heavy load is placed on the electrical system. It also furnishes field current for the alternator and helps start the alternator producing current.

For many years, DC generators were the prime source of electrical energy for aircraft as well as for automobiles. But with the advent of efficient solid-state diodes, the DC alternator has replaced the generator on almost all small and medium-size aircraft.

Alternators have two main advantages over generators: They normally have more pairs of field poles than generators do, allowing them to produce their rated current at a lower RPM; and their load current is produced in the

generator. A mechanical device that transforms mechanical energy into electrical energy by rotating a coil inside a magnetic field. As the conductors in the coil cut across the lines of magnetic flux, a voltage is generated that causes current to flow.

alternator. An electrical generator that produces alternating current. The popular DC alternator used on light aircraft produces three-phase AC in its stator windings. This AC is changed into DC by a six-diode, solid-state rectifier before it leaves the alternator.

fixed stator winding and then taken out through solid connections. Generators produce their load current in the rotating element, and it is taken out through carbon brushes riding on copper commutator segments.

In this section we will first consider DC alternator circuits, then DC generator circuits. In the section on large-aircraft electrical systems, AC alternator circuits are discussed. The theory of electrical generation is covered in the *General* textbook of the *AMTS*, and the *Powerplant* textbook looks at the mechanisms and internal circuitry of generators and alternators, and their controls.

The DC Alternator Circuit

A DC alternator converts some of the aircraft engine's mechanical energy into electrical energy. A rotating electromagnetic field with four to eight pairs of poles is turned by the engine. The magnetic flux produced by this field cuts across some heavy windings, called stator coils, or stator windings, which are wound in slots in the housing of the alternator. As the magnetic field cuts across these windings, it produces three-phase alternating current in them. This alternating current is changed into direct current by six solid-state rectifier diodes mounted inside the alternator housing.

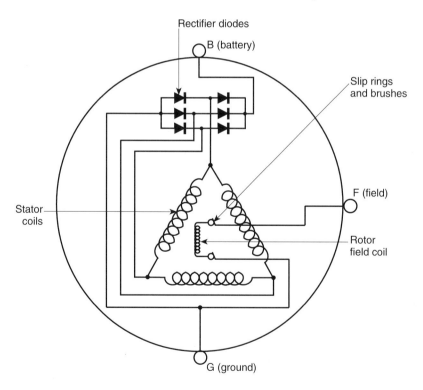

Figure 7-30. *The internal circuit of a typical light-aircraft DC alternator*

The amount of voltage the alternator produces is controlled by a voltage regulator which acts much like a variable resistor between the battery bus and the coil in the alternator rotor. The strength of the magnetic field is controlled by the amount of current flowing through the field coil, and the voltage regulator varies this current to keep the alternator output voltage constant as the amount of current it produces changes with the electrical load. Figure 7-31 shows how the alternator ties into the electrical system at the main battery bus.

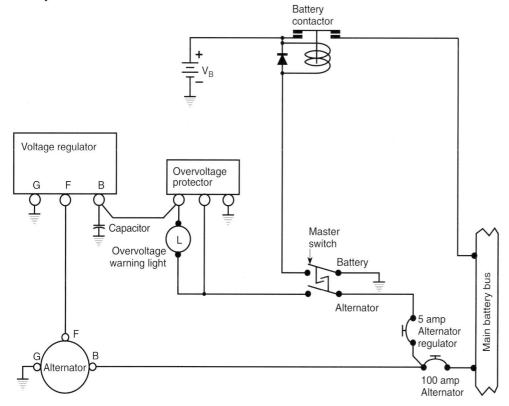

Figure 7-31. *A typical light-aircraft DC alternator system*

The B, or battery, terminal of the alternator connects to the main bus through a 100-amp circuit breaker. Since an alternator can be destroyed if it is operated without a load connected to it, this circuit breaker must always be closed unless the alternator malfunctions. The field current is also supplied from this circuit breaker, so the alternator cannot be disconnected from the bus without also shutting off the field current.

The alternator field current flows through the alternator circuit breaker, then through a 5-amp alternator regulator circuit breaker, through the alternator side of the master switch, through the overvoltage protector, and into the voltage regulator at its B terminal.

bus. A point within an electrical system from which the individual circuits get their power.

The voltage regulator senses the voltage the alternator is producing. If this voltage is too high, it decreases the field current flowing to the coil in the rotor. If the output voltage is too low, it increases the current. The field current leaves the voltage regulator through its F terminal. The alternator and the voltage regulator are grounded through their G terminals.

The master switch is a double-pole, single-throw split-rocker switch that controls the battery circuit and the alternator field circuit at the same time. The rocker for this switch is split so that the battery side of the switch can be turned on without turning on the alternator side, but the alternator side cannot be turned on without also turning on the battery side. The alternator side can be turned off, as it would have to be if the alternator malfunctioned in flight, without turning off the battery side of the switch. You cannot turn off the battery side of the switch without also turning off the alternator field side.

The overvoltage protector is a device in the alternator field circuit that senses the voltage the alternator is producing; if this voltage gets too high, the overvoltage protector opens the field circuit, stopping any further output from the alternator.

The overvoltage warning light turns on when the master switch is first closed, and it turns off when the engine is started and the alternator produces the correct amount of voltage. If the voltage gets too high, the overvoltage protector opens the alternator field circuit, which turns on the overvoltage warning light, showing that the alternator has been shut off because of an overvoltage condition.

The capacitor installed between the battery input of the voltage regulator and ground acts as a shock absorber. During operation, the electric motors in the aircraft can produce a spike of voltage in the electrical system high enough for the overvoltage protector to sense, which prompts it to open the alternator field circuit, shutting off the alternator. To prevent this, the capacitor absorbs the spike so it will not trip the overvoltage protector.

Twin-Engine Alternator System Using a Shared Voltage Regulator

One of the simplest alternator systems for use in a twin-engine aircraft is one that uses a single voltage regulator to control the output of both alternators, so that they will increase their current output when the current load on the aircraft electrical system is heavy, or decrease their output current when the demand is low.

Figure 7-32 is a basic schematic diagram of such a system. The output from each of the alternators goes directly to the main bus through 60-amp circuit breakers. Notice in the diagram that each of these circuit breakers is connected to a normally open switch by a dashed line. This symbol indicates that the circuit breaker is mechanically linked to a precision switch, such as a Microswitch, whose contacts open when the circuit breaker is tripped, but are held closed when the circuit breaker is allowing current to flow. An alternator can be destroyed if it is operated into an open circuit, so when the

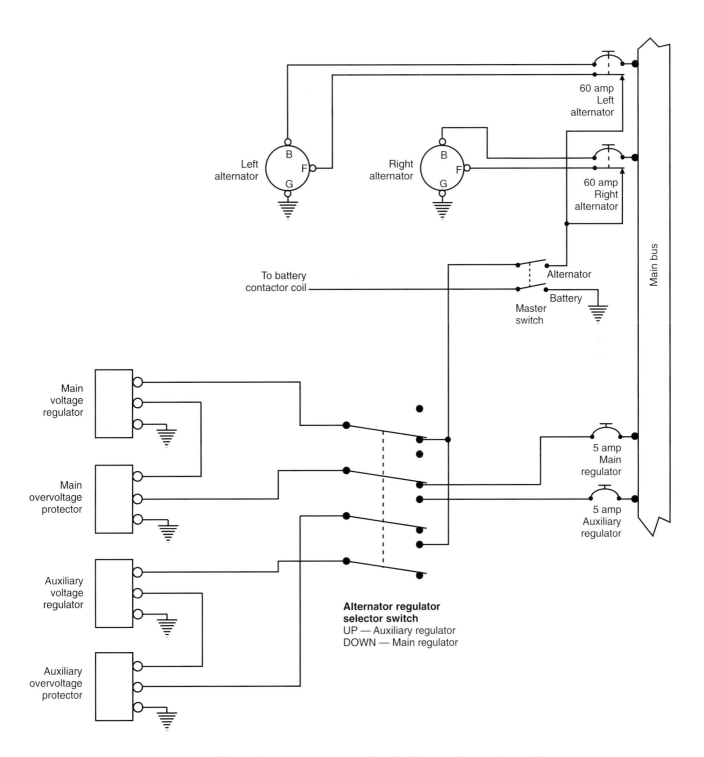

Figure 7-32. *Light twin-engine aircraft electrical power system using a shared voltage regulator and overvoltage protector*

circuit breaker opens, disconnecting the alternator output from the main bus, the Microswitch opens the alternator field circuit and stops the alternator from producing current.

The two Microswitches are connected in series with the field terminals of the two alternators. The two fields are connected to the alternator side of the aircraft master switch.

This alternator system has two voltage regulators, one main regulator and one auxiliary, or backup, regulator that can be switched into the system if the main regulator should fail. The alternator regulator selector switch is a four-pole, double-throw toggle switch. When the switch handle is in the down position, the main voltage regulator is in the circuit. When it is moved into the up position, the main voltage regulator is taken out of the circuit and the auxiliary voltage regulator takes its place.

When the main voltage regulator is selected, alternator field current flows from the main bus through a 5-amp main-regulator circuit breaker, through the regulator selector switch, and through the overvoltage protector. The current then flows through the voltage regulator back through the alternator selector switch, the alternator side of the master switch, and through the Microswitches to the F terminals of both alternators.

If the main voltage regulator fails in flight, the pilot can switch the voltage regulator selector switch to the auxiliary-regulator position. The alternator field current will follow the same path to the selector switch, but from there it will flow through the auxiliary overvoltage protector and the auxiliary voltage regulator.

overvoltage protector. A component in an aircraft electrical system that opens the alternator field circuit any time the alternator produces too high an output voltage.

The overvoltage protectors are located in the alternator field circuits, so if the voltage regulator malfunctions and the alternators produce too high a voltage, the contacts inside the overvoltage protector will open the alternator field circuit. If that happens, both alternators will go off line until the auxiliary voltage regulator is selected.

Twin-Engine Alternator System Using Individual Voltage Regulators

A more modern control system for small twin-engine aircraft uses a solid-state voltage regulator and an overvoltage protector for each alternator. Figure 7-33 shows this type of system.

The output of each alternator goes directly to the main bus through 100-amp circuit breakers. Field current is supplied to each alternator through its own 5-amp circuit breaker, alternator field switch, overvoltage protector, and voltage regulator.

This circuit has one feature that has not yet been discussed: the paralleling feature on the voltage regulators. The two regulators are connected through their P terminals so that circuits inside the regulators can compare the field voltages.

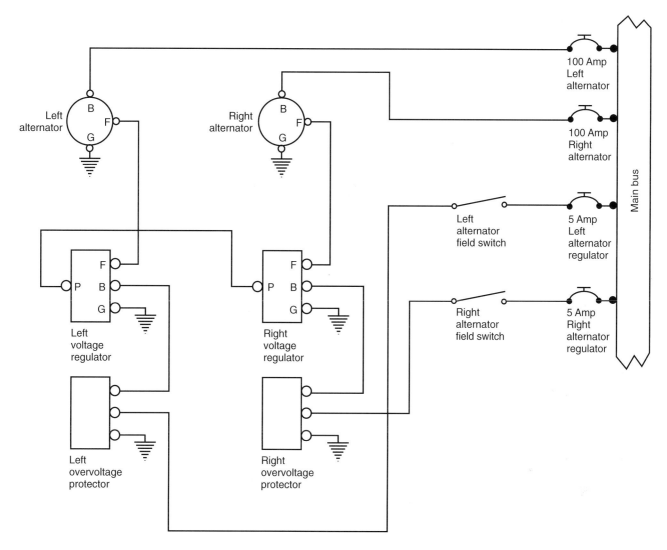

Figure 7-33. *Light twin-engine aircraft electrical power system using individual electronic voltage regulators and overvoltage protectors. The alternator paralleling circuit is built into the voltage regulators.*

If one alternator is producing more current than the other, its field voltage will be higher. This difference is sensed by the circuitry inside the voltage regulators, which decreases the field current flowing to the high-output alternator and increases the field current sent to the low-output alternator. This adjusts the alternator output voltages so they share the load equally.

The overvoltage protectors sense the main-bus voltage. If this voltage becomes too high, the overvoltage protector opens the alternator field circuit and shuts off the alternator.

The DC Generator Circuit

Because there are still a lot of older aircraft with DC generator systems installed, we need to understand these systems.

There are three basic differences between an alternator and a generator: the component in which the load current is generated, the type of rectifier used, and the method of field excitation.

Generator output current is produced in the rotating armature. The output current in an alternator is produced in the stationary stator.

Both generators and alternators produce AC, which must be changed into DC before it can be used. In a generator, this conversion is done by brushes and a commutator which act as a mechanical rectifier that switches between the various armature coils so that the current leaving the armature always flows in the same direction. An alternator produces three-phase AC in its stator windings, which is changed into DC by a six-diode solid-state rectifier mounted inside the alternator housing.

Generator fields are self-excited. This means that the field current comes from the armature. As the voltage produced in the armature rises, the field current rises and causes the armature voltage, and consequently the load current, to increase even more. If some provision were not made for limiting the current, a generator would burn itself out. For this reason, all generators must use some type of current limiter as well as a voltage regulator. Because alternator field current is supplied by the aircraft battery and the regulated output of the alternator, an alternator does not need a current limiter.

Most light aircraft use a basic electrical system that has been adapted from automobile systems. The generators and regulators are similar in appearance to those used in automobiles, but there are internal differences, differences in materials, and especially differences in the inspections used to certificate the components for use in aircraft. It is not permissible to use an automobile component in an FAA-certificated aircraft even though the parts do look alike.

There are two types of generator circuits used in aircraft electrical systems. Both are shown in Figure 7-34. The A-circuit's field coils are connected to the insulated brush inside the generator, and the voltage regulator acts as a variable resistor between the generator field and ground. In the B-circuit, the field coils are connected to the grounded brush, and the voltage regulator acts as a variable resistor between the generator field and the armature. The electrical systems that use these two types of generators work in the same way. The only difference is in the connection and servicing of the two systems. The fact that the components used in these different types of systems look much alike makes it very important that you use only the correct part number for the component when servicing these systems.

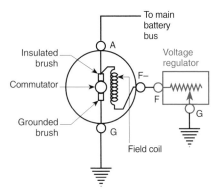

Voltage regulator used with A-circuit generator system is between shunt field and ground.

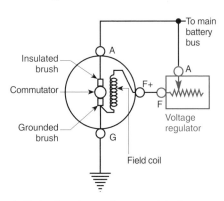

In B-circuit system, voltage regulator is between shunt field and armature.

Figure 7-34. *The placement of voltage regulators in the field circuits of generators for light aircraft*

The generator control contains three units: the voltage regulator, the current limiter, and the reverse-current cutout. This unit is shown in Figure 7-35 and is described in more detail in the *Powerplant* textbook of the *AMTS*, Chapter 17.

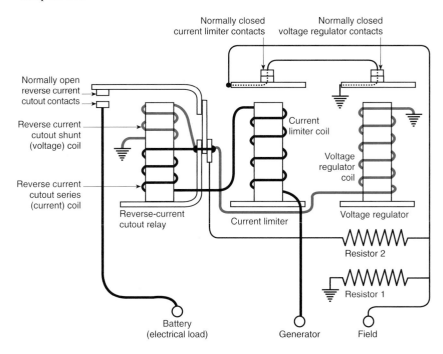

Figure 7-35. *An A-circuit, three-unit generator control such as is used on light aircraft.*

The voltage regulator senses the generator output voltage, and its normally closed contacts vibrate open and closed many times a second, limiting the amount of current that can flow through the field.

The current limiter is actuated by a coil in series with the armature output. When the generator puts out more than its rated current, the current limiter's normally closed contacts open and put a resistance in the field circuit to lower the generator output voltage to a level that will not produce excessive current.

The normally open contacts of the reverse-current cutout disconnect the generator from the aircraft bus when the generator voltage drops below that of the battery, and they automatically connect the generator to the bus when the generator voltage rises above that of the battery.

Simple Light-Aircraft Generator System

The A-circuit type generator system in Figure 7-36 is typical for most single-engine light airplanes.

The armature terminal of the generator connects to the G terminal of the generator control unit. The contacts of the reverse-current cutout are between the G and the B terminals. When the generator output reaches a specified voltage, the reverse-current cutout contacts close and connect the generator to the main bus.

Field current produced in the generator flows from the field terminal of the generator, through the generator side of the master switch, into the F terminal of the control unit, and through the voltage regulator and current limiter contacts to ground. If either the voltage or the current are too high, one set of normally closed contacts opens and this field current must flow through the resistor to ground.

The zero-center ammeter shows the amount of current flowing either from the battery to the main bus (−) or from the generator through the main bus into the battery (+) to charge it.

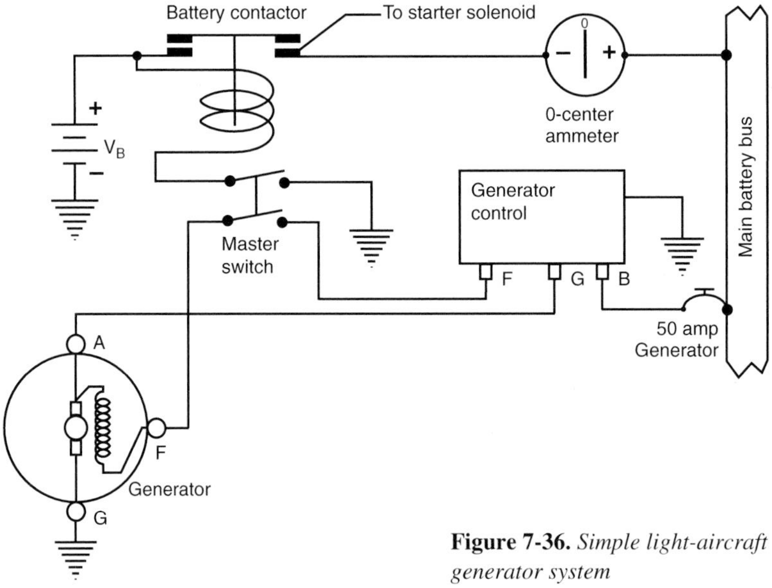

Figure 7-36. *Simple light-aircraft generator system*

Twin-Engine Generator System Using Vibrator-Type Voltage Regulators

The generator system shown in Figure 7-37 uses generators and regulators similar to those just discussed, except that the voltage regulator relay in the generator control has an extra coil wound on it through which paralleling current flows. This coil is connected between the regulator's P (paralleling) terminal and G (generator) terminal.

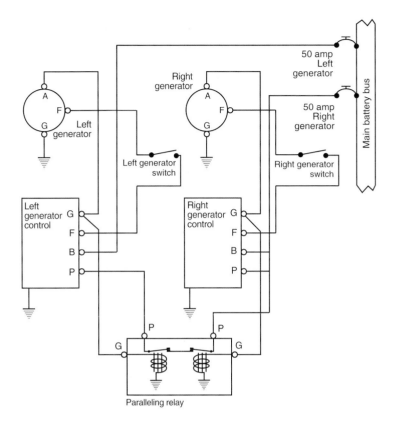

Figure 7-37. *Twin-engine aircraft generator system using vibrator-type voltage regulators and a paralleling relay*

The paralleling relay unit contains two relays, whose coils are supplied with current from the G terminals of the two voltage regulators. This current is supplied at the generator output voltage. The contacts of the relays are connected in series and to the P terminals of each of the voltage regulator units.

When both generators are operating and supplying current to the main bus, the two paralleling relays are closed and the paralleling coils in the two voltage regulators are connected. If the output voltage of one generator rises above that of the other, it will put out more current than the other. Current will flow through the paralleling coils from the generator producing the high voltage output to the one producing the lower voltage. The magnetic field caused by this current will aid the field from the voltage coil in the voltage regulator for the high generator and will oppose the field from the voltage coil in the voltage regulator for the low generator. This will decrease the voltage of the high generator and increase the voltage of the low generator so that they will share the load equally.

When the output voltage of either generator drops to zero, the paralleling relay for that generator automatically opens the paralleling circuit so that a working generator will not be affected by the one that is producing no current.

paralleling circuit. A circuit in a multiengine aircraft electrical system that causes the generators or alternators to share the electrical load equally.

paralleling relay. A relay in a multiengine aircraft electrical system that controls a flow of control current which is used to keep the generators or alternators sharing the electrical load equally.

The relay opens automatically to shut off the flow of paralleling current any time the output of either alternator or generator drops to zero.

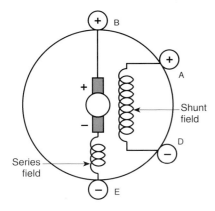

Figure 7-38. *Internal circuit of a compound-wound generator*

carbon-pile voltage regulator. A type of voltage regulator used with large aircraft generators.

Field current is controlled by varying the resistance of a stack of thin carbon disks. This resistance is varied by controlling the pressure on the stack with an electromagnet whose force is proportional to the generator output voltage.

differential-voltage reverse-current cutout. A type of reverse-current cutout switch used with heavy-duty electrical systems. This switch connects the generator to the electrical bus when the generator voltage is a specific amount higher than the battery voltage.

shunt winding. Field coils in an electric motor or generator that are connected in parallel with the armature.

generator series field. A set of heavy field windings in a generator connected in series with the armature. The magnetic field produced by the series windings is used to change the characteristics of the generator.

generator shunt field. A set of field windings in a generator connected in parallel with the armature. Varying the amount of current flowing in the shunt field windings controls the voltage output of the generator.

Twin-Engine Generator System Using Carbon-Pile Voltage Regulators

Carbon-pile voltage regulators and heavy-duty, compound-wound generators with differential-voltage reverse-current cutout relays were used to produce current for all older large aircraft. While these systems are not used on aircraft now being produced, a lot of them are still in operation.

The generators used in these systems have both a shunt field used for voltage control and a series field wound in such a way that it helps minimize armature reaction that causes brush arcing as the generator load changes. The positive brushes are connected to terminal B, and the negative brushes are connected through the series field to terminal E (Figure 7-38). The positive end of the shunt field winding is connected to terminal A and its negative end is connected to terminal D. The carbon-pile voltage regulator used with this type of system acts as a variable resistor between the positive end of the field terminal, terminal A, and the armature output, terminal B.

The differential-voltage reverse-current cutout relay senses both the generator output voltage and the battery voltage, and its contacts close when the generator output is a specified amount higher than the battery voltage. The contacts remain closed until the generator output drops low enough that current flows from the battery back through the generator armature and the series field coils. This control unit has a switch terminal supplied with current from its generator terminal through a generator control switch mounted on the instrument panel. When this switch is closed, the generator can be connected to the main bus as soon as its voltage rises to the proper value. When this switch is open, the generator cannot be connected to the bus regardless of its voltage.

A current limiter, a form of slow-blow fuse, is installed in the heavy cable between the B terminal of the generator and the G terminal of the reverse-current cutout. This type of current limiter allows current in excess of its rating to flow through it for a short time, but its fuse link will melt and open the circuit if its rated current flows through it for a longer than specified length of time. These current limiters are normally located in the engine nacelle, and cannot be changed in flight. The generator output current is carried into the main bus from the reverse-current cutout through a circuit breaker.

The carbon-pile voltage regulator uses a stack of pure carbon disks inside a ceramic tube to act as a variable resistance in the shunt-field circuit to control the generator output. This stack of carbon disks, the carbon pile, is connected between terminals A and B of the regulator, which is between the armature output and the positive end of the shunt field (*see* Figure 7-39). The stack is held tightly compressed by a heavy spring to decrease its resistance.

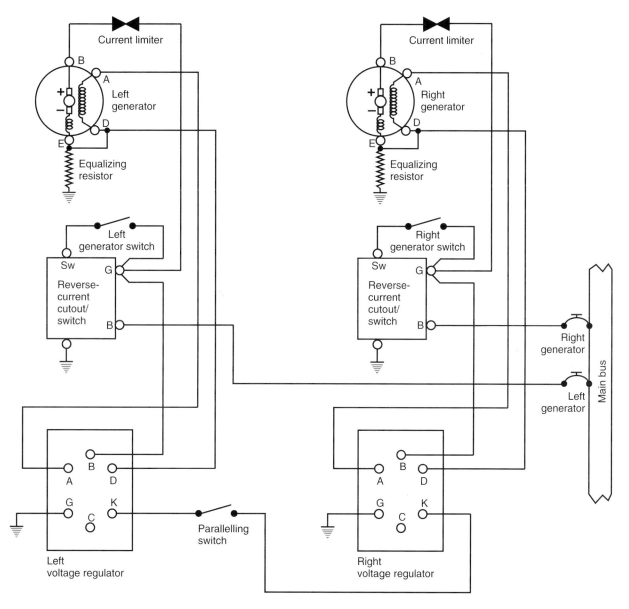

Figure 7-39. *Heavy-duty aircraft generator system using differential-voltage reverse-current cutout relays and carbon-pile voltage regulators.*

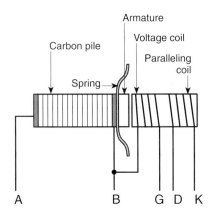

Figure 7-40. *Internal circuit of a carbon pile voltage regulator*

equalizing resistor. A large resistor in the ground circuit of a heavy-duty aircraft generator through which all of the generator output current flows.

The voltage drop across this resistor is used to produce the current in the paralleling circuit that forces the generators to share the electrical load equally.

Two coils, a voltage coil and a paralleling coil, are wound around an iron core so that the magnetic pull caused by current flowing through them attracts the armature, which pulls against the spring and loosens the pressure on the carbon stack. This increases the resistance of the carbon stack and decreases the current flowing in the field coils.

The voltage coil is connected between terminals B and G, so the current flowing through it is directly related to the output voltage the generator is producing. When this voltage rises above the value for which the regulator is set, its magnetic field pulls on the spring and loosens the carbon stack. Loosening the stack increases its resistance and decreases the field current. This lowers the generator output voltage.

Notice in Figure 7-39 that the E terminals of the two generators, the negative ends of the armatures, do not go directly to ground, but rather go to ground through equalizing resistors, also called equalizing shunts. These shunts are heavy-duty resistors that produce a voltage drop of 0.5 volt when the rated current of the generator flows through them. One end of each equalizing resistor connects to ground, and the other end connects to generator terminals E and D. This ground point of the generators is connected to terminal D of the voltage regulator, which connects to one end of the paralleling coil. The other end of the paralleling coil is connected to terminal K of the regulator. The K terminals of both regulators are connected through a cockpit-mounted paralleling switch.

The paralleling circuit ensures that the generators produce the same amount of current when both are connected to the main bus. All of the current the generators produce flows through the equalizing resistors and produces a voltage drop across them. When the generators are producing exactly the same amount of current, the voltage drops across the two equalizing resistors are the same and no current flows through the paralleling coils of the regulators. But if the left generator furnishes more current to the bus than the right generator does, for example, the top end of the left generator's equalizing resistor has a higher voltage than the top end of the right generator's equalizing resistor, and current flows through both of the paralleling coils.

The magnetic pull caused by the current in the paralleling coil of the left regulator aids the pull from the voltage coil and loosens the carbon stack in the left regulator. This decreases the left generator field current and lowers its output voltage. At the same time, the magnetic field from the paralleling coil in the right generator opposes the pull caused by the voltage coil, and the carbon pile tightens up so that its resistance decreases. The field current and the output voltage of the right generator increases until the generators share the load equally.

Turbine-Engine Starter-Generator System

Most of the smaller turbine engines installed in business jet airplanes have a combination starter-generator rather than a separate starter and generator. These units resemble heavy-duty, compound-wound DC generators, but they have an extra set of series windings. The series motor windings are switched into the circuit when the engine is started, but as soon as it is running, they are switched out.

Figure 7-42 shows a typical starter-generator circuit. When the start switch is placed in the START position, current flows through the start/ignition circuit breaker and the upper contacts of the start switch to the coil of the starter relay. This current produces a magnetic pull that closes the relay and allows current to flow to the starter-generator through its C+ terminal, the series motor windings, the armature, and the starter-generator series windings, to ground. At the same time, current flows through the ignition-cutoff switch into the igniter unit to provide the intense heat needed to ignite the fuel.

When ignition is achieved, the start switch is moved into the RUN position. Current flows from the bus through the generator field circuit breaker to the coil of the generator field relay, producing the magnetic pull needed to close the field relay contacts to connect the generator field to the voltage regulator. When generator field current flows, the generator produces current. As soon as the voltage builds up to the specified value, the contacts inside the reverse-current cutout relay close and the large amount of current produced in the generator flows from the B+ terminal through the reverse-current relay to the bus, through the generator circuit breaker.

When the start switch is placed in the OFF position, the current is shut off to the generator-field relay; it opens, disconnecting the generator field from the voltage regulator, and the generator stops producing load current.

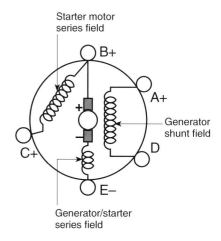

Figure 7-41. *Internal circuit of a turbine-engine starter-generator*

starter-generator. A single-component starter and generator used on many of the smaller gas-turbine engines.

It is used as a starter, and when the engine is running, its circuitry is shifted so that it acts as a generator.

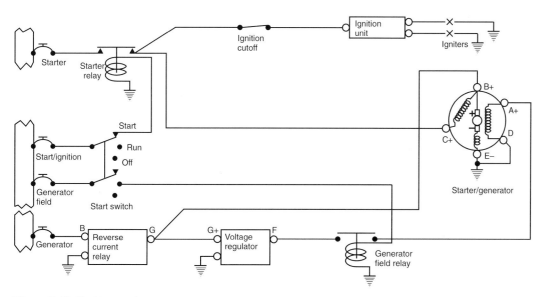

Figure 7-42. *Turbine-engine starter-generator system*

Voltage and Current Indicating Circuits

Almost all aircraft have some means of monitoring the current flow in some portion of the electrical system. The simplest system uses a zero-center ammeter connected between the system side of the battery contactor and the main bus, as shown in Figure 7-43. This type of system can be used only when the electrical loads on the aircraft are quite low, as the wire that carries all of the load current must go up to the ammeter on the instrument panel. Typically, this is an 8- or 10-gage wire.

The ammeter has zero in the center of its scale, so it can deflect in either direction. When the battery is supplying all of the current, the ammeter deflects to the left, showing that the battery is being discharged. When the voltage of the alternator, which is connected to the main bus, is higher than that of the battery, the battery is being charged, and the ammeter deflects to the right. An ammeter in this location does not show the amount of current the alternator is producing.

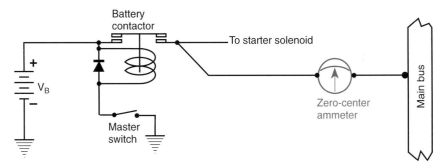

Figure 7-43. *A zero-center ammeter in this location gives an indication of the current flowing into or out of the battery.*

loadmeter. A current meter used in some aircraft electrical systems to show the amount of current the generator or alternator is producing. Loadmeters are calibrated in percent of the generator rated output.

millivoltmeter. An electrical instrument that measures voltage in units of millivolts (thousandths of a volt).

voltmeter multiplier. A precision resistor in series with a voltmeter mechanism used to extend the range of the basic meter or to allow a single meter to measure several ranges of voltage.

A loadmeter is a type of ammeter installed between the alternator output and the aircraft main bus. It does not give any indication of whether or not the battery is delivering current to the system, or whether it is receiving current from the alternator. The dial of the loadmeter is calibrated in terms of percentage of the alternator's rated output.

Figure 7-44 shows the way a loadmeter is connected into an alternator circuit. The loadmeter shunt is a precision resistor that has a large terminal on each end and two smaller terminals located between the larger ones. When the rated current for the alternator flows through the shunt, there is a fifty-millivolt (0.050-volt) drop between the two smaller terminals, which are connected to a millivoltmeter in the instrument panel with 20- or 22-gage wire.

The millivoltmeter is calibrated in percentage from zero to 100 percent. If the aircraft is equipped with a 100-amp alternator and the loadmeter reads 50%, the alternator is supplying 50 amps of current to the main bus.

Some twin-engine aircraft have a volt-ammeter that can measure the current furnished by either the left or the right alternator and the current supplied by the battery, as well as the voltage on the aircraft electrical bus.

Figure 7-45 shows such a system, with an instrument shunt in the output of both alternators and a similar shunt in the cable between the battery contactor and the main bus. Small-gage wires attach the three shunts to the instrument selector switch, and two small wires connect the switch to the volt-ammeter mounted in the instrument panel.

The pilot can read the amount of current being produced by the left or the right alternator or the amount of current the battery is furnishing to the system, as well as the voltage on the system bus.

The voltmeter multiplier is a precision resistor in series with the meter movement. It allows the millivoltmeter to read the voltage of the system.

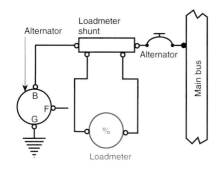

Figure 7-44. *A loadmeter in this location shows, in percentage of its rated output, the amount of current the alternator is producing.*

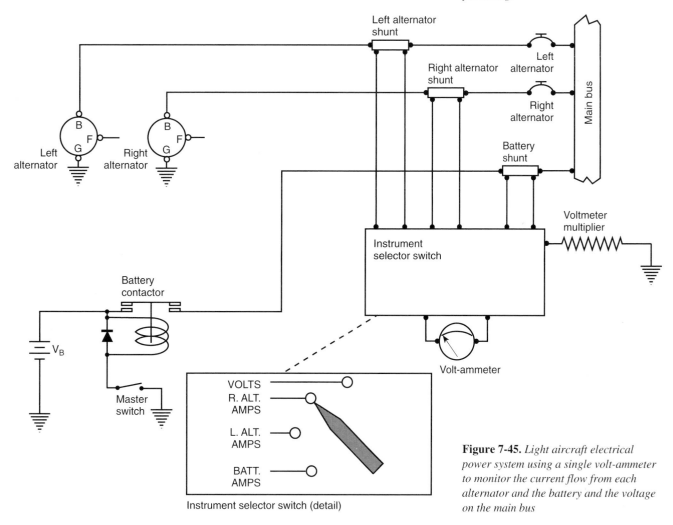

Instrument selector switch (detail)

Figure 7-45. *Light aircraft electrical power system using a single volt-ammeter to monitor the current flow from each alternator and the battery and the voltage on the main bus*

*Answers begin on Page 580. **Page numbers refer to chapter text.***

26. The reference from which all voltage is measured in an aircraft electrical system is called the _____ . *Page 507*

27. Return current from devices installed in an aircraft electrical system flows back to the battery through the _____ . *Page 507*

28. The battery terminal that is normally grounded is the _____ (negative or positive) terminal. *Page 507*

29. Circuit breakers and fuses are installed in a circuit primarily to protect the _____ (wiring or circuit devices). *Page 508*

30. The one circuit in an aircraft electrical system that is not required to be protected by a circuit protection device is the main _____ circuit. *Page 508*

31. Circuit breakers used in aircraft electrical systems must be of the _____ type. *Page 509*

32. A trip-free circuit breaker _____ (can or cannot) be manually held closed in the presence of a fault. *Page 509*

33. Automatic reset circuit breakers _____ (are or are not) approved for use in aircraft electrical circuits. *Page 509*

34. An electrical circuit that has 12 fuses rated at 30 amps is required to carry at least _____ 30-amp fuses as spares. *Page 509*

35. Current that is induced into a conductor by a changing current in another nearby conductor is called _____ current. *Page 509*

36. The amount of current that is induced by a changing magnetic field is determined by the _____ of change of the magnetic field. *Page 510*

37. The direction of flow of induced current is _____ (the same as or opposite) that of the current that caused it. *Page 510*

38. The diode that is placed across the coil of a battery contactor is _____ (forward or reverse) biased by the battery. *Page 510*

39. Refer to Figure 7-29. The device that prevents the GPU from overcharging a fully charged battery is _____ . *Page 511*

40. Refer to Figure 7-29. The device that prevents the GPU from being connected to the aircraft electrical system if its polarity is incorrect is _____ . *Page 511*

41. Refer to Figure 7-29. The device that prevents the GPU from being connected to the aircraft electrical system if there is a short in the battery is _____ . *Page 511*

42. The prime source of electrical power in an aircraft is the _____ (battery or alternator). *Page 511*

43. The load current produced in a DC alternator is produced in the _____ (rotor or stator). *Page 511*

44. The voltage produced in the stator windings of a DC alternator is _____ (AC or DC). *Page 511*

45. DC electricity is produced in a DC alternator by the _____ . *Page 512*

46. If an alternator fails in flight and is disconnected from the main bus, the alternator field circuit should be _____ (opened or closed). *Page 514*

47. If an alternator produces too high a voltage, the overvoltage protector opens the _____ (load or field) circuit. *Page 514*

48. The load current produced in a DC generator is produced in the _____ (rotating or stationary) coils. *Page 512*

49. A DC alternator can produce its rated current at a lower RPM than a DC generator because of the greater number of _____ in the alternator. *Page 511*

50. DC electricity is produced in a DC generator by the _____ and _____ . *Page 512*

51. A DC alternator _____ (does or does not) require a current limiter. *Page 518*

52. A DC generator _____ (does or does not) require a current limiter. *Page 518*

Continued

53. In an A-circuit generator, the voltage regulator is between the field terminal of the generator and _____ (ground or the armature). *Page 518*

54. The three units in a generator control used with low-output DC generators are:
    a. _____
    b. _____
    c. _____
    Page 519

55. The contacts of a reverse-current cutout relay are normally _____ (open or closed). *Page 519*

56. The contacts of a vibrator-type voltage regulator are normally _____ (open or closed). *Page 519*

57. The contacts of a vibrator-type current limiter are normally _____ (open or closed). *Page 519*

58. A carbon-pile voltage regulator acts as a variable _____ in the generator field circuit. *Page 523*

59. The output current produced by the two generators in a twin-engine installation are kept the same by the _____ circuit in the voltage regulators. *Page 521*

60. Current through the paralleling circuit in a twin-engine electrical system using carbon-pile voltage regulators is provided by the voltage drops across the _____ resistors. *Page 524*

61. Many general aviation turbine-powered aircraft combine the _____ and _____ into one single unit. *Page 525*

62. The starter windings in a starter-generator are _____ (series or shunt) windings. *Page 525*

63. A zero-center ammeter _____ (does or does not) show the amount of current the alternator is producing. *Page 526*

64. A loadmeter is calibrated in _____ of the rated alternator or generator output. *Page 527*

Aircraft Electrical Load Circuits

The electrical systems just discussed are used to place electrical power on the main bus from the battery, the alternator, and the generator.

This section will examine some typical aircraft load circuits. A load circuit is simply any circuit that connects to the main electrical bus and provides a load for the electrical system. These circuits, all typical, are shown here to help illustrate the way these systems operate.

The Starter Circuit

The starter circuit differs from any other load circuit in the extremely large amount of current it carries. It is the only circuit in most aircraft electrical systems that is not required to have some kind of circuit protection device. The amount of current the starter motor needs to crank the engine is so high that it would be impractical to use any type of fuse or circuit breaker.

Though a starter solenoid is similar to a battery contactor, they are not normally interchangeable because the battery contactor must be energized the entire time the aircraft is operating, while the solenoid used for the starter is energized only when the engine is being cranked. The battery contactor is called a continuous-duty solenoid; the starter solenoid is called an intermittent-duty solenoid.

One end of the starter solenoid coil goes to ground, usually inside the solenoid housing, and the other end connects to the terminal on the ignition switch marked START (Figure 7-46). Power comes from the battery bus through the circuit breaker and the BATT terminal of the ignition switch. Since so little current is used by the starter solenoid coil, and it is used for such a short time, it is often taken from a circuit breaker that is also used for some other circuit. For example, some aircraft tie the starter solenoid coil to the instrument light circuit breaker. When troubleshooting the starter circuit, you must have a wiring diagram of the aircraft so you know which circuit breaker this current comes from.

When the master switch is turned on, the battery contactor closes and power is supplied to the battery bus and the ignition switch. As soon as the ignition switch is placed in the START position, the starter solenoid closes and current flows to the starter motor to crank the engine.

continuous-duty solenoid. A solenoid-type switch designed to be kept energized by current flowing through its coil for an indefinite period of time. The battery contactor in an aircraft electrical system is a continuous-duty solenoid. Current flows through its coil all of the time the battery is connected to the electrical system.

intermittent-duty solenoid. A solenoid-type switch whose coil is designed for current to flow through it for only a short period of time. The coil will overheat if current flows through it too long.

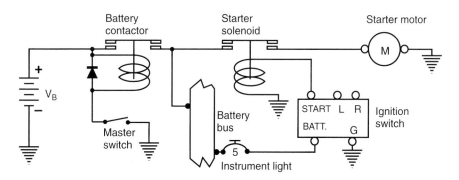

Figure 7-46. *A typical starter circuit for a light aircraft engine*

Navigation Light Circuit

Figure 7-47 shows a typical navigation light circuit. Current flows from the main bus through the 5-amp Navigation Light circuit breaker and the Navigation Light switch. The current then splits and flows through the red light on the aircraft's left wing tip, the green light on the right wing tip, and the white light on the tail.

This is an example of a series-parallel, or complex, circuit. The three lights are connected in parallel with one another, and all three are in series with the switch and the circuit breaker.

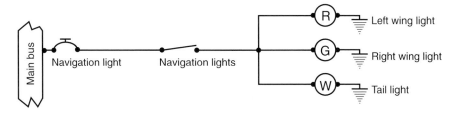

Figure 7-47. *Navigation light circuit typical for smaller aircraft*

Landing and Taxi Light Circuit

The circuit in Figure 7-48 is just slightly more complicated than that for the navigation lights. The landing light and the taxi light get their current from the main bus through their own circuit breakers. The landing light is connected to a 10-amp circuit breaker, and the taxi light circuit breaker is rated at 5 amps. The diode connected between the two sides of the switch is the reason for the difference between the ratings of the two circuit breakers.

The landing light shines ahead of the aircraft at the correct angle to light up the end of the runway when the aircraft is descending for a landing. The taxi light is aimed so that it shines ahead of the aircraft when it is taxiing. Both lights are on during landing, but only the taxi light is on during taxiing.

When the landing-light switch is turned on, current flows from the main bus through the landing light circuit breaker, through the landing light switch to the landing light, and also through the diode to the taxi light. Both lights are on.

After the aircraft is on the ground, the pilot can turn the landing light off and the taxi light on. Current then flows through the taxi-light circuit breaker and the taxi-light switch and turns the taxi light on. The diode blocks current to the landing light.

Another way of doing the same thing is to use a special type of split-rocker switch. This is a double-pole, single-throw switch that turns on both lights when the landing-light side of the switch is depressed. The landing-light side of the switch can be turned off without affecting the taxi-light side, but when the taxi-light side of the switch is depressed, both lights turn off. The taxi light

press-to-test light fixture. An indicator light fixture whose lens can be pressed in to complete a circuit that tests the filament of the light bulb.

can also be turned on without affecting the landing light. When this type of switch is used, each light is connected to the bus through a 5-amp circuit breaker.

Landing Gear Actuation and Indicating Circuit

Figure 7-49 shows the circuit for the retractable landing gear system of a typical twin-engine airplane as it is with the aircraft on the ground. All three landing gear struts are down and locked and the gear-selector switch is in the GEAR-DOWN position.

Current for the green indicator light flows through the 5-amp circuit breaker, wire 6, the nose-gear down switch, wire 5, the left gear-down switch, wire 4, the right gear-down switch, and wire 3 to the green light, causing it to illuminate.

You will notice that the red and green lights both have two power terminals and one ground terminal. The lower power terminals of both lights receive power through the 5-amp circuit breaker and wires 7 and 17, or 7 and 18. When the lens of either light is pressed in, the circuit through wire 3 or 8 is opened and the circuit through wire 17 or 18 is closed. This sends current through the bulb to show that the filament is not burned out. This type of light fixture is called a press-to-test light.

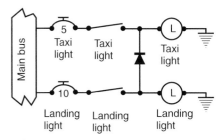

Circuit using two independent switches

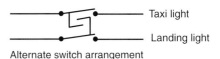

Circuit using a split rocker switch

Figure 7-48. *Landing light and taxi light circuits typical for smaller aircraft*

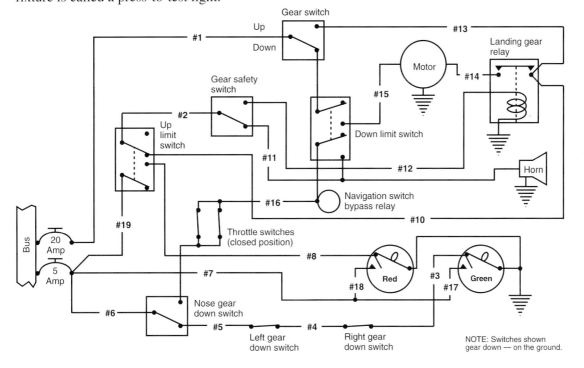

Figure 7-49. *Retractable landing gear control and indicating system. The airplane is on the ground, the landing gear handle is down, and all three landing gears are down and locked.*

When the aircraft takes off and the weight is off of the landing gear, the gear-safety switch (the squat switch) changes its position, as shown in Figure 7-50. When the pilot moves the landing-gear selector handle into the GEAR-UP position, its switch changes position, and the circuit is completed from the 20-amp circuit breaker through wires 1 and 13 to the right-hand terminal of the landing-gear relay.

Current flows from this connection on the relay through wire 10, through the upper contacts of the up-limit switch, through the gear-safety switch, and through wire 12, to the coil of the landing-gear relay. This current produces a magnetic pull, which closes the relay so that current can flow through the relay contacts and the winding of the reversible DC motor to raise the landing gear.

As soon as the landing gear is released from its downlocks, the three landing-gear-down switches open and the green light goes out. The landing gear has not reached its up-and-locked position, so the red light is off.

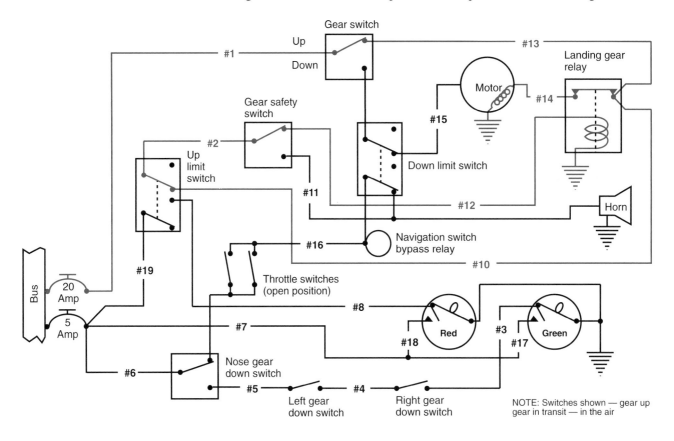

Figure 7-50. *The airplane is in the air, the landing gear handle is up, the landing gear is in transit, and the throttles are open.*

Figure 7-51 shows the condition of the landing-gear circuit when the landing gear is up and locked in flight. The gear switch is in the GEAR-UP position and the up-limit switch is in the gear-up-and-locked position. There is no weight on the landing gear, so the gear safety switch is in the position shown here. The down-limit switch is not in the gear-down-and-locked position, and the three gear-down switches are open.

No current can flow to the relay coil because of the up-limit switch, and no current can flow to the gear-down side of the motor because of the gear-selector switch. Current flows through the lower contacts of the up-limit switch, through wires 19 and 8, to the red light, showing that the landing gear is up and locked.

If either throttle is closed when the landing gear is not down and locked, current will flow through the nose-gear-down switch, the throttle switch, and the down-limit switch and will sound the gear-warning horn. This horn warns the pilot that the landing gear has not been lowered in preparation for landing.

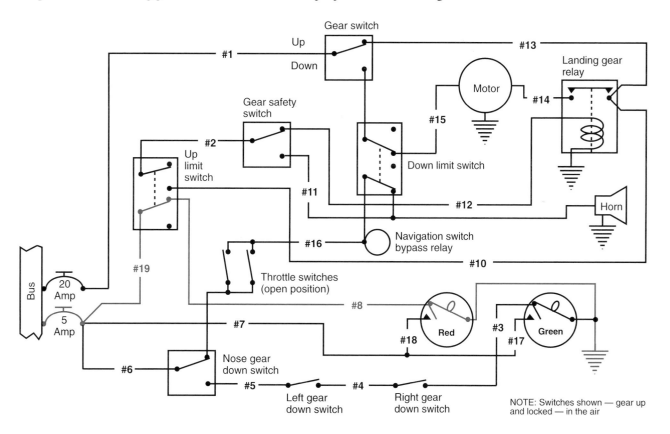

Figure 7-51. *The airplane is in the air, the landing gear handle is up, all three landing gears are up and locked, and the throttles are open.*

When the landing-gear-selector switch is moved into the GEAR-DOWN position, current flows through it and the down-limit switch to the gear-down side of the reversible DC motor that lowers the landing gear. As soon as the gear is down and locked, the down-limit switch opens and shuts off the landing-gear motor. The three gear-down switches close and the green light comes on.

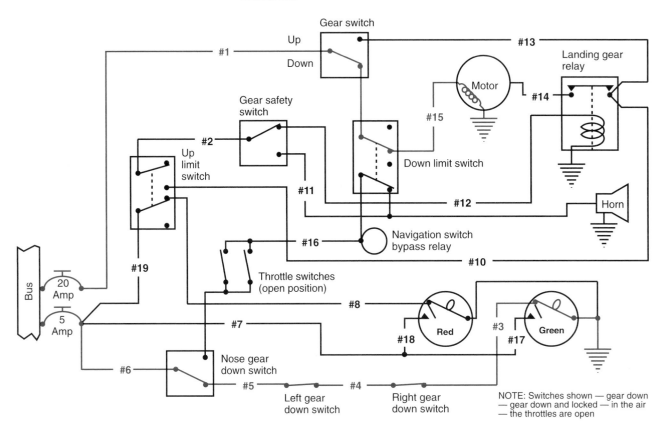

Figure 7-52. *The airplane is in the air, the landing gear handle is down, all three landing gears are down, and the throttles are open.*

Antiskid Brake System

The high landing speed of modern turbojet and turboprop airplanes, together with the small contact area between the tires and the runway, makes hydroplaning and brake skidding a real problem.

When the antiskid-control switch in Figure 7-53 is ON and the airplane is on the ground with the squat switches closed, current flows from the bus, through the antiskid-test circuit breaker and the antiskid-control circuit breaker, to the antiskid control box.

Each of the wheels has a wheel-speed sensor—a small AC generator—mounted inside the landing gear axle. The rotor for this generator is driven by a spring clip mounted in the inboard wheel bearing cover. Excitation for the sensor is supplied through the antiskid control box, and its AC output is returned to the control box. *See* Figure 7-53 on the next page.

The frequency of the AC produced by the wheel-speed sensor is determined by the rotational speed of the wheel. The AC from each of the sensors is sent into the control box, where its frequency is compared with that from the other sensors, and with a built-in program tailored to the particular type of aircraft.

If any wheel starts to slow down faster than its mate or faster than the program allows, the control box sends a signal to the antiskid valve in the brake line for that wheel. The valve opens and allows fluid from the brake to flow back into the hydraulic system return manifold. As soon as the brake releases and the wheel stops slowing down, the valve closes and directs fluid back into the brake. The brake valve modulates, or turns off and on, to keep the tire on the threshold of a skid, but does not allow a skid to develop. *See* Figure 7-53 on the next page.

When the aircraft is in the air and the antiskid-control switch is ON, current cannot flow to the antiskid control box because the squat switches mounted on the landing gear struts are open, removing the ground from the antiskid control circuit. The pilot can hold the brake pedals fully depressed, but no hydraulic pressure will reach the brakes because the antiskid valves are open, and the fluid flows into the hydraulic system return manifold.

As soon as the weight of the aircraft is on the landing gear and the squat switches close, current flows through the antiskid control box and energizes its computing circuits. The signals from the wheel-speed sensors are entered into the computing circuits, and when the wheels spin up to a specified speed or a specified number of seconds after the squat switches close, the antiskid valves close and direct hydraulic pressure into the brake. The computer senses the output of the wheel-speed sensors for a second or so to detect the braking action the runway provides, and then it applies pressure to the brakes. The control valves modulate the application of the brakes and bring the wheels to a stop at a rate that keeps them from skidding.

antiskid brake system. A system used with aircraft brakes that keeps the wheels from skidding on wet or icy runways.

squat switch. A switch on a landing gear strut that is actuated when weight is on the strut. Squat switches are used to prevent certain operations when the aircraft is on the ground and to prevent other operations when the aircraft is in the air.

If, for any reason, one of the antiskid control valves dumps fluid back into the hydraulic system for a longer time than is allowed, the antiskid-failure light comes on, and the brake system returns to normal action without antiskid protection.

As soon as the aircraft slows to about 10 knots, the low-speed circuit in the antiskid control box deactivates the antiskid system, and braking is done as though no antiskid system were installed.

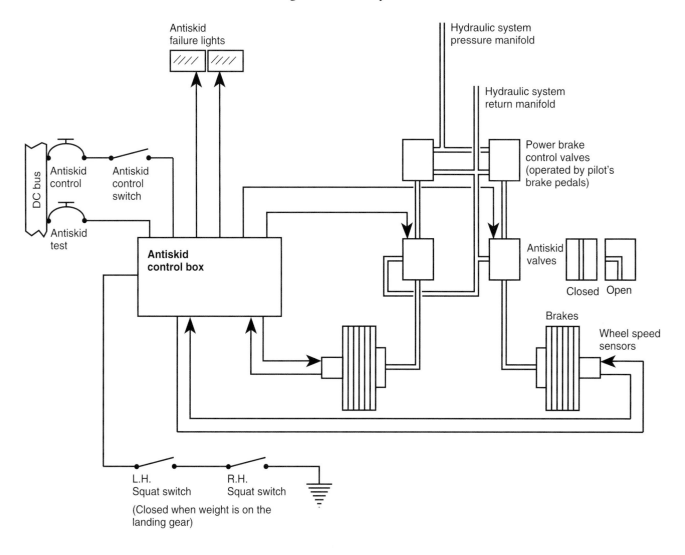

Figure 7-53. *Antiskid brake system used on a typical light turbine-engine-powered airplane*

Electrical Propeller Deicing System

Many modern aircraft are certificated to fly into known icing conditions. They can do this because they are equipped with deicing systems to remove ice from the wings, the tail surfaces, and the propellers, and anti-icing systems to prevent the formation of ice on the windshield and pitot tube.

deicing system. A system in an aircraft that removes ice after it has formed. Propellers are deiced with heat produced when current flows through deicer boots bonded to the propeller blades.

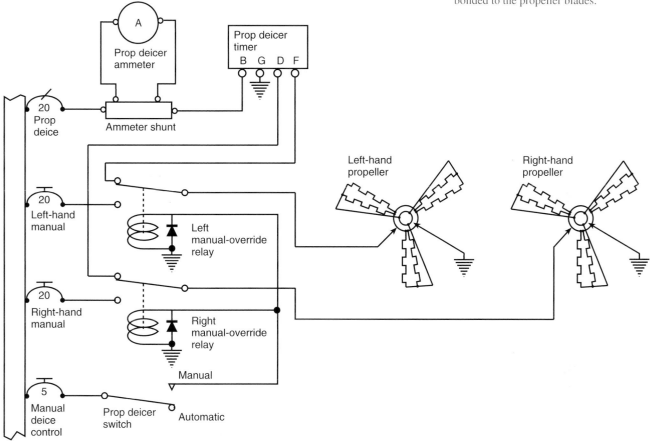

Figure 7-54. *Electrothermal propeller deicing system*

Deicing the propellers is done with an electrothermal system made of rubber boots bonded to the leading edge of the propeller blades. These boots have electrical heating elements embedded in them that are supplied with current from a propeller deicing timer.

Figure 7-54 shows a typical system used on a twin turboprop airplane. Current flows from the bus through a 20-amp prop deice circuit breaker switch into the deicer timer unit. When the manual-override relays are not energized, this current flows into the heating elements on the propeller blades through brushes riding on slip rings mounted on the propeller spinner bulkhead. The slip rings are connected to the heater elements through flexible conductors that allow the blades to change their pitch angle.

The timer sends current through the right propeller for about 90 seconds, then shifts and sends current through the left propeller for 90 seconds.

Some propeller deicing systems have two separate heating elements on each blade. Current flows through the right-propeller outboard element for about 30 seconds, then through the right-propeller inboard element for the same length of time. After the right propeller is deiced, the timer shifts and sends current through the left-propeller outboard elements and then through the left-propeller inboard elements.

Current cycles of the two propellers are controlled by the timer if the propeller deicer switch is in the AUTOMATIC position. When the prop deicer switch is moved to its momentary MANUAL position, the two manual-override relays are energized and current flows directly from the bus to the blades without going through the timer.

The pilot can easily tell whether the deicing system is operating correctly in the AUTOMATIC mode by watching the propeller ammeter. It will show a flow of current each time one of the heater elements draws current.

Turbine-Engine Autoignition Circuit

The ignition system for a turbine engine is used only for starting the engine, but it is important that it be energized so that it can relight the engine if it should flameout. Autoignition systems such as the one shown in Figure 7-55 are installed on some turboprop engines to serve as a backup for takeoff and landing, during flight in conditions in which the engine is more likely to flameout.

The engine-start switch has three positions. In the ENGINE START AND IGNITION position, current flows to the generator control and to the coil of the starter relay, as well as to the coil of the ignition-power relay. Current flowing in the generator control opens the generator-field circuit for the starter-generator and connects the series starter winding to the electrical system. *See* Figure 7-42 on Page 525. Current flowing in the coil of the ignition-power relay closes its contacts, allowing current to flow from the electrical bus to the ignition exciter unit and to a light on the annunciator panel, showing that the ignition is on.

When the engine-start switch is placed in the STARTER ONLY position to motor the engine without starting it, current flows to the coil of the starter-only relay and moves its contacts so that it no longer supplies a ground for the ignition-power relay. Since the ignition-power relay cannot be actuated, no current flows to the ignition exciters or to the ignition light on the annunciator panel. But current does flow to the generator control and to the coil of the starter relay.

autoignition system. A system on a turbine engine that automatically energizes the igniters to provide a relight if the engine should flame-out.

flameout. A condition in the operation of a gas turbine engine in which the fire in the engine unintentionally goes out.

annunciator panel. A panel of warning lights in plain sight of the pilot. These lights are identified by the name of the system they represent and are usually covered with colored lenses to show the meaning of the condition they announce.

When the pilot turns the autoignition control switch to the ON, or ARMED, position, current flows from the bus through the 5-amp starter-control circuit breaker to the compressor-discharge pressure switch. When the engine is producing a specified amount of compressor-discharge pressure, the pressure switch moves its contacts so that current can flow to the autoignition-armed light on the annunciator panel.

If the engine loses power and the compressor-discharge pressure drops below the specified value, the pressure-switch contacts shift and send current to the coil of the ignition-power relay. When this relay shifts position, current flows from the bus through the ignition-power circuit breaker to the ignition exciter and the ignition-on light on the annunciator panel.

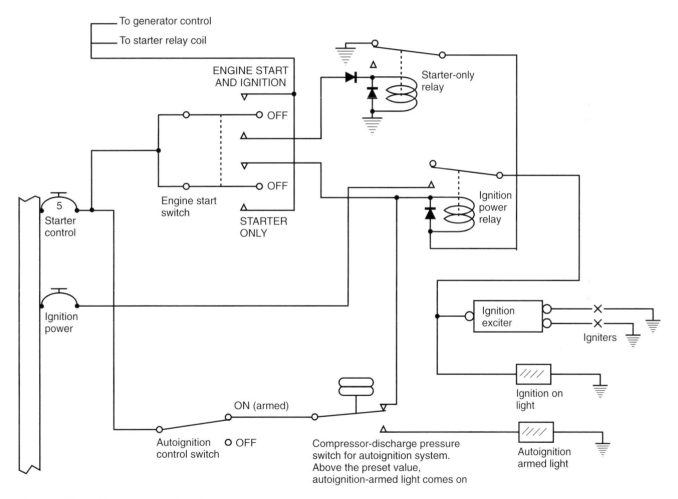

Figure 7-55. *Turbine-engine autoignition system*

Reciprocating-Engine Starting and Ignition Circuit

The high voltage supplied to the spark plugs in an aircraft reciprocating engine is produced in a magneto. For a magneto to produce a spark hot enough to jump the gap in the spark plug, it must be turned at a high rate of speed. Magnetos on most small aircraft engines reach this high speed when the engine is being cranked by using an impulse coupling between the engine and the magneto. Most larger reciprocating engines use a vibrator to produce a pulsating direct current that is fed into the primary winding of one of the magneto coils. This pulsating DC produces a high-voltage AC in the secondary of the coil, and this high voltage is sent through the distributor to the correct spark plug.

Not only must the spark for starting the engine be hot, but it must also occur after the piston passes over its top-center position so the engine will not kick back. At one time, this late, or retarded, spark was produced by a trailing finger on the distributor rotor, but modern systems use a second set of breaker points in one of the magnetos to interrupt the pulsating DC after the piston has passed top center, producing a retarded spark in the cylinder.

Figure 7-56 shows a circuit used on many modern reciprocating-engine aircraft. When the ignition switch is in the OFF position, the primary coils of both the right and the left magnetos are grounded through the ignition switch. Current from the aircraft bus cannot reach the coil of the starter solenoid because the battery contacts inside the starter switch are open.

When the switch is placed in the spring-loaded START position, the primary circuit of the right magneto remains grounded, but the ground is opened on the left magneto. Current flows from the main bus through the battery contacts in the switch, to the coil of the starter solenoid, and then to the starting vibrator. The vibrator changes the DC flowing through its coil into pulsating DC. This pulsating DC flows through the BO contacts and the LR contacts of the switch to ground through the retard set of breaker points in the left magneto. Current also flows from the BO contacts through the L contacts of the switch to ground through the normal, or run, set of breaker points in the left magneto. These breaker points are in parallel with the primary coil of the left magneto. The pulsating DC tries to flow to ground through the primary coil, but since it finds a low-resistance path to ground through the closed breaker points, it follows that path, and no current flows through the coil.

As the engine rotates to the correct advanced position for the magnetos to fire normally, the run breaker points open but current continues to flow to ground through the closed retard points. After the engine rotates far enough for the pistons to be in position for the spark to occur for starting, the retard points open and the pulsating DC flows to ground through the primary winding of the left magneto coil. When AC or pulsating DC flows through the primary winding of a transformer, such as the magneto coil, a high voltage is induced into the secondary winding. The secondary winding of the coil connects to the rotor of the distributor, a high-voltage selector switch, and high voltage goes to the correct spark plug.

retard breaker points. A set of breaker points in certain aircraft magnetos that are used to provide a late (retarded) spark for starting the engine.

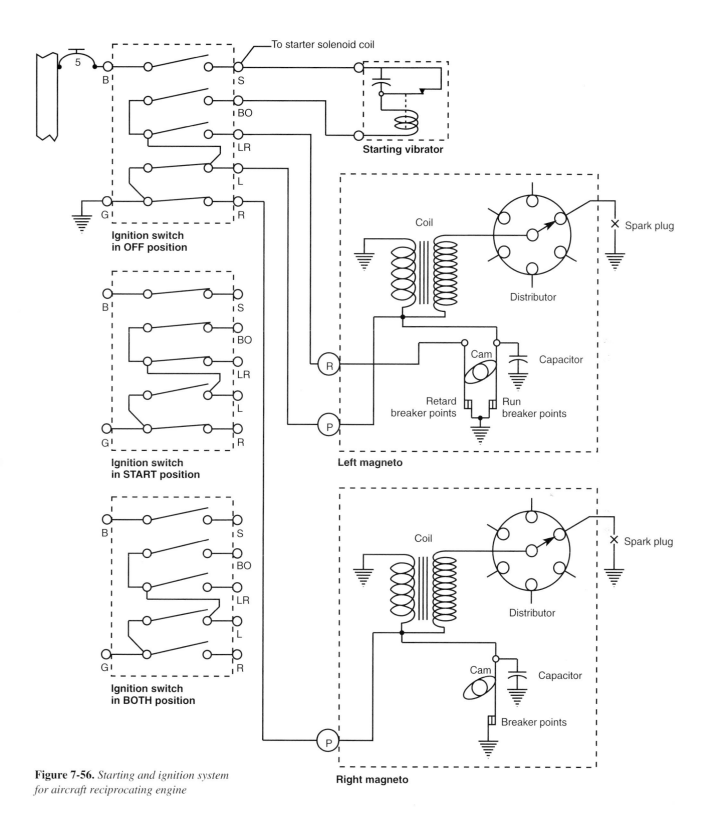

Figure 7-56. *Starting and ignition system for aircraft reciprocating engine*

As soon as the engine starts, the ignition switch is returned to the BOTH position and all of the contacts open, removing the ground from both of the magnetos and disconnecting the battery from the starter-relay coil and the vibrator. The L and R contacts in the switch can be closed individually in the course of a magneto check, to ground out the right and left magnetos.

Split-Bus Circuits for Avionics Protection

In the review of induced current beginning on Page 509, we saw that any time current is shut off to a motor or a relay, the magnetic field that actuated these devices collapses, cuts across their windings, and induces a spike of high voltage in the electrical system. These high-voltage spikes can destroy any solid-state electronic equipment connected to the electrical system.

To prevent damage to radio equipment, all radio equipment should be turned off before the engine is shut down, and a careful check made to be sure all of it is turned off before the engine is started. Most modern aircraft carry so much electronic equipment that it is possible to fail to turn off some system when the engine is started or shut down, or when the external power source is connected to the aircraft. To prevent this kind of damage, modern practice is to connect all of the voltage-sensitive electronic and avionic equipment to a separate bus and connect this bus to the main bus with either a switch-type circuit breaker or a relay.

Figure 7-57. *Avionics bus protected from inductive spikes by a switch-type circuit breaker*

Figure 7-57 shows a popular system that uses a switch-type circuit breaker to connect the avionics bus to the main bus. Before starting or shutting down the engine, the pilot opens the circuit breaker and all of the avionics equipment is isolated from the main bus. Any spikes of high voltage are absorbed by the battery, and there is no danger of damage to this equipment.

split bus. A type of electrical bus that allows all of the voltage-sensitive avionic equipment to be isolated from the rest of the aircraft electrical system when the engine is being started or when the ground-power unit is connected.

avionics. Electronic equipment installed in an aircraft.

In another type of split-bus system, the two buses are joined with a normally closed relay that connects the two buses at all times except when the starter is being used or when the ground power source is plugged into the aircraft. Figure 7-58 shows how this system works. When the starter switch is placed in the START position, current flows through the diode and the coil and opens the relay. When the engine starts, the starter switch is released and the relay closes, connecting the avionics bus to the main bus.

When the external power source is plugged into the aircraft, current flows through its diode and energizes the relay, isolating the avionics bus from the main bus as long as the ground-power source is plugged in.

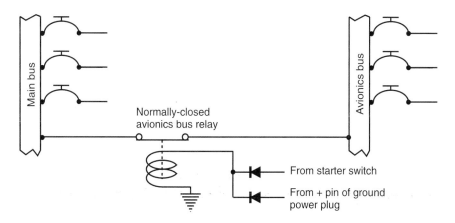

Figure 7-58. *Avionics bus protected from inductive spikes by a normally closed relay. This relay opens, isolating the avionics bus when the starter switch is closed or when the ground-power plug is connected.*

STUDY QUESTIONS: AIRCRAFT ELECTRICAL LOAD CIRCUITS

Answers begin on Page 580. Page numbers refer to chapter text.

65. A battery contactor is a/an _____ (continuous or intermittent) -duty solenoid. *Page 531*

66. A starter solenoid is a/an _____ (continuous or intermittent) -duty solenoid. *Page 531*

67. Normally the only circuit in an aircraft electrical system that does not require a circuit breaker or fuse is the _____ circuit. *Page 531*

68. The navigation light circuit in Figure 7-47 is an example of a _____ (series, parallel, or complex) circuit. *Page 532*

Continued

---

69. In the landing light circuit shown in Figure 7-48 it _____ (is or is not) possible to turn on the landing light without the taxi light also coming on. *Page 533*

70. In the landing gear circuit shown in Figure 7-49, three switches that must be in the correct position for current to flow to the landing gear relay coil are:

    a. _____

    b. _____

    c. _____
       Page 533

71. In the landing gear circuit shown in Figure 7-50, the landing gear warning horn _____ (will or will not) sound if only one throttle is pulled back to the idle position. *Page 534*

72. When the antiskid brake system shown in Figure 7-53 is operating properly, the aircraft cannot be landed with the brakes applied because the brakes cannot be applied until weight is on the landing gear and both _____ switches are closed. *Page 537*

73. According to the circuit of the propeller deicing system in Figure 7-54, the prop deicer ammeter shows the current flowing to the deicers when the system is operating _____ (manually or automatically). *Page 539*

74. In the turbine-engine autoignition circuit seen in Figure 7-55, the autoignition-armed light turns _____ (on or off) when the compressor-discharge pressure drops low enough for its pressure switch to supply power to the ignition power relay. *Page 541*

75. According to the reciprocating engine starting and ignition system seen in Figure 7-56, the engine is started on the _____ (left or right) magneto. *Page 542*

76. Avionic equipment must be isolated from the aircraft electrical system when the engine is being started because of spikes of high _____ voltage. *Page 544*

Electrical Power Systems for Large Aircraft

The electrical systems for large turbojet transport aircraft are different than those used with smaller aircraft, primarily because these aircraft use alternating current for their primary power. The DC needed for charging the battery and for certain motor and instrument systems is produced by transformer-rectifier, or TR, units. They reduce the voltage of the AC produced by the engine-driven generators to 28 volts and then rectify it, or change it, from AC into DC. *See* Figure 7-59 on the next page.

Figure 7-59 shows a simplified block diagram of the electrical power system of a Boeing 727 jet transport airplane. Electrical power is produced by three 115-volt, three-phase, 400-hertz alternating-current generators driven by the engines through constant-speed drive (CSD) units. The CSDs hold the speed of the generators constant to keep the frequency of the AC they produce constant as the engine speed varies over their normal operating range.

Each generator is connected to its own bus through a generator breaker (GB), and the three buses can be connected at the tie bus by the use of bus-tie breakers (BTB) that are controlled from the flight engineer's control panel.

A turbine-powered auxiliary power unit (APU) drives a three-phase AC generator that can be connected to the tie bus through the APU generator breaker to supply electrical power to the aircraft when the engines are not running. An external power unit can also be connected to the aircraft, and its AC output can be connected to the tie bus through the EXT breaker.

All the circuits that are essential to the operation of the aircraft are connected to an essential bus, which can be supplied with AC from any of the three engine-driven generators: the APU; the external power unit; or a standby inverter that produces 115-volt, 400-hertz AC from 28-volt DC battery power. A selector switch on the panel allows the flight engineer to select the source of power for the essential bus.

Direct current is produced by two transformer-rectifier (TR) units that take AC from buses 1 and 2 and supply DC to DC buses 1 and 2. A third TR unit takes AC from the essential bus and produces DC for the essential DC bus.

The battery supplies power for starting the APU and for emergency operation of certain essential radio and instrument systems. The battery is kept charged by a battery-charger unit that receives its AC power from the AC transfer bus. Monitoring circuits inside the battery are connected into the battery-charger circuit so that if the battery temperature becomes too high, the charging current will automatically decrease.

The battery is connected to the hot battery bus at all times, but is automatically disconnected from most of the DC loads in normal operation. These loads are supplied from the two DC buses and the essential DC bus.

transformer rectifier. A component in a large aircraft electrical system used to reduce the AC voltage and change it into DC for charging the battery and for operating DC equipment in the aircraft.

TR unit. A transformer-rectifier unit. A TR unit reduces the voltage of alternating current and changes it into direct current.

constant-speed drive. A special drive system used to connect an alternating current generator to an aircraft engine. The drive holds the generator speed (and thus its frequency) constant as the engine speed varies.

auxiliary power unit (APU). A small turbine or reciprocating engine that drives a generator, hydraulic pump and air pump. The APU is installed in the aircraft and is used to supply electrical power, and air and hydraulic pressure when the main engines are not running.

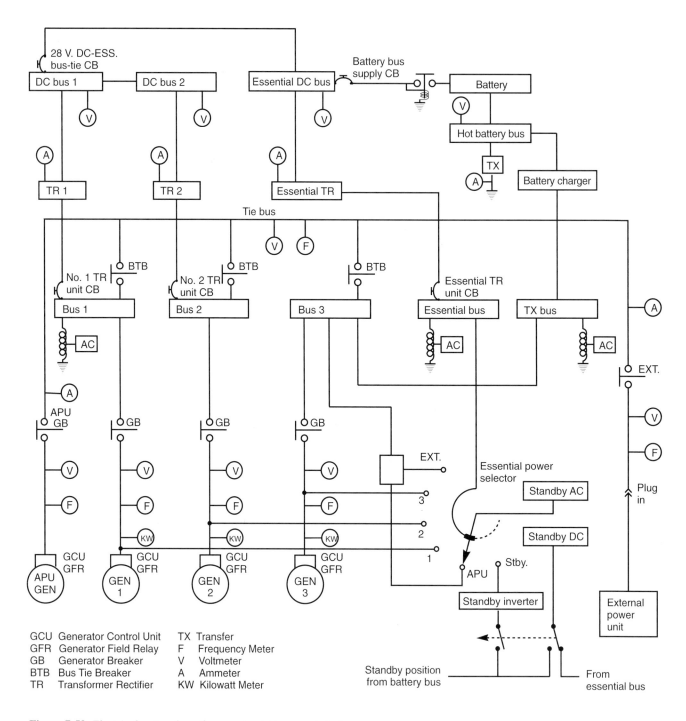

Figure 7-59. *Electrical system for a three-engine jet transport airplane.*

GCU Generator Control Unit
GFR Generator Field Relay
GB Generator Breaker
BTB Bus Tie Breaker
TR Transformer Rectifier

TX Transfer
F Frequency Meter
V Voltmeter
A Ammeter
KW Kilowatt Meter

Answers begin on Page 580. Page numbers refer to chapter text.

77. The generators installed on large turbojet aircraft produce _____ (AC or DC) electricity. *Page 547*

78. Direct current is produced in the electrical system seen in Figure 7-59 by the _____ .
    Page 547

79. The frequency of the AC produced by generators driven by turbine engines is held constant by the
    _____ units. *Page 547*

80. Three measurements that are made of the output of the three main generators in Figure 7-59 are:
    a. _____
    b. _____
    c. _____
       Page 548

81. Six sources of current that can be used to supply the essential bus in the electrical system shown in
    Figure 7-59 are:
    a. _____
    b. _____
    c. _____
    d. _____
    e. _____
    f. _____
       Page 548

82. The bus that is continuously supplied with battery power in the electrical system shown in Figure 7-59
    is the _____ . *Page 548*

Aircraft Electrical System Installation

The installation of an electrical system in an aircraft differs greatly from industrial and commercial installations. Absolute dependability is of utmost importance, and this must be maintained in an environment of vibration and drastically changing temperatures. The weight of the electrical installation is critical, as every pound used in the electrical system costs a pound in payload.

This next section addresses the actual installation of the circuits.

Electrical Wire

The wire used in aircraft electrical systems must stand up under extremes of vibration and abrasion without breaking and without wearing away the insulation. Most of the wire installed in a civil aircraft meets Military Specifications and may be made of either copper or aluminum. Copper conductors are coated with tin, nickel, or silver to prevent oxidation and to facilitate soldering.

Both copper and aluminum wires are stranded for protection against breakage from vibration and, for low temperature installations, are encased in polyvinylchloride or nylon insulation. If the wire is to be used in a high-temperature environment, it must have glass braid insulation.

Wire size is measured according to the American Wire Gage. The most common sizes range from AN-22 for wires that carry a small amount of current, to AN-0000 (pronounced "four aught") for battery cables that carry several hundred amps of current. In this numbering system, the smaller the number, the larger the wire. *See* Figure 7-60 on the next page.

Figure 7-60 shows the current-carrying capability of both copper and aluminum wire. An aluminum wire must be about two wire-gage numbers larger than a copper wire for it to carry the same amount of current. For example, an AL-4 aluminum wire should be used to replace an AN-6 copper wire if it is to carry the same amount of current. Six-gage copper wire can carry 101 amps in free air; 4-gage aluminum wire can carry 108 amps in the same installation.

A convenient rule of thumb regarding the current-carrying ability of copper aircraft wire is that each time you increase the wire size by four gage numbers, you approximately double the current-carrying capability of the wire. A 20-gage wire will carry 11 amps in free air, a 16-gage wire will carry 22 amps, a 12-gage wire will carry 41 amps, and an 8-gage wire will carry 73 amps.

Aluminum wire is more susceptible than copper wire to breakage and corrosion. As a result, several limitations are placed on the use of aluminum wire in aircraft electrical systems, including:

- Aluminum wire is restricted to 6-gage and larger.
- Aluminum wire should neither be attached to engine-mounted accessories nor installed in other areas of severe vibration.
- Aluminum wire should not be installed where frequent connections and disconnections are required. All installations of aluminum wire should be relatively permanent.
- Aluminum wire should not be used where the length of run is less than 3 feet.
- Aluminum wire should not be used in areas where corrosive fumes exist.
- Aluminum wire is not recommended for use in communications or navigation systems.

**Copper Wire
Current Carrying Capability**

Wire Size	Maximum Amps Single Wire in Free Air	Maximum Amps Wire in Bundle or Conduit
AN-20	11	7.5
AN-18	16	10
AN-16	22	13
AN-14	32	17
AN-12	41	23
AN-10	55	33
AN-8	73	46
AN-6	101	60
AN-4	135	80
AN-2	181	100
AN-1	211	125
AN-0	245	150
AN-00	283	175
AN-000	328	200
AN-0000	380	225

**Aluminum Wire
Current Carrying Capability**

Wire Size	Maximum Amps Single Wire in Free Air	Maximum Amps Wire in Bundle or Conduit
AL-6	83	50
AL-4	108	66
AL-2	152	90
AL-0	202	123
AL-00	235	145
AL-000	266	162
AL-0000	303	190

Figure 7-60. *Current-carrying capability of aircraft electrical wire*

Selection of Wire Size

In any kind of electrical installation, it is important that the correct size of wire be used. When choosing wire size, two factors must be considered: the voltage drop caused by current flowing through the resistance of the wire, and the current-carrying capability of the wire. Current-carrying capability is determined by the amount of heat generated in the wire by the current flowing through it.

The Federal Aviation Administration has established a maximum allowable voltage drop for aircraft electrical systems, as shown in Figure 7-61.

It is possible to use Ohm's law to determine the wire size needed to meet the voltage-drop requirements, but the FAA has produced a handy chart that makes selection easier. This chart, shown in Figure 7-62, gives both the allowable voltage drop for any installation and a good indication of the wire's current-carrying capability.

The vertical lines in Figure 7-62 represent the various wire gages. The horizontal lines are for the different lengths of wire that produce the maximum allowable voltage drop for continuous operation in each voltage system. The diagonal lines represent the number of amps of current the wire carries. The three heavy curves across the center of the chart show the current-carrying limitations of the wires.

Nominal System Voltage	Allowable Voltage Drop	
	Continuous Operation	Intermittent Operation
14	0.5	1.0
28	1.0	2.0
115	4.0	8.0
200	7.0	14.0

Figure 7-61. *Maximum allowable voltage drop for aircraft electrical systems*

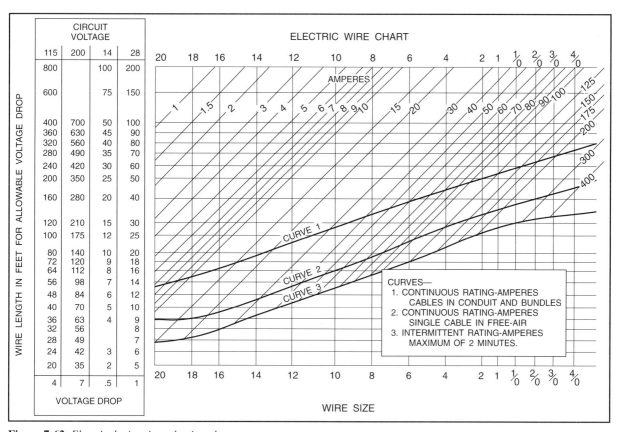

Figure 7-62. *Electrical wire size selection chart*

Use the chart in Figure 7-62 to find the size of copper wire needed for installation of a component that draws 20 amps continuously in a 28-volt system, if the wire needs to be 30 feet long and is to be installed in a bundle.

First, follow the 20-amp diagonal line down until it crosses the horizontal line for 30 feet in the 28-volt column. These two lines cross between the vertical lines for 12-gage and 10-gage wire. Always choose the larger wire when the lines cross between two wire sizes (in this case, the 10-gage wire).

Follow the horizontal line from the intersection of the 20-amp current line and the 10-gage wire line; it takes about 45 feet of this wire to give the maximum allowable 1-volt drop. Since the wire is only 30 feet long, we are perfectly safe as far as voltage drop is concerned.

The intersection of the 20-amp diagonal line and the 10-gage vertical line is well above curve 1. This means that a 10-gage copper wire can safely carry 20 amps when it is routed in a bundle or in conduit. (The chart in Figure 7-60 shows that a 10-gage copper wire routed in a bundle can carry 33 amps.)

Now, assume that a battery in a 14-volt aircraft is installed in such a way that it requires a 15-foot cable to supply 200 amps to the starter.

First, see Figure 7-60; it shows that an AN-1 wire is needed to carry 200 amps in free air. Now, using Figure 7-62, follow the 200-amp diagonal line down until it crosses the 1-gage vertical line. The intersection is between curves 2 and 3, which means that a 1-gage wire can carry 200 amps if it is routed in free air and is used for intermittent operation (2 minutes or less). The starter is an intermittent load, and the starter cable will be run by itself in free air.

By projecting a horizontal line from this intersection to the column for a 14-volt system, we see that 16 feet of this wire will produce only a 0.5-volt drop when 200 amps flows through it, so the voltage drop in 15 feet of wire is well below the 1 volt allowed for an intermittent load in a 14-volt system. *See* Figure 7-61.

Special Types of Wire

Most of the wire used in an aircraft electrical system is made of stranded, tinned copper and insulated with white polyvinylchloride (PVC) which is often covered with a clear nylon jacket. This type of wire is suitable for installations in which the temperature does not exceed 221°F (105°C). The insulation has a voltage rating of 1,000 volts.

If the wire is to be used in an application in which the temperature is too high for the PVC insulation some form of fluorocarbon insulation can be used. This insulation is normally good to a temperature of about 392°F (200°C).

When wires carry alternating current in an area where the electromagnetic field caused by the AC could interfere with other wires or with sensitive electronic equipment, the wires may be shielded. A shielded wire is one in which the stranded wire is insulated with PVC and then encased in a braid of tinned copper. Most shielded wire is covered with a clear PVC or nylon jacket

PVC. Polyvinylchloride. A thermoplastic resin used to make transparent tubing for insulating electrical wires.

shielded wire. Electrical wire that is enclosed in a braided metal jacket. Electromagnetic energy radiated from the wire is trapped by the braid and is carried to ground.

to protect it from abrasion. Several individual wires grouped together and enclosed in a common shield is called a shielded cable; in certain applications, the wires inside the shield are twisted to further reduce the effect of the magnetic fields that surround the individual wires.

Coaxial cable, commonly called coax, is a type of shielded wire used between a radio antenna and the equipment and between other special types of electronic equipment. Coaxial cable is made of a solid or stranded center conductor surrounded by thick insulation. Around this inner insulation are one or two layers of tinned copper braid enclosed in an outer jacket of tough plastic to protect it from abrasion.

Coaxial cables are normally used to carry alternating current at radio frequencies. It is important when carrying this type of electrical signal that the two conductors (the inner conductor and the braid) be held so that they have the same center. Coaxial cable must not be crushed or bent with too small a bend radius or the relationship between the two conductors will be destroyed.

Normally, wire bundles are routed in straight lines throughout the aircraft following the structural members, but coaxial cable may be routed as directly as possible to minimize its length.

coaxial cable. A special type of electrical cable that consists of a central conductor, an inner insulator, a braided metal outer conductor, and an outer insulation. Coaxial cable is used to connect a radio transmitter with its antenna.

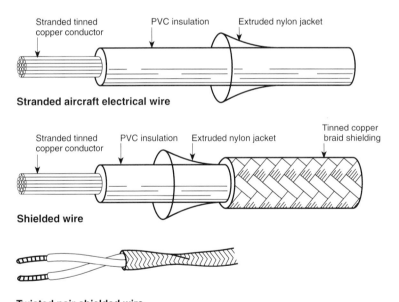

Stranded aircraft electrical wire

Shielded wire

Twisted pair shielded wire

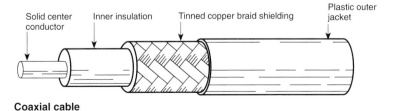

Coaxial cable

Figure 7-63. *Types of aircraft electrical wire*

Terminal and Connector Installation

The wiring for an aircraft electrical system is assembled into harnesses in the aircraft factory and is installed in the aircraft without the use of solder. Permanently attached wires are fastened to terminal strips; wires that must be connected and disconnected frequently are terminated with AN or MS quick-disconnect connectors.

Quick-Disconnect Connectors

Wire bundles that connect an electrical or electronic component into an aircraft electrical system are usually terminated with quick-disconnect plugs that allow the component to be changed without disturbing the wiring.

Wires carrying power to a component (hot wires) are fitted with connectors that have sockets. The mating connectors on the ground side of the circuit have pins. This minimizes the possibility of a short between a connector and ground when the connectors are separated.

quick-disconnect connector. A type of wire connector used in aircraft electrical systems. The wires terminate inside an insulated plug with pins or sockets that mate with the opposite type of terminals in a similar plug. The two halves of the connector push together and are held tight with a special nut.

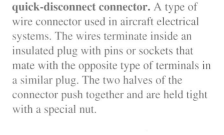

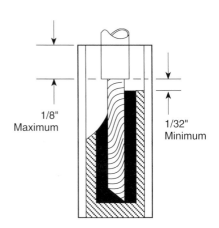

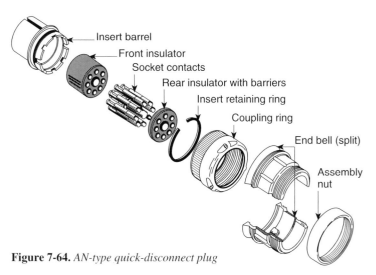

Figure 7-64. *AN-type quick-disconnect plug*

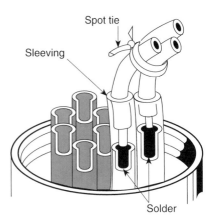

Figure 7-65. *Method of attaching wires in a quick-disconnect plug by soldering*

The wires are installed in the pins or sockets of the connector by crimping or soldering, and the connector is reassembled. A cable clamp is screwed onto the end of the connector and all of the wires are securely clamped so that when the cable is handled, no strain is put on the wires where they are attached.

Wires are attached to most of the older quick-disconnect plugs by soldering, as shown in Figure 7-65. About $\frac{1}{32}$-inch of bare wire is left between the top of the solder in the pots and the end of the insulation, to ensure that no solder wicks up into the strands of wire and destroys its flexibility where it is attached. After all of the wires are soldered into the connector, transparent PVC sleeving is slipped over the end of each wire and the pot into which the wire is soldered. These wires are then tied together with a spot tie of waxed linen or nylon cord.

Most modern quick-disconnect plugs use crimped-on tapered terminals that are pressed into tapered holes in the ends of the pins or sockets. A tapered pin is crimped onto the end of each wire to be inserted into the plug, and all necessary rings and clamps are slipped over the wires. A special insertion tool, shown in Figure 7-66, is used to force the tapered terminals into the holes and lock them in place. After the wires are in place, the connector is assembled and a wire clamp is tightened on the wire to take all of the strain.

Some components have two or more identical quick-disconnect plugs. In such cases, if the wrong socket is connected to the plug the equipment will not work, or worse, it may be damaged. To prevent this, the inserts in the connectors are designed so that they may be positioned in several different ways inside the shells. The last letter in the identification number marked on the shell is always one of the last letters in the alphabet, and it identifies the insert rotation. In Figure 7-67, the insert rotation letter is X, and the slot into which the key of the mating connector fits is near socket B. The inserts in both halves of the connector can be rotated so that the key and slot are near socket A. If this were done, the insert rotation identifier would be another letter, possibly Y. Only a plug with a Y identifier will fit into a socket with a Y identifier.

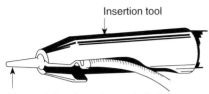

Insertion tool

Tapered pin crimped on end of wire

Figure 7-66. *Tapered pins are crimped onto the wires and are pushed into tapered holes in the connectors with a tool such as this.*

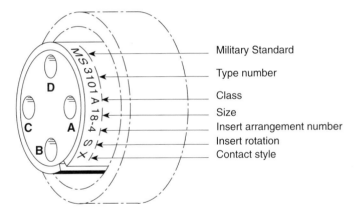

Military Standard

Type number

Class

Size

Insert arrangement number

Insert rotation

Contact style

Figure 7-67. *Identification and insert orientation marking on a quick-disconnect connector*

Terminal Strips

Wires which are installed when the aircraft is built and are disconnected only during a major repair or alteration are connected to terminal strips inside junction boxes. Most terminal strips in an aircraft electrical system are of the barrier type and are made of a phenolic plastic material. Barrier posts stick up between each terminal lug to keep the wires separated.

Most terminal lugs have 6-32, 8-32, or 10-32 machine screw threads and are held in the terminal strip with a flat washer and a cadmium-plated plain nut. Electrical power circuits normally use terminal lugs no smaller than 10-32, but most load circuits use smaller lugs.

terminal strips. A group of threaded studs mounted in a strip of insulating plastic. Electrical wires with crimped-on terminals are placed over the studs and secured with nuts.

phenolic plastic. A plastic material made of a thermosetting phenol-formaldehyde resin, reinforced with cloth or paper. Phenolic plastic materials are used for electrical insulators and for chemical-resistant table tops.

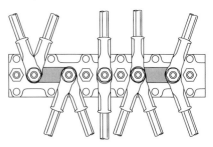

When it is necessary to connect more than 4 wires to a single point, 2 or more studs are connected with a bus strap.

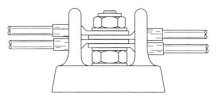

Correct method of stacking wire terminals on a stud

Figure 7-68. *A barrier-type terminal strip*

Copper-wire terminals are placed directly on top of the nut, followed either by a plain washer and an elastic stop nut or by a plain washer, a split steel lockwasher, and a plain nut. The wire terminals are stacked on the studs, as shown in Figure 7-68, with no more than four terminals per stud. When it is necessary for more than four wires to be attached to a single point, a bus strip is used to join two studs, and the wires are divided between the studs. No single stud should have more than four terminal lugs or three terminal lugs and a bus strap.

Wire Terminals

Pre-insulated crimp-on terminals are used on all wires connected to terminal strips. The insulation is stripped from the end of the wire, which is inserted into the terminal until the insulation butts up against the sleeve of the terminal and the end of the wire sticks out slightly beyond the end of the sleeve. When the terminal is crimped with a special crimping tool, the terminal sleeve grips the wire tightly enough to make a joint that is as strong as the wire itself.

The insulation around the sleeve is crimped at the same time, so it is forced tightly against the insulation on the wire and helps remove some of the strain from the wire strands when the wire is subjected to movement and vibration.

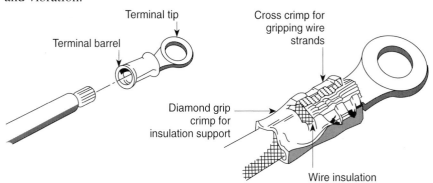

Figure 7-69. *Method of installing crimped-on terminals*

The color of the insulation on the terminal indicates the wire size the terminal is designed to fit. A small yellow terminal fits on wire gages 26 through 22, a red terminal fits wires from 20 through 18, a blue terminal fits wires from 16 through 14, and a large yellow terminal fits wire gages 12 through 10.

Terminals for wires larger than 10-gage are non-insulated and are installed on the wires with an air-powered squeezer. After the terminal is squeezed onto the end of the wire, slip a piece of PVC tubing over the sleeve of the terminal and secure it by tying it in place with waxed string or by shrinking the insulation over the terminal with heat.

Large aluminum wires are installed in aluminum terminal lugs by the method shown in Figure 7-70. Strip the insulation from the end of the wire, being very careful to not nick any of the wire strands. (Any nicked strand will very likely break and reduce the current carrying capability of the wire.)

Partially fill the terminal with a petrolatum and zinc-dust compound and slip the wire into the terminal until the end of the wire shows in the inspection hole. As the wire is inserted into the terminal, the zinc-dust compound is forced back to cover the strands. When the terminal is crimped with a pneumatic crimper, the zinc dust abrades the oxide from the wire strands and the petrolatum keeps air away from the wire and prevents oxides from forming on the wire. After the terminal is crimped on, insulate the barrel with PVC tubing and either tie it in place or shrink it around the terminal with heat.

petrolatum-zinc dust compound.
A special abrasive compound used inside an aluminum wire terminal that is being swaged onto a piece of aluminum electrical wire. When the terminal is compressed, the zinc dust abrades the oxides from the wire, and the petrolatum prevents oxygen reaching the wire so no more oxides can form.

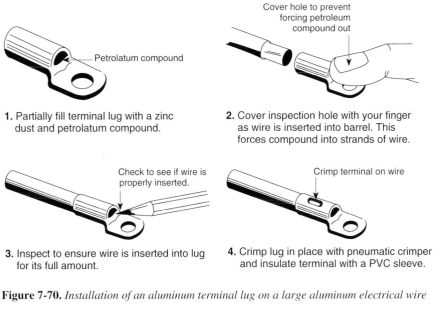

1. Partially fill terminal lug with a zinc dust and petrolatum compound.

2. Cover inspection hole with your finger as wire is inserted into barrel. This forces compound into strands of wire.

3. Inspect to ensure wire is inserted into lug for its full amount.

4. Crimp lug in place with pneumatic crimper and insulate terminal with a PVC sleeve.

Figure 7-70. *Installation of an aluminum terminal lug on a large aluminum electrical wire*

The three most popular types of wire terminals are ring, hook, and slotted terminals, shown in Figure 7-71. Most of the wires installed in an aircraft electrical system are terminated with ring-type terminals. If the nut on the terminal stud should become loose, the ring-type terminal will remain on the stud, whereas a hook or slotted terminal will slip off.

Ring-type terminal
— Tongue
— Barrel
— Color-coded insulation
— Insulation grip

Hook-type terminal

Slotted-type terminal

Figure 7-71. *Types of wire terminals*

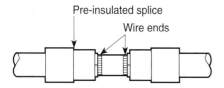

Figure 7-72. *Pre-insulated wire splice before it is crimped onto the wire*

Wire Splices

At one time it was common practice to splice wires by wrapping the ends of the wires together and soldering them, but now almost all wire splicing is done with the proper size pre-insulated solderless splices. To install the terminals, strip the insulation off the ends of the wires, slip the ends of the two wires into the splice, and crimp the splice, using the proper crimping tool.

There should not be more than one splice in any wire segment between any two connections or other disconnect points. When several wires in a bundle are to be spliced, the wires should be cut so that the splices are staggered along the bundle, as in Figure 7-73.

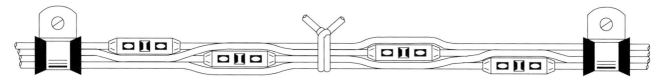

Figure 7-73. *Wire splices should be staggered when the wires are installed in a bundle.*

Wire Number GE4B-22N

GE This wire is in the landing gear indicator light circuit. *See* Figure 7-75.

4 This is wire number 4 in this circuit.

B This is the second segment of wire number 4.

22 This is a 22-gage wire.

N This wire is connected to aircraft ground.

Figure 7-74. *Interpretation of wire identification numbers*

Wire Identification

Wires installed in an aircraft are usually identified by a series of letters and numbers, including code letters for the circuit function, the number of the wire in the circuit, a letter to indicate the segment of the wire, a number for the wire gage, and the letter N if the wire goes to ground. *See* Figures 7-74 and 7-75 for the interpretation of a wire identification number.

Most aircraft wires are identified near each end and at 12- to 15-inch intervals along their length. The numbers are stamped on the wire in the aircraft factory. If you must install a wire in the field, where you do not have access to a wire-stamping machine, write the wire number on a piece of pressure-sensitive tape and wrap the tape around the ends of the wire in the form of a small flag.

Wire Bundling

The complex wiring installed in a modern aircraft is not normally installed one wire at a time. Rather, the entire wiring assembly is made in the form of a harness on jig boards in the aircraft factory, and the harness is installed in the aircraft. If an aircraft is damaged to the extent that it must be rewired, it is usually more economical to buy a new harness and install it, rather than to install individual wires.

After an aircraft is in the field, new equipment is often added, requiring new wire bundles to be made up and installed. When making up a wire bundle, it is important that all of the wires be kept parallel and not allowed to cross over one another and make a messy-looking bundle. One way of keeping the wires straight is to use a guide made of the plastic insert from a discarded AN or MS

wire bundle. A compact group of electrical wires held together with special wrapping devices or with waxed string. These bundles are secured to the aircraft structure with special clamps.

A Armament

B Photographic

C Control Surface
  CA - Automatic Pilot
  CC - Wing Flaps
  CD - Elevator Trim

D Instrument (Other than Flight or Engine Instrument)
  DA - Ammeter
  DB - Flap Position Indicator
  DC - Clock
  DD - Voltmeter
  DE - Outside Air Temperature
  DF - Flight Hour Meter

E Engine Instrument
  EA - Carburetor Air Temperature
  EB - Fuel Quantity Gage and Transmitter
  EC - Cylinder Head Temperature
  ED - Oil Pressure
  EE - Oil Temperature
  EF - Fuel Pressure
  EG - Tachometer
  EH - Torque Indicator
  EJ - Instrument Cluster

F Flight Instrument
  FA - Bank and Turn
  FB - Pitot Static Tube Heater and Stall Warning Heater
  FC - Stall Warning
  FD - Speed Control System
  FE - Indicator Lights

G Landing Gear
  GA - Actuator
  GB - Retraction
  GC - Warning Device (Horn)
  GD - Light Switches
  GE - Indicator Lights

H Heating, Ventilating and Deicing
  HA - Anti-icing
  HB - Cabin Heater
  HC - Cigar Lighter
  HD - Deice
  HE - Air Conditioners
  HF - Cabin Ventilation

J Ignition
  JA - Magneto

K Engine Control
  KA - Starter Control
  KB - Propeller Synchronizer

L Lighting
  LA Cabin

L Lighting (cont'd)
  LB - Instrument
  LC - Landing
  LD - Navigation
  LE - Taxi
  LF - Rotating Beacon
  LG - Radio
  LH - Deice
  LJ - Fuel Selector
  LK - Tail Floodlight

M Miscellaneous
  MA - Cowl Flaps
  MB - Electrically Operated Seats
  MC - Smoke Generator
  MD - Spray Equipment
  ME - Cabin Pressurization Equipment
  MF - Chem O_2 - Indicator

P DC Power
  PA - Battery Circuit
  PB - Generator Circuits
  PC - External Power Source

Q Fuel and Oil
  QA - Auxiliary Fuel Pump
  QB - Oil Dilution
  QC - Engine Primer
  QD - Main Fuel Pumps
  QE - Fuel Valves

R Radio (Navigation and Communication)
  RA - Instrument Landing
  RB - Command
  RC - Radio Direction Finding
  RD - VHF
  RE - Homing
  RF - Marker Beacon
  RG - Navigation
  RH - High Frequency
  RJ - Interphone
  RK - UHF
  RL - Low Frequency
  RM - Frequency Modulation
  RP - Audio System and Audio Amplifier
  RR - Distance Measuring Equipment (DME)
  RS - Airborne Public Address System

S Radar

U Miscellaneous Electronic
  UA - Identification - Friend or Foe

W Warning and Emergency
  WA - Flare Release
  WB - Chip Detector
  WC - Fire Detection System

X AC Power

Figure 7-75. *Circuit function and circuit code identifiers for aircraft electrical wire*

connector. Slip the wires through the holes in the guide before they are secured into the connector. Then slip the guide along the wire bundle as you tie the wires together with nylon straps or spot ties made with waxed linen or nylon cord.

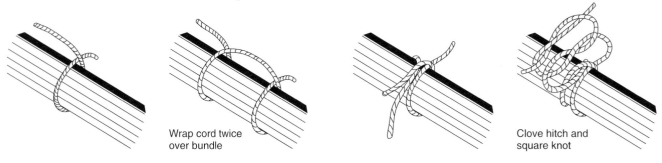

Wrap cord twice
over bundle

Clove hitch and
square knot

Figure 7-76. *Wire bundles can be tied together with waxed linen or nylon cord using two half hitches (a clove hitch) secured with a square knot.*

Junction Boxes

Terminal strips are mounted inside of junction boxes to protect the wires from physical damage and electrical short circuits. Junction boxes are usually made of aluminum alloy or stainless steel, and are installed at locations where they cannot be used as a step or the wire bundles used as a handhold. When possible, the boxes are mounted with their open side facing downward or at an angle so that any dropped nuts or washers will tend to fall out rather than wedge between the terminals.

The holes where the wires enter the junction box are fitted with protective grommets to prevent the wires from chafing, thereby damaging their insulation. Junction boxes are equipped with close-fitting lids to keep water and loose debris out and away from the wires.

Wiring Installation

When installing a wire bundle in an aircraft, use cushion clamps to attach the bundle to the aircraft structure. As mentioned above, be sure the bundles are not routed in a location where they are likely to be used as a handhold or where they can be damaged by persons entering or leaving the aircraft or by cargo or baggage being pulled across them or resting on them.

Wire bundles should not be routed below a battery or closer than 6 inches from the bilge of the fuselage (the lowest point where water can collect). Wire bundles should not be run closer than 3 inches from any control cable unless a suitable mechanical guard is installed over the wire so the cable cannot contact it.

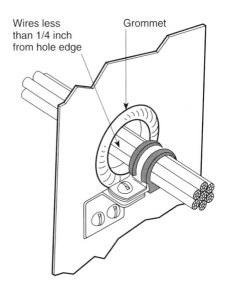

Wires less
than 1/4 inch
from hole edge

Grommet

Figure 7-77. *When electrical wires pass through a bulkhead, the edges of the hole should be protected with a grommet, and the wire bundle secured with a cushioned clamp.*

If an electrical wire bundle is run through a compartment parallel to a line carrying a combustible fluid or oxygen, the bundle must be separated from the line as much as possible. The wires should be above or on the same level as the fluid line and must be no closer than 6 inches from the line.

Most wire installation in modern aircraft is open wiring. This means that the wires are bundled and fastened together, but are not installed in protective covering, such as a conduit. In some locations, however, such as wheel wells, where additional protection is needed for the wires, they are run through either a rigid or a flexible conduit.

open wiring. An electrical wiring installation in which the wires are tied together in bundles and clamped to the aircraft structure rather than being enclosed in conduit.

When wires are run through rigid conduit, the ends of the conduit must have all burrs removed to prevent wire damage. The inside diameter of the conduit must be at least 25% greater than the outside diameter of the wire bundle in it, and the conduit must be bent carefully so that it does not collapse in the bend and decrease to less than 75% of its original diameter.

rigid conduit. Aluminum alloy tubing used to house electrical wires in areas where they are subject to mechanical damage.

Wire bundles are often run inside a piece of clear PVC tubing for protection. A trick that makes this hard job easier is to use compressed air to blow some tire talcum through the tubing, then blow a length of rib lacing cord through it. Tie the end of the wire bundle to the rib lacing cord and pull it through.

Circuit Control and Protection Devices

The purpose of an electrical system in an aircraft is to create a flow of current that can perform work by the heat it produces or the magnetic field it causes. For this work to be done, the flow must be controlled and the system protected against an excess of either current or voltage.

Switches

All switches used in aircraft electrical systems must have sufficient contact capacity to break, make, and carry continuously the connected load current. Snap-action switches are preferred because their contacts open rapidly, regardless of the speed of the operating toggle or plunger. This rapid movement minimizes contact arcing.

Type of Load	Derating Factors	
	24 VDC System	12 VDC System
Lamp	8	5
Inductive (relay–solenoid)	4	2
Resistive (heater)	2	1
Motor	3	2

Figure 7-78. *Switch derating factors*

The rating stamped on the switch housing is the amount of continuous current the switch can safely carry with the contacts closed. When switches are used in certain types of circuits, they must be derated by the factors shown in Figure 7-78.

derated. Reduction in the rated voltage or current of an electrical device. Derating is done to extend the life or reliability of the device.

A switch installed in a circuit that controls incandescent lamps is exposed to a very high inrush of current. When the lamp filament is cold, its resistance is very low. When the switch is first closed, the flow of current is 15 times more than the continuous current. As the filament heats up, its resistance increases and the current decreases. If the switch is not derated, the contacts may burn or weld shut when they are closed.

Wire AN Gage Copper	Circuit Breaker (Amp.)	Fuse (Amp.)
22	5	5
20	7.5	5
18	10	10
16	15	10
14	20	15
12	25 (30)	20
10	35 (40)	30
8	50	50
6	80	70
4	100	70
2	125	100
1		150
0		150

Figures in parentheses may be substituted where protectors of the indicated rating are not available.

Figure 7-79. *Wire and circuit protection chart*

When a switch opens an inductive circuit, such as a relay or solenoid, the magnetic field surrounding the turns of the coil collapses and induces a high voltage that causes an arc across the contacts.

DC motors draw a large amount of current when the switch is first closed. As soon as the armature starts to turn, a back voltage, or counter EMF, is generated and the load current decreases. When the switch is opened to stop the motor, the magnetic field surrounding the coils collapses and induces a high voltage in the circuit.

A switch controlling a DC motor in a 24-volt system has a derating factor of 3. If the motor draws 4 amps for its normal operation, the switch must be rated at 4 · 3 = 12 amps to allow it to safely start and stop the motor.

Switches must be mounted in such a way that their operation is logical and consistent with other controls. For example, two-position ON-OFF switches should be mounted in such a way that the switch is turned on by an upward or forward movement of the control. If the switch controls movable aircraft elements, such as landing gear or flaps, the handle should move in the same direction as the desired motion. The operating control of switches whose inadvertent operation must be prevented should be covered with an appropriate guard.

Fuses and Circuit Breakers

Circuit protection devices such as fuses and circuit breakers are installed as close to the source of electrical energy as is practical. Their function is to protect the wiring. The circuit protection device should open the circuit before enough current flows to heat the wire and cause its insulation to smoke.

Figure 7-79 shows the size of fuse or circuit breaker that should be used to protect various sizes of wires.

STUDY QUESTIONS: AIRCRAFT ELECTRICAL SYSTEM INSTALLATION

Answers begin on Page 580. Page numbers refer to chapter text.

83. A 20-gage wire will carry _____ (more or less) current than an 18-gage wire. *Page 550*

84. A continuous electrical load in a 28-volt electrical system is allowed to produce a voltage drop of _____ volt/s. *Page 551*

85. An intermittent electrical load in a 14-volt electrical system is allowed to produce a voltage drop of _____ volt/s. *Page 551*

86. If a 4-gage copper wire routed in free air is to be replaced with an aluminum wire that is to carry the same amount of current, a _____-gage aluminum wire will have to be used. *Page 550*

87. The smallest size aluminum wire recommended for use in aircraft electrical systems is _____-gage. *Page 550*

88. When selecting the size wire to use in an aircraft electrical system, two things must be considered. These are:
    a. _____
    b. _____
    Page 551

89. Use the wire chart in Figure 7-62 on Page 551 to find the wire size needed to carry a continuous load of 50 amps for 60 feet in a 28-volt electrical system. The wire is to be routed in a bundle. The smallest wire is a _____ gage. *Page 551*

90. Use the wire chart in Figure 7-62 on Page 551 to find the size electrical cable needed to carry an intermittent load of 150 amps for 20 feet in a 14-volt electrical system without exceeding a 1-volt drop. The smallest wire is a _____ gage. *Page 551*

91. The electromagnetic field surrounding wires carrying alternating current can be prevented from interfering with sensitive electronic equipment by using _____ wires. *Page 552*

92. A radio transmitter is normally connected to its antenna with a _____ cable. *Page 553*

93. The half of an AN or MS quick-disconnect connector that carries the power is fitted with _____ (pins or sockets). *Page 554*

94. A barrier-type terminal strip should not have more than _____ terminals installed on any single lug. *Page 556*

95. If more than four wires need to be connected to a single point on a terminal strip, two or more lugs can be connected with a metal _____ . *Page 556*

96. The correct size preinsulated terminal to use on a 18-gage wire would have a _____ (what color) insulation. *Page 556*

Continued

97. The correct size preinsulated terminal to use on a 12-gage wire would have a _____ (what color) insulation. *Page 556*

98. The type of wire terminal that should be installed on a barrier-type terminal strip is a _____ type. *Page 557*

99. Refer to Figure 7-75. Answer these questions about a wire identified as HD3A-20.
    a. This wire is in the _____ system.
    b. This is wire number _____ in this circuit.
    c. This is the _____ segment in this wire.
    d. This is a _____-gage wire.
    e. This wire _____ (does or does not) go to ground.
       Pages 558 and 559

100. The only type lubricant that should be used when pulling a wire bundle through a piece of polyvinyl tubing is _____ . *Page 561*

101. Wire bundles should be secured to the aircraft structure using _____ clamps. *Page 560*

102. If an electrical wire bundle is routed parallel to a fuel line, the wire bundle should be _____ (above or below) the fuel line. *Page 561*

103. A wire bundle should be no closer than _____ inches from any control cable unless a suitable mechanical guard is installed over the wire so the cable cannot contact it. *Page 560*

104. The maximum-diameter wire bundle that may be enclosed in a rigid conduit with an inside diameter of one inch is _____ inch . *Page 561*

105. The edges of a hole through which a wire bundle passes must be covered with a _____ .
     Page 560

106. A switch used to control a 3-amp continuous flow of current in a 24-volt DC incandescent lamp circuit should be rated for at least _____ amps. *Page 561*

107. A switch used to control a 12-volt DC motor that draws a 3-amp continuous flow of current should be rated for at least _____ amps. *Page 562*

108. A circuit that is wired with an 18-gage wire should be protected with a _____-amp circuit breaker.
     Page 562

Electrical System Troubleshooting

At one time, it was easy to see what was wrong with an ailing airplane, but much skill and knowledge were needed to get it back in the air. Today, the situation has drastically changed. With the complex systems used in modern aircraft, a high degree of knowledge and skill is needed to identify problems, but specialization has made it possible to get an aircraft back into the air quickly. Faulty components are sent to a shop where specialists with sophisticated test equipment can find and fix the trouble.

Remove and replace, or R and R, maintenance is the only way flight schedules can be maintained today. When an aircraft is down, it is the responsibility of the technician to find out as quickly as possible which component is causing the trouble, remove it, and replace it with a component known to be good, in order to get the aircraft back into the air quickly. Maintenance of this type requires a good knowledge of systematic troubleshooting so that only the offending component is changed.

One major air carrier has recently stated that more than 60% of the "black boxes" removed from aircraft throughout their system have been sent to the shop only to find that there was nothing wrong with them. Needless to say, this is inefficient use of the technician's time, and it cannot be tolerated if the airline is to operate cost-effectively.

To help reduce unnecessary R and R of good components, this next section will describe how to develop a system of logical, or systematic, troubleshooting that will allow you to locate a problem and fix it in the shortest period of time.

Rules for Systematic Troubleshooting

Efficient troubleshooting begins with a few very simple rules:

1. Know the way the system should operate. This sounds absurdly simple, but it is the secret of successful troubleshooting. You must know the way a component works. This includes knowledge of correct voltage and current at specified test points and the correct frequency and wave form of alternating current at these test points.

2. Observe the way the system is operating. Any difference between the way a system is operating and the way it should operate is an indication of trouble. Current or voltage that is too low or too high, or components that show signs of overheating, are indications that a system is not operating correctly.

3. Divide the system to find the trouble. Time is valuable in aviation maintenance; it is important that lost motion be kept to a minimum. When we know a system is not operating as it should, we must first find whether the trouble is in the beginning of the system or near its end. To do this, open the system near its middle and check the conditions there. If

Continued

troubleshooting. A procedure used in aircraft maintenance in which the operation of a malfunctioning system is analyzed to find the reason for the malfunction and to find a method for returning the system to its condition of normal operation.

black box. A term used for any portion of an electrical or electronic system that can be removed as a unit. A black box does not have to be a physical box.

everything is OK at this point, the trouble is between there and the end. If things at that point are not as they should be, the trouble is between the power source and that point.

4. Look for the obvious problem first, and make all measurements at the points where they are easiest to make.

    Popped circuit breakers, blown fuses, and corroded ground connections are usually easy to check, and are the cause of many electrical system malfunctions.

An Example of Systematic Troubleshooting

Let's examine a very simple troubleshooting problem. Most of the steps we will discuss will seem quite obvious, but bear with us. We are building a system that works on a simple inoperative dome light as well as on a malfunctioning ignition or alternator system.

In this example, the only information we have is a complaint left by a pilot that tells us "the dome light doesn't work." This is a simple problem, and in all probability, it is a burned-out bulb. But since we are analyzing systematic troubleshooting, let's not close our minds to all of the possibilities.

Below are some of the first points that might come to mind:

1. When troubleshooting a problem, you must know how the system SHOULD work: In this case, the dome light should light up.

2. You should know all of the possible problems that can keep the dome light from burning.

    a. Is there power on the airplane? There must be, or the pilot would have complained about more than just the dome light.

    b. Was the dome light switch turned on? Surely the pilot would have checked this.

    c. Is the bulb burned out? This is our most likely suspect, but let's not jump to conclusions.

    d. What else could be the problem? There are several other possibilities, including a bad switch, a bad connection, a broken wire, or a bad ground connection.

To make the most efficient use of your time, you must make only one trip to the airplane, and you must fix the problem on your first attempt. First, gather the tools and equipment you'll need. You'll need a copy of the wiring diagram for the dome light circuit; you can get a copy from the microfiche reader or from a service manual. And you'll need a spare bulb. You can get the correct part number from the circuit diagram. You will also need a multimeter (a volt-ohm-milliammeter, or VOM), and a screwdriver or two.

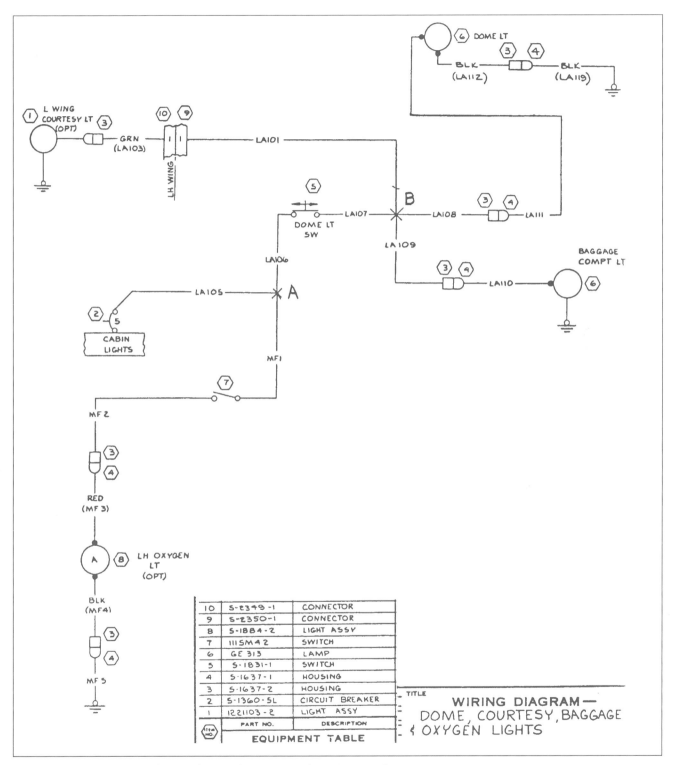

Figure 7-80. *Typical electrical circuit diagram from an aircraft service manual*

Before going any further, let's take a few minutes to consider the dome light circuit. Look at Figure 7-80 and answer the following questions:

1. Which circuit breaker supplies power to the dome light?

   Answer—Cabin lights

2. What other lights are on the same circuit breaker?

   Answer—L.H. Oxygen light, baggage compartment light, L. wing courtesy light

3. What is the part number of the dome light bulb?

   Answer—GE 313

Now you are ready to go to the airplane.

When you turn on the master switch, you hear the familiar "klunk" of the battery contactor, which tells you that there is electrical power on the main bus.

But, when you try the dome light switch, sure enough, the dome light doesn't light up. But the left-wing courtesy light does, so the baggage compartment light is probably burning too.

Next in line is the bulb and its ground circuit. Take the cover off of the dome light so you can see the bulb. Before taking the bulb out of the socket, make sure that the ground for the light is good. Using one of the test leads from your multimeter, touch one end to the outside of the lamp socket and the other end to some part of the aircraft that you know connects to the main structure and is not insulated with paint or a protective oxide coating. If the lamp burns with this temporary ground, you know the bulb is good and the trouble is in the ground circuit. The trouble could be:

1. At the point where the black wire, LA112, connects to the lamp socket

2. At the connection between the two sections of black wire

3. At the point where black wire, LA119, grounds to the aircraft structure

If this temporary ground did not cause the bulb to light up, it is time to take the bulb out of its socket and look at the filament. If it is broken, you have found the problem, and a new bulb will fix it. If the filament is not broken, check it for continuity. It is possible for a filament to look good and still be open. Switch the VOM to the low-resistance scale and measure the resistance of the filament. The amount of resistance is not important—you are just concerned that the filament has continuity. If the filament does have continuity, your problem is in the electrical system.

You now know that there is power through the dome light switch (since the left-wing courtesy light came on when you turned on the dome light switch), the lamp filament is good, and the ground for the light fixture is good. Now check to see whether there is power to the center contact of the dome light socket. Turn the selector switch on the VOM to the range of DC voltage that will allow the battery voltage to move the pointer up to around mid-scale. (The 24- or 50-volt scale is good for either a 12-volt or a 24-volt system.) Clip the black, or negative, lead to the outside of the lamp socket, and carefully touch the center contact with the red, or positive, lead. If there is power to the bulb, the meter will show the battery voltage. If there is no voltage at this point, check the wiring diagram. You will find that there are three possible places to look:

1. There could be a bad connection between wire LA111 and the lamp socket.

2. There could be a bad connection where wire LA111 joins wire LA108.

3. Wire LA108 could be loose where it joins wires LA101, LA107, and LA109. This is not likely, because the left-wing courtesy light burns, and it comes from the same point.

Begin by checking the easiest place to get to and work your way back to the point that has power. Now you can find the bad connection and fix it in the way the manufacturer recommends. Put the cover back over the dome light and turn the master switch off. The job has been finished in the shortest possible time.

Troubleshooting Review

Now that you have completed a simple, but typical, troubleshooting problem, let's review a few basic points on how to make the most efficient use of your time when you have a problem like this:

1. Again, first of all, you must know what the system does when it is operating correctly.

2. Next, collect all of the information possible on the trouble. Ask the pilot or flight crew as many questions as possible. Did the problem happen suddenly? Did anything unusual happen before the trouble started? Have you noticed anything like this happening before? Was there any unusual noise when the trouble started? Was there any smoke or unusual smell?

3. When you have all of the information from the flight crew, study the wiring diagram. Figure out all of the possible causes of the problem and plan your troubleshooting in a systematic way.

4. Work on the most likely causes first:
   • Blown fuses
   • Burned-out bulbs
   • Loose connections
   • Shorted or open diodes

5. When something is proven to be good, forget about it and keep looking until you find something that is not as it should be.

6. Remember that an aircraft electrical system is a high-performance system. To save weight, it uses the smallest wire possible and the lightest possible connectors and components, all of which are subjected to vibration that would shake an automobile system apart in a short time.

   Keep this in mind when you have a specially troublesome problem. Shake the connections and look for connections that appear to be good but which open up when they are vibrated.

7. If your troubleshooting requires a lot of power, such as you would need for landing lights, flap motors, or landing gear retraction motors, be sure to use a ground power supply, or GPU, so that you do not discharge the aircraft battery. When connecting the GPU, be sure to follow the aircraft manufacturer's instructions in detail. Airplanes differ in the way the GPUs are to be connected.

8. When a problem really has you stumped, draw a simple logic flow chart to help find where the trouble is.

Logic Flow Charts for Troubleshooting

Figure 7-81 shows a logic flow chart for the simple electrical system troubleshooting problem just discussed. This type of chart not only allows us to visualize the problem clearly, but it helps us see all of the alternatives.

An oval is used to show the beginning and the end of the problem. A diamond is used when there is a decision to be made. The instructions in a rectangle tell what to do next.

The first oval instructs us to turn the master switch on, and the last oval states that the job is done.

When the master switch is turned on, two possible conditions can occur. The battery relay will click, or it will not click. The first diamond depicts these two alternatives. If it clicks, there is power to the battery relay and you can follow the YES route to the next instruction. If it does not click, follow the NO route to the box that tells that the problem is between the battery and the battery relay. The battery could be discharged, the battery ground connection could be loose or corroded, or there may be a loose or corroded connection between the battery and the master relay.

If there is power to the battery relay and it closes as it should, then turn on the dome light switch and go to the next diamond. If the dome light burns, follow the YES route to the oval that tells you that the job is done. If it does not burn, follow the NO route to the diamond that asks if the left-wing courtesy light is burning. If this light is burning there is power to point B on the circuit in Figure 7-80. Follow the next instruction, which tells you to ground the dome light socket to the airframe, and then go to the next diamond. If the dome light burns, go with the YES route and follow the next instruction to fix the problem in the light socket ground wire. When this is fixed, follow

logic flow chart. A type of graphic chart that can be made up for a specific process or procedure to help follow the process through all of its logical steps.

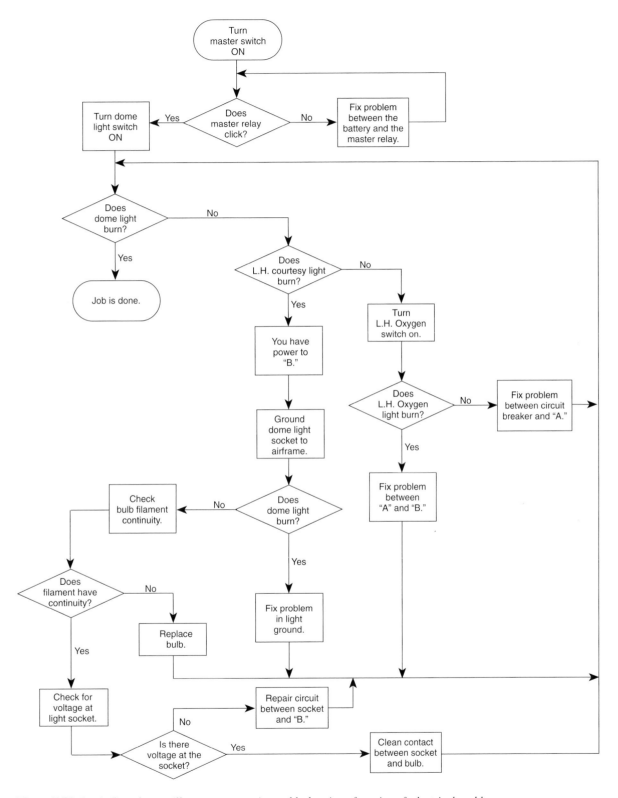

Figure 7-81. *Logic flow chart to illustrate systematic troubleshooting of an aircraft electrical problem.*

continuity tester. A troubleshooting tool that consists of a battery, a light bulb, and test leads.

The test leads are connected to each end of the conductor under test, and if the bulb lights up, there is continuity. If it does not light up, the conductor is open.

multimeter. An electrical test instrument that consists of a single current-measuring meter and all of the needed components to allow the meter to be used to measure voltage, resistance, and current.

Multimeters are available with either analog or digital-type displays.

clamp-on ammeter. An electrical instrument used to measure current without opening the circuit through which it is flowing.

The jaws of the ammeter are opened and slipped over the current-carrying wire and then clamped shut. Current flowing through the wire produces a magnetic field which induces a voltage in the ammeter that is proportional to the amount of current.

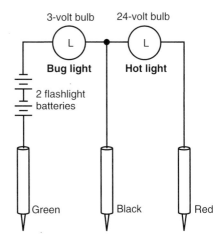

Figure 7-82. *A combination "bug light" and "hot light" is a handy tool for detecting continuity and power in an aircraft electrical system.*

the line from the instruction box back to the diamond that asks if the dome light is burning. If it is burning, follow the YES route to the oval that tells you that the job is finished.

Now, go back to the third diamond that asks if the left-wing courtesy light is burning. If it is not burning, follow the NO route to the instruction box that tells you to turn the left-hand oxygen light on. Then go to the diamond that asks if the left-hand oxygen light is burning. If it is burning, the problem is between points A and B, and the most likely trouble spot is in the dome light switch itself. If the left-hand oxygen light is not burning, the problem is between the cabin lights circuit breaker and point A.

With a flow chart such as this, you can logically trace the steps that allow you to locate any trouble and fix it with the least amount of lost motion.

To make a flow chart, start with the first logical step in the operation of the system on which you are working (turn on the master switch) and end with the condition you want to occur (the dome light burns). Ask questions that can be answered YES or NO about every condition that exists between the beginning and the end of the problem. All YES answers should take you to the end, and all NO answers should require you to take some action that will put you back on the path to the solution.

Once you get into the habit of systematically analyzing your troubleshooting problems, you will be able to follow a logical sequence of action that will take you to a solution to the problem in the shortest time with the least amount of lost motion and expense.

Troubleshooting Tools

Because electrical system troubleshooting requires that you open up the system and measure values of voltage and current, you need specialized equipment. This can be as simple as a continuity light or as complex as an oscilloscope. Let's look at some of the most frequently used instruments.

Continuity Light

The simplest electrical system troubleshooting tool you can use is a "bug light," or continuity tester, consisting of two flashlight batteries, a 3-volt flashlight bulb, and two test leads. With this simple homemade tool, you can trace wires through a system, locate shorts and open circuits, and quickly determine whether a fuse is good or bad.

Many technicians augment their bug light with a 24-volt bulb and another test lead. This part of the circuit is called a "hot light," and it is used to determine whether there is voltage in the part of the system you are testing. Since you want to know only if voltage is present, a 24-volt bulb will allow you to test both 12- and 24-volt systems.

When using the continuity tester, all electrical power must be off to the circuit. Connect the black test lead to one end of the circuit and the green lead to the other end. If there is continuity, the bulb will light up. If there is an open circuit, the bulb will not light.

Note: It is not a good policy when troubleshooting an aircraft electrical system to follow the automotive practice of piercing the insulation with a sharp needle point on the test lead to contact the wire for checking continuity or voltage. The insulation is different and there is a danger of damaging the small wire.

The hot light feature is handy for determining the presence of voltage at various points in the system. If you touch the red test leads of the hot light to the point you want to check for voltage, and the black lead to some ground point on the aircraft structure, the light will come on if there is voltage, or stay off if there is no voltage.

Multimeters

Continuity lights are simple, inexpensive to make, and can be easily carried in your toolbox, but they are limited in what they can do. The next logical choice in troubleshooting tools is a small, toolbox-size multimeter, about 2.5 inches deep by 3 inches wide, and less than 6 inches tall. These multimeters measure AC and DC voltages, direct current in the milliamp range, and resistance. The meter sensitivity is 1,000 ohms per volt, which places too much load on the circuit for it to be used for making measurements in certain electronic circuits, but its ruggedness and small size make it ideal for troubleshooting aircraft electrical systems. The accuracy of this type of meter is about 3% of full scale for the DC measurements and 4% of full scale for AC measurements.

The most popular multimeter for aircraft electrical system troubleshooting is the one in Figure 7-83. This instrument is slightly more than 5 inches by 7 inches and is a little more than 3 inches deep. It does not require any outside power and its range of scales and sensitivities makes it ideal for much more complex troubleshooting than the smaller multimeter.

This larger meter has full-scale DC voltage ranging from 0.25 volt to 1,000 volts. The full-scale AC ranges are from 2.5 volts to 1,000 volts. DC current ranges are from 50 microamperes to 10 amps. Alternating current up to 250 amps can be measured with a special clamp-on ammeter adapter. Resistance is measured in three ranges, with center-scale readings of 12 ohms, 1,200 ohms, and 120,000 ohms.

Digital Multimeter

The digital multimeter (DMM) is a new test instrument that is replacing, to a great extent, the older and more conventional analog multimeter. Digital multimeters have internal circuits that convert analog values of voltage, current, and resistance into digital signals and produce an indication in the form of numbers in a liquid crystal display.

Figure 7-83. *This high-sensitivity multimeter can be used for most serious troubleshooting of aircraft electrical systems.*

digital multimeter. An electrical test instrument that can be used to measure voltage, current, and resistance. The indication is in the form of a liquid crystal display in discrete numbers.

oscilloscope. An electrical instrument that displays on the face of a cathode-ray tube the wave form of the electrical signal it is measuring.

analog-type indicator. An electrical meter that indicates values by the amount a pointer moves across a numerical scale.

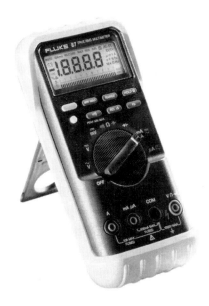

Figure 7-84. *Digital multimeters like this one have replaced analog instruments for many troubleshooting jobs. Their main advantages are their high input impedance and their inherent accuracy.*

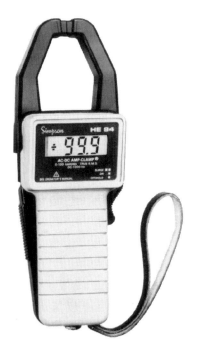

Figure 7-85. *This clamp-on ammeter measures current flowing through a conductor without having to open the circuit.*

DMMs cover a wide range of AC and DC measurements, have an extremely high input impedance—usually between 10 and 11 megohms—and an accuracy between about 0.03% and 0.25%. This contrasts with between 1.5% and 3% for analog-type multimeters.

Most DMMs can be used to check the condition of semiconductor diodes, and some of them even have an audible tone for indicating continuity. The main limitation of digital meters for troubleshooting is the difficulty in determining the trends of changing values. The needle of an analog instrument rises or falls to show trends, but it is more difficult to interpret the trends as the digits change. To compensate for this limitation, some DMMs have a small analog meter in parallel with the digital readout, and others have a bar graph liquid crystal display that shows trends, peaks, and nulls.

Clamp-on Ammeter

One very handy tool for electrical-system troubleshooting is a clamp-on ammeter. This instrument has a set of jaws that can be opened, slipped over a current-carrying wire and then clamped shut. Current flowing in the wire produces a magnetic field that acts on a special type of semiconductor material to produce a voltage proportional to the strength of the magnetic field. The strength of this field is proportional to the amount of current flowing in the wire.

Clamp-on ammeters are also used for troubleshooting hydraulic and fuel systems that have electrically operated pumps. The load on a pump can be determined fairly well by the amount of current the pump motor is drawing. By clamping an ammeter over the lines to the pumps, you can determine which pumps are operating and get an idea of the amount of load they are carrying.

Oscilloscopes

One of the most sophisticated pieces of test equipment used for aircraft electrical system troubleshooting is a cathode-ray oscilloscope. The display on a cathode-ray tube shows the wave form and frequency of the voltage being measured.

Modern electronic systems have made dual-trace oscilloscopes the most popular type of instrument. With a dual-trace oscilloscope, you can look at the signals on the input and output of a circuit at the same time. Oscilloscopes used for troubleshooting normally have a small screen—usually about a three-inch diagonal—and are small enough that they are easy to carry to the aircraft.

Answers begin on Page 580. Page numbers refer to chapter text.

109. The four basic rules for systematic troubleshooting are:

    a. _____

    b. _____

    c. _____

    d. _____

    Page 565

110. One of the first things to check if an electrical component does not operate is the _____ . *Page 566*

111. A decision point in a logic flow chart is enclosed in a _____-shaped box. *Page 570*

112. Two characteristics of a digital multimeter that make it a valuable troubleshooting tool are its:

    a. _____

    b. _____

    Page 574

113. Analog multimeters have an advantage over digital multimeters in their ease to identify _____ in voltage and current changes. *Page 574*

114. Current can be measured in a circuit without having to open the circuit if a/an _____ -type ammeter is used. *Page 574*

115. Wave form and frequency of the voltage in an electric circuit can be observed with a/an _____ . *Page 574*

Appendix A — Electrical Symbols

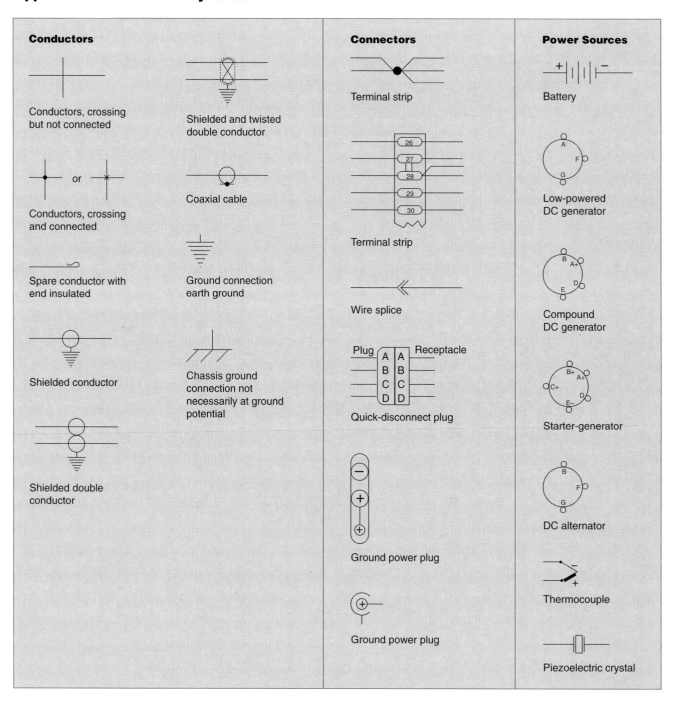

Conductors

Conductors, crossing but not connected

Conductors, crossing and connected
or

Spare conductor with end insulated

Shielded conductor

Shielded double conductor

Shielded and twisted double conductor

Coaxial cable

Ground connection earth ground

Chassis ground connection not necessarily at ground potential

Connectors

Terminal strip

26
27
28
29
30

Terminal strip

Wire splice

Plug   Receptacle

A   A
B   B
C   C
D   D

Quick-disconnect plug

Ground power plug

Ground power plug

Power Sources

Battery

Low-powered DC generator

Compound DC generator

Starter-generator

DC alternator

Thermocouple

Piezoelectric crystal

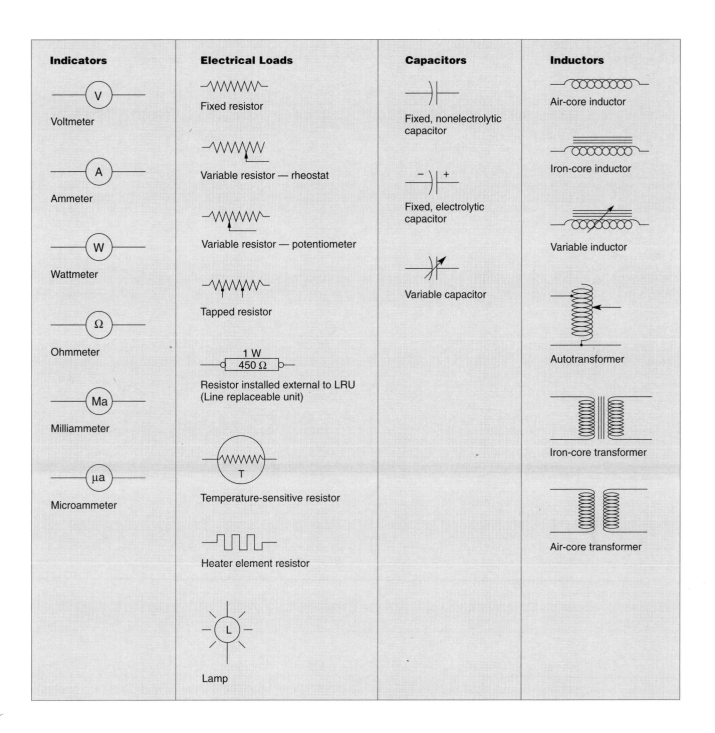

Indicators

Voltmeter

Ammeter

Wattmeter

Ohmmeter

Milliammeter

Microammeter

Electrical Loads

Fixed resistor

Variable resistor — rheostat

Variable resistor — potentiometer

Tapped resistor

1 W
450 Ω

Resistor installed external to LRU
(Line replaceable unit)

T

Temperature-sensitive resistor

Heater element resistor

L

Lamp

Capacitors

Fixed, nonelectrolytic
capacitor

− +

Fixed, electrolytic
capacitor

Variable capacitor

Inductors

Air-core inductor

Iron-core inductor

Variable inductor

Autotransformer

Iron-core transformer

Air-core transformer

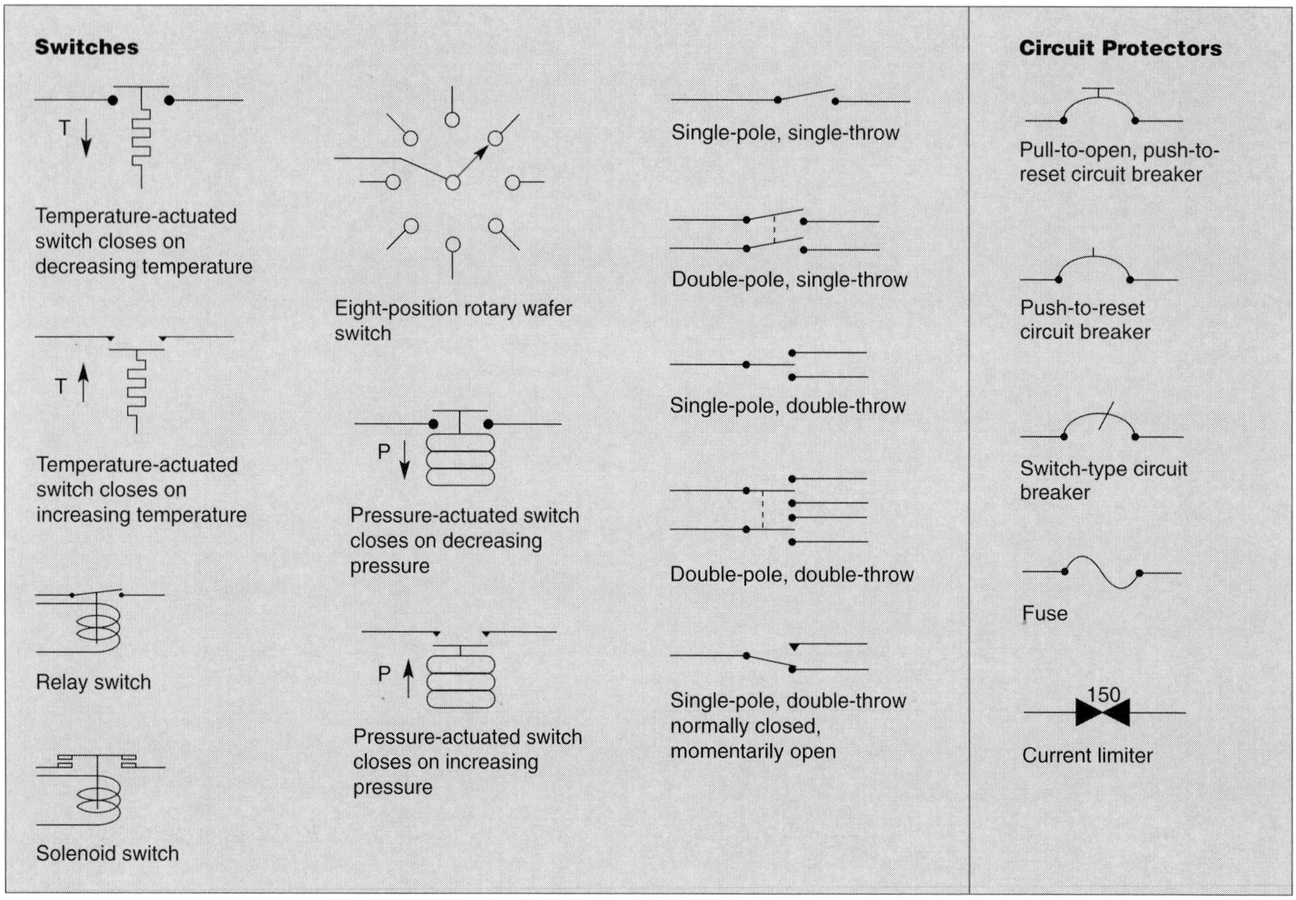

Switches

Temperature-actuated switch closes on decreasing temperature

Temperature-actuated switch closes on increasing temperature

Relay switch

Solenoid switch

Eight-position rotary wafer switch

Pressure-actuated switch closes on decreasing pressure

Pressure-actuated switch closes on increasing pressure

Single-pole, single-throw

Double-pole, single-throw

Single-pole, double-throw

Double-pole, double-throw

Single-pole, double-throw normally closed, momentarily open

Circuit Protectors

Pull-to-open, push-to-reset circuit breaker

Push-to-reset circuit breaker

Switch-type circuit breaker

Fuse

Current limiter

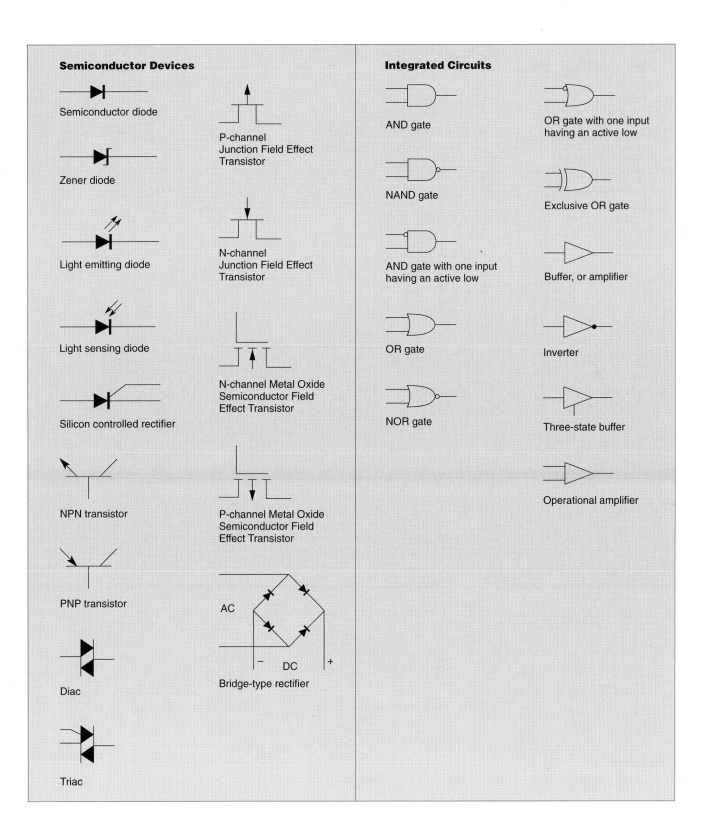

Semiconductor Devices

Semiconductor diode

Zener diode

Light emitting diode

Light sensing diode

Silicon controlled rectifier

NPN transistor

PNP transistor

Diac

Triac

P-channel
Junction Field Effect
Transistor

N-channel
Junction Field Effect
Transistor

N-channel Metal Oxide
Semiconductor Field
Effect Transistor

P-channel Metal Oxide
Semiconductor Field
Effect Transistor

AC

DC

Bridge-type rectifier

Integrated Circuits

AND gate

NAND gate

AND gate with one input
having an active low

OR gate

NOR gate

OR gate with one input
having an active low

Exclusive OR gate

Buffer, or amplifier

Inverter

Three-state buffer

Operational amplifier

Answers to Aircraft Electrical Systems Study Questions

1. I
2. E, V
3. R
4. bus
5. a. heat is produced in the conductor
   b. a magnetic field surrounds the conductor
   c. voltage is dropped across the load
6. positive
7. opposite
8. same
9. a. a source of electrical energy
   b. an electrical load
   c. conductors to join the source with the load
10. forward
11. closed
12. 0.7
13. does not
14. zener diode
15. reverse
16. fixed
17. movable
18. closed
19. increases
20. silicon controlled rectifier
21. true
22. battery voltage
23. zero volts
24. resistance
25. battery
26. ground
27. aircraft structure
28. negative
29. wiring
30. starter

31. trip-free
32. cannot
33. are not
34. 6
35. induced
36. rate
37. opposite
38. reverse
39. resistor R
40. diode D_1
41. the fuse
42. alternator
43. stator
44. AC
45. diodes
46. opened
47. field
48. rotating
49. field poles
50. commutator, brushes
51. does not
52. does
53. ground
54. a. voltage regulator
   b. current limiter
   c. reverse-current cutout
55. open
56. closed
57. closed
58. resistor
59. paralleling
60. equalizing
61. starter, generator
62. series
63. does not
64. percent
65. continuous
66. intermittent

67. starter
68. complex
69. is not
70. a. gear switch
   b. up-limit switch
   c. gear safety switch
71. will
72. squat
73. automatically
74. off
75. left
76. induced
77. AC
78. TR units
79. constant-speed drive
80. a. voltage
   b. frequency
   c. power
81. a. external power unit
   b. generator 1
   c. generator 2
   d. generator 3
   e. auxiliary power unit
   f. standby inverter
82. hot battery bus
83. less
84. 1.0
85. 1.0
86. 2
87. 6
88. a. current-carrying capability
   b. allowable voltage drop
89. 4
90. 4
91. shielded
92. coaxial
93. sockets
94. 4

95. bus strap
96. red
97. yellow
98. ring
99. a. deicing
    b. 3
    c. first
    d. 20
    e. does not
100. tire talcum
101. cushion
102. above
103. 3
104. ¾
105. grommet
106. 24
107. 6
108. 10
109. a. Know the way the system should operate.
     b. Observe the way the system is operating.
     c. Divide the system to find the trouble.
     d. Look for the obvious problems first.
110. circuit breaker
111. diamond
112. a. high input impedance
     b. high degree of accuracy
113. trends
114. clamp-on
115. oscilloscope

AIRCRAFT FUEL SYSTEMS

8

Continued

AIRCRAFT FUEL SYSTEMS

Aviation Fuels

Aircraft engines convert the chemical energy in fuel into heat energy. It is the function of the aircraft fuel system to store the fuel until it is needed, and then supply the engine with the volume of uncontaminated fuel that will allow it to develop the required power.

The development of aviation fuels has closely paralleled the development of aviation itself. In the early days of flying, the reciprocating engines used just about any type of gasoline that was available. But when more power was demanded of the lightweight aircraft engines, additives were mixed with the gasoline that allowed the engines to produce more power without detonating.

Turbine engines, with their voracious appetite for fuel, have led the petroleum industry to produce fuels that are especially adapted to the requirements of these engines.

This text discusses the basic requirements of fuels in aircraft fuel systems. The *Powerplant* textbook of the *Aviation Maintenance Technician Series* discusses the actual chemical transformation that allows the engines to use these fuels.

Reciprocating Engine Fuel

Reciprocating engines were the primary power for aircraft up through World War II. The military services and the airlines used tremendous amounts of aviation gasoline in their high-powered engines, and private, or general, aviation used much less fuel in their low-powered engines. The two fuels used for the two types of engines differ in the additives they contain to suppress detonation.

After World War II the turbine engine became the standard propulsion system for the military and the airlines, and the demand for aviation gasoline has decreased drastically. The petroleum industry is finding it increasingly uneconomical to produce all the grades of aviation gasoline needed to supply small reciprocating-engine-powered aircraft. As a result, the engines in the smaller aircraft use fuel that contains far more lead than they were designed to use. The unavailability of the correct fuel along with the high cost of aviation gasoline has propelled much research into the use of automotive gasoline in aircraft.

hydrocarbon. An organic compound that contains only carbon and hydrogen. The vast majority of our fossil fuels such as gasoline and turbine-engine fuel are hydrocarbons.

fractional distillation. A method of separating the various components from a physical mixture of liquids.

The material to be separated is put into a container and its temperature is increased. The components having the lowest boiling points boil off first and are condensed. Then as the temperature is further raised, other components are removed. Kerosine, gasoline and other petroleum products are obtained by fractional distillation of crude oil.

vapor lock. A condition in which vapors form in the fuel lines and block the flow of fuel to the carburetor.

vapor pressure. The pressure of the vapor above a liquid needed to prevent the liquid evaporating. Vapor pressure is always specified at a specific temperature.

detonation. An explosion, or uncontrolled burning inside the cylinder of a reciprocating engine. Detonation occurs when the pressure and temperature inside the cylinder become higher than the critical pressure and temperature of the fuel.

octane rating. A rating of the antidetonation characteristics of a reciprocating engine fuel. It is based on the performance of the fuel in a special test engine. When a fuel is given a dual rating such as 80/87, the first number is its antidetonating rating with a lean fuel-air mixture, and the higher number is its rating with a rich mixture.

Aviation Gasoline Grades

When military and airline aircraft were powered by reciprocating engines, four grades of aviation gasoline were widely available. But now that most of the aircraft are turbine-powered, only three grades of aviation gasoline are produced, and two of these are being phased out. The petroleum industry would like to produce only one type of gasoline that would meet the needs of all gasoline engines.

Grade	Old Rating	Tetraethyl Lead Content ml/gallon	Color	Availability
80	80/87	0.5	Red	Being phased out
91			Blue	Phased out
100	100/130	4.0	Green	Being phased out
100LL		2.0	Blue	Available
115	115/145	4.6	Purple	Phased out

Figure 8-1. *Aviation gasoline grades*

Aviation Gasoline Characteristics

Aviation gasoline is a highly refined hydrocarbon fuel obtained by fractional distillation of crude petroleum. Its important characteristics are: purity, volatility, and antidetonation qualities.

Purity

Every precaution is taken to ensure purity of aviation gasoline, but certain contaminants do get into it. The most prevalent contaminant is water. Fortunately, water is heavier than aviation gasoline and it settles to the bottom of the tank and to the lowest point in the fuel system. Aircraft fuel tanks are required to have a sump, or low area, where the water can collect, and these sumps are fitted with a quick drain valve so the pilot on a preflight inspection can drain water from these low points.

Water gets into the fuel tanks by condensation. If a fuel tank remains partially empty for several days, the changing temperature will cause air to be drawn into the tank, and this air will contain enough moisture to condense and settle to the bottom of the tank. All fuel tanks should be filled as soon after flight as possible.

Jet engine fuels have a higher viscosity than aviation gasoline, and they hold contaminants in suspension better than gasoline, so water contamination causes additional problems with jet aircraft fuel systems. These problems are discussed in more detail in the section on jet engine fuel.

Volatility

Liquid gasoline will not burn. It must be vaporized so it will mix with oxygen in the air and form a combustible mixture. Aviation gasoline must be volatile enough to completely vaporize in the engine induction system. If it does not vaporize readily enough, it can cause hard starting, poor acceleration, uneven fuel distribution, and excessive dilution of the oil in the crankcase. If it vaporizes too readily it can cause vapor lock, which prevents the flow of fuel to the engine.

The measure of the ease with which a fuel vaporizes is the Reid vapor pressure. This is the pressure of the vapor above the fuel required to prevent further vaporization at a specified temperature.

The maximum vapor pressure allowed for aviation gasoline is 7 psi at 100°F, which is lower than that of most automotive gasoline. If the vapor pressure of the fuel is too high, it is likely to vaporize in the lines in hot weather or high altitude and starve the engine of fuel.

Antidetonation Qualities

Detonation occurs in an aircraft engine when the fuel-air mixture inside the cylinders reaches its critical pressure and temperature and explodes rather than burning smoothly. The extreme pressures produced by detonation can cause severe structural damage to the engine.

Aviation gasoline is rated according to its antidetonation characteristics by its octane rating or performance number. The procedure for obtaining this rating is described in the section on Aviation Fuels in the *General* textbook of this *Aviation Maintenance Technician Series*. This procedure compares the performance of the rated fuel to that of a fuel made up of a mixture of iso-octane and normal heptane. Grade 80 fuel has characteristics similar to that of a mixture of 80% octane and 20% heptane, and grade 100 and 100LL have the same antidetonation characteristics as iso-octane.

Fuel Additives

Various grades of aviation gasolines differ in the types and amounts of additives they contain. The basic additive is tetraethyl lead (TEL) which increases the critical pressure and temperature of the fuel.

Not only does TEL improve the antidetonation characteristics of the fuel, but it provides the required lubrication for the valves. Engines that must use fuel with less lead than they are designed to use suffer from valve problems.

One problem associated with using a fuel with too much TEL is the buildup of lead deposits in the spark plugs. Other additives such as ethylene dibromide and tricresyl phosphate are used in leaded fuel to help scavenge the residue left from the lead.

performance number. The anti-detonation rating of a fuel that has a higher critical pressure and temperature than iso-octane (a rating of 100). Iso-octane that has been treated with varying amounts of tetraethyl lead is used as the reference.

iso-octane. A hydrocarbon, C_8H_{18}, which has a very high critical pressure and temperature. Iso-octane is used as the high reference for measuring the anti-detonation characteristics of a fuel.

normal heptane. A hydrocarbon, C_7H_{16}, with a very low critical pressure and temperature. Normal heptane is used as the low reference in measuring the anti-detonation characteristics of a fuel.

tetraethyl lead (TEL). A heavy, oily, poisonous liquid, $Pb(C_2H_5)_4$, that is mixed into aviation gasoline to increase its critical pressure and temperature.

ethylene dibromide. A chemical compound added to aviation gasoline to convert some of the deposits left by the tetraethyl lead into lead bromides. These bromides are volatile and will pass out of the engine with the exhaust gases.

tricresyl phosphate (TCP). A chemical compound, $(CH_3C_6H_4O)_3PO$, used in aviation gasoline to assist in scavenging the lead deposits left from the tetraethyl lead.

Aromatic additives such as toluene, xylene, and benzene are used in some aviation gasoline to improve its antidetonation characteristics. Fuel that contains aromatic additives must be used only in fuel systems specifically approved for it, because these additives soften some of the rubber compounds used in fuel hoses and diaphragms.

Turbine Engine Fuels

There are two basic types of turbine engine fuel: Jet A and A-1, and Jet B. Jet A and A-1 are similar to commercial kerosine, having characteristics similar to those of military JP-5. They have a low vapor pressure and their flash points are between 110°F and 150°F. Their freezing points are -40°F for Jet A, -58°F for Jet A-1, and -55°F for JP-5.

Jet B is called a wide-cut fuel because it is a blend of gasoline and kerosine fractions, and it is similar to military JP-4. Jet B has a low freezing point, around -60°F, and its vapor pressure is higher than that of kerosine, but lower than that of gasoline.

Turbine Fuel Volatility

Volatility of turbine fuel is important because it is a compromise between conflicting factors. Its volatility should be high enough for good cold weather starting and aerial restarting, but low enough to prevent vapor lock and to reduce fuel losses by evaporation.

Under normal temperature conditions, gasoline, with its 7-psi vapor pressure, can give off so much vapor in a closed container or tank that the fuel-air mixture is too rich to burn. Under these same conditions, the vapor given off by Jet B, with its 2- to 3-psi vapor pressure, will produce a fuel-air mixture that is explosive. Jet A, with its extremely low vapor pressure of around 0.125 psi, has such low volatility that under normal conditions it does not give off enough vapor to form an explosive fuel-air mixture.

Turbine Fuel Viscosity

Turbine fuel is more viscous than gasoline, so it holds contaminants and prevents their settling out in the tank sumps.

Water is held in an entrained state in turbine fuel, and at high altitude and low temperature, it can collect on the fuel strainers and freeze, blocking the flow of fuel.

Microbial Growth in Turbine Fuel Tanks

Water in turbine fuel causes problems that do not exist in reciprocating engine fuel. During flight at high altitude and low temperature, water condenses out of the fuel and settles in the bottom of the fuel tank, where it collects around the sealant used in the seams of integral fuel tanks. Microscopic organisms live and multiply at the interface between the water and the fuel and form a scum that holds water in contact with the tank structure. Corrosion forms, with this water acting as the electrolyte.

flash point. The temperature to which a material must be raised for it to ignite, but not continue to burn, when a flame is passed above it.

petroleum fractions. The various components of a hydrocarbon fuel that are separated by boiling them off at different temperatures in the process of fractional distillation.

microbial contaminants. The scum that forms inside the fuel tanks of turbine-engine-powered aircraft that is caused by micro-organisms.

These micro-organisms live in water that condenses from the fuel, and they feed on the fuel. The scum they form clogs fuel filters, lines, and fuel controls and holds water in contact with the aluminum alloy structure. This causes corrosion.

To prevent the formation of the scum in the tanks, turbine fuel may be treated with a biocidal additive. This kills the microbes and bacteria and prevents their forming the scum. This additive may be put in at the refinery, or added into the fuel as it is pumped into the aircraft tanks.

Fuel Anti-Icing

When water condenses out of the fuel and freezes on the fuel filters, it can shut off the flow to the engine. To prevent this, some aircraft use fuel heaters that are a form of heat exchanger. Compressor bleed air or hot engine oil flows through one part of the heater and fuel flows through another part. The air or oil gives up some of its heat to the fuel and raises its temperature enough to prevent ice from forming on the filter.

The fuel additive that prevents the formation of the microbial scum in the fuel tanks also acts as an anti-icing agent, or antifreeze. It mixes with the water that condenses out of the fuel and lowers its freezing point enough that it cannot freeze on the filters.

anti-icing additive. A chemical added to the turbine-engine fuel used in some aircraft. This additive mixes with water that condenses from the fuel and lowers its freezing temperature so it will not freeze and block the fuel filters. It also acts as a biocidal agent and prevents the formation of microbial contamination in the tanks.

STUDY QUESTIONS: AIRCRAFT FUELS

Answers begin on Page 649. Page numbers refer to chapter text.

1. One of the basic differences between the various grades of aviation gasoline is in the amount of additive used to suppress _____ . *Page 589*

2. The most prevalent contaminant in aviation gasoline is _____ . *Page 588*

3. Jet engine fuels have a _____ (higher or lower) viscosity than aviation gasoline. *Page 588*

4. Hard starting, slow warm-up, poor acceleration, and uneven fuel distribution to the cylinders will result if the vapor pressure of the fuel is too _____ (high or low). *Page 589*

5. Gasoline does not vaporize easily if its vapor pressure is too _____ (high or low). *Page 589*

6. Aviation gasoline is not allowed to have a Reid vapor pressure higher than _____ psi at 100°F. *Page 589*

7. Most automotive gasoline has a _____ (higher or lower) vapor pressure than aviation gasoline. *Page 589*

8. The antidetonation characteristics of aviation gasoline are specified by its _____ rating or _____ number. *Page 589*

Continued

9. The basic fuel additive used to suppress detonation in a reciprocating engine is
_____ . *Page 589*

10. Aromatic additives are used in aviation gasoline to increase the antidetonation characteristics of the fuel but they also cause deterioration of _____ parts. *Page 590*

11. The jet-engine fuel that is similar to kerosine is _____ (Jet A or Jet B). *Page 590*

12. Turbine engine fuels are more susceptible to water contamination than aviation gasoline because they are _____ (more or less) viscous than gasoline. *Page 590*

13. Micro-organisms live in the water which condenses and collects in the integral fuel tanks of a jet airplane. They form a scum that holds the water against the aluminum alloy structure and cause _____ . *Page 590*

14. The additive that is put into turbine engine fuel to kill the micro-organisms also acts as an _____ agent. *Page 591*

Fuel System Requirements

More aircraft accidents and incidents are attributable to fuel systems than to any other system in an aircraft. System mismanagement has caused engines to quit due to fuel starvation when fuel was still available in some of the other tanks. Bladder-type fuel tanks have partially collapsed, decreasing the amount of fuel that can be carried without warning the pilot of this shortage. Fuel systems serviced with the wrong grade of fuel have caused severe detonation and the loss of an engine on takeoff, the most critical portion of a flight. Undetected contaminants can cause engine failure by plugging the fuel lines or by replacing fuel with water.

It is the responsibility of the pilot-in-command of an aircraft to ensure that the aircraft has a sufficient quantity of the correct grade of uncontaminated fuel for each flight. But aviation maintenance technicians must maintain the fuel systems in such a way that they can hold the full amount of fuel and deliver this fuel at the correct rate under all operating conditions. It is the responsibility of the person fueling an aircraft to use only the correct grade of fuel and to take all precautions to ensure that the fuel is free from water and other contaminants.

Federal Aviation Regulations Part 23 *Airworthiness Standards: Normal, Utility, Acrobatic and Commuter Category Airplanes* gives the requirements for the fuel systems of these aircraft. In this text, we will consider these requirements. Transport category airplanes have somewhat different requirements, and they are specified in FAR Part 25.

§ 23.951 General. Each fuel system must be constructed and arranged to insure a flow of fuel at a rate and pressure established for proper engine functioning under each likely operating condition.

No fuel pump can draw fuel from more than one tank at a time unless there is a means of preventing air from being introduced into the system.

Each turbine engine fuel system must be capable of sustained operation throughout its flow and pressure range with fuel initially saturated with water at 80°F and having 0.75 cc of free water per gallon added and cooled to the most critical condition for icing likely to be encountered in operation.

§ 23.953 Fuel system independence. Each fuel system for a multi-engine airplane must be arranged so that, in at least one system configuration, the failure of any one component (other than a fuel tank) will not result in the loss of power of more than one engine or require immediate action by the pilot to prevent the loss of power of more than one engine.

Each fuel tank for a multi-engine fuel system must have independent tank outlets for each engine, each incorporating a shutoff valve at the tank.

Each fuel tank for a multi-engine fuel system must have at least two vents arranged to minimize the probability of both vents becoming obstructed simultaneously, and the filler caps must be designed to minimize the probability of incorrect installation or in-flight loss.

§ 23.955 Fuel flow. Gravity fuel systems must have a flow rate of 150% of the takeoff fuel consumption of the engine, and pump-fed systems for reciprocating engines must flow 125% of the takeoff fuel flow of the engine at the maximum power approved for the engine.

If the fuel system incorporates a flowmeter, it must be blocked during the flow test and the fuel must flow through the meter bypass.

If a reciprocating engine can be supplied with fuel from more than one tank, it must be possible in level flight to regain full power and fuel pressure to that engine in not more than 10 seconds (for single-engine airplanes) or 20 seconds (for multi-engine airplanes) after switching to any full tank, after engine malfunctioning due to fuel depletion becomes apparent while the engine is being supplied from any other tank.

Each turbine engine fuel system must provide 100% of the fuel flow required by the engine under each intended operation condition and maneuver.

§ 23.957 Flow between interconnected tanks. It must be impossible, in a gravity feed system with interconnected tank outlets, for enough fuel to flow between the tanks to cause an overflow of fuel from any tank vent.

§ 23.961 Fuel system hot weather operation. Each fuel system conducive to vapor formation must be free from vapor lock when using fuel at a temperature of 110°F under critical operating conditions.

§ 23.963 Fuel tanks: general. The total usable capacity of the fuel tanks must be enough for at least one-half hour of operation at maximum continuous power.

§ 23.965 Fuel tank tests. Each fuel tank must be able to withstand the following pressures without failure or leakage:

For each conventional metal tank and nonmetallic tank with walls not supported by the airplane structure, a pressure of 3.5 psi, or that pressure developed during maximum ultimate acceleration with a full tank, whichever is greater.

For each nonmetallic tank with walls supported by the airplane structure and constructed in an acceptable manner using acceptable basic tank material, and with actual or simulated support conditions, a pressure of 2 psi for the first tank of a specific design.

§ 23.967 Fuel tank installation. No fuel tank may be on the engine side of the firewall. There must be at least one-half inch of clearance between the fuel tank and the firewall.

No fuel tank may be installed in the personnel compartment of a multi-engine airplane.

§ 23.969 Fuel tank expansion space. Each fuel tank must have an expansion space of not less than two percent of the tank capacity, unless the tank vent discharges clear of the airplane.

It must be impossible to fill the expansion space inadvertently with the airplane in the normal ground attitude.

§ 23.971 Fuel tank sump. Each fuel tank must have a drainable sump with an effective capacity, in the normal ground and flight attitudes, of 0.25 percent of the tank capacity or $\frac{1}{16}$ gallon, whichever is greater.

§ 23.975 Fuel tank vents and carburetor vapor vents. Each fuel tank must be vented from the top part of the expansion space.

Air spaces of tanks with interconnected outlets must be interconnected.

§ 23.977 Fuel tank outlet. There must be a fuel strainer for the fuel tank outlet or for the booster pump.

§ 23.991 Fuel pumps. There must be an emergency pump immediately available to supply fuel to the engine if any main pump (other than a fuel injection pump approved as part of an engine) fails.

§ 23.995 Fuel valves and controls. There must be a means to allow appropriate flight crew members to rapidly shut off, in flight, the fuel to each engine individually.

No shutoff valve may be on the engine side of any firewall.

§ **23.995** *(Continued)* Fuel tank valves must require a separate and distinct action to place the selector in the OFF position. And the tank selector positions must be located in such a manner that it is impossible for the selector to pass through the OFF position when changing from one tank to another.

§ **23.997 Fuel strainer or filter.** There must be a fuel strainer or filter between the fuel tank outlet and the inlet of either the fuel metering device or an engine-driven positive displacement pump, which ever is nearer the fuel tank outlet.

§ **23.999 Fuel system drains.** There must be at least one drain to allow safe drainage of the entire fuel system with the airplane in its normal ground attitude.

§ **23.1001 Fuel jettisoning system.** If the design landing weight is less than the allowable takeoff weight, the airplane must have a fuel jettisoning system installed that is able to jettison enough fuel to bring the maximum landing weight down to the design landing weight.

STUDY QUESTIONS: FUEL SYSTEM REQUIREMENTS

Answers begin on Page 649. Page numbers refer to chapter text.

15. In the design of a fuel system, it _____ (is or is not) permissible for a fuel pump to draw fuel from more than one tank at a time. *Page 593*

16. In the design of a multiengine fuel system it _____ (is or is not) permissible for one tank outlet to feed both engines. *Page 593*

17. If an engine supplied with a gravity fuel system requires 25 gallons of fuel per hour for takeoff, the fuel system must be capable of supplying _____ gallons per hour. *Page 593*

18. If an engine supplied with a pump-fed fuel system requires 25 gallons of fuel per hour for takeoff, the fuel system must be capable of supplying _____ gallons per hour. *Page 593*

19. A turbine engine fuel system must provide at least _____ percent of the fuel flow required by the engine under each intended operation condition and maneuver. *Page 593*

20. A conventional metal fuel tank must be able to withstand an internal pressure of _____ psi without leaking. *Page 594*

21. A nonmetallic fuel tank with walls supported by the aircraft structure (a bladder tank) must be able to withstand an internal pressure of _____ psi without leaking. *Page 594*

Continued

22. When the outlets of two fuel tanks are interconnected, the vent space above the fuel in the tanks must be _____ . *Page 594*

23. If the design landing weight of an airplane is less than its allowable takeoff weight, the airplane must have a _____ system installed. *Page 595*

Aircraft Fuel Systems

The weight of the fuel is a large percentage of an aircraft's total weight, and the balance of the aircraft in flight changes as the fuel is used. These conditions add to the complexity of the design of an aircraft fuel system. In small aircraft the fuel tank or tanks are located near the center of gravity so the balance changes very little as the fuel is used. In large aircraft, fuel tanks are installed in every available location and fuel valves allow the flight engineer to keep the aircraft balanced by scheduling the use of the fuel from the various tanks. In high-performance military aircraft, the fuel scheduling is automatic.

Gravity-Feed Fuel System for a Float Carburetor

The simplest fuel system is a gravity-feed system like those used on some of the small high-wing training airplanes.

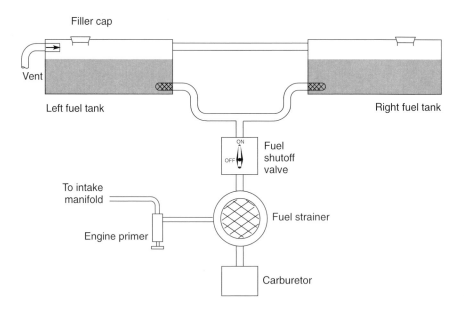

Figure 8-2. *Fuel system of a high-wing training airplane*

The fuel is carried in two tanks, one in the root of each wing. The outlets of these tanks are interconnected and they flow into a simple ON/OFF fuel valve. Because the tank outlets are interconnected, the airspace above the fuel in the two tanks is also interconnected and the tanks vent to the atmosphere through an overboard vent in the top of the left tank.

The fuel flows from the shutoff valve through a strainer to the carburetor. A small, single-acting primer pump draws fuel from the strainer and sprays it into the intake manifold to furnish fuel for starting the engine.

Gravity-Feed System for a Fuel-Injected Engine

Figure 8-3 diagrams the fuel system of a high-wing airplane equipped with a fuel-injected engine.

The fuel flows by gravity from the main fuel tanks into small reservoir tanks and into the tank selector valve, which has three positions: OFF, LEFT ON, and RIGHT ON.

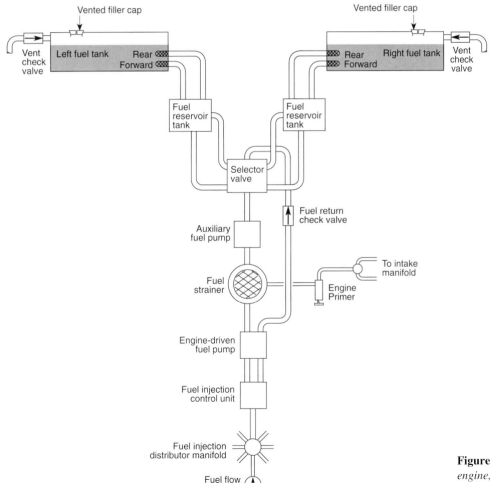

Figure 8-3. *Fuel system for a single-engine, high-wing airplane equipped with a fuel-injected engine*

Fuel flows from the selector valve through a two-speed electric auxiliary pump that has a LOW and a HIGH position. After leaving the pump it passes through the main fuel strainer into the engine-driven fuel pump.

This engine uses a Teledyne-Continental fuel-injection system in which part of the fuel is returned by the mixture control to the pump and from there through a check valve and the selector valve to the tank that is being used.

A priming system uses a manually operated plunger-type pump that draws fuel from the strainer and sprays it into the aft end of each of the two intake manifolds on the engine.

Low-Wing, Single-Engine Fuel System for a Float Carburetor

The fuel system in Figure 8-4 is found on some low-wing single-engine airplanes whose engines are equipped with float carburetors.

Fuel flows from the tanks to a fuel selector valve that has three positions, LEFT TANK ON, RIGHT TANK ON, and OFF. From the selector valve the fuel flows through a strainer and the pumps to the carburetor. The plunger-type electric pump and the diaphragm-type engine pump are connected in parallel. The electric pump moves the fuel for starting the engine, and as soon as it starts, the diaphragm pump supplies the fuel for normal operation. The electric pump is turned on for takeoff and landing to supply fuel in the event the engine pump should fail.

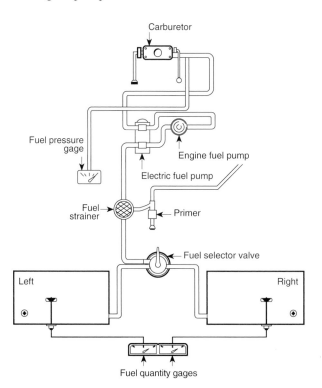

Figure 8-4. *Fuel system for a low-wing, single-engine airplane whose engine is equipped with a float carburetor*

Low-Wing, Twin-Engine Fuel System for Fuel-Injected Engines

Figure 8-5 shows the fuel system for a low-wing, twin-engine airplane with fuel-injected engines. This airplane has two 51-gallon main fuel tanks, which are mounted on the wing tips, and two 36-gallon bladder-type auxiliary tanks, one in each wing. Two additional 26-gallon tanks can be installed in the nacelle lockers at the aft end of the engine nacelles. These locker tanks do not feed the engines directly, but are equipped with transfer pumps that allow the fuel to be pumped into the main tanks and from there to the engines.

This fuel system has a fuel selector valve for each engine. The valve for the left engine has the positions LEFT MAIN, RIGHT MAIN, LEFT AUXILIARY, and OFF. The valve for the right engine has the positions RIGHT MAIN, LEFT MAIN, RIGHT AUXILIARY, and OFF.

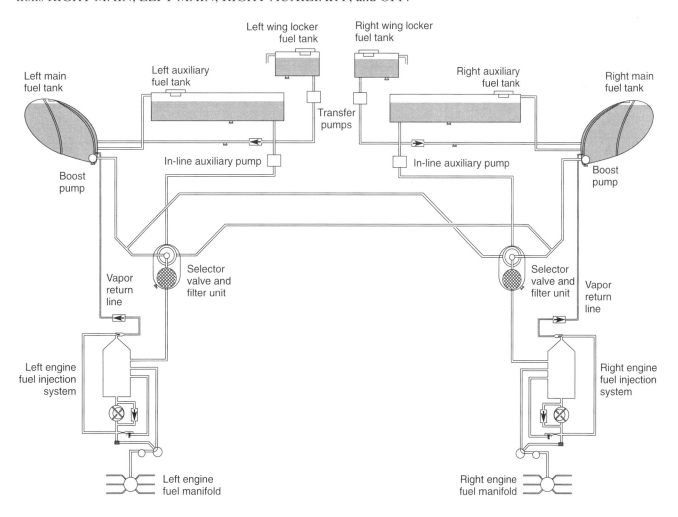

Figure 8-5. *Fuel system for a low-wing, twin-engine airplane with fuel-injected engines*

Fuel flows from the selected tanks through the selector valves and the filters to the engine-driven pumps which are part of the Teledyne-Continental fuel-injection system. There is a small but steady stream of fuel through the vapor return lines from fuel-injector pumps to the main tanks. This return fuel picks up any vapors that have formed in the system and returns them to the tank, rather than allowing them to disturb the fuel metering.

The selector valves allow the pilot to operate either engine from either of the main fuel tanks and the left engine from the left auxiliary tank and the right engine from the right auxiliary tank. The fuel in the nacelle locker tanks can be pumped into the main tanks on their respective sides.

There is a submerged centrifugal-type auxiliary fuel pump in each of the main fuel tanks. These pumps are controlled by three electrical switches: for priming, for purging, and for backing up the engine-driven pumps for takeoff and landing. When the Prime switch is placed in the ON position, the auxiliary pump operates at high speed. When the Auxiliary Fuel Pump switch is placed in LOW position, the pump operates at low speed for purging the lines of vapor. When it is placed in the ON position, the pump operates at low speed, but in the event of the failure of the engine-driven pump, it automatically shifts to high speed. In the OFF position, the auxiliary pump does not operate.

Electric plunger-type pumps are installed in the lines between the wing locker tanks and the main tanks to transfer the fuel, and between the auxiliary tanks and the fuel selector valve to supply fuel to the fuel-injector pumps and prevent vapors forming in the lines between the auxiliary tanks and the injector pumps.

Twin-Engine Cross-feed Fuel System

The fuel system in Figure 8-6 has two fuel tanks, two shutoff valves, and two cross-feed valves. Either engine can draw fuel from either tank, or the tanks can be connected.

Each of these tanks has a boost-pump sump and a fuel transfer ejector to keep the boost-pump sumps full. Part of the boost-pump discharge flows through the ejector and creates a low pressure which pulls fuel from the tank into the sump. Flapper valves in the sump prevent fuel flowing from the sump back into the tank.

If either of the boost pumps should fail, the other pump can supply both engines through the pump cross-feed valve. The check valve prevents fuel from the tank with the functioning pump from flowing into the other tank under these conditions.

cross-feed valve. A valve in a fuel system that allows all engines of a multiengine aircraft to draw fuel from any fuel tank.

Cross-feed systems are used to allow a multi-engine aircraft to maintain a balanced fuel condition.

ejector. A form of jet pump used to pick up a liquid and move it to another location. Ejectors are used to assure that the compartment in which the boost pumps are mounted is kept full of fuel. Part of the fuel from the boost pump flowing through the ejector produces a low pressure that pulls fuel from the main tank and forces it into the boost-pump sump area.

boost pump. An electrically driven centrifugal pump mounted in the bottom of the fuel tanks in large aircraft. Boost pumps provide a positive flow of fuel under pressure to the engine for starting and serve as an emergency backup in the event an engine-driven pump should fail. They are also used to transfer fuel from one tank to another and to pump fuel overboard when it is being dumped.

Boost pumps keep pressure on the fuel in the line to the engine-driven pump, and in doing this, prevent vapor lock from forming in these lines.

Centrifugal boost pumps have a small agitator propeller on top of the pump impeller. This agitator releases the vapors in the fuel before the fuel leaves the tank.

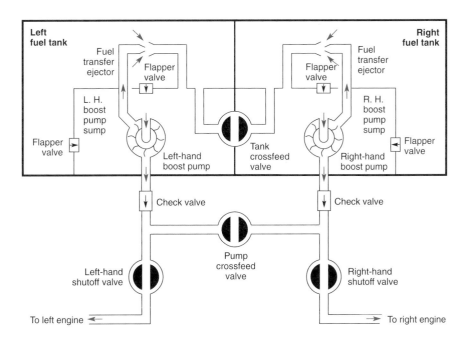

Figure 8-6. *Twin-engine cross-feed fuel system*

Four-Engine Manifold Cross-feed Fuel System

Large aircraft have a number of fuel tanks that may be filled, drained, or used from a manifold that connects all tanks and all engines. Figure 8-7 shows such a system. *See* Figure 8-7 on the next page.

The characteristics of a manifold cross-feed fuel system are:

1. All tanks can be serviced through a single refueling receptacle. This pressure fueling reduces the chances of fuel contamination, as well as reducing the danger of static electricity igniting fuel vapors.

2. Any engine can be fed from any tank. This lets the pilot balance the fuel load to maintain good stability of the aircraft.

3. All engines can be fed from all tanks simultaneously.

4. A damaged tank can be isolated from the rest of the fuel system.

Each tank has a boost pump and a tank shutoff valve, and each engine has a firewall shutoff valve. There is a manifold valve for each of the engines.

manifold cross-feed fuel system. A type of fuel system commonly used in large transport category aircraft. All fuel tanks feed into a common manifold, and the dump chutes and the single-point fueling valves are connected to the manifold. Fuel lines to each engine are taken from the manifold.

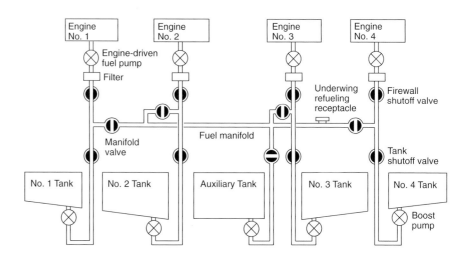

Figure 8-7. *A typical manifold cross-feed fuel system*

By opening the tank shutoff valve and the firewall shutoff valve, each engine is fed from its own fuel tank. And, by opening the manifold valve for any engine, the boost pump in the tank feeding that engine can pressurize the manifold. This allows pilot or flight engineer to balance the load in flight to maintain good stability

This fuel system allows for single-point pressure fueling and defueling. This reduces the chances of fuel contamination, as well as reducing the danger of static electricity igniting fuel vapors.

Pressure fueling is done through an underwing fueling and defueling receptacle and a fuel control panel that contains all of the controls and gages necessary for a person to fuel or defuel any or all of the tanks. When the aircraft is being refueled, the fueling hose is attached to the refueling receptacle on the manifold. All the manifold valves and tank valves are open and the firewall shutoff valves are closed. The valve on the fueling hose is opened and fuel flows into all the tanks. When a tank is full, or when it reaches the level preset on the fuel control panel, the valve for that tank shuts off. When all the tanks have the correct amount of fuel in them, the system automatically shuts off.

Helicopter Fuel System

Helicopters have unique requirements for their fuel systems. The spaces in which the fuel tanks can be located are far more limited than they are in an airplane because a helicopter has no wings in which the tanks can be installed. Another complication is that the center of gravity range is so limited that the fuel tanks as well as most of the payload must be located in close proximity to the rotor mast.

Figure 8-8 shows the airframe fuel system for a single-engine turbine-powered helicopter. The bladder-type fuel cell is mounted in the fuselage and is connected to the fuel filler port on the outside of the fuselage. Two centrifugal-type submerged boost pumps are mounted in the bottom of the tank, one forward and one aft. Fuel is picked up by the boost pumps and directed through integral check valves to a single fuel supply line. After the fuel leaves the tank, it passes through a solenoid-operated shutoff valve, through an airframe system filter, and through the engine filter to the engine fuel control unit.

bladder-type fuel cell. A plastic-impregnated fabric bag supported in a portion of an aircraft structure so that it forms a cell in which fuel is carried.

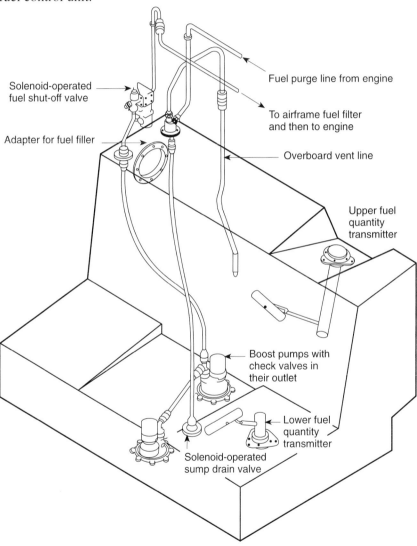

Figure 8-8. *Simplified diagram of the fuel system of a turbine-engine-powered helicopter*

Large Turbine-Engine Transport Fuel System

The fuel system of the Boeing 727 is typical of the systems used in this type of aircraft. The fuel is held in three tanks. Tanks 1 and 3 are located in the wings and have a nominal capacity of 12,000 pounds. Tank 2 has a nominal capacity of 24,000 pounds and consists of three sections. An integral section of tank 2 is located in each wing, and a bladder section is located in the wing center section. *See* Figure 8-9.

Tanks 1 and 3 have two centrifugal-type submerged boost pumps each that are driven by 3-phase AC motors. Tank 2 has four boost pumps of the same type. Each boost pump has a check valve in its outlet so fuel will not flow back into the tank through any pump if it is inoperative.

The boost pumps in each tank feed their respective engines through electric motor-driven engine shutoff valves. Three cross-feed valves allow the boost pumps in any tank to supply fuel to any engine and to defuel any of the tanks or transfer fuel from one tank to another.

Vent lines in tanks 1 and 3 are connected to vent surge tanks outboard of their respective tanks. Vent lines in tank 2 are connected to both of the surge tanks. The vent-surge tank outlets are in a non-icing flush scoop on the lower surface of the wing tips. This scoop allows positive ram pressure to be in the tanks during all airplane attitudes.

The surge tanks are protected against the entry of flames in the vent duct. A flame-sensitive detector is mounted in each vent duct between the vent scoop and the surge tank. If a flame enters the duct, the detector will electrically discharge an inerting agent into the vent-surge tank which will prevent the flame from reaching the fuel tanks. The flight engineer has a test switch that tests the integrity of the system.

The electrically operated engine shutoff valves are operated by DC motors that are controlled by switches on the flight engineer's panel. When any fire pull handle is pulled, the engine fuel shutoff valve is closed and the switch on the flight engineer's panel is deactivated until the fire pull handle is pushed back in.

Fueling and Defueling

The Boeing 727 is equipped for pressure fueling and defueling, but provisions are also made for overwing fueling and suction defueling.

The single-point refueling panel, (as shown in Figure 8-10 on Page 607), located in the leading edge of the right wing contains two fueling hose couplings, fuel quantity indicators for the three tanks, and the control switches for the fueling valves.

Before fueling, test the fuel quantity indicators by turning the fueling test switch to ON. All three indicators should drive toward zero. When the switch is returned to its OFF position, the gages will return to their original indication.

fire pull handle. The handle in an aircraft cockpit that is pulled at the first indication of an engine fire. Pulling this handle removes the generator from the electrical system, shuts off the fuel and hydraulic fluid to the engine, and closes the compressor bleed air valve. The fire extinguisher agent discharge switch is uncovered, but it is not automatically closed.

pressure fueling. The method of fueling used by almost all transport aircraft. The fuel is put into the aircraft through a single underwing fueling port. The fuel tanks are filled to the desired quantity and in the sequence selected by the person conducting the fueling operation.
Pressure fueling saves servicing time by using a single point to fuel the entire aircraft, and it reduces the chances for fuel contamination.

Connect the two fuel hoses and pressurize the fueling manifold. When the fueling valve switch is moved to the OPEN position, the valve opens and fuel flows from the fueling manifold into the tank. If the tank is to be completely filled, a float-operated shutoff valve, labeled ACO in Figure 8-9, will close the valve when the tank is full. If the tank is to be only partially filled, the fueling valve switch can be moved to the CLOSE position when the desired quantity is indicated on the fuel quantity gage.

Tanks 1 and 3 have provisions for overwing fueling. If tank 2 needs to be fueled by this method, fuel can be transferred from tanks 1 and 3 by opening the cross-feed valves and using the boost pumps in tanks 1 and 3.

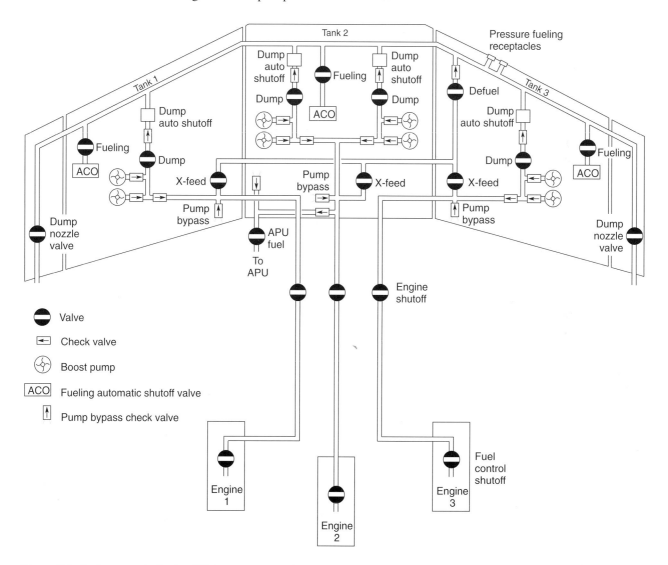

Figure 8-9. *Fuel system of a Boeing 727 jet transport airplane*

Pressure defueling is done by connecting a fuel-servicing truck to the servicing manifold. Open all three of the cross-feed valves and turn on one or more boosts pump in each tank. Open the manually operated defuel valve and fuel will be pumped from the cross-feed manifold into the servicing manifold and into the servicing truck.

Suction defueling can be done by using the same connections and valve positions as for pressure defueling. Close the manifold vent shutoff valve at the fuel panel and use the suction provided by the servicing truck to get the fuel from the tanks. The fuel will flow from the tank through the pump-bypass check valves.

Fuel Dumping

Fuel can be jettisoned in flight from all three tanks through either or both of the dump nozzles located in the wing tips. Fuel under boost pump pressure flows through the four electrically operated dump valves, through the automatic dump level control valves, into the fueling and dump manifold. The fuel leaves this manifold through the electrically operated dump nozzle valves and exits the aircraft through the dump nozzles.

The normal dumping rate is approximately 2,300 pounds per minute. The mechanically operated dump level control valves will shut the fuel off automatically when the level reaches 3,500 pounds in each tank. If these valves should not operate, the dumping can be terminated by closing the electrically operated dump valves.

Instruments and Controls

The switches and instruments for the fuel system are located at the single-point refueling panel in the leading edge of the right wing and at the flight engineer's panel.

Refueling Panel

The refueling panel has three fuel quantity gages, one for each of the three tanks. These gages indicate the usable fuel in each tank, measured in pounds. *See* Figure 8-10. Directly below each of these gages is a guarded fueling shutoff valve switch and a valve-in-transit light. When the valve switch is moved, the light comes on until the valve reaches the position called for by the switch, and then goes out.

The fueling power switch controls power for the fueling operation with the external or APU power connected.

When the fueling test switch is moved to the ON position, all three indicators on the fueling panel are driven toward zero. The indicators on the flight engineer's panel are driven toward full. When the switch is turned to the OFF position, the indicators all return to their original position.

The manifold vent shutoff valve is a manual valve that is normally open, but is closed when the tanks are being defueled by suction.

fuel jettison system. A system installed in most large aircraft that allows the flight crew to jettison, or dump, fuel to lower the gross weight of the aircraft to its allowable landing weight.

Boost pumps in the fuel tanks move the fuel from the tank into a fuel manifold. From the fuel manifold it flows away from the aircraft through dump chutes in each wing tip.

The fuel jettison system must be so designed and constructed that it is free from fire hazards.

Flight Engineer's Panel

The fuel system control switches and indicators on the flight engineer's panel are illustrated in Figures 8-11 and 8-12.

The digital total fuel quantity indicator indicates the total usable fuel aboard to the nearest 100 pounds. The three analog-type indicators give the usable amount of fuel in each of the three tanks. The large pointers indicate the thousands of pounds, and the small vernier pointers indicate the hundreds of pounds. These indicators are driven by a capacitance bridge system that compensates for variations in fuel temperature and density.

When the test switch for each indicator is depressed, the analog indicators move toward empty and the indication on the total quantity indicator increases. When the switch is released, the indications return to their normal values.

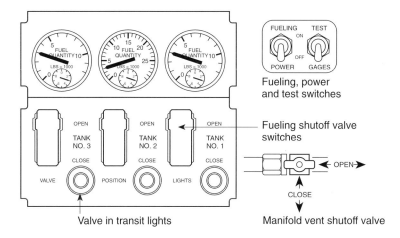

Figure 8-10. *Refueling panel controls and indicators*

The boost pump switches control the boost pumps. The low-pressure lights associated with each pump come on if the boost pump is not producing any pressure.

The engine fuel valve control switch controls the engine fuel valves as long as the fire pull handles are not pulled. When these handles are pulled, the valve control switch is disarmed and cannot operate until the fire pull handle is pushed back in. The valve-in-transit light comes on, indicating power to the valve motor, and it turns off when the valve reaches the position called for by the switch.

The cross-feed valve control switch is a rotary switch that has a bar on its knob that lines up with lines on the panel that show whether the valve is open or closed. When bar is aligned with the line, the engine fuel system is connected to the cross-feed manifold. *See* Figure 8-11 on the next page.

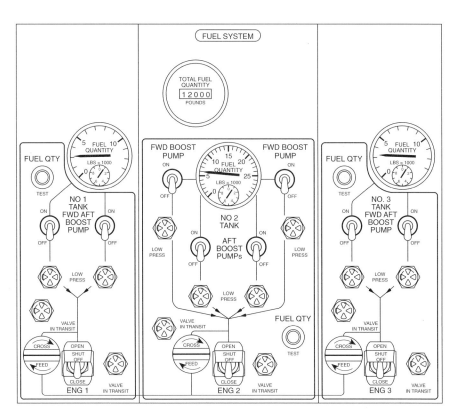

Figure 8-11. *Fuel system controls on the flight engineer's panel*

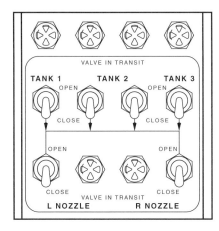

Figure 8-12. *Fuel dump control switches on the flight engineer's auxiliary panel*

The left and right dump nozzle valve switches and the dump valve switches are located on the flight engineer's auxiliary panel. Each switch has an accompanying valve-in-transit light that shows that there is power to the valve, and the light goes out when the valve reaches the position called for by the switch.

To dump fuel, open the appropriate nozzle valves and dump valves and turn on the boost pump or pumps. The fuel will dump until the dump level sensor in the tank shuts off the dump flow when the fuel in the tank reaches approximately 3,500 pounds.

STUDY QUESTIONS: AIRCRAFT FUEL SYSTEMS

Answers begin on Page 649. Page numbers refer to chapter text.

24. Refer to Figure 8-2. Because fuel can feed from both tanks at the same time, the air space above the fuel in the tanks must be _____ . *Page 596*

25. The electric fuel pump and the engine fuel pump in Figure 8-4 are connected in _____ (series or parallel). *Page 598*

26. In the fuel system shown in Figure 8-5, vapors in the engine-driven fuel pump are returned to the _____ (main or auxiliary) fuel tanks. *Page 599*

27. In the cross-feed fuel system in Figure 8-6, the boost-pump sumps are kept filled by the fuel transfer _____ . *Page 601*

28. The manifold cross-feed system like that in Figure 8-7 allows any engine to be operated from any fuel tank. This allows the pilot to maintain a _____ fuel load to maintain good stability. *Page 601*

29. In the jet transport fuel system in Figure 8-9 the pressure for dumping fuel is provided by the _____ . *Page 606*

30. When pressure-fueling the jet transport fuel system in Figure 8-9, the fuel being directed into a tank is _____ (manually or automatically) shut off when the tank is full. *Page 605*

Fuel Tanks

Three types of fuel tanks are used in aircraft; built-up tanks, integral tanks, and bladder tanks.

Large fuel tanks have baffles to keep the fuel from surging back and forth, which could cause aircraft control difficulties. And some tanks have special baffles with flapper-type check valves around the tank outlet to prevent the fuel from flowing away from the outlet during certain unco-ordinated flight maneuvers.

All fuel tanks have a low point, called a sump, with a drain valve or fitting which allows this sump to be drained from outside the aircraft. Any water or contaminants in the tank collect in the sump and are removed when the sump is drained.

All fuel tanks must be vented to the atmosphere, with the vents having sufficient capacity to allow the rapid relief of excessive pressure between the interior and the exterior of the tank. The vents keep the pressure above the fuel in the tank the same as that at the fuel metering system.

If a gravity-fed fuel system can supply fuel from both tanks at the same time, the air space above the fuel in the tanks must be interconnected and vented overboard.

It is especially important that the vents in bladder-type tanks be open. If the vent should become clogged, it is possible for the tank to collapse and pull away from its attachments.

Fuel tanks on small aircraft should be marked with the word "FUEL" and the minimum grade or designation of fuel for the engine.

The fuel tanks on transport category aircraft must be marked with the word "FUEL," the minimum grade of fuel allowed for the engines, and the maximum permissible fueling and defueling pressures for pressure fueling systems.

Built-Up Fuel Tanks

Built-up tanks are made of sheet aluminum alloy or stainless steel and are riveted or welded. Some of the tanks in older aircraft are made of thin lead-coated steel called terneplate. These tanks use folded seams and are soldered to make them leak proof.

Some aircraft use fuel tanks ahead of the main spar in the wing that forms the leading edge of the wing. The components of these tanks are electrically seam-welded together, and to prevent their leaking, they are coated on the inside with a sealing compound.

Figure 8-13 shows a typical welded-aluminum fuel tank installed in the fuselage of an aircraft. The filler neck extends to the outside of the fuselage and is surrounded by a scupper, which collects any fuel that spills during fueling and carries it overboard through the drain line. The outlet line to the main fuel strainer is connected to a standpipe inside the tank, which puts the finger screen above the bottom of the tank and provides a sump to collect water and contaminants. The quick-drain valve at the bottom of the sump allows the sump to be drained during the walk-around inspection to check for the presence of water. A small perforated container of potassium dichromate crystals is mounted inside the tank in the sump area. The crystals change any water that collects in the sump into a weak chromate solution that inhibits corrosion.

Observe special caution when repairing a welded aluminum fuel tank, because the fuel vapors inside a tank can explode during the welding process if the tank is inadequately cleaned.

Before a fuel tank is welded, it should be thoroughly washed out with hot water and a detergent. Then live steam should be passed through the tank for at least 30 minutes. The steam vaporizes any fuel left in the tank and carries out the vapors.

After welding an aluminum fuel tank, remove all of the welding flux by scrubbing the weld area with a 5% solution of either sulfuric or nitric acid. After the tank repairs have been completed, the tank should be pressure checked for leakage. Restrain the tank with restraints in the same location as those used in the aircraft, and apply regulated compressed air at a pressure of 3.5 psi. This does not sound like very much pressure, but consider a typical wing tank that is 24 inches wide and 36 inches long. This tank has an area of 864 square inches. When 3.5-psi air pressure is put into the tank, a force of 3,024 pounds acts on the top and bottom of the tank. If the tank is not adequately restrained, it will be damaged.

scupper. A recess around the filler neck of an aircraft fuel tank. Any fuel spilled when the tank is being serviced collects in the scupper and drains to the ground through a drain line rather than flowing into the aircraft structure.

sump. A low point in an aircraft fuel tank in which water and other contaminants can collect and be held until they can be drained out.

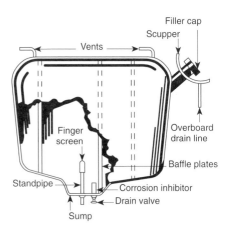

Figure 8-13. *A typical welded aluminum fuel tank*

Integral Fuel Tanks

Almost all large aircraft and many small ones have a part of the structure sealed off and used as a fuel tank. This type of tank reduces weight and uses as much of the space as possible for carrying fuel.

Figure 8-14 shows an integral fuel tank used in a high-wing general-aviation airplane. All the seams are sealed with a rubber-like sealant that remains resilient so vibration will not crack it. Three inspection holes in the structure allow access to the inside of the tank for replacement of the fuel quantity probes or repairing any damaged sealant.

Integral fuel tanks must be thoroughly "inerted," or purged of any fuel vapors, before they can be repaired. This is done by allowing an inert gas such as carbon dioxide or argon to flow through the tank until all of the gasoline fumes have been purged. Both argon and carbon dioxide are heavier than air and will remain in the tank while the repairs are being made.

Integral tanks on large aircraft may be entered for inspection and repair. It is extremely important that before anyone enters these tanks, the tanks must be thoroughly purged by forcing a continuous flow of air through them for at least 2 hours. After purging the tank for the required time, test it to be sure that

integral fuel tank. A fuel tank which is formed by sealing off part of the aircraft structure and using it as a fuel tank. An integral wing tank is called a "wet wing." Integral tanks are used because of their large weight saving.

The only way of repairing an integral fuel tank is by replacing damaged sealant and making riveted repairs, as is done with any other part of the aircraft structure.

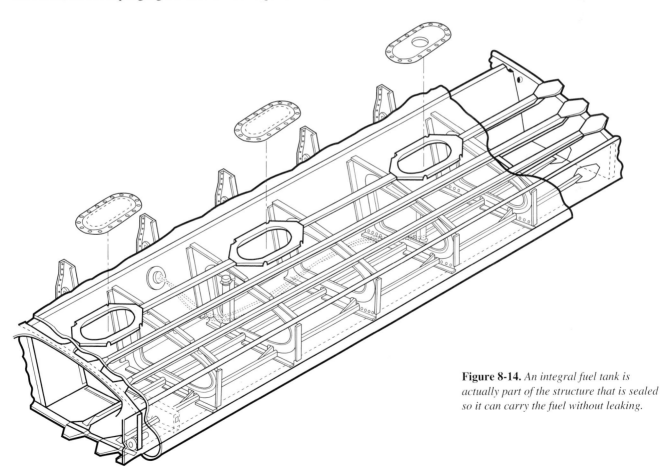

Figure 8-14. *An integral fuel tank is actually part of the structure that is sealed so it can carry the fuel without leaking.*

the vapor level is safe before allowing anyone to enter the tank. The person entering the tank must wear the proper protective clothing and an air supply respirator with full face mask. Another person, similarly equipped, must remain on the outside of the tank to monitor his or her progress and act as a safety agent for the person inside.

Many integral fuel tanks have a series of baffles with flapper-type check valves installed around the boost pumps to prevent fuel flowing away from the pump and the tank discharge line. This check valve allows fuel to flow to the boost pump, but it closes to prevent the fuel flowing away from it. Some tanks also have a pump-removal flapper-type check valve that allows a booster pump to be removed from the tank without having to first drain the tank.

Repair an integral fuel tank the same way you repair any other part of the structure with the exception that you must seal all seams with two-part sealant that is available in kit form from the aircraft manufacturer.

When new riveted joints are made in a fuel tank, the parts are fabricated, all rivet holes are drilled, and the metal parts cleaned with methyl-ethyl-ketone (MEK) or acetone. A layer of sealant is applied to one of the mating surfaces and the parts are riveted together. After the riveting is completed, sealant is applied in a fillet as is shown in Figure 8-15.

Leaks are repaired by removing all of the old sealant from the area suspected of leaking. This is best done with a chisel-shaped tool made of hard fiber and the residue cleaned away with aluminum wool. Be sure that you do not use steel wool or sandpaper. Vacuum out all the chips, filings, and dirt, and thoroughly clean the entire area with MEK or acetone. Apply the sealant as shown in Figure 8-15, and allow it to cure as specified in the instructions that come with the sealer kit.

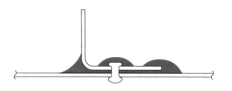

Figure 8-15. *Typical sealant application for a wing rib in an integral fuel tank*

Bladder-Type Fuel Tanks

Some aircraft use rubberized fabric liners inside a part of the structure that has been especially prepared by covering all sharp edges of the supporting structure with chafing tape. Figure 8-16 shows a typical bladder-type installation in the inboard portion of the wing ahead of the main spar. These bladders are carefully folded and inserted into the wing through the available inspection holes. Inside the wing they are unfolded and attached to the structure with clamps, clips, or lacing. The interconnecting hoses are attached, and the clamps are torqued in place to complete the installation.

If bladder tanks are to remain empty for an extended period of time, wipe the inside of the tank with clean engine oil to prevent the rubber from drying out and cracking. *See* Figure 8-16.

A technician can repair bladder tanks by patching them, but it is usually more economical to send them to a repair station that is certificated for this specific repair. Technicians working in these shops are familiar with the bladders and can evaluate the condition of the tank and make all of the repairs that are needed to restore the cell to an airworthy condition.

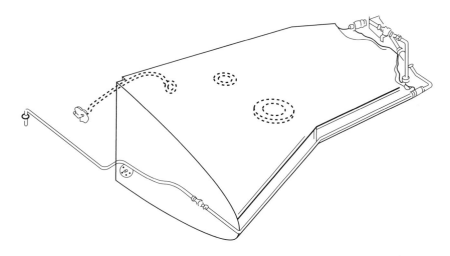

Figure 8-16. *Bladder-type fuel tank installed in the inboard portion of the wing ahead of the main spar*

Leaks in bladder cells are located by plugging all of the holes, inserting ammonia gas into the cell, and rounding the cell out with about $\frac{3}{4}$-psi air pressure. Place a white cloth saturated with a phenolphthalein solution over the cell. If there are any leaks, the ammonia gas will escape and react with the phenolphthalein and produce a bright red mark on the white cloth.

Fuel Tank Filler Caps

For a component to which is so little attention is paid, the fuel tank filler cap is vitally important. Fuel tanks are often located in the wings, and the filler opening is in a low pressure area. If the cap does not seal properly, the low pressure will draw the fuel from the tank. Leaking filler caps will also allow water to enter the tank when the aircraft is parked outside in the rain.

Fuel tanks must be vented to the outside air. If air cannot enter the tank to take the place of the fuel as it is used, the resulting low pressure will cause fuel to cease flowing to the engine. If the tank is a bladder type, it will probably collapse and pull loose from its fastenings inside the structure. Some fuel tanks are vented through the filler cap, and others use vents that are independent of the cap. Be sure to install only the proper cap when replacing a filler cap. Many light aircraft in the past required a slight positive air pressure inside the fuel tank to assure proper feed to the engine. These filler caps have a piece of tubing sticking up from the cap that must be pointed forward in flight.

One popular type of fuel filler cap, shown in Figure 8-17, seals the tank opening with an O-ring and vents the tank through a vent safety valve. This valve is closed when the air pressure in the tank and outside air are the same, but it opens when the pressure inside the tank is lower than the outside air pressure. It also acts as a safety valve and opens if the pressure in the tank should ever get as much as 5 psi above the pressure outside the tank.

An extremely serious problem develops if a reciprocating-engine-powered aircraft is inadvertently fueled with turbine engine fuel. Turbine engine fuel used in a reciprocating engine will detonate and destroy the engine. To prevent improper fueling, adapters may be installed in the fuel tank filler openings that prevent a jet fuel nozzle entering the tank.

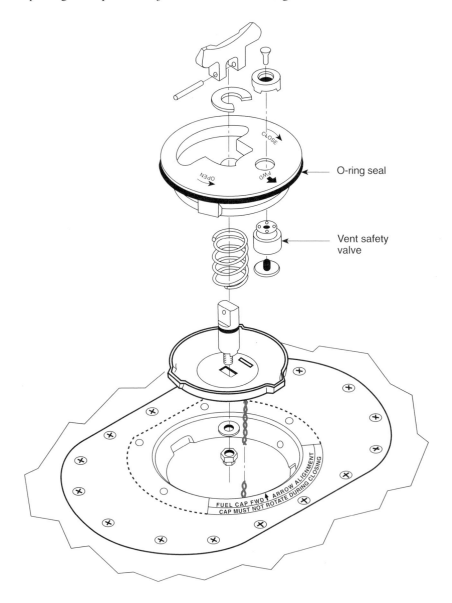

Figure 8-17. *Fuel tank filler cap with a vent safety valve*

Answers begin on Page 649. **Page numbers refer to chapter text.**

31. Fuel is prevented from surging back and forth in a fuel tank by the installation of _____ inside the tank. *Page 609*

32. Water and other contaminants inside a fuel tank collect in the low point that is called the tank _____ . *Page 609*

33. The air pressure above the fuel in a fuel tank is kept the same as the pressure at the fuel metering system by fuel tank _____ . *Page 609*

34. The area around the fuel tank filler neck of an aircraft that has a pressure fueling system must be marked with the word FUEL, the maximum permissible fueling and defueling pressure and the _____ . *Page 610*

35. Before making a welded repair to an aluminum fuel tank, wash it out with hot water and detergent and purge it with live steam for at least _____ minutes. *Page 610*

36. After a welded repair to an aluminum fuel tank is completed, the welded area should be washed with hot water and drained, then the area soaked with a 5% solution of _____ or _____ acid. *Page 610*

37. A welded aluminum fuel tank whose walls are not supported by the aircraft structure must be leak tested with a pressure of _____ psi. *Page 610*

38. A part of the aircraft structure that is sealed off and used as a fuel tank is called a/an _____ fuel tank. *Page 611*

39. Integral fuel tanks on small general aviation airplanes can be purged of gasoline fumes by flowing _____ or _____ through the tank and allowing it to remain in the tank while repairs are being made. *Page 611*

40. Before a person can work inside an integral fuel tank, all of the vapors must be thoroughly purged from the tank by flowing air through the tank for at least _____ hours. *Page 611*

41. Bladder-type fuel cells are checked for leaks by filling the inside of the cell with _____ gas and covering the outside of the cell with a white cloth saturated with a _____ solution. *Page 613*

Fuel Pumps

Several types of fuel pumps are used in aircraft fuel systems. The simplest low-power, low-wing airplanes use a diaphragm pump on the engine and a plunger-type electrically operated auxiliary pump mounted in parallel with the engine pump. Larger reciprocating engines use sliding vane-type pumps driven by the engine and electrically driven centrifugal pumps inside the tanks for starting, backup, and fuel transfer. Turbine engine fuel pumps are normally gear-type pumps.

Electrical Auxiliary Pumps

Fuel boost, or auxiliary, pumps are used to provide a positive flow of fuel from the tank to the engine. They are used for engine starting, as a backup for takeoff and landing, and, in many cases, to transfer fuel from one tank to another.

Plunger-Type Pumps

Many smaller general aviation aircraft use a plunger-type auxiliary fuel pump such as the one in Figure 8-18, installed in parallel with a diaphragm-type engine-driven pump.

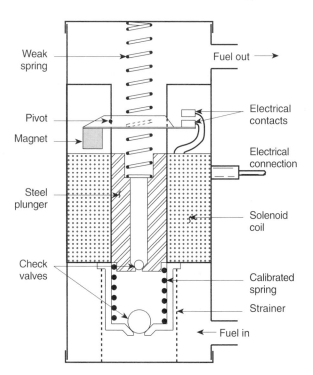
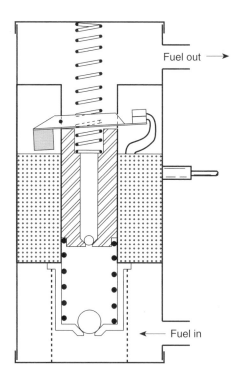

A Coil has been energized and pulled plunger into solenoid. Then electrical contacts opened.

B Calibrated spring has pushed plunger up and fuel out of pump. Magnet is attracted to plunger and contacts close, sending current through solenoid coil.

Figure 8-18. *An electrical plunger-type auxiliary fuel pump*

These simple single-acting pumps have a steel plunger that is moved on its return stroke by an electromagnetic coil, and on its pumping stroke by a calibrated spring. In Figure 8-18A, the pump is shown at the beginning of its pumping stroke. When the switch is first turned on, the magnetic field pulls the steel plunger into the solenoid and opens the contacts. The calibrated spring then forces the plunger up, pushing fuel out of the top of the pump, simultaneously pulling more fuel into the bottom of the pump. When the plunger is out of the solenoid, as in Figure 8-18B, the magnet is attracted to it. As it moves toward the plunger, the contact arm rotates on its pivot and the contacts close, sending current through the coil. This current produces a magnetic field that pulls the plunger back into the solenoid. As soon as the plunger is in the coil, the magnet is attracted to the steel case of the pump, and the contacts open, de-energizing the coil.

When the pressure in the line to the carburetor is low, the pump cycles rapidly, but as the pressure in the discharge line rises, the fuel prevents the calibrated spring forcing the plunger up, and the pump cycles slower.

Centrifugal Boost Pump

Most of the larger aircraft that operate at high altitude use centrifugal boost pumps in the fuel tanks. These pumps supply fuel under positive pressure to the inlet of the engine-driven fuel pumps under conditions where the ambient pressure is too low to assure a positive supply. Pressurizing the fuel lines prevents vapor lock at high altitude. Many of these boost pumps have a two-speed motor. Low speed is used to supply fuel to the engine for starting and as a backup for takeoff and landing. High speed is used to transfer fuel from one tank to another.

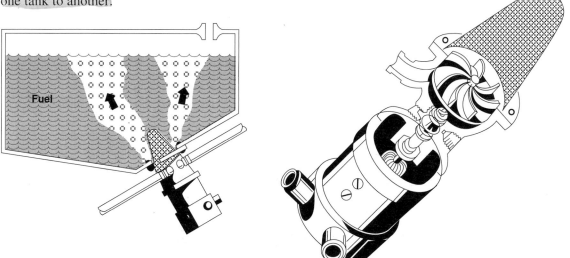

Figure 8-19. *A centrifugal boost pump mounted outside the fuel tank. An agitator on the impeller shaft stirs up the fuel, causing it to release its vapors before the fuel is taken into the fuel lines.*

Figure 8-19 on the previous page shows a centrifugal boost pump mounted on the outside of the tank, but a more common installation is seen in Figure 8-20, in which the electric motor is enclosed in an explosion-proof housing and submerged inside the tank.

A centrifugal boost pump is a variable-displacement pump, and it does not require a relief valve; its output pressure is determined by the impeller speed. The pressure produced by a single-speed centrifugal fuel pump is determined by the pump's design and its internal clearances and characteristics.

Centrifugal boost pumps have a small agitator built onto the impeller that agitates the fuel before it enters the pump impeller. This causes the pump to release much of its vapors before it enters the fuel lines.

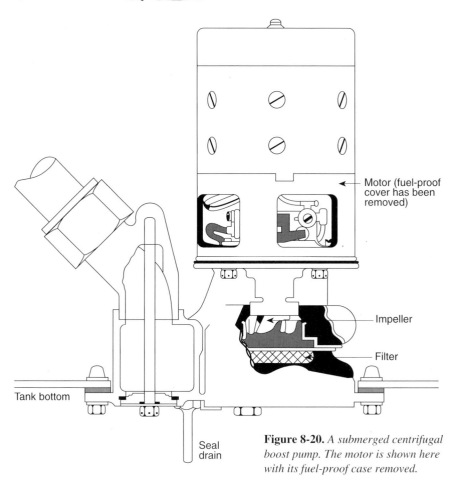

Motor (fuel-proof cover has been removed)

Impeller

Filter

Tank bottom

Seal drain

Figure 8-20. *A submerged centrifugal boost pump. The motor is shown here with its fuel-proof case removed.*

Ejector Pump Systems

It is extremely important that submerged boost pumps always be completely covered with fuel. To prevent fuel flowing away from the pump in any flight attitude, some aircraft are equipped with boost pump sumps that are kept filled by an ejector pump system. *See* Figure 8-21. In Figure 8-22, the fuel tank has a surge box and a sump. The boost pump is installed in the sump, and some of its discharge is routed back into the tank through three ejector pumps.

An ejector pump is a type of jet pump that produces a low pressure when fuel from the boost pump flows through a venturi, as in Figure 8-21. Some of the fuel is taken from the discharge of the boost pump and directed through the ejector pump. This fuel flows through the venturi in the pump at high velocity, and the resulting low pressure draws fuel from the tank and from the surge box and discharges it into the boost pump sump.

The bulkhead between the surge box and the fuel tank has several flapper-type check valves that allow fuel to flow from the tank into the surge box, but prevent it from flowing in the opposite direction. These flapper valves ensure that fuel cannot flow away from the boost pump in any normal flight attitude. Some aircraft also equip the boost pump sump with pump-removal flapper-type check valves that allow you to remove a booster pump from the tank without having to drain the tank first.

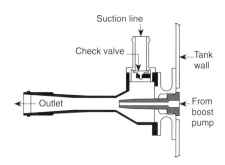

Figure 8-21. *An ejector pump uses a flow of fuel from the boost pump to produce a low pressure that draws fuel from the tank and sends it into the boost pump sump.*

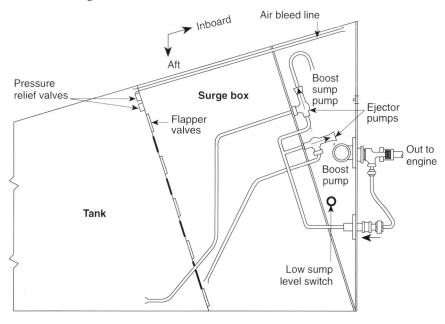

Figure 8-22. *This fuel tank has a surge box with flapper valves that allow the fuel to flow to the boost pump sump but prevent its flowing away from the pump. Ejector pumps draw fuel from the tank and the surge box into the boost pump sump.*

Engine-Driven Fuel Pumps

Three types of engine-driven fuel pumps are generally used on aircraft engines. The smallest engines use a diaphragm-type pump similar to that used on automobile engines, most of the large engines use vane-type pumps, and most turbine engines use gear-type pumps.

Diaphragm-Type Fuel Pump

Some of the smaller engines use diaphragm-type fuel pumps like the one in Figure 8-23. This type of pump is actuated by a plunger that is operated by an eccentric on one of the accessory gears or the camshaft. When the plunger presses against the rocker arm, the diaphragm is pulled down. This pulls fuel into the pump from the fuel tank. When the plunger drops away from the arm, a spring under the diaphragm pushes it up and forces the fuel out of the pump and into the carburetor. The pressure produced by the pump is determined entirely by the compressive strength of the diaphragm spring. This is a variable-displacement pump. When the demand of the engine is great, the pump moves a large volume of fuel, but when the needle valve in the carburetor is closed, the fuel pressure in the line between the carburetor and the fuel pump minimizes the movement of the diaphragm, and very little fuel is moved.

Diaphragm-type pumps are normally installed in parallel with a plunger-type auxiliary pump.

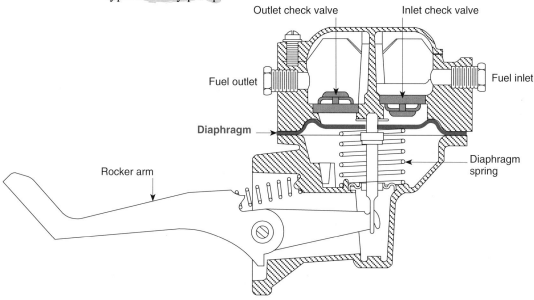

Figure 8-23. *A diaphragm-type engine-driven fuel pump is a variable-displacement pump that is normally installed in parallel with a plunger-type electric auxiliary pump.*

Vane-Type Fuel Pump

The most popular type of fuel pump for larger reciprocating engines is the vane-type pump shown in Figure 8-24. These pumps can be driven by the engine or by an electric motor.

As the pump rotor turns, steel vanes slide in and out of slots, changing the volume of the space between the rotor and the pump cylinder. On the inlet side of the pump this space increases its volume and pulls in fuel. On the discharge side its volume decreases and fuel is forced from the pump.

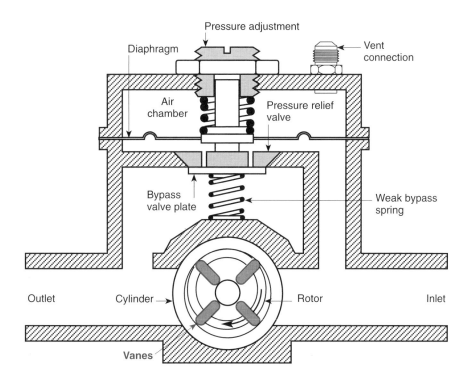

Figure 8-24. *A compensating vane-type fuel pump*

A vane-type pump is a constant-displacement pump that moves a specific volume of fuel each time it rotates. Therefore it must have a relief valve to bypass back to the pump inlet all the fuel in excess of that required by the engine. When the outlet pressure rises above that for which the relief valve is set, the fuel lifts the relief valve from seat and the excess fuel returns to the inlet side of the vanes.

This pump, called a compensated fuel pump, can be used on a turbosupercharged engine equipped with a pressure carburetor. In these engines, the inlet fuel pressure must be maintained a given amount above the inlet air pressure. To do this, the fuel pump must automatically vary its discharge pressure as the carburetor inlet air pressure changes. The diaphragm in the top of this pump is connected to the relief valve shaft and forms one side of the air chamber which senses the air pressure at the carburetor inlet through the vent connection. When the turbosupercharger increases the carburetor inlet air pressure, the increased pressure inside the fuel pump air chamber forces down on the diaphragm, aiding the spring, and increasing the fuel pressure needed to force the relief valve off its seat.

constant-displacement pump. A fluid pump that moves a specific volume of fluid each time it rotates. Some form of pressure regulator or relief valve must be used with a constant-displacement pump when it is driven by an aircraft engine.

compensated fuel pump. A vane-type, engine-driven fuel pump that has a diaphragm connected to the pressure-regulating valve. The chamber above the diaphragm is vented to the carburetor upper deck where it senses the pressure of the air as it enters the engine.

The diaphragm allows the fuel pump to compensate for altitude changes and keeps the carburetor inlet fuel pressure a constant amount higher than the carburetor inlet air pressure.

When used as an engine-driven pump, a vane-type pump is installed in series with the boost pump. For starting the engine, fuel flows from the boost pump into the pump inlet and forces the bypass valve plate on the bottom of the relief valve down. This allows fuel to flow to the engine with only a very slight pressure drop caused by the weak spring trying to hold the bypass valve closed.

Turbine-Engine Fuel Pump

The high fuel pressure required by turbine engines makes gear or piston pumps the most widely used types. The pump in Figure 8-25 is a constant-displacement, high-pressure pump with two gear-type pump elements. Each element is fitted with a shear section that will break if either element becomes jammed. The jammed element will stop, but the other element will continue to produce fuel pressure for the engine.

The gear-driven impeller at the inlet of the pump increases the fuel pressure from 15 to 45 psi before it enters the high-pressure gear sections of the pump. The two gear sections increase the pressure to about 850 psi and discharge it in a common outlet compartment in which the pump pressure relief valve is located. Pressure in excess of that for which the relief valve is set is bypassed to the gear section inlet.

shear section. A necked-down section of an engine-driven pump shaft that is designed to shear if the pump should seize. When the shear section breaks, the shaft can continue to turn without causing further damage to the pump or to the engine.

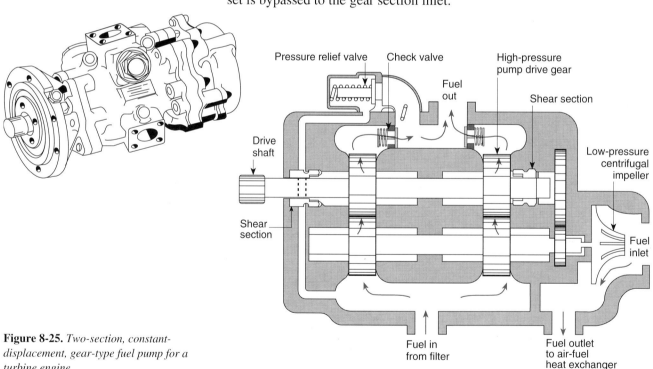

Figure 8-25. *Two-section, constant-displacement, gear-type fuel pump for a turbine engine*

*Answers begin on Page 649. **Page numbers refer to chapter text.***

42. The pressure produced by a plunger-type auxiliary pump is determined by the strength of the _____ spring. *Page 617*

43. A centrifugal boost pump is a _____ (constant or variable) -displacement pump. *Page 618*

44. The small agitator that spins with the impeller of a centrifugal boost pump is used to separate the _____ from the fuel before the fuel enters the lines to the carburetor. *Page 618*

45. Fuel is prevented from flowing away from the boost pump by flapper-type _____ in the fuel tank baffles. *Page 619*

46. Fuel is pulled into the boost pump sump from the fuel tank by a/an _____-type pump. *Page 619*

47. A diaphragm-type engine-driven pump is a _____ (constant or variable) -displacement pump. *Page 620*

48. The pressure produced by a diaphragm-type fuel pump is determined by the _____ . *Page 620*

49. A vane-type fuel pump is a _____ (constant or variable) -displacement pump. *Page 621*

50. Constant-displacement pumps _____ (do or do not) require a relief valve. *Page 621*

51. An engine-driven vane-type pump is installed in _____ (series or parallel) with the boost pump. *Page 622*

52. The air chamber on one side of the diaphragm in a compensated fuel pump senses the air pressure at the inlet to the _____ . *Page 621*

53. A gear-type fuel pump is a _____ (constant or variable) -displacement pump. *Page 622*

54. If the gears in a gear-type fuel pump should seize, the _____ on the drive shaft will prevent the engine being damaged. *Page 622*

Fuel Filters and Strainers

A review of aircraft accidents caused by powerplant failure shows a large portion of them are due to fuel contamination. Filters or strainers clogged with debris and water in the carburetor are chief offenders.

Types of Contaminants

Contaminants likely to be found in an aircraft fuel system include: water, solid particles, surfactants, and micro-organisms. The procedures to use to avoid fuel system contamination are covered later in this chapter.

Though always present in aviation fuel, water is now considered to be a major source of fuel contamination. Modern jet aircraft fly at altitudes where the temperature is low enough to cause water that is entrained, or dissolved, in the fuel to condense out and form free water. This free water can freeze, and the resulting ice will clog the fuel screens. This may be prevented by using an antifreeze additive in the fuel.

Sand blown into the storage tanks or in the aircraft fuel tanks during fueling operation or rust from unclean storage tanks are solid particles which clog strainers and restrict the flow of fuel.

Surfactants are partially soluble compounds which are by-products of the fuel processing or from fuel additives. Surfactants reduce the surface tension of the liquid contaminants and cause them to adhere to other contaminants and drop out of the fuel and form sludge.

Micro-organisms are one of the serious contaminants found in jet aircraft fuel tanks. Grown from airborne bacteria, these tiny organisms collect in the fuel and lie dormant until they come into contact with free water. The bacteria grow at a prodigious rate as they live in the water and feed on the hydrocarbon fuel and on some of the surfactant contaminants. The scum which they form holds water against the walls of the fuel tanks and causes corrosion. The antifreeze additive that is used with turbine engine fuel also acts as a biocidal agent and kills the micro-organisms, preventing them from forming the scum inside the tanks.

Required Fuel Strainers

All fuel systems are required to have a strainer in the outlet of each tank and at the inlet to the fuel metering system or the engine-driven pump. The strainer in the tank outlet is normally a coarse mesh finger screen that traps any large contaminants to prevent their obstructing the fuel line.

The main strainer, located before the inlet to the carburetor or fuel pump and in the lowest point in the system, may be similar to the gascolator in Figure 8-26. If the strainer is located in the lowest point in the system, it can trap any small amount of water that is present in the system.

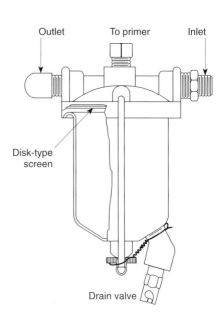

Figure 8-26. *A gascolator fuel filter is installed at the low point in the fuel system.*

The filtering element of some of the larger fuel screens is made of a coarse screen formed into a cylinder with a cone in its center. This coarse screen is covered with a fine screen that does the actual filtering. Any water or contaminants in the fuel collect in the bottom of the strainer housing where they can be drained out on a daily or preflight inspection. *See* Figure 8-27.

Turbine engine fuel controls contain such close tolerance components that even the smallest contaminants can cause serious problems. For this reason, turbine engine fuel systems often use a microfilter that uses a replaceable cellulose filter element that is capable of removing foreign matter as small as 10 to 25 microns. A human hair has a diameter of approximately 100 microns. Such a filter is shown in Figure 8-28.

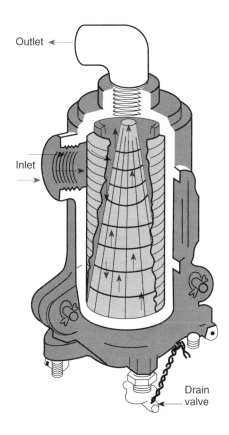

Figure 8-27. *A main fuel strainer*

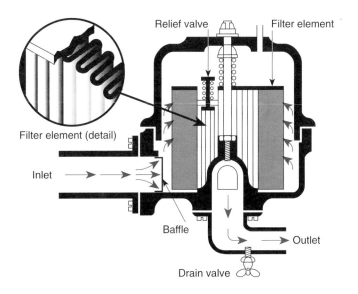

Figure 8-28. *Microfilter used in a turbine engine fuel system*

Another type of filter that is widely used for turbine engine fuel systems is the wafer screen filter seen in Figure 8-29 (Page 626). The filtering element is a stack of wafer-type screen disks made of a 200-mesh bronze, brass, or stainless steel wire screen. This type of filter can remove very tiny particles from the fuel and at the same time can withstand the high pressures found in a turbine engine fuel system.

Some of the fuel filters used in jet transport aircraft have a pressure switch across the filtering element. If ice should form on the filter and block the flow of fuel, the pressure drop across the filter will increase enough to close the contacts and turn on a light on the flight engineer's panel, warning that ice is forming on the filter.

micron. A measurement equal to one millionth of a meter, or 0.000 039 inch.

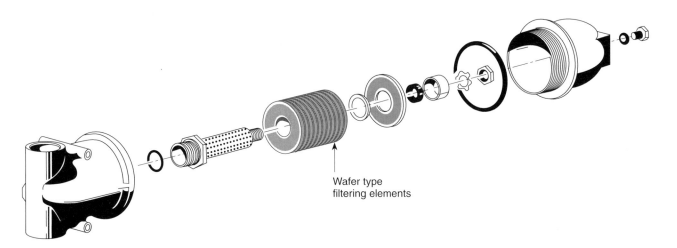

Wafer type
filtering elements

Figure 8-29. *A wafer-screen-type fuel filter*

Answers begin on Page 649. Page numbers refer to chapter text.

STUDY QUESTIONS: FUEL FILTERS AND STRAINERS

55. It _____ (is or is not) possible to get rid of all of the water in aviation fuel. *Page 624*

56. One problem with the water that condenses from turbine engine fuel is that it clogs the fuel screens when it _____ . *Page 624*

57. Water can be prevented from freezing on the fuel screens by adding an _____ additive to the fuel. *Page 624*

58. Micro-organisms that form scum inside a fuel tank are killed by the _____ additive that is used in the fuel. *Page 624*

59. The main fuel strainers are located at the lowest point in the fuel system so it will trap and hold any _____ in the system. *Page 624*

60. The fuel filters on some jet transport aircraft have a pressure switch across the filtering element. This switch will turn on a warning light on the flight engineer's panel if _____ clogs the filter. *Page 625*

Fuel Valves

Aircraft fuel systems are complex and usually have several tanks, pumps, strainers and much plumbing. The valves that control the flow of fuel through these systems are vital components of the fuel system.

The valves must be capable of carrying all of the required fuel flow without an excessive pressure drop, and all valves must have a positive method of determining when they are in the fully open or fully closed position.

Plug-Type Valves

Some of the smaller aircraft use a simple plug-type selector valve in which a conical cork or brass plug is rotated in a mating hole in the valve body. The plug is drilled in such a way that it can connect the inlet to any one of the outlets that is selected.

A spring-loaded pin slips into a detent in the housing when the cone is accurately aligned with the holes in the valve body. This detent allows the pilot to tell by feel when the valve is in its fully open or fully closed position. *See* Figure 8-30.

Poppet-Type Selector Valve

The poppet-type selector valve has many advantages over other types of hand-operated valves. It has a positive feel when any tank is in the full ON position and its design assures that the line to a tank is either fully open or fully closed, with no possibility of an intermediate position.

Figure 8-31 shows a typical poppet-type selector valve. The handle rotates a cam which forces the poppet for the selected tank off its seat and fuel flows from that tank to the engine. Springs hold the poppets for all the other tanks tight against their seat. A spring-loaded indexing pin drops into a notch, or detent, in an indexing plate each time a poppet is fully off of its seat. It also drops into the notch when the valve in the OFF position and all of the poppets are seated.

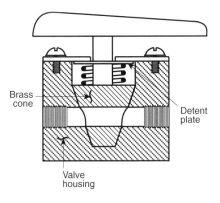

Figure 8-30. *Plug-type fuel selector or shutoff valve*

detent. A spring-loaded pin or tab that enters a hole or groove when the device to which it is attached is in a certain position. Detents are used on a fuel valve to provide a positive means of identifying the fully on and fully off position of the valve.

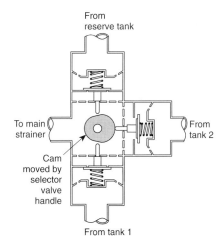

Figure 8-31. *A typical poppet-type fuel selector valve*

Electric Motor-Operated Sliding Gate Valve

All large aircraft use electrically operated valves in their fuel systems. Common types of electrically operated valves are motor-driven gate valves and solenoid-operated poppet valves.

The valve in Figure 8-32 is a motor-driven gate valve. The geared output of a reversible electric motor drives a crank arm which moves the gate through a slot to cover the opening for the fuel line. Reversing the motor rotates the arm so it pulls the gate back and uncovers the fuel line opening.

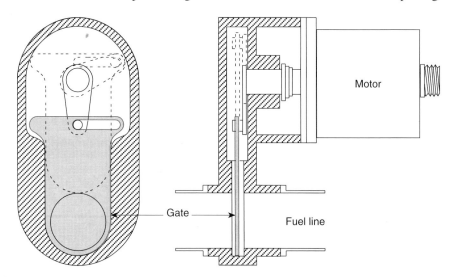

Figure 8-32. *Electric motor-operated sliding gate-type fuel valve*

Solenoid-Operated Poppet-Type Fuel Shutoff Valve

The solenoid-operated poppet-type shutoff valve in Figure 8-33 uses a pulse of DC electricity in one circuit to open the valve and a pulse in another circuit to close it.

To open the valve, the opening solenoid is energized with a pulse of electricity. The magnetism produced by the pulse pulls the valve stem up until the spring behind the locking stem can force it into the notch in the valve stem. The locking stem holds the valve open.

To close the valve, the closing solenoid is energized with a pulse of electricity. The magnetism produced by this pulse pulls the locking stem back and allows the valve spring to close the valve.

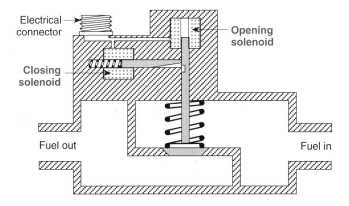

Figure 8-33. *Solenoid-operated shutoff valve*

STUDY QUESTION: FUEL VALVES

Answer is on Page 649. Page number refers to chapter text.

61. A device on a fuel valve that allows the pilot to know when the valve is in its fully open or fully
    closed position is called a/an _____ . *Page 627*

Fuel Heaters

Because turbine-engine-powered aircraft fly at high altitudes where the
temperature is very low, the fuel systems are susceptible to the formation of
ice on the fuel filters.

A fuel temperature indicator on the flight engineer's panel warns when
the fuel temperature is low enough for ice crystals to form in the fuel.

Fuel filter icing lights warn that ice is forming on the fuel filter and
restricting the flow of fuel. Fuel heat switches can open the fuel heat valves
to direct hot, high-pressure compressor bleed air through the fuel heater to
increase the temperature of the fuel.

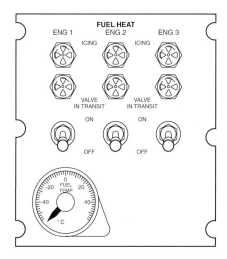

Figure 8-34. *Fuel heat control panel. The
top lights indicate that ice is forming on
the filters. The lower lights are on while
the fuel heat valves are moving to the
position called for by the fuel heat switch.
The fuel heat switches open or close the
valve that directs hot, high-pressure
compressor bleed air into the heat
exchanger. The fuel temperature gage on
the flight engineer's panel warns of the
danger of ice clogging the fuel filters.*

Two types of fuel heaters can be used to prevent ice clogging the filters in turbine engine fuel systems: air-to-fuel and oil-to-fuel heat exchangers. Air-to-fuel systems use hot compressor bleed air for the source of heat, and oil-to-fuel systems use the heat from the engine lubricating oil.

Figure 8-35 shows a typical air-to-fuel heat exchanger. Cold fuel flows through the tubes in the heat exchanger, and the fuel temperature sensor controls the amount of warm air that flows around the tubes. Heat from the air enters the fuel and raises its temperature enough to prevent ice crystals forming on the fuel filter.

All the fuel that flows to the engine must pass through the heat exchanger, and it can raise the fuel temperature enough to thaw ice that has formed on the fuel screen.

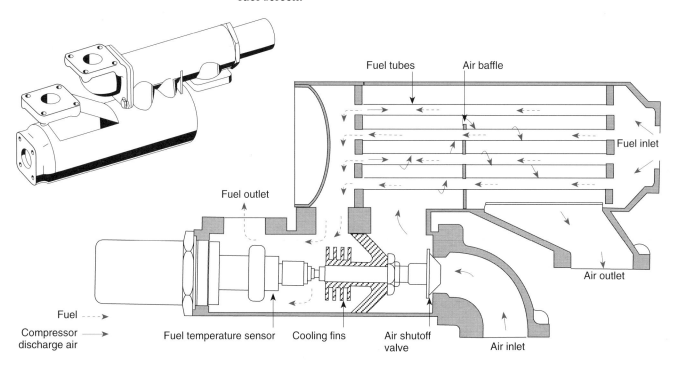

Figure 8-35. *An air-to-fuel heat exchanger for a jet aircraft*

STUDY QUESTIONS: FUEL HEATERS

Answers begin on Page 649. Page numbers refer to chapter text.

62. Two sources of heat for fuel heaters are:

    a. _____

    b. _____

    Page 630

63. Ice is prevented from clogging the filter of a turbine engine fuel system by routing warm
    _____ through an air-to-fuel heat exchanger. *Page 629*

64. A fuel heater _____ (can or cannot) be used to thaw ice that has already formed on the fuel
    screen. *Page 630*

Fuel System Instruments

All aircraft, regardless of their size, must have some means of indicating the quantity of fuel in each tank. Other information that fuel system instrumentation must provide is fuel pressure, fuel flow, and fuel temperature.

Fuel Quantity Measuring Systems

Fuel quantity measuring systems range from extremely simple floats riding on the surface of the fuel to electronic systems that compensate for fuel temperature and indicate the number of pounds of fuel on board the aircraft.

Each fuel quantity indicator must be calibrated to read zero during level flight when the quantity of the fuel remaining in the tank is equal to the unusable fuel supply.

Direct-Reading Fuel Gages

One simple type of direct-reading fuel quantity indicating system is a sight glass. A transparent tube connected between the top and the bottom of the fuel tank shows the level of the fuel in the tank. To make the level of the fuel easier to read, some of the tubes for shallow tanks are slanted, and the quantity is indicated against a calibrated scale behind the tube.

Some direct indicators use a simple cork float with a wire sticking through a hole in the fuel tank cap. The higher the wire protrudes from the tank, the more fuel there is. This type of system does not give an accurate indication of the amount of fuel in the tank, only a relative indication.

A combination of sight glass and cork has been used for fuel tanks in the wings of high-wing airplanes and in the upper wing of biplanes. A transparent tube, whose length is the same as the depth of the fuel tank, sticks out below the wing. A cork float rides on the top of the fuel in the tank and a wire protrudes from the bottom of the float. This wire rides inside the transparent tube and a knob, or indicator, on the end of the wire shows the level of the fuel in the tank.

Some fuel tanks have a float mounted on a wire arm that rides on the top of the fuel. *See* Figure 8-36. The wire arm moves a bevel gear which drives a pinion. Attached to the pinion is a pointer which rides over a dial to indicate the level of the fuel in the tank. All of this mechanism is sealed inside the fuel tank.

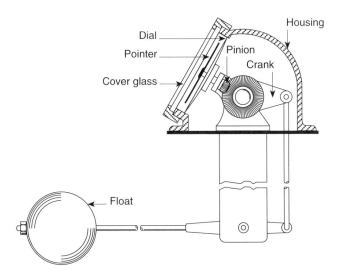

Figure 8-36. *A direct-reading fuel quantity gage indicates the level of the fuel in the tank by converting the movement of the float arm into rotation of the pointer in front of the dial.*

A similar type of indicator to that in Figure 8-36 mounts the pointer on the outside of the tank. A magnet on the pointer is magnetically coupled to a magnet inside the tank that is moved by the float arm mechanism. Movement of the float arm rotates the pointer, and there is no possibility of fuel leaking through this type of indicator.

Electrical Resistance-Type Fuel Quantity Indicating System

For many years the most widely used fuel quantity measuring system has been the electrical resistance-type system. These systems use a sender, or transmitter, that consists of a variable resistor mounted on the outside of the fuel tank and operated by an arm connected to a float that rides on the surface of the fuel in the tank. Movement of the arm is transmitted through a metal bellows-type seal to operate the wiper of the resistor.

The indicator used with this system is a current-measuring instrument calibrated in fuel quantity. When the tank is empty, the float is on the bottom and the resistance is maximum. This drives the indicator pointer to the EMPTY mark on the dial. When the tank is full, the float is near the top of the tank, the resistance is minimum, and the pointer is driven to the FULL mark.

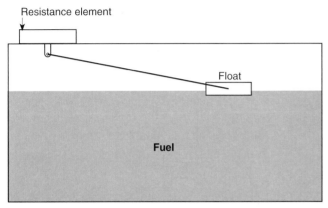

Resistance element

Float

Fuel

Float rides on top of fuel in tank and drives wiper across resistance element on the outside of tank through metal bellows-type seal.

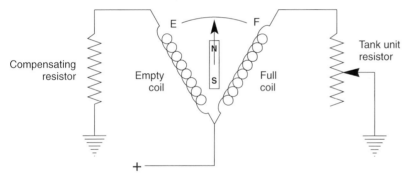

Compensating resistor

Empty coil

Full coil

Tank unit resistor

When tank is full, the tank unit resistance is minimum and current through the full coil is maximum. Permanent magnet attached to pointer pulls pointer into alignment with the full coil.

Figure 8-37. *Electrical resistance-type fuel quantity indicator*

Capacitance-Type Electronic Fuel Quantity Measuring System

The electronic (capacitance-type) fuel-quantity-indicating system has no moving parts inside the tank, and is more accurate than other types of systems used for measuring fuel quantity.

These systems use several capacitor-type probes extending across each tank from top to bottom. When the attitude of the aircraft changes, fuel rises

capacitance-type fuel quantity measuring system. A popular type of electronic fuel quantity indicating system. The tank units are cylindrical capacitors, called probes, mounted across the tank from top to bottom, and the indicator is a servo-type instrument driven by a capacitance bridge and a signal amplifier. There are no moving parts of the system in the fuel tank.

The dielectric between the plates of the capacitance probes is made up of the fuel and the air above the fuel in the tank. The capacitance of the probe varies with the amount of fuel in the tank.

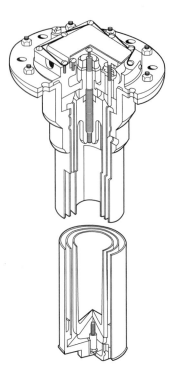

Flange-mounted tank unit

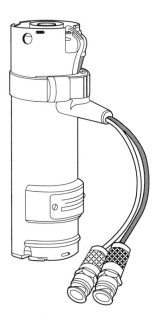

Internally-mounted tank unit

Figure 8-38. *Probes for a capacitance type fuel quantity measuring system*

in some probes and lowers in others, and the total capacitance of all probes remains constant. This makes the fuel-quantity indication independent of attitude changes.

The dielectric constant of the fuel changes with its temperature and thus its density. The system measures the weight, actually the mass, of the fuel rather than its volume. Cold fuel is denser than warm fuel, and there are more pounds in one gallon of cold fuel than there are in a gallon of warm fuel. Knowing the number of pounds of fuel available is more important than knowing the number of gallons, because the power produced by an aircraft engine is determined by the pounds of fuel burned, not the gallons.

By measuring the total capacitance of all of the capacitors in all of the fuel tanks, a totalizing system can indicate, on one instrument, the total number of pounds of fuel on board the aircraft.

The components in electronic (capacitance-type) fuel-quantity-indicating systems are:

* Capacitor probes mounted in the fuel tanks
* A bridge circuit to measure the capacitance of the probes
* An amplifier to increase the amplitude of the signal from the bridge circuit to a value high enough to drive the indicator
* An indicator mounted in the instrument panel to show the amount of fuel in the tanks

A capacitor is an electrical component made up of two conductors separated by a dielectric, or insulator. It stores an electrical charge, and the amount of charge it can store is determined by three things: the area of the plates, the separation between the plates, and the dielectric constant, or characteristic, of the material between the plates.

Probes like those in Figure 8-38 extend across the fuel tanks from top to bottom. These probes are capacitors and are made of thin metal tubes that act as the plates. These plates have a fixed area, and they are separated by a fixed distance. The dielectric is the fuel or air inside the tank. Air has a dielectric constant, or K, of 1 and the fuel has a K of approximately 2, depending upon its temperature. When the tank is full, fuel is the dielectric and the probe has a given amount of capacity. As the fuel is used, the dielectric becomes less fuel and more air, and the capacitance of the probe decreases.

Several probes can be installed in a fuel tank to measure the quantity of fuel in odd-shaped tanks. These capacitors are connected in parallel and their total capacitance is the sum of the individual capacitances. The probes are connected into a bridge circuit and the indicator is servo-driven to make the bridge self-balancing.

Figure 8-39 is a simplified diagram of a basic capacitance bridge circuit. The bridge is excited with 400-hertz AC through the center-tapped secondary of a transformer. One half of the secondary winding is in series with the tank-unit capacitors and the other half is in series with a reference capacitor. The two halves of the center-tapped winding are 180° out of phase with each other, and if the capacitance of the tank units and the reference capacitor are exactly the same, their capacitive reactances will be the same, and the current through the top half of the bridge will exactly cancel the current through the bottom half. There will be no current flow through the indicator.

The self-balancing bridge in Figure 8-40 works in the same way as the one just considered. When the fuel level in the tank changes, the capacitance of the probes change and shift the phase of the current in the top half of the bridge. The bridge is now unbalanced and a signal is sent to the amplifier. The amplifier sends a resulting out-of-phase current through one set of windings in the two-phase motor inside the indicator. The other set of windings in the indicator motor is fed with a reference AC, and when the bridge is unbalanced, the motor will turn and drive the rebalancing potentiometer until the AC in the lower half of the bridge is in phase with that in the upper half. The bridge balances and the motor stops turning. The pointer of the fuel quantity indicator is attached to the motor shaft, and it indicates the number of pounds of fuel remaining in the aircraft.

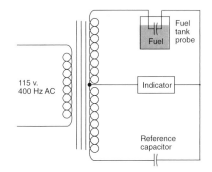

Simplified diagram of a capacitance bridge

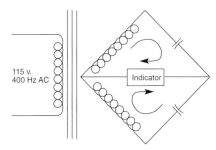

Bridge circuit showing the way current in each half of bridge cancel out

Figure 8-39. *Capacitance bridge diagrams*

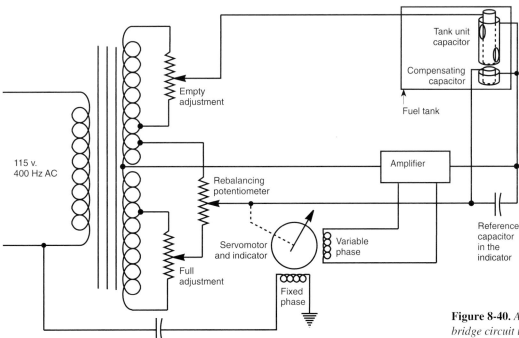

Figure 8-40. *A simplified self-balancing bridge circuit used in a capacitance-type fuel quantity indicating system*

fuel totalizer. A fuel quantity indicator that gives the total amount of fuel remaining on board the aircraft on one instrument. The totalizer adds the quantities of fuel in all of the tanks.

drip stick. A fuel quantity indicator used to measure the fuel level in the tank when the aircraft is on the ground.

The drip stick is pulled down from the bottom of the tank until fuel drips from its open end. This indicates that the top of the gage inside the tank is at the level of the fuel. Note the number of inches read on the outside of the gage at the point it contacts the bottom of the tank, and use a drip-stick table to convert this measurement into gallons of fuel in the tank.

Aircraft instrument panel space is always limited, and one advantage of the capacitance-type fuel quantity indicating system is its ability to measure the fuel in several tanks and give the pilot an indication of the total number of pounds of fuel remaining on one indicator, called a totalizer.

A computerized fuel system indicates the amount of time remaining at the existing fuel flow rate, and is described in the section on fuel flow indication.

Drip Gage and Sight Gage

The fueling crew can use any of several types of external underwing fuel gaging devices to check the actual level of the fuel in the tank. These gages give a purely physical indication of the fuel level in the tank and are used to verify the indications of the electronic measuring systems.

The drip stick is a hollow tube that mounts in the bottom of the fuel tank and sticks up to the top of the tank. To check the amount of fuel in the tank, the drip stick is unlocked and slowly pulled down until fuel begins to drip from its open end. The fuel quantity in the tank relates to the distance the drip stick is pulled from the tank before fuel begins to drip. Some drip sticks are graduated in inches or centimeters and a drip-stick table is used to convert the drip stick reading into pounds of fuel.

The sight gage seen in Figure 8-41 works on the same basic principle as a drip stick, but no fuel actually drips from it. The gage is a long acrylic plastic rod that sticks across the tank from bottom to top. To use the gage, the technician unlocks it and pulls it down while watching the rod through the sight window. When the quartz tip is above the fuel, it reflects light back down the rod. As the rod is pulled and the tip enters the fuel, the amount of reflected light decreases. When the entire tip is in the fuel, no more light is reflected. The level of the fuel in the tank is at the point where the line of reflected light is visible, but is minimum in size. The amount of fuel is read on the calibrated scale opposite the reference mark on the bottom of the tank.

Fuel Flowmeters

Fuel quantity indication is an after-the-fact measurement. Much more useful information is obtained from the fuel flowmeters, which actually show the amount of fuel the engines are burning.

Flowmeters for Large Reciprocating Engines

Many large reciprocating engines use a vane-type flowmeter in the fuel line between the engine-driven pump and the carburetor. The measuring vane, shown in Figure 8-42, is moved by the flow of fuel, and its movement is measured with an Autosyn transmitter. The pointer on the Autosyn fuel flow indicator in the cockpit follows the movement of the vane and shows the fuel flow in gallons per hour. *See* Figure 8-43 on Page 638. This type of instrument is accurate and reliable, but shows only the volume of fuel being used, not its mass. Some of the indicators used with this type of system have a scale on the inside of the gallons indication that gives the amount of fuel burned in pounds. This indication is only approximate, as it is based on the nominal weight of gasoline being six pounds per gallon. It does not take changes in fuel density into consideration.

Autosyn system. The registered trade name of a remote-indicating instrument system. An Autosyn system uses an electromagnet excited with 400-hertz AC for its rotor and a three-phase distributed-pole stator.

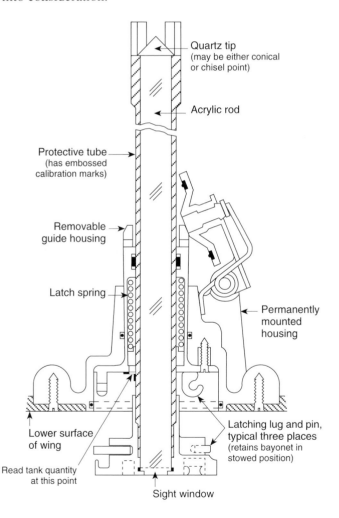

Figure 8-41. *Sight gage for measuring the level of fuel in a tank from underneath the wing.*

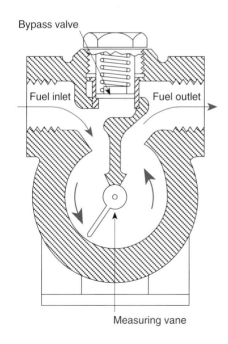

Figure 8-42. *Fuel chamber of a volume-type fuel flowmeter used with large reciprocating engines*

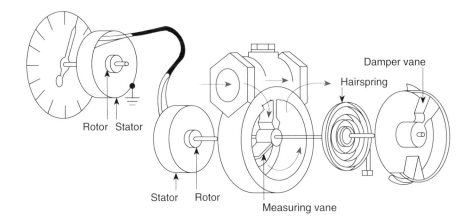

Figure 8-43. *An indication of the movement of the measuring vane in a volume-type flowmeter is electrically transmitted to the indicator in the cockpit.*

Flowmeters for Fuel-Injected Horizontally Opposed Reciprocating Engines

The flowmeter used with fuel injection systems installed on horizontally opposed reciprocating engines does not measure mechanical movement. Rather, it measures the pressure drop across the injector nozzles as seen in Figure 8-44.

The principal fault of this arrangement is the fact that a plugged injector nozzle discharges less fuel than a clear nozzle, yet the pressure drop across it is greater than it is across a clear nozzle.

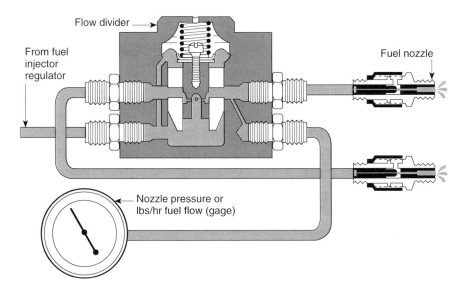

Figure 8-44. *The fuel flowmeter used with a fuel-injected horizontally opposed engine is a pressure gage that measures the pressure drop across the injector nozzles.*

Flowmeters for Turbine Engines

Turbine engine fuel flow is measured in mass flow rather than volume flow, and the transmitting system is shown in Figure 8-45.

The impeller and the turbine are mounted in the main fuel line leading to the engine. The impeller, driven at a constant speed by a special three-phase motor, imparts a swirling motion to the fuel passing through it, and this swirling fuel deflects the turbine. The turbine is restrained by two calibrated restraining springs, and the amount it deflects is affected by both the volume and the density of the fuel.

The amount of turbine deflection is transmitted to an electrical indicator in the cockpit by a Magnesyn transmitter built into the flowmeter.

Magnesyn system. The registered trade name of a remote indicating instrument system. A Magnesyn system uses a permanent magnet as its rotor and a toroidal coil excited by 400-hertz AC as its stator.

A small magnet in the indicator follows the movement of a larger magnet in the transmitter.

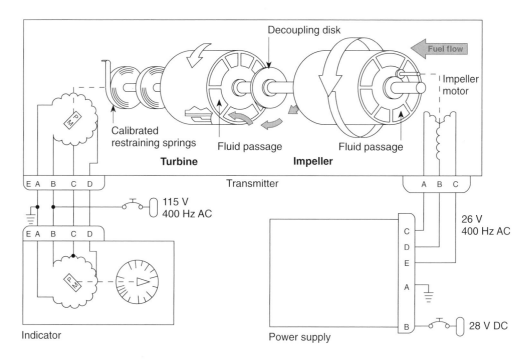

Figure 8-45. *Mass flowmeter used on a large turbine engine*

Computerized Fuel System

Dedicated computers have found serious applications in all sizes of aircraft. One important computerized application is the Computerized Fuel System, or CFS. This versatile instrument uses a small turbine rotor mounted in the fuel line between the fuel injection unit and the flow divider to which the fuel injection nozzles attach. All the fuel that flows to the cylinders must pass through the turbine, which spins at a speed proportional to the rate of fuel flow. As it spins, it interrupts a beam of light between a light-emitting diode and a phototransistor. The resulting pulses of light are converted into pulses of electricity and entered into the computer.

When the instrument is properly programmed with the amount of fuel on board at engine startup, it can inform the pilot of the number of pounds or gallons of fuel on board, the fuel flow in gallons or pounds per hour, the fuel time remaining at the present rate of flow, and the number of gallons of fuel used since the engine was initially started.

Fuel Pressure Warning System

Most fuel pressure is measured with a differential-pressure gage that measures the difference between the fuel pressure and the air pressure at the carburetor. These pressure gages are sensitive enough for all normal operation, but an indicator with a more rapid response and positive indication is needed to warn the pilot of a dangerous drop in fuel pressure.

The fuel pressure warning system senses the pressure at the carburetor inlet and generates an electrical signal to give the first indication that a tank is empty and the selector valve should be switched to a full tank. As soon as the pump begins to draw air from the tank, the fuel pressure drops and the pressure warning system contacts close, sending an electrical signal which turns on a warning light or flashes a warning on an annunciator panel.

The pressure-sensitive mechanism is generally a bellows, and it can be adjusted to change the pressures at which it actuates. Maintenance and troubleshooting procedures for fuel pressure warning systems are found in the manufacturer's maintenance manuals.

Fuel Temperature Indicators

Fuel-temperature sensors are installed in the fuel tanks of some jet-powered aircraft to indicate to the flight engineer when the fuel is getting cold enough to begin forming ice crystals that could clog the fuel filters and shut off the flow of fuel to the engines.

When the fuel temperature gets near 0°C, hot compressor bleed air can be directed through the fuel heater to prevent the formation of ice.

STUDY QUESTIONS: FUEL SYSTEM INSTRUMENTATION

*Answers begin on Page 649. **Page numbers refer to chapter text.***

65. Each fuel quantity indicator must be calibrated to read zero during level flight when the quantity of the fuel remaining in the tank is equal to the _____ fuel supply. *Page 631*

66. The tank unit used in an electronic fuel quantity indicating system is a/an _____ . *Page 633*

67. A capacitance-type fuel quantity indicating system measures fuel quantity in _____ (gallons or pounds). *Page 634*

68. The two things that make up the dielectric of the capacitor-type fuel probe are _____ and _____ . *Page 634*

69. A capacitance-type fuel quantity indicating system measures the weight of the fuel because the temperature of the fuel affects its _____ . *Page 634*

70. A volume of cold fuel contains _____ (more or less) heat energy than an equal amount of warm fuel. *Page 634*

71. Three things affect the capacitance of a capacitor; these are:
   a. _____
   b. _____
   c. _____
      Page 634

72. A bridge circuit measures the capacitance of the fuel tank probes and a/an _____ increases the strength of the signal from this bridge to make it strong enough to drive the servo indicator. *Page 635*

73. The Autosyn-type fuel flowmeter transmits the movement of the metering vane from the engine to the cockpit _____ . *Page 638*

74. The flowmeter used on a fuel-injected horizontally opposed engine is actually a pressure gage that measures the pressure drop across the _____ . *Page 638*

75. If a fuel injector nozzle becomes plugged and flows less fuel to the engine, the pressure-type fuel flowmeter will indicate _____ (more or less) flow. *Page 638*

Fuel System Plumbing

The lines and fittings used in an aircraft fuel system carry highly flammable fuel through the aircraft. They must be of the highest quality materials and must be properly installed. This section discusses some of the requirements for fuel system plumbing.

Fuel Line Routing

The line must not chafe against control cables or airframe structure or come in contact with electrical wiring or conduit. Where physical separation of the fuel line from electrical wiring or conduit is impracticable, locate the fuel line below the wiring and clamp it securely to the airframe structure. In no case may the wiring be supported by the fuel line.

Fuel Line Alignment

Locate all bends accurately so that the tubing is aligned with all the support clamps and end fittings and is not drawn, pulled, or otherwise forced into place by them. Never install a straight length of tubing between two rigidly mounted fittings. Always incorporate at least one bend between such fittings to absorb strain caused by vibration and temperature changes.

Bonding

When fuel flows through a fuel line, it generates static electricity. If any portion of the system is electrically insulated from the aircraft structure, these charges can build up high enough to cause a spark.

All fuel system components must be electrically bonded and grounded to drain off all charges of static electricity before they can cause a spark.

Bond metallic fuel lines at each point where they are clamped to the structure. Integrally bonded and cushioned line-support clamps are preferred to other clamping and bonding methods.

Support of Fuel System Components

To prevent failure of the fuel lines, all fittings heavy enough to cause the line to sag should be supported by means other than the tubing.

Place support clamps or brackets for metallic lines as recommended in Figure 8-46.

Tubing O.D. (inch)	Approximate Distance Between Supports (inches)
1/8 to 3/16	9
1/4 to 5/16	12
3/8 to 1/2	16
5/8 to 3/4	22
1 to 1 1/4	30
1 1/2 to 2	40

Figure 8-46. *Support spacing for rigid fuel lines*

Answers begin on Page 649. Page numbers refer to chapter text.

76. If a fuel line is routed through a compartment parallel with an electrical bundle, the fuel line should be _____ (above or below) the wire bundle. *Page 641*

77. It _____ (is or is not) permissible to clamp a wire bundle to a fuel line if a cushion clamp is used. *Page 641*

78. It _____ (is or is not) permissible to install a straight length of tubing between two rigidly mounted fittings. *Page 642*

79. The clamps used to support a fuel line should be _____ cushion clamps. *Page 642*

80. Fuel lines are bonded to the aircraft structure to prevent a buildup of _____ . *Page 642*

81. A 1/2-inch O.D. fuel should be supported every _____ inches along the run of the line. *Page 642*

Fuel Jettisoning System

Transport category aircraft and general aviation aircraft are both allowed to have a higher takeoff weight than landing weight if they have a fuel jettisoning system. The jettisoning system allows the flight crew to dump enough fuel to lower the gross weight of the aircraft to its maximum allowable landing weight.

The fuel-jettisoning system must be so designed that its operation is free from fire hazards and the fuel must discharge clear of any part of the aircraft. The system must be so designed that fuel or fumes will not enter any part of the airplane, and the jettisoning operation must not adversely affect the controllability of the airplane.

A fuel jettisoning system consists of lines, valves, dump chutes, and the chute operating mechanism, and the fuel is pumped overboard by boost pumps located inside the fuel tanks. The controls allow the flight personnel to close the dump valve to stop dumping during any part of the jettisoning operation.

Fuel tanks whose fuel can be jettisoned are equipped with a dump limit switch that will shut off the flow to the dump chute if the pressure drops below that needed to supply the engine with adequate fuel, or when the tank level reaches a preset dump shutoff level. This prevents more fuel from being jettisoned from any tank than is allowed by Federal Aviation Regulations.

Lateral stability of the aircraft is maintained while dumping fuel by having two separate and independent jettisoning systems, one for each side of the aircraft.

STUDY QUESTIONS: FUEL JETTISONING SYSTEM

Answers begin on Page 649. Page numbers refer to chapter text.

82. If an aircraft is allowed to have a higher takeoff weight than its landing weight, it must have a _____ system. *Page 643*

83. Fuel is forced out of the jettisoning system by the _____ in the fuel tanks. *Page 643*

84. It _____ (is or is not) possible for the flight crew to terminate the fuel jettisoning operation at any time. *Page 643*

85. Lateral stability during fuel jettisoning is maintained by having _____ . *Page 643*

Fueling and Defueling

Aviation maintenance technicians are often required to fuel aircraft and to maintain the fueling equipment, and so should be intimately familiar with fuel handling.

Each fuel bulk storage facility is protected from discharges of static electricity and from contamination as much as is practicable. It is the responsibility of the operator of these facilities to make absolutely certain that the proper grade of fuel is put into the fuel truck and that the truck is electrically grounded to the bulk facility when the fuel is being pumped. The fuel filters should be cleaned before pumping begins, and all of the water traps must be carefully checked for any indication of water.

It is extremely important to identify the fuel properly when fueling an aircraft. The use of fuel with a lower-than-allowed octane or performance rating can cause detonation, which can destroy an engine.

A number of reciprocating-engine-powered airplanes have crashed because they have been inadvertently fueled with turbine engine fuel. Turbine engine fuel will cause severe detonation when a reciprocating engine is operated at takeoff power.

When an aircraft is fueled from a tank truck, the driver must position the truck well ahead of the aircraft and headed parallel with the wings. The brakes must be set so there will be no possibility of the truck rolling into the aircraft. The truck sumps must be checked and a record made of the purity of the fuel.

The truck should be equipped with a fully charged fire extinguisher, ready for instant use if the need should arise. A static bonding wire should be attached between the truck and the aircraft and the truck should be grounded to the earth.

A ladder should be used if it is needed, and a soft mat should be placed over the top of the wing to keep the fuel hose from damaging the skin. The fuel nozzle must be free from any loose dirt which could fall into the tank, and when inserting the nozzle, special care must be taken not to damage the light metal of which the tank is made. The end of the nozzle must never be allowed to strike the bottom of the tank.

After the fueling operation is completed, replace the nozzle cover and secure the tank cap. Remove the wing mat and put all of the equipment back onto the truck and remove the hose and bonding wire and roll them back onto their storage reels.

The fueling and defueling procedures vary widely from aircraft to aircraft, and this makes it important to follow the instructions issued by the aircraft manufacturer. Normally, when defueling an aircraft that has fuel tanks in sweptback wings, you must defuel the outboard wing tanks first. This minimizes the twisting effect on the wing caused by the fuel being located behind the wing attachment points on the fuselage.

Pressure fueling, or single-point fueling, is used in large aircraft because of the tremendous amount of time saved by allowing the entire aircraft to be fueled from a single location. This not only saves time, but also makes for a much safer operation, as the pressure fueling reduces the chance of static electricity igniting fuel vapors.

When fueling an aircraft using the pressure fueling method, be sure the truck pump pressure is correct for the aircraft. The required pressures and the fueling procedures are normally shown on placards on the fuel control panel access door. No one should fuel an aircraft with a fuel pressure fueling system unless he or she has been thoroughly checked out on the procedure for the specific aircraft.

The fuel tank sumps and the main fuel strainer must be periodically drained to prevent contaminated fuel reaching the engine. Even if the aircraft is fueled from a truck or storage tank that is known to be uncontaminated, the sumps and strainers should be checked because contamination may enter from other sources.

Fire Protection

All fueling operations must be done under conditions that allow for a minimum possibility of fire. All fueling and defueling operations should be done in the open, NEVER in a hangar.

All electrical equipment that is not absolutely necessary for the fueling operation should be turned off, and fueling should not be done in the proximity of radar operation. Radar systems radiate enough electrical energy that a spark could be caused to jump and ignite the fuel vapors.

Fires can be best brought under control with a dry-powder or carbon dioxide (CO_2) fire extinguisher. Soda-acid or water-type extinguishers should not be used, because the fuel is lighter than water and will float away, spreading the fire. Both the dry-powder and the CO_2 should be swept back and forth across the fire, allowing the agent to settle into the fire so it will cut off the supply of oxygen and extinguish the flame.

STUDY QUESTIONS: FUELING AND DEFUELING

Answers begin on Page 649. Page numbers refer to chapter text.

86. When fueling an aircraft from a fuel truck, the truck should be positioned ahead of the aircraft and headed _____ (parallel to or perpendicular with) to the wings. *Page 644*

87. Before beginning the fueling operation, the aircraft and the fuel truck should be connected with a _____ . *Page 644*

Continued

88. If a reciprocating engine is operated with turbine engine fuel, it will most likely be damaged by _____ . *Page 644*

89. It _____ (is or is not) permissible to defuel an aircraft inside a hangar. *Page 645*

90. Pressure fueling is safer than overwing fueling because there is less danger of static electricity igniting the _____ . *Page 645*

91. The correct pressure to use for pressure fueling is normally noted on a placard in or adjacent to the _____ . *Page 645*

92. Unless the service manual specifies otherwise, the outboard fuel tanks on an aircraft with swept-back wings should be defueled _____ (first or last). *Page 644*

Fuel System Contamination Control

Draining a sample of fuel from the main strainers has long been considered an acceptable method of assuring that the fuel system is clean. However, tests on several designs of aircraft have shown that this cursory sampling is not adequate to be sure that no contamination exists.

In one test reported to the FAA, three gallons of water were added to a half-full fuel tank. After time was allowed for this water to settle, it was necessary to drain 10 ounces of fuel before any water showed up at the strainer. In another airplane, one gallon of water was poured into a half-full fuel tank and more than a quart of fuel had to be drained out before water showed up at the strainer. The fuel tank sumps had to be drained before all of the water was eliminated from the system.

A commercial water test kit is available that consists of a small glass jar and a supply of capsules that contain a grayish-white powder. A 100-cc sample of fuel is taken from the tank or from the fuel truck and is put into the bottle. One of the test capsules is emptied into this sample of fuel, the lid is screwed onto the jar, and the sample is shaken for about 10 seconds. If the powder changes color from gray-white to pink or purple, the fuel has a water content of more than 30 parts per million, and it is not considered safe for use. This test is fail-safe because any error in performing it will show an unsafe indication.

Protection Against Contamination

All fuel tanks must have the discharge line from the tank protected by an 8- to 16-mesh finger screen. Downstream from this finger screen is the main strainer, usually of the fine-wire mesh type or of the paper Micronic type.

Each fuel tank is normally equipped with a quick-drain valve, where a sample of the fuel may be taken from each tank on the preflight inspection. When draining the main strainer, some fuel should flow with the tank selector set for each of the tanks individually. Drawing fuel when the selector valve is on the BOTH position will not necessarily drain all of the water that has collected in all of the fuel lines.

Micronic filter. The registered trade name of a filter that uses a porous paper element.

Importance of Proper Grade of Fuel

Aircraft engines are designed to operate with a specific grade of fuel, and they will operate neither efficiently nor safely if an improper grade is supplied to the engine.

The required minimum grade of fuel must be clearly marked on the filler cap of the aircraft fuel tanks, and the person fueling the aircraft must know the grade of fuel required and that the proper grade of fuel is being supplied.

If the tanks have been serviced with aviation gasoline of a lower grade than allowed or with turbine-engine fuel, the following procedure is recommended:

If the engine has not been operated:

1. Drain all improperly filled tanks.
2. Flush out all lines with the proper grade of fuel.
3. Refill the tanks with the proper grade of fuel.

If the engine has been operated:

1. Perform a compression check on all cylinders.
2. Inspect all cylinders with a borescope, paying special attention to the combustion chambers and to the domes of the pistons.
3. Drain the oil and inspect all oil screens.
4. Drain the entire fuel system, including all of the tanks and the carburetor.
5. Flush the entire system with the proper grade of fuel.
6. Fill the tanks with the proper grade of fuel.
7. Perform a complete engine run-up check.

Fuel System Troubleshooting

A schematic diagram of the fuel system is one of the most useful documents you can use when troubleshooting the system. The schematic diagram shows the components as they function in the system, but not necessarily as they are installed in the aircraft.

One of the most difficult problems to trace down in a fuel system is an internal leak. It is often possible to isolate a portion of a large-aircraft fuel system that has an internal leak by watching the fuel-pressure gage and operating the selector valves. If the fuel pressure drops, or if the boost pumps must run continually to maintain the pressure, the selected portion of the system may have the internal leak.

You can check fuel valves in small aircraft for internal leakage by draining the strainer bowl, turning the valve off, and turning on the boost pump. If the valve is leaking internally, fuel will flow into the strainer bowl.

When inspecting any fuel system for leaks, turn on the boost pump, and visually inspect all valves located downstream of the pump for indication of leaks.

STUDY QUESTIONS: FUEL SYSTEM TROUBLESHOOTING

Answers begin on Page 649. Page numbers refer to chapter text.

93. One of the most useful documents for use in troubleshooting an aircraft fuel system is a/an
_____ . *Page 648*

94. When checking a fuel system for external leaks, the system should be pressurized with the
_____ . *Page 648*

Answers to Aircraft Fuel Systems Study Questions

1. detonation
2. water
3. higher
4. low
5. low
6. 7
7. higher
8. octane, performance
9. tetraethyl lead
10. rubber
11. Jet A
12. more
13. corrosion
14. anti-icing
15. is not
16. is not
17. 37.5 gph
18. 31.25 gph
19. 100
20. 3.5
21. 2.0
22. interconnected
23. fuel jettisoning
24. interconnected
25. parallel
26. main
27. ejectors
28. balanced
29. boost pumps
30. automatically
31. baffles
32. sump
33. vents

34. minimum allowable fuel grade
35. 30
36. nitric, sulfuric
37. 3.5
38. integral
39. argon, carbon dioxide
40. 2
41. ammonia, phenolphthalein
42. calibrated
43. variable
44. vapor
45. check valves
46. ejector
47. variable
48. diaphragm spring
49. constant
50. do
51. series
52. carburetor
53. constant
54. shear section
55. is not
56. freezes
57. antifreeze
58. antifreeze
59. water
60. ice
61. detent
62. a. compressor bleed air
    b. engine lubricating oil
63. compressor bleed air
64. can
65. unusable

66. capacitor
67. pounds
68. fuel, air
69. dielectric constant
70. more
71. a. area of the plates
    b. separation between the plates
    c. dielectric constant
72. amplifier
73. electrically
74. injector nozzles
75. more
76. below
77. is not
78. is not
79. bonded
80. static electricity
81. 16
82. fuel jettisoning
83. boost pumps
84. is
85. two separate jettisoning systems
86. parallel to
87. static bonding wire
88. detonation
89. is not
90. fuel vapors
91. fueling control panel
92. first
93. schematic diagram
94. boost pumps

CABIN ATMOSPHERE CONTROL SYSTEMS

9

Continued

CABIN ATMOSPHERE CONTROL SYSTEMS

9

Human Needs in Flight

Flight has become such a standard means of transportation, it's easy to forget the importance of the atmosphere control systems that make high-altitude flight possible. Unaided, people cannot survive at the high altitudes where most airliners fly. The air temperature is about -50°F (-45.6°C) and the atmospheric pressure is so low that the human body cannot get enough oxygen from the air to survive.

Without heating and pressurizing the air in an aircraft cabin, it would be impossible to fly at the high altitudes where turbine engines run most efficiently and where most bad weather can be avoided.

A complete cabin atmosphere control system regulates the pressure to force oxygen into our lungs, and temperature, humidity, and air movement to make the aircraft cabin comfortable.

Pressure

The human body requires oxygen. One way to provide this oxygen when flying at a high altitude is to increase the pressure of the air inside the aircraft cabin. When the air pressure inside the cabin is near to that on the earth's surface, enough oxygen will pass through the lungs and enter the blood stream to allow the brain and body to function normally.

Temperature

In the hot summertime, we feel comfortable when our bodies (which usually have a temperature of about 98°F) can pass off heat to the air around us. For this reason, the air in the aircraft cabin should be maintained in the comfort range of between 70°F (21°C) and 80°F (27°C).

In the wintertime, when the temperature of the outside air is much lower than that of our bodies, we lose heat from our bodies to the air so rapidly that we are uncomfortable. To allow our bodies to maintain their heat, heaters keep the temperature of the air inside the cabin within the comfort range.

Humidity

It is true that it is not only the heat, but the humidity that makes summertime uncomfortable. Humidity is the amount of water vapor in the air, and it affects our comfort.

The human body has a natural air conditioning system that works best when the humidity is low. When our body is hot, water, or sweat, comes out of the pores of our skin, and air blowing over our bodies evaporates it. The heat that changes this water from a liquid into a vapor comes from our skin, and losing this heat makes us feel cooler.

But, when the humidity is high, the air already has a lot of water vapor in it and the sweat does not evaporate as readily. With less evaporation, less heat is removed, and we feel uncomfortable.

An effective cabin atmosphere control system maintains the humidity in the air at a level that allows our bodies to lose excessive heat, while at the same time containing enough moisture that our throats do not become dry.

Air Movement

We usually feel comfortable and alert when cool air blows over our face and head, as long as it blows at a rate fast enough to take away the unwanted heat but not hard enough to make us consciously aware of it.

Warm air feels comfortable when it blows over the lower part of our body, but it makes us drowsy and sluggish when it blows over our face and head.

A properly designed and operating cabin atmosphere control system moves air at the right temperature and moisture content over and around our bodies. This allows the flight crew to operate most efficiently and the passengers to be most comfortable.

The Atmosphere

The air that surrounds the earth is a physical mixture of gases made up of approximately 78% nitrogen, 21% oxygen, and traces of several other gases that include carbon dioxide and water vapor.

Oxygen is the most important gas in the air because no human or animal life can exist for more than a few minutes without it. Depriving our bodies of oxygen for even a few seconds can damage our brain. Nitrogen, which makes up the bulk of the air we breathe, is an inert gas. It provides volume to the air and dilutes the oxygen.

The earth's atmosphere extends upward for more than 20 miles, and since the gases that make up the atmosphere are compressible, the air near the surface is denser than the air higher up. As a result of this compression, about one half of the total atmosphere is below 18,000 feet.

While the pressure of the air changes with altitude, its composition remains relatively constant. There is the same percentage of oxygen in the air at sea level as there is at 30,000 feet, but because there is so little air at this altitude, the actual amount of oxygen is much less.

Standard Conditions

Standard conditions have been established for atmospheric pressure and temperature. Under these standards, the atmosphere is considered to press down on the surface of the earth with a pressure of 14.69 pounds per square inch. This much pressure will hold up a column of mercury 29.92 inches, or 760 millimeters, high. The pressure of the atmosphere decreases as the altitude increases, as is illustrated in Figure 9-1.

ICAO Standard Atmosphere						
Altitude Feet	Temperature		Pressure			Speed of Sound Knots
	°F	°C	In. Hg	Mm Hg	PSI	
0	59.00	15.0	29.92	760.0	14.69	661.7
1,000	55.43	13.0	28.86	733.0	14.18	659.5
2,000	51.87	11.0	27.82	706.7	13.66	657.2
3,000	48.30	9.1	26.82	681.2	13.17	654.9
4,000	44.74	7.1	25.84	656.3	12.69	652.6
5,000	41.17	5.1	24.90	632.5	12.23	650.3
6,000	37.60	3.1	23.98	609.1	11.77	647.9
7,000	34.04	1.1	23.09	586.5	11.34	645.6
8,000	30.47	-0.8	22.23	564.6	10.92	643.3
9,000	26.90	-2.8	21.39	543.3	10.51	640.9
10,000	23.34	-4.8	20.58	522.7	10.10	638.6
15,000	5.51	-14.7	16.89	429.0	8.30	626.7
20,000	-12.32	-24.6	13.75	349.5	6.76	614.6
25,000	-30.15	-34.5	11.12	284.5	5.46	602.2
30,000	-47.90	-44.4	8.885	226.1	4.37	589.5
35,000	-65.82	-54.2	7.041	178.8	3.64	576.6
*36,089	-69.70	-56.5	6.683	169.7	3.28	573.8
40,000	-69.70	-56.5	5.558	141.2	2.73	573.8
45,000	-69.70	-56.5	4.355	110.6	2.14	573.8
50,000	-69.70	-56.5	3.425	87.4	1.70	573.8
55,000	-69.70	-56.5	2.693	68.8	1.33	573.8
60,000	-69.70	-56.5	2.118	54.4	1.05	573.8
65,000	-69.70	-56.5	1.665	42.3	0.82	573.8
70,000	-69.70	-56.5	1.310	33.5	0.64	573.8
75,000	-69.70	-56.5	1.030	26.2	0.51	573.8
80,000	-69.70	-56.5	0.810	20.9	0.40	573.8
85,000	-64.80	-53.8	0.637	16.2	0.31	577.4
90,000	-56.57	-49.2	0.504	13.0	0.25	583.4
95,000	-48.34	-44.6	0.400	10.2	0.20	589.3
100,000	-40.11	-40.1	0.320	8.0	0.16	595.2
*Geopotential of the tropopause						

Figure 9-1. *Table of the ICAO Standard Atmosphere*

The standard temperature at sea level is 15°C, or 59°F. The temperature drops as the altitude increases until about 36,000 feet, which marks the beginning of the stratosphere, where the temperature stabilizes at -56.5°C (-69.7°F).

The density of air increases as its temperature decreases but it decreases as its pressure decreases. Decreased density lessens the aerodynamic drag of an aircraft, but the power the engines can develop also lessens as the density decreases. The temperature remains constant in the stratosphere, so the density change lessens as the altitude changes. For this reason, jet aircraft perform best at the beginning of the stratosphere, at an altitude of about 36,000 feet.

The Characteristics of Oxygen

Oxygen is one of the most abundant chemical elements on the earth. It is found in the rocks and soil that make up the crust of the earth, and it accounts for most of the weight of the water that covers the majority of the earth. As a free gas, oxygen is one of the two major elements that make up the air that surrounds the earth.

Oxygen is colorless, odorless, and tasteless, and is extremely active chemically. This means that it unites with most of the other chemical elements to form compounds. Often it reacts with other elements so violently that it produces a large amount of heat and light.

Oxygen is produced commercially by lowering the temperature of air until it changes from a gas into a liquid. The oxygen is separated from the other gases by increasing the temperature enough for the various gases to boil off. Each of the constituent gases boils off at a different temperature.

Oxygen can also be produced in a very pure state by an electrolytic process in which electrical current is passed through water. The current causes the water to break down into its two chemical elements, hydrogen and oxygen.

Oxygen does not burn, but it supports combustion so well that you must take special care not to use oxygen where anyone is smoking or where there is any fire, hot metal, or open petroleum products.

Oxygen Partial Pressure

partial pressure. The percentage of the total pressure of a mixture of gases produced by each of the individual gases in the mixture.

Air is a physical mixture of gases rather than a chemical compound, and while the percentages of the gases remain constant, the amount of each gas in the air decreases as altitude increases.

Twenty-one percent of the gas in the air is oxygen, so the pressure caused by oxygen in the air is 21% of the total atmospheric pressure. Under standard sea level atmospheric conditions, oxygen exerts a pressure of 3.08 psi. This pressure forces oxygen into our lungs. At 10,000 feet, the total pressure is down to 10.10 psi, and the oxygen partial pressure is only 2.12 psi.

Generally speaking, there is not enough oxygen partial pressure in the air above 10,000 feet to allow the human body to function properly. If we fly at this altitude without supplemental oxygen for several hours, we will get a headache and will become fatigued.

At 15,000 feet, the oxygen partial pressure is down to 1.74 psi. Flight at this altitude for more than thirty minutes will cause us to become sleepy, and our judgment and coordination will be impaired.

At 35,000 feet, where the oxygen partial pressure is down to 0.76 psi, we can only function for about 15 to 30 seconds before losing consciousness.

There are two ways to increase the oxygen partial pressure while flying at high altitude: increase the pressure of the air in the cabin by pressurization, or provide supplemental oxygen for the occupants.

The Function of Oxygen

Gasoline is a compound of hydrogen and carbon. When it is mixed with air inside the cylinder of an aircraft engine, and its temperature is raised, it combines with the oxygen in the air. The hydrogen and carbon react with the oxygen and change into carbon dioxide (CO_2) and water (H_2O). When this change takes place, heat and light are released. The fuel is said to be burned, or oxidized.

The same kind of reaction, only not nearly so violent, takes place in our bodies when the oxygen we breathe furnishes our brain and muscles with the energy we need to operate.

When we inhale, our lungs fill with air, which is primarily a mixture of oxygen and nitrogen. A wonderfully complex system in our lungs separates the oxygen from the air and loads it onto the hemoglobin in our blood, which then carries it to our brain and to all our other organs that need oxygen. The oxygen reacts with hydrocarbons in our body to release the energy that we need.

In the human body, as in an aircraft engine, oxygen and carbon combine to form carbon dioxide. This CO_2 is picked up by the blood and carried back to the lungs where it is expelled into the air when we exhale.

We can go without food for days without suffering any permanent damage, but if our body is deprived of oxygen for even a short while, we develop a condition known as hypoxia. Its first symptoms are an increase in breathing rate, headaches, and a tingling sensation in the fingers. Judgment and vision are both impaired, and we become sleepy. Hypoxia degrades our night vision, and severe hypoxia causes unconsciousness and death.

Altitude (Feet)	Effect
5,000	Deteriorated vision
10,000	Judgement and abilities impaired
14,000	Blurred thinking
16,000	Disorientation and belligerence
18,000	Possible unconciousness
Above 18,000	Unconciousness and possible death

Figure 9-2. *Effects of lack of oxygen on the human body*

hypoxia. A physiological condition in which a person is deprived of the needed oxygen. The effects of hypoxia normally disappear as soon as the person is able to breathe air containing sufficient oxygen.

Federal Aviation Regulations Part 91, *General Operating and Flight Rules*, gives the requirements for supplemental oxygen for unpressurized aircraft.

§91.211

(a) *General.* No person may operate a civil aircraft of U.S. registry—

> (1) At cabin pressure altitudes above 12,500 feet (MSL) up to and including 14,000 feet (MSL) unless the required minimum flight crew is provided with and uses supplemental oxygen for that part of the flight at those altitudes that is of more than 30 minutes duration;
>
> (2) At cabin pressure altitudes above 14,000 feet (MSL) unless the required minimum flight crew is provided with and uses supplemental oxygen during the entire flight time at those altitudes; and
>
> (3) At cabin pressure altitudes above 15,000 feet (MSL) each occupant of the aircraft is provided with supplemental oxygen.

The Function of Carbon Dioxide

Our bodies produce carbon dioxide, most of which is expelled as we exhale, but we need a small amount of carbon dioxide to control the rate and depth of our breathing.

When we exercise or work hard, our blood contains an excess of carbon dioxide. This causes us to breathe deep and fast to get rid of this excess and take in the oxygen we need. Fear, stress, and pain also signal our lungs to breathe deeply, and under these conditions we get rid of much of the carbon dioxide we need. This condition, known as hyperventilation, causes symptoms similar to those of hypoxia, and can cause nausea and unconsciousness.

The Threat of Carbon Monoxide

While our bodies need a small amount of carbon dioxide (CO_2), carbon monoxide (CO) serves no useful function, and we must guard against its presence. Only a small amount of CO can starve the brain by displacing the oxygen it needs.

CO is a colorless, odorless, tasteless, unstable gas that results from incomplete combustion of hydrocarbon fuels. It is found in the smoke and fumes from burning aviation fuels and lubricants, and in the smoke inhaled into our lungs from burning tobacco.

Hemoglobin is a part of our blood that carries oxygen from our lungs to our brain and all other organs that must have oxygen to function properly. But hemoglobin has a much higher affinity for CO than it has for oxygen. If CO is present in the air, the hemoglobin will fill up with it rather than with oxygen. When our brain is supplied with blood that does not have enough oxygen in it, we lose our ability to reason, and it becomes difficult to make correct decisions.

pressure altitude. The altitude in standard air at which the pressure is the same as the existing pressure.

MSL. Mean sea level. When the letters MSL are used with an altitude, it means that the altitude is measured from mean, or average, sea level.

The effect of CO poisoning is cumulative; that is, breathing air that is even slightly contaminated with CO over a prolonged period of time is as bad as breathing a heavy concentration for a shorter period of time. Either will affect our ability to safely operate an aircraft.

The early stages of carbon monoxide poisoning are similar to any other form of oxygen starvation. First, we feel sluggish and too warm, and there is usually a tight feeling across the forehead. This is usually followed by a headache, ringing ears, and throbbing temples. If we don't heed the warning from these early symptoms, severe headaches, dizziness, unconsciousness, and even death will result.

Aircraft, especially those that use heat produced by the engine exhaust system, should be equipped with carbon monoxide detectors. These are simply small containers of colored chemical crystals that change their color in the presence of carbon monoxide. The color of the crystals warns occupants of an aircraft of the presence of carbon monoxide long before they could detect it by other means.

STUDY QUESTIONS: HUMAN NEEDS IN FLIGHT

Answers begin on Page 713. Page numbers refer to chapter text.

1. A decrease in the temperature of the air causes the density to _____ (increase or decrease).
   Page 658

2. A decrease in the pressure of the air causes the density to _____ (increase or decrease).
   Page 657

3. The two gases that make up the majority of the atmosphere are _____ and _____ . *Page 656*

4. Oxygen _____ (does or does not) burn. *Page 658*

5. Long exposure at an altitude of 10,000 feet without supplemental oxygen will result in _____ and fatigue. *Page 658*

6. A condition in which the human body is deprived of the oxygen it needs is called _____ .
   Page 659

7. The rate and depth of our breathing is controlled by _____ in our blood. *Page 660*

8. Carbon monoxide is dangerous because it takes the place of the _____ the brain needs to function. *Page 660*

The Physics of Cabin Atmosphere Control

To best understand the way a cabin atmosphere control system works, we should review some of the concepts of basic physics.

Heat

All matter is made up of extremely tiny particles called molecules. These molecules are too small to see, even with a high-powered microscope. And the molecules in all substances are held together by strong forces of attraction for each other.

All molecules contain heat energy, which causes them to move about in all directions. If a material contains only a small amount of heat energy, its molecules move about relatively slowly; but if heat is added, the molecules move faster. If it were possible to remove all the heat energy from a material, its molecules would stop moving altogether.

Heat energy can transfer from one object to another, and the transfer is always from an object with a high level of energy to one with a lower level of energy—from a hotter object to a cooler one.

When an object loses or gains heat energy, the molecules change their speed of movement enough that the object can actually change its physical state.

If a solid material such as a block of ice, a block of frozen water, sits in a pan, the molecules that make up the water are all moving about, but they don't have a great deal of energy. They all stay pretty much together so the ice holds its form and keeps its size and shape.

If the ice sits in a warm room, its molecules absorb some heat energy from the air, and their movement speeds up. As they speed up, they change their positions, and the block of ice changes form—it melts and turns into liquid water.

If the pan of water is put on a stove and heated, the molecules speed up even more. They move so fast that they leave the surface of the water and become steam, or water vapor.

Ice, water, and steam are all H_2O. They have the same chemical composition, but they are in different physical states, or conditions. The only difference is the amount of heat energy the H_2O has absorbed.

Units of Heat

There are two standard units of heat measurement, the calorie in the metric system and the British thermal unit, or Btu, in the English system. One calorie is the amount of heat energy needed to raise the temperature of one gram of pure water 1°C. One Btu is the amount of heat energy needed to raise the temperature of one pound of water 1°F.

Types of Heat

If a pan of water with a temperature of 80°F is placed on a stove and heated, the water will remain a liquid, but its temperature will increase. This is an example of sensible heat, heat added to a material that causes its temperature to change, but does not change its physical state.

Keep the pan of water on the stove, and its temperature will continue to rise, but only until the water begins to boil. As soon as it begins to boil, or change from a liquid into a vapor, its temperature stops rising.

It takes 970 Btu of heat energy to change one pound of water from a liquid into a vapor. This is called the latent heat of vaporization. When the water changes from a liquid into a vapor, this heat energy remains in it. When the water vapor cools enough to revert into a liquid, this same 970 Btu of heat energy is given up. The heat returned when the water vapor changes into a liquid is called the latent heat of condensation.

Specific heat is the number of Btu of heat energy needed to change the temperature of one pound of a substance 1°F. One Btu of heat energy will raise the temperature of one pound of water 1°F, so water has a specific heat of 1.0.

Refrigerant R-12 (which we'll study in more detail) has a much lower specific heat. One Btu of heat energy will raise the temperature of 4.6 pounds of R-12 1°F. Its specific heat is 0.217.

Movement of Heat

Heat, like any other kind of energy, always moves from a high level of energy to a lower level. There are three ways this energy can move: by conduction, by convection, and by radiation.

If we touch a hot stove, we get burned. There is a big difference between the amount of heat energy in the stove and the heat energy in our skin. And, since our skin is in direct contact with the hot stove, this heat energy flows directly into our skin and burns it.

The heat from the stove is transferred to our skin by conduction.

Convection is a method in which heat is transferred by vertical currents in a liquid or gas.

All of the water in a pan sitting on a hot stove will eventually become uniformly hot. But only the water on the bottom of the pan in direct contact with the hot metal is heated by conduction.

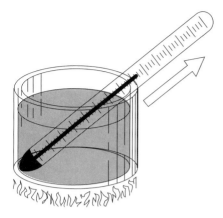

Figure 9-3. *Heat added to a liquid that causes it to change its temperature is called sensible heat.*

Figure 9-4. *Heat absorbed by a liquid as it changes to a gas without changing its temperature is called latent heat.*

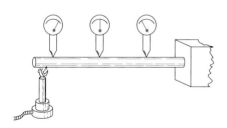

Figure 9-5. *Heat travels along this bar by conduction. The heat moves in the bar from a point of high heat energy to a point of lower heat energy.*

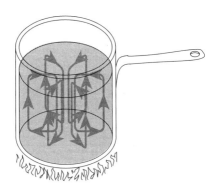

Figure 9-6. *Convection transfers heat through a fluid by vertical currents. Warm liquid is less dense than the colder liquid, and it rises. This forces the colder liquid down so it can be heated.*

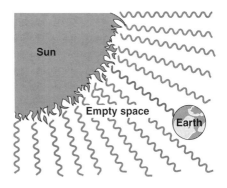

Figure 9-7. *Heat from the sun reaches the earth by radiation. Heat can transfer by radiation even through a vacuum.*

absolute zero. The point at which all molecular motion ceases. Absolute zero is -460°F and -273°C.

As this water gets hot, its molecules move faster, the water becomes less dense, and it rises. As it rises, it forces the colder water above it to go down to the bottom. This process continues until all of the water in the pan is heated.

The third way heat can be moved is by radiation. This is the method of heat transfer by electromagnetic waves.

Heat energy causes electromagnetic waves, much like radio waves, to radiate, or spread out, in all directions from an object. These waves can travel through space from one object to another without any contact between the objects, and can travel through a vacuum.

The tremendous amount of heat energy released by the sun reaches the earth by the process of radiation.

Temperature

Temperature is a measure of the amount of hotness or coldness of an object, and it is a measure of the effect of the heat energy an object has absorbed.

Temperature is measured on a scale that has two practical reference points. One of these is the temperature at which pure water changes from a liquid into a solid. At this point, the water has lost enough heat energy that the moving molecules slow down enough to turn the liquid into a solid. The other is the point at which water has gained enough heat energy to change from a liquid into a vapor. At this point, the molecules have sped up enough that they can no longer remain in liquid form, but they bounce out of the surface and become a gas.

Four different scales are used to measure temperature. Two of these scales, Fahrenheit and Celsius, are used in most of our everyday temperature measurements, and the other two, Kelvin and Rankine, are absolute temperature scales used primarily in scientific work.

The Fahrenheit temperature scale has 180 equal divisions between the point at which water freezes and the temperature at which it boils. The point at which water freezes is 32°F, and it boils 180 degrees higher, at 212°F. Absolute zero, or the temperature at which all molecules stop moving, is 460°F below zero or -460°F.

Celsius temperature has 100 equal divisions between the point at which water freezes and the point at which it boils. This is the reason Celsius temperature was formerly called Centigrade (100 graduations) temperature. Water freezes at 0°C and boils at 100°. Absolute zero is -273°C.

Absolute temperature is measured from the point at which all molecular movement stops, and the two absolute scales are used in scientific work.

Kelvin temperature uses absolute zero as its zero value, and the divisions are the same as those used in Celsius temperature. Water freezes at 273°K and it boils at 373°K.

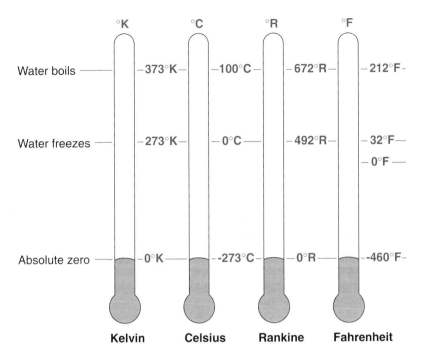

Figure 9-8. *The temperature scales*

Rankine temperature also uses absolute zero as its zero value. Its divisions are the same as those used in Fahrenheit temperature. Water freezes at 492°R and boils at 672°R.

Pressure

Pressure is a measure of the amount of force that acts on a unit of area. It is always measured from a reference, and there are three commonly used references. Absolute pressure is measured from zero pressure, or a vacuum. Gage pressure is measured from the existing atmospheric pressure, and differential pressure is the difference between two pressures.

Units of Pressure

Most of the positive pressures (or pressure greater than that of the atmosphere), used in air conditioning system servicing are measured in pounds per square inch, gage (psig). A typical high-side pressure gage is calibrated from zero to about 500 psi.

Negative pressure (or pressure lower than that of the atmosphere), is typically measured in units of inches of mercury (in. Hg) and is called a vacuum. One inch of mercury is the amount of pressure that will hold up a column of mercury one inch high.

absolute pressure. Pressure measured from zero pressure, or a vacuum.

gage pressure. Pressure referenced from the existing atmospheric pressure.

differential pressure. The difference between two pressures.

micron ("micro meter"). A unit of linear measurement equal to one millionth of a meter, or one thousandth of a millimeter. A micron is also called a micrometer.

The pressure caused by the weight of the atmosphere pressing down on the surface of the earth is 14.69 pounds per square inch, and this much pressure will support a column of mercury 29.92 inches, or 760 millimeters high. This is called one atmosphere of pressure. For quick computations, a pressure of 1 psi is approximately the same as a pressure of 2 in. Hg.

A micron is one thousandth of a millimeter (0.001 mm). A vacuum measured in microns is often spoken of as a "deep vacuum." Its absolute pressure is so low that it will support a column of mercury only a few thousandths of a millimeter high.

STUDY QUESTIONS: THE PHYSICS OF CABIN ATMOSPHERE CONTROL

Answers begin on Page 713. Page numbers refer to chapter text.

9. The basic difference between ice, water, and steam is the amount of _____ each contains. *Page 662*

10. The basic unit of heat in the English system is the _____ , and in the metric system it is the _____ . *Page 662*

11. Heat energy that causes a material to change its temperature is called _____ heat. *Page 663*

12. Heat energy that causes a material to change its physical state without changing its temperature is called _____ heat. *Page 663*

13. The two reference points used for measuring temperature are:
    a. _____
    b. _____
       Page 664

14. Absolute zero is the temperature at which there is no _____ motion. *Page 664*

15. The absolute temperature scale that uses the same graduations as the Celsius scale is the _____ scale. *Page 664*

16. Pressure that is referenced from zero pressure is called _____ pressure. *Page 665*

17. Pressure that is referenced from the existing atmospheric pressure is called _____ pressure. *Page 665*

18. Pressure that is referenced from another pressure is called _____ pressure. *Page 665*

19. The number of Btu of heat energy needed to change the temperature of one pound of a substance one degree Fahrenheit is called the _____ of the substance. *Page 663*

20. Three methods of heat transfer are:
    a. _____
    b. _____
    c. _____
       Page 663

21. A vacuum is usually measured in units of _____ . *Page 665*

22. A "deep vacuum" is usually measured in units of _____ . *Page 666*

Aircraft Supplemental Oxygen Systems

There are two ways to provide high-flying aircraft with the oxygen needed to sustain life. The cabin can be pressurized to increase the total pressure of the air surrounding the occupants. This raises the partial pressure of the oxygen enough that it can enter the blood stream from the lungs. The other way is to furnish the occupants with supplemental oxygen. When the percentage of oxygen in the air is increased, its partial pressure becomes high enough to force it into the blood.

Types of Oxygen Supply

Oxygen can be carried in an aircraft in four ways: in its gaseous form, in a liquid form, as a solid chemical compound, and in some military aircraft the oxygen is extracted from the air by mechanical methods.

Gaseous Oxygen

Gaseous oxygen is stored in high-pressure steel cylinders that keep the oxygen under a pressure of between 1,800 and 2,400 pounds per square inch. At one time low-pressure oxygen systems were used in which the oxygen was carried in large cylinders under a pressure of 450 psi, but since these cylinders took up so much space in the aircraft, they are no longer used.

Gaseous oxygen has been carried in aircraft since World War I, when it was used by the Germans to allow their fleet of huge lighter-than-air Zeppelins to fly at a higher altitude than possible for British fighter aircraft.

High-flying aircraft between World Wars I and II carried gaseous oxygen in large, low-pressure tanks. In many installations the oxygen was fed to the pilot through a pipestem mouthpiece.

Most of the air battles of World War II were fought at high altitude. Air crews breathed gaseous oxygen from low-pressure cylinders. This oxygen was metered to the masks through continuous-flow or demand-type regulators.

aviators oxygen. Oxygen that has had all of the water and water vapor removed from it.

Oxygen used for welding and cutting, for industrial chemical processes, and for hospital and ambulance use is not suited for use in aircraft oxygen systems because of its water content. Just a tiny drop of moisture can freeze in the regulator and shut off the flow of oxygen to the mask. Aircraft oxygen systems must be serviced exclusively with aviators oxygen that meets military specifications MIL-O-21749 or MIL-O-27210. This oxygen is at least 99.5% pure and contains no more than 0.02 milligram of water per liter at 21.1°C (70°F).

Liquid Oxygen

Liquid oxygen (LOX) systems are used in most modern military aircraft because of their efficiency and small space requirements, but they find little application in civilian aircraft because of the special handling LOX requires.

LOX is a pale blue transparent liquid that boils under standard pressure at a temperature of about -180°F. To keep it in its liquid form, it is stored in a vented Dewar bottle, a special double-wall, spherical container made of steel. The inner surfaces of the container's double walls are reflective, which minimizes the transfer of heat by radiation, and all the air is pumped out of the space between the walls to minimize the transfer of heat by conduction.

The expansion rate of LOX is about 862:1. This means that one liter of LOX will produce about 862 liters of gaseous oxygen.

A converter in the oxygen system controls the gaseous oxygen that boils out of the liquid and delivers it to the oxygen regulator at the proper pressure.

chemical oxygen candle system. An oxygen system used for emergency or backup use. Solid blocks of a material that release oxygen when they are burned are carried in special fireproof fixtures. When oxygen is needed, the candles are ignited with an enclosed lighter, and oxygen flows into the tubing leading to the masks.

Chemical Oxygen Candle

Chemical oxygen candles are used when oxygen is used only occasionally, as it is in smaller general aviation aircraft, or when it is used as an emergency backup, as in some transport aircraft.

Sodium chlorate, mixed with a binding material, is molded into a specially shaped solid block. This block is installed inside an insulated stainless steel case. When oxygen is needed, a spring-loaded igniter starts the sodium chlorate burning. As it burns, it releases a quantity of oxygen. Once the candle, as this block is called, is ignited, it must burn until it is consumed, because there is no way to shut it off.

Chemical oxygen candles have an extremely long shelf life, they are safe to store and to handle, they are lightweight, and in use they produce very little fire hazard. With the exception of the routine inspection they require for security of mounting and general condition, chemical oxygen candles require no attention or servicing until after they have been used.

Chemical oxygen candle systems have the following characteristics:

1. Once the candle is ignited, it releases its oxygen at a predetermined rate which cannot be shut off or changed until the candle is exhausted.

2. The storage capacity is about three times that of a gaseous oxygen system.

3. The system generators are inert below 400°F even under severe impact.

4. The distributing and regulating system is self-contained. It consists of a stainless steel cylinder attached to manifolded hose nipples. The nipples contain orifices that assure an equal flow to all masks.

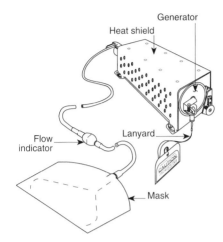

Figure 9-9. *A chemical oxygen generator with a simple rebreather-bag-type mask*

Mechanically Separated Oxygen

The fire hazard of manufacturing and storing liquid oxygen aboard aircraft carriers and the difficulty of providing liquid oxygen at forward locations during battle conditions led the military services to study other ways of supplying oxygen for flight crews. One method that overcomes the dangers inherent with both high-pressure gaseous oxygen and liquid oxygen is mechanically separated breathing oxygen. This system is called OBOGS, or Onboard Oxygen Generating System.

The air we breathe is a physical mixture rather than a chemical compound, and its constituents, oxygen, nitrogen, and the traces of other gases, all have different physical characteristics. A patented material called a "molecular sieve" will pass oxygen, but effectively blocks nitrogen and the other gases. Compressor bleed air from the turbine engine is directed through containers of molecular sieve material, and only oxygen passes through it to the oxygen regulator. Part of the oxygen that passes through the sieve material is used to regularly back-flush the container and force all of the nitrogen and other gases out of the system.

Mechanically separated oxygen is used for many medical applications, and its use in aircraft is sure to increase.

Two Types of Oxygen Systems

Most small general aviation aircraft only require oxygen occasionally, and use a system that meters a continuous flow of oxygen whose amount is based on the altitude flown. Aircraft that regularly fly at altitudes above 18,000 feet typically have a diluter-demand system that meters oxygen based on the altitude flown, but directs it to the mask only when the user inhales. Aircraft that fly at very high altitudes, where the outside air pressure is too low to force oxygen into the lungs, use pressure-demand systems. These systems send oxygen to the mask under a slight positive pressure that forces it into the lungs.

Continuous-Flow Oxygen System

Continuous-flow systems, such as the one in Figure 9-10, are usually used in passenger oxygen systems and systems where oxygen is needed only occasionally. These systems are wasteful of oxygen, but because of their simplicity, they are the type installed in most small general aviation aircraft.

Unpressurized aircraft that fly at high altitudes may have a continuous-flow oxygen system for the passengers and a diluter-demand or pressure-demand system for the pilots.

The oxygen is carried in a steel, high-pressure bottle. The pressure is reduced from that in the bottle to between 300 and 400 psi by a pressure reducing valve, and the oxygen metered by a pressure regulator before it is delivered to the masks. A pressure relief valve is incorporated in the system to prevent damage in the event of a failure of the pressure reducing valve. If the pressure is relieved by the relief valve, a green "blowout" disk on the outside of the aircraft will blow out.

continuous-flow oxygen system. A type of oxygen system that allows a metered amount of oxygen to continuously flow into the mask. A rebreather-type mask is used with a continuous-flow system. The simplest form of continuous-flow oxygen systems regulates the flow by a calibrated orifice in the outlet to the mask, but most systems use either a manual or automatic regulator to vary the pressure across the orifice proportional to the altitude being flown.

pressure reducing valve. A valve used in an oxygen system to change high cylinder pressure to low system pressure.

pressure relief valve. A valve in an oxygen system that relieves the pressure if the pressure reducing valve should fail.

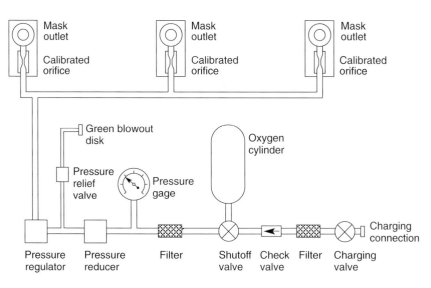

Figure 9-10. *A typical continuous-flow oxygen system*

Continuous-Flow Regulators

There are automatic and manual continuous-flow oxygen regulators. The automatic regulator contains an aneroid that senses the altitude the aircraft is flying and meters the correct amount of oxygen accordingly. The manual regulator has a control that allows the pilot to adjust the flow based on the altitude of flight.

A calibrated orifice in the mask outlet determines the amount of oxygen the regulator delivers to the mask. The orifice for the pilot's mask usually meters more oxygen than those for the passenger masks, and some oxygen systems have provisions for a therapeutic mask outlet for passengers who have difficulty breathing or who have a known heart problem. The orifice in a therapeutic outlet allows approximately twice the normal flow.

Continuous-Flow Masks

Continuous-flow oxygen systems use rebreather-type oxygen masks. These masks may be as simple as a transparent plastic rebreather bag like the one in Figure 9-9. This mask is held loosely over the mouth and nose with an elastic band, and oxygen continuously flows into the bottom of the bag through a plastic hose that is plugged into the mask outlet.

When the user exhales, the air that was in the lungs for the shortest period of time is the first out, and it fills the bag. The last air expelled from the lungs has the least oxygen in it, and by the time it is exhaled, the bag is full and it spills out of the mask. When the user inhales, the first air to enter the bag, now enriched with pure oxygen, is rebreathed.

More sophisticated continuous-flow masks are used in pressurized aircraft. In the event of the loss of cabin pressure, an automatic turn-on valve sends oxygen into the passenger oxygen system. *See* Figure 9-13, Page 673. The oxygen pressure actuates the door actuator valve, which opens the door to the overhead mask compartment. A mask of the type in Figure 9-11 drops down. The passenger pulls on the mask tube, which opens the rotary, lanyard-operated valve and starts the flow of oxygen. The passenger then places the cup over his or her mouth and nose and breathes normally. Valves mounted in the base plate of the mask allow some cabin air to enter the mask and allow the air that has been exhaled from the lungs to leave it. At the beginning of the inhale, the pure oxygen from the bag is taken into the lungs. When the bag is empty, cabin air is taken in through one of the mask valves and mixes with oxygen flowing through the tube. The pure oxygen that is taken in first fills most of the lungs and is absorbed into the blood, and the diluted oxygen fills only that part of the respiratory system where no absorption takes place.

During the exhale, the air from the lungs leaves the mask through one of the valves while pure oxygen is flowing from the regulator into the reservoir bag to be ready for the next inhale.

therapeutic mask adapter. A calibrated orifice in the mask adapter for a continuous-flow oxygen system that increases the flow of oxygen to a mask being used by a passenger who is known to have a heart or respiratory problem.

rebreather oxygen mask. A type of oxygen mask used with a continuous-flow system. Oxygen continuously flows into the bottom of the loose-fitting rebreather bag on the mask. The wearer of the mask exhales into the top of the bag. The first air exhaled contains some oxygen, and this air goes into the bag first. The last air to leave the lungs contains little oxygen, and it is forced out of the bag as the bag is filled with fresh oxygen. Each time the wearer of the mask inhales, the air first exhaled, along with fresh oxygen, is taken into the lungs.

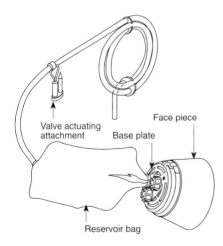

Figure 9-11. *Passenger oxygen mask*

Demand-Type Oxygen System

The cockpit crew of most commercial aircraft are supplied with oxygen
through a diluter-demand system. This system meters oxygen only when the
user inhales, and the amount of oxygen metered depends upon the altitude
being flown. Figure 9-12 is a simplified diagram of a typical demand-type
oxygen system.

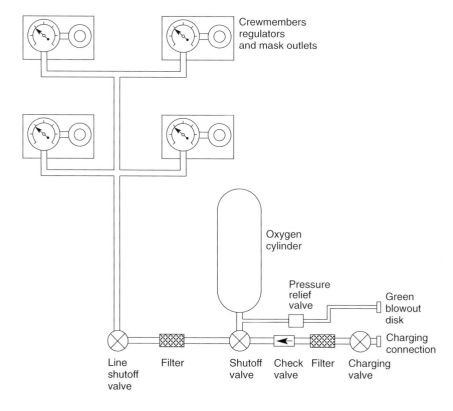

Figure 9-12. *A typical demand-type oxygen system*

Almost all pressurized turbine-powered aircraft have a demand-type oxygen
system for the flight crew and a continuous-flow system as a backup for the
passengers. Figure 9-13 shows this system. Two oxygen cylinders are
installed in the aircraft, and selector valves allow either cylinder to supply the
crew or the passengers.

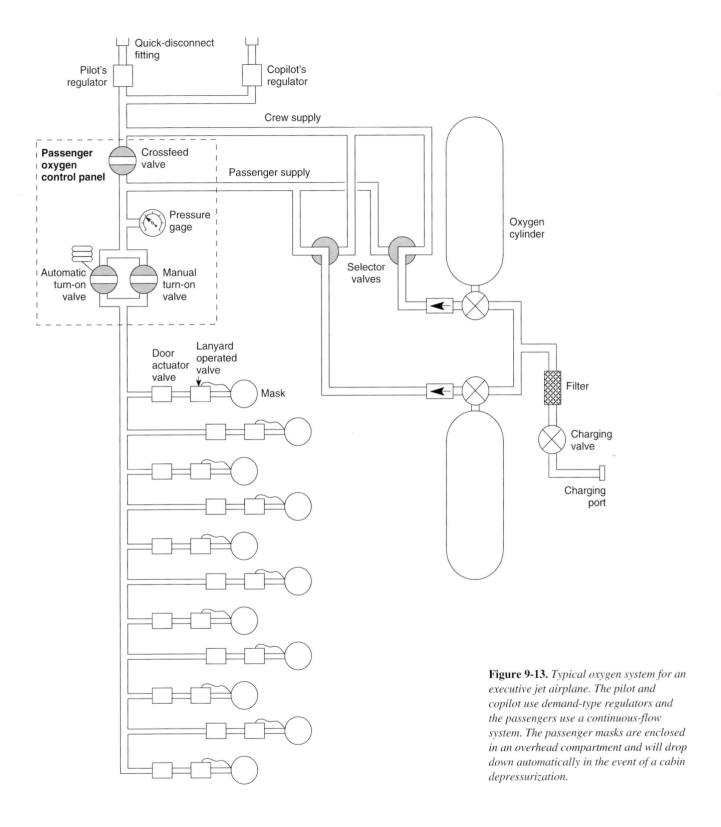

Figure 9-13. *Typical oxygen system for an executive jet airplane. The pilot and copilot use demand-type regulators and the passengers use a continuous-flow system. The passenger masks are enclosed in an overhead compartment and will drop down automatically in the event of a cabin depressurization.*

Diluter-Demand-Type Regulator

Figure 9-14 shows a typical diluter-demand-type oxygen regulator, and Figure 9-15 shows the way this regulator operates.

For normal operation, the Supply lever is in the ON position, the Oxygen lever is in the NORMAL position, and the Emergency lever is OFF. Oxygen flows into the regulator through the supply valve, and when the user inhales, the pressure inside the regulator decreases and the demand valve opens, allowing oxygen to flow to the mask.

The aneroid-operated air metering valve mixes cabin air with the oxygen. When the aircraft is flying at low altitudes, the user gets mostly cabin air and a small amount of oxygen. As the altitude increases, the aneroid progressively shuts off the cabin air and opens the oxygen line until, at approximately 34,000 feet, the cabin air is completely shut off and the mask receives 100% oxygen.

If there is smoke in the cockpit, or if the user feels a need for pure oxygen, the oxygen lever can be moved to the 100% position. The cabin air will be shut off from the regulator and only pure oxygen taken into the mask when the user inhales.

If the regulator malfunctions, the emergency lever can be placed in the ON position. This opens the demand valve and pure oxygen flows continually to the mask.

aneroid. An evacuated and sealed metallic bellows that is used as a pressure measuring element for absolute pressure.

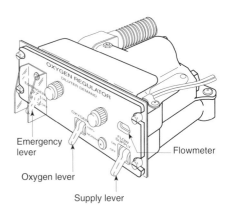

Figure 9-14. *A typical diluter-demand oxygen regulator*

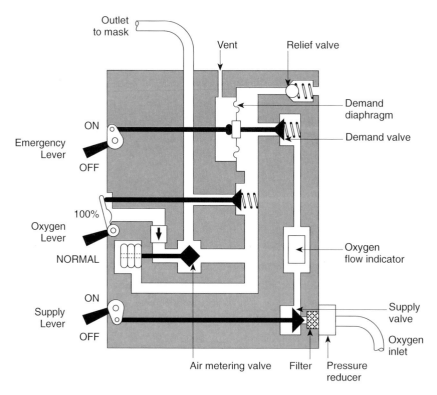

Figure 9-15. *The operational schematic of a diluter-demand oxygen regulator*

Pressure-Demand Oxygen Regulator

At altitudes above 40,000 feet the oxygen in the air has such a low partial pressure that even 100% oxygen must be forced into the lungs under a slight positive pressure from the regulator. Aircraft that operate at this altitude are equipped with pressure-demand regulators.

A pressure-demand regulator looks much like a diluter-demand regulator, but at altitudes above 40,000 feet, it supplies oxygen to the mask under a low positive pressure rather than depending upon the low pressure from the user's lungs to pull in the oxygen.

Gaseous Oxygen Cylinders

High-pressure oxygen cylinders, or bottles, carried in modern aircraft may be made of either heat-treated steel or Kevlar-wrapped aluminum alloy. They are painted green and have the words AVIATORS OXYGEN stenciled in letters one inch high.

These bottles must meet either ICC or DOT specification 3AA 1800 for the standard bottle or 3HT 1850 for the lightweight bottle. The specification number must be stamped on the bottle.

All oxygen bottles carried in aircraft must be hydrostatically tested within the required time interval. DOT 3AA cylinders must be tested to $\frac{5}{3}$ of their working pressure (3,000 psi) every five years, and DOT 3HT cylinders must be tested to a pressure of 3,083 psi every three years, and retired from service after 15 years or 4,380 pressurizations, whichever occurs first. The date of the hydrostatic test must be stamped on the cylinder, near its neck.

Never let oxygen bottles become empty, nor let their pressure drop below about 50 psi. When the cylinder is empty, air containing water vapor may enter it and cause corrosion inside, where it is difficult to detect.

Up through World War II, oxygen was carried in low-pressure bottles. These steel bottles are much larger than the high-pressure bottles and are painted yellow. Oxygen inside them is under a pressure of approximately 450 psi.

Oxygen System Servicing

Servicing a gaseous oxygen system, though not complicated, requires strict attention to details and must be done in direct accordance with the instructions furnished by the aircraft manufacturer. Servicing consists of filling the system, purging it of all air, and checking the system for leaks.

Oxygen System Filling

Most oxygen systems are filled from an oxygen service cart similar to the one in Figure 9-16 (Page 676). This cart contains several oxygen bottles along with the necessary valves, gages, service hoses, and an oxygen purifier. Some oxygen carts also carry bottles of compressed nitrogen. The valves of nitrogen bottles face in the opposite direction, to prevent the accidental connection of a nitrogen bottle into the oxygen system.

pressure-demand oxygen system. A type of oxygen system used by aircraft that fly at very high altitude. This system functions as a diluter-demand system (*See* diluter-demand oxygen system) until, at about 40,000 feet, the output to the mask is pressurized enough to force the needed oxygen into the lungs, rather than depending on the low pressure produced when the wearer of the mask inhales to pull in the oxygen.

hydrostatic test. A pressure test used to determine the serviceability of high-pressure oxygen cylinders. The cylinders are filled with water and pressurized to $\frac{5}{3}$ of their working pressure. Standard-weight cylinders must be hydrostatically tested every five years, and lightweight cylinders (DOT 3HT) must be tested every three years.

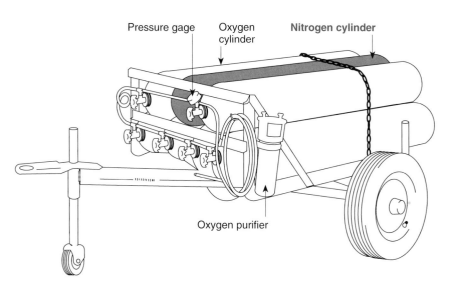

Figure 9-16. *A typical gaseous oxygen servicing trailer*

Ambient Temperature °F	Filling Pressure For	
	1,800 psi At 70°F	1,850 psi At 70°F
0	1,600	1,650
10	1,650	1,700
20	1,675	1,725
30	1,725	1,775
40	1,775	1,825
50	1,825	1,875
60	1,875	1,925
70	1,925	1,975
80	1,950	2,000
90	2,000	2,050
100	2,050	2,100
110	2,100	2,150
120	2,150	2,200
130	2,200	2,250

Figure 9-17. *Pressure-temperature chart for filling an oxygen cylinder*

ambient temperature. The temperature of the air surrounding a person or an object.

purge. To remove all of the moisture and air from a cooling system by flushing the system with a dry gaseous refrigerant.

To fill an oxygen system, first purge the service line of all air by releasing some oxygen through it. Then connect it to the aircraft filler valve. Open the lowest pressure bottle on the service cart and let it flow into the aircraft system until the system pressure reaches that in the bottle. Shut this bottle valve and then open the valve on the bottle with the next higher pressure.

The ambient temperature determines the final pressure required by the aircraft system. A pressure-temperature chart for each type of oxygen bottle should be on the service cart. Figure 9-17 is a typical pressure-temperature chart. If the ambient temperature is 90°F, the system should be charged until the pressure gage reads 2,000 psi. When the temperature of the oxygen stabilizes, its pressure should be approximately 1,800 psi at 70°F.

Purging

If an oxygen system is opened and air has gotten into the lines, charge the system and purge it by letting oxygen flow through all the lines and masks for about ten minutes, until all the contaminating air has been removed.

Leak Checking

If a loss of oxygen indicates a leak in the system, check the fittings by spreading a special nonpetroleum soap solution over all suspected areas and watching for bubbles. When you find a leak, release the pressure from the system before tightening any fittings.

System Discharge Indication

The pressure relief valve in an installed gaseous oxygen system vents to a blowout plug on the side of the fuselage. If, for any reason, the pressure builds up in the system enough to open the pressure relief valve, the green disk over the outlet will blow out, showing that the oxygen system has discharged.

Special Precautions

Never use petroleum products on oxygen systems; there is a fire danger. The oxygen will react with oil or grease and produce enough heat to cause a fire.

Never lubricate threaded fittings used in oxygen systems with any type of thread lubricant that contains petroleum. Teflon tape is generally approved to seal tapered pipe thread connections in an oxygen system, and a special water-base lubricant is used for other applications.

Fire Safety

Oxygen itself will not burn, but because it supports the combustion of other products, you should observe special safety precautions when working with oxygen. Some of these are:

1. Display "No Smoking" placards when an oxygen system is being serviced.

2. Provide adequate fire-fighting equipment in the immediate vicinity of the servicing.

3. Keep all tools and oxygen-servicing equipment free from oil or grease.

4. Avoid checking aircraft radio or electrical systems during the servicing operation.

STUDY QUESTIONS: AIRCRAFT SUPPLEMENTAL OXYGEN SYSTEMS

Answers begin on Page 713. Page numbers refer to chapter text.

23. When oxygen is needed for a backup in a pressurized aircraft the _____ system is used because of its simplicity, efficiency, and minimum maintenance required. *Page 668*

24. Aviators oxygen is different from hospital oxygen because of its low _____ content. *Page 668*

25. The type of contaminant most generally found in gaseous oxygen systems is _____ . *Page 668*

26. In the onboard oxygen generating system (OBOGS), engine compressor bleed air flows through beds of a _____ material that mechanically filters the oxygen from the nitrogen and other constituents of the air. *Page 669*

Continued

---

27. The rate of release of the oxygen from a chemical oxygen candle system _____ (may or may not) be adjusted for the altitude flow. *Page 669*

28. The generators used in a chemical oxygen candle system are inert below _____°F even under a severe impact. *Page 669*

29. Supplemental oxygen is normally provided for passengers of a pressurized aircraft by the _____ (continuous-flow or demand)-type system. *Page 670*

30. In a continuous-flow oxygen system, the pressure of the oxygen in the high-pressure cylinder is reduced before it goes to the regulator by a/an _____ valve. *Page 670*

31. If the pressure reducer valve in a continuous-flow oxygen system should malfunction, a _____ valve will prevent damage to the system. *Page 670*

32. Two types of regulators that may be used in a continuous-flow oxygen system are _____ and _____ regulators. *Page 671*

33. The amount of oxygen a regulator will deliver to flow to a continuous-flow mask is determined by a _____ in the mask outlet. *Page 671*

34. The continuous-flow oxygen mask worn by a person with a known respiratory or heart problem should receive its oxygen from a _____ mask outlet. *Page 671*

35. A rebreather-bag-type oxygen mask is used with a _____ (continuous-flow or demand)-type oxygen system. *Page 671*

36. The cockpit crew of a pressurized aircraft normally have their supplemental oxygen supplied by a _____ (continuous-flow or demand)-type oxygen system. *Page 672*

37. A diluter-demand oxygen regulator dilutes the oxygen it meters at the lower altitudes with _____ . *Page 674*

38. The demand valve on a diluter-demand oxygen regulator opens each time the wearer of the mask _____ . *Page 674*

39. High-pressure oxygen cylinders installed in an aircraft must meet the specifications of the _____ or the _____ . *Page 675*

40. Oxygen cylinders are required to be _____ tested periodically and the date of the test stamped on it. *Page 675*

41. Standard high-pressure oxygen cylinders should be hydrostatically tested every _____ years. *Page 675*

42. Lightweight high-pressure oxygen cylinders should be hydrostatically tested every _____ years. *Page 675*

43. A lightweight high-pressure oxygen cylinder should be hydrostatically tested to a pressure of _____ psi. *Page 675*

44. A lightweight high-pressure oxygen cylinder should be retired from service after _____ years. *Page 675*

45. The pressure inside an oxygen bottle should never be allowed to drop below _____ psi. *Page 675*

46. High-pressure oxygen bottles are painted _____ . *Page 675*

47. Low-pressure oxygen bottles are painted _____ . *Page 675*

48. The amount of oxygen in a gaseous oxygen bottle is indicated by its _____ . *Page 676*

49. If a gaseous oxygen system is to be charged to 1,850 psi at 70°F when the ambient temperature is 60°F, the filling pressure should be _____ psi. *Page 676*

50. Any time an oxygen system has been opened, it should be purged for about _____ minutes to remove all of the air from the oxygen lines. *Page 676*

51. Thread lubricants used with oxygen system components must contain no _____ . *Page 677*

52. Leaks in an oxygen system are located by spreading a _____ soap solution over the suspected area and watching for bubbles. *Page 676*

53. A blowout plug on the side of the fuselage will be blown out if the oxygen system has been discharged through the _____ . *Page 677*

54. Thread lubricants approved for use in an oxygen system have a/an _____ base. *Page 677*

Aircraft Pressurization Systems

Although high altitude is a hostile environment in which the human body cannot subsist without a great deal of help, it is the ideal environment for high-speed flight. Turbine engines operate efficiently and the resistance caused by the low density air decreases drag. The humidity is low at high altitude, so weather conditions are excellent.

As early as the 1850s the American balloonist John Wise predicted that at high altitudes there was a fast moving "great river of air that could not only sweep him across the Atlantic ocean, but on around the world."

In the 1920s the U.S. Army Air Service experimented with pressurized flight. They built an oval steel tank in the cockpit of an airplane. There was a glass port through which the pilot could see, and the airplane controls were built into the tank. The tank was pressurized by a gear-driven supercharger, and the pilot was able to control an exhaust valve manually to maintain the pressure at the required level. An airplane flew with this system in 1921, but the experiment proved unsuccessful.

In 1934, Wiley Post, who had already proven his aeronautical expertise by flying twice around the world, once by himself, began to experiment with a pressure suit that would let him take advantage of high-altitude flight. Post's suit was made of rubberized fabric and topped with an aluminum helmet with a round porthole for him to see through. The suit was pressurized with air from the engine supercharger through two lines. One line ran direct, and the other wrapped around one of the exhaust stacks to pick up heat. The temperature inside the suit was controlled by metering the air from the two lines with needle valves. A liquid oxygen generator provided oxygen in the event of engine or supercharger failure.

Post's suit let him attain an altitude of 48,000 feet. He proved the existence of high-velocity winds at these altitudes, and his efforts spurred further study and development.

In 1936 Lockheed made a special version of their Model 10 Electra with a fully pressurized cabin. This airplane was powered by two turbosuper-charged engines and was able to make flights to an altitude of 25,000 feet. The cabin altitude was maintained at 10,000 feet or less. The developments made by this airplane and the potential it created earned it the Collier trophy for the most valuable contribution to aircraft development in 1937.

In 1940, Transcontinental and Western Air put the Boeing 307B into service. This was the first airliner to have a fully pressurized cabin. Today all airliners and many general aviation aircraft are pressurized.

Principles of Pressurization

Aircraft are pressurized by sealing off a strengthened portion of the fuselage, called the pressure vessel, and pumping air into it. The cabin pressure is controlled by an outflow valve, usually located at the rear of the pressure vessel. The opening of this valve is controlled by the cabin pressure controller to regulate the amount of air allowed to leave the cabin.

Sources of Pressurization Air

Pressurization systems do not have to move a huge volume of air. Their function is to raise the pressure of the air inside closed containers. Small reciprocating-engine-powered aircraft receive their pressurization air from the compressor of the engine turbocharger. Large reciprocating-engine-powered aircraft have engine-driven air compressors to provide pressurization air, and turbine-powered aircraft use engine compressor bleed air.

Reciprocating-Engine-Powered Aircraft

Turbochargers are driven by engine exhaust gases flowing through a turbine. A centrifugal air compressor is connected to the turbine shaft. The compressor's output goes to the engine's cylinders to increase the manifold pressure and let the engine develop its power at altitude. Part of the compressed air is tapped off between the turbocharger and the engine and used to pressurize the cabin. This air passes through a sonic venturi, or flow limiter, and then through an intercooler into the cabin. *See* Figure 9-18 on the following page.

Large reciprocating-engine-powered transports use either a positive-displacement Roots blower-type air compressor or a variable-displacement centrifugal compressor driven by the engine through an accessory drive or by an electric or hydraulic motor.

These large multi-engine airplanes have more than one cabin air compressor, and they are connected together through a delivery-air-duct check valve, or isolation valve, that prevents the loss of pressurization through a disengaged compressor.

pressure vessel. The strengthened portion of an aircraft structure that is sealed and pressurized in flight.

outflow valve. A valve in the cabin of a pressurized aircraft that controls the cabin pressure by opening to relieve all pressure above that for which the cabin pressure control is set. The outflow valve is controlled by the cabin pressure controller and it maintains the desired cabin pressure.

sonic venturi. A venturi in a line between a turbine engine or turbocharger and a pressurization system. When the air flowing through the venturi reaches the speed of sound, a shock wave forms across the throat of the venturi and limits the flow. A sonic venturi is also called a flow limiter.

Roots-type air compressor. A positive-displacement air pump that uses two intermeshing figure-8-shaped rotors to move the air.

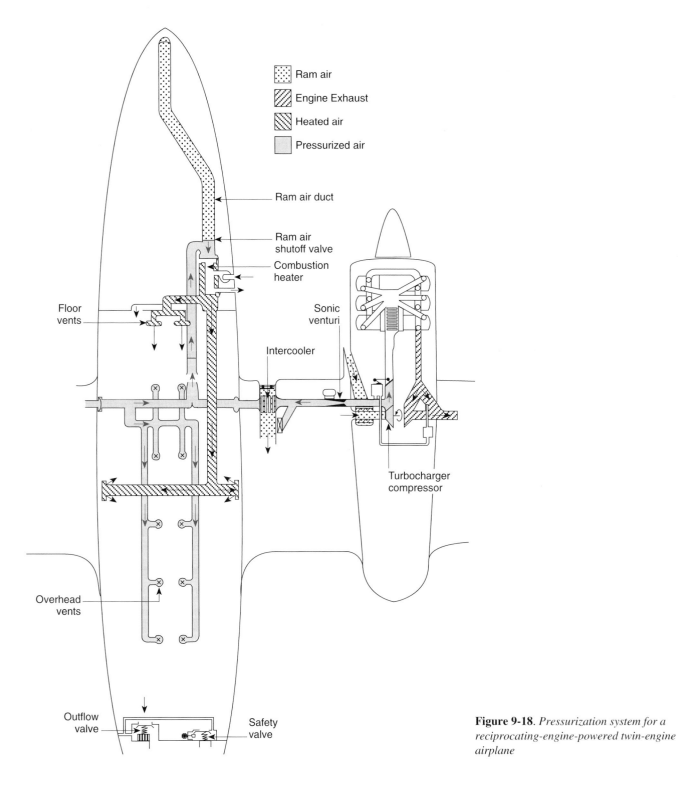

Figure 9-18. *Pressurization system for a reciprocating-engine-powered twin-engine airplane*

Ram air

Engine Exhaust

Heated air

Pressurized air

Ram air duct

Ram air shutoff valve

Combustion heater

Floor vents

Sonic venturi

Intercooler

Overhead vents

Turbocharger compressor

Outflow valve

Safety valve

Turbine-Engine-Powered Aircraft

Usually the air bled from a gas turbine engine compressor is free from contamination and can be used safely for cabin pressurization, but some aircraft use independent cabin compressors driven by compressor bleed air.

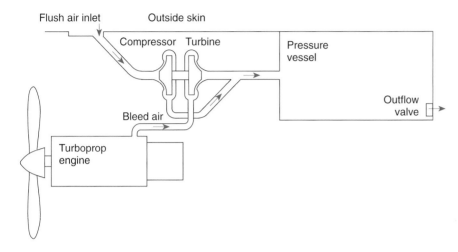

Figure 9-19. *Pressurization system of a turboprop airplane that uses compressor bleed air to drive a flow multiplier*

Some aircraft use a jet pump flow multiplier to increase the amount of air taken into the cabin. The jet pump is essentially a special venturi inside a line from the outside of the aircraft, like the one in Figure 9-20. A nozzle blows a stream of high-velocity compressor bleed air into the throat of the venturi, and this produces a low pressure that draws air in from the outside. This is mixed with the compressor bleed air and carried into the aircraft cabin.

jet pump. A special venturi in a line carrying air from certain areas in an aircraft that need an augmented flow of air through them. High-velocity compressor bleed air is blown into the throat of a venturi where it produces a low pressure that pulls air from the area to which it is connected. Jet pumps are often used in the lines that pull air through galleys and toilet areas.

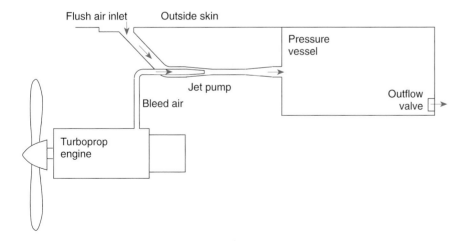

Figure 9-20. *A jet pump flow multiplier increases the air available for cabin pressurization.*

Modes of Pressurization

There are three modes of pressurization: the unpressurized mode, the isobaric mode, and the constant-differential mode. In the unpressurized mode, the cabin altitude is always the same as the flight altitude. In the isobaric mode, the cabin altitude remains constant as the flight altitude changes, and in the constant-differential mode, the cabin pressure is maintained a constant amount above that of the outside air pressure. This amount of differential pressure is determined by the structural strength of the pressure vessel.

The Unpressurized Mode

In the unpressurized mode, the outflow valve remains open and the cabin pressure is the same as the ambient air pressure.

The Isobaric Mode

In the isobaric mode, the cabin pressure is maintained at a specific cabin altitude as flight altitude changes. The cabin pressure controller begins to close the outflow valve at a chosen cabin altitude. The outflow valve opens and closes, or modulates, to maintain the selected cabin altitude as the flight altitude changes. The controller will maintain the selected cabin altitude up to the flight altitude that produces the maximum differential pressure for which the aircraft structure is rated.

The Constant-Differential Mode

Cabin pressurization puts the structure of an aircraft fuselage under a tensile stress as the pressure inside the pressure vessel tries to expand it. The cabin differential pressure, expressed in psid, is the ratio between the internal and external air pressure and is a measure of the stress on the fuselage. The greater the differential pressure, the greater the stress.

When the cabin differential pressure reaches the maximum for which the aircraft structure is designed, the cabin pressure controller automatically shifts to the constant-differential mode and allows the cabin altitude to increase, but maintains the maximum allowable pressure differential.

Pressurization Controls

The pressurization controller in Figure 9-21 provides the control signals for a typical pressurization system. The dial is graduated in cabin altitude up to approximately 10,000 feet. One knob sets the desired cabin altitude, another corrects the barometric scale, and the third knob sets the cabin rate of climb.

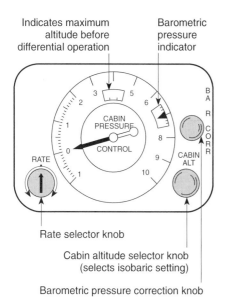

Indicates maximum altitude before differential operation

Barometric pressure indicator

Rate selector knob

Cabin altitude selector knob (selects isobaric setting)

Barometric pressure correction knob

Figure 9-21. *Typical cabin pressurization controller*

Pressurization Instruments

The main instruments used with a pressurization system are shown in Figure 9-22. These are a cabin rate-of-climb indicator and a combination cabin altitude and differential pressure gage.

Cabin Air Pressure Regulator

The cabin pressure regulator maintains cabin altitude at a selected level in the isobaric range and limits cabin pressure to a preset differential value in the differential range by regulating the position of the cabin outflow valve. Normal operation of the regulator requires only the selection of the desired cabin altitude, the adjustment of the barometric scale, and the selection of the desired cabin rate of climb.

The regulator in Figure 9-23 (Page 686) is a typical differential-pressure-type regulator that is built into the normally closed, pneumatically operated outflow valve. It uses cabin altitude for its isobaric control and barometric pressure for the differential range of control. A cabin rate-of-climb controller controls the rate of pressure change inside the cabin.

There are two principal sections of this regulator: the head and reference chamber section, and the outflow valve and diaphragm section.

The balance diaphragm extends outward from the baffle plate to the outflow valve, creating a pneumatic chamber between the fixed baffle plate and the inner face of the outflow valve. Cabin air flowing into this chamber through holes in the side of the outflow valve exerts a force against the inner face of the valve that tries to open it. This force is opposed by the force of the spring around the valve pilot that tries to hold the outflow valve closed.

The actuator diaphragm extends outward from the outflow valve to the cover assembly, creating a pneumatic chamber between the cover and the outer face of the outflow valve. Air from the head and reference chamber section flows through holes in the cover, filling this chamber, exerting a force against the outer face of the outflow valve and helping the spring hold the valve closed.

The position of the outflow valve controls the amount of cabin air allowed to leave the pressure vessel, and this controls the cabin pressure. The position of the outflow valve is determined by the amount of reference-chamber air pressure (cabin air pressure) that presses on the outer face of the outflow valve.

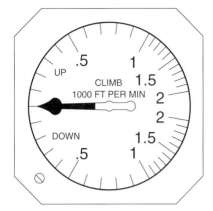

Cabin rate-of-climb indicator

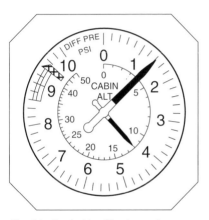

Combination cabin altimeter and differential pressure gage

Figure 9-22. *Typical instruments used with a cabin pressurization system*

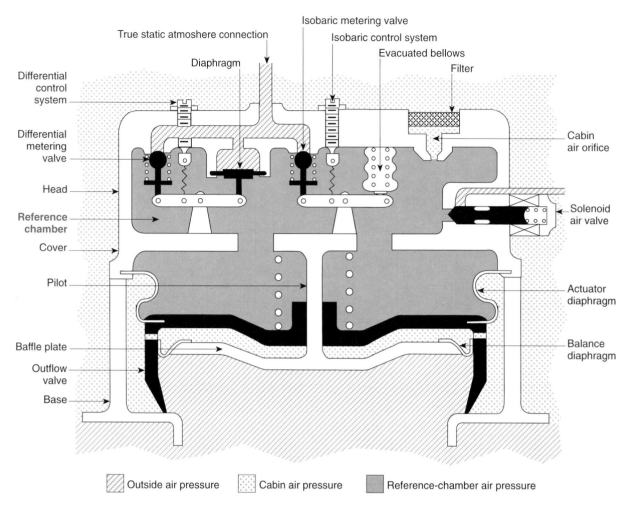

Figure 9-23. *A typical cabin pressure regulator*

Isobaric Control

The isobaric system of the cabin pressure regulator in Figure 9-23 incorporates an evacuated bellows, a rocker arm, a follower spring, and a ball-type isobaric metering valve. One end of the rocker arm is connected to the head by the evacuated bellows, and the other end of the arm holds the metering valve in a closed position against a passage in the head. A follower spring between the metering valve seat and a retainer on the valve causes the valve to move away from its seat as far as the rocker arm permits.

When the cabin pressure increases enough for the reference-chamber air pressure to compress the bellows, the rocker arm pivots about its fulcrum and allows the metering valve to move away from its seat an amount proportional to the compression of the bellows. When the metering valve opens, reference-chamber air flows from the regulator to the atmosphere through the true static atmosphere connection.

When the regulator is operating in the isobaric range, cabin pressure is held constant by reducing the flow of reference-chamber air through the metering valve. This prevents a further decrease in the reference pressure.

The isobaric control system responds to slight changes in reference-chamber pressure by modulating to maintain a substantially constant pressure in the chamber throughout the isobaric range of operation.

Anytime an increase in cabin pressure causes the isobaric metering valve to move toward the OPEN position, the reference pressure decreases and the outflow valve opens, decreasing the cabin pressure.

Differential Control

The differential control system incorporates a diaphragm, a rocker arm, a differential metering valve, and a follower spring. One end of the rocker arm is attached to the head by the diaphragm which forms a pressure-sensitive face between the reference chamber and a small chamber in the head. This small chamber is opened to atmosphere through a passage to the true static atmosphere connection.

Atmospheric pressure acts on one side of the diaphragm, and reference-chamber pressure acts on the other side. The opposite end of the rocker arm holds the metering valve in a closed position against a passage in the head. A follower spring between the metering valve seat and a retainer on the valve causes the valve to move away from its seat the amount the rocker arm allows.

When reference-chamber pressure becomes enough greater than the decreasing atmospheric pressure that it moves the diaphragm, the metering valve moves away from its seat an amount proportional to the movement of the diaphragm. When the metering valve opens, reference-chamber air flows to the atmosphere through the true static atmosphere connection and reduces the reference pressure. This causes the outflow valve to open and decrease the cabin pressure.

Cabin Rate of Climb

The cabin rate control determines the rate of pressure change inside the cabin by controlling the speed with which the outflow valve closes. If the cabin pressure is changing too rapidly (the cabin rate of climb is too great) the rate controller knob can be turned back to close the outflow valve faster.

Negative-Pressure Relief Valve

A pressurized aircraft structure is designed to operate with the cabin pressure higher than the outside air pressure. If the cabin pressure were to become lower than the outside air pressure, the cabin structure could fail. Because of this design feature, all pressurized aircraft require some form of negative pressure relief valve that opens when the outside air pressure is greater than the cabin pressure.

The negative-pressure relief valve may be incorporated into the outflow valve, or it may be a separate unit.

Cabin Air Pressure Safety Valve

The cabin air pressure safety valve is a combination pressure relief, vacuum relief, and dump valve.

The pressure relief valve prevents cabin pressure from exceeding a predetermined differential pressure above the ambient pressure.

The vacuum relief valve prevents ambient pressure from exceeding cabin pressure by allowing external air to enter the cabin when the ambient pressure is greater than the cabin pressure.

The dump valve is actuated by a switch in the cockpit. When the switch is in the ram, or auxiliary-ventilation, position, the solenoid air valve opens, dumping cabin air to the atmosphere. If the auxiliary ventilation position is selected while in cruising flight, the cabin pressurization will be dumped and the cabin pressure will decrease—the cabin altitude will rapidly increase until it is the same as the flight altitude.

The dump valve is also controlled by a squat switch on the landing gear so it will open when the aircraft is on the ground. This removes all positive pressure from the cabin and prevents the cabin from being pressurized when the aircraft is on the ground.

Augmented Airflow

Some aircraft use a jet pump (essentially a special venturi) in a line carrying air from certain areas that need increased airflow. Jet pumps are often used in the lines that pull air through galleys and toilet areas.

A nozzle blows a stream of high-velocity compressor bleed air into the throat of the venturi. This increases the velocity of the air flowing through the venturi and produces low pressure, which pulls air from the compartment to which it is connected.

Answers begin on Page 713. Page numbers refer to chapter text.

55. Pressurization air for reciprocating-engine-powered general aviation aircraft is compressed by the _____ . *Page 681*

56. Two types of mechanical compressors used to supply pressurizing air for a reciprocating-engine-powered airplane are:
    a. _____
    b. _____
       Page 681

57. When two or more mechanical air compressors supply the cabin pressure for a pressurized aircraft, the loss of cabin pressure if one compressor should fail is prevented by a delivery air duct _____ valve. *Page 681*

58. In a turbine-engine-powered aircraft the air for pressurization comes from the _____ section of the engine. *Page 683*

59. The air used for pressurizing a turbine-engine-powered aircraft is called _____ air. *Page 683*

60. The cabin altitude is the same as the flight altitude when the aircraft is operating in the _____ mode. *Page 684*

61. The cabin altitude is maintained at a constant value as the flight altitude changes when the pressurization system is operating in the _____ mode. *Page 684*

62. The cabin pressure is maintained a given amount higher than the outside air pressure when the pressurization system is operating in the _____ mode. *Page 684*

63. The maximum differential pressure allowed in a pressurized aircraft is determined by the strength of the _____ . *Page 684*

64. The amount of air the cabin pressure regulator in Figure 9-23 allows to leave the cabin is determined by the _____ pressure. *Page 685*

65. When the cabin pressure regulator in Figure 9-23 is operating in the isobaric mode, cabin pressure is held constant by reducing the flow of reference-chamber air through the isobaric _____ valve. *Page 686*

Continued

66. Refer to Figure 9-23. Anytime an increase in cabin pressure causes the isobaric metering valve to move toward the OPEN position, the outflow valve _____ (opens or closes). *Page 687*

67. Refer to Figure 9-23. When the outside air pressure decreases enough that the difference between the cabin pressure and the outside pressure reaches the pressure-differential limit allowed by the airframe manufacturer, the differential metering valve _____ (opens or closes). *Page 687*

68. Refer to Figure 9-23. The isobaric metering valve is controlled by the _____ (bellows or diaphragm). *Page 686*

69. Refer to Figure 9-23. The differential metering valve is controlled by the _____ (bellows or diaphragm). *Page 686*

70. If the cabin rate of climb is too great, the rate control will cause the outflow valve to close _____ (faster or slower). *Page 687*

71. A negative-pressure relief valve is incorporated in a pressurization system to prevent cabin pressure ever becoming _____ (lower or higher) than the surrounding air pressure. *Page 688*

72. All positive pressure inside the cabin is relieved when the aircraft is on the ground by the _____ valve opening. *Page 688*

73. If "auxiliary ventilation" is selected on the pressurization control while cruising at altitude, cabin pressurization will be dumped, and the cabin altitude will _____ (increase or decrease). *Page 688*

74. Airflow is increased in some areas of an aircraft by using a _____ to augment the airflow. *Page 688*

Aircraft Heaters

Aircraft environmental control systems include heaters, cooling systems, pressurization systems, and supplemental oxygen.

The most widely used environmental control devices are heaters, which are installed in almost all aircraft, from the smallest trainers to the largest transport aircraft. In this section we discuss exhaust system heaters and combustion heaters. The section on air-cycle air-conditioning systems discusses cabin heat taken from engine compressor bleed air.

Exhaust System Heaters

Most of the smaller aircraft use jackets, or shrouds, around part of the engine exhaust system to provide heat for the cabin. Air flows around the exhaust component and picks up heat before it is carried into the cabin.

When the cabin heat valve is ON, the heated air is directed into the cabin. When it is OFF, this hot air is dumped overboard.

Aircraft that use this type of heater should have their exhaust system regularly inspected for cracks or other leaks. One acceptable way of checking exhaust systems is to remove the heater shroud, pressurize the system with the pressure discharge of a vacuum cleaner, and paint the outside of the system with a soap and water solution. Leaks will cause bubbles to appear.

Carbon monoxide detectors should be used in the cabin to detect any trace of carbon monoxide. These are simply small packets of crystals that are stuck to the instrument panel in plain sight of the occupants. These crystals are normally a bright color, but when they are exposed to carbon monoxide, they darken. They turn black when exposed to a level of CO that could cause illness.

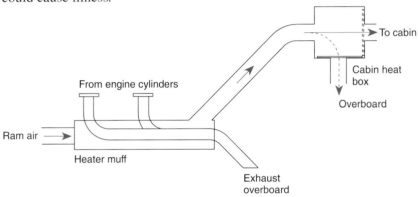

Figure 9-24. *A shroud around part of the exhaust system serves as a source of heat for some of the smaller aircraft cabins.*

Combustion Heaters

Some aircraft are heated with combustion heaters that use fuel from the aircraft fuel tanks. A typical combustion heater system schematic is shown in Figure 9-25 on the next page.

Fuel flows from the tank through a filter and an electric fuel pump and relief valve, then through an overheat solenoid valve into the fuel control assembly. In this assembly there is another filter, a fuel-pressure regulator, and a thermostat-operated solenoid valve. From this assembly, the fuel flows to the spray nozzle inside the combustion chamber.

combustion heater. A type of cabin heater used in some aircraft. Gasoline from the aircraft fuel tanks is burned in the heater.

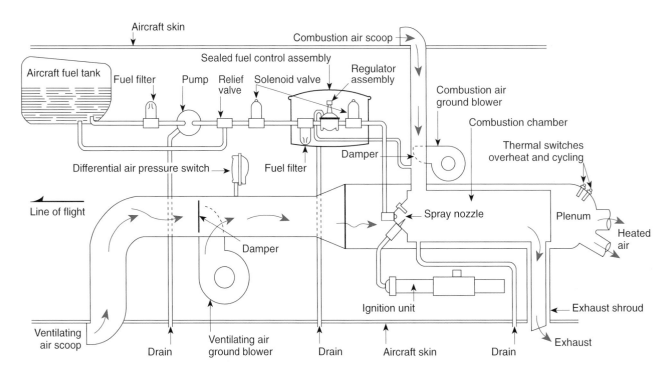

Figure 9-25. *A typical combustion heater schematic*

In flight, ventilating air flows into the air ducts from a scoop on the outside of the aircraft. On the ground, an electrically driven blower supplies ventilating air. This air flows through the heater housing to pick up heat and carry it where it is needed.

Combustion air is taken into the heater from the main air intake or from a separate outside air scoop, and the air pressure varies with the airspeed. A differential-pressure regulator or a combustion-air relief valve prevents too much air from entering the heater as the airspeed increases. An electrically driven blower ensures a consistent flow of air into the combustion chamber.

The heat produced by a combustion heater is controlled by a thermostat cycling switch that cycles the fuel on and off. When more heat is required, the fuel is turned on. When the correct temperature is reached, the fuel is turned off automatically. An overheat switch shuts the fuel off if the temperature at the discharge of the heater becomes too high.

Combustion heaters are maintained by cleaning the heater fuel filters. After the filters are replaced, the system must be pressurized and all connections carefully checked for traces of fuel leaks.

Answers begin on Page 713. Page numbers refer to chapter text.

75. Aircraft that are heated with exhaust system heaters should have _____ detectors installed on the instrument panel. *Page 691*

76. Two types of airflow through a combustion heater are _____ air and _____ air. *Page 692*

77. Too much combustion air is prevented from flowing through a combustion heater by either a combustion air _____ valve or a _____ regulator. *Page 692*

78. Regular maintenance of a combustion heater consists of cleaning or replacing the fuel _____ and checking all connections for _____ . *Page 692*

79. The temperature produced by a combustion heater is controlled by the thermostat which controls the _____ going to the heater. *Page 692*

Aircraft Cooling Systems

It has not been too many years since cooling aircraft was considered to be a needless expense both in weight and complexity. Airplanes flew in the low temperatures of high altitude and heating was the needed temperature control. Now, with people accustomed to more creature comfort, cooling systems are used to make the cabins more comfortable when the aircraft is on the ground.

Air-Cycle Cooling System

Transport aircraft use the compressor bleed air for pressurizing the cabins with temperature controlled air. Figure 9-26 (Page 694) shows the air-conditioning system for a twin-engine jet transport airplane with the engines mounted on the aft fuselage. This airplane has two independent air-conditioning systems that supply the cabin with heated and cooled air that is mixed to produce pressurizing air at the right temperature. Hot compressor bleed air is taken from the engines and from the auxiliary power unit. It passes through pressure regulating and shutoff valves, flow limiters, and flow control valves to the air-cycle machines where it is cooled. Some of the hot air is tapped off before it goes through the cooler, and is mixed with the cold air by a temperature control valve to get air of the correct temperature.

The cold air for cooling the airplane shown in Figure 9-26 is produced by removing heat energy from the hot compressor bleed air.

air-cycle cooling system. A system for cooling the air in the cabin of a turbojet-powered aircraft. Compressor bleed air passes through two heat exchangers where it gives up some of its heat; then it drives an expansion turbine where it loses still more of its heat energy as the turbine drives a compressor. When the air leaves the turbine it expands and its pressure and temperature are both low.

heat exchanger. A device used to exchange heat from one medium to another. Radiators, condensers, and evaporators are all examples of heat exchangers. Heat always moves from the object or medium having the greatest level of heat energy to a medium or object having a lower level.

Hot compressor bleed air from the engines and the APU flows into the primary heat exchanger where it gives up some of its heat to ram air that flows through ducts.

After leaving the primary heat exchanger, it flows through the air-cycle machine where it is further compressed by the centrifugal compressor. The temperature rise caused by this compression allows more heat energy to be removed as the air flows through the secondary heat exchanger. After leaving this heat exchanger, the air gives up much of its energy as it spins the expansion turbine, which drives the air-cycle machine compressor. Still more energy is extracted in the last stage of cooling as the air expands upon leaving the turbine. When it leaves the expansion turbine, the air is cold.

As the air cools, moisture condenses out of it and is collected in the water separator. As the air leaves the air-cycle machine, it is so cold that the water will freeze in the water separator and shut off the flow of cooling air. To prevent this, the thermostat senses the temperature of the air leaving the water

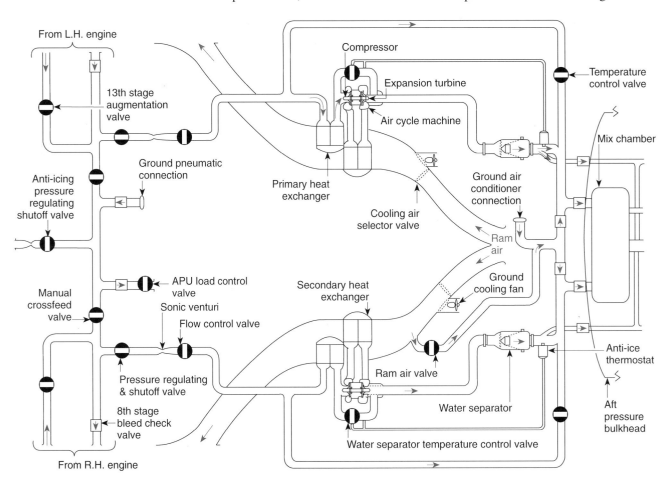

Figure 9-26. *Air-conditioning system for a twin-engine jet transport airplane*

separator. If the temperature drops below 38°F, the water separator temperature control valve opens and lets warm air mix with the cold air to raise the temperature enough that the moisture will not freeze.

Temperature Control

The cabin air temperature is controlled by the temperature control valve taking the hot air that has bypassed the air-cycle machine and mixing it with the cold air as it leaves the water separator.

Vapor-Cycle Cooling System

To better understand the way heat is moved in a vapor-cycle cooling system, consider the events that take place when heat from the sun is absorbed in the water of a lake.

When the sun shines on a lake during a hot summer day, some of the heat is absorbed by the water, which gets warmer. The warmed water on the surface evaporates, or changes from a liquid into a gas.

When the water evaporates, it takes some of the heat from the air immediately adjacent to the surface, and this air is cooled.

The water that evaporated from the surface of the lake is still water, only now it is in the form of invisible water vapor that is only slightly more than half as heavy as the air surrounding it. This water vapor still contains the energy from the sun that changed it from a liquid into a gas.

The lightweight water vapor rises in the air, and because the temperature of the air drops as altitude increases, the water vapor cools. Soon, its temperature becomes so low that it can no longer remain a vapor, and it changes back into a liquid, into tiny droplets that form clouds.

When the water vapor reverts into liquid water, the heat it absorbed from the sun is released, and this heat raises the temperature of the air surrounding the cloud.

Heat is moved in a vapor-cycle air cooling system in the same way it is moved from the surface of the lake to the air surrounding the clouds.

Under standard conditions, water is a liquid. If heat energy is added to a pan of water on a hot stove, and the temperature of the water goes up until it reaches 212°F, then the water boils. As long as the water is allowed to boil, its temperature will never rise above 212°F. But, if a tight-fitting lid is placed on the pan and more heat is added to the water, its temperature will go higher. The lid keeps pressure on the water, and it must get much hotter before it can boil.

A refrigerant, such as R-12 (*see* description of Refrigerant-12 on Page 706), remains a liquid under standard pressure only at temperatures below -21.6°F. Above this temperature, it boils, or changes into a vapor.

R-12 in an open container will have a gage pressure above it of 0 psi, and its temperature will be -21.6°F. *See* Figure 9-27. If a lid with a closed valve is put on the container, the refrigerant reaches the temperature of the surrounding air, which in this case is 70°F. The pressure above the liquid reaches approximately 70 psi, where it stabilizes. If the valve is cracked slightly, some of the vapor escapes, the pressure drops, and more liquid evaporates. When the pressure drops to approximately 47 psi, the temperature of the refrigerant drops to 50°F. If the valve is cracked still more, the pressure continues to drop and more refrigerant evaporates. When the pressure is down to 10 psi, the temperature of the refrigerant reaches 2°F.

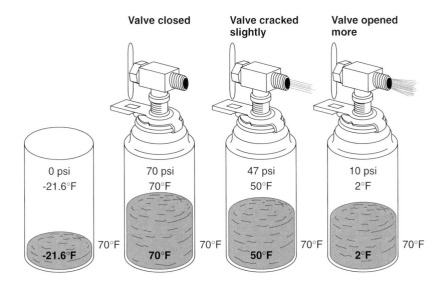

Figure 9-27. *There is a direct relationship between the temperature of R-12 and the pressure of the gas above it.*

To better understand the operation of a vapor-cycle cooling system, think of it as divided into two sides: the low side and the high side. The low side is the part of the system that picks up the heat, and the high side is the part of the system that gets rid of the heat.

The low side starts at the expansion valve, goes through the evaporator, and ends at the inlet of the compressor. The high side starts at the discharge of the compressor, goes through the condenser and the receiver-dryer, and ends at the expansion valve.

The pressure and the temperature are both low in the low side, and they are both high in the high side. *See* Figure 9-28.

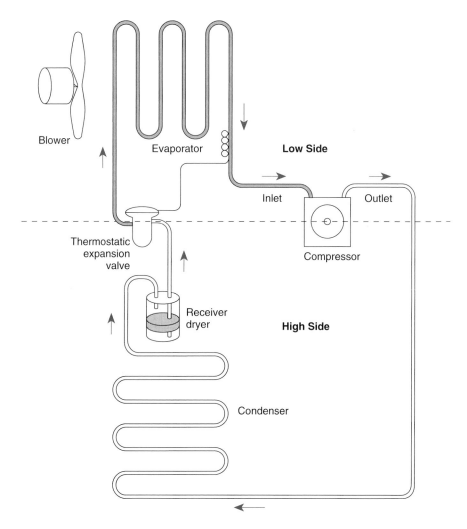

Figure 9-28. *A vapor-cycle cooling system is divided into a high side and a low side.*

The Compressor

The compressor is the heart of an air-conditioning system. It moves the refrigerant through the system, and it divides the system into its high side and low side.

The compressor pulls the low-pressure refrigerant vapor from the evaporator and compresses it. And when the vapor is compressed, its pressure and temperature both go up.

The compressor carries a specified amount of special moisture-free refrigeration oil that lubricates and seals the compressor, and circulates through the system with the refrigerant.

compressor. The component in a vapor-cycle cooling system in which the low-pressure refrigerant vapors, after they leave the evaporator, are compressed to increase both their temperature and pressure before they pass into the condenser. Some compressors are driven by electric motors, others by hydraulic motors and, in the case of most light airplanes, are belt driven from the engine.

Some compressors are driven from the aircraft engine by a V belt through an electromagnetic clutch. When the system calls for cooling, the clutch engages, and the pulley drives the compressor. When cooling is not needed, the clutch disengages and the pulley continues to turn, but the compressor is not driven. Other compressors are driven by an electric or hydraulic motor.

Typical air-conditioning compressors use reed valves mounted in a valve plate between the top of the cylinders and the cylinder head.

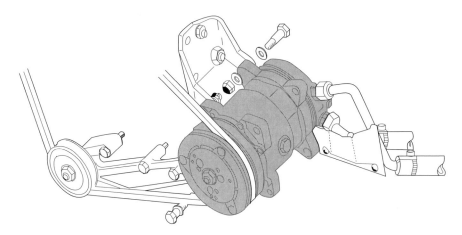

Figure 9-29. *A five-cylinder axial compressor that is belt-driven from the engine*

The Compressor Drive System

When the compressor is driven by the engine with a V belt, an electromagnetic clutch inside a grooved pulley is used so the compressor can be engaged and disengaged as the demands of the system require.

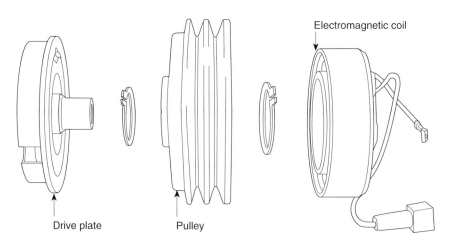

Figure 9-30. *Electromagnetic clutch for an engine-driven compressor*

The pulley is not rigidly connected to the compressor shaft, but it rides on a double-row ball bearing so it is free to turn without turning the compressor.

A clutch drive plate is keyed to the compressor shaft, and when the clutch is disengaged, there is a small amount of clearance between the plate and the pulley.

An electromagnetic coil is installed inside the pulley housing in such a way that when the air conditioning controls call for cooling, current flows through the coil, and a magnetic field is set up between the drive plate and the pulley. This magnetic field locks the pulley to the drive plate, and the pulley turns the compressor.

The compressor in some aircraft air conditioning systems is driven by a hydraulic motor whose pressure is supplied by an engine-driven pump.

A hydraulic manifold assembly contains a filter and a solenoid valve. When no cooling is required, the solenoid is de-energized and the valve allows fluid to bypass the motor and flow back to the reservoir. When the temperature control switch calls for cooling, the solenoid is energized and the valve shifts, closing off the return to the reservoir. The fluid flows through the pump so it can drive the compressor.

The Condenser

The refrigerant leaves the compressor as a hot, high-pressure gas, and flows to the condenser mounted where outside air can pass through its fins.

The condenser is made of high-pressure tubing wound back and forth, with thin sheet metal fins pressed over the tubes.

The hot refrigerant gas enters one side of the condenser and gives up some of its heat to the air flowing through the condenser fins.

When the system is working properly, about two thirds of the condenser is filled with refrigerant gas, and the rest contains liquid refrigerant.

condenser. The component in a vapor-cycle cooling system in which the heat taken from the aircraft cabin is given up to the ambient air outside the aircraft.

The Receiver-Dryer

High-pressure, high-temperature liquid refrigerant leaves the condenser and flows into the receiver-dryer, which acts as a reservoir to hold the supply of refrigerant until it is needed by the evaporator. *See* Figure 9-31.

As the hot liquid refrigerant enters the receiver-dryer, it passes through a filter that removes any solid contaminants. Then it passes through a layer of a drying agent such as silica gel or activated alumina. This drying agent, called a desiccant, absorbs any moisture that may be circulating through the system in the refrigerant. Some receiver-dryers have two filters; the one below the desiccant prevents any particles of the desiccant getting into the system.

receiver-dryer. The component in a vapor-cycle cooling system that serves as a reservoir for the liquid refrigerant. The receiver-dryer contains a desiccant that absorbs any moisture that may be in the system.

desiccant. A drying agent used in a refrigeration system to remove water from the refrigerant. A desiccant is made of silica-gel or some similar material.

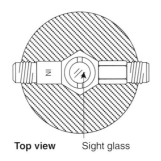

Top view   Sight glass

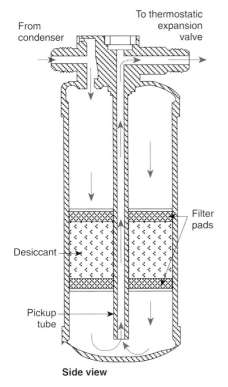

Side view

Figure 9-31. *Liquid refrigerant from the condenser is stored in the receiver-dryer.*

sight glass. A small window in the high side of a vapor-cycle cooling system. Liquid refrigerant flows past the sight glass, and if the charge of refrigerant is low, bubbles will be seen. A fully charged system has no bubbles in the refrigerant.

volatile liquid. A liquid that easily changes into a vapor.

If moisture were allowed to remain in the system, it would mix with the refrigerant and form acids that could eat away the thin-wall tubing in the evaporator and cause leaks.

Another reason it is so important to remove all the moisture from the refrigerant is that it takes only a single drop of water to freeze in the expansion valve and block the flow of refrigerant into the evaporator. This stops the cooling action of the system.

Sometimes the refrigerant leaving the condenser has vapor in it, and the receiver-dryer acts as a separator. The liquid settles to the bottom and is picked up by the pickup tube that reaches almost to the bottom of the tank.

Some receiver-dryers include a sight glass that allows you to check the amount of refrigerant in the system. The sight glass is on the discharge side of the receiver-dryer, and if the system has enough refrigerant in it, only liquid flows to the expansion valve. But if the system is low on refrigerant, you will see bubbles in the sight glass.

Thermostatic Expansion Valves

The thermostatic expansion valve (TEV) is a metering device that measures the temperature of the discharge end of the evaporator to allow the correct amount of refrigerant to flow into the evaporator. All of the liquid refrigerant should be turned into a gas (it should evaporate) by the time it gets to the end of the evaporator coil.

Several types of thermostatic expansion valves are installed in aircraft air-conditioning systems. This section discusses both internally and externally equalized TEVs.

Before discussing these valves, we must understand the term "superheat." Superheat is heat energy added to a refrigerant after it has changed from a liquid into a vapor. Refrigerant that has superheat in it is not hot, it is very cold.

Figure 9-32 shows a typical internally equalized thermostatic expansion valve. The outlet attaches to the inlet of the evaporator, and the inlet is connected to the tubing that comes from the receiver-dryer.

A diaphragm in the top of the valve rides on the top of two pushrods that press against the superheat spring.

A capillary tube, which is a metal tube with a very small inside diameter, connects into the TEV just above the diaphragm. The end of this capillary tube is wound into a tight coil, and acts as the temperature pickup bulb. This bulb is clamped to the discharge line of the evaporator, and is wrapped with an insulating tape so it will not be affected by any temperature other than that of the evaporator discharge.

The capillary tube and the space above the diaphragm is partially filled with a highly volatile liquid. When the bulb is heated, the pressure of the vapor above the liquid increases. It produces a force that pushes the diaphragm

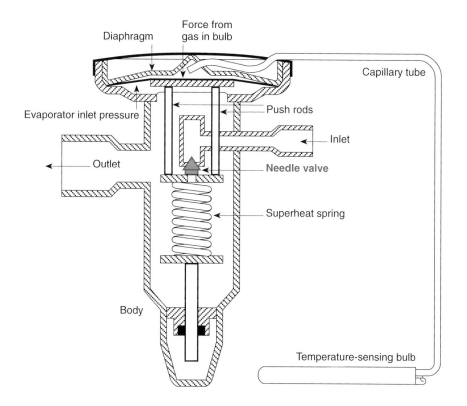

Diaphragm

Force from gas in bulb

Capillary tube

Evaporator inlet pressure

Push rods

Inlet

Outlet

Needle valve

Superheat spring

Body

Temperature-sensing bulb

Figure 9-32. *Internally equalized thermostatic expansion valve*

down against the force caused by the superheat spring and the force caused by the evaporator inlet pressure acting on the bottom of the diaphragm. The temperature of the refrigerant in the discharge of the evaporator determines the amount of force that acts against the superheat spring.

A needle valve is located between the inlet and the outlet of the TEV. The position of the needle in the valve is determined by the balance between the force caused by the pressure of the gas above the diaphragm and the forces produced by the superheat spring and the pressure of the refrigerant in the evaporator.

When the system is started, the evaporator is warm, and the pressure inside the bulb is high, so the TEV allows the maximum amount of refrigerant to enter the evaporator.

As the refrigerant evaporates, the temperature at the outlet of the evaporator drops and the pressure above the diaphragm decreases. This decreased pressure allows the superheat spring to close the needle valve and restrict the amount of refrigerant that flows into the evaporator. Just enough refrigerant is metered into the evaporator for it all to be turned into a gas by the time it reaches the end of the evaporator coils.

thermal expansion valve (TEV). The component in a vapor-cycle cooling system that meters the refrigerant into the evaporator.

The amount of refrigerant metered by the TEV is determined by the temperature and pressure of the refrigerant as it leaves the evaporator coils.

The TEV changes the refrigerant from a high-pressure liquid into a low-pressure liquid.

evaporator. The component in a vapor-cycle cooling system in which heat from the aircraft cabin is absorbed into the refrigerant. As the heat is absorbed, the refrigerant evaporates, or changes from a liquid into a vapor. The function of the evaporator is to lower the cabin air temperature.

superheat. Heat energy that is added to a refrigerant after it changes from a liquid to a vapor.

If the heat load inside the cabin of the aircraft increases, and all of the refrigerant is turned into a gas before it reaches the end of the evaporator coils, heat is added to the refrigerant vapor. This is superheat, and it increases the temperature of the refrigerant, but it does not increase its pressure. The increased temperature raises the pressure inside the bulb and on top of the diaphragm, and this forces the needle valve off its seat and allows more refrigerant to flow into the evaporator.

The amount of compression of the superheat spring is set at the factory, and it is important when installing a new TEV that the superheat setting be correct for the particular installation.

A TEV is equalized by having the pressure of the refrigerant inside the evaporator work on the bottom of the diaphragm. It works in such a way that it assists the superheat spring in opposing the force of the gas inside the temperature bulb. An internally equalized TEV has a passage inside the valve that allows the pressure at the inlet of the evaporator to press against the diaphragm.

An externally equalized TEV is used with large evaporators that have a fair amount of pressure drop across the coils. This makes the outlet pressure significantly lower than the inlet pressure. An externally equalized TEV has a small tube connected to the discharge of the evaporator that carries this pressure to the space below the diaphragm.

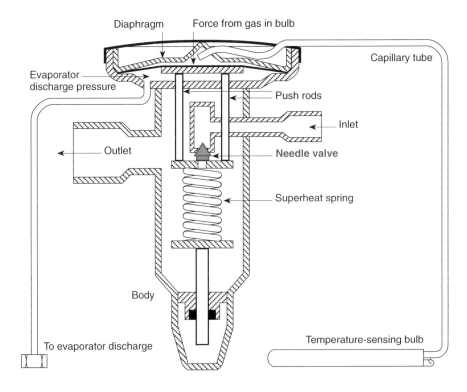

Figure 9-33. *Externally equalized thermostatic expansion valve*

The Evaporator

The evaporator is the part of the air conditioning system where the cold air is produced. It is made of a series of tubes over which thin sheet aluminum fins have been pressed. The area provided by the fins allows a maximum amount of heat to be picked up from the air inside the cabin and transferred into the refrigerant inside the evaporator tubing.

The evaporator is usually mounted inside a shroud in such a way that a blower can pull hot air from inside the cabin and force it through the evaporator fins. After the air leaves the evaporator, it blows over the occupants of the cabin. The blower is equipped with a speed control that allows the pilot to vary the amount of air blowing across the evaporator coils. The thermostatic expansion valve is mounted at the inlet of the evaporator, and it breaks the refrigerant up into a fine mist and sprays it out into the coils. The refrigerant flowing through the coils picks up heat from the fins, is warmed, and turns into a gas. The air passing through the fins loses some of its heat and is cooled.

The temperature-sensing bulb of the TEV is clamped to the discharge line of the evaporator, and it is insulated with tape so it is not affected by any temperature except that caused by the refrigerant vapors inside the evaporator.

The temperature of the refrigerant vapor is controlled by regulating the amount of refrigerant allowed to enter the evaporator through the TEV. The vapor at the discharge of the evaporator is a few degrees warmer than the liquid refrigerant because of the superheat put into it. This superheat ensures that none of the refrigerant will be in its liquid state when it enters the inlet of the compressor because liquid refrigerant will damage the reed valves in the compressor.

In addition to absorbing heat from the air and cooling the air that is blown out into the cabin, the evaporator serves the very important function of dehumidifying the air. When warm, humid air is blown through the cold evaporator fins, the moisture condenses out of the air in the same way moisture condenses and forms as water on the outside of a glass holding a cold drink. This moisture drips down off the fins and collects in a pan, and is carried outside the aircraft through a drain tube. Pressurized aircraft have a float-operated drain valve in the drain line. When there is no water in the valve housing, the valve is closed. But when enough water collects in the housing, it raises the float, opens the valve and allows the water to be blown overboard. When there is no more water in the housing, the float drops down and the valve closes.

The fins on the evaporator must be kept open so that air can flow through them and add heat to the refrigerant. If the flow of air is blocked, the refrigerant cannot absorb enough heat, and the evaporator will get so cold that the moisture which condenses out of the air will freeze in the evaporator fins and block the air. The system will then stop producing cold air.

reed valve. A thin, leaf-type valve mounted in the valve plate of an air conditioning compressor to control the flow of refrigerant gases into and out of the compressor cylinders.

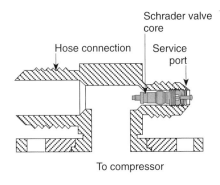

Schrader valve core

Hose connection

Service port

To compressor

Detail of Schrader valve core

Figure 9-34. *Schrader-type valve air conditioning service valve*

Schrader valve. A type of service valve used in an air conditioning system. This is a spring-loaded valve much like the valve used to put air into a tire.

compound gage. A pressure gage used to measure the pressure in the low side of an air conditioning system. A compound gage is calibrated from zero to 30-inches of mercury vacuum, and from zero to about 150-pounds per square inch positive pressure.

Service Valves

A vapor-cycle air conditioning system is a sealed system that operates under pressure. In order to measure the pressure in the system and to add refrigerant when the supply is low, provisions must be made for getting into the system while it is under pressure.

Schrader-type service valves are used on most aircraft air conditioning systems because of their light weight and reliability. A Schrader valve can be installed at any point in the system, and these valves keep the system closed until a service hose is screwed onto the valve. When the hose fitting is screwed down, a valve depressor inside the fitting presses down on the valve stem and opens the system.

Air-Conditioning System Servicing Equipment

Because an air-conditioning system is a sealed system, it requires specialized equipment to properly service it. The refrigerants currently used are considered to be a threat to the ozone and can no longer be vented to the atmosphere. In this section we will consider the manifold gage set, the charging station, refrigerant recovery systems, and leak detectors.

The Manifold Gage Set

The most useful single piece of service equipment for working with a vapor-cycle cooling system is a manifold gage set, like the one in Figure 9-35.

A manifold gage set has two pressure gages and two hand-operated valves, mounted on a manifold that has connections for three service hoses.

A red, high-pressure service hose attaches to a fitting connected directly to the high-side gage. A blue, low-pressure hose attaches to a fitting connected to the compound low-side gage. A yellow service hose connects to the center fitting.

The two valves shut off the center fitting from either of the two gages, but they may be opened to connect the center hose to either the low side or the high side of the system.

The zero position of the compound low-side gage is not at the end of the scale, but is placed in such a position that the pointer can move down scale to measure between zero and 30 inches of mercury vacuum, or up scale to measure from zero to 150 pounds per square inch pressure.

The high-pressure gage is marked so it can measure from zero to 500 pounds per square inch.

A manifold gage set is used to measure the pressures that exist inside the air conditioning system, to evacuate the system of refrigerant, to pump down, or purge, the system of all water vapor, and to charge the system with refrigerant.

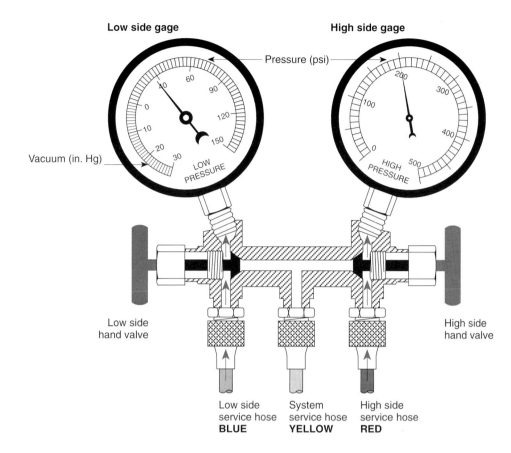

Figure 9-35. *The manifold gage set is the most important single piece of equipment for servicing an air-conditioning system.*

Charging Stand

A charging stand is a piece of equipment that contains everything needed to service an air-conditioning system. All the equipment is mounted in a single unit that can easily be moved to the aircraft whose air-conditioning system is being serviced.

A charging stand usually contains a cylinder of refrigerant and a heating system that allows the refrigerant to be heated to speed its entry into the system. This cylinder is fitted with valves that allow the refrigerant to be added to the system in either liquid or gaseous form.

A vacuum pump and a vacuum holding valve are included to allow a system to be pumped down and checked for leaks. All the hoses, adapters, and valves needed to connect the charging stand to the aircraft system are included.

charging stand. A handy and compact arrangement of air conditioning servicing equipment. A charging stand contains a vacuum pump, a manifold gage set, and a method of measuring and dispensing the refrigerant.

Vacuum Pumps

When servicing an air-conditioning system, you must remove every trace of moisture from the system. Water combines with the refrigerant to form hydrochloric acid, which can eat away the inside of the evaporator and condenser tubes and cause leakage. It also takes only a small droplet of water to freeze inside the thermostatic expansion valve and shut off the operation of the system.

Vacuum pumps may be of either the piston type or the rotary vane type and they are capable of producing a "deep vacuum," a very low absolute pressure. A good pump can produce a pressure as low as 29.99 inches of mercury (250 microns). At this extremely low pressure, water boils at a temperature of well below 0°F, and any water will turn into a vapor and be pulled out of the system.

Leak Detectors

An air-conditioning system must be sealed so none of the refrigerant can leak out of it. Occasionally, though, a leak allows the refrigerant to escape. The leak must be found before the system is returned to service.

The only type of leak detector suited for servicing an aircraft air-conditioning system is an electronic oscillator-type leak detector. The oscillator produces a tone, and if even an extremely small trace of refrigerant is picked up by the pickup tube, the tone will change. An electronic leak detector is simple to use, extremely sensitive, and causes no danger when servicing the system.

Gaseous refrigerant is heavier than air, and the probe is passed below locations where leakage is suspected.

Refrigerant-12

Refrigerant-12 is sold under many different trade names. One of the most common is Freon-12, the registered trade name by E.I. DuPont de Nemours and Company. (Note: other refrigerants, such as R-13 and R-22, have entirely different characteristics. Using them in a system designed for R-12 will cause a great deal of trouble.)

You can buy R-12 in 14-ounce cans (commonly called one-pound cans), 2- and 2½-pound cans, 10- and 12-pound disposable cylinders, and in 25- and 145-pound refillable cylinders.

R-12 is being replaced with R-134a, which is more environmentally friendly. Automotive air-conditioning systems have been given a date beyond which R-12 can no longer be used, and it is probable that aircraft air-conditioning systems will soon be similarly constrained.

deep-vacuum pump. A vacuum pump capable of removing almost all of the air from a refrigeration system. A deep-vacuum pump can reduce the pressure inside the system to a few microns of pressure.

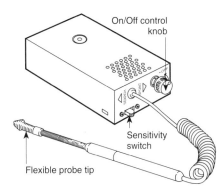

On/Off control knob

Sensitivity switch

Flexible probe tip

Figure 9-36. *An electronic oscillator-type leak detector detects extremely small refrigerant leaks and is safe for servicing aircraft air-conditioning systems.*

Freon. The registered trade name for the refrigerant used in a vapor-cycle cooling system. Freon-12 is the most commonly used refrigerant.

Refrigeration Oil

The sealed air-conditioning system is lubricated by a special high-grade refrigeration oil that circulates through the system with the refrigerant.

Fresh refrigeration oil is free of water, is a pale yellow color, almost clear, and has very little odor. Since refrigeration oil has a tendency to absorb moisture from the air, it must be kept in a tightly closed container until it is put into the system.

Air-Conditioning System Checks

With the system turned on and the engine running at a fast idle, a normally-functioning air-conditioning system will blow a stream of cold air out from the evaporator. All of the components in the high side of the system should feel hot or warm to the touch. All of the components in the low side of the system should feel cold or cool to the touch.

The actual temperature of the air as it leaves the evaporator depends on the air's humidity and the ambient air temperature, but it should be in the range of 35° to 45°F.

Visual Inspection

The entire air-conditioning system should be checked visually for its condition. Begin with one part of the system and check it through the entire system.

Check the evaporator to be sure it is mounted securely and that there is a clear airflow path through its shroud.

The fins must be free of lint and dirt, and there must not be any fins bent over to obstruct the air flowing through them. The blower must operate at all speeds and not rub against its housing.

The sensor for the thermostatic expansion valve must be securely taped to the discharge of the evaporator, and covered so it will not be affected by any temperature other than that of the evaporator coil.

The thermostat switch must be secured in such a way that its sensor is in the fins of the evaporator so it can sense the temperature at the point the manufacturer specifies.

Check the compressor for security of mounting, for freedom of operation of the clutch, and for the proper belt tension. The load the compressor places on its mounting as it cycles on and off puts a big strain on the castings, so you should carefully inspect the area around which the compressor is mounted. Check the mounting bolts to be sure none of them have vibrated loose.

The condenser is much like the evaporator, except that it is made to withstand much higher temperatures and pressures. It must be inspected for security of mounting and for any bent or damaged fins. The housing that holds the condenser must be securely mounted in the aircraft structure, and it must be free from any obstruction to the airflow.

Many aircraft systems have a blower that forces air over the condenser when the aircraft is on the ground. Check this blower and its motor for proper operation, and be sure there is no indication that the blower is rubbing on its housing.

Check the receiver-dryer, which is usually located near the condenser, for proper and secure mounting. If it has a sight glass in it, check to see if there is an adequate supply of liquid refrigerant in the system. You shouldn't see any bubbles in the refrigerant.

Since the receiver-dryer is in the high side of the system, it is hot when the system is operating properly.

The entire air-conditioning system is connected with hoses and tubing. Inspect every fitting and section of hose for any indication of oil leakage that would indicate a refrigerant leak.

All plumbing in the aircraft should be supported by the method the manufacturer specifies. If you install anything differently from the method used by the factory, the installation must be made according to approved data.

Operational Check

After a careful visual check confirms that the air-conditioning system is properly mounted in the aircraft, you can give it an operational check. This check consists of connecting a manifold gage set to the system and measuring the pressure of the refrigerant in the system.

Remove the protective cap from the service port in the high side of the system and, after checking to be sure the high-side valve on the manifold gage set is closed, connect the high-side service hose to the valve. Open the high-side valve slightly and allow refrigerant to flow out of the center hose for about three to five seconds, then close the valve.

Remove the protective cap from the low-side service port and connect the low-side service hose. Open the low-side valve and allow refrigerant to flow out of the center hose for three to five seconds, then close the valve.

Allow the system to operate with the engine running at a relatively fast idle for about five minutes, with the blowers operating at high speed and the air conditioning controls calling for maximum cooling. After the system has run five minutes, check the evaporator air discharge temperature and the high-side pressure. The pressures are affected by the ambient temperature, but the pressures in Figure 9-37 are typical.

Installing a Partial Charge of Refrigerant

If the sight glass shows there is no refrigerant in the system, or if the pressure on the gages of the manifold gage set is below 50 psi, you must install a partial charge in the system before making any further operational checks.

Connect a can-tap valve to a one-pound can of refrigerant and puncture the can seal. Connect the valve to the center hose of the manifold gage set and

Ambient Temperature °F	High-Side Pressure psi	Low-Side Pressure psi
60°	105 – 110	4 – 8
70°	125 – 130	10 – 15
85°	170 – 180	15 – 30
100°	215 – 225	25 – 50
110°	255 – 260	30 – 60

Figure 9-37. *Pressures in a normally operating vapor-cycle air-conditioning system*

loosen the hose at the manifold. Open the can valve and allow refrigerant to flow through the hose for a few seconds to purge the hose of any air, then tighten the hose fitting.

Open the high-side manifold valve and allow refrigerant to flow into the system until the pressure is above 50 psi.

Leak Testing

A leakage of about $\frac{1}{2}$-pound of refrigerant in a one-year period is not considered excessive, but a leak test must be performed if leakage is any greater than that.

With the system pressure above 50 pounds per square inch, hold the probe of an electronic leak detector below any point at which a leak is suspected. The detector changes the tone of the sound it produces when it detects a leak.

Air-Conditioning System Servicing

Servicing an air-conditioning system is different from other types of aircraft maintenance because the system is sealed and operates under pressure. Follow normal good operating practices in any type of maintenance work, and follow the instructions furnished by the aircraft manufacturer in detail. Some of the most commonly performed service procedures are as follows.

Discharging the System

When it is necessary to change any of the components in an air-conditioning system or to replace contaminated refrigerant, drain the old refrigerant from the system. In the past this was done by connecting a manifold gage set to the system and holding a shop towel over the end of the center hose, then slowly opening both the high- and low-side valves and allowing the refrigerant to escape into the atmosphere. R-12 is nontoxic, but it does displace oxygen from the area and it should not be discharged from a system in a closed area.

Concern for the environment has changed the way R-12 is handled. R-12 must now be emptied into a recovery and recycling system, rather than being vented into the atmosphere. The refrigerant is emptied into a container in the recycling system and pumped through a series of filters to remove all the refrigerant oil and clean the refrigerant for reuse.

Replacing System Components

The procedure for replacing components in an air-conditioning system is similar to that used for replacing components in any other aircraft system, except that the openings in the components must be kept capped until they are ready to be installed. Moisture is always present in the air, and the absolute minimum amount of moisture must be allowed to get into the system.

When installing hoses with hose clamps, lubricate the inside of the hose with clean refrigeration oil and work the fitting into the hose with a twisting motion.

Hoses that are screwed onto a component should be tightened by using two wrenches, one on the fitting in the component and one on the hose fitting. The use of two wrenches prevents straining the component.

Checking Compressor Oil

Compressors used in air-conditioning systems are lubricated by oil sealed in the system. Any time the system is opened, it is a good idea to check the amount of oil in the compressor.

Because the compressors may be mounted in different ways on different aircraft, it is important that the instructions in the aircraft maintenance manual be followed to check the compressor oil. The oil in some compressors can be checked with the compressor installed on the engine; on other installations, the compressor must be removed and the oil checked with the compressor on the bench.

Flushing the System

If a system has been contaminated, it can be flushed by removing the receiver-dryer and flushing the system. This is done by connecting a can of refrigerant to the system and allowing the liquid refrigerant to flow through the system. Install a new receiver-dryer after the system has been flushed.

Evacuating the System

After the system has been repaired by replacing any faulty components and flushing the lines, all the air must be pumped out so any trapped moisture will be changed into water vapor and removed with a vacuum pump.

Connect a vacuum pump to the center service hose of the manifold gage set, open both valves, and start the pump. Allow the pump to pull as much vacuum as it will, and hold the system at this low pressure for at least thirty minutes. After the system has been pumped down, close the valves on the manifold gage set and check to see that there is no leak in the system. A leak would be indicated by a rise in the negative pressure shown on the low-side gage.

Charging the System

After the system has been evacuated and is still under vacuum, close both valves on the manifold gage set and disconnect the vacuum pump. Connect the hose to a container of refrigerant and purge the air from the hose.

Open the high-side valve and allow the amount of liquid refrigerant specified in the aircraft service instructions to flow into the system. The correct amount is usually specified in units of weight rather than volume.

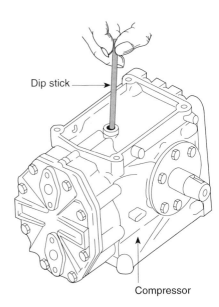

Dip stick

Compressor

Figure 9-38. *Checking the oil in a two cylinder in-line compressor*

If the full amount of refrigerant fails to flow into the system, close the high-side valve, turn the container of refrigerant upright, start the engine, and slowly open the low-side valve. Allow the compressor to pull enough refrigerant vapors into the system to give it a full charge. Filling the system may be hastened by putting the cans of refrigerant in warm water, but be sure the temperature of the water is not higher than 125°F.

Never put liquid refrigerant into the low side of an operating system unless the low-side pressure is below 40 psi, and the ambient temperature is above 80°F. If the refrigerant has not all evaporated by the time it reaches the compressor it is likely to cause compressor damage.

When the system is fully charged and is operating properly with no bubbles visible in the sight glass, close both service valves and remove the manifold gage set. Replace the protective caps over the service valves.

STUDY QUESTIONS: AIRCRAFT COOLING SYSTEMS

Answers begin on Page 713. Page numbers refer to chapter text.

80. Heat for the cabin of a jet transport airplane is provided by _____ air. *Page 693*

81. In a jet transport airplane, hot compressor bleed air is mixed with cold air from the _____ machine to get air of the correct temperature for the cabin. *Page 693*

82. The first heat that is lost from the hot compressor bleed air in an air-cycle machine is removed by the _____ heat exchanger. *Page 694*

83. After the air leaves the primary heat exchanger it is heated as it is compressed by the _____ compressor. *Page 694*

84. After leaving the air-cycle machine centrifugal compressor the air gives up some of its heat as it passes through the _____ heat exchanger. *Page 694*

85. More heat is removed from the pressurizing air after it leaves the secondary heat exchanger as it spins the _____ which drives the centrifugal compressor. *Page 694*

86. The final stage of cooling is done when the air _____ upon leaving the turbine. *Page 694*

87. Moisture that condenses from the pressurizing air after it leaves the expansion turbine is removed by the _____ . *Page 694*

88. Water is prevented from freezing in the water separator by routing some _____ around the air-cycle machine to mix with cold air and raise its temperature. *Page 695*

Continued

89. In a vapor-cycle cooling system, heat from the cabin is absorbed into the refrigerant in the
    _____ . *Page 703*

90. Heat taken from the cabin is transferred into the outside air by the _____ . *Page 699*

91. The refrigerant enters the evaporator as a _____ (high or low)-pressure _____
    (liquid or vapor). *Page 700*

92. The refrigerant leaves the evaporator as a _____ (high or low)-pressure _____
    (liquid or vapor). *Page 697*

93. The refrigerant enters the condenser as a _____ (high or low)-pressure _____
    (liquid or vapor). *Page 697*

94. The refrigerant leaves the condenser as a _____ (high or low)-pressure _____
    (liquid or vapor). *Page 699*

95. The receiver-dryer holds the refrigerant in its _____ (liquid or vapor) state. *Page 699*

96. The two units that divide an air conditioning system into a high side and a low side are the
    _____ and the _____ . *Page 697*

97. The component in an air conditioning system that increases both the temperature and the pressure of the
    gaseous refrigerant is the _____ . *Page 697*

98. Cycling of a compressor that is belt-driven from the aircraft engine is accomplished by using an electro-
    magnetic _____ in the drive pulley. *Page 698*

99. The condenser is in the _____ (high or low) side of an air conditioning system. *Page 697*

100. The air conditioning system component that meters liquid refrigerant into the evaporator coils is the
     _____ . *Page 700*

101. The evaporator is in the _____ (high or low) side of an air conditioning system. *Page 697*

102. The air leaving the evaporator of a properly functioning air conditioning system should have a
     temperature of between _____°F and _____°F. *Page 707*

103. When using an electronic leak detector, the probe should be held _____ (above or below)
     a location of a suspected leak. *Page 706*

Answers to Cabin Atmosphere Control Systems Study Questions

1. increase
2. decrease
3. nitrogen, oxygen
4. does not
5. headaches
6. hypoxia
7. carbon dioxide
8. oxygen
9. heat energy
10. British thermal unit, calorie
11. sensible
12. latent
13. a. the freezing point of water
    b. the boiling point of water
14. molecular
15. Kelvin
16. absolute
17. gage
18. differential
19. specific heat
20. a. conduction
    b. convection
    c. radiation
21. inches of mercury
22. microns
23. chemical oxygen candle
24. water
25. water
26. molecular sieve
27. may not
28. 400
29. continuous flow
30. pressure reducer
31. pressure relief
32. manual, automatic
33. calibrated orifice
34. therapeutic
35. continuous flow
36. demand
37. cabin air
38. inhales
39. Interstate Commerce Commission (ICC), Department of Transportation (DOT).
40. hydrostatically
41. 5
42. 3
43. 3,083
44. 15
45. 50
46. green
47. yellow
48. pressure
49. 1,925
50. 10
51. petroleum
52. nonpetroleum
53. pressure relief valve
54. water
55. turbocharger
56. a. Roots blower type
    b. Centrifugal type
57. check
58. compressor
59. compressor bleed
60. unpressurized
61. isobaric
62. constant differential
63. aircraft structure
64. reference chamber
65. metering
66. opens
67. opens
68. bellows
69. diaphragm
70. faster
71. lower
72. dump
73. increase
74. jet pump
75. carbon monoxide
76. combustion, ventilating
77. relief, differential-pressure
78. filter, leaks
79. fuel
80. compressor bleed
81. air cycle
82. primary
83. centrifugal
84. secondary
85. expansion turbine
86. expands
87. water separator
88. warm air
89. evaporator
90. condenser
91. low, liquid
92. low, vapor
93. high, vapor
94. high, liquid
95. liquid
96. thermostatic expansion valve, compressor
97. compressor
98. clutch
99. high
100. thermostatic expansion valve
101. low
102. 35, 45
103. below

AIRCRAFT INSTRUMENT SYSTEMS

10

Continued

AIRCRAFT
INSTRUMENT SYSTEMS

10

An Overview of Aircraft Instruments

The progress attained in serious flight has been made possible by the development of accurate and dependable instruments. The first aircraft had no instruments at all, but as engines became more dependable, instruments were developed to tell the pilot the amount of fuel on board and the speed and temperature of the engine.

The first flight instruments were primitive altimeters and compasses. All flying had to be done when the horizon was visible because the pilot had no way to knowing when the aircraft was flying straight or turning. The development of a sensitive altimeter and gyro instruments allowed the first excursions into the realm of "blind flying." When radio became developed enough to be used as a navigation aid, true blind flight became possible. The first flight without any outside visual reference was made by Jimmy Doolittle in September of 1929.

Today, even small general aviation aircraft have sophisticated instruments that allow the pilot to know his or her exact location and to monitor the performance of the aircraft and its engine. With this knowledge, safe flight in almost all situations is a reality.

Most of the instruments used in the past and present give mechanical indications. Pointers rotate across calibrated dials in an analog fashion to indicate the values being measured. The mechanisms that convert the parameter being measured into rotation of a pointer are quite complex and delicate.

Today, with the rapid developments in solid-state electronics and microcomputer technology, much instrumentation uses solid-state pickups and light-emitting diodes or liquid crystal displays on the instrument panels.

This portion of the *Aviation Maintenance Technician Series* discusses the basic operating principles of engine and flight instruments and many of the physical and electrical principles on which these instruments work.

Classifications of Aircraft Instruments

Aircraft instruments can be classified according to their function or their operating principles. Here, they are classified by their means of operation, and their function will be explained with each instrument.

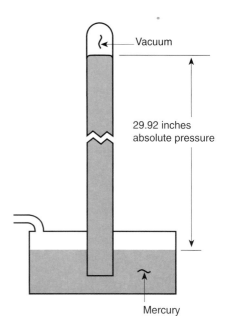

Figure 10-1. *A mercury barometer is the most accurate instrument to measure absolute pressure.*

Pressure Measuring Instruments

Pressure is the amount of force acting on a given unit of area, and all pressure must be measured from some known reference. Absolute pressure is measured from zero pressure, or a vacuum. Gage pressure is measured from the existing atmospheric pressure, and differential pressure is the difference between two pressures.

Absolute Pressure Instruments

The most accurate device for measuring absolute pressure is the mercury barometer, a glass tube about 34 inches long and one inch in diameter closed at one end and filled with mercury. Its open end is immersed in a bowl of mercury. *See* Figure 10-1. The mercury drops down in the tube and leaves an empty space, or a vacuum, above it. The weight of the air pressing down on the mercury in the bowl holds the mercury up in the tube at a height proportional to the pressure of the air. Standard atmosphere at sea level holds the mercury up in the tube until the top of the column is 29.92 inches, or 760 millimeters, above the top of the mercury in the bowl.

A mercury barometer is not a convenient instrument to carry in an aircraft, so the aneroid (no liquid) barometer has been developed. This instrument uses a sealed, evacuated, concentrically corrugated metal capsule as its pressure-sensitive mechanism.

absolute pressure. Pressure referenced from zero pressure, or a vacuum.

aneroid. The sensitive component in an altimeter or barometer that measures the absolute pressure of the air. The aneroid is a sealed, flat capsule made of thin corrugated disks of metal soldered together and evacuated by pumping all of the air out of it. Evacuating the aneroid allows it to expand or collapse as the air pressure on the outside changes.

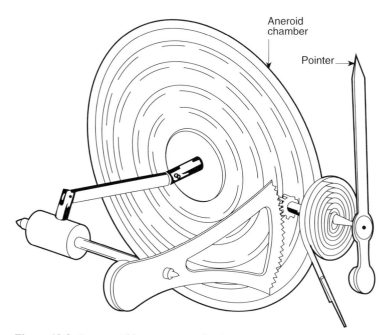

Figure 10-2. *An aneroid barometer mechanism*

The concentric corrugations provide a degree of springiness that opposes the pressure of the air. As the air pressure increases, the thickness of the capsule decreases, and as the pressure decreases, the capsule expands. A rocking shaft, sector gear, and pinion multiply the change in dimension of the capsule and drive a pointer across a calibrated dial.

rocking shaft. A shaft used in the mechanism of a pressure-measuring instrument to change the direction of movement by 90° and to amplify the amount of movement.

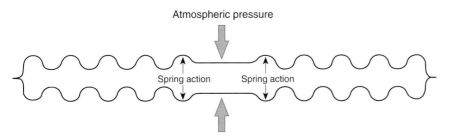

Figure 10-3. *The spring action of the corrugations opposes the pressure of the air to measure any changes in the air pressure.*

sector gear. A part of a gear wheel that contains the hub and a portion of the rim with teeth.

pinion. A small gear that meshes with a larger gear, a sector of a gear, or a toothed rack.

Absolute pressure is measured in an aircraft to determine altitude. The knob in the lower left-hand corner of the altimeter in Figure 10-4 adjusts the barometric scale in the window on the right side of the dial to set the pressure level from which the absolute pressure is referenced. The absolute pressure is expressed in feet of altitude from the referenced pressure level.

barometric scale. A small window in the dial of a sensitive altimeter in which the pilot sets the barometric pressure level from which the altitude shown on the altimeter is measured. This window is sometimes called the "Kollsman" window.

Figure 10-4. *An altimeter measures absolute pressure and displays it as feet of altitude above the pressure reference level that has been set into the barometric window.*

gage pressure. Pressure referenced from the existing atmospheric pressure.

Gage Pressure Instruments

Gage pressure is measured from the existing barometric pressure and is actually the pressure that has been added to a fluid.

A Bourdon tube is typically used to measure gage pressure. This tube is a flattened thin-wall bronze tube formed into a curve as in Figure 10-5. One end of the tube is sealed and attached through a linkage to a sector gear. The other end is connected to the instrument case through a fitting that allows the fluid to be measured to enter.

Bourdon tube. A type of pressure-indicating mechanism used in most oil pressure and hydraulic pressure gages. It consists of a sealed, curved tube with an elliptical cross section. Pressure inside the tube tries to straighten it, and as it straightens, it moves a pointer across a calibrated dial. Bourdon tube pressure gages can be used to determine temperature when they measure the pressure of a sealed container of a volatile liquid, such as methyl chloride, whose pressure varies with its temperature.

When the pressure of the fluid inside the tube increases, it tries to change the cross-sectional shape of the tube from flat to round. As the cross section changes, the curved tube tends to straighten out. This in turn moves the sector gear, which rotates the pinion gear on which the pointer is mounted.

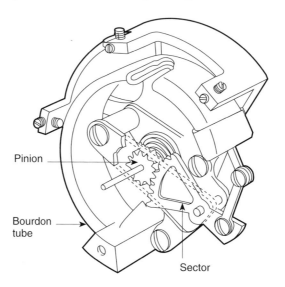

Figure 10-5. *A Bourdon tube mechanism is used to measure such gage pressures as engine lubricating oil pressure and hydraulic fluid pressure.*

Bourdon tube instruments measure relatively high pressures like those in engine lubricating systems and hydraulic systems. Lower pressures such as instrument air pressure, deicer air pressure, and suction are often measured with a bellows mechanism much like an aneroid capsule. Figure 10-6 shows this mechanism. The pressure to be measured is taken into the bellows. As the pressure increases, the bellows expands and its expansion rotates the rocking shaft and the sector gear. Movement of the sector gear rotates the pinion gear and the shaft on which the pointer is mounted.

differential pressure. The difference between two pressures. An airspeed indicator is a differential-pressure gage. It measures the difference between static air pressure and pitot air pressure.

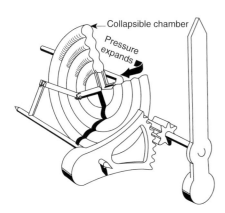

Figure 10-6. *A bellows mechanism is used to measure low gage pressures.*

Differential Pressure Instruments

A differential pressure is simply the difference between two pressures. The indication on an airspeed indicator is caused by the difference between pitot, or ram, air pressure and static, or still, air pressure. Pitot pressure is taken into the inside of the diaphragm and static pressure is taken into the sealed instrument case. As the speed of the aircraft increases, the pitot pressure increases and the diaphragm expands, rotating the rocking shaft and driving the pointer across the dial.

A differential bellows like that in Figure 10-8 is a popular instrument mechanism that can be used to measure absolute, differential, or gage pressure.

When a differential bellows is used to measure absolute pressure, as it is when used in a manifold pressure gage, one of the bellows is evacuated and sealed and the other bellows senses the pressure inside the engine intake manifold.

When used to measure differential pressure, as it is when used as a fuel pressure gage, one bellows senses the air pressure at the carburetor inlet, and the other bellows senses the fuel pressure at the carburetor fuel inlet. A differential bellows can be used to measure gage pressure by leaving one of the bellows open to the atmosphere and the other connected to the pressure to be measured.

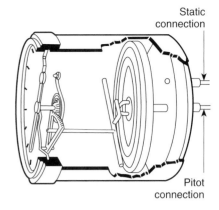

Figure 10-7. *An airspeed indicator is a differential pressure gage which measures the difference between pitot, or ram air, pressure and static, or still air, pressure. The resulting differential pressure is displayed on the dial as knots, miles per hour, or kilometers per hour.*

airspeed indicator. A flight instrument that measures the pressure differential between the pitot, or ram, air pressure and the static pressure of the air surrounding the aircraft. This differential pressure is shown in units of miles per hour, knots, or kilometers per hour.

static air pressure. Pressure of the ambient air surrounding the aircraft. Static pressure does not take into consideration any air movement.

pitot pressure. Ram air pressure used to measure airspeed. The pitot tube faces directly into the air flowing around the aircraft. It stops the air and measures its pressure.

manifold pressure gage. A pressure gage that measures the absolute pressure inside the induction system of a reciprocating engine. When the engine is not operating, this instrument shows the existing atmospheric pressure.

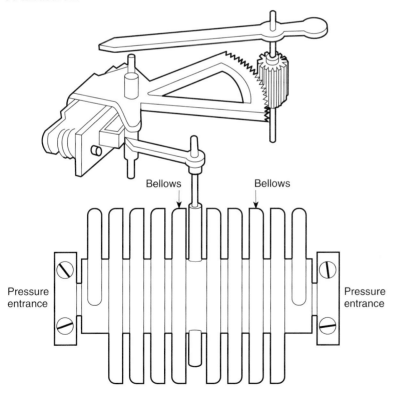

Figure 10-8. *Differential bellows mechanism that may be used to measure absolute, differential, or gage pressure*

Answers begin on Page 786. Page numbers refer to chapter text.

1. Pressure referenced from a vacuum is called _____ pressure. *Page 720*

2. An altimeter measures _____ (absolute, differential, or gage) pressure. *Page 721*

3. Pressure referenced from the existing atmospheric pressure is called _____ pressure. *Page 720*

4. Engine oil pressure is an example of _____ (absolute, differential, or gage) pressure. *Page 722*

5. A Bourdon tube instrument is used to measure _____ (absolute, differential, or gage) pressure. *Page 722*

6. Pressure that is the difference between two pressures is called _____ pressure. *Page 720*

7. The pressure measured by an airspeed indicator is _____ (absolute, differential, or gage) pressure. *Page 723*

Temperature Measuring Instruments

Pilots need to know the temperatures in aircraft that range all of the way from the low temperatures of the outside air at high altitude to the high temperatures of the engine exhausts. Three basic temperature measurement methods are discussed here: nonelectrical measurement, used for measuring outside air temperature and oil temperature in most small general aviation aircraft; resistance-change electrical instruments for measuring low temperatures; and thermocouple instruments for measuring high temperatures.

Nonelectrical Temperature Measurements

Most solids, liquids, and gases change dimensions proportional to their temperature changes. These dimensional changes may be used to move pointers across a dial to indicate changes in temperature.

Most small general aviation aircraft have an outside air temperature gage protruding through the windshield. This simple thermometer is made of strips of two metals having different coefficients of expansion welded together, side by side, and twisted into a helix, or spiral. When this bimetallic strip is heated, one strip expands more than the other and the spiral tries to straighten out. A pointer is attached to the metal strip in such a way that, as the temperature changes, the pointer moves across a dial to indicate the temperature.

helix. A screw-like, or spiral, curve.

Liquids also change their dimensions as their temperature changes. The most common example of this is the glass-tube mercury thermometer often used in chemistry and physics laboratories and as home fever thermometers. These thermometers are simply thick-wall glass tubes that have a small reservoir on one end and a precision small-diameter bore through the entire length of the tube. The reservoir holds a supply of mercury that extends part-way up into the bore. When the temperature of the reservoir changes, the mercury expands or contracts, and its top end moves up or down against graduated marks that are engraved into the glass tube. Because of their delicacy, mercury thermometers find no practical use as aircraft instruments.

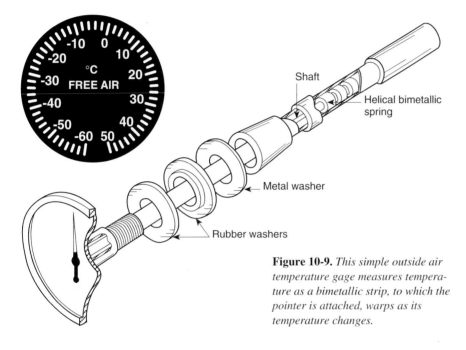

Figure 10-9. *This simple outside air temperature gage measures temperature as a bimetallic strip, to which the pointer is attached, warps as its temperature changes.*

Temperature is also determined by measuring the pressure of the vapors above a highly volatile liquid. The vapor pressure varies directly as the temperature of the liquid.

A Bourdon tube is connected to a thin-wall, hollow metal bulb by a capillary tube. This is a length of copper tubing that has a very small inside diameter. The bulb is filled with a volatile liquid such as methyl chloride which has a high vapor pressure, and the entire bulb, capillary, and Bourdon tube are sealed as a unit. The bulb is placed where the temperature is to be measured and, as its temperature changes, the pressure of the vapors above the liquid changes. This pressure change is sensed by the Bourdon tube, which moves a pointer across a dial that is calibrated in degrees Fahrenheit or Celsius.

capillary tube. A soft copper tube with a small inside diameter. The capillary tube used with a vapor-pressure thermometer connects the temperature sensing bulb to the Bourdon tube. The capillary tube is protected from physical damage by enclosing it in a braided metal wire jacket.

Electrical Temperature Measurements

Two principles are used to measure temperature electrically, resistance change and voltage generation. The resistance of certain metals changes with their temperature, and this principle is used to measure relatively low temperatures such as oil temperature, outside air temperature, and carburetor air temperature. The voltage generation, or thermocouple principle, is used for measuring higher temperatures such as cylinder-head temperature and exhaust-gas temperature of both reciprocating and turbine engines.

Resistance-Change Instruments

A length of fine nickel wire wound around an insulator and enclosed in a thin-wall stainless steel tube serves as the pickup for resistance-change thermometers. The resistance of the wire in this bulb changes from approximately 30 ohms at -70°F to 130 ohms at 300°F.

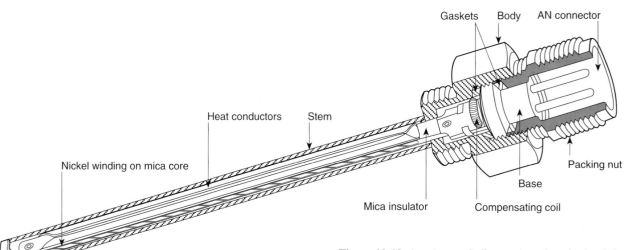

Figure 10-10. *A resistance bulb contains a length of nickel wire whose resistance changes linearly with changes in its temperature.*

The resistance of the bulb is measured by either a Wheatstone bridge circuit like the one in Figure 10-11 or ratiometer circuits like those in Figures 10-12 and 10-13.

Wheatstone Bridge Circuit

Some resistance thermometers measure temperature changes by placing the bulb in one of the legs of a Wheatstone bridge, as in Figure 10-11.

The bridge is balanced and no current flows through the indicator when the ratio $R_1 : R_3$ is the same as the ratio of $R_2 : R_{Bulb}$. As the temperature sensed by the bulb decreases, the bulb resistance decreases and the bridge unbalances, sending current through the indicator that drives the needle toward the low side of the dial. An increase in temperature increases the bulb resistance and drives the indicator needle toward the high side of the dial.

Ratiometer Circuits

There are two types of ratiometer circuits for measuring temperatures: moving-coil and moving-magnet ratiometers.

The moving-coil ratiometer in Figure 10-12 uses an instrument with two coils mounted on the indicator needle as seen in illustration A. The electrical circuit for this instrument is shown in illustration B. When the temperature is low and the bulb resistance is low, more current flows through coil 1 and the bulb than flows through coil 2 and resistor R_1. The resulting magnetic field pulls the needle toward the low side of the dial. When the temperature is high, the bulb resistance is high, and more current flows through coil 2 and R_1 than through coil 1 and the bulb, and the needle deflects toward the high side of the dial.

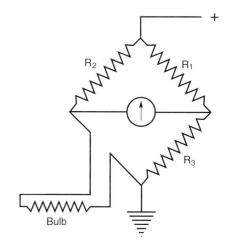

Figure 10-11. *A Wheatstone bridge circuit used to measure temperature*

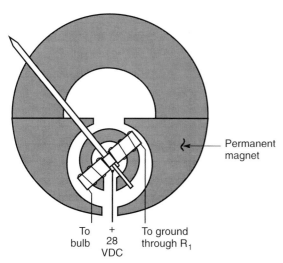

A Indicator has two coils mounted on its needle. These coils rotate over C-shaped core inside the strong magnetic field of the permanent magnet.

Figure 10-12. *A moving-coil ratiometer*

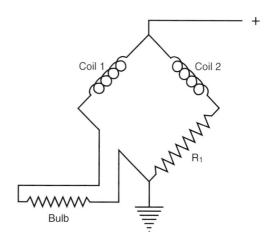

B Basic electrical circuit of the moving-coil ratiometer

thermocouple. A loop consisting of two kinds of wire, joined at the hot, or measuring, junction and at the cold junction in the instrument. The voltage difference between the two junctions is proportional to the temperature difference between the junctions. In order for the current to be meaningful, the resistance of the thermocouple is critical, and the leads are designed for a specific installation. Their length should not be altered. Thermocouples used to measure cylinder head temperature are usually made of iron and constantan, and thermocouples that measure exhaust gas temperature for turbine engines are made of chromel and alumel.

A moving-magnet ratiometer has its needle attached to a small permanent magnet that is influenced by the magnetic fields of two fixed coils arranged like those in Figure 10-13A.

Follow the circuit in Figure 10-13B to see the way this instrument measures temperature. When the temperature is low and the bulb resistance is low, more current flows through resistor A, the low-end coil, and the bulb, than flows through resistors A, E, and D. The magnetic field from the low-end coil pulls the needle on the permanent magnet toward the low side of the dial. When the temperature and the resistance of the bulb increase, current flows through resistors B, C, the high-end coil, and resistor D. The resulting magnetic field from the high-end coil moves the needle toward the high side of the dial.

Notice that this instrument can be used in either a 14-volt or a 28-volt aircraft depending upon the pin in the indicator to which the power is connected. A dropping resistor lowers the voltage if the instrument is used in a 28-volt aircraft.

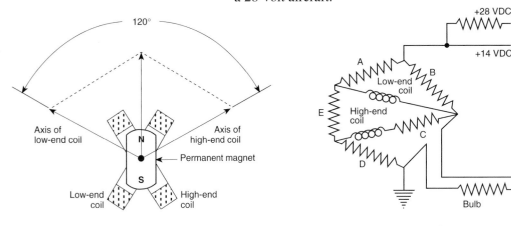

A Indicator has two fixed coils whose magnetic fields determine position of a small permanent magnet to which indicator needle is attached.

B Basic electrical circuit of a moving-magnet ratiometer

Figure 10-13. *A moving-magnet ratiometer*

Thermocouple Instruments

Cylinder head temperature for reciprocating engines and exhaust gas temperature for both reciprocating and turbine engines are measured with thermocouple instruments. These instruments do not require any external power, since a thermocouple is an electrical generator.

A thermocouple used for measuring cylinder head temperature is a loop made of two different types of wire, as in Figure 10-14. One wire is made of constantan, a copper-nickel alloy, and the other wire is made of iron. One end

constantan. A copper-nickel alloy used as the negative lead of a thermocouple for measuring the cylinder head temperature of a reciprocating engine.

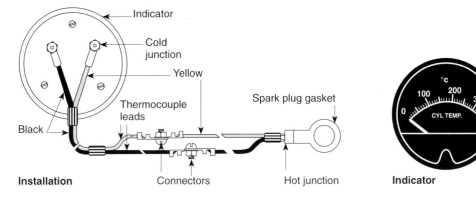

Installation **Connectors** **Hot junction** **Indicator**

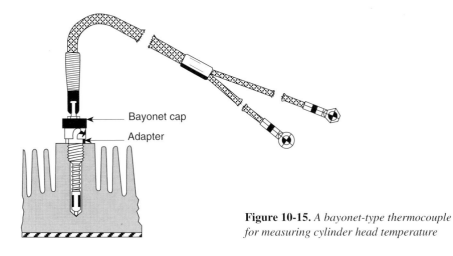

Figure 10-14. *A typical cylinder head temperature indicator installation using a spark plug gasket as the hot, or measuring, junction*

of each wire is embedded in a copper spark-plug gasket or is joined inside a bayonet like that in Figure 10-15. This end of the loop is called the hot, or measuring, junction. The other ends of the wires are connected to the instrument movement to form the cold, or reference, junction. A voltage is produced between the two junctions that is proportional to the temperature difference between the junctions. This voltage causes current to flow, and this current is measured on the indicator that is calibrated in degrees Celsius or degrees Fahrenheit.

Since the indicator is a current-measuring instrument, the resistance of the thermocouple leads must have a specific value. These leads usually have a resistance of either two or eight ohms, and their length must not be altered to suit the installation. If they are too long they may be coiled neatly so they will not cause any mechanical interference. If the resistance is too low, a special constantan-wire resistor may be installed in the negative lead.

For accurate temperature indication, the reference-junction temperature must be held constant. It is not practical to do this in an aircraft instrument, so the indicator needle is mounted on a bimetallic hairspring in such a way that it moves back as the cockpit temperature increases. This compensates for reference-junction temperature changes.

Figure 10-15. *A bayonet-type thermocouple for measuring cylinder head temperature*

Higher temperatures, like those found in the exhaust gases of both reciprocating and turbine engines, are measured with thermocouples made of chromel and alumel wires. Chromel is an alloy of nickel and chromium and is used as the positive element in the thermocouple. Alumel is an alloy of nickel, aluminum, manganese, and silicon and is used as the negative element. Figure 10-16 shows a typical exhaust gas temperature system for a reciprocating engine. The thermocouple is mounted in the exhaust pipe, usually within about six inches of the cylinder.

The indicator is a current-measuring instrument similar to that used for measuring cylinder head temperature. *See* Figure 10-16.

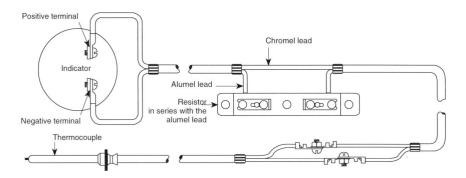

Figure 10-16. *A typical exhaust gas temperature indication system for installation on a reciprocating engine*

The exhaust gas temperature (EGT) system for a turbine engine is similar to that for a reciprocating engine except that several thermocouples are used. These are arranged around the tail cone so they can sample the temperature in several locations. These indications are averaged to give one indication that is the average temperature of the gases leaving the turbine. Figure 10-17 shows a typical circuit for a turbine engine EGT system.

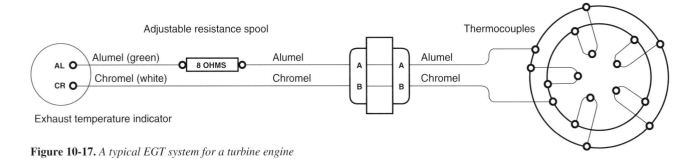

Figure 10-17. *A typical EGT system for a turbine engine*

Answers begin on Page 786. Page numbers refer to chapter text.

8. A bimetallic-strip thermometer measures temperature because the two strips of metals have different coefficients of _____ . *Page 724*

9. A Bourdon tube thermometer measures temperature by measuring the pressure of the _____ of a volatile liquid. *Page 725*

10. The temperature-sensitive element in a resistance thermometer is a coil made of _____ wire. *Page 726*

11. As the temperature sensed by a resistance bulb increases, the resistance of the bulb _____ (increases or decreases). *Page 726*

12. Thermocouples used for measuring cylinder head temperature are usually made of _____ and _____ . *Page 728*

13. Most cylinder head temperature and exhaust gas temperature gages are _____ (current or voltage) measuring instruments. *Page 729*

14. The thermocouple junction formed by the instrument movement of a cylinder head temperature gage is the _____ (measuring or reference) junction. *Page 729*

15. Thermocouples used for measuring exhaust gas temperature are usually made of _____ and _____ . *Page 730*

16. The negative lead in an EGT thermocouple is made of _____ . *Page 730*

Mechanical Movement Measuring Instruments

Instruments that measure mechanical movement include all of the position-indicating lights as well as remote-indicating synchro systems. This section also discusses such devices as tachometers and accelerometers.

Position-Indicating Lights

There are a number of indications in an aircraft for which the only information needed is a simple yes or no. The flight crew needs to know if the landing gear is down and locked or if it is not down and locked, and if the cabin door is closed and locked or if it is not closed and locked. This information can be generated and displayed by simple switches and lights.

Microswitch. The registered trade name for a precision switch that uses a short throw of the control plunger to actuate the contacts. Microswitches are used primarily as limit switches to control electrical units automatically.

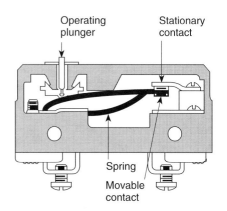

Figure 10-18. *A typical precision switch used to indicate that some device is in a specific position*

synchro system. A remote instrument indicating system. A synchro transmitter is actuated by the device whose movement is to be measured, and it is connected electrically with wires to a synchro indicator whose pointer follows the movement of the shaft of the transmitter.

Selsyn system. A synchro system used in remote indicating instruments. The rotor in the indicator is a permanent magnet and the stator is a tapped toroidal coil. The transmitter is a circular potentiometer with DC power fed into its wiper. The transmitter is connected to the indicator in such a way that rotation of the transmitter shaft varies the current in the indicator toroidal coil. The magnet in the indicator follows the rotation of the transmitter shaft.

Precision switches, often called Microswitches after the trade name of the most popular manufacturer, detect a specific position of the item being measured. Figure 10-18 shows a typical precision switch. The operating plunger must be in a very specific position for the contacts to snap to their opposite condition. One switch can be placed on each of the three landing gears in such a way that their plunger will close the contacts only when each gear is fully down and correctly locked.

The down-and-locked position of the three landing gears may close switches that are in series. The indicator light will turn on only when all three switches are closed. In more modern installations, a signal may be sent from the three switches to a three-input AND gate circuit. When all three landing gears are down and locked, a signal at the output of the AND gate will cause a light to show that they are all down and locked.

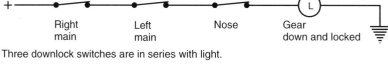

Three downlock switches are in series with light.

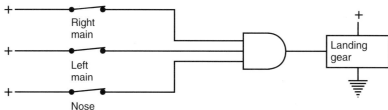

Electronic indicator is actuated by three switches connected to three inputs of an AND gate. Light on annunciator panel will illuminate only when all three gears are down and locked.

Figure 10-19. *A simplified diagram of a position indicating system that turns on a light only when all three landing gears are down and locked*

Synchro Systems

A synchro system is a remote-indicating system in which the needle of an indicator moves in synchronization with the device whose movement is being monitored. There are three commonly used systems: the DC Selsyn system, the AC Magnesyn system, and the AC Autosyn system.

DC Selsyn System

A typical DC Selsyn system like that used to measure such movements as cowl flap position or stabilizer position is shown in Figure 10-20. A coil of resistance wire is wound around a circular form, and two wipers are driven by the device whose movement is being measured. One of the two wipers has a positive DC potential and the other is at ground potential. Current from these two wipers flows through the resistance element and then to the three coils inside the indicator. These coils are connected into a delta arrangement. As the wipers move over the resistance element, the current through the three coils changes and produces a moving magnetic field. A permanent magnet inside the coils locks with this field and rotates as the field changes. The pointer attached to the magnet moves across a calibrated dial to follow the movement being measured. The two wiper arms may be moved in relation to each other to adjust the position of the pointer on the dial when the device being measured is at either end of its travel.

delta connection. A method of connecting three electrical coils into a ring or, as they are drawn on a schematic diagram as a triangle, a delta (Δ).

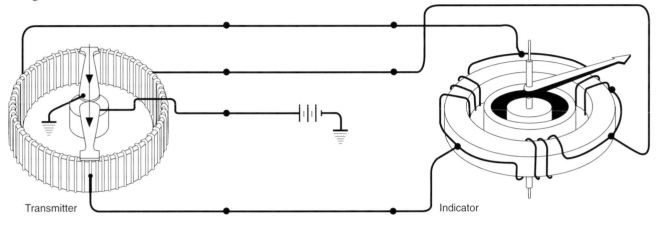

Figure 10-20. *A typical DC Selsyn system used to measure such mechanical movement as that of engine cowl flaps*

AC Magnesyn System

The Magnesyn (Magnetic Synchro) system is an AC remote-indicating system that uses permanent magnets for the moving elements and toroidal coils wound on highly permeable ring-type cores for the stationary elements.

   The toroidal coils in the transmitter and indicator are tapped at two points and are connected as shown in Figure 10-21 (Page 734). The ends of the coils are excited with 26-volt, 400-Hz AC. A permanent magnet mounted on a shaft is free to rotate in the center of the coil. The magnet in the transmitter is driven by the device whose movement is to be measured, and the needle of the indicator is mounted on the shaft of the magnet in the indicator coil.

   When no current is flowing in the coils, the flux from the permanent magnets flows through the ring-shaped cores surrounding them. But when current is flowing through the coils, the cores become magnetically saturated so they can no longer accept the flux from the permanent magnets. The coils are excited with 26-volt, 400-Hz AC so the cores become saturated and then demagnetized 800 times a second. This causes the flux from the permanent magnets to cut across the windings each time the flux from the AC in the

Magnesyn system. A synchro system used in remote indicating instruments. The rotors in a Magnesyn system are permanent magnets, and the stators are tapped toroidal coils, excited with 26-volt, 400-hertz AC. The rotor in the indicator will exactly follow the movement of the rotor in the transmitter.

toroidal coil. An electrical coil that is wound around a ring-shaped core of highly permeable material.

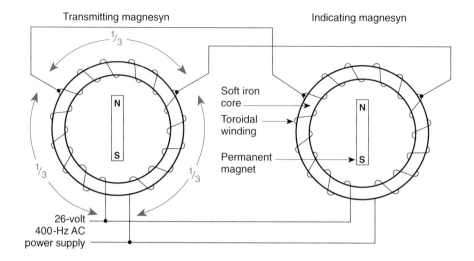

Figure 10-21. *A simplified circuit of a Magnesyn remote position indicating system*

windings drops through zero. The flux from the permanent magnets induces a voltage in the coils that causes a current to flow in the three segments of the coils. This current varies with the position of the magnets.

The magnet in the transmitter is considerably larger than that in the indicator, and the voltage it induces causes the small permanent magnet in the indicator to follow its movement.

One of the popular applications of the Magnesyn system is the Magnesyn remote-indicating compass. The compass transmitter is mounted in the wing or tail of the aircraft away from any interfering magnetic fields. This transmitter consists of a metal float, housing a rather large permanent magnet. The float rides inside a plastic housing that is filled with a damping liquid, and the toroidal coil is mounted on the outside of the housing. The magnet remains aligned with the earth's magnetic field, and as the airplane rotates around it, the current in the indicator coils changes, and the small permanent magnet in the indicator to which the pointer is attached retains its relationship with the magnet in the transmitter. The pointer attached to the magnet shaft rides over a calibrated dial to indicate the compass heading of the aircraft.

AC Autosyn System

The Autosyn (Automatic Synchro) system is used for many of the same purposes as the Magnesyn system, but it uses an electromagnet for its rotor. The Autosyn system, seen in Figure 10-22, uses delta-wound, distributed-pole, three-phase stators and single-phase rotors. The rotors are excited with 26-volt, 400-Hz AC. The AC in the rotor induces a voltage in the three-phase windings of the stator, and since the two stators are connected together in parallel, the voltages in the three stator windings of the indicator are exactly the same as those in the transmitter. The rotor in the transmitter is moved by

Autosyn system. A synchro system used in remote indicating instruments. The rotors in an Autosyn system are two-pole electromagnets, and the stators are delta-connected, three-phase, distributed-pole windings in the stator housings. The rotors in the transmitters and indicators are connected in parallel and are excited with 26-volt, 400-hertz AC. The rotor in the indicator follows the movement of the rotor in the transmitter.

the object whose movement is being measured, and as it moves, the magnetic field it induces in the three windings of the transmitter stator changes. The current in the indicator stator windings is the same as that in the transmitter stator, and the magnetic field it produces causes the rotor in the indicator to follow the rotor in the transmitter.

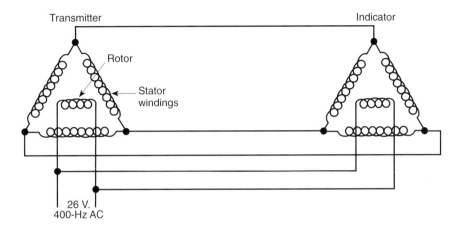

Figure 10-22. *A simplified circuit of an Autosyn remote position indicating system*

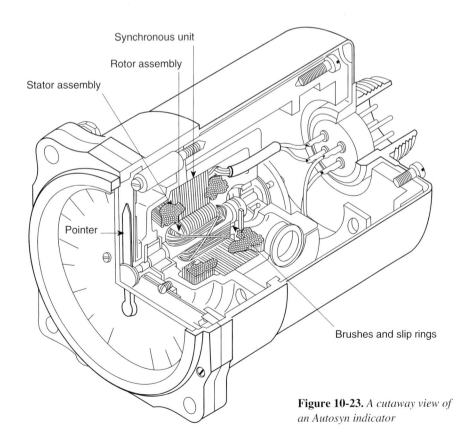

Figure 10-23. *A cutaway view of an Autosyn indicator*

Tachometers

One of the earliest aircraft instruments was a tachometer, used to let the pilot know the RPMs of the engine. Today, tachometers are required instruments in all powered aircraft, and their indications allow the pilots to monitor the performance of the engines. Tachometers for reciprocating engines indicate the engine speed in RPM times 100. Turbine-engine tachometers indicate the compressor speed in percent of the rated RPM.

The earliest tachometers were centrifugal instruments that used the same principle as the governors for steam engines. During World War II, a popular tachometer used a rather complicated clockwork mechanism that momentarily coupled a shaft from the engine directly to the indicating needle about once a second.

The mechanism in some modern mechanical tachometers resembles automobile speedometers, and the most popular electrical tachometer is based on a three-phase synchronous motor. New technology tachometers are digital electronic devices that count pulses from a tachometer generator or from the reciprocating-engine ignition system and display the engine speed in a digital format.

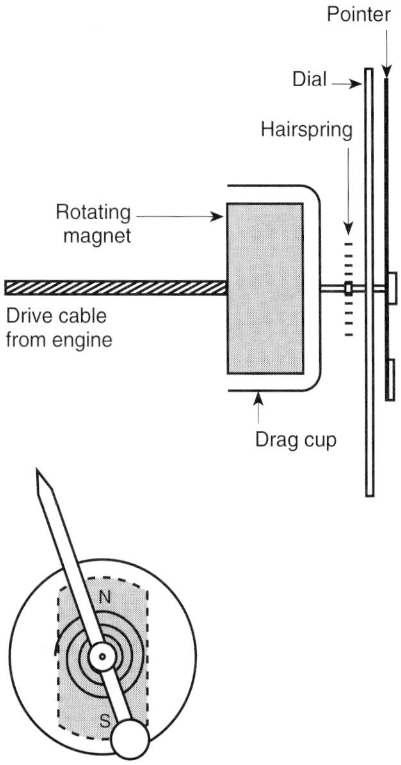

Mechanical Tachometer

The most widely used tachometer for smaller reciprocating engines is of the magnetic drag type. *See* Figure 10-24. A relatively small permanent magnet inside the instrument case is driven by a steel cable from the engine at one-half the crankshaft speed. Riding on the outside of this magnet, but not touching it, is an aluminum drag cup. A steel shaft attached to the outside center of this cup rides in bearings in the instrument so it is free to rotate. The instrument pointer is attached to this shaft and its rotation is restrained by a calibrated hairspring.

When the engine is operating, the magnet is spinning inside the instrument. As it spins, its lines of flux cut across the aluminum drag cup and induce an eddy current in it. This current produces a magnetic field which interacts with that of the rotating magnet and tries to drive the drag cup. But rotation of the cup is restrained by the calibrated hairspring so it rotates only a portion of a revolution. The pointer on the shaft moves in front of a dial that is marked in RPM times 100 to indicate the speed of the crankshaft.

This type of tachometer is mounted inside a steel case that prevents the magnetic flux produced by the rotating magnet from interfering with other instruments in the panel.

Most magnetic drag tachometers have an hourmeter built into them that is the counterpart to the odometer on an automobile speedometer. A series of drums with numbers on their outer surfaces are turned by a worm gear from the magnet drive shaft. The numbers on these drums indicate the number of hours the engine has run. The hours indication is derived from a shaft whose number of revolutions in a given time is a function of the speed of the engine. Because of this, the hours indication is accurate only at the cruise RPM of the

Figure 10-24. *A simplified diagram of a mechanically operated magnetic drag tachometer.*

RPM. Revolutions per minute.

engine. When replacing a magnetic drag tachometer, be sure to use one that is designed for the cruise RPM of the engine whose speed it is measuring. This RPM is stamped on the instrument case. The hours indication on this type of tachometer is normally considered sufficiently accurate for measuring inspection intervals and total engine operating time.

Magnetic drag tachometers are not known for their accuracy, and since engine RPM is extremely important, the tachometer indication should be checked with a stroboscopic tachometer any time there is reason to doubt the accuracy of the instrument.

Electric Tachometer

In the past, electric tachometers have used either an AC or DC permanent-magnet generator driven at one-half crankshaft speed. The voltage of these generators is proportional to their RPM, and this voltage was measured and displayed as RPM on the dial of a voltmeter. This system is limited because its accuracy depends on the strength of the permanent magnet in the generator, and this strength deteriorates with time.

A much more accurate system uses a three-phase permanent magnet generator on the engine that drives a small synchronous motor inside the indicator case. This motor in turn drives a magnet assembly and a drag disk such as the one in Figure 10-25. The drag disk, with its calibrated hairspring and pointer, operates in exactly the same way as the drag cup in the mechanical tachometer. This instrument is inherently accurate, as the frequency of the generator is determined only by the RPM of the engine, and variations of the strength of the generator magnet have little or no effect on the accuracy.

stroboscopic tachometer. A tachometer used to measure the speed of any rotating device without physical contact. A highly accurate variable-frequency oscillator triggers a high-intensity strobe light. When the lamp is flashing at the same frequency the device is rotating, the device appears to stand still.

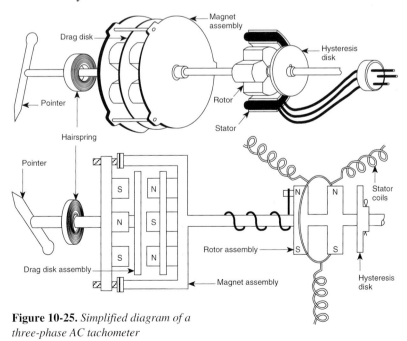

Figure 10-25. *Simplified diagram of a three-phase AC tachometer*

Synchroscopes

Some tachometers designed for use on multi-engine aircraft have synchroscopes built into them. These instruments simply show a small disk in a cutout on the instrument dial. This disk is marked with light- and dark-colored segments so it is easy to see when it is turning. The disk is driven by two synchronous motor windings on its shaft, and these windings are excited by the output of the two engine tachometer generators. When the engines are turning at the same speed, the torque produced by the two windings cancel, and the disk remains still. But when one engine is turning faster than the other, one set of windings puts out more torque than the other and the disk rotates in the direction of the faster engine. The speed of rotation is one half of the difference in the speed of the two engines.

Accelerometers

In high-performance flight, it is often important to know the dynamic load acting on the aircraft. This load is a function of the force of acceleration and is indicated on an accelerometer in G units (gravity units).

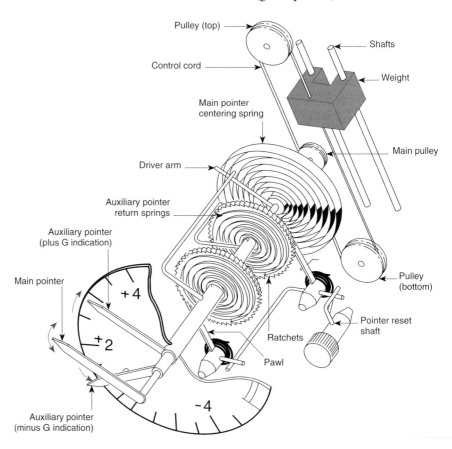

Figure 10-26. *An accelerometer gives the pilot an indication of the dynamic load acting on the aircraft.*

angle of attack. The acute angle between the chord line of the wing and the relative wind.

angle-of-attack indicator. An instrument that measures the angle between the local airflow around the direction detector and the fuselage reference plane.

The accelerometer mechanism shown in Figure 10-26 has a small lead weight that rides up and down on two polished steel shafts. When the aircraft is sitting still on the ground or is flying in smooth, straight, and level flight, the pointer-centering spring holds all three pointers pointing to 1G on the dial. This indicates that one force of gravity is acting on the aircraft. When the aircraft is pulled up sharply in flight, inertia acting on the weight pulls it down, and the main pointer and the +G pointers indicate a positive acceleration. When the aircraft returns to straight and level flight, the +G auxiliary pointer remains at the maximum positive acceleration and the main pointer returns to 1G. When the pilot forces the nose down suddenly, the weight moves up and the main and -G pointers move to indicate the negative acceleration. On return to straight and level flight, the -G pointer remains at the maximum negative acceleration and the main pointer returns to 1G. The two auxiliary pointers may be reset to 1G by pushing in the reset knob on the front of the instrument. This releases the pawls that hold the ratchets on the two auxiliary pointer shafts, and the auxiliary pointer-return springs return the pointers to 1G.

Angle of Attack Indicating Systems

The lift produced by an aircraft wing is a function of the air density and velocity, the size of the wing and shape of the airfoil, and the angle of attack. For many years the main instrument for indicating the approach to a stall has been the airspeed indicator. But this instrument does not tell the whole story. A stall can occur at any airspeed, but it can occur at only one angle of attack. For this reason, many airplanes have angle of attack indicators that allow them to safely fly at high angles of attack.

Small general aviation airplanes such as those used for training have very simple indicators. One of the very simplest is an aural-type indicator. There is a hole at a very specific location in the leading edge of the wing near the root. Inside the wing, attached to this hole, is a reed that vibrates and makes a sound when air flows through it from inside the wing outward. When the angle of attack is low, air flows into this hole, and the reed does not vibrate. But when the angle of attack is high enough to warn of an impending stall, the air flows across the hole and creates a low pressure that draws air from inside the wing. As the air flows through the reed, it produces a sound loud enough to warn the pilot of an impending stall.

A more popular type of stall-warning device uses a small metal tab protruding from the leading edge of the wing at the stagnation point. This is the point at which the airflow separates into some flowing over the top of the wing and the rest below the wing. At low angles of attack, the air holds the tab down, but when the angle of attack increases, the stagnation point moves down, and as the wing approaches a stall, the air flows upward over the tab and raises it. This closes an electrical switch that turns on a stall warning light on the instrument panel.

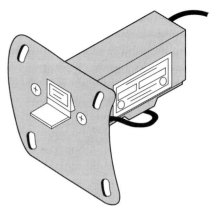

Stall-warning transmitter as it is installed in the leading edge of the wing

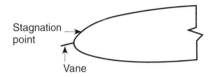

At low angles of attack, tab is below stagnation point and air holds it down, holding switch open.

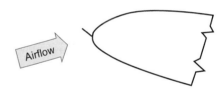

As angle of attack increases to point that a stall could occur, the stagnation point moves down, causing air to flow upward. This raises tab, closes switch and initiates a stall warning signal.

Figure 10-27. *A tab-type stall-warning indicator*

stagnation point. The point on the leading edge of a wing at which the airflow separates, with some flowing over the top of the wing and the rest below the wing.

For true precision flying, an angle of attack system as shown in Figure 10-28 may be installed. In this system the probe is installed so that it senses the direction of the airflow relative to a fuselage reference plane. As the angle of attack changes, relative amounts of air flowing into the two slots in the probe change. This causes the pressure inside the chambers formed by the upper and lower halves of the paddle to change. When the paddle moves, it moves the wiper of a potentiometer, which causes the pointer in the indicator to move over its dial to indicate the actual angle of attack.

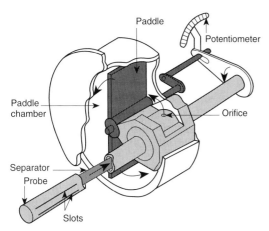

The airstream-direction detector senses the angle of attack the aircraft is flying by the pressure differential inside the paddle chamber.

The angle of attack indicator shows the actual angle of attack being flown.

Figure 10-28. *An angle of attack indicating system*

STUDY QUESTIONS: MECHANICAL MOVEMENT MEASURING INSTRUMENTS

Answers begin on Page 786. Page numbers refer to chapter text.

17. A three-input digital logic AND gate can be used in a position indicating system to give the same information as three switches installed in _____ (series or parallel). *Page 732*

18. The moving element in the pickup for a DC Selsyn system is the wiper of a/an _____ . *Page 732*

19. The moving element in the indicator of a DC Selsyn system is a/an _____ . *Page 733*

20. The moving element in the transmitter for an AC Magnesyn system is a/an _____ . *Page 734*

21. The coil used in an AC Magnesyn system is a _____-wound coil. *Page 734*

22. The coil used in an AC Magnesyn system is tapped so it has _____ (how many) sections. *Page 734*

23. The moving element in the transmitter for an AC Autosyn system is a/an _____ . *Page 734*

24. The rotor of an AC Autosyn system has a _____ (single or three) -phase winding. *Page 734*

25. The stator of an AC Autosyn system has a _____ (single or three) -phase winding. *Page 734*

26. The Magnesyn and Autosyn remote indicating systems both are excited with _____-volt, _____-hertz AC. *Page 734*

27. The tachometer for a reciprocating engine gives the engine speed in RPM times _____ . *Page 736*

28. The magnetic drag tachometer measures engine RPM by the interaction of the magnetic field of the rotating permanent magnet and the field produced by _____ in the aluminum drag cup. *Page 736*

29. Most magnetic drag tachometers are mounted in cases made of _____ (steel or plastic). *Page 736*

30. Three-phase AC tachometers measure engine speed by the _____ (voltage or frequency) of the AC they produce. *Page 737*

31. An instrument that shows the pilot or flight engineer the difference in the speeds of the engines in a multi-engine aircraft is called a/an _____ . *Page 738*

32. The dynamic load acting on an aircraft in flight is indicated on an accelerometer in _____ units. *Page 738*

33. An accelerometer in an airplane that is not moving will indicate _____ (0G or 1G). *Page 739*

34. The airspeed of an airplane _____ (is or is not) always an indication of an impending stall. *Page 739*

35. The most accurate stall warning systems measure the _____ . *Page 740*

36. Angle of attack indicating systems for high-performance aircraft sense the direction of the airflow over the aircraft relative to the fuselage _____ . *Page 740*

Direction-Indicating Instruments

All certificated aircraft are required to have some type of magnetic direction indicator. The magnetic compass is one of the simplest of all instruments and is one of the oldest. The origin of the magnetic compass dates back to the early sea peoples who discovered that a piece of lodestone, when suspended in the air or floated on a chip of wood, would always point toward the North Star. The simple concept of the magnetic compass has not changed since these early days, and the physical appearance of the aircraft compass has changed very little over the decades. Modern navigation systems have relegated the magnetic compass to a backup status, but its familiar face is present even in jet transport aircraft with their panels full of exotic electronic displays.

The earth is a huge permanent magnet, with magnetic north and south poles located near, but not at, the geographic poles. The magnets in a magnetic compass align with the earth's field and serve as a directional reference for the pilot.

The magnets are attached to the bottom of a metal float suspended on a pivot riding in a cup-shaped jewel in a bowl of compass fluid. Mounted around the float is a ring-shaped dial, called a card, marked with the directions. The four cardinal compass points are marked with the letters N, E, S, and W, and there are marks every five degrees. The alternate marks, which represent 10-degree increments, are longer than the 5-degree marks. Every 30-degree mark has the value of the heading marked above it with the last zero omitted.

A glass lens is mounted in the front of the instrument, and a straight vertical marker, called a lubber line, allows the pilot to relate the heading of the aircraft to the specific degree mark on the card.

lodestone. A magnetized piece of natural iron oxide.

cardinal compass points. The four principal directions on a compass: North, East, South, and West.

lubber line. A reference on a magnetic compass and directional gyro that represents the nose of the aircraft. The heading of the aircraft is shown on the compass card opposite the lubber line.

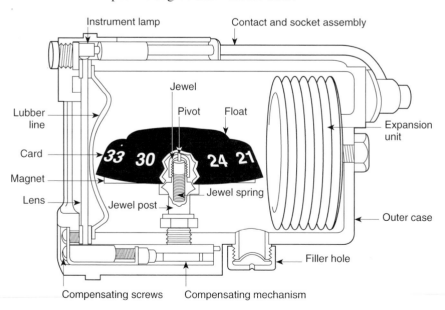

Figure 10-29. *A cutaway view of a direct-reading magnetic compass*

The compass is filled with compass fluid, a highly refined petroleum product similar to kerosine. This fluid damps the oscillations of the compass card. Since the bowl is completely full of fluid, a diaphragm or bellows assembly like the one in Figure 10-29 must compensate for changes in volume of the fluid as its temperature changes.

compass fluid. A highly refined, water-clear petroleum product similar to kerosine. Compass fluid is used to damp the oscillations of magnetic compasses.

Compass Errors

The magnetic compass requires no electrical power, and needs no other components to function. But it has three basic errors to be aware of: variation, deviation, and dip errors.

Variation

The magnetic compass error caused by the fact that the earth's magnetic and geographic poles are not at the same location is called variation error. In land navigation, this is called declination error.

The compass magnets always align with the earth's magnetic field, and the lines of force of this field leave the earth at its magnetic north pole and return at its magnetic south pole. All aeronautical charts are drawn with reference to the earth's geographic north and south poles. Since the magnetic and geographic poles are not at the same physical location, the compass indication cannot be used directly with an aeronautical chart.

Aeronautical charts have isogonic lines drawn across them, and anywhere along a given isogonic line, there is a specific angular difference between the magnetic north pole and the geographic pole. For example, along the 15° east isogonic line that passes roughly through Denver, Colorado, the compass points to a location that is 15° east of the geographic north pole. When a pilot flying in the area of Denver wants to fly due east (090°), he or she must subtract this 15° and fly a magnetic course of 075°.

There is one line along which magnetic and geographic poles are in alignment. This is called the agonic line and it runs roughly through Chicago, Illinois. *See* Figure 10-30. East of the agonic line, the compass points to a location that is west of true north and the variation must be added to the true direction to find the magnetic course. The variation error is the same regardless of the heading the aircraft is flown, but it varies with the location on the earth's surface, and it continually changes. These changes, while small, are great enough that the position of the isogonic lines are redrawn on aeronautical charts each time the charts are revised.

isogonic line. A line drawn on an aeronautical chart along which the angular difference between the magnetic and geographic north poles is the same.

agonic line. A line drawn on an aeronautical chart along which there is no angular difference between the magnetic and geographic north poles.

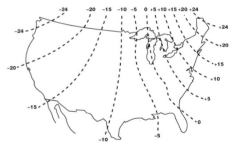

Figure 10-30. *Isogonic lines of equal compass variation*

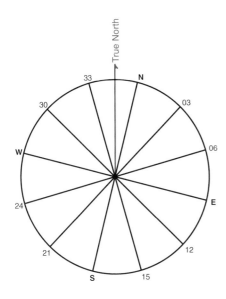

Figure 10-31. *Compass roses are laid out on many airports to be used to swing magnetic compasses.*

compass rose. A location on an airport where an aircraft can be taken to have its compasses "swung." Lines are painted on the rose to mark the magnetic directions in 30° increments.

compass swinging. A maintenance procedure that corrects a magnetic compass for deviation error. The aircraft is aligned on a compass rose, and the compensating magnets in the compass case are adjusted to get the compass to align with the direction marked on the rose. After the deviation error is minimized on all headings, a compass correction card is completed and mounted on the instrument panel next to the compass.

deviation error. An error in a magnetic compass caused by localized magnetic fields in the aircraft. Deviation error, which is different on each heading, is compensated by the technician "swinging" the compass. A compass must be compensated so the deviation error on any heading is no greater than 10 degrees.

Deviation

The floating magnets in a compass are affected not only by the earth's magnetic field, but by all other magnetic fields near them. They align with the composite field produced by the earth's field and the magnetic influence of steel structural members, current-carrying wires, and steel instrument cases. The effect of this composite field varies with the heading of the aircraft, and a correction must be made by the pilot for each different heading flown. Deviation error is minimized by two small permanent magnets inside the compensating mechanism in the compass.

Many airports have a compass rose on which an airplane is placed to swing the compass to minimize the deviation error. The compass rose is usually painted on a taxi strip well away from any magnetic interference caused by electrical power lines or buried pipes. The north-south line is aligned exactly magnetic north and south, and intersecting lines are laid out every 30°. *See* Figure 10-31.

A compass is "swung," to compensate it for deviation error, by following these steps:

1. Taxi the airplane onto the compass rose and align it along the north-south line, pointing north. Leave the engine running at a speed that allows the alternator to produce current.

2. Using a nonmagnetic screwdriver, turn the N-S compensating screw seen in Figure 10-32 until the compass reads N (360°).

3. Move the airplane until it aligns with the east-west line, pointed east. Adjust the E-W compensating screw until the compass reads E (090°).

4. Move the airplane until it aligns with the north-south line, pointed south. Adjust the N-S screw to remove one half of the N-S error. Record the compass indication with the radio off and again with it on.

5. Move the airplane until it aligns with the east-west line, pointed west. Adjust the E-W screw to remove one half of the E-W error. Record the compass indication with the radio off and again with it on.

6. Move the airplane until it aligns with the 300° line and record the compass indication with the radio both off and on.

7. Continue to move the airplane until it aligns with each line in the compass rose and record the compass indications with the radio both off and on.

8. Make a compass correction card similar to the one in Figure 10-33.

There should be no compass error greater than 10° on any heading. If there is an error greater than this, the cause must be found and corrected. Some part of the structure may have to be demagnetized, some equipment may have to be moved, or some electrical wires may have to be rerouted.

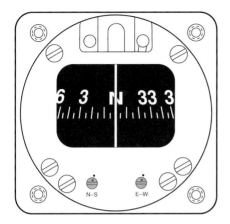

Figure 10-32. *The deviation compensating screws on a magnetic compass*

Figure 10-33. *A compass correction card*

FOR	000	030	060	090	120	150
STEER						
RDO. ON	001	032	062	095	123	155
RDO. OFF	002	031	064	094	125	157

FOR	180	210	240	270	300	330
STEER						
RDO. ON	176	210	243	271	296	325
RDO. OFF	174	210	240	273	298	327

The compass is lighted with a tiny DC light bulb. The wiring used to carry the current to and from this bulb should be twisted and grounded at a location well away from the compass. Twisting the wires effectively cancels the magnetic fields caused by the current.

Dip Errors

The earth's magnetic field leaves the surface vertically at the North Pole and re-enters vertically at the South Pole. Near the equator, the field parallels the surface of the earth. The compass magnets align with the magnetic field, and near the poles, the magnetic field pulls one end of the magnet down. To compensate for this tilt, the compass float is weighted so it will float relatively level in all but the extremely high latitudes. This tilt and its correction cause two errors: acceleration error and northerly turning error.

When an aircraft accelerates while flying on an east or west heading, the inertia of the dip-compensating weight causes the compass card to swing toward the north. When it decelerates on either of these headings, the inertia causes the card to swing toward the south.

When an aircraft is flying on a northerly heading and is banked for a turn, the downward pull of the vertical component of the magnetic field causes the card to start to move in the direction opposite to the direction of the turn. When banking for a turn from a southerly heading, the card starts to turn in the correct direction, but it turns faster than the airplane is turning.

Vertical-Card Magnetic Compass

The traditional magnetic compass in Figure 10-32 has a built-in error potential in reading the heading indication. Notice that when the aircraft is flying on a northerly heading, the indications for easterly directions are on the

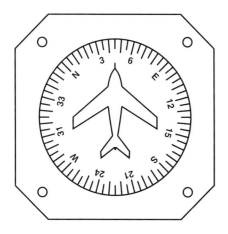

Figure 10-34. *A vertical-card magnetic compass minimizes the error of turning in the wrong direction to reach a desired heading.*

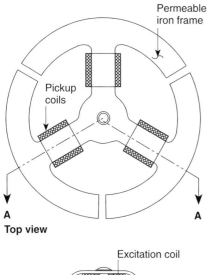

Top view

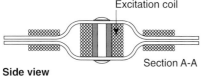

Side view

Figure 10-35. *The flux valve has a highly permeable segmented-ring frame suspended as a pendulum. An excitation coil mounted in the center of the frame carries 400-Hz AC which magnetically saturates the frame 800 times each second.*

west side of the compass. The reason is that the pilot is looking at the back side of the compass card, and the airplane turns around the card. This error potential is minimized by the vertical card compass in Figure 10-34.

The dial of the instrument is driven by gears from the magnet, which is mounted on a shaft rather than floating in a bowl of liquid. Oscillations of the magnet are damped by eddy currents induced into a damping cup. The nose of the symbolic airplane serves as the lubber line, and it is easy for the pilot to immediately visualize the direction to turn to reach a given heading.

Flux Gate Compass System

The magnetic compass has so many limitations that much study has been made to determine direction relative to the earth's magnetic field by methods other than simply observing a card or dial attached to a floating magnet.

The successful New York-to-Paris flight by Charles Lindbergh in 1927 was made possible, in part, by an earth inductor compass that overcame the oscillation and dip errors and minimized the deviation error. A wind-driven generator was mounted behind the cabin where magnetic interference from the engine was minimum. This generator contained coils in which the earth's magnetic field induced a voltage whose phase was altered by the heading of the aircraft. A controller allowed Lindbergh to set in the compass heading he wished to fly.

An electrical indicator on the instrument panel showed him when his actual heading was either to the right or left of the desired heading. By keeping the needle centered, he was able to fly a constant heading. Modern flux-gate compasses work on this same basic principle, but the hardware has been vastly improved.

A flux valve like the one in Figure 10-35 is mounted in a location in the aircraft where magnetic interference is minimum, often near a wing tip or in the vertical fin. The sensitive portion of the flux valve consists of a highly permeable segmented-ring frame, suspended as a pendulum and sealed in a housing filled with a damping fluid, as in Figure 10-36. A coil is mounted in the center of the frame and is excited with 400-Hz AC. Pickup coils are wound around each of the three legs, and they are connected into a Y-circuit as shown in Figure 10-38 on Page 748.

When the aircraft is flying, the earth's magnetic field is picked up by the permeable frame. During each peak of the excitation AC, the frame is magnetically saturated and rejects the earth's field. But 800 times a second, as the AC drops back through zero, the earth's field cuts across the windings of the three pickup coils and induces a voltage in them. The relationship of the voltage in each of the three coils is determined by the heading of the aircraft.

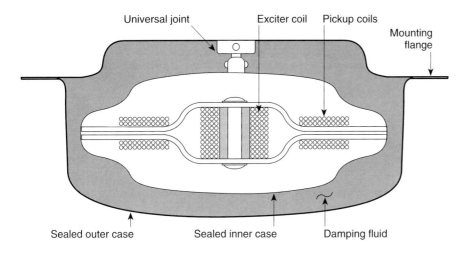

eddy current damping. Decreasing the amplitude of oscillations by the interaction of magnetic fields.

In the case of a vertical-card magnetic compass, flux from the oscillating permanent magnet produces eddy currents in a damping disk or cup. The magnetic flux produced by the eddy currents opposes the flux from the permanent magnet and decreases the oscillations.

Figure 10-36. *The flux valve is sealed inside a case which is suspended as a pendulum in a housing filled with a damping fluid.*

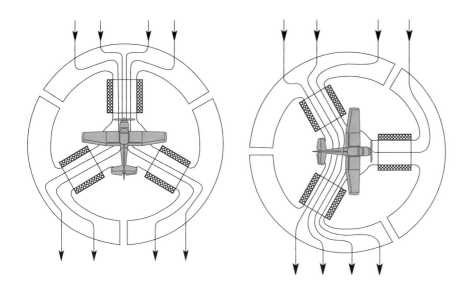

Figure 10-37. *When the frame is not saturated, it accepts flux from the earth's magnetic field. This flux cuts across the windings of the three pickup coils. The heading of the aircraft determines the voltage relationships existing in the coils.*

The output of the three pickup coils in the flux valve is fed into the flux-valve synchro in Figure 10-38. The three-phase voltage in the stator causes its rotor to follow the rotation of the aircraft relative to the earth's magnetic field. The voltage output of this rotor is fed into a compass-slaving amplifier whose output excites one phase of a two-phase slaving torque motor. This motor applies a force to the slaved attitude gyro, causing it to precess and rotate its gimbals until the rotor of the flux-valve synchro is in a position determined by the relationship of the earth's magnetic field and the pickup coils. Also connected to the gyro gimbals and the flux-valve synchro rotor is the rotor of the heading synchro. As the gyro turns to indicate the rotation of the aircraft relative to the earth's magnetic field, the rotor of the heading synchro turns. This causes the rotor in the movable-dial synchro to rotate the dial of the remote gyro heading indicator.

As we will see in the study of some of the electronic navigation systems, the flux gate compass system is an extremely important component in many modern flight instruments.

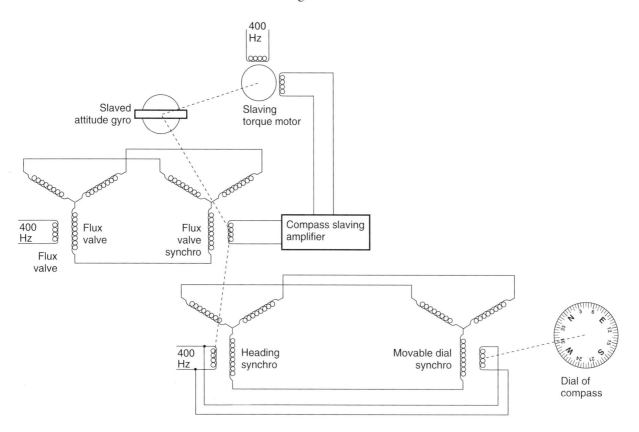

Figure 10-38. *A basic schematic diagram of a flux gate compass system*

Answers begin on Page 786. Page numbers refer to chapter text.

37. The reference mark in a magnetic compass that allows the pilot to determine the exact compass heading is called the _____ . *Page 742*

38. The marks on a magnetic compass card are spaced every _____ degrees. *Page 742*

39. The magnetic and geographic poles of the earth _____ (are or are not) at the same location. *Page 743*

40. Variation error of a compass _____ (does or does not) change with the heading of the aircraft. *Page 743*

41. The compass error caused by local magnetic fields is called _____ (deviation or variation). *Page 744*

42. Deviation error of a compass _____ (does or does not) change with the heading of the aircraft. *Page 744*

43. A technician swings a compass to minimize and plot the _____ (variation or deviation) error. *Page 744*

44. The maximum deviation error allowed for a magnetic compass is _____ degrees. *Page 744*

45. The magnetic fields caused by the current used to power the built-in compass light are minimized by _____ the wires carrying the current. *Page 745*

46. Two compass errors caused by the vertical component of the earth's magnetic field are:
    a. _____
    b. _____
    Page 745

47. The nose of the symbolic airplane on a vertical-card magnetic compass serves as the _____ . *Page 746*

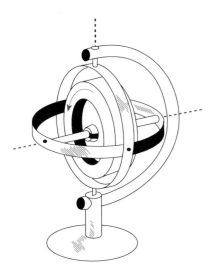

Figure 10-39. *A spinning gyroscope mounted in a double gimbal will remain in the same attitude, relative to the earth, even if its stand is moved, tilted, or twisted.*

gyro (gyroscope). The sensing device in an autopilot system. A gyroscope is a rapidly spinning wheel with its weight concentrated around its rim. Gyroscopes have two basic characteristics that make them useful in aircraft instruments: rigidity in space and precession. *See* rigidity in space and precession.

rigidity in space. The characteristic of a gyroscope that prevents its axis of rotation tilting as the earth rotates. This characteristic is used for attitude gyro instruments.

gimbal. A support that allows a gyroscope to remain in an upright condition when its base is tilted.

attitude indicator. A gyroscopic flight instrument that gives the pilot an indication of the attitude of the aircraft relative to its pitch and roll axes. The attitude indicator in an autopilot is in the sensing system that detects deviation from a level-flight attitude.

Gyroscopic Instruments

A gyroscope is a small wheel with its weight concentrated in its rim. When it spins at a high speed, it exhibits two interesting characteristics: rigidity in space and precession. Directional gyros and gyro horizons are attitude gyros, and they make use of the characteristic of rigidity in space. Rate gyros such as turn and slip indicators and turn coordinators use the characteristic of precession.

Attitude Gyros

If a gyroscope is mounted in a double gimbal like the one in Figure 10-39 and spun at a high speed, it will remain in the attitude in which it was spun even though the stand in which it is mounted is moved, tilted, or twisted. This is the characteristic of rigidity in space and is used in attitude gyro instruments.

Attitude Indicator

The gyro in the attitude indicator seen in Figure 10-40 is mounted in a double gimbal with its spin axis vertical. The older attitude indicator, normally called a gyro horizon, or artificial horizon, has a simple horizon bar that retains its relationship with the gyro as the aircraft pitches and rolls. The amount the aircraft rotates about its pitch and roll axes is indicated by the relationship of the horizon bar with the miniature airplane in the center of the instrument face. This miniature airplane is fixed in its relationship with the aircraft.

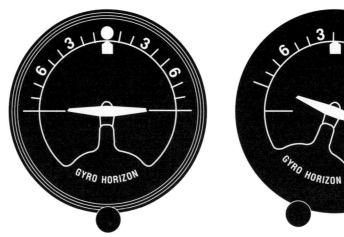

Airplane is flying straight and level.   Airplane is in a 20° bank to the right.

Figure 10-40. *The horizon bar of the gyro horizon remains level with the natural horizon, and the miniature airplane attached to the instrument case depicts the attitude of the aircraft relative to the horizon.*

Modern attitude indicators have replaced the simple horizon bar with a two-color dial like the one in Figure 10-41. The top of this dial is blue to represent the sky and the bottom is brown for the earth. Straight horizontal lines, marked in degrees, align with the miniature airplane to indicate the amount of pitch, and angled lines all pointing into the center indicate the degree of bank.

Heading Indicator

A heading indicator is an attitude gyro instrument with the spin axis of the gyro in a horizontal plane. It senses rotation about the vertical axis of the aircraft. The early heading indicators were called directional gyros, or simply DGs. These instruments had a drum-type card much like that of a floating-magnet compass surrounding the gyro. Modern heading indicators use vertical cards shown in Figure 10-42.

A gyro heading indicator is not a direction-seeking instrument, and it must be set to agree with the magnetic compass. The gyro remains rigid in space and the aircraft turns around it. The symbolic airplane on the glass is fixed, and as the heading of airplane changes, the card rotates and the indication under the extended nose of the airplane is the actual heading. Markers around the instrument dial at 45° and 90° increments make it easy for a pilot to turn 45°, 90°, or 180° without having to do any mental arithmetic.

Rate Gyros

Rate gyros are mounted in single gimbals, and they operate on the characteristic of precession. A force acting on a spinning gyroscope is felt, not at the point of application, but at a point 90° from the point of application in the direction of rotation.

In Figure 10-43, an upward force is applied to one end of the gyro shaft. This is the same as a force applied to the top of the wheel. Rather than tilting the shaft upward, the force is felt at the right side of the wheel, which is 90° from the point of application in the direction the wheel is rotating. Precession causes the upward force on the shaft to rotate the shaft in a counterclockwise

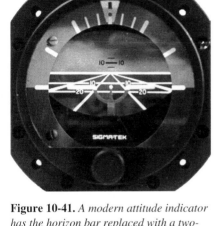

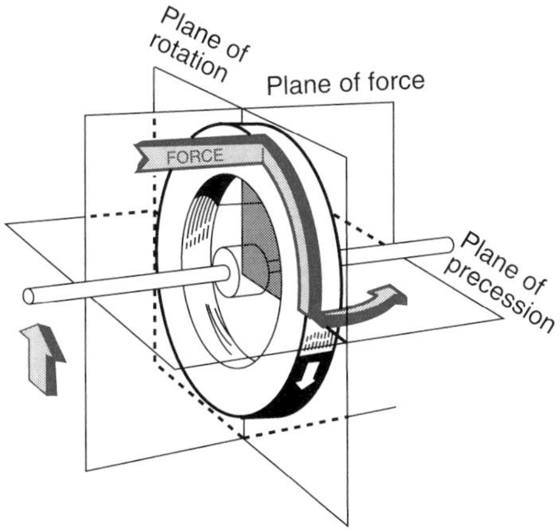

Figure 10-41. *A modern attitude indicator has the horizon bar replaced with a two-color dial with graduations to show the degrees of pitch and bank.*

Figure 10-42. *A vertical-card gyro heading indicator*

heading indicator. A gyroscopic flight instrument that gives the pilot an indication of the heading of the aircraft.

precession. The characteristic of a gyroscope that causes a force to be felt, not at the point of application, but at a point 90° in the direction of rotation from that point.

Figure 10-43. *Precession of a gyroscope. An upward force on one end of the shaft causes the gyro to rotate in a counterclockwise direction as viewed from above.*

turn and slip indicator. A rate gyroscopic flight instrument that gives the pilot an indication of the rate of rotation of the aircraft about its vertical axis.

A ball in a curved glass tube shows the pilot the relationship between the centrifugal force and the force of gravity. This indicates whether or not the angle of bank is proper for the rate of turn. The turn and slip indicator shows the trim condition of the aircraft and serves as an emergency source of bank information in case the attitude gyro fails. Turn and slip indicators were formerly called needle and ball and turn and bank indicators.

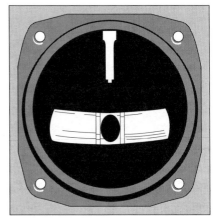

Two-minute turn indicator

Four-minute turn indicator

Figure 10-44. *Turn and slip indicators*

direction (when viewed from above) in a horizontal plane. Figure 10-43 summarizes this action. The plane of rotation, plane of force, and plane of precession are all at 90° to each other. An upward force in the plane of the force will cause a counterclockwise rotation in the plane of precession.

Turn and Slip Indicator

The turn and slip indicator in Figure 10-44 is the oldest gyroscopic instrument used in aircraft. It was originally called a needle and ball, then a turn and bank indicator, and in the last couple of decades, it has been more accurately called a turn and slip indicator.

The turn mechanism in this instrument is a gyro wheel mounted in a single gimbal with its spin axis horizontal and the axis of the gimbal aligned with the longitudinal axis of the aircraft. When the aircraft yaws, or rotates about its vertical axis, a force is applied to the front and back of the gimbal, which, because of precession, causes the gimbal to lean over. This leaning is restrained by a calibration spring, and the amount the gimbal leans over is determined by the rate at which the aircraft is yawing. *See* Figure 10-45.

The rotation of the gimbal drives a paddle-shaped pointer across the instrument dial. There are no graduation numbers on the dial, just an index mark at the top. The calibration spring is adjusted so that the needle moves over with its left edge aligned with the right edge of the index mark when the aircraft is yawing at the rate of 3° per second. This is called a standard-rate turn and will result in a 360° turn in two minutes.

Since fast airplanes must turn at a rate of yaw less than 3° per second, turn and slip indicators for these airplanes are calibrated so that when the left edge of the needle is aligned with the right edge of the index mark, the airplane is yawing $1\frac{1}{2}°$ per second. The dials of four-minute turn indicators have, in addition to the index mark, two doghouse-shaped marks located one needle-width away from each side of the index mark. When the needle is aligned with one of the doghouses, the airplane is making a 3° per second turn.

The ball in a turn and slip indicator shows the pilot when the turn is coordinated; that is, when the angle of bank is correct for the rate of turn. In a coordinated turn the force of gravity and the centrifugal force are balanced and the ball remains in the center of the curved glass tube, between the two wires. If the rate of turn is too great for the angle of bank, the centrifugal force is greater than the force of gravity and the ball rolls toward the outside of the turn. If the angle of bank is too great for the rate of turn, the effect of gravity is greater than the centrifugal force and the ball rolls toward the inside of the turn.

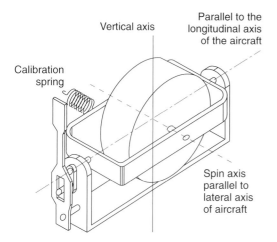

Figure 10-45. *The rate gyro in a turn and slip indicator precesses an amount that is proportional to the rate of rotation about its vertical axis.*

Turn Coordinator

A turn and slip indicator measures rotation only about the vertical axis of the aircraft. But a turn is started by banking the aircraft, or rotating it about its roll axis. When the aircraft is banked, the lift produced by the wings has a horizontal component that pulls the aircraft around in curved flight. An instrument that could sense roll as well as yaw would allow the pilot to keep the aircraft straight and level better than a turn and slip indicator. To this end, the turn coordinator in Figure 10-46 was developed.

A turn coordinator is much like a turn and slip indicator except that the gimbal axis is tilted upward about 30°. This allows it to sense both roll and yaw. The needle has been replaced by a small symbolic airplane, and marks by the wing tips indicate a standard rate turn.

Figure 10-46. *A turn coordinator*

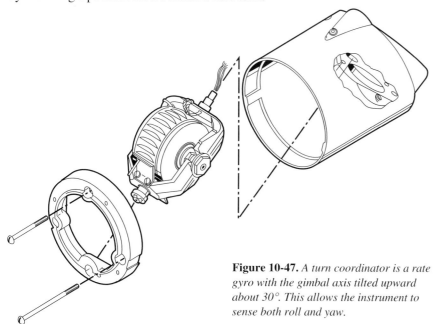

Figure 10-47. *A turn coordinator is a rate gyro with the gimbal axis tilted upward about 30°. This allows the instrument to sense both roll and yaw.*

Answers begin on Page 786. Page numbers refer to chapter text.

48. Attitude gyros operate on the gyroscopic principle of _____ (rigidity in space or precession). *Page 750*

49. Attitude gyros are mounted in _____ (single or double) gimbals. *Page 750*

50. An attitude indicator senses rotation about the _____ and _____ axes of an aircraft. *Page 750*

51. The spin axis of the gyro in an attitude indicator is _____ (horizontal or vertical). *Page 750*

52. The heading indicator senses rotation about the _____ axis of the aircraft. *Page 751*

53. The spin axis of the gyro in a heading indicator is _____ (horizontal or vertical). *Page 751*

54. A gyro heading indicator _____ (is or is not) a direction-seeking instrument. *Page 751*

55. Rate gyros operate on the gyroscopic principle of _____ (rigidity in space or recession). *Page 751*

56. A rate gyro is mounted in a _____ (single or double) gimbal. *Page 751*

57. A turn and slip indicator senses rotation about the _____ axis of the aircraft. *Page 752*

58. The spin axis of the gyro in a turn and slip indicator is _____ (horizontal or vertical). *Page 752*

59. A one-needle-width turn with a two-minute turn indicator means that the aircraft is yawing _____ degrees per second. *Page 752*

60. When the needle of a four-minute turn indicator is aligned with one of the doghouses, the aircraft is yawing _____ degrees per second. *Page 752*

61. A turn coordinator senses rotation of an aircraft about its _____ and _____ axes. *Page 753*

Aircraft Instrument Systems

Knowing the basic operating principles of the various types of instruments will help understand the way these instruments relate to the entire aircraft. This section discusses the various systems in which specific instruments are installed.

Pitot-Static Systems

One of the most important instrument systems is the pitot-static system. This system serves as the source of the pressures needed for the altimeter, airspeed indicator, and vertical speed indicator.

A tube with an inside diameter of approximately ¼ inch is installed on the outside of an aircraft in such a way that it points directly into the relative airflow over the aircraft. This tube, called a pitot tube, picks up ram air pressure and directs it into the center hole in an airspeed indicator.

Small holes on either side of the fuselage or vertical fin or small holes in the pitot-static head sense the pressure of the still, or static, air. This pressure is taken into the case of the altimeter, airspeed indicator, and vertical speed indicator.

Figure 10-48 shows a typical pitot-static head. Ram, or impact, air is taken into the front of the head and directed up into the pitot pressure chamber. It is taken out of this chamber through the pitot-tube riser to prevent water from getting into the instrument lines. Any water that gets into the pitot head from flying through rain is drained overboard through drain holes in the bottom of the front of the head and in the back of the pressure chamber. Static air pressure is taken in through holes or slots in the bottom and sides of the head. An electrical heater in the head prevents ice from forming on the head and blocking either the static holes or pitot air inlet.

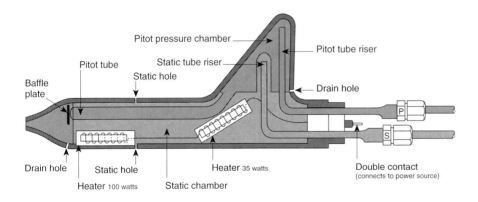

Figure 10-48. *An electrically heated pitot-static head*

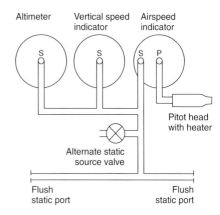

Figure 10-49. *A typical pitot-static system for a small general aviation airplane*

Pitot-static systems for light airplanes are similar to the one in Figure 10-49. The pitot tube for these aircraft is connected directly to the center opening of the airspeed indicator. The two flush static ports, one on either side of the fuselage, are connected together and supply pressure to the airspeed indicator, altimeter, and vertical-speed indicator. An alternate static air valve is connected into this line to supply static air to the instruments if the outside static ports should ever cover over with ice. The alternate air is taken directly from the cockpit of unpressurized aircraft, but pressurized aircraft pick it up from outside of the pressure vessel.

Large jet transport aircraft have a more complex pitot-static system. Figure 10-50 shows such a system. The pitot tube on the left side of the aircraft supplies the captain's Machmeter and airspeed indicator. Static pressure for all of the captain's instruments is obtained from the captain's static source, but the alternate static source valve allows this to be taken from the alternate static sources.

The right-hand pitot tube supplies pitot air pressure to the first officer's Machmeter, airspeed indicator, and No. 2 Mach/Indicated Airspeed warning system. All the first officer's static instruments connect to the F/O static source, and can also be connected to the alternate static source.

The auxiliary pitot tube picks up ram air for the auto pilot, yaw dampers, No. 1 Mach/IAS warning system, and flight recorder. The alternate static source supplies air to these instruments plus the two flight directors and the reference for cabin differential pressure.

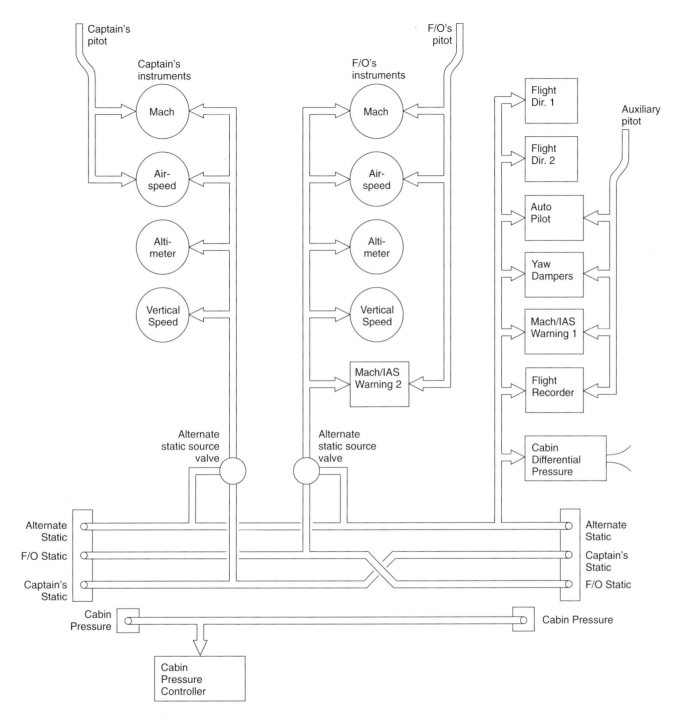

Figure 10-50. *Pitot-static system for a jet transport airplane*

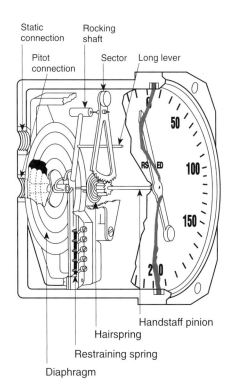

Static
connection

Rocking
shaft

Pitot
connection

Sector   Long lever

Handstaff pinion

Hairspring

Restraining spring

Diaphragm

Figure 10-51. *Cutaway view of an airspeed indicator*

Figure 10-52. *A True Speed indicator is an airspeed indicator with a manually rotated subdial that allows the pilot to correct the indicated airspeed for nonstandard pressure and temperature. The true airspeed indication is read at the end of the pointer on the white subdial.*

Airspeed Indicators

An airspeed indicator is a differential pressure indicator that takes ram, or pitot, air pressure into a diaphragm assembly and static air pressure into the instrument case. *See* Figure 10-51. As the aircraft flies faster, the diaphragm expands, and this expansion is transmitted through the rocking shaft and sector gear to the pinion which is mounted on the same shaft as the pointer.

The indication on the airspeed indicator is called indicated airspeed (IAS), and two corrections must be applied before this is of value in precision flying.

The air passing over the aircraft structure does not flow smoothly over all parts, and its flow pattern changes with the airspeed. The pressure of the air picked up by the static ports changes with the airspeed, and this change in pressure causes an error in the airspeed indication called position error. When indicated airspeed is corrected for position error, the result is calibrated airspeed (CAS). True airspeed (TAS) is obtained by correcting calibrated airspeed for nonstandard pressure and temperature. This correction is done by the pilot with a flight computer.

True Airspeed Indicator

A true airspeed indicator contains a temperature-compensated aneroid bellows that modifies the movement of the levers as the pressure and temperature change. The pointer indicates the true airspeed being flown.

An airspeed indicator installed in many of the small general aviation aircraft is called a True Speed indicator. *See* Figure 10-52. This instrument has two cutouts in the dial, with a movable subdial which has altitude graduations visible in one cutout and true airspeed visible in the other. A knob on the front of the instrument allows the pilot to rotate the subdial to align the existing outside air temperature with the pressure altitude being flown. When these two parameters are aligned, the instrument pointer will show on the subdial the true airspeed being flown.

Maximum-Allowable Airspeed Indicator

An airplane is limited to a maximum true airspeed by structural considerations and also by the onset of compressibility at high speeds. As the air becomes less dense at high altitude, the indicated airspeed for a given true airspeed decreases. Relatively low-performance airplanes have a fixed red line on the instrument dial which is the never-exceed mark (V_{NE}), but airplanes that fly at high altitudes often use a maximum-allowable airspeed indicator. This instrument has two pointers: one, the ordinary airspeed indicator pointer and the other, a red or red and black-striped or checkered pointer that is actuated by an aneroid altimeter mechanism. This pointer shows the maximum indicated airspeed allowed for the altitude being flown, and it moves down the dial as the altitude increases. The small numbers on the dial indicate the limiting Mach numbers for the altitude being flown.

The indicator in Figure 10-53 is a combination pointer and drum indicator. The white pointer shows at a glance that the airspeed is something over 400 knots, and the number in the center of the drum is 31. The indicated airspeed shown here is 431 knots.

Machmeter

The airspeed limit placed on many airplanes is caused not by structural strength, but by the onset of compressibility and the formation of shock waves as the airplane approaches the speed of sound. For this reason many airplanes are Mach limited. For the pilot to know just how near the aircraft is to the speed of sound, a Machmeter such as the one whose dial is seen in Figure 10-54 may be installed.

A Machmeter uses an airspeed indicator mechanism whose pointer movement is modified by an altimeter aneroid. The dial is calibrated in Mach numbers, and the pointer shows the pilot, at a glance, the relationship between the speed of the aircraft and the speed of sound. The Machmeter in Figure 10-54 shows that the airplane is flying at Mach .83, which is 83% of the speed of sound.

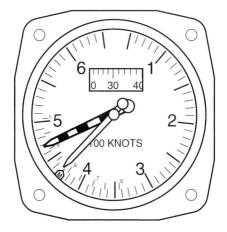

Figure 10-53. *The dial of a maximum-allowable airspeed indicator*

Figure 10-54. *This Machmeter shows that the airplane is flying at 83% of the speed of sound.*

indicated airspeed (IAS). The airspeed as shown on an airspeed indicator with no corrections applied.

position error. The error in pitot-static instruments that is caused by the static ports not sensing true static air pressure. Position error changes with airspeed and is usually greatest at low airspeeds.

calibrated airspeed (CAS). Indicated airspeed corrected for position error. *See* position error.

true airspeed (TAS). Calibrated airspeed corrected for nonstandard pressure and temperature.

knot. A speed measurement that is equal to one nautical mile per hour. One knot is equal to 1.15 statute mile per hour.

Mach number. The ratio of the speed of an airplane to the speed of sound under the same atmospheric conditions. An airplane flying at Mach 1 is flying at the speed of sound.

Figure 10-55. *A three-pointer sensitive altimeter*

altimeter setting. The barometric pressure at a given location corrected to mean (average) sea level.

pressure altitude. The altitude read on an altimeter when the barometric scale is set to the standard sea level pressure of 29.92 inches of mercury.

Altimeters

A pneumatic, or pressure, altimeter is actually an aneroid barometer whose dial is calibrated in feet of altitude above some specified reference level.

Some of the very early altimeters had a range of approximately 10,000 feet and had a knob that allowed the pilot to rotate the dial. Before takeoff, the dial was rotated to indicate zero feet if the flight was to be local, or, more accurately, to the surveyed elevation of the airport. This simple altimeter did not take into consideration the changes in barometric pressure along the route of flight that have a great effect on the altimeter indication.

The altimeter that has been used for all serious flying since the 1930s is the three-pointer sensitive altimeter, a recent version of which is seen in Figure 10-55.

The long pointer of the three-pointer altimeter in Figure 10-55 makes one round of the dial for every 1,000 feet. The dial is calibrated so that each number indicates 100 feet and each mark indicates 20 feet. The short pointer makes one round of the dial for every 10,000 feet, and each number represents 1,000 feet. The third pointer is actually a partial disk with a triangle that rides around the outer edge of the dial so that each number represents 10,000 feet. A cutout in the lower part of this disk shows a barber-pole striped subdial. Below 10,000 feet, the entire striped area is visible, but above this altitude the solid part of the disk begins to cover the stripes, and by 15,000 feet all the stripes are covered.

The altimeter in Figure 10-55 shows a pressure altitude of 10,180 feet. The small window in the right side of the dial shows the barometric scale. This scale is adjusted by the altitude set knob. When this knob is turned, both the barometric scale and the pointers move. Before takeoff and when flying below approximately 18,000 feet, the pilot sets the barometric scale to the altimeter setting given by the control tower or by an air traffic controller for an area within 100 miles of the aircraft. The altimeter setting is the local barometric pressure corrected to mean sea level. When the barometric scale is adjusted to the correct altimeter setting, the altimeter shows indicated altitude, which is the altitude above mean, or average, sea level. By keeping the barometric scale adjusted to the current altimeter setting, the pilot can tell the height of the aircraft above objects whose elevations are marked on the aeronautical charts.

When the aircraft is flying above 18,000 feet, the barometric scale must be adjusted to 29.92 inches of mercury, or 1013 millibars. This causes the altimeter to measure the height above standard sea-level pressure. This is called pressure altitude, and even though its actual distance from mean sea level varies from location to location, all aircraft flying above 18,000 feet are flying at pressure altitudes, and vertical separation is accurately maintained.

Some of the modern altimeters are drum-pointer-type indicators like that in Figure 10-56. The barometric scale of this instrument shows both inches of mercury and millibars, and it has a single pointer that makes one round for 1,000 feet. A drum counter shows the altitude directly. The altimeter in Figure 10-56 shows an indicated altitude of -165 feet.

Encoding Altimeter

Air traffic control radar displays returns from the aircraft that ATC controls. These returns show not only location of the aircraft, but also the pressure altitude the aircraft is flying. An encoding altimeter supplies the pressure altitude, in increments of 100 feet, to the transponder that replies to the ground radar interrogation. Some encoding altimeters are the indicating instrument used by the pilot, and others are blind instruments that have no visible display of the altitude. They only furnish this information to the transponder.

FAR 91.217 requires that the indication from the encoding altimeter not differ more than 125 feet from the indication of the altimeter used by the pilot to maintain flight altitude.

Figure 10-56. *A drum-pointer-type altimeter*

Vertical-Speed Indicators

A vertical-speed indicator (VSI), often called a rate-of-climb indicator, is an unusual type of differential pressure gage. It actually measures only changing pressure. Static pressure is brought into the instrument case from the static air system. This air flows into a diaphragm capsule similar to the one used in an airspeed indicator and into the instrument case through a calibrated restrictor.

When the aircraft is flying at a constant altitude, the air pressure is not changing and the pressures inside the capsule and inside the instrument case are the same. The indicating needle is horizontal and represents no vertical speed. When the aircraft goes up, the air becomes less dense and the pressure inside the capsule changes immediately, but the calibrated restrictor causes the pressure inside the case to change more slowly. As long as the aircraft is going up, the pressure is changing, and the needle deflects to indicate the number of hundred feet per minute the altitude is changing. When the altitude is no longer changing, the pressure inside the case becomes the same as that inside the capsule, and the needle returns to zero. When the aircraft descends, the pressure becomes greater and the indicator shows a downward vertical speed.

Figure 10-57. *A vertical-speed indicator*

Instantaneous Vertical-Speed Indicator

A vertical-speed indicator cannot show a climb or descent until it is actually established. For this reason, there is a noticeable lag in its indication, and the VSI is not able to detect the changes in pitch attitude that precede the actual change in altitude. To make the VSI more useful for instrument flying, the instantaneous vertical-speed indicator, or IVSI, has been developed. This instrument uses two accelerometer-actuated air pumps, or dashpots, installed across the capsule. When the aircraft is flying level, the IVSI indicates zero, but when the pilot drops the nose to begin a descent, the accelerometer causes a slight pressure increase inside the capsule, and the indicator needle immediately deflects downward. As soon as the actual descent begins, the changing pressure keeps the needle deflected. When the pilot raises the nose to begin a climb, the accelerometer causes a slight pressure drop inside the capsule and the needle immediately deflects upward.

STUDY QUESTIONS: PITOT-STATIC SYSTEMS

Answers begin on Page 786. Page numbers refer to chapter text.

62. The instruments that connect to the static air system are the _____ , _____ , and _____ . *Page 756*

63. The instrument that connects to the pitot system is the _____ . *Page 756*

64. Ice is prevented from forming on a pitot-static head by a/an _____ . *Page 756*

65. If the static ports on the side of an aircraft ice over in flight, the pilot can restore service to the static instruments by opening the _____ valve. *Page 756*

66. The airspeed as read directly from the airspeed indicator is called _____ airspeed. *Page 758*

67. Indicated airspeed corrected for position error is called _____ airspeed. *Page 758*

68. Calibrated airspeed corrected for nonstandard pressure and temperature is called _____ airspeed. *Page 758*

69. The indication of a true airspeed indicator is modified by a/an _____ bellows that compensates for pressure and temperature changes. *Page 758*

70. As altitude increases, the maximum allowable indicated airspeed _____ (increases or decreases). *Page 758*

71. When an airplane is flying at 75% of the speed of sound, it is flying at Mach _____ . *Page 759*

72. When the barometric scale of an altimeter is adjusted to the local altimeter setting, the altitude shown is the height above _____ . This is called _____ altitude. *Page 760*

73. When the barometric scale of an altimeter is set to 29.92 inches of mercury, the altimeter is showing _____ altitude. *Page 760*

74. When aircraft fly at an altitude of 18,000 feet or above, the barometric scale of the altimeter should be adjusted to _____ inches of mercury or _____ millibars. *Page 760*

75. An encoding altimeter furnishes altitude information to the _____ which transmits this information to the air traffic controller on the ground. *Page 761*

76. An encoding altimeter must agree with the altimeter used by the pilot to maintain flight altitude within _____ feet. *Page 761*

77. A vertical-speed indicator measures the rate of _____ of the static pressure surrounding the aircraft. *Page 761*

78. One limitation of a vertical-speed indicator is that its indication _____ (lags or leads) the actual pressure changes. *Page 761*

79. An instantaneous vertical speed indicator uses _____-actuated air pumps to start the indication when the aircraft pitches up or down. *Page 761*

Gyro Instrument Power Systems

Gyro instruments are essential for safe flight when the natural horizon is not visible. Almost all current production aircraft are equipped with at least an attitude gyro and a gyroscopic heading indicator. These instruments are backed up by a turn and slip indicator or turn coordinator and an airspeed indicator.

For safety, the attitude gyros may be electrically driven and the rate gyro driven by air, or the attitude instruments may be air driven and the rate gyro electrically driven. By using this type of power arrangement, failure of either the instrument air source of the electrical power will not deprive the pilot of all of the gyro instruments. Some gyroscopic instruments are dual powered. The gyro wheel contains the windings of an electric motor, and buckets are cut into its periphery so it can also be spun by a jet of air.

Gyro Pneumatic Systems

The gyro wheels in pneumatic flight instruments are made of brass and have notches, or buckets, cut in their periphery. Air blows through a special nozzle into the buckets and spins the gyro at a high speed. *See* Figure 10-58 on the next page.

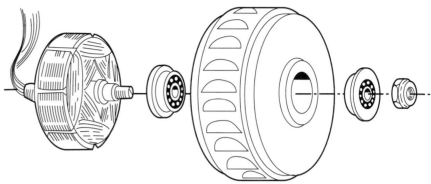

Figure 10-58. *This dual-powered gyro has buckets cut into its periphery so it can be driven by air. It also has a fixed winding inside the gyro that allows it to be driven as an electric motor.*

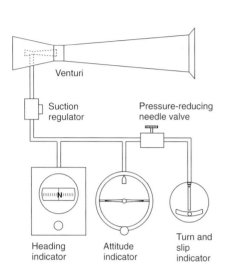

Figure 10-59. *A gyro instrument system using a venturi tube for the source of suction*

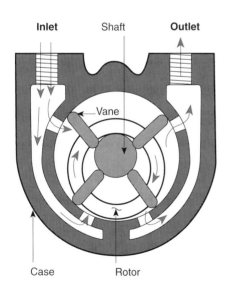

Figure 10-60. *A vane-type air pump can be used either to evacuate the instrument case or to provide a flow of pressurized air to drive the instrument gyros.*

There are two ways of producing the airflow over the gyro wheels: suction and pressure. The air can be evacuated from the instrument case, and air drawn in through a filter flows through the nozzles to drive the gyro. Or, air moved by a vane-type air pump can be directed through the nozzles to spin the gyros.

Suction Systems

Some gyro instrument-equipped aircraft do not have an air pump, and the gyros on these aircraft must be driven by low pressure produced by a venturi tube mounted on the outside of the fuselage. Air flowing through the venturi produces a low pressure inside the instrument case. Air flows into the instrument cases through built-in filters to spin the gyros. *See* Figure 10-59. The gyro horizon and directional gyros used in these systems each require four inches of mercury suction to drive the gyro at its proper speed, and the turn and slip indicator requires two inches of mercury.

A venturi tube capable of providing enough airflow through the three instruments is mounted on the outside of the fuselage. The line connecting the venturi tube to the instruments contains a suction regulator. This regulator is adjusted in flight to provide four inches of mercury suction at the cases of the heading indicator and the attitude indicator. A needle valve between the attitude instruments and the turn and slip indicator is then adjusted to provide two inches of mercury suction at the case of the turn and slip indicator.

Venturi systems are not dependable for flight into instrument meteorological conditions because the venturi tube will likely ice up and become inoperative.

Modern aircraft equipped with pneumatic gyros use vane-type air pumps similar to the one in Figure 10-60. Two types of air pumps are wet pumps and dry pumps.

Wet Vacuum Pump System

Wet vacuum pumps were the only type of pump available for many years. These pumps have steel vanes riding in a steel housing. They are lubricated by engine oil taken in through the base of the pump. This oil seals, cools, and lubricates the pump and is then removed from the pump with the discharge air. Before this air is dumped overboard or used for inflating deicer boots, the oil is removed by routing the air through an air-oil separator. The oily air is blown through a series of baffles where the oil collects and is drained back into the engine crankcase, and the air is either directed overboard or to the deicer distributor.

wet-type vacuum pump. An engine-driven air pump that uses steel vanes. These pumps are lubricated by engine oil drawn in through holes in the pump base. The oil passes through the pump and is exhausted with the air. Wet pumps must have oil separators in their discharge line to trap the oil and return it to the engine crankcase.

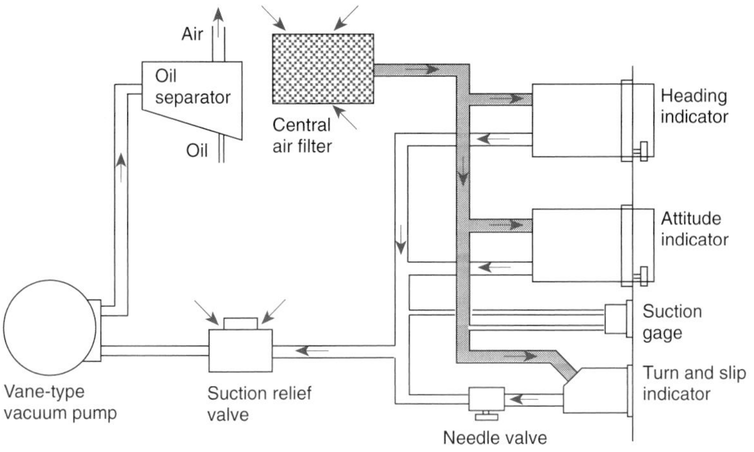

Figure 10-61. *A wet-pump vacuum system used to drive gyro instruments*

The air to drive the gyros is taken in through a central air filter, and then flows directly to the nozzles in the heading indicator, attitude indicator, and turn and slip indicator. The cases of the heading and attitude indicators are connected to the suction side of the system, and the case of the turn and slip indicator is also connected to the suction side, but there is a needle valve in the line. Air flows from the instruments through the suction-relief valve to the pump and then is discharged. The suction-relief valve is a spring-loaded flat disk valve that opens at a preset amount of suction to allow air to enter the system. If the spring is set with too much compression, the suction will have to be greater to allow the disk to offseat and allow air to enter the system. The suction relief valve is adjusted to four inches of mercury as read on the instrument panel suction gage, and the needle valve in the turn and slip line is adjusted so there will be a suction of two inches of mercury in the turn and slip case.

Dry Air Pump Systems

Dry air pumps have almost completely replaced wet pumps for instrument air systems. These pumps are lighter in weight and require no lubrication or oil separators in their discharge lines. They can drive instruments with either the suction they produce or by their positive air pressure.

Dry air pumps are vane-type pumps with the rotors and vanes made of a special carbon compound that wears in microscopic amounts to provide the needed lubrication.

Figure 10-62 shows a typical twin-engine dual vacuum pump system for gyro instruments. Each pump is connected to a manifold check valve through a vacuum regulator that allows just enough outside air to enter the system to maintain the desired suction.

In case either pump should fail, the manifold check valve will prevent the inoperative side of the system interfering with the working side. The manifold is connected to the outlet ports of the attitude indicator and the heading indicator and to the suction gage. The inlet ports of both indicators are connected to an inlet air filter. The line that goes to the filter also goes to the suction gage so that it reads the pressure drop across the gyros. The suction gage has two red buttons visible when the pumps are not operating, but as soon as either pump is producing a vacuum, its button pulls into the instrument and is not visible. The lines to these pump-failure buttons are taken off of the manifold before the check valves.

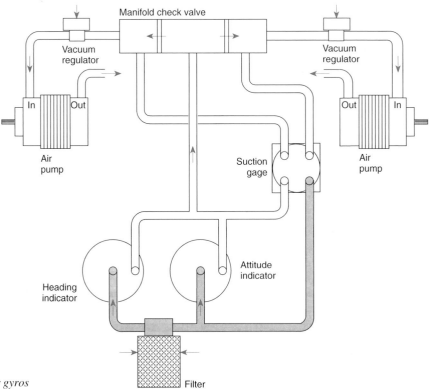

Figure 10-62. *A twin-engine vacuum system for gyros*

Pressure System

Many modern airplanes fly at altitudes so high, there is not enough ambient air pressure to drive the gyro instruments. For these aircraft, the output of the air pumps can be used to drive the gyros. A typical twin-engine pressure-instrument system is seen in Figure 10-63.

The inlets of the pumps are fitted with an inlet filter and the outlet air flows through a pressure regulator that vents all the air above the pressure for which it is adjusted. The air then flows through an in-line filter and into the manifold check valve to the inlet of the gyro instruments. After passing through the gyros, the air is vented into the cabin. Pump-failure buttons on the pressure gage pop out to show when either pump is not producing the required pressure.

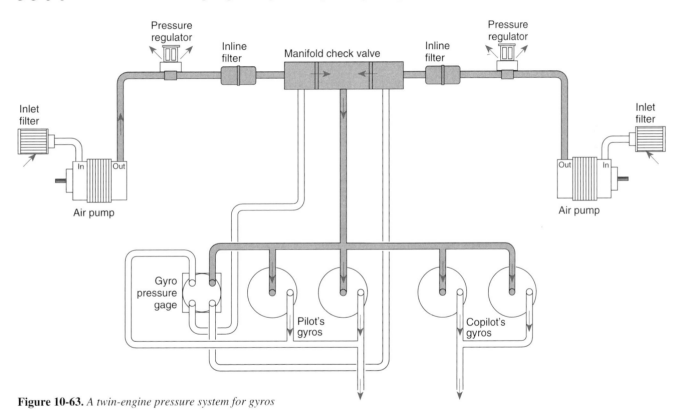

Figure 10-63. *A twin-engine pressure system for gyros*

*Answers begin on Page 786. **Page numbers refer to chapter text.***

80. An aircraft that has pneumatic attitude gyros normally has rate gyros that are driven by
_____ . *Page 763*

81. A "wet" vacuum pump is lubricated with _____ . *Page 765*

82. A "dry" vacuum pump does not need any lubrication because the vanes and rotor are made of
_____ . *Page 766*

83. The discharge from a vacuum pump is often used to furnish compressed air for the _____
system. *Page 765*

84. Aircraft that operate at high altitudes have their pneumatic gyro instruments driven by a
_____ (vacuum or pressure) system. *Page 767*

Automatic Flight Control Systems

automatic flight control system (AFCS). The full system of automatic flight control that includes the autopilot, flight director, horizontal situation indicator, air data sensors, and other avionics inputs.

automatic pilot. An automatic flight control device that controls an aircraft about one or more of its three axes. The primary purpose of an autopilot is to relieve the pilot of the control of the aircraft during long periods of flight.

Automatic flight has been investigated since the early days of aviation, and in 1914, Lawrence Sperry demonstrated successful automatic flight in a Curtiss C-2 flying boat. In 1933 Wiley Post had an experimental Sperry automatic pilot installed in his Lockheed *Vega*, the *Winnie Mae*. He had flown around the world in this airplane in 1931 with Harold Gatty as his navigator, but with the automatic pilot, he completed a similar flight alone.

Automatic flight is important, not only because it frees the human pilot from continuously flying the aircraft, but it flies the aircraft with a greater degree of precision and can navigate by coupling onto the various electronic navigation aids. Many modern high-performance fighter aircraft are designed to be conditionally stable and cannot be flown manually, but must be flown with automatic flight control systems.

Early automatic pilots used two attitude gyro instruments, a directional gyro and an artificial horizon. Pneumatic pickoffs from these gyros controlled three balanced oil valves that supplied hydraulic fluid to one side or the other of linear servo cylinders in the aileron, rudder, and elevator control systems.

Modern automatic flight control systems use attitude gyros, rate gyros, altimeter aneroids, and signals from various electronic navigation aids to program the desired flight profile that the aircraft can follow with extreme precision. These pickoffs and servos are now considered to be input and output devices for the flight computers.

The simplest autopilot is a single-axis wing-leveler using a single canted rate gyro that senses roll or yaw and sends a signal to pneumatic servos in the aileron system that keeps the wings level. Three-axis autopilots are the most common type. Pitch errors are corrected by the elevator channel, roll errors are corrected by the aileron channel, and a heading is maintained by the rudder channel.

A yaw damper is installed in many swept wing airplanes to counteract Dutch roll, which is an undesirable low-amplitude oscillation about both the yaw and roll axes. These oscillations are sensed by a rate gyro and signals are sent to the rudder servo that provides the correct rudder movement to cancel these oscillations.

An automatic flight control system consists of four subsystems: command, error-sensing, correction, and follow-up.

The pilot programs the desired flight parameters into the command subsystem. The error-sensing subsystem detects when the aircraft is not in the condition called for by the command. A signal is sent to the correction subsystem, which moves a control to achieve the appropriate changes. The follow-up subsystem senses the changes in the parameter and removes the error signal as soon as the correction is completed.

canted rate gyro. A rate gyro whose gimbal axis is tilted so it can sense rotation of the aircraft about its roll axis as well as its yaw axis.

yaw damper. An automatic flight control system that counteracts the rolling and yawing produced by Dutch roll. *See* Dutch roll.

Dutch roll. An undesirable, low-amplitude oscillation about both the yaw and roll axes that affects many swept wing airplanes. Dutch roll is minimized by the use of a yaw damper.

Command Subsystem

The command subsystem is the portion of the automatic flight control system that allows the pilot to program the aircraft to do what is needed. A sketch of a typical controller is seen in Figure 10-64.

flight controller. The component in an autopilot system that allows the pilot to maneuver the aircraft manually when the autopilot is engaged.

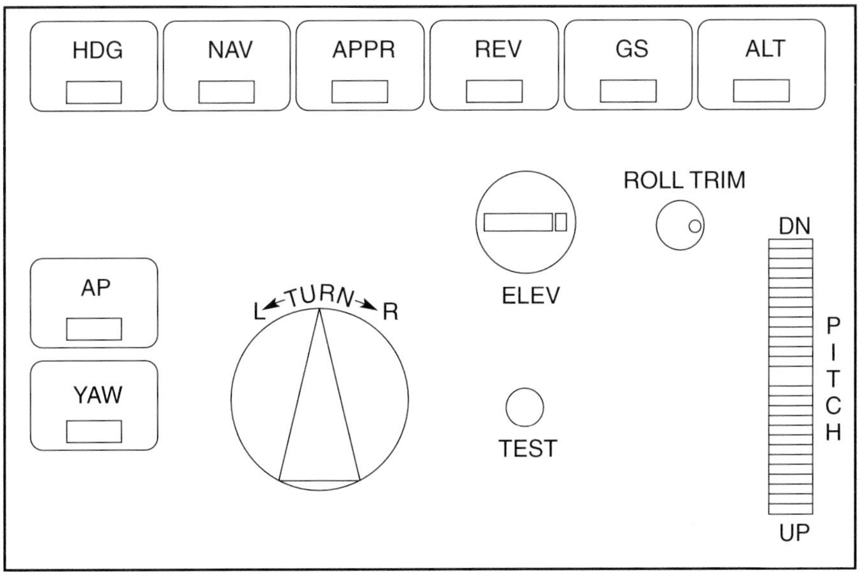

Figure 10-64. *The controller for a typical automatic flight control system*

To engage the autopilot, the pilot depresses the AP button. An indicator light shows that it is engaged. Depressing the HDG button ties the system to the horizontal situation indicator and the aircraft will fly the heading that is selected on it.

Depressing the NAV button commands the aircraft to fly along the VOR radial or RNAV course selected on the appropriate navigation source.

Depressing the APPR button causes the system to capture the chosen ILS localizer and follow it to the runway. If a back-course approach is to be made, the pilot can depress the REV button to see back-course information. When the GS button is depressed, the light will indicate that it is armed, and when the aircraft intercepts the glide slope, it will lock on it and will descend along its electronic path.

Depressing the ALT button commands the aircraft to fly to a selected barometric altitude and hold it.

The YAW button engages the rudder trim, which automatically trims the rudder for changes in airspeed.

Rotating the TURN knob commands the aircraft to initiate a banked turn to the left or right.

The PITCH control can be moved to the UP or DN position to command a change in pitch attitude. When it is released, it returns to its spring-loaded center position.

The ELEV indicator shows whether or not the elevator is in its neutral position, and indicates any needed pitch-trim changes.

The ROLL TRIM allows the pilot to trim the aircraft about its roll axis when no other command is active.

Error-Sensing Subsystem

Gyros normally do error-sensing. The gyro in an attitude indicator senses any deviation from level flight, either in pitch or roll. The gyro in a heading indicator senses any deviation from the heading selected by the pilot. The amount of error signal is related to the amount the aircraft has deviated from its chosen attitude or heading.

Rate gyros are used in some simpler automatic flight control systems to sense deviation from the selected flight condition. These instruments normally use a canted-rate gyro such as that used in a turn coordinator to sense rotation about both the roll and yaw axes. When the aircraft rolls or yaws, the gyro rolls over, or precesses, an amount proportional to the rate of deviation. A signal is sent to the appropriate servos to return the aircraft to a condition of level flight.

Because of the ease with which modern electronic systems can interface with automatic flight control systems, the output from the VOR and ILS as well as other navigation systems can be used to produce error signals. The pilot can tune to the appropriate localizer frequency on the VHF nav receiver and command the aircraft to follow an ILS approach. Any time the aircraft deviates from the glide slope or the localizer, an error signal is established that returns the aircraft to the desired flight path.

Altimeters can be included in the error-sensing subsystem. If the pilot has commanded the aircraft to fly to a given altitude, an error signal is established when the aircraft is not at that altitude, and the controls are adjusted to cause it to attain that altitude and level off. The altitude-hold command causes an error signal any time the aircraft departs from the specified altitude.

Correction Subsystem

The error-sensing subsystem acts as the brains of the system to detect when a correction is needed. Its signal is sent to the controller and then to the servos, which act as the muscles of the system.

Some automatic flight control systems have hydraulic servos that are balanced actuators in the control cable system as seen in Figure 10-65A. When fluid is directed to one side of the piston, the piston moves and pulls on the cable to move the appropriate control. To turn this type of autopilot off, the valve between the two sides of the servo cylinder is opened and the piston is free to move back and forth as the controls are moved.

Some systems use electric motors with drum-type capstans mounted on their shafts as servos. In some installations the primary control cable is wrapped around the capstan, Figure 10-65B. In other installations a smaller bridle cable is wrapped around the capstan and secured to the primary control cable with clamps as shown in Figure 10-65C.

Some smaller wing-lever autopilots use a canted-rate gyro for the sensor and two pneumatic servos like the one in Figure 10-65D. The small cable attached to the diaphragm in this servo is clamped to the primary aileron cable. When the rate gyro senses a roll or yaw, it shifts an air valve and directs suction to the servo that pulls on the correct aileron cable to return the aircraft to level flight. As long as the wings remain level, the airplane cannot turn.

Electric servos have the unusual requirement that they must start, stop, and reverse their direction rapidly when the controller directs, and they must have sufficient torque to move the controls. Some of the larger aircraft use three-phase AC motors to drive the capstan, and the smaller aircraft use DC motors. *See* Figure 10-65 on the following page.

servo. The component in an autopilot system that actually applies the force to move the flight control surfaces.

balanced actuator. A linear hydraulic actuator that has the same area on each side of the piston.

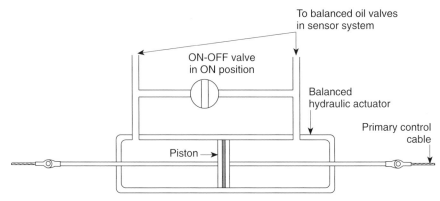

A Hydraulic servo using a balanced actuator

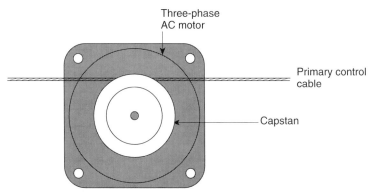

B Capstan driven by a three phase AC motor in the primary control system

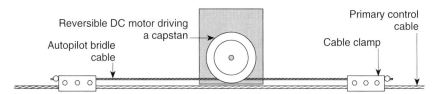

C The capstan, driven by a reversible DC motor, pulls on the bridle cable which is clamped to the primary control cable.

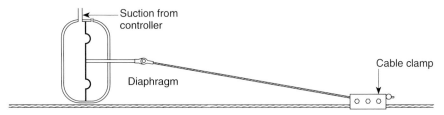

D Pneumatic servo for a wing-leveler autopilot. Two such servos are used to pull the aileron cables in the correct direction.

Figure 10-65. *Automatic flight control servos*

Follow-Up Subsystem

The follow-up system stops the control movement when the surface has deflected the proper amount for the signal sent by the error sensor. There are two basic types of follow-up systems, rate and displacement.

The rate follow-up used on some of the smaller autopilot systems takes its signals from a canted-rate gyro that senses both roll and yaw. When the aircraft rolls or yaws, a signal is generated by the rate gyro that relates to both the direction and rate of deviation. The signal is amplified and sent to the servos, which move the aileron, and in some installations the rudder, to bring the aircraft back to straight and level flight.

A displacement follow-up system uses position pickups on each of the primary flight controls. When a signal from the error-sensing system causes a control to deflect, the position pickup follows the movement of the surface and nulls out the signal from the error sensor when the surface attains the correct deflection.

For example, if the left wing drops, the gyro senses an error and sends a signal to the aileron servo that moves the left aileron down. When the aileron moves an amount proportional to the amount the wing has dropped, the follow-up system generates a signal equal in amplitude, but opposite in polarity, to the error signal and cancels it.

The left wing is still down and the aileron is deflected, and since the signals have canceled, the autopilot does not call for any more aileron deflection. As the aerodynamic forces bring the wing back to its level-flight attitude, an error signal opposite to the one that started the action is produced. This signal is gradually canceled, and by the time the wing is level, the aileron is in the streamlined position and there is no overshooting or oscillation.

Flight Director Indicator and Horizontal Situation Indicator

One advance in flight instrumentation is the flight director, shown in Figure 10-66. This instrument functions like an attitude indicator with the addition of the "bow-tie-shaped" steering bars. The triangular delta symbol represents the airplane, and the steering bars are controlled by the autopilot command and error-sensing systems. Rather than sending the signals to the appropriate servos to actually control the aircraft, the signals are sent to the steering bars that tell the pilot what to do. The flight director in Figure 10-66 is telling the pilot to pitch the nose up and turn to the right. The flight director shows the pilot the changes to make in pitch and roll in the same way the horizontal situation indicator (HSI) shows the pilot the proper changes to make in directional flight.

follow-up signal. A signal in an autopilot system that nulls out the input signal to the servo when the correct amount of control surface deflection has been reached.

HSI. Horizontal Situation Indicator

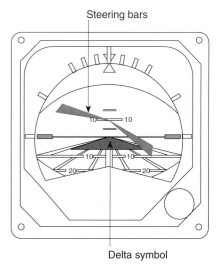

Steering bars

Delta symbol

Figure 10-66. *The bow-tie steering bars in this flight director show the pilot that the aircraft should be pitched up and turned to the right. The object is to fly the delta symbol so that it rests in the V of the steering bars.*

The HSI in Figure 10-67 shows the pilot the relationship of the aircraft to the VOR radial or ADF bearing, the magnetic direction, the desired course and heading, and also the relationship of the aircraft to the glide slope.

The pilot wants to approach the VOR station by flying inbound on the 120° radial. This gives a course of 300° to the station. This is set into the HSI with the course select knob. The airplane is flying a compass heading of 330° as shown opposite the lubber line, and is slightly to the left of the desired course as is shown by the lateral deviation bar which is to the right of the airplane symbol. If the pilot continues on this heading, the 330° radial will be intercepted, but the pilot has turned the heading select knob until the selected heading marker, or "bug," is over 315°. This commands the autopilot to change the heading of the airplane 15° to the left. In this case the pilot believes that the 15° difference between the heading and the course will correct for wind drift and allow the airplane to track inbound on the 120° radial.

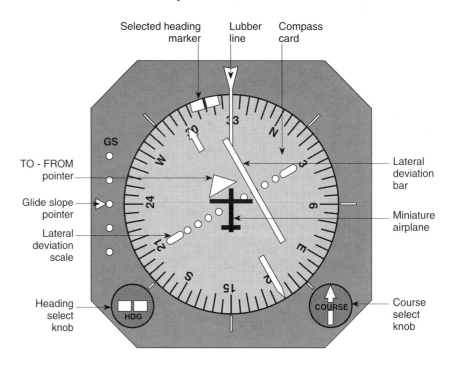

Figure 10-67. *This horizontal situation indicator (HSI) shows the pilot to be inbound to the station on the 120° radial. The selected course is 300°, the heading is 330°, and the pilot has selected a change in heading to 315°.*

Answers begin on Page 786. **Page numbers refer to chapter text.**

85. The four subsystems of an automatic flight control system are:
    a. _____
    b. _____
    c. _____
    d. _____
    Page 769

86. The pilot is able to maneuver the aircraft when the autopilot is engaged by turning knobs or pressing buttons on the _____ . *Page 769*

87. Most autopilot systems sense deviation from straight and level flight with _____ . *Page 770*

88. The type gyro used by a wing-lever type of autopilot is a/an _____ (attitude or rate) gyro. *Page 770*

89. The component in an automatic flight control system that actually applies force to move the control surface is the _____ . *Page 771*

90. Autopilot servos are driven by signals supplied by the _____ . *Page 771*

91. The subsystem in an autopilot that stops the control movement when its deflection is correct for the amount of error is called the _____ system. *Page 773*

92. The two types of follow-up systems are the _____ and the _____ systems. *Page 773*

Aural Warning Systems

FAR Part 23.729 requires that every landplane with a retractable landing gear have an aural or equally effective warning device that functions continuously when one or more throttles are closed if the landing gear is not fully extended and locked.

Transport aircraft operating under FAR Part 25 have much more stringent requirements for aural warning systems. Figure 10-68 shows some of the aural warnings used on transport aircraft.

Warning System	Stage of Operation	Signal	Cause of Signal
Landing gear	Landing	Continuous horn	Landing gear is not down and locked when flaps are less than full up and throttle is retarded to idle.
Mach warning	In flight	Clacker	EAS or Mach number limits exceeded
Flight controls	Takeoff	Intermittent horn	Thrust levers are advanced and any of these conditions exist: 1. Speed brakes not down 2. Flaps not in takeoff range 3. APU exhaust door is open 4. Stabilizer not in takeoff setting
Pressurization	In flight	Intermittent horn	If cabin pressure becomes equal to atmospheric pressure at the specific altitude
Fire warning	Any stage	Continuous bell	Any overheat condition or fire in any engine or nacelle, or main wheel or nose wheel well, APU engine or any compartment having fire warning system installed. Also when fire warning system is being tested.
Communications	Any stage	High chime	Any time captain's call button is pressed at external power panel forward, or rearward cabin attendant's panel
Communications	Any stage	Two-tone or high-low chime or single low chime	When a signal has been received by an HF or VHF communications system and decoded by the Selcal decoder

Figure 10-68. *Aural warning signals used in transport category aircraft*

Answers begin on Page 786. Page numbers refer to chapter text.

93. The takeoff warning system alerts the flight crew when a flight control is not properly set prior to takeoff. This system is activated by a switch on the _____ . *Page 776*

94. The aural signal for a fire in an engine compartment is a/an _____ . *Page 776*

95. The aural signal for a flight control being in an unsafe condition for takeoff is a/an _____ . *Page 776*

96. The aural signal for the landing gear being in an unsafe condition for landing is a/an _____ . *Page 776*

Instrument Installation and Maintenance

Aircraft instrument maintenance is different from any other maintenance. According to FAR 65.81(a), a certificated technician may perform or supervise the maintenance, preventive maintenance, or alteration of an aircraft or appliance, or a part thereof, for which he or she is rated (but excluding major repairs to, and major alterations of propellers, and *any repair to, or alteration of, instruments.*)

Aviation maintenance technicians are authorized to perform the required 100-hour inspections on instruments and instrument systems and to conduct the static system checks. They can remove and replace instruments and instrument components and replace the range markings on instruments if these marks are on the outside of the glass and do not require opening the instrument case.

Any actual repair or calibration to an instrument must be made by the instrument manufacturer or by an FAA-certificated repair station approved for the particular repair to the specified instrument.

Instrument Range Marking

Some instruments have colored range marks that let the pilot see at a glance whether a particular system or component is operating in a safe and desirable range of operation or in an unsafe range. The colored marks direct attention to approaching operating difficulties. Figure 10-69 shows the colors used and the meaning of each.

Color and type of mark	Meaning
Green arc	Normal operating range
Yellow arc	Caution range
White arc	Special operations range
Red arc	Prohibited range
Red radial line	Do not exceed indication
Blue radial line	Special operating condition

Figure 10-69. *Meanings of instrument range mark colors*

Instrument	Range Marking	Instrument	Range Marking
Airspeed indicator		**Oil temperature gauge**	
White arc	Flap operating range	Green arc	Normal operating range
Bottom	Flaps-down stall speed	Yellow arc	Precautionary range
Top	Maximum airspeed for flaps-down flight	Red radial line	Maximum and/or minimum permissible oil temperature
Green arc	Normal operating range		
Bottom	Flaps-up stall speed	**Tachometer (Reciprocating engine)**	
Top	Maximum airspeed for rough air	Green arc	Normal operating range
Blue radial line	Best single-engine rate of climb airspeed	Yellow arc	Precautionary range
		Red arc	Restricted operating range
Yellow arc	Structural warning area	Red radial line	Maximum permissible rotational speed
Bottom	Maximum airspeed for rough air		
Top	Never-exceed airspeed	**Tachometer (Turbine engine)**	
Red radial line	Never-exceed airspeed	Green arc	Normal operating range
		Yellow arc	Precautionary range
Carburetor air temperature		Red radial line	Maximum permissible rotational speed
Green arc	Normal operating range		
Yellow arc	Range where carburetor ice is most likely to form	**Tachometer (Helicopter)**	
		Engine tachometer	
Red radial line	Maximum allowable inlet air temperature	Green arc	Normal operating range
		Yellow arc	Precautionary range
		Red radial line	Maximum permissible rotational speed
Cylinder head temperature		Rotor tachometer	
Green arc	Normal operating range	Green arc	Normal operating range
Yellow arc	Operation approved for limited time	Red radial line	Maximum and minimum rotor speed for power-off operational conditions
Red radial line	Never-exceed temperature		
		Torque indicator	
Manifold pressure gage		Green arc	Normal operating range
Green arc	Normal operating range	Yellow arc	Precautionary range
Yellow arc	Precautionary range	Red radial line	Maximum permissible torque pressure
Red radial line	Maximum permissible manifold absolute pressure		
		Exhaust gas temperature indicator (Turbine engine)	
Fuel pressure gage		Green arc	Normal operating range
Green arc	Normal operating range	Yellow arc	Precautionary range
Yellow arc	Precautionary range	Red radial line	Maximum permissible gas temperature
Red radial line	Maximum and/or minimum permissible fuel pressure		
Oil pressure gage			
Green arc	Normal operating range		
Yellow arc	Precautionary range		
Red radial line	Maximum and/or minimum permissible oil pressure		

Figure 10-70. *Range markings for specific instruments*

It is the responsibility of the technician installing an instrument in an aircraft and a technician conducting an inspection to be sure the instruments are properly marked for the aircraft in which they are being installed. Type Certificate Data Sheets for the aircraft and the engine specify the range marks that are required.

Some instruments have the range marking on the glass rather than on the dial, and instruments marked in this way must have a slip mark to show if the glass has slipped and the marks are no longer properly aligned. The slip mark is a white line painted across the instrument bezel and onto the glass at the bottom of the instrument. If the glass should slip and get the markings out of alignment with the numbers on the dial, the slip mark will be broken and the pilot warned that the range markings are not correct.

Instrument Installation

A technician is allowed to install instruments in an instrument panel, and it is his or her responsibility on an inspection to be sure that the instruments are secure in their mounting and that all the hoses and wires attached to the instruments are in good condition and do not interfere with any of the controls.

Many of the electrical instruments are mounted in iron or steel cases to prevent interference from outside magnetic fields. Lines of magnetic flux cannot flow across iron or steel, and these cases entrap the lines of flux, rather than allowing them to affect nearby instruments. Even with this precaution, electrical instruments should not be mounted near the magnetic compass, and the wires carrying current into the compass light should be twisted to prevent the lines of flux from this small current from causing a compass error.

Most instruments are installed in the panel with four brass machine screws that screw either into brass nuts mounted in holes in the instrument case or into nut plates installed in the panel. Because panel space is so limited, many modern instrument cases are flangeless and are held in clamps attached to the back of the panel. The instrument is connected to its electrical harness or hose and slipped through the hole in the panel until it is flush and properly aligned, then the clamp-tightening screw in the panel is turned to tighten the clamp around the instrument case.

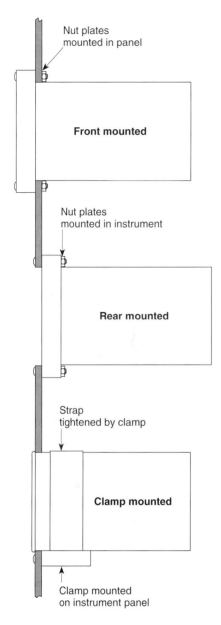

Figure 10-71. *Instrument mounting methods*

bezel. The rim that holds the glass cover in the case of an aircraft instrument.

Figure 10-72. *The basic "T" arrangement of the flight instruments*

shock mounts. Resilient mounting pads used to protect electronic equipment by absorbing low-frequency, high-amplitude vibrations.

bonding. The process of electrically connecting all isolated components to the aircraft structure. Bonding provides a path for return current from the components, and it provides a low-impedance path to ground to minimize radio interference from static electrical charges. Shock-mounted instrument panels have bonding braids connected across the shock mounts, so that return current from the instruments can flow into the main structure and thus return to the alternator or battery.

For many years the arrangement of the instruments in the panel was haphazard, at best. The directional gyro and gyro horizon were much larger than the other instruments and were often placed in inappropriate locations. Now that instrument flight has become so important, there is a standard arrangement for basic flight instruments. This is known as the basic "T" arrangement.

Aircraft instrument panels are shock-mounted to absorb low-frequency, high-amplitude shocks. The type, size, and number of shock mounts required for an instrument panel are determined by the weight of the complete panel unit with all of the instruments installed. For heavy panels, two shock mounts like those in Figure 10-73A are mounted between brackets attached to the structure and to the panel. Lighter weight panels are supported from the structure with the type of shock mounts shown in Figure 10-73B. Any time a panel is supported by shock mounts, a bonding strap must be installed across the mounts to carry any return current from the instruments into the aircraft structure. When inspecting instrument installation, check the bonding straps to be sure that they are in good condition and securely fastened.

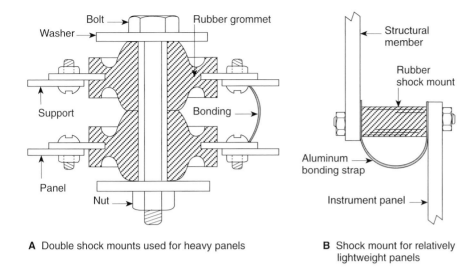

A Double shock mounts used for heavy panels
B Shock mount for relatively lightweight panels

Figure 10-73. *Instrument panel shock mounts*

Instrument Maintenance

An aircraft instrument in need of any repair or alteration must be returned to the instrument manufacturer or to a certificated repair station approved for the particular instrument. A technician can install instruments and inspect them, but is not authorized to do any type of repair or alteration.

Such operations as replacing range markings on the outside of the instrument glass, tightening loose mounting screws, tightening leaking B nuts in the plumbing, and retouching chipped case paint are not considered to be instrument repairs or alterations and may be done by an appropriately rated technician.

Instruments that have a leaking case or a cracked glass or instruments that are fogged or whose pointers will not zero must be replaced.

Static System Leak Checks

Altimeters, vertical speed indicators, and airspeed indicators all connect to the static air system. As the airplane goes up in altitude, the static air pressure lowers, and the altimeter indicates a higher altitude. The air pressure inside the airspeed indicator case lowers, and the pitot pressure can more easily expand the diaphragm capsule.

If the static pressure line should become disconnected inside a pressurized cabin in flight, the static pressure in the instrument cases will increase. This will cause the altimeter to read a lower altitude and the airspeed indicator to indicate a lower airspeed.

A certificated technician with an airframe rating can check the static air system for leakage as is required by FAR 91.411 and described in FAR Part 43, Appendix E. All openings into the static system are closed, and a negative pressure, or suction, of 1.07 inches of mercury is applied to the static system, to cause an equivalent altitude increase of 1,000 feet to be indicated on the altimeter. The line to the tester is then shut off and the altimeter is watched. It must not leak down more than 100 feet in one minute.

If a leak is indicated, isolate portions of the system and check each portion systematically. Begin at the connection nearest the instruments and check it. If this is good, reseal the connection and check the next portion, working your way out to the static ports until the leak is found.

A static system leak checker may be made from components that can be purchased from a surgical supply house. You will need an air bulb such as is used for measuring blood pressure and two or three feet of thick-walled surgical hose. Slip the hose over the suction end of the bulb as seen in Figure 10-74 and clamp it in place with a hose clamp.

To check the system, close the pressure bleed-off valve and then squeeze the air bulb to expel as much air as possible. Hold the suction hose firmly against the static pressure opening and slowly release the bulb while watching the altimeter and vertical speed indicator. Do not release the bulb rapidly enough for the needle on the VSI to peg. When the altimeter indicates an increase in altitude of 1,000 feet, pinch the hose to trap the suction in the system, and hold it for one minute. The altimeter indication should not decrease by more than 100 feet.

Most aircraft have more than one static port, and when performing this test, the port not used must be taped over to prevent it interfering with the test. One handy method of doing this is to use black plastic electrical tape to make a large X over the static port. This tape is easy to remove without damaging the finish, and the large black X is so easy to see that you are not likely to forget and leave the static port covered.

The pressure end of the checker can be used for checking the integrity of the pitot system.

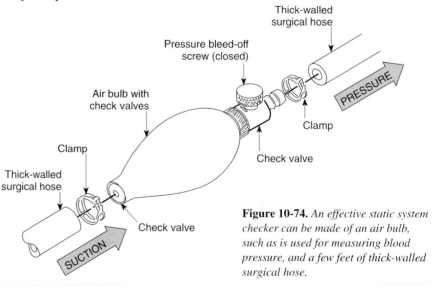

Figure 10-74. *An effective static system checker can be made of an air bulb, such as is used for measuring blood pressure, and a few feet of thick-walled surgical hose.*

Instrument Handling

Aircraft instruments are delicate and sensitive devices that require special care in handling. Many of the cases of airspeed indicators, vertical speed indicators, and manifold pressure gages are made of thermosetting plastic and can be cracked if the fittings are overtightened. Be sure to observe the caution marked on these instruments, and do not blow into the openings.

Cylinder head temperature and exhaust gas temperature gages are thermocouple-type instruments whose moving coils are damped through the thermocouple. When the thermocouple is not connected, the instrument is not damped and the pointer can swing violently enough to knock it out of balance, which will result in inaccurate indications. Any time a thermocouple instrument is not connected to its thermocouple, a loop of uninsulated wire should be wrapped around the terminals to short-circuit them and allow damping current to flow. Be sure that this wire is removed before the thermocouple is connected.

Gyro instruments are especially easy to damage by rough handling. If the instrument is fitted with a caging device, cage it when it is not in the panel. Never handle a gyro instrument when the rotor is spinning, and when preparing it for shipment to a repair facility, use only the packing boxes specified by the manufacturer or the repair shop. Some gyro instruments require special handling, and when packing this type of instrument be sure to follow all instructions in detail.

cage. To lock the gimbals of a gyroscopic instrument so it will not be damaged by abrupt flight maneuvers or rough handling.

*Answers begin on Page 786. **Page numbers refer to chapter text.***

97. An aviation maintenance technician with an airframe rating _____ (is or is not) permitted to make a minor repair to an airspeed indicator. *Page 777*

98. An aviation maintenance technician with a powerplant rating _____ (is or is not) permitted to calibrate an oil temperature gage. *Page 777*

99. An aviation maintenance technician with an airframe rating _____ (is or is not) permitted to perform an instrument system static check on an aircraft. *Page 777*

100. Instruments can be repaired only by the manufacturer or by a/an _____ approved by the FAA for the particular instrument. *Page 777*

101. The proper range marks for an instrument may be found in the _____ for the aircraft or engine. *Page 779*

102. The white arc on an airspeed indicator is the _____ range. *Page 778*

103. The yellow arc on an airspeed indicator is the _____ area. *Page 778*

104. An airspeed indicator is marked to show the best rate of climb speed with one engine inoperative with a _____ radial line. *Page 778*

105. A red arc on a tachometer indicates a _____ range. *Page 778*

106. A green arc on an instrument indicates the _____ range. *Page 777*

107. A white slip mark between the instrument bezel and the glass is required when the instrument range marks are on the _____ . *Page 779*

108. The maximum or minimum safe operating limits are indicated on an instrument dial with a _____ . *Page 777*

109. An AMT certificate with an airframe rating _____ (is or is not) authorization to replace a cracked glass in an aircraft instrument. *Page 781*

110. The person responsible for making sure an instrument is properly marked when it is installed in an aircraft is the instrument _____ . *Page 779*

111. There are two ways instruments can be held in the instrument panel. These are:

a. _____

b. _____

Page 779

112. Aircraft instrument panels are usually shock mounted to absorb _____ (low or high)-frequency, _____ (low or high) -amplitude shocks. *Page 780*

113. A certificated technician with airframe and powerplant ratings _____ (may or may not) perform minor repairs to engine instruments. *Page 781*

114. The result of the instrument static pressure line becoming disconnected inside a pressurized cabin during high altitude cruising flight will be that the altimeter will read _____ (high or low) and the airspeed indicator will read _____ (high or low). *Page 781*

115. When an unpressurized aircraft's static pressure system is leak-checked to comply with the requirements of FAR 91.411, the _____ may be used in lieu of a pitot-static system tester. *Page 782*

116. The maximum altitude loss permitted during an unpressurized aircraft instrument static pressure system integrity check is _____ feet in _____ minute(s). *Page 782*

117. The minimum requirements for testing and inspection of instrument static pressure systems required by FAR Section 91.411 are contained in FAR _____ Appendix _____ . *Page 781*

118. When performing the static system leakage check required by FAR 91.411, the technician uses a _____ (positive or negative) pressure. *Page 782*

119. If a static pressure system check reveals excessive leakage, the leak(s) may be located by isolating portions of the line and testing each portion systematically, starting at the _____ (instrument or static port) end of the system. *Page 782*

Answers to Aircraft Instrument Systems Study Questions

1. absolute
2. absolute
3. gage
4. gage
5. gage
6. differential
7. differential
8. expansion
9. vapor
10. nickel
11. increases
12. iron, constantan
13. current
14. reference
15. chromel, alumel
16. alumel
17. series
18. variable resistor
19. permanent magnet
20. permanent magnet
21. toroidal
22. three
23. electromagnet
24. single
25. three
26. 26, 400
27. 100
28. eddy currents
29. steel
30. frequency
31. synchroscope
32. G
33. 1G
34. is not
35. angle of attack
36. reference plane
37. lubber line
38. 5
39. are not
40. does not
41. deviation
42. does
43. deviation
44. 10
45. twisting
46. a. acceleration error
    b. northerly-turning error
47. lubber line
48. rigidity in space
49. double
50. roll, pitch
51. vertical
52. vertical
53. horizontal
54. is not
55. precession
56. single
57. vertical
58. horizontal
59. 3
60. 3
61. roll, yaw
62. airspeed indicator, altimeter, vertical speed indicator
63. airspeed indicator
64. electric heater
65. alternate static air
66. indicated
67. calibrated
68. true
69. aneroid
70. decreases
71. .75
72. mean sea level, indicated
73. pressure
74. 29.92, 1013
75. transponder
76. 125
77. change
78. lags
79. accelerometer
80. electricity
81. engine oil
82. carbon
83. deicer
84. pressure
85. a. command
    b. error-sensing
    c. correction
    d. follow-up
86. controller
87. gyros
88. rate
89. servo
90. controller
91. follow-up
92. rate, displacement
93. thrust lever
94. continuous bell
95. intermittent horn
96. continuous horn
97. is not
98. is not
99. is
100. repair station
101. Type Certificate Data Sheets
102. flap operating
103. structural warning
104. blue
105. restricted operating
106. normal operating
107. glass
108. red radial line
109. is not
110. installer
111. a. screws
     b. clamps
112. low, high
113. may not
114. low, low
115. altimeter
116. 100, 1
117. 43, E
118. negative
119. instrument

COMMUNICATION AND NAVIGATION SYSTEMS

11

Continued

Electronic Systems Installation and Maintenance   843

COMMUNICATION AND NAVIGATION SYSTEMS

Communication Systems

For many years the only electronics involved in aviation were used for communication and navigation, and all electronic equipment was classified simply as "radio." Today's aircraft employ vast quantities of electronic equipment, much of it unrelated to either communication or navigation. This equipment is now classified as avionics. This section considers the portion of avionics that deals with communication and navigation, and the section on electronic instrument systems discusses some of the other aspects of avionics.

avionics. The branch of technology that deals with the design, production, installation, use, and servicing of electronic equipment mounted in aircraft.

Components in the communication and electronic navigation systems are considered aircraft instruments, and as such, can only be repaired by the manufacturer or by an FAA-certificated repair station. To perform certain tuning operations on radio transmitters, technicians must hold the appropriate license issued by the Federal Communications Commission (FCC). Each radio transmitter installed in an aircraft must have an FCC-issued radio station license, and this license must be displayed in the aircraft. Each person operating a radio transmitter must hold at least a valid restricted-radio-telephone permit, which is also issued by the FCC.

Basic Radio Theory

Radio is a method of transmitting intelligence from one location to another by means of electromagnetic radiation.

A block diagram of an extremely basic radio transmitter is shown in Figure 11-1. This transmitter contains a crystal-controlled oscillator that produces alternating current with a very accurate frequency in the radio frequency (RF) range. This is above approximately 10 kilohertz (10,000 cycles per second). The intelligence to be transmitted is changed into an audio frequency (AF) electrical signal by the microphone, and this AF modulates, or changes, the carrier so that its voltage varies in exactly the same way as the voltage from the microphone. Notice that both sides of the modulated carrier are the same as the AF signal. The voltage of the modulated carrier is amplified so that it has enough power to radiate into space when it goes to the antenna.

antenna. A special device used with electronic communication and navigation systems to radiate and receive electromagnetic energy.

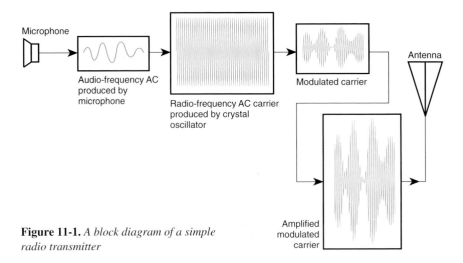

Figure 11-1. *A block diagram of a simple radio transmitter*

The signal radiates out into space from the transmitter antenna, and is picked up by the receiver antenna, as shown in Figure 11-2.

The signal picked up by the antenna is a very weak imitation of the amplified modulated RF signal that was sent to the transmitter antenna. The weak modulated RF signal is amplified, and then demodulated. This removes the RF carrier but leaves both halves of the AF signal. Since the resultant voltage of the AF signal is zero, one half must be removed. This is done in the detector, or rectifier. The resulting voltage has the same waveform as that produced by the microphone attached to the transmitter. This signal has too low a voltage to be useful, so it is amplified and then used to drive a speaker. The audio output of the speaker is the same as the input to the microphone.

The transmitter uses a crystal oscillator to produce an accurately controlled carrier frequency, and only this one frequency radiates from the transmitter antenna. The receiver antenna picks up not only the signal from the desired transmitter, but signals from every other transmitter in the area as well as electromagnetic radiation from all sorts of electrical devices. In order

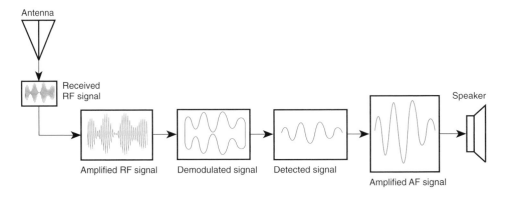

Figure 11-2. *A block diagram of a simple radio receiver*

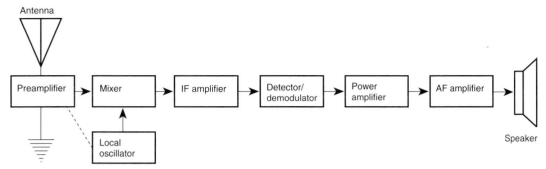

Figure 11-3. *A simplified block diagram of a superheterodyne receiver*

for a receiver to be useful, it must filter out every frequency except the one that is wanted. To do this, it employs a special superheterodyne circuit.

The antenna picks up all the radio signals in the area, and they are taken into a tunable preamplifier. This preamplifier uses an electronic filter circuit that passes only the frequency to which the receiver is tuned and sends all of the other frequencies to ground. To better understand filters, review the section on filters in the *General* textbook of this *Aviation Maintenance Technician Series*, beginning on Page 237. In this explanation, we will consider the receiver to be a broadcast receiver tuned to 1,200 kilohertz. The preamplifier amplifies any signal with a frequency of 1,200 kHz and passes all other frequencies to ground.

A tunable local oscillator is included in this circuit. The frequency of this oscillator is varied so it is always a specific frequency higher than the frequency to which the preamplifier is tuned. For most broadcast band receivers, the frequency of the local oscillator is always 455 kilohertz higher than the frequency tuned on the preamplifier. In this case, the local oscillator produces a signal with a frequency of 1,655 kilohertz (1,200 + 455).

The signals from the preamplifier and the local oscillator are sent to the mixer. When signals with two frequencies are mixed, they produce two other signals, one with a frequency that is the sum of the original two frequencies and the other with a frequency that is the difference between the two. The four signals will have frequencies of 1,200 kHz, 1,655 kHz, 2,855 kHz (1,200 + 1,655), and 455 kHz (1,655 – 1,200). The four signals from the mixer are sent into the intermediate frequency (IF) amplifier. This is a very narrow-band amplifier that is tuned to 455 kHz. It amplifies the 455 kHz signal and attenuates, or diminishes, all other frequencies.

The amplified 455 kHz signal is sent to the detector/demodulator, which removes the 455 kHz IF carrier and leaves the AF envelope that has both halves of the audio signal. The detector rectifies the AF signal and removes one half of the envelope. The resulting signal is an exact copy of the AF that modulated the carrier that is being received. The AF signal is amplified by a power amplifier stage and drives the speaker. The output of the speaker is the same as the input to the microphone at the transmitter.

superheterodyne circuit. A sensitive radio receiver circuit in which a local oscillator produces a frequency that is a specific difference from the received signal frequency. The desired signal and the output from the oscillator are mixed, and they produce a single, constant intermediate frequency. This IF is amplified, demodulated, and detected to produce the audio frequency that is used to drive the speaker.

Communication receivers such as those used in aircraft are more sensitive than the normal household broadcast receiver, and they have more stages. Figure 11-4 shows a block diagram of a very high frequency (VHF) communication receiver.

The signal is picked up on the antenna and amplified by the tuned preamplifier. The local oscillator produces a frequency that is 10.8-megahertz different from the frequency to which the preamplifier is tuned. These two frequencies are fed into the mixer where they produce a 10.8-MHz intermediate frequency. This IF is amplified by two stages of IF amplification and sent into the detector/demodulator, where it emerges as an audio frequency signal that duplicates the AF produced by the microphone at the transmitter.

To hold the output constant as the input signal voltage changes, some of the output from the detector goes to an automatic volume control (AVC). This is fed back into the preamplifier in such a way that it increases the preamp amplification when the signal is weak and attenuates it when the signal is too strong.

Some of the detector output is sent into a squelch circuit that controls the audio frequency amplifier. When no signal is being received, the AF amplifier output is attenuated, or decreased, so the background noise that makes a hissing sound in the speaker is not loud enough to be annoying. But as soon as a signal is received, the attenuation is removed, allowing the audio output to be loud enough to be comfortably heard.

The output of the AF amplifier goes to a power amplifier where it is further amplified so it can drive the speaker.

noise (electrical). An unwanted electrical signal within a piece of electronic equipment.

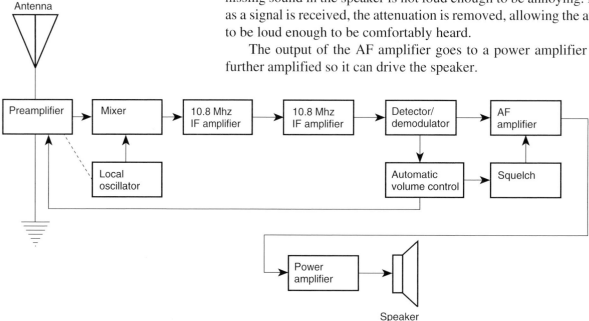

Figure 11-4. *A simplified block diagram of a VHF superheterodyne communication receiver*

Modulation

As you have seen in the simplified explanation of a transmitter and receiver, the carrier wave that is generated in the transmitter is just that, a device that carries the information from the transmitter to the receiver. The carrier has a frequency high enough to produce electromagnetic waves that radiate from the antenna, and this frequency is accurately controlled so that a sensitive receiver can select the carrier from a specific transmitter and reject the carriers from all other transmitters.

The carrier itself serves no function other than to carry the signal from the transmitter to the receiver, and the carrier is routed to ground after the intelligence is removed from it. It is the intelligence, or information, produced by the microphone or other type of input device that is important. The process of placing intelligence on a carrier is called modulation, and there are several ways to do it. Three ways most often used in aviation communication equipment are amplitude modulation (AM), frequency modulation (FM), and single-sideband (SSB).

Amplitude Modulation (AM)

Amplitude modulation, or AM, is a method of modulation in which the voltage of the carrier is changed by the audio signal. Figure 11-5 shows a sine-wave audio signal that has been used to modulate a carrier. The voltage of the resulting carrier varies with the voltage of the modulating audio frequency.

Frequency Modulation (FM)

Man-made interference, such as that caused by electric motors and ignition systems, and natural interference, like that caused by lightning in the atmosphere, amplitude-modulate all radio signals in their vicinity. Frequency modulation is used to obtain interference-free communication.

The voltage variations of the audio frequency signal produced by a microphone are used to change the frequency of the carrier. As shown in Figure 11-6, as the voltage of the AF rises in a positive direction, the frequency of the carrier increases, and as it goes negative, the frequency of the carrier decreases.

The amplitude of an FM carrier is held constant by limiter circuits, and any interference, which amplitude-modulates the carrier, is clipped off so it does not appear in the output.

When an FM signal is received, the deviations in frequency are changed into amplitude variations in an audio-frequency voltage that is amplified and used to drive the speaker.

Single-Sideband (SSB)

Both AM and FM are limited in that they require a wide band of frequencies for their transmission. For example, if a 25-MHz carrier is modulated with an audio-frequency signal that contains frequencies up to 5,000 hertz, the transmitted signal occupies a band of frequencies from 24.995 to 25.005

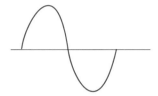

Waveform of the audio frequency used to modulate the carrier

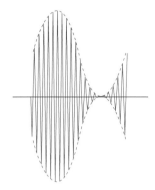

Amplitude of the modulated carrier varies with amplitude of modulating AF

Figure 11-5. *Amplitude modulation*

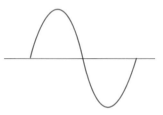

Waveform of audio frequency used to modulate the carrier

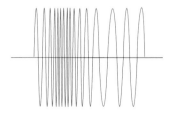

Frequency of modulated carrier varies with amplitude of modulating AF

Figure 11-6. *Frequency modulation*

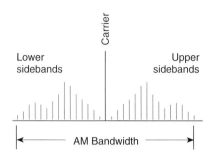

An AM transmitter must transmit carrier and both upper and lower sidebands. This requires much power and twice the bandwidth needed for the information.

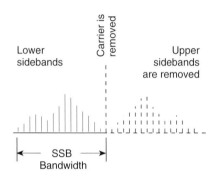

An SSB transmitter removes carrier and transmits only one sideband, in this case, the lower sideband.

Figure 11-7. *Advantage of SSB over AM*

noise (electrical). An unwanted electrical signal within a piece of electronic equipment.

megahertz. This band includes the carrier, the lower sideband, which is the carrier frequency minus the modulating frequency; and the upper sideband, which is the carrier frequency plus the modulating frequency.

Figure 11-7 shows the advantages of SSB over AM. The upper illustration shows the bandwidth required for an AM signal, and the lower illustration shows shows the bandwidth required for an SSB signal. The carrier and the upper sideband have been removed.

All the information needed is carried in either one of the sidebands, and it is inefficient use of energy to transmit the carrier and both the upper and lower sidebands. Removing the carrier and one of the sidebands and using all of the available energy for transmitting the other sideband give the transmitter a much greater range.

Radio in the United States typically uses the lower sideband, but the upper sideband is used overseas. When an SSB transmission is picked up by an AM receiver, it is heard as a muffled noise because it has no carrier to mix with to produce an audible tone. But inside the SSB receiver, a carrier of the proper frequency is inserted and the original sound is reproduced.

At present, SSB is the primary type of transmission for communication in the high-frequency (HF) band.

Radio Waves

When a high-frequency AC signal is placed on a special conductor called an antenna, two fields exist: electric fields, called E fields; and magnetic fields, called H fields. In Figure 11-8, view A shows an electrical generator connected between the two halves of the antenna. View B shows the development of the magnetic field whose strength is determined by the amount of current flowing. Since this is AC, which periodically reverses, the current is not uniform throughout the antenna, but is minimum at the end of each section, where it reverses, and maximum in the center. The current flows in the direction shown by the arrow I for one alternation and then reverses during the next. C shows the development of the electric field. The polarity is shown for one alternation, and the intensity of the E field is determined by the amount of voltage. D shows the two fields that exist in the antenna at the same time.

When the AC changes fast enough, the fields do not entirely collapse before the next buildup occurs, and some of the energy is radiated out into space as an electromagnetic, or radio, wave. This wave has two components, the electric wave and the magnetic wave. The waves are at right angles to each other, and both are at right angles to the direction of propagation, or the direction the wave is traveling. *See* Figure 11-9.

When a radio wave leaves the transmitter antenna, it travels out in space at the speed of light, 186,000 miles per second, or 300,000,000 meters per second. When this wave strikes the antenna of a radio receiver, it generates a voltage that is a much weaker replication of the voltage in the transmitter antenna.

A Transmitter is actually an AC generator placed between two halves of the antenna.

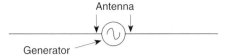

B Alternating current flowing in antenna produces magnetic field whose strength varies along length of antenna. Direction of field reverses with each alternation.

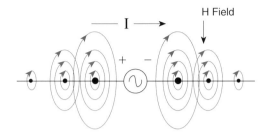

C Voltage that exists between the ends of antenna produces an electric field. Polarity of this field reverses with each alternation of the AC.

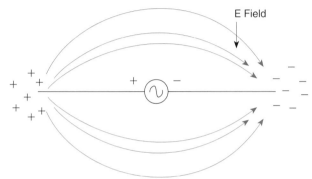

D Magnetic (H) and electric (E) fields exist in antenna at same time.

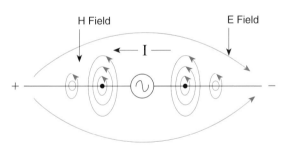

Figure 11-8. *Fields surrounding a radio antenna*

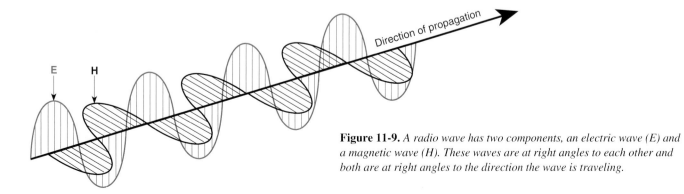

Figure 11-9. *A radio wave has two components, an electric wave (E) and a magnetic wave (H). These waves are at right angles to each other and both are at right angles to the direction the wave is traveling.*

Polarization

To induce the maximum amount of voltage into the receiving antenna, the antenna must be installed in such a way that it is perpendicular to the magnetic, H, field, and parallel to the electric, E, field in the radio waves. When the transmitting antenna is vertical, the E field is vertical, and the radiation is said to be vertically polarized. The maximum reception is picked up with a vertical antenna. When the transmitting antenna is horizontal, the radiation is horizontally polarized, and is best received on a horizontal antenna.

Wavelength

A radio wave is essentially a sine wave that radiates from the transmitting antenna. There is a definite relationship between the length of the wave and its frequency, and this relationship is extremely important. The higher the frequency, the shorter the distance between the ends of the wave. This relationship is seen in the formula in Figure 11-10.

$$\lambda = v \div f$$
λ = wavelength in meters
v = velocity of light (300,000,000 meters per second for radio waves) ÷ 1,000,000
f = frequency in megahertz

Example: Find the length of a VHF wave whose frequency is 108 megahertz.

$$\lambda = v \div f$$
$$= 300 \div 108$$
$$= 2.8 \text{ meters}$$

Figure 11-10. *Relationship between frequency and wavelength*

Frequency Allocation

Radio did not become a successful means of communication until a method was devised to separate one frequency of electromagnetic energy from all the others. This is commonly done by the use of electronic filters, and it has reached an extremely high level of perfection.

It is now practical to produce many frequencies in a transmitter by using only a single high-precision crystal in a circuit called a synthesizer. The oscillators inside the receivers are also crystal controlled, and it is now common practice to have adjacent communication channels separated by only 25 kilohertz.

Since it is possible to separate frequencies accurately, the usable range of frequencies has been divided and bands assigned for various communication and navigation purposes. The frequencies used for aviation communication and navigation are shown in Figure 11-11.

Band and Function	Frequency
Very low frequency (VLF)	**3 – 30 kHz**
Omega	10 – 14 kHz
Low frequency (LF)	**30 – 300 kHz**
Decca	70 – 130 kHz
Loran C	100 kHz
ADF	200 – 1,700 kHz
Medium frequency (MF)	**300 kHz – 3 MHz**
Commercial broadcast	535 kHz – 1.6 MHz
High frequency (HF)	**3 – 30 MHz**
HF communications	2 – 25 MHz
Very high frequency (VHF)	**30 – 300 MHz**
Marker beacons	75 MHz
ILS localizer	108.1 – 111.95 MHz
VOR	108.0 – 117.95 MHz
VHF communications	118.0 – 135.975 MHz
Ultrahigh frequency (UHF)	**300 MHz – 3 GHz**
ILS glideslope	320 – 340 MHz
DME	960 MHz – 1.215 GHz
Secondary surveillance radar	1.03 GHz and 1.09 GHz
Superhigh frequency (SHF)	**3 – 30 GHz**
Radar altimeter	2.2 – 2.4 GHz
Weather radar (C band)	5.5 GHz
Doppler radar (X band)	8.8 GHz
Weather radar (X band)	9.4 GHz
Doppler radar (K band)	13.3 GHz
Extremely high frequency (EHF)	**30 – 300 GHz**

Figure 11-11. *Frequency allocation for aviation navigation and communication*

Communication radios use highly sensitive and selective transmitters and receivers for two-way communication between aircraft and ground stations or between aircraft in flight.

Aircraft flying over the oceans typically use HF communication because it can travel great distances. HF equipment operates in the frequency range of 2 to 25 megahertz and is normally single-sideband.

Very high frequency (VHF) radio transmissions operate in the 118.000 to 135.975 megahertz range. This frequency range is used for air traffic control (ATC) communication and for communication between civil aircraft operated domestically. VHF communication use single-channel simplex operation in which a single frequency is used for both transmitting and receiving (single-channel), but only one person can talk at a time (simplex). This differs from duplex communication where both people can talk at the same time, as on a telephone.

VHF. Very High Frequency

Radio Wave Propagation

When a radio wave is transmitted from the antenna it moves out along three paths, depending primarily upon its frequency. These paths are surface waves, sky waves, and space waves, as in Figure 11-12.

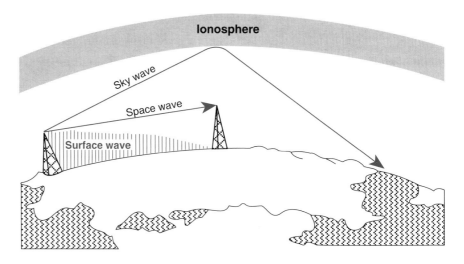

Figure 11-12. *Electromagnetic energy radiated from a transmitter antenna travels in surface waves, sky waves, or space waves, depending primarily on its frequency.*

The lower frequencies such as VLF, LF, and MF normally follow the curvature of the earth in surface waves. These waves travel great distances and are used for very long-distance communication and navigation. Commercial broadcast signals follow this path in the daytime.

HF communication and commercial broadcast at night are carried primarily by sky waves. This energy tries to radiate into space, but it bounces off the ionosphere and returns to the earth at a distance from the transmitter. This "skip distance," as it is called, varies and is responsible for the fading of many signals heard from a long distance.

Frequencies in the VHF and higher bands follow a straight line from the transmitting antenna to the receiving antenna and are said to travel by space waves.

Antenna

An antenna is a special conductor connected to a radio transmitter to radiate the electromagnetic energy produced by the transmitter into space. An antenna is also connected to the receiver to intercept this electromagnetic energy and carry it into the receiver circuits, where it is changed into signals that can be heard and used. The characteristics that make an antenna good for transmitting also make it good for receiving.

skip distance. The distance from a radio transmitting antenna to the point on the surface of the earth the reflected sky wave first touches after it has bounced off of the ionosphere.

dipole antenna. A straight-wire, half-wavelength, center-fed radio antenna. The length of each of the two arms is approximately one fourth of the wavelength of the center frequency for which the antenna is designed.

Three characteristics of an antenna are critical: its length, polarization, and directivity. For an antenna to be most efficient, its length must be one-half the wavelength of the signal being transmitted or received, as shown in Figure 11-13. This length allows the antenna current to be maximum.

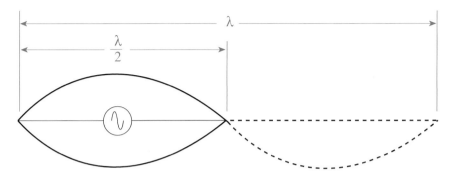

Figure 11-13. *For maximum efficiency, an antenna should have a length of one-half the wavelength it is carrying.*

When the transmitting antenna is vertical, its electric field is vertical and the magnetic field is horizontal. It is picked up best by a vertical antenna. Most LF, MF, and HF communication use horizontally polarized antennas, and higher frequency systems use vertically polarized antennas.

Figure 11-14 shows three types of antennas and their directional characteristics. The dipole antenna in **A** transmits its signal strongest in a direction perpendicular to its length. The vertical whip antenna in **B** has a uniform field strength in all directions and is called an omnidirectional antenna. The loop antenna in **C** is highly directional. Its strength is sharply reduced in the direction perpendicular to its plane.

Transmission Lines

In order for a transmitter to get the maximum amount of energy into its antenna, and for the receiving antenna to get the maximum amount of energy into its receiver, the antennas must be connected to the equipment with a special type of conductor called a coaxial cable. This cable has a central conductor surrounded by a special insulating material. This is, in turn, surrounded by a braided metal shield. All of this is encased in a protective plastic coating. A coaxial cable, commonly called coax, has a specified characteristic impedance that must be matched to the antenna and the transmitter or receiver. Normally this impedance is 50 ohms.

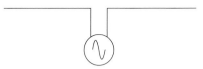

A A dipole antenna has its strongest field perpendicular to its length.

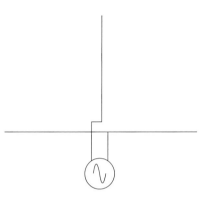

B A vertical whip antenna is omnidirectional. Its field strength is equal in all directions.

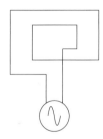

C A loop antenna is highly directional. Its maximum strength is in line with its plane and decreases sharply perpendicular to its plane.

Figure 11-14. *Directional characteristics of typical antennas*

coaxial cable. A special type of electrical cable that consists of a central conductor held rigidly in the center of a braided outer conductor.

Coaxial cable, or coax, as it is normally called, is used for attaching radio receivers and transmitters to their antenna.

Coax is relatively rugged, but care must be exercised to not bend it around too tight a radius or to allow it to become overheated. Anything that distorts the spacing between the central conductor and the outer conductor can change the characteristics of the coax and decrease the efficiency of the installation.

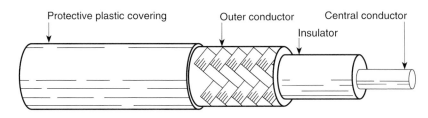

Figure 11-15. *Coaxial cable is used to connect transmitters and receivers to their antenna.*

Communication Radio Antenna

In the past, long-wire trailing antennas were used for HF communication. But advances in communication technology have developed tuned antennas that are actually part of the aircraft structure. Other aircraft use a copper-clad steel wire enclosed in a polyethylene covering run from outside the fuselage above the cockpit to the top of the vertical fin.

VHF communication uses the frequencies between 118 and 136 megahertz, which are just above the VOR frequencies, and the antenna used is normally a quarter-wavelength, vertically polarized whip. The metal in the aircraft structure provides the other quarter-wavelength to make the antenna electrically a half-wavelength long. Many whip antennas are bent so they can also pick up horizontally polarized signals.

Broad-band blade antennas provide more efficient transmission and reception than simple whips.

Aircraft Communication Addressing and Reporting System (ACARS)

ACARS is a communication link between an airliner in flight and the airline's main ground facilities. Data is collected in the aircraft by the digital flight data acquisition unit, which interfaces with the communication systems, navigation systems, engines, flight controls, automatic flight control system, landing gear, cabin doors, and the flight management computer. Status messages are compiled and coded to compress them. The compressed message is then transmitted via the VHF communication equipment to remote ground stations scattered throughout the United States. The signal is then relayed from the station that received it to the Central Processor and Electronic Switching System, located in the Chicago area and operated by Aeronautical Radio Incorporated (ARINC). The signal is then sent by ground line to the airline's operations center. Here it is routed to the appropriate departments.

ACARS (Aircraft Communication Addressing and Reporting System). A two-way communication link between an airliner in flight and the airline's main ground facilities. Data is collected in the aircraft by digital sensors and is transmitted to the ground facilities. Replies from the ground may be printed out so the appropriate flight crewmember can have a hard copy of the response.

ARINC (Aeronautical Radio Incorporated). A corporation whose principal stockholders are the airlines. Its function is to operate certain communication links between airliners in flight and the airline ground facilities.

ARINC also sets standards for communication equipment used by the airlines.

Replies from the airline ground facilities regarding weather and dispatch updates or other pertinent data are sent via ground line to the Chicago facility and then transmitted from the appropriate remote station. Information received in the aircraft is decoded and printed so the appropriate flight crewmember can have a hard copy of the information.

Information transferred between the aircraft and the ground facility by ACARS greatly increases safety and efficiency of operation.

Selective Calling *(SELCAL)*

The flight crew members of a modern airliner have such a heavy work load that they are not able to spare the concentration needed to monitor the frequencies used by the airline company in order to select from all of the traffic only the messages directed at their specific aircraft. The radio communication facilities operated by the FAA cannot be used for any purpose other than the control of air traffic, and therefore no company business can be conducted on these frequencies.

An airline ground facility can communicate with any of its aircraft in flight through an ARINC facility. ARINC assigns a four-tone code to each aircraft, and when it needs to communicate with a particular aircraft, this code is used. When the receiver in the aircraft identifies its code, the SELCAL decodes it and operates a chime or a light to alert the crew to the fact that a message is being directed to them. The crew can then use the appropriate receiver to hear the message.

Audio Integrating System *(AIS)*

Modern airliners have a complex interphone system that allows flight crewmembers to communicate with each other and ground crewmembers to communicate with the flight crew or with other members of the ground crew. The pilots and flight attendants can make announcements to the passengers, and the conversations in the cockpit are recorded for investigative use in the event of an air crash. Each of the subsystems of the AIS of a large jet transport aircraft are considered below.

Flight Interphone

All communications from the flight deck, both internal and external, are directed through audio selection panels at each one of the crew stations. By using switches on these panels, the crewmembers can receive and transmit on any of the VHF or HF transceivers, can listen to any of the navigation receivers, and can talk over the interphone or the public address system.

Cabin Interphone

The cabin interphone control panel allows communication between the flight attendants and the captain and allows either the flight attendants or the captain to make announcements over the public address (PA) system. The pilot has full priority over all others in making PA announcements.

Service Interphone

Phone jacks are located throughout the aircraft that allow service personnel to communicate with each other. A switch on the flight engineer's panel connects the service and flight interphone systems.

Passenger Address

Good communication between the flight crew and the passengers is extremely important in airline flying. There are four levels of priority assigned to the passenger address system. Announcements by the pilot have first priority, then announcements by the flight attendants. Prerecorded announcements follow as third level, and finally boarding music. A chime is produced when the pilot turns on the "fasten seat belt" or "no smoking" signs.

Prerecorded emergency announcements may be initiated by the pilot or by a flight attendant, and these messages are initiated automatically in the event of a cabin depressurization.

Passenger Entertainment

The passenger entertainment system is complex in that it allows 10 tape-deck channels, four movie audio channels, and the PA channel to be fed to each of the individual seats. This is done by a time-multiplexing system. The passenger can select the channel that is heard over the stethoscope-type headset.

Ground Crew Call

The ground crew has a flight-deck call button in the nosewheel well that, when depressed, sounds a low chime on the flight deck and illuminates a ground-crew call light. When the ground-crew call button on the flight deck is depressed, a horn in the nosewheel well sounds. When the chime or the horn sounds, the appropriate crew members can use the interphone system to communicate with the one who initiated the call.

Cockpit Voice Recorder

The cockpit voice recorder, or CVR, is an important device for determining the cause of an aircraft accident. An endless tape allows for 30 minutes of recording, and then it is automatically erased and recorded over. There are four inputs to the recording heads: the microphones of the captain, the first officer, the flight engineer, and a microphone that picks up received audio and cockpit conversations. These microphones are always "hot" and do not require any type of keying.

The pickups are all in the cockpit, but the actual tape recorder is in a fire-resistant box usually located near the tail of the aircraft, and is painted bright orange so that it is easily identified among the wreckage.

Emergency Locator Transmitter (ELT)

An emergency locator transmitter (ELT) is a small, self-contained radio transmitter mounted in a location where it is least likely to be damaged in a crash. It has an inertia switch that closes in the event of a crash and starts the transmitter emitting a series of down-sweeping tones simultaneously on two emergency frequencies, 121.5 MHz in the VHF band and 243.0 MHz in the UHF band. The battery in an ELT has a design life long enough to operate the transmitter continuously for 48 hours.

ELTs are installed as far aft in the fuselage as it is practical to place them, and they are connected to a flexible whip antenna. The installation must be such that orients the inertia switch so that it is sensitive to a force of approximately 5G along the longitudinal axis of the aircraft.

When an ELT is properly installed, it requires little maintenance other than ensuring that it remains securely mounted and connected to its antenna. There must be no evidence of corrosion, and the battery must be replaced according to a specific schedule. Nonrechargeable batteries must be replaced or chargeable batteries recharged when the transmitter has been used for more than one cumulative hour, or when it has reached 50% of its usable life, or if it is rechargeable 50% of its useful life of charge. The date required for its replacement must be legibly marked on the outside of the transmitter case and recorded in the aircraft maintenance records.

An ELT can be tested by removing it and taking it into a shielded or screened room to prevent its radiation from causing a false alert. An operational check may be made with the ELT in the aircraft by removing the antenna and connecting a dummy load. If it is not possible to use a dummy load, the antenna may be left in place and the ELT operated for no more than three audible sweeps, and the test must be conducted within the first five minutes after any hour. If the ELT must be operated outside of this time frame, the nearest FAA control tower must be contacted and the test coordinated with them.

The pilot should check at the end of each flight to be sure that the ELT has not been triggered. This is done by tuning the VHF receiver to 121.5 MHz and listening for the tone. If no tone is heard, the ELT is not operating.

key *(verb)*. To initiate an action by depressing a key or a button.

ELT (emergency locator transmitter). A self-contained radio transmitter that automatically begins transmitting on the emergency frequencies any time it is triggered by a severe impact parallel to the longitudinal axis of the aircraft.

Answers begin on Page 855. Page numbers refer to chapter text.

1. A radio station license issued by the _____ must be displayed in all aircraft equipped with two-way radio. *Page 791*

2. The minimum license required for a person to operate an aircraft radio transmitter is a/an _____ . *Page 791*

3. The radio-frequency carrier used in a radio transmitter is produced by a/an _____-controlled oscillator. *Page 792*

4. A superheterodyne circuit is used in a radio _____ (receiver or transmitter). *Page 793*

5. Most communication between civilian aircraft and ground facilities is in the _____ (HF, VHF, or UHF) frequency band. *Page 799*

6. Most radio communication by aircraft operating over the oceans is done in the _____ (HF, VHF, or UHF) frequency band. *Page 799*

7. SSB is the primary type of transmission for communication in the _____ (HF or VHF) band. *Page 796*

8. One difference between AM and SSB radio communication is that SSB communication requires a _____ (wider or narrower) band of frequencies for its transmission. *Page 796*

9. The two fields that exist in a radio antenna are the:
   a. _____
   b. _____
   Page 796

10. Radio waves travel through space at a speed of _____ miles per second, or _____ meters per second. *Page 796*

11. The radio waves emitted from a vertical whip antenna are _____ (vertically or horizontally) polarized. *Page 801*

12. A radio wave with a frequency of 136 MHz has a wavelength of _____ meters. *Page 798*

13. VHF radio communication travel primarily by the _____ (ground, sky, or space) waves. *Page 800*

14. Three critical characteristics of a radio antenna are:
    a. _____
    b. _____
    c. _____
       Page 801

15. For an antenna to be most effective, its length should be _____ (¼ or ½) of a wavelength. *Page 801*

16. A loop antenna _____ (is or is not) directional. *Page 801*

17. An antenna is connected to a transmitter with a _____ cable. *Page 802*

18. The system that allows an airline ground facility to monitor conditions existing in an aircraft in flight is called the _____ . *Page 802*

19. When an airline ground facility wishes to contact one of its aircraft in flight the _____ system is used. *Page 803*

20. A prerecorded emergency announcement in flight may be automatically initiated over a large aircraft's passenger address system in the event of a _____ . *Page 804*

21. An emergency locator transmitter (ELT) transmits on two frequencies. These are: _____ and _____ megahertz. *Page 805*

22. Most ELTs are powered by _____ (the aircraft electrical system or a self-contained battery). *Page 805*

23. An ELT is activated by an inertial switch that senses impact forces that are parallel to the _____ (lateral or longitudinal) axis to the aircraft. *Page 805*

24. An ELT is normally installed in the aircraft as far _____ (aft or forward) as possible. *Page 805*

25. When activated, the battery installed in an ELT must be capable of furnishing power for signal transmission for at least _____ hours. *Page 805*

Continued

26. An ELT battery must be replaced when it has been installed for _____ percent of its rated usable life. *Page 805*

27. The replacement date for an ELT battery must be legibly marked on the outside of the _____ . *Page 805*

28. Operation of an ELT is verified by tuning the VHF communication receiver to _____ megahertz and activating the transmitter momentarily. *Page 805*

29. If you are going to test an ELT, the test should be performed within _____ minutes after any hour. *Page 805*

Electronic Navigation Systems

Air travel became practical when radio navigation made it possible for pilots to navigate without having to depend upon visual recognition of landmarks.

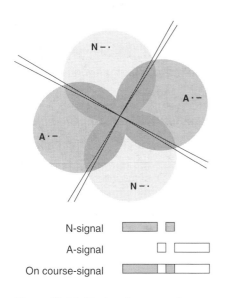

Figure 11-16. *The low-frequency, four-course radio range was the earliest successful radio navigation system. When the pilot heard the overlapping signals as a solid tone, the airplane was flying along one of the four course legs.*

Much early radio navigation made use of the fact that a loop antenna was highly directional. Some airplanes had a wire loop wound inside the fuselage, behind the cabin. If the pilot tuned in a commercial broadcast station and turned the airplane until the volume was minimum, the airplane would fly to the station. There were a number of problems with this simple system; not the least was the problem of 180° ambiguity. The same minimum volume would be obtained when the aircraft was flying directly away from the station as when it was flying directly toward it. To be assured of flying to the station, the pilot had to listen carefully to the change in volume. If the signal got louder, the aircraft was, indeed, flying toward the station.

The first really practical radio navigation system was the low-frequency, four-course radio range. Radio transmitters were located on the airports and along the designated Federal airways. The antenna system for these ranges transmitted overlapping figure-eight-shaped signals. *See* Figure 11-16. One set of antennas transmitted the International Morse code letter N (— •), and the other set transmitted the letter A (• —). These characters were so spaced that, in the area where they were received with equal strength, the pilot heard a continuous tone. An identification signal was transmitted every 30 seconds.

When flying into an airport equipped with this system, the pilot would tune the receiver to the radio range frequency and identify the station. The signal heard would be an A or an N along with the identifier. An orientation pattern was flown until the pilot heard the continuous tone and then turned toward the station. If the turn was made in the correct direction, the signal became louder, but if it was made in the wrong direction, the signal faded. By flying a heading that kept the solid tone with increasing volume, the pilot approached the antennas. When directly over the antenna, the signal built up quite strong and then faded rapidly. This was called the cone of silence and identified the aircraft position as directly over the antenna.

The low-frequency, four-course range had serious limitations. It operated in the low-frequency range that was highly susceptible to interference from atmospheric static. During bad weather, when the system was needed most, it was least reliable. Variations in the strength of the two signals often caused the legs to swing in such a way that they could lead the pilot over dangerous terrain. Finally, successful use of this system required a high degree of skill on the part of the pilot.

Automatic Direction Finder (ADF)

A loop antenna receives a signal at maximum strength when its plane is pointed toward the station it is receiving, and at minimum strength when its plane is broadside to the station. This fact was made use of in radio direction finding (RDF). A station could be tuned in on the RDF receiver, and a loop antenna mounted on the outside of the aircraft could be rotated by the pilot or navigator to vary the strength of the received signal. When the signal strength was the weakest, the station was either directly ahead of or directly behind the aircraft. By carefully listening to whether the signal built up or faded, the location of the station could be determined. This system worked, but during World War II it was perfected into the popular rotating-loop ADF, or automatic direction finder.

An ADF receiver operates in the LF and MF frequency bands and has inputs for two different antennas, a loop and a long wire-type sense antenna. The output of the loop antenna varies with the direction between the plane of the loop and the station being received. The output of the sense antenna is omnidirectional, meaning that its signal strength is the same in all directions. The field of the two antennas, when mixed in the ADF receiver, is heart-shaped with a very definite and sharp null.

When the frequency of a radio beacon is selected on the ADF receiver, the signals from the two antennas mix and a voltage is generated in the receiver that causes the loop-drive motor to rotate the loop. The loop will rotate until the combined field is the weakest, the null. The same signal that drives the loop antenna drives the needle of the ADF indicator. When the station is directly ahead of the aircraft, the needle points to the 0° position. When the station is directly off the right wing, the needle points to 90°. The needle always indicates the direction of the station from the nose of the aircraft in a clockwise direction.

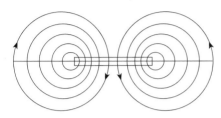

The loop antenna is highly directional with the maximum strength received when the antenna is pointing either directly toward or away from the transmitting antenna.

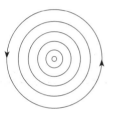

The sense antenna is omnidirectional. It receives with equal strength from all directions.

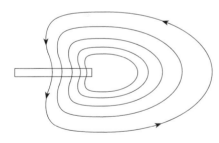

When the signals from the loop and the sense antennas are combined, the field from the sense antenna cancels the field from one side of the loop and adds to that of the other side. The resulting field is heart-shaped with a definite and sharp null.

Figure 11-17. *Reception patterns for ADF antennas*

Figure 11-18 is a highly simplified block diagram of a rotating-loop ADF system. The output of the loop antenna is amplified and mixed with the output of the sense antenna. This combined signal is amplified by a tuned amplifier that filters out all but the desired signal. The signal is mixed with the output of a local oscillator to produce an intermediate frequency. The IF is amplified, demodulated, and detected and sent to an audio power amplifier and then to the speaker. A voltage is taken from the output of the detector, filtered and amplified, and used to drive the loop-drive motor. This voltage has the correct polarity to drive the loop in the proper direction to reach its null position. The needle of the ADF indicator is driven by the same signal, and it shows the position of the station relative to the nose of the aircraft.

The beat frequency oscillator (BFO) connected to the IF amplifier is used when the ADF receiver is tuned to an unmodulated transmitter. The transmissions from radio beacons in some foreign countries are not modulated, and in order to hear the station, a signal is generated in a BFO that is near that of the IF amplifier. When the BFO signal mixes with the IF, an audio signal is produced whose frequency is the difference between the two signals. In the United States, almost all radio beacons are modulated, so the BFO is not switched in.

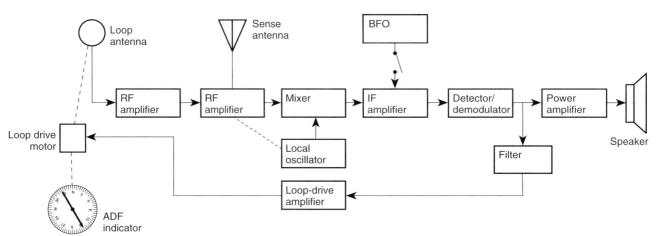

Figure 11-18. *A simplified block diagram of a rotating-loop ADF*

The principle of the ADF has changed very little over the years, but the hardware has changed dramatically to keep up with the state of the art. Modern high-speed aircraft do not use an actual long-wire sense antenna, but part of the structure is made to function in the same way as the long wire. The rotating loop antenna has been replaced with a nonrotating fixed loop as seen in Figure 11-19.

The nonrotating loop is actually two fixed-loop antennas connected to two fixed stator windings in a resolver, or goniometer. The fields of the two stator windings induce a voltage in the rotor, and this voltage is sent into the

goniometer. Electronic circuitry in an ADF system that uses the output of a fixed loop antenna to sense the angle between a fixed reference, usually the nose of the aircraft, and the direction from which the radio signal is being received.

loop input of the RF amplifier in the ADF receiver. The signal is processed in the receiver in the way shown in Figure 11-18. The output of the loop-drive amplifier drives a small motor inside the ADF indicator that drives the rotor of the goniometer until it aligns with the null produced by the of the two fixed coils and the output of the sense antenna. The motor also rotates the needle of the ADF indicator so that it indicates the direction of the station received relative to the nose of the aircraft.

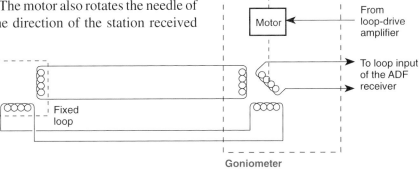

Figure 11-19. *A simplified block diagram of an ADF fixed loop and the goniometer that produces the loop input for the ADF receiver. The motor that drives the goniometer rotor also drives the needle of the indicator.*

Very High Frequency Omnidirectional Range Navigation System (VOR)

Immediately after the end of World War II, the Civil Aeronautics Administration, forerunner of the present FAA, realized that the tremendous growth of aviation as a serious means of transportation would demand better radio navigation facilities than the low-frequency, four-course system then in use. Aircraft approaching or departing from a busy airport should be able to use more than four courses. Also, the system should not operate in the low frequency band, which is susceptible to all types of atmospheric interference. Finally, the inherent accuracy of the system should be in the ground equipment. The accuracy of the equipment in an aircraft would relate to the type of flying being done and the amount of money the user was willing to spend for precision. This allowed relatively inexpensive equipment to be installed in light aircraft that operated under visual flight rules (VFR) and yet allowed airliners and military aircraft to navigate with a high degree of precision.

VOR operates in the 108- to 118-MHz band with 50-kHz channel spacing, making 360 channels available. VOR transmitters located along the airways have about 200 watts of output power and are usable for approximately 200 nautical miles. Terminal VORs (TVOR) are located on the airports, and they operate with about 50 watts of output power and have a usable range of approximately 25 nautical miles.

VOR is a phase-comparison type of navigation system that provides direction to a station, and when it is combined with distance measuring equipment (DME), it provides a specific fix. Since VOR is such a popular navigation system, it has been developed to a very high degree of sophistication, especially in the presentation of information to the pilot. This text discusses the basic principles as they apply to the early type of display, and the way the new systems relate.

VOR. Very high frequency Omni Range navigation.

terminal VOR. A low-powered VOR that is normally located on an airport.

The VOR ground station transmits two signals modulated with 30-hertz on the same frequency. One signal is an omnidirectional reference signal and the other is a rotating signal. The ground station is set up in such a way that the two signals are in phase as the rotating signal sweeps past magnetic north. They get farther apart until it sweeps past 180° magnetic, and then are back in phase at 360°.

The equipment in the aircraft consists of the horizontally polarized antenna, the VHF VOR receiver, the omni bearing selector (OBS), the course deviation indicator (CDI), and the TO/FROM indicator.

The antenna is a horizontally polarized V-dipole that is installed above the aircraft cabin or on the vertical fin. The more modern antenna is a "towel rack" that mounts on the vertical fin and acts as a highly efficient horizontal dipole. The receiver may be the VHF communication receiver with the additional circuitry needed to process the VOR signals and also the circuitry to process the instrument landing system (ILS) localizer signals. The localizer signals are in the same frequency range as the terminal VOR signals, and the localizer uses the same instrument as is the VOR, but its operation is entirely different. The localizer is described with the ILS on Page 816.

Follow the block diagram in Figure 11-20 to see the way the VOR functions. The VOR signal from the receiver contains an AM 30-Hz variable signal (this is the one that rotates), and a 10-kHz subcarrier that is frequency modulated with a 30-Hz reference signal.

A 10-kHz filter passes the FM reference signal and it is demodulated to remove the subcarrier and is passed into the omni bearing selector as a 30-Hz signal. The OBS is a variable phase shifter that can shift the phase of the reference signal. When it is shifted, the OBS indicator shows the number of degrees it has been shifted.

A 30-Hz filter passes the variable signal, and it is put into the phase detector with the output from the OBS. The phases of the two signals are compared and they drive the needle of the course-deviation indicator.

Another phase detector is parallel to the one that drives the course-deviation, or L-R, indicator, but this one is in series with a 90° phase shifter. Its signals are always 90° out of phase with the signals that drive the L-R indicator. The output of this phase detector drives the TO-FROM indicator.

Figure 11-21 shows the way the VOR operates. The pilots in airplanes A and B can select the frequency of the VOR station on the receiver and identify it by the three-letter code identifier or the voice identifier. He or she then turns the OBS knob until the needle of the L-R indicator centers. It will center at two different settings of the OBS. In this case, it centered when the OBS read 030° and the TO-FROM indicator indicated FROM. This means that if the airplane were turned to a heading of 030°, it would be flying *from* the station. It will also center on 210° and the TO-FROM indicator will indicate TO. If the airplane is turned to a heading of 210°, it will go *to* the station.

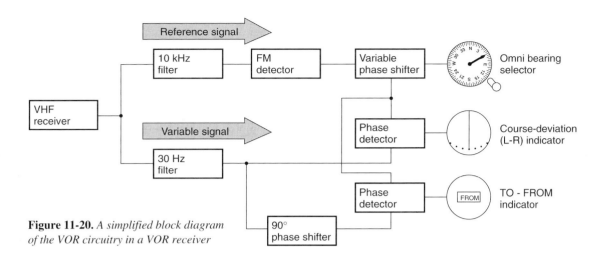

Figure 11-20. *A simplified block diagram of the VOR circuitry in a VOR receiver*

The pilots in airplanes C and D will also have the L-R indicator centered when the OBS reads 030° and 210°. When it reads 030°, the TO-FROM indicator will indicate TO, and when it reads 210°, the TO-FROM will indicate FROM. If either of these two airplanes was turned to a heading of 030°, it would go to the station. When the aircraft is off the radial, the needle will deflect toward the radial by an amount proportional to the amount it is off course. The needle will deflect full scale when the aircraft is approximately 15° off course.

radial. A directional line radiating outward from a radio facility, usually a VOR.

When an aircraft is flying outbound on the 330° radial, it is flying away from the station on a line that has a magnetic direction of 330° from the station.

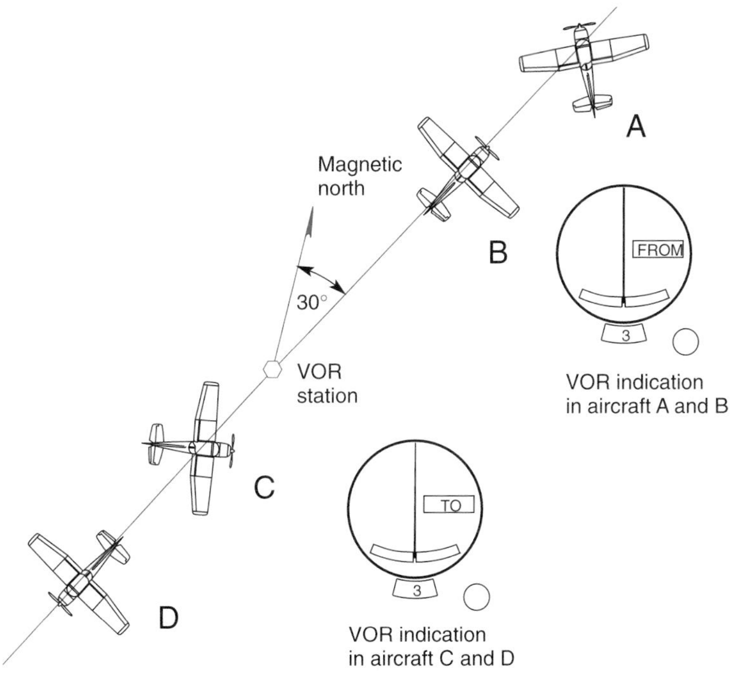

Figure 11-21. *The indication of a VOR has nothing to do with the heading of the aircraft. It is entirely dependent upon the location of the aircraft relative to the station.*

RMI. Radio Magnetic Indicator

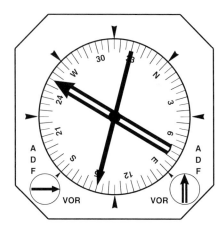

Figure 11-22. *An RMI shows the magnetic heading of the aircraft, the VOR radial on which it is flying, and the magnetic direction from the aircraft to a station being received on the ADF.*

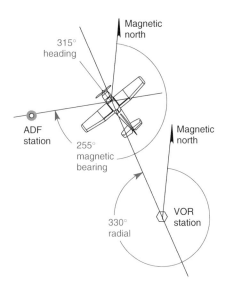

Figure 11-23. *This is the position of the aircraft shown by the instrument in Figure 11-22. It is heading 315° magnetic and is flying outbound on the 330° radial from the VOR. The ADF station has a magnetic bearing from the aircraft of 255°.*

Notice one important fact about VOR. It has nothing to do with the heading of the aircraft; it is only sensitive to the location of the aircraft directionally in relation to the station. This is different from ADF, which computes the direction of the station relative to the direction the nose of the aircraft is pointed.

Radio Magnetic Indicator (RMI)

In an effort to minimize the number of instruments on a modern instrument panel and to combine information from various indicators to make their interpretation easier, the radio magnetic indicator, or RMI, has been developed and is now widely used. This instrument combines the remote indicating compass with the indicators for the ADF and VOR.

A flux-gate compass drives the dial of the instrument, and the head of the VOR needle points to the TO bearing to the station. Figure 11-22 shows the dial of an RMI, and Figure 11-23 shows the location and heading of the aircraft relative to the two radio stations.

The single arrow that indicates for the VOR is pointing to 150°. This is the TO bearing to the station, and if the aircraft were turned to a heading of 150° it would go to the station. This places the aircraft on the 330° radial (180° + 150° = 330°). VOR radials are always numbered by the magnetic direction FROM the station.

The flux-gate compass has rotated the dial of the indicator to show that the aircraft is flying with a magnetic heading of 315°. The dial has turned until 315° is under the marker at the top of the instrument, which is the lubber line. This means that there is probably a wind from the west and the aircraft is crabbing 15° to the left to prevent the wind blowing it off the 330° radial.

The double arrow that indicates for the ADF shows that the station being received on the ADF is to the left of the aircraft between the wing and the nose. The station has a magnetic bearing from the aircraft of 255°. Remember that an ADF arrow always points to the station relative to the nose of the airplane, which is the top of the indicator. *See* Figures 11-22 and 11-23.

Instrument Landing System (ILS)

VOR, ADF, and RNAV allow navigation between airports, but it is the ILS, or instrument landing system, that allows pilots to get safely on the ground once they've reached their destination.

The ILS system has been used for years, and is extremely efficient. The system consists of these electronic components: compass locators for the outer marker and the middle marker, localizer, marker beacons, and glide slope. This system is illustrated in Figure 11-24.

localizer. The portion of an instrument landing system that directs the pilot along the center line of the instrument runway.

glide slope. The portion of an instrument landing system that provides the vertical path along which an aircraft descends on an instrument landing.

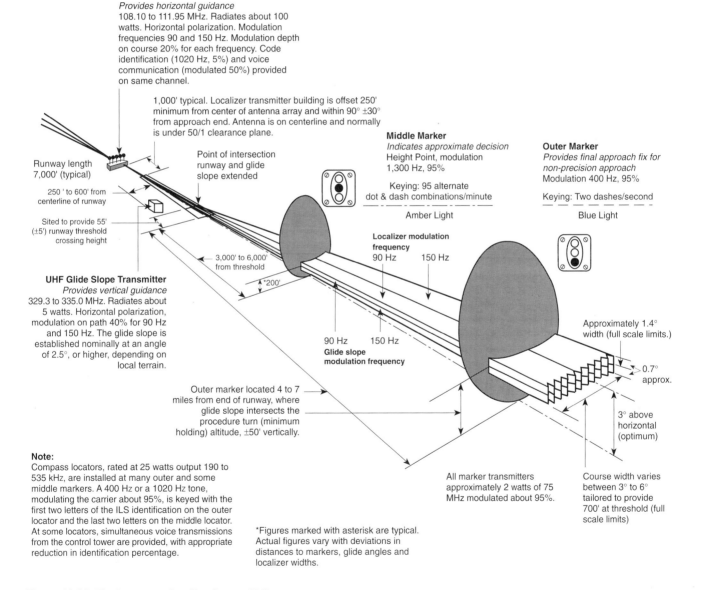

VHF Localizer
Provides horizontal guidance
108.10 to 111.95 MHz. Radiates about 100 watts. Horizontal polarization. Modulation frequencies 90 and 150 Hz. Modulation depth on course 20% for each frequency. Code identification (1020 Hz, 5%) and voice communication (modulated 50%) provided on same channel.

1,000' typical. Localizer transmitter building is offset 250' minimum from center of antenna array and within 90° ±30° from approach end. Antenna is on centerline and normally is under 50/1 clearance plane.

Runway length 7,000' (typical)

250 ' to 600' from centerline of runway

Sited to provide 55' (±5') runway threshold crossing height

Point of intersection runway and glide slope extended

Middle Marker
Indicates approximate decision Height Point, modulation 1,300 Hz, 95%

Keying: 95 alternate dot & dash combinations/minute

Amber Light

Outer Marker
Provides final approach fix for non-precision approach Modulation 400 Hz, 95%

Keying: Two dashes/second

Blue Light

UHF Glide Slope Transmitter
Provides vertical guidance
329.3 to 335.0 MHz. Radiates about 5 watts. Horizontal polarization, modulation on path 40% for 90 Hz and 150 Hz. The glide slope is established nominally at an angle of 2.5°, or higher, depending on local terrain.

3,000' to 6,000' from threshold

*200'

Localizer modulation frequency
90 Hz   150 Hz

90 Hz   150 Hz
Glide slope modulation frequency

Approximately 1.4° width (full scale limits.)

0.7° approx.

3° above horizontal (optimum)

Outer marker located 4 to 7 miles from end of runway, where glide slope intersects the procedure turn (minimum holding) altitude, ±50' vertically.

Note:
Compass locators, rated at 25 watts output 190 to 535 kHz, are installed at many outer and some middle markers. A 400 Hz or a 1020 Hz tone, modulating the carrier about 95%, is keyed with the first two letters of the ILS identification on the outer locator and the last two letters on the middle locator. At some locators, simultaneous voice transmissions from the control tower are provided, with appropriate reduction in identification percentage.

*Figures marked with asterisk are typical. Actual figures vary with deviations in distances to markers, glide angles and localizer widths.

All marker transmitters approximately 2 watts of 75 MHz modulated about 95%.

Course width varies between 3° to 6° tailored to provide 700' at threshold (full scale limits)

Figure 11-24. *The Instrument Landing System (ILS)*

Compass Locators

Compass locators are low-frequency nondirectional beacons that operate between 190 and 535 kHz. They transmit a continuous carrier and keyed identifier and have a range of approximately 15 miles. When the ADF is tuned to the published frequency of the compass locator at the outer marker, the aircraft can fly directly to the marker that begins the instrument approach. Compass locators are typically installed at the outer marker and the middle marker.

Localizer

A localizer is a VHF facility that provides course guidance down the extended center line of the instrument runway from approximately 18 miles out to the point of touchdown. The localizer uses the same receiver, antenna, and indicator as the VOR, but operates on an entirely different principle.

The localizer antenna arrays are located at the far end of the instrument runway, and they transmit a horizontally polarized signal on frequencies between 108.10 and 111.95 MHz. The carrier is transmitted with two sets of antenna. The signal from one set is modulated with a 90-Hz tone and the signal from the other is modulated with a 150-Hz tone. Refer to Figure 11-24. The antennas that radiate the 90-Hz tone have a pattern that is about $1\frac{1}{2}°$ to $3°$ wide and it extends from the center line of the instrument runway toward the left side, as viewed from the approach end. The pattern of the 150-Hz modulated signal is on the right side of the runway center line.

When the VHF Nav receiver is tuned to a localizer frequency, the VOR circuitry is switched out and the localizer circuitry activated. The signal from the antenna is taken into the receiver and passed through two filters. One filter passes the 90-Hz tone and the other passes the 150-Hz tone. This audio signal is rectified and changed to a DC voltage that drives the pointer of the same Left-Right indicator that is used with the VOR. When the aircraft is to the right of the runway center line, it is in the 150-Hz modulation area, and the needle deflects to the left, showing that the runway is to the left. The needle deflects full scale when the aircraft is approximately $2.5°$ off of the center line. This translates to about 1,500 feet at five miles out, but becomes less as the runway is approached. If the aircraft moves to the left of the runway center line, it is in the 90-Hz area and the needle is driven to the right, indicating that the runway is to the right of the aircraft. While the localizer indicator is the same instrument used with VOR, when it is displaying the localizer, it is approximately four times as sensitive as it is when it is displaying VOR.

The localizer signals extend from both ends of the instrument runway. When the aircraft is approaching the runway from the end that has the glide slope, it is said to be making a front-course approach and the pilot turns toward the needle when the aircraft is off course. When approaching from the opposite end of the runway, the aircraft is making a back-course approach. When the aircraft drifts off course the pilot must turn it away from the needle to get back on course. This, you will notice, differs from the way VOR is flown.

back course. The reciprocal of the localizer course for an ILS (Instrument Landing System).

Marker Beacons

The outer marker beacon transmitter is located between four and seven miles from the end of the runway. This is a low-power 75-MHz transmitter that radiates its signal straight up. The outer marker is modulated with a 400-Hz audio tone in a series of dashes.

When the aircraft is directly above the outer marker, this signal is received and the modulation is filtered. The 400-Hz modulation turns on a blue light in the three-light display on the instrument panel and the pilot hears the series of 400-Hz dashes.

When the aircraft is about 3,500 feet from the threshold of the runway, it passes over the middle marker. This is the same type of transmitter and antenna, but it is modulated with a 1,300-Hz tone in a series of alternating dots and dashes. When this modulation is filtered, it turns on the amber light and the pilot hears the dots and dashes.

Some instrument landing systems have an inner marker that uses the same type of transmitter and antenna. This is located at the point at which the aircraft should be at its decision height. It is modulated with a 3,000-Hz tone in a series of dots, and its filtered audio signal turns on the white light.

Glide Slope

The glide slope transmitter and antenna are located about 750 to 1,250 feet from the approach end of the runway and offset about 250 to 600 feet from the runway center line. It transmits a highly directional signal that is approximately 1.4° wide and is angled upward from the transmitter at an angle of approximately 3°.

The signal from the glide slope is transmitted on one of 40 UHF channels between 329.30 MHz and 335.00 MHz, and the antenna is a small UHF dipole that is sometimes built into the front of the VOR/localizer antenna.

Each glide slope channel is paired with a specific localizer frequency and is automatically selected when the pilot tunes the VHF nav receiver to the localizer frequency. Two signals using the same carrier are transmitted from the antenna system in such a way that they overlap to form the glide slope. The upper signal is modulated with a 90-Hz tone and the lower signal is modulated with a 150-Hz tone.

When the signal is received, the audio modulations are filtered and converted into DC voltages that drive the horizontal cross pointer seen in Figure 11-26. If the aircraft is above the glide slope, it is in the 90-Hz modulation and the pointer is driven downward to show the pilot to fly down. If the aircraft is below the glide slope, it is in the 150-Hz modulation and the pointer is driven up to instruct the pilot to fly up.

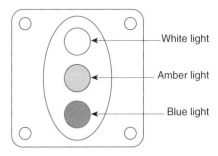

Figure 11-25. *A three-light display for the marker beacons located along an ILS approach.*

The blue light illuminates in a series of dashes to indicate passage over the outer marker (OM).

The amber light illuminates in a series of alternate dots and dashes to indicate passage over the middle marker (MM).

The white light illuminates in a series of dots to indicate passage over the inner marker (IM).

UHF. Ultrahigh Frequency.

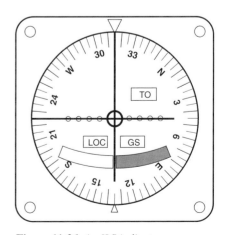

Figure 11-26. *An ILS indicator*

Radar Beacon Transponder

Radar is one of the most important systems for the control of aircraft along our airways and in busy terminal areas. The ground radar at an air traffic control center sends out highly directional pulses of UHF or SHF energy. This energy travels in a straight line, and if it does not hit anything, it continues out into space and does not return, but if it hits an aircraft, part of the energy is returned to the ground antenna. This returned energy is processed by the receiver and displayed on a radar scope as a bright dot.

With the large number of aircraft in the air at any one time, traffic controllers need to identify the dot on the scope made by a specific aircraft. They use radar beacon transponders for this purpose.

The transponder contains a receiver and a transmitter that can respond to a received signal with any of 4,096 discrete codes. The ground controller will assign the pilot of an aircraft a specific code to select on the transponder. When the transponder is operating, it receives the pulse of energy from the ground station and replies with the assigned code. Instead of being just a dot on a crowded scope, the controller can filter out and eliminate all of the aircraft other than those responding with the assigned code. The returns for these aircraft appear as a double slash. If the controller wants to know which one of the returns is from the particular aircraft, the pilot may be asked to ident. To do this, the pilot pushes the IDENT button on the instrument. The return modifies the two-slash image so the controller can easily identify the proper return.

Most transponders are now equipped for Mode C operation. When Mode C, or ALT, is selected on the control, the transponder receives a signal from the encoding altimeter and responds on a code that places an alphanumeric display beside the double slashes that shows the pressure altitude of the aircraft.

The controls for a typical transponder are seen in Figure 11-27. The four selector knobs allow the pilot to select the code the controller requests. The selector switch on the left has an OFF, STANDBY, ON, ALT, and TEST position. There is also an IDENT button and a REPLY light. When the switch is in the OFF position, the transponder is turned off. When it is in the STANDBY position, the equipment is warmed up, but it is not replying to any interrogations. In the ON position, it replies with the selected code when it is interrogated. When the ALT position is selected it replies with the altitude code as furnished by the encoding altimeter. When the IDENT button is pressed, the return is modified so the controller can instantly identify the aircraft. The reply light blinks each time the transponder replies to a ground interrogation.

Transponder Checks

Because an accurate reply is so important, the FAA requires that all transponders be checked every 24 calendar months and found to comply with the requirements that are specified in FAR Part 43, Appendix F.

alphanumeric symbols. Symbols made up of all of the letters in our alphabet, numerals, punctuation marks, and certain other special symbols.

pressure altitude. The altitude in standard atmosphere at which the pressure is the same as at the existing altitude.

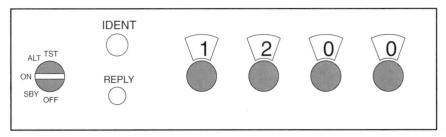

Figure 11-27. *The control head of an ATC transponder*

Distance Measuring Equipment *(DME)*

VOR gives the pilot the direction from the station, but it tells nothing about the distance from the station. In order to get a definite location fix, two VOR receivers would have to be used. DME, or distance measuring equipment, has been developed and is installed in most modern aircraft to give the pilot an actual readout of the distance of the aircraft from the station.

DME is a UHF pulse system that is actually part of the military TACAN (Tactical Air Navigation) system that gives military pilots both direction and distance from the station. VOR and TACAN stations are installed at the same location and are called VORTAC stations. Civilian pilots receive their direction information from the VOR and their distance from the DME.

DME operates on a frequency in the band between 987 and 1,213 MHz and is tuned with the VOR. The antenna is a short UHF blade mounted on the belly of the aircraft.

In operation, the DME transmits approximately 150 pairs of randomly-spaced pulses each second. The ground station receives these pulses as well as the pulses from every other aircraft flying in the area and retransmits them all. The DME receives all of these retransmitted pulses and locks onto the pulse pairs it recognizes as having the same spacing as those it transmitted.

When the DME recognizes the pulse pairs it transmitted, it measures the difference between the time they were transmitted and the time the retransmitted pulses were received. This time difference in microseconds is converted into nautical miles and displayed on the DME indicator. This distance is called slant-line distance because it is the distance through the air to the station, and not the distance over the ground. When the aircraft is directly over the station at an altitude of 6,000 feet it will indicate that it is about one nautical mile from the station. It is one mile above the station.

Modern DME has circuits in it that measure the change in distance for a given time and give direct readout of the ground speed, and time en route to the station.

DME. Distance Measuring Equipment

TACAN (Tactical Air Navigation). A radio navigation facility used by military aircraft for both direction and distance information. Civilian aircraft receive distance information from a TACAN on their DME.

Area Navigation (RNAV)

The main limitation of VOR as a navigation system is that it can only direct the pilot to or from VOR stations, and often flights must be made to some location that does not have a VOR. This limitation has been overcome with Area Navigation, or RNAV, as it is generally called.

If a pilot wants to fly directly to an airport that does not have a VOR on the field, but is located near a VORTAC station, a way point can be set on the field that appears to the RNAV receiver to be a VOR station. The way point is established by entering the radial and the distance from the VORTAC into the RNAV. In Figure 11-28, the destination airport is 36 miles from the VORTAC station on its 140° radial. The RNAV knows the radial on which the aircraft is located and its distance from the VORTAC. By knowing the length and direction of two sides of a triangle, the RNAV computer can easily determine the direction of a straight line from the aircraft to the destination airport and the distance to the airport.

The RNAV uses a course deviation indicator similar to that used with VOR to show any deviation from a straight line between the aircraft present position and the way point. As the aircraft flies toward the way point, the computer keeps track of the decreasing distance and displays on its indicator the distance to go, the ground speed, and the estimated time en route. Some sets can display the estimated time of arrival.

There is one important difference between the CDI of a VOR and that of an RNAV. Deviation from the desired course on a VOR is an angular deviation. The actual distance the aircraft is off course depends upon its distance from the station. Deviation on an RNAV indicator is a linear deviation. If the indicator shows the aircraft to be 2 nautical miles off course, this distance will not change as the aircraft approaches the way point.

Loran

Loran is a LOng RAnge Aid to Navigation. It was developed during World War II and was originally used for marine navigation. Aircraft that carried a navigator could effectively use Loran but its use was too complicated for a lone pilot to use in addition to the other flying chores. The advent of the microcomputer has changed all of this and Loran might well become the navigation system of choice in the near future.

Loran C, the system used in modern aircraft, is a hyperbolic navigation system that operates in the low-frequency range, transmitting on 100 kHz.

Twelve Loran chains serve the United States and Canada. A chain is a linked group of transmitters, one master station and between two and five secondaries. The master station in each chain transmits a series of groups of nine pulses. The time interval between these groups of pulses is called the group repetition interval, or GRI, and is the identifier for the particular chain.

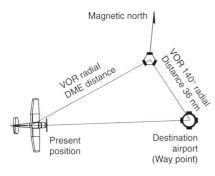

Figure 11-28. *RNAV is able to direct an aircraft to a way point that is defined in terms of a radial from a VORTAC station and the distance in nautical miles between the station and the way point. The computer in the RNAV solves the trig problem of finding the length and direction of the unknown side of a triangle when the length and direction of the other two sides are known.*

The groups of pulses are transmitted from the master station and are received by the secondary stations and then retransmitted by each of them. Figure 11-29 shows a master station, M, and one secondary, V. Radio signals require a definite length of time to travel, and because of the difference in distance between the aircraft and the master station and the aircraft and secondary station V, the signals from these two stations will not be received at the same time, but will be received a few microseconds apart. The computer in the Loran receiver measures the time difference between the reception of the two signals and stores this difference in its memory. The time difference will be the same anywhere along the line identified in Figure 11-29 as the line of equal time difference, or a line of position (LOP). It is possible for the aircraft to be located anywhere along this line.

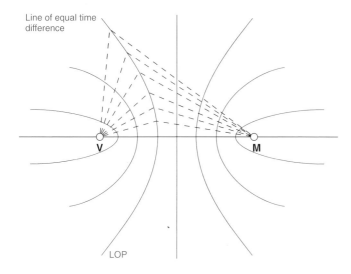

Figure 11-29. *A plot of the locations along which the time difference between the reception of signals from stations M and V are the same will form a hyperbola. Each hyperbola is called a line of equal time difference, or a line of position (LOP).*

To determine the exact location of the aircraft, the Loran receiver automatically selects another secondary station in the same chain and finds the same time difference between the reception of the signals from it and from the master station. The aircraft is at the intersection of the lines of position V and W, Figure 11-30 on the next page.

Data stored in the computer allows the Loran to convert the intersections of the two LOPs along which the aircraft is flying into a latitude and longitude location which can be shown on the Loran display.

The Loran can also store the latitude and longitude locations of up to 500 way points, and a database that includes the location of airports and navigation facilities as well as special use airspace, worldwide.

If the pilot calls up a particular airport or way point, the Loran displays information about the facility and shows the direction of the course directly to it, its distance in nautical miles, the ground speed the aircraft is making toward the facility, the estimated time en route, and estimated time of arrival. It shows the direction and distance the aircraft is off the straight-line course and, if the Loran is coupled with a fuel computer, shows the amount of fuel that will be on board when the aircraft arrives at the facility.

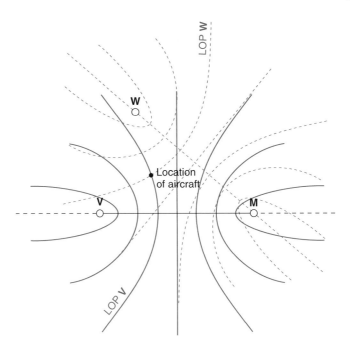

Figure 11-30. *The Loran receiver determines the LOPs from secondary stations V and W along which the aircraft is flying. The intersection of these two LOPs is the location of the aircraft.*

Global Positioning System (GPS)

GPS is extensively used by the military services and is becoming widely used in civilian flying because of its accuracy and dependability in all types of weather.

GPS receives signals from satellites that orbit the earth at altitudes in the range of 11,000 miles. These satellites transmit signals on 1,575.42 and 1,227.6 MHz. These signals, unlike those of Loran, are line-of-sight frequencies, so there must be no obstructions between the antenna and the satellite.

The database in the GPS receiver knows exactly where each satellite is at all times. When signals are received from a satellite, the computer in the GPS receiver computes the actual distance from the satellite by measuring the time required for the signal to reach the aircraft. Signals are received from four satellites and when the accurate distance from each of them is known, the latitude and longitude location of the aircraft can be pinpointed with a high degree of accuracy.

GPS receivers can be combined with Loran receivers and display the same information. The location of the aircraft is displayed, and the way points, airports, and special use airspace can be retrieved from the database and used as a destination.

database. A body of information that is available on any particular subject.

Moving-Map Display

Information from a Loran or GPS can be displayed on a moving map which is a video display from a stored database that shows airports, navigational aids, intersections, and the outline of special use airspaces. A selector allows the pilot to choose the range that is being displayed. This can be typically from one nautical mile to 240 nautical miles. The display can be oriented with the heading of the aircraft up, or with north up.

Inertial Navigation System (INS)

The INS is an extremely accurate navigation system that does not depend upon outside navigation signals to direct the pilot to any chosen destination. The INS has three accelerometers and three attitude gyros mounted at right angles to each other on a gyro-stabilized inertial platform that remains parallel to the earth's surface regardless of the earth's rotation or the airplane's position or attitude.

The exact location of the aircraft in terms of latitude and longitude is entered into the INS computer before the aircraft is pushed back from the gate, and as the aircraft moves, the computer integrates the signals from the accelerometers with time to track the movement of the aircraft longitudinally, laterally, and vertically.

The latitude and longitude of the aircraft are continually updated in the computer, and the direction, distance, and time to any way point entered into the computer are displayed for the pilot to see. This information is also fed into the automatic flight control system to direct the aircraft to fly to the way point.

Microwave Landing System (MLS)

MLS is a new state-of-the-art system that has been considered by the FAA as a replacement for the currently used Instrument Landing System (ILS), but at present, has been rejected.

MLS has the advantage of allowing multiple approach paths to the instrument runway rather than the single approach path allowed by ILS.

Like ILS, MLS uses two transmitters, one to form the azimuth beam, similar to the ILS localizer, and the other to form the elevation beam, similar to the ILS glide slope.

MLS is a time-referenced scanning-beam (TRSB) system that operates in the superhigh frequency (SHF) range of 3 to 30 GHz. Its signal is fed into a phased-array antenna that transmits the signal in a scanning beam from the runway. As the beam scans, it sweeps back and forth, or to and fro, as it is called in this system. The airborne equipment determines the time each scan sweep starts and the time the pulse is received in the aircraft. By using accurate timing circuits, the equipment can determine the location of the aircraft along the approach path, with regard to both azimuth and elevation.

The output of the airborne MLS equipment is displayed on a conventional course deviation indicator (CDI), horizontal situation indicator (HSI), and attitude direction indicator (ADI).

Radar and Radio Altimeters

Pneumatic altimeters measure the absolute pressure of the air in which the aircraft is flying. By adjusting a reference pressure level in the barometric window, the altimeter will show the height, in feet, above this reference level. This instrument does not show the height of the aircraft above the terrain over which it is flying, and it is not adequate for the extreme precision needed for some of the very-low-visibility instrument approaches approved for modern, well-equipped aircraft.

Radar altimeters were developed during World War II when certain types of bombing and torpedo release demanded an extremely accurate knowledge of the height of the aircraft above the surface of the water. These altimeters transmitted a pulse of energy vertically downward, which hit the surface and bounced back and was received. The lapsed time between transmission and reception was measured and displayed on an instrument in terms of feet of altitude.

Modern aircraft use radio altimeters which, instead of transmitting pulses of energy, transmit a 50-MHz frequency-modulated continuous-wave signal on a carrier frequency of 4,300 MHz. The modulation causes the frequency of this wave to vary from 4,250 to 4,350 MHz, and this variation occurs 100 times each second.

This signal is transmitted downward by a directional antenna, and it strikes the ground and bounces back to the aircraft where it is received on another antenna. The frequency of the signal changes a specific number of Hertz each second, and the transmitted energy travels a specific number of feet each second. The equipment measures the difference in frequency between the signal transmitted and that received, and the difference relates to the distance the wave has traveled from the aircraft to the ground and back to the aircraft.

The distance, in feet, between the aircraft and the surface is displayed on an instrument. The pilot is able to set the decision height into the instrument. When the aircraft descends to this height above the ground, a light warns that the decision must be made to continue the approach to landing, or if the approach lights are not visible, to execute a missed approach.

Ground Proximity Warning System (GPWS)

It has been proven that a human voice can attract a person's attention more than a warning light or other visual indication. For this reason aural warnings are used in the GPWS when the aircraft is in a dangerous position relative to the ground.

During operation, a GPWS senses the nearness of the ground and warns the pilot if the aircraft has gotten too near the ground when it is not in a configuration for landing. It does this by monitoring the radar altimeter to determine the actual height above the ground. It also monitors the air data computer, instrument landing system, and landing gear and flap position to determine if the aircraft is properly configured for its distance from the ground. If it is too near the ground for its location or configuration, the system will warn the pilot.

A typical GPWS in a transport aircraft will warn the flight crew of five types of hazards. These are listed in Figure 11-31.

Mode 1 warnings occur when the aircraft is below 2,450 feet radio altitude and the barometric altimeter shows an excessive rate of descent. When the excessive descent rate is first detected, the amber GROUND PROXIMITY light will illuminate and the aural warning will say "SINK RATE...." If the excessive sink rate continues, the red PULL UP light will illuminate and the aural warning will repeat "WHOOP! WHOOP! PULL UP!"

Mode 2 warnings occur when the terrain is rising at an excessively fast rate. When this is first encountered the amber GROUND PROXIMITY light illuminates and the aural warning says the word "TERRAIN" twice. If the excessive closure rate continues, the red PULL UP light illuminates and the aural warning will repeat "WHOOP! WHOOP! PULL UP!"

Mode 3 warnings occur when the aircraft has initiated a climb after takeoff or after a missed approach. If there is a loss of altitude under these conditions, the amber GROUND PROXIMITY light will illuminate and the aural warning will say "DON'T SINK...."

Mode 4 warnings occur during the landing phase of a flight. If there is insufficient terrain clearance when the landing gear is up and the airspeed is below 190 knots, the amber GROUND PROXIMITY light will illuminate and the aural warning will say "TOO LOW...GEAR...."

If there is insufficient terrain clearance when the landing gear is down, but the flaps are less than 25° and the airspeed is below 154 knots, the amber GROUND PROXIMITY light will illuminate and the aural warning will say "TOO LOW...FLAP...."

If there is insufficient terrain clearance when the landing gear is up, and the airspeed is greater than 190 knots, the amber GROUND PROXIMITY light will illuminate and the aural warning will say "TOO LOW... TERRAIN...."

Mode	Condition
1	Excessive descent rate
2	Excessive closure rate with respect to rising terrain
3	Excessive altitude loss during climb-out in takeoff or during go-around when not in landing configuration
4	Insufficient terrain clearance when not in landing configuration
5	Excessive deviation below glide slope when making a front-course approach with the gear down

Figure 11-31. *Classifications of hazards warned by the GPWS*

If there is insufficient terrain clearance when the landing gear is down, with the flaps less than 25°, and the airspeed is greater than 154 knots, the amber GROUND PROXIMITY light will illuminate and the aural warning will say "TOO LOW…TERRAIN…."

Mode 5 warnings occur when the aircraft is on a front-course approach when the aircraft is below 1,000 feet radio altitude and the landing gear is down. If the aircraft sinks below the glide slope, the amber GROUND PROXIMITY light will illuminate and the aural warning will repeat "GLIDE SLOPE…GLIDE SLOPE."

Traffic Alert Collision Avoidance System (TCAS)

The crowded skies and busy workloads of the flight crews make traffic avoidance extremely important. When operating under Visual Flight Rules, it is the responsibility of the pilot-in-command of an aircraft to see and avoid any traffic, and when operating under Instrument Flight Rules, it is the responsibility of the air traffic controller to space the aircraft so there is no danger of in-flight collisions. But, with the large number of aircraft in the air around busy airports, visual contact is sometimes not possible and as a result there have been several fatal accidents.

There is no universally accepted TCAS system available for aircraft during the middle 1990s. There is, however, research being done on systems that detect the presence of aircraft that are in a position to cause a threat. Computers determine the likely flight path of the threat aircraft and warn the pilot by an aural signal of the appropriate action to take to avoid a collision.

Radar

One of the most important developments to come out of World War II was that of radar (RAdio Detection And Ranging). This system, brought to a high level of operation by the British, allowed ships and aircraft to be detected and tracked when they could not be seen because of distance or clouds.

Radar transmits a pulse of high-energy electromagnetic waves at a superhigh frequency from a highly directional antenna. This pulse travels from the antenna until it strikes an object, then part of the energy is reflected and it returns to the antenna and is directed into the receiver. The returned pulse is displayed as a light dot on a cathode-ray tube at a specific distance and direction from a reference on the tube.

A basic primary radar system can be explained by using the block diagram in Figure 11-32.

The synchronizer is the timing device that produces the signals that synchronize the functions of the transmitter, receiver, and indicator. The modulator produces pulses of high-voltage DC that are built up and stored until a timing, or trigger, pulse from the synchronizer releases them into the transmitter. In the transmitter, the high-voltage pulses are changed into pulses of SHF energy of extremely short duration. These pulses are directed into the

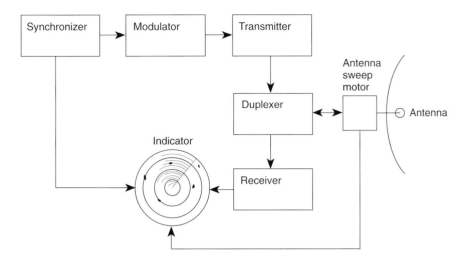

Figure 11-32. *A simplified block diagram of a primary radar system*

duplexer, which acts as an automatic selector switch, connecting the transmitter to the antenna, and then disconnecting it and connecting the antenna to the receiver. The pulse of SHF energy is radiated from a short dipole antenna and is focused by a parabolic reflector into a beam. The beam of SHF electromagnetic energy travels in a straight line until it hits some object, and then some of it bounces back and is picked up by the reflector and focused on the antenna and is carried into the duplexer. The duplexer, again acting as a switch, directs the returned energy into the receiver. The receiver manipulates this energy so it is usable by the indicator.

The returned energy is displayed on a cathode-ray tube (CRT) indicator, such as the one in Figure 11-33, as a bright spot of light. The location of the spot is determined in azimuth by the position of the antenna when the return was received, and in its distance from the center of the scope by the time between the transmission of the energy and the reception of the returned energy. In this way, the location of the spot shows the direction and distance between the antenna and the object causing the return.

As the antenna rotates, the sweep on the indicator follows it and leaves a light dot for each return. The phosphors on the inside of the CRT have a characteristic called persistence that causes them to continue to glow for a short time after the sweep has past. This persistence allows the returns to remain on the indicator long enough to form a meaningful pattern.

Radar has made precision control of air traffic possible. All of the airways are covered by radar surveillance, and the terminal radar control is able to track all of the aircraft in the vicinity of the airports. Precision-radar-controlled approaches assist pilots in safe landings in all types of weather conditions.

cathode-ray tube. A display tube used for oscilloscopes and computer video displays.

An electron gun emits a stream of electrons that is attracted to a positively charged inner surface of the face of the tube. Acceleration and focusing grids speed the movement of the electrons and shape the beam into a pinpoint size. Electrostatic or electromagnetic forces caused by deflection plates or coils move the beam over the face of the tube.

The inside surface of the face of the tube is treated with a phosphor material that emits light when the beam of electrons strikes it.

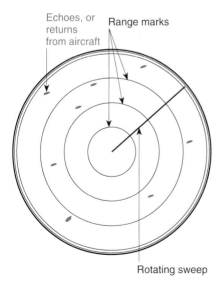

Figure 11-33. *A circular, or P-scan, radar indicator*

Band	Application	Frequency
	Radar altimeter	2.2 – 2.4 GHz
C	Weather radar	5.4 GHz
X	Doppler radar	8.8 GHz
X	Weather radar	9.4 GHz
K	Doppler radar	13.3 GHz

Figure 11-34. *Radar bands and their frequency ranges*

The radar described above is ground-based radar. Two types of radar are carried in aircraft, doppler radar and weather radar. The band names and frequencies for airborne radar are shown in Figure 11-34.

Doppler Navigation Radar

Doppler radar is a navigation system that requires no ground facilities. It works on the principle that the frequency of a signal appears to change as the source of the signal moves.

Most airborne doppler transmits four highly directional beams of frequency-modulated continuous-wave energy with a frequency of 8.8 GHz. These beams are directed from the aircraft as shown in Figure 11-35.

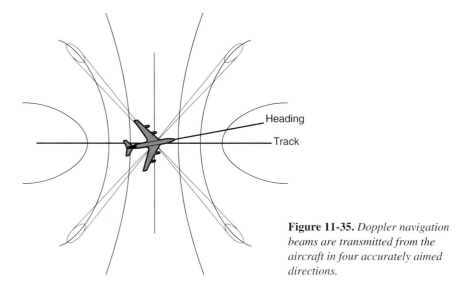

Figure 11-35. *Doppler navigation beams are transmitted from the aircraft in four accurately aimed directions.*

The beams of energy reach the ground and are reflected back to the antenna where they are analyzed by the doppler computer. The difference in frequency between the signal transmitted and that received is caused by the movement of the aircraft in the direction of the beam. By integrating the frequency changes of the four beams, the computer can accurately determine the distance the aircraft has moved vertically as well as horizontally over the ground. Since the beams are transmitted in a specific direction relative to the longitudinal axis of the aircraft, the information produced by the computer shows the aircraft heading as well as the track, and this allows it to compute the drift from the desired course and thus determine the wind direction and speed.

Doppler navigation systems are used for the same purpose as inertial navigation systems, but they are not as popular as INS.

Weather Radar

Weather radar, the most widely used airborne radar, is available for general aviation aircraft as well as airliners.

Weather radar operates in the same way as the primary radar previously described. Its purpose is to detect turbulence and display it in such a way that the pilot can alter the flight direction to avoid it.

Turbulence is often associated with clouds that contain rain, and when rain is present, the radar beam will reflect from the droplets and furnish a return. The electromagnetic energy has a frequency that gives the best return from the water droplets. Most current weather radar operates in the X or the C band. X-band radar has a frequency of 9.4 GHz and a wavelength of approximately 3.2 cm. C-band radar has a frequency of 5.4 GHz and a wavelength of approximately 5.5 cm.

The typical modern weather radar uses a flat-plate planar-array antenna rather than a dipole and parabolic reflector. The beam sweeps approximately 60° to either side of the nose of the aircraft and the returns are displayed on a fan-shaped plan position indicator (PPI) scope similar to that in Figure 11-36.

Most modern weather radars have color displays. The intensity of the returned energy determines the color of the display on the screen. Minimum precipitation shows up as a green return, medium precipitation shows up as yellow, and heavy precipitation shows up as a red area.

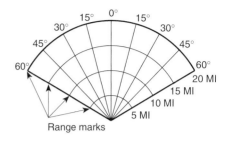

Figure 11-36. *The fan-shaped PPI scope commonly used with weather radar. Different distance scales can be selected.*

PPI (Plan Position Indicator). A type of radar scope that shows both the direction and distance of the target from the radar antenna. Some radar antenna rotate and their PPI scopes are circular. Other antenna oscillate and their PPI scopes are fan shaped.

Stormscope Weather Mapping System

It has long been known that an ADF radio would home in on a thunderstorm as well as on a conventional radio transmitter. This principle is made use of in the Stormscope weather mapping system.

Weather radar requires precipitation to produce its return, but the Stormscope does not. Turbulence is caused by the upward and downward movement of air currents, and as these currents move against each other, static electrical charges build up. The voltage increases until it has an opportunity to discharge to an area that has an opposite charge. It often builds up to such a high value that the discharge is the visible lightning with which we are all familiar. Discharges at a lower voltage are not visible, but are intense enough to be detected by the Stormscope.

The Stormscope works essentially in the same way as an ADF. It has a fixed loop and sense antenna built into a single unit, a computer and processor, and a small-diameter cathode-ray tube or liquid crystal display. When the unit is turned on, it picks up the static electricity discharges from within the storm and shows each discharge on the display as a small green dot. The azimuth location of the dot is determined in the same way ADF determines the direction to a station. The distance is determined by the computer, which among other things measures the intensity of the discharge and places the dot a specific distance from the center of the display. The Stormscope detects only electrical discharges and is not affected by rain.

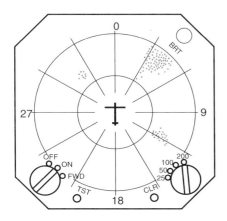

Figure 11-37. *A Stormscope picks up electrical disturbances and displays them on the indicator as dots, showing their direction and distance from the aircraft.*

The controls on a typical Stormscope indicator are seen in Figure 11-37. Turning the switch on the left to ON turns the system on. When electrostatic discharges are detected, they show up as small green dots on the screen the correct distance and direction from the nose of the symbolic airplane. These dots accumulate and show the extent of the storm. To prevent the screen from becoming too cluttered, when the maximum number of dots allowed by the system is reached, each new dot bumps the oldest dot off of the screen.

When this switch is turned to FWD, only the dots from disturbances ahead of the aircraft are shown.

When the TST button is depressed, a series dots is generated that shows that the entire system is functioning properly.

The right-hand selector switch is the range switch and the pilot is able to select a range of 25, 50, 100, or 200 nautical miles. The outer ring on the display represents the selected distance.

The CLR button clears the screen and allows new dots to form. The screen is typically cleared when the aircraft is turned to a new heading. It takes approximately 20 seconds for the screen to fill with new dots after it has been cleared.

STUDY QUESTIONS: ELECTRONIC NAVIGATION SYSTEMS

Answers begin on Page 855. Page numbers refer to chapter text.

30. The old four-course radio range operated in the _____ (low or high) -frequency range. *Page 809*

31. The Automatic Direction Finder (ADF) operates in the _____ and _____ bands. *Page 809*

32. An ADF system requires two antenna. These are a/an _____ and a/an _____ antenna. *Page 809*

33. The loop antenna used with an ADF system _____ (is or is not) a directional antenna. *Page 809*

34. The indication on an ADF indicator _____ (does or does not) change as the heading of the aircraft changes. *Page 809*

35. VOR navigation equipment operates in the _____ (VHF or UHF) band. *Page 811*

36. The antenna used with a VOR system is _____ (horizontally or vertically) polarized. *Page 812*

37. The antenna and receiver used for VOR are also used for the _____ (glide slope or localizer) portion of the instrument landing system. *Page 812*

38. The indication on a VOR Course Deviation Indicator _____ (does or does not) change as the aircraft heading changes. *Page 814*

39. When a Radio Magnetic Indicator is driven by a VOR, the needle points to the _____ (TO or FROM) bearing. *Page 814*

40. The dial of an RMI indicates the _____ (true or magnetic) heading of the aircraft. *Page 814*

41. Compass locators used with an ILS operate in the _____ (LF, VHF, or UHF) band. *Page 816*

42. The signals from the compass locators are received by the _____ (ADF or VOR) receiver. *Page 816*

43. The portion of an ILS that provides guidance down the center line of the instrument runway is the _____ . *Page 816*

44. The localizer used with an ILS operates in the _____ (LF, VHF, or UHF) band. *Page 816*

45. When the Left-Right indicator is used with a localizer signal, it is _____ (more or less) sensitive than it is when it is used with a VOR signal. *Page 816*

46. The glide slope used with an ILS operates in the _____ (LF, VHF, or UHF) band. *Page 817*

47. The carrier transmitted by a marker beacon used with an ILS has a frequency of _____ MHz. *Page 817*

48. A pilot _____ (does or does not) manually tune the glide slope receiver. *Page 817*

49. Distance Measuring Equipment (DME) is a _____ (pulse or phase comparison) system. *Page 819*

50. DME operates in the _____ (VHF or UHF) band. *Page 819*

51. The distance shown on a DME indicator _____ (is or is not) the actual distance over the ground from the location of the aircraft to the station. *Page 819*

52. When a radar beacon transponder is replying with an indication of its altitude, it is operating in Mode _____ . *Page 818*

Continued

53. Radar beacon transponders must be checked every _____ calendar months. *Page 818*

54. RNAV is able to direct a pilot to a way point that has been defined and entered into the equipment as the radial and distance from a/an _____ . *Page 820*

55. The deviation indicator for an RNAV receiver shows the _____ (angular or linear) deviation from the desired course. *Page 820*

56. Loran C operates in the _____ (LF, MF, HF, or VHF) range. *Page 820*

57. GPS signals _____ (are or are not) line of sight signals. *Page 822*

58. The location of an aircraft can be shown on a moving map display by using the signals from _____ or _____ . *Page 823*

59. The inertial navigation system (INS) _____ (is or is not) dependent upon ground-based electronic signals. *Page 823*

60. Microwave landing system (MLS) operates in the _____ (VHF, UHF, or SHF) range. *Page 824*

61. A radio altimeter shows the pilot the actual height of the aircraft above _____ (the ground or sea level). *Page 824*

62. The GPWS warns the flight crew of a dangerous situation with both visual and _____ warnings. *Page 825*

63. During operation, a GPWS typically monitors the radio (radar) altimeter, air data computer, instrument landing system, and the _____ and _____ positions. *Page 825*

64. Weather radar returns show energy that is reflected from _____ . *Page 829*

65. An area of the heaviest precipitation shows up on a color weather radar as _____ (green, yellow, or red). *Page 829*

66. The Stormscope system detects electrostatic discharges within a storm and it _____ (does or does not) require water for its signal. *Page 829*

Electronic Instrument Systems

One reason aviation is such a fascinating branch of science is the speed with which it changes. And in no aspect have changes occurred as rapidly as they have in the field of instrumentation and control. Miniaturization of electronic components has made possible the development of circuits that could never have been built with vacuum tubes or even with discrete components such as transistors and coils.

It was integrated circuits that made electronic computers practical, and it was the replacement of analog computers with digital computers that made possible the electronic instrument systems that are used in modern aircraft.

Microcomputers

Computers operate with numbers, and an electrical computer must assign a definite value of voltage to each digit. Using the decimal number system requires the computer to be able to manipulate ten different values, or conditions, and this requires precision measurement and complicates the process of computing. But there are other number systems than the decimal system. The binary number system will do everything the decimal system will do, and it uses only two conditions: 0 and 1 or, electrically, voltage and no voltage.

Computers have become such an important part of our life that we use them every day whether we recognize it or not. Almost all schools and many homes have personal computers, or PCs, and most businesses have access to larger computers. In this text, we are not concerned with these devices, but rather we want to examine the principle on which the many dedicated computers that are part of an aircraft instrument or control system operate.

Figure 11-38 is a very simple diagram of a digital computer. This computer has three components: a central processing unit, or CPU, a memory, and input/output devices. *See* Figure 11-38 on the next page.

The CPU is the heart of the computer and it contains a clock, a control unit, and an arithmetic/logic unit (ALU). The memory contains all of the instructions and data stored in the form of binary numbers, called words. The input devices receive signals from temperature, position, or pressure sensors, and commands from the pilot. The output devices can be anything from a video display to electric motors or other types of actuators.

The memory section contains two types of memory, ROM and RAM. ROM, or Read-Only Memory, is permanent memory built into the computer and cannot be changed. ROM contains the instructions that allow the computer to start up and perform a number of diagnostic tests to assure that everything is working as it should. It also contains all the steps the computer should take to process signals from the input devices and give the desired results in the output.

dedicated computer. A small digital computer, often built into an instrument or control device, that contains a built-in program that causes it to perform a specific function.

The RAM, or Random-Access Memory, is a read-write memory in which data can be held in storage until it is needed and then called out and manipulated by the ALU and put back into storage. RAM is called volatile memory, because anything that is in it when the power is turned off is lost.

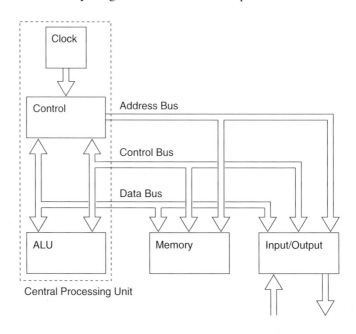

Figure 11-38. *An extremely simplified block diagram of a dedicated digital computer*

Let's consider a hypothetical dedicated computer designed to maintain cylinder head temperature within an optimum range and warns the pilot if it gets out of this range. The aircraft has a digital cylinder head temperature indicator with a two-line remarks display such as the one in Figure 11-39. Up to a temperature of 100°C, the light bars on the indicator are green. Between 100°C and 230°C, they are blue, and above 230°C, they are red. Above 260°C, the bars flash.

These are the requirements for this computer:

1. The cowl flaps are to be open when aircraft is on the ground.

2. The cowl flaps should close when the aircraft becomes airborne.

3. The cowl flaps should be automatically regulated to maintain the CHT between 100°C and 248°C.

4. When the temperature is between 100°C and 230°C, the display reads AUTO-LEAN OK.

5. When the temperature reaches 230°C, the readout in the bottom of the instrument displays AUTO-RICH ONLY.

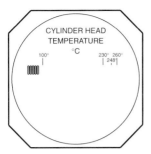

CHT is 90°C. Bars are green, and no remarks are displayed.

CHT is 185°C. Bars are blue, and notation shows that engine can be operated with carburetor mixture set to AUTO LEAN.

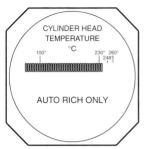

CHT is 235°C. Bars are red, and notation shows AUTO RICH must be used.

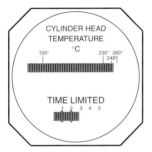

CHT is 250°C. Bars are red, and engine is in time limited range. It has been operating in this range for almost 3 minutes out of the allowable 5 minutes.

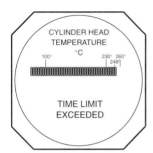

CHT is still 250°C and has been above 248°C limit for more than the allowable 5 minutes. TIME LIMIT EXCEEDED warning is flashing.

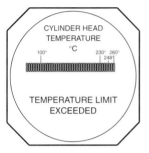

CHT is 260°C and light bars and TEMPERATURE LIMIT EXCEEDED warning is flashing.

6. If the temperature reaches 248°C, the display reads TIME LIMITED. A timer begins, and when it counts five minutes, the display flashes the words TIME LIMIT EXCEEDED.

7. If the temperature reaches 260°C, the light bars flash and the display flashes the words TEMPERATURE LIMIT EXCEEDED.

The computer takes these basic steps, and while it takes a while for us to read them, the computer steps through them continuously. Each step takes only a few thousandths of a second.

1. When the master switch is turned on, the first signal from the clock tells the control to clear all of the storage areas in the computer and perform all of the necessary diagnostic tests.

2. The next signal from the clock tells the control to fetch the first instruction. The program in ROM tells the control to determine from the landing gear squat switch (an input device) if weight is on the landing gear.

3. If the squat switch says that weight is on the landing gear, an instruction is sent to the controller signaling the cowl flap motor to open the cowl flaps.

Continued

Figure 11-39. *This type of digital cylinder head temperature indicator can be driven by a computer. Each bar in the display represents 5°C.*

4. The clock continually tells the control to fetch instructions from the memory. These steps amount to a loop of instructions that tell the controller to sense the input from the CHT thermocouple and light up the correct light bars on the indicator display.

5. The loop of instructions also continually monitors the landing gear squat switch, and when it signals that the weight is off of the landing gear, an instruction is sent that causes the cowl flap motor (an output device) to close the cowl flaps.

6. The loop continues to search all of the input devices until the temperature sensor indicates that the CHT has reached 100°C. At this time the display at the bottom of the indicator shows the words AUTO-LEAN OK.

7. The loop continues to search all of the input devices until the temperature sensor indicates that the CHT has reached 230°C. At this time the display at the bottom of the indicator changes to show the words AUTO-RICH ONLY.

8. The loop continues to search all of the input devices until the temperature sensor shows that the CHT has reached 248°C. A signal is sent to the cowl flap motor to open the cowl flaps enough to keep the temperature below 248°C. Any time the loop detects that the CHT is above 248°C, the display shows the words TIME-LIMITED. The control directs a display on the CHT indicator to light up a bar graph that shows the length of time the engine is allowed to operate in this temperature range. Each 15 seconds a red bar lights up.

9. If the loop sampling the temperature finds that it remains above 248°C for the full five minutes that are allowed, the display changes to TIME LIMIT EXCEEDED, and the display flashes.

10. If the temperature sampled by the loop ever reaches 260°C, the light bars and the display TEMPERATURE LIMIT EXCEEDED flash.

Digital Indicating and Control Systems

Digital electronics has opened an extremely wide door for new developments.

Cathode-ray tubes (CRTs) are used as multifunction displays (MFDs) in the modern "glass cockpits." A single MFD replaces a number of mechanical analog-type indicators and has the added advantage that only those indicators that show abnormal conditions are displayed. In addition to displaying instrument indications, CRTs may be used to display check lists and operational history of the portions of a system that are showing trouble, suggest corrective action, and display any performance reduction caused by the malfunction.

Digital systems lend themselves to self-examination of their operating condition and the diagnosis of faults that are detected. This is done by the portion of the system known as BITE, or Built-In Test Equipment. BITE

MFD. Multi-Function Display

glass cockpit. An aircraft instrument system that uses a few cathode-ray-tube displays to replace a large number of mechanically actuated instruments.

BITE. Built-In Test Equipment

checks the system, and when a malfunction is detected it traces it to the nearest line replaceable unit, or LRU, and informs the flight crew of the action that should be taken.

In this section of the text we will discuss three digital electronic instrument systems that are presently in use: Electronic Flight Instrument System (EFIS), Engine Indicating and Crew Alerting System (EICAS), and Electronic Centralized Aircraft Monitor (ECAM) system.

LRU. Line Replaceable Unit

EFIS. Electronic Flight Instrument System

EICAS. Engine Indicating and Crew Alerting System

ECAM. Electronic Centralized Aircraft Monitor

Electronic Flight Instrument Systems (EFIS)

EFIS consists of a pilot's display system and a copilot's display system. Each system has two color CRT display units: an electronic attitude director indicator (EADI), and an electronic horizontal situation indicator (EHSI). These indicators are driven by symbol generators and are controlled by display controllers.

EADI. Electronic Attitude Director Indicator

EHSI. Electronic Horizontal Situation Indicator

The symbol generators receive data from such sensors as those listed in Figure 11-41 and process it. This data is then sent to the appropriate indicator. The center symbol generator can be switched by the display controllers so it will furnish data to either set of indicators in the event that their symbol generator should fail.

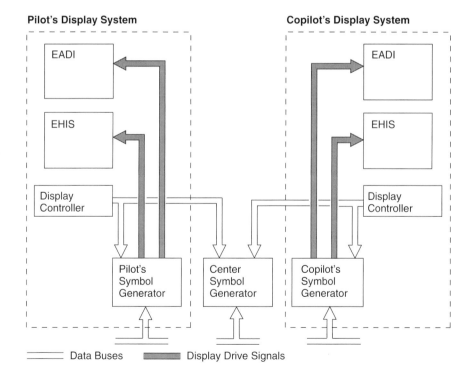

Figure 11-40. *Simplified block diagram of an Electronic Flight Instrument System*

VOR
DME
ILS
Radio altimeter
Weather radar
Inertial reference system
Flight control computer
Flight management computer
Display controller

Figure 11-41. *Typical sources of data that are fed into the symbol generators for an EFIS*

data bus. A wire or group of wires that are used to move data within a computer system.

The EADI shows such information as the pitch and roll attitude of the aircraft, the flight director commands, deviation from the localizer and glide slope, selected airspeed, ground speed, radio altitude, and decision height.

The display controller allows the pilot to select the appropriate mode of operation for the current flight situation.

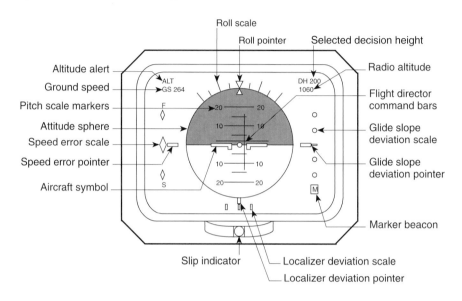

Figure 11-42. *An electronic attitude director indicator, an EADI*

The EHSI has four selectable modes: MAP, PLAN, ILS, and VOR.

In the MAP mode the EHSI takes its signals from the flight management computer and shows its display against a movable map display. This display shows heading and track information, distance to go, ground speed, and estimated time of arrival. It shows the location of various airports, navaids, and way points. And it also shows the wind speed and direction.

In the PLAN mode, the EHIS shows a static map with the active route of the flight plan drawn out on it.

In the VOR mode, the display shows the compass rose with heading and course information. In the ILS mode, the heading and localizer and glide slope information are shown. Information furnished by the weather radar is shown on the EHSI when it is in the expanded scale format of both the VOR and ILS modes.

When any function such as navigation (NAV), compass (HDG), localizer (LOC) or glide slope (GS) shown on the EHSI is not operative, or if the signals being received or used are too weak to give a proper indication, a warning flag will show up that warns the pilot not to depend upon that function.

way point. A phantom location created in certain electronic navigation systems by measuring direction and distance from a VORTAC station or by latitude and longitude coordinates from loran or GPS.

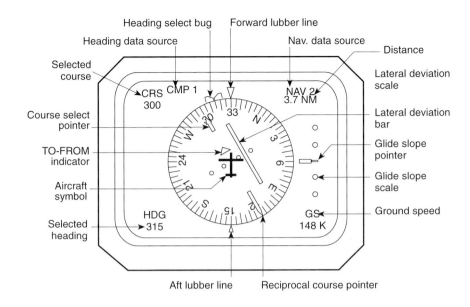

Heading select bug
Forward lubber line
Heading data source
Nav. data source
Distance
Selected course
Lateral deviation scale
CRS CMP 1
300
NAV 2
3.7 NM
Course select pointer
Lateral deviation bar
TO-FROM indicator
Glide slope pointer

Aircraft symbol
Glide slope scale
HDG
315
GS
148 K
Ground speed
Selected heading
Aft lubber line
Reciprocal course pointer

Figure 11-43. *An electronic horizontal situation indicator, an EHSI, in the VOR mode*

Engine Indicating and Crew Alerting System (EICAS)

The EICAS, or engine indicating and crew alerting system, takes the place of a myriad of individual instruments and furnishes the needed information to the flight crew. A typical EICAS senses the parameters seen in Figure 11-44, and in addition it interfaces with such systems as the maintenance control display panel (MCDP) of the flight control computer (FCC), the thrust management system (TMS), the electronic engine control (EEC), the flight management computer (FMC), the radio altimeter, and the air data computer (ADC).

The EICAS consists of two color CRT displays, mounted one above the other. The right-hand side of the upper display shows the engine primary displays such as EPR, EGT, and N_1 speed. These parameters are shown in the form of an analog display with the actual value in digits. The left-hand side of the display shows warnings and cautions.

The lower display shows engine secondary parameters such as N_2 and N_3 speeds, fuel flow, oil quantity, oil pressure, and oil temperature, and engine vibration. The status of systems other than engine systems may be displayed as well as maintenance data.

Caution and warning lights as well as aural signals back up the displays on the EICAS.

Engine sensors

Compressor speeds
N_1, N_2, and N_3
Engine pressure ratio
Exhaust gas temperature
Fuel flow
Oil pressure
Oil quantity
Oil temperature
Vibration

System sensors

Hydraulic quantity
Hydraulic pressure
Control surface positions
Electrical system voltage
Electrical system current
Electrical system frequency
Generator drive temperature
Environmental control system
temperatures
APU exhaust gas temperature
APU speed
Brake temperature

Figure 11-44. *Parameters sensed by the EICAS*

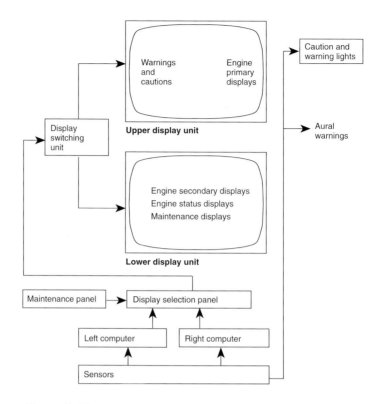

Figure 11-45. *Simplified block diagram of an EICAS*

Electronic Centralized Aircraft Monitor System (ECAM)

The ECAM system monitors the functions and condition of the entire aircraft and displays the information on two color CRT displays that are mounted side by side in the cockpit. The left-hand display shows the status of a system, and the right-hand display shows diagrams and additional information about the system on the left-hand display.

Three automatic display modes can be selected: flight-phase, advisory, and failure-related modes. A manually selected mode displays diagrams and information about the various systems in the aircraft.

The automatic flight-phase mode is normally displayed and it shows the conditions for the current phase of flight. These phases are: preflight, takeoff, climb, cruise, descent, approach, and after-landing. The failure-related mode has priority over the other modes. When some parameter exceeds its operating limit, a diagram of the system appears in the right-hand display and the recommended corrective action is shown on the left-hand display.

When some unit fails, the failure-related mode actuates, and the left-hand display shows the flight crew any changes that must be made in the operation of the aircraft as a result of the failure.

Air Data Computer

Small aircraft sample static air pressure to drive the altimeter and vertical speed indicator. In addition, pitot, or ram, air pressure is sampled to work with the static pressure to give an indication of airspeed.

Large aircraft also sample static and pitot pressures, but, rather than simply driving the mechanical instruments, these pressures are taken into an air data computer. In this computer they expand bellows in a conventional manner, but these bellows operate electrical pickoffs that convert the pressures into digital signals that are used by the various instruments and other computers.

Altitude information is used by the autopilot in its altitude-acquire and altitude-hold modes. It is used by the transponder to furnish pressure altitude information to the ATC ground radar. It is used to determine rate of altitude change and is furnished to the Mach module to convert indicated airspeed into Mach number. It is also used by the cabin-pressure computer and the flight recorder.

Airspeed information is used by the flight director and the autopilot and is used with the altitude information to produce Mach number. A total air temperature pickup converts air temperature into an electrical signal which is used to convert indicated airspeed into true airspeed.

Flight Management Computer System (FMCS)

The FMCS is a single-point system that allows a flight crew to initiate and implement a flight plan and to monitor its operation. The FMCS is the point at which the flight crew inputs the information to initialize the inertial reference units (IRUs). *See* Figure 11-46.

The FMCS consists of two Flight Management Computers (FMCs) and two Control Display Units (CDUs). An extensive data base that contains all of the navigational and operational information needed for the flights can be stored in the two FMCs. The CDUs have an alphanumeric key pad that allows the flight crew to display and update data and to call up any of the information stored in its data base. The output of the key pad is displayed on a portion of the display called the scratch pad. This information can be transferred to the appropriate data field by pressing one of the line select keys along either side of the display.

FMC. Flight Management Computer

- Receives and transmits digital data to and from the various systems on board the aircraft.
- Checks to determine that all of the received data is valid.
- Formats and updates data and sends it to the CDU for display.
- Provides alerting and advisory messages to the CDU for display on the scratch pad.
- Performs a self-test during the power-up operation, and on request. Any failures are recorded on nonvolatile memory for use at a later date.
- Computes the aircraft's current position, velocity and altitude.
- Selects and automatically tunes the VORs and DMEs.
- Determines the aircraft position by measuring the distance from two automatically tuned DME stations.
- Computes velocity by using the IRU inputs, and altitude by using IRU and ADC inputs.
- Monitors aircraft and engine parameters and computes and displays the vertical path of the flight profile.
- Compares the actual lateral position of the aircraft with its desired position and generates steering commands which are input to the appropriate flight control computer (FCC).
- Compares the actual vertical profile data with the desired altitude and altitude rate and generates pitch and thrust commands which are input to the appropriate FCC and thrust management computer (TMC).
- Provides navigational data to the EFIS Symbol generators.

Figure 11-46. *Some of the major functions performed by the Flight Management Computer System*

Answers begin on Page 855. Page numbers refer to chapter text.

67. The three basic components in a digital computer are:

    a. _____

    b. _____

    c. _____

       Page 833

68. Two types of memory in a digital computer are:

    a. _____

    b. _____

       Page 833

69. RAM _____ (does or does not) allow data to be written into the memory as well as read from it.
    Page 834

70. RAM is normally _____ (volatile or nonvolatile). *Page 834*

71. The self-diagnostic portion of a digital system installed in an aircraft is called _____ . *Page 836*

72. A component that can be changed by the technicians on the flight line is called a/an _____ .
    Page 837

73. The unit in an EFIS that receives and processes the input signals from the aircraft and engine sensors and sends it to the appropriate display is the _____ . *Page 837*

74. The unit in an EFIS that allows the pilot to select the appropriate system configuration for the current flight situation is the _____ . *Page 838*

75. The two displays that are part of an EFIS are:

    a. _____

    b. _____

       Page 837

76. When a warning flag appears on an EHSI or HSI for a function such as NAV, HDG, or GS, the function is _____ . *Page 838*

77. Three engine primary parameters that are displayed on the upper display of an EICAS are:

    a. _____

    b. _____

    c. _____

      Page 839

78. The mode that takes priority over all of the other display modes in an ECAM is the _____ mode. *Page 840*

79. The air data computer uses total air temperature to convert indicated airspeed into _____ . *Page 841*

80. The air data computer uses altitude information to convert indicated airspeed into _____ . *Page 841*

81. A single-point system that allows a flight crew to initiate and implement a flight plan and monitor its operation is the _____ . *Page 841*

Electronic Systems Installation and Maintenance

The electrical and electronic systems are some of the most important systems in a modern aircraft. These aircraft have many complex electronic devices that must be properly installed and maintained. They must have the proper type and amount of electrical power, they must have adequate cooling, and their sensitive pickups must be protected from interference by electromagnetic radiation from other devices.

Most of the components in these electronic systems must be repaired only by FAA-certificated repair stations that are approved for the specific work, and the AMT must be able to restore a malfunctioning system to its normal operation by replacing only the faulty components.

The profitability of modern airline operation depends upon every flight departing on schedule, and any maintenance-caused delay must be kept to an absolute minimum. Because of this, the manufacturers have designed into the aircraft built-in test equipment, or BITE. When a system malfunctions, BITE checks it out and informs the flight crew of the system status and the action that must be taken to restore normal operation. BITE normally traces the problem down to a line replaceable unit, or LRU, that can be replaced at the next stop.

General aviation maintenance is not as structured as airline maintenance and the AMT must often design the installation of electrical and electronic systems. This section discusses the installation and maintenance of electrical and electronic systems in general aviation aircraft.

Approval for the Installation of Electronic Equipment

The addition of any equipment to an aircraft constitutes an alteration, and must be made according to approved data. If the equipment to be installed is included in the equipment list that is furnished with the aircraft, its installation is considered to be a minor alteration. The installation may be done and the aircraft approved for return to service by an AMT holding an Airframe rating.

Much of the newer equipment is not included in the equipment list, but its approval for installation has been obtained by the manufacturer of the equipment in the form of a Supplemental Type Certificate (STC). Instructions for its installation are included with the STC. The installation can be done by an AMT holding an Airframe rating, and when the installation is completed, the work must be inspected for conformity with the approved data by an AMT holding an Inspection Authorization. Installation of any electronic equipment that is done according to an STC constitutes a major alteration, and its completion must be recorded and submitted to the FAA on an FAA Form 337.

When equipment is installed without the use of an STC, approval must be obtained from the local FAA District Office before the work is begun. Approval for some installations is quite complex and may require engineering approval.

Electrical Considerations

All electrical and electronic components must have an uninterrupted supply of electricity that has the correct voltage, and if AC, the correct frequency and phase. The system must be so designed that an adequate supply of current can reach the equipment, and all of the wiring terminations must be of an approved type that prevents accidental disconnection and minimizes the chance of improper connection.

Load Limits

Generators or alternators are the primary sources of electrical energy in an aircraft. Their combined output must be great enough that the total connected electrical load does not exceed their current rating, and the system must keep the battery fully charged.

Most multi-engine aircraft have normal electrical loads that exceed the capacity of either alternator alone. If one engine or alternator should fail, the flight crew must be able to reduce enough of the electrical load to bring the required current down until it is within the rating of the remaining alternator. This must be done without turning off any system or component that is essential to the safety of flight.

Aircraft that have complex electrical and electronic systems normally have loadmeters installed between the alternator and the system bus. These indicators are calibrated in the percentage of the alternator rated output, and by monitoring their indication, the flight crew can keep the electrical load safely below the alternator maximum output.

Circuit Protection

All electrical systems must have fuses or circuit breakers installed as close to the main power buses as practical to protect the wiring from overheating.

Electronic equipment must also be protected from voltage spikes. These spikes are lethal to solid-state electronic components, and during the starting and shutdown procedure all of the sensitive electronic components are especially vulnerable. To protect them, almost all aircraft electrical systems have some provision for isolating the avionics bus from the main electrical system. Figure 11-47 shows two such systems. A switch-type circuit breaker can be installed that should be opened before the engine is shut down and closed only after the engine is started. This system works, but the avionics bus can be isolated automatically by installing a normally closed relay between the two buses. Without power on the relay coil, the relay is closed and the avionics bus has power. But when the engine starter switch is closed, or when the ground power unit is plugged in, current flows in the relay coil and the contacts are opened, preventing voltage spikes damaging anything attached to the avionics bus.

Wiring

The wiring practices used for avionics installations must be the same as those used for other electrical systems in an aircraft, except that special attention must be paid to the effect of electromagnetic fields radiating from wires carrying AC. Much avionic equipment is extremely sensitive to electromagnetic radiation, and the wires carrying signals are protected from this interference by shielding them.

A shielded wire is encased in a metal braid that intercepts any radiated energy and conducts it to ground rather than allowing it to cause interference. Since intercepted current flows in the shielding, the fields from this current are minimized by grounding the shielding at only one point, rather than at both of its ends.

Bundling and Routing

Wires that carry alternating current are normally not bundled with wires that carry the signals into sensitive avionic equipment. Be very careful when installing an electronic component to follow the instructions from the manufacturer in detail. Some wires are required to be twisted, and others must be shielded.

Wire bundles should be tied with special plastic straps or waxed cord. The bundles should be attached to the structure with cushion clamps. The edges of any hole in a structural member through which the wire passes must be

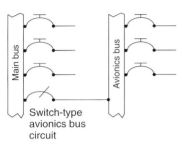

Switch-type circuit breaker is used to isolate avionics bus from main bus when engine is being shut down or started.

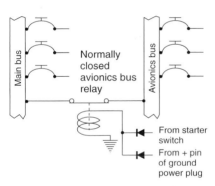

Normally closed relay is installed to isolate avionics bus from main bus when engine is being started or when ground power unit is plugged in.

Figure 11-47. *Avionics bus protection*

1. Cut outer insulation back about 1/4 inch from end of cable and remove insulation from braid.

2. Separate braid and fan it out, being careful not to break any strands.

3. Remove about 1/8 inch of insulation from around center conductor, being very careful not to nick conductor when insulation is cut.

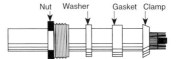

4. Slip nut, washer, gasket, and clamp over wire.

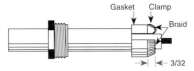

5. Fold strands of outer conductor back over tapered clamp and trim them flush with end of taper.

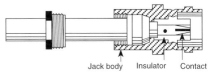

6. Tin exposed inner conductor with good grade of 60-40 resin-core solder. Slip center contact over end until it butts flush against the dielectric. Very carefully solder it to conductor. Heat contact with soldering iron and flow solder through hole in contact body. Do not burn insulation and use only enough solder to form good connection. Slip insulator and connector over end of cable and secure it with nut.

Figure 11-48. *Proper installation of a connector on a coaxial cable*

protected with a rubber grommet. Most wire bundles are installed so they parallel the structural members, but certain critical wires, such as transmission lines, are run as directly as possible to minimize their length.

Transmission Lines

For the maximum amount of energy to be transferred between a piece of avionic equipment and its antenna, the impedance of the antenna and that of the equipment must be matched. For this reason, antennas are normally connected to the equipment with coaxial cable that has a very specific characteristic impedance.

Coaxial cable, or coax, as it is normally called, has an inner conductor, a heavy insulation, an outer conductor braid, and a plastic insulation around the entire cable. Figure 11-48 on the next page shows the proper way to install a connector on a piece of coax.

The coax, furnished with certain pieces of avionics equipment, has been cut to the required length and its length should not be changed. If the cable is too long, it should be carefully coiled up and attached to the aircraft structure with cushion clamps. Normally coax may be run directly between the equipment and the antenna, and it should not be bundled with other wires.

It is a good practice when installing a coaxial cable to secure it firmly along its entire length with cushion clamps every two feet or so. The spacing between the inner and outer conductors is critical and the cable must not be crushed. Because of this, coax should not be bent with a radius smaller than 10 times the cable diameter.

Protection from Electrostatic Discharge Damage

Much sensitive electronic equipment is highly susceptible to electrostatic discharge damage. The normal rubbing of our clothing on our bodies builds up a high voltage that can transfer into the equipment when we handle it. This high voltage can cause enough current to flow to destroy some of the sensitive integrated circuit components. To prevent damaging any of this equipment, be sure that your body is completely discharged by touching some piece of grounded metal. Before opening up any of this equipment on a bench, attach a grounding strap to your wrist and be sure it is adequately electrically grounded.

Weight and Balance

The installation of any avionics equipment affects the empty weight of the aircraft, its CG, and its useful load. The weight-and-balance record must be updated to show the change in the empty weight and empty-weight CG of the aircraft. The addition of equipment decreases the useful load, and if the installation is ahead of the forward limit or behind the aft limit, it is possible for it to move the aircraft EWCG outside of its allowable limits.

Cooling

Electronic equipment often produces heat that must be carried away to prevent the equipment from being damaged. Installations in large aircraft produce so much heat that special ducts from the air-conditioning system are routed to blow cool air over or through the installation racks. Smaller aircraft often have air intakes on the outside of the fuselage, with a scoop opening forward to pick up ram air for cooling. These systems normally require some form of baffle to prevent water from getting into the equipment when the aircraft is flown in rain.

Shock Mounting

Electronic equipment is easily damaged by vibration. To prevent this, much of the equipment is mounted in special shock-mounted racks like the one in Figure 11-49. The equipment is slid into the rack and the locking screws are tightened to hold it tightly in place. When the equipment is slid into the rack, pins in the electrical connector fit into sockets in the rack, and electrical connection is made with the aircraft system.

When electronics are installed in a stationary instrument panel, the installation must be strong enough to withstand a 2.0-G load forward, 1.5 G sideways, 6.6 G downward, and 3.0 G upward.

Shock mounts such as the typical mount seen in Figure 11-50 are designed to isolate the equipment from high-frequency, low-amplitude vibration. They allow considerable freedom of movement of the equipment, and before the installation is complete, be sure to check for the full deflection of the mount to be sure that the equipment cannot move enough to contact adjacent equipment or the aircraft structure itself. Be sure that the permanently installed wiring is not strained when the equipment deflects.

The shock mounts are not only vibration isolators, they are also electrical insulators, and provisions must be made for carrying all of the return current from the equipment back into the aircraft structure. Braided tinned copper bonding jumpers seen in Figure 11-50 must be installed to carry this current. The braid must be large enough to carry the current, and the voltage drop across the jumper must be negligible. The resistance between the equipment rack and the aircraft structure must not be more than three milliohm (0.003 ohm).

Some electronic equipment may be mounted under the seats. When this type of installation is made, you must prove that there will be at least one inch of clearance when the seat is deflected to its maximum. This deflection is measured when the seat is loaded with 6.6 times the amount the seat is designed to carry. Most seats are designed to carry 170 pounds, and so it must be loaded with 1,122 pounds to check the clearance.

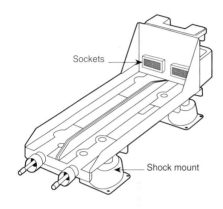

Figure 11-49. *A typical shock-mounted electronic equipment rack. When the equipment is slid into the rack, electrical contact is made between the plugs on the equipment and the sockets installed in the rack.*

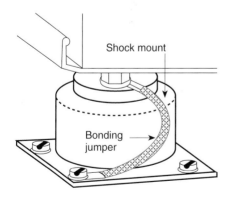

Figure 11-50. *All shock-mounted equipment must have provisions for carrying the return current back to the aircraft structure. Bonding jumpers should be as short as practical and must not produce any appreciable voltage drop.*

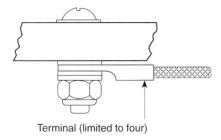

Terminal (limited to four)

Figure 11-51. *Method of attaching a bonding jumper to a flat surface*

static dischargers. Devices connected to the trailing edges of control surfaces to discharge static electricity harmlessly into the air. They discharge the static charges before they can build up high enough to cause radio receiver interference.

Static Protection

The movement of air over an aircraft surface can cause a buildup of static electricity. When the voltage builds up high enough, electrons will jump to some component that has a lower voltage. This electron movement is in the form of a spark which causes enough electromagnetic radiation to interfere with the sensitive radio receivers. Two steps can be taken to minimize static interference, bond all of the movable structural components together, and install static dischargers on all of the control surfaces.

Bonding jumpers are normally made of tinned copper wire braid and are fastened between the movable components and the main structure. When a static charge builds up, it finds a low-resistance path to flow to the main structure. With all of the structure at the same electrical potential, there is no static discharge.

Be sure to remove all of the paint and anodized film before installing the jumpers, and install them as shown in Figure 11-51. There should be no more than four terminals installed at any one point. The jumpers should be as short as practicable and the resistance across the jumper should be no more than three milliohm (0.003 ohm).

Static electrical charges tend to build up as air flows over the control surfaces, and to prevent this buildup, many control surfaces have static dischargers installed on their trailing edges. These dischargers carry the static charges into the atmosphere before their voltage builds up high enough to cause the high current to flow that causes radio interference. By the proper design and location of these dischargers, the static charges will be dissipated while their current level is low.

Figure 11-52. *Nullfield static dischargers are installed on the trailing edges of control surfaces to carry static electrical charges into the atmosphere, before they build up a high enough voltage to interfere with the electronic equipment.*

Antenna Installation

Regardless of the excellence of the equipment, no radio installation is better than its antenna. Each piece of equipment must have a specific antenna, and this antenna must be mounted in a specific location for the most efficient operation. Most antennas are used for both reception and transmitting. They are connected to the equipment through a duplexer, which is an electrically operated switch that switches the antenna to the transmitter when the press-to-talk switch on the microphone is closed.

Types of Antenna

The length, polarization, and location of an antenna is of extreme importance in getting the most efficient transmission and reception from the installed equipment. The types of antennas used with several pieces of avionic equipment are examined here.

VHF Communication

VHF transmitters and receivers use a vertically polarized antenna that may be mounted either above or below the aircraft fuselage. Some of the simpler installations use wire whip antennas like the one in Figure 11-53, while the more efficient installations use a broad-band blade antenna like the one in Figure 11-54. Some wire antennas are bent aft at about a 45° angle, which allows them to receive horizontally as well as vertically polarized signals.

A VHF communication antenna is a quarter-wavelength antenna that uses the metal of the aircraft as the other quarter wavelength to give the antenna the required half wavelength. When installing this type of antenna on a fabric-covered aircraft, you must provide a ground plane. This is done by using strips of aluminum foil or a piece of aluminum screen wire that extends out for approximately one-quarter wavelength from the center of the antenna on the inside of the fabric.

HF Communication

Aircraft that fly over the water for long distances rely on high-frequency communications. The lower frequencies used by this equipment require long antenna. The horizontally polarized radiation used by HF communications allows long wires to be used. These are often installed between a point above the cockpit and the tip of the vertical fin. The wire is often a copper-plated steel wire, but the more efficient systems use an antenna wire encased in a plastic sheath to minimize precipitation static.

Some modern high-speed aircraft have the HF communications antennas built into some part of the structure, such as the leading edge of the vertical fin.

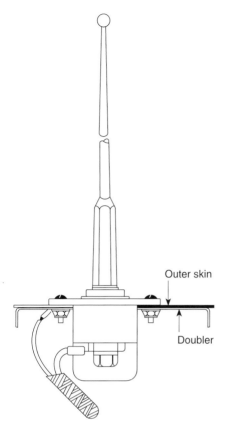

Figure 11-53. *Installation of a wire-type VHF communication antenna. This type of antenna is often bent back at an angle of 45° to allow it to receive both vertically and horizontally polarized signals.*

Figure 11-54. *Broad-band VHF communications blade-type antenna.*

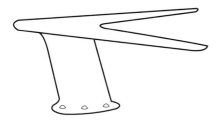

Figure 11-55. *A typical "ram's horn" VOR/LOC antenna. Some antennas of this type have a small horizontally polarized UHF dipole glide slope antenna mounted in the front of the housing.*

VOR/LOC

The VOR and the localizer function of the ILS share the same antenna. Figure 11-55 shows a "ram's-horn" VHF V-dipole antenna. The favored location for this type of antenna is on top of the aircraft above the cabin with the apex pointing forward.

Some more modern high-efficiency VOR antennas are of the type shown in Figure 11-56. The two antennas are designed to mount on the upper section of the vertical stabilizer of a single-finned airplane or on either side of a helicopter tail boom. The two antennas are connected together through a phasing coupler to provide a single 50-ohm input in the VOR, localizer, and glide slope bands. .

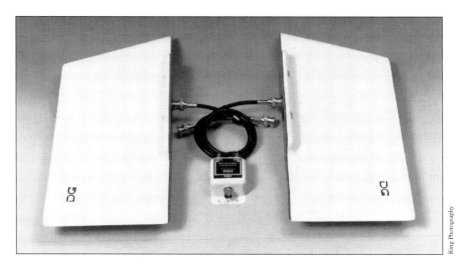

Figure 11-56. *VOR/LOC/GS antenna system that mounts on the sides of the upper portion of the vertical fin of a single-fin airplane or on the sides of the tail boom of a helicopter.*

Glide Slope

The glide slope portion of the ILS operates in the UHF range. Its antenna is a UHF dipole mounted near the front of the aircraft, sometimes on the same mast as the VOR/LOC antenna. Some general aviation aircraft mount the glide slope antenna inside the cabin in roughly the same location as the rear view mirror in an automobile.

Marker Beacons

Marker beacons transmit horizontally polarized signals vertically upward on a frequency of 75 MHz. They are received in the aircraft by an antenna like the one in Figure 11-57, mounted on the bottom of the fuselage.

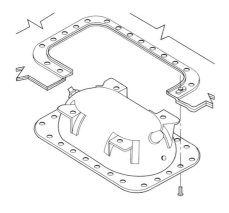

Figure 11-57. *A flush-mounted marker beacon receiver antenna*

ADF

The automatic direction finder requires two antenna, a loop and a sense antenna. The loop has traditionally been a rotating device enclosed in a rather large housing. Now, almost all ADF installations use fixed loops mounted in thin streamlined housings below the fuselage. Since the metal in the aircraft affects the reception of the signal by the loop antenna, the loop must be mounted on the fuselage center line. Some faster aircraft have the loop antennas mounted flush with the aircraft skin.

Because the LF and MF bands are relatively close together, the same antenna used as the ADF sense antenna for picking up LF NDBs can also pick up standard commercial broadcast stations.

Figure 11-58. *ADF fixed-loop antenna*

DME

Distance measuring equipment uses a short, vertically polarized UHF whip or blade antenna. It is mounted on the center line of the bottom of the fuselage as far from any other antenna as is practical. This location is chosen to prevent an interruption in DME operation by the antenna being blanked by the wing when the aircraft is banked. *See* Figure 11-59.

ATC Transponder

The air traffic control transponder uses the same type of antenna as the DME. It is also mounted on the bottom center line of the fuselage. It and the DME antenna must be as far apart as practical. Both installations require that the coax between the equipment and the antenna be as short as possible.

Radio Altimeter

Radio altimeters transmit vertically downward and receive their reflected signal from the surface beneath them. This system requires two antennas mounted on the bottom of the fuselage. In most installations these antennas are flush with the skin.

Figure 11-59. *A typical UHF blade antenna such as is used with the DME and ATC transponder*

ELT

The emergency locator transmitter antenna typically uses a thin wire whip antenna mounted as far aft in the fuselage as possible, but ahead of the empennage. It is usually mounted on top of the fuselage, where it is least likely to be damaged.

$D = 0.000327\ AV^2$

D = Drag, or air load, on the antenna, in pounds

0.000327 = a constant

A = Frontal area of the antenna in square feet

V = Never exceed airspeed of the aircraft in miles per hour

Figure 11-60. *Formula for finding the air load on an antenna*

Antenna Structural Attachment

When you attach an antenna to an aircraft structure, consider not only the radiation pattern and interference from other antennas or electromagnetic fields, but the structural aspects as well. The installation must be made in such a way that all of the air loads are transmitted into the aircraft structure rather than concentrating in the skin.

Most antennas in small general aviation aircraft are attached to the fuselage skin. This skin is normally too thin to support the antenna by itself, so a doubler must be installed inside the fuselage to absorb some of the loads from the antenna and carry them into the skin so that there are no stress concentrations. A gasket or sealant is used between an antenna mast and the fuselage skin to prevent the entry of moisture into the fuselage.

The person designing an antenna installation must prove to the FAA that the installation is strong enough to carry all the air loads.

The formula used in Advisory Circular 43.13-2A for determining the air loads is shown in Figure 11-60.

We can use the formula in Figure 11-60 to find the air load imposed on an antenna with a frontal area of 0.137 square feet installed on an aircraft with a V_{NE} of 275 mph. In this installation the antenna would have to withstand an air load of 3.39 pounds.

$$
\begin{aligned}
D &= 0.000327\ AV^2 \\
&= 0.000327 \cdot 0.137 \cdot 275^2 \\
&= 0.000327 \cdot 0.137 \cdot 75{,}625 \\
&= 3.39 \text{ pounds}
\end{aligned}
$$

Flutter and vibration must also be considered in the installation of an antenna. When any rigid antenna is mounted on a vertical stabilizer, the flutter and vibration characteristics must be carefully evaluated, as the weight and air loads on the antenna can change the resonant frequency of the vertical surface. If the particular antenna has not been previously approved for installation on the vertical fin, be sure to have the installation approved by the FAA before beginning the actual work.

When an automatic direction finder is installed on a particular type of aircraft for the first time, check the loop antenna for quadrantal error.

Quadrantal error is caused when the metal in the aircraft structure distorts the electromagnetic field of the received signal. It causes azimuth inaccuracies, which are greatest between the four cardinal points with respect to the center line of the aircraft.

Answers begin on Page 855. Page numbers refer to chapter text.

82. The installation of a piece of electronic equipment that is included in the aircraft equipment list is considered to be a _____ (minor or major) alteration. *Page 844*

83. When a piece of electronic equipment is installed on an aircraft according to the data included with a Supplemental Type Certificate, the work must be recorded on an FAA Form _____ . *Page 844*

84. The primary source of electrical energy in an aircraft is the _____ (battery or alternator). *Page 844*

85. Fuses and circuit breakers are required in an aircraft electrical system to protect the _____ (equipment or wiring). *Page 845*

86. Electromagnetic radiation is prevented from interfering with signals carried to sensitive avionic equipment by using _____ wires. *Page 845*

87. Coaxial cable _____ (should or should not) be included in a bundle with other wires. *Page 846*

88. Coaxial cable should be secured along its entire length at intervals of approximately every _____ feet. *Page 846*

89. Coaxial cable should not be bent with a bend radius of less than _____ times the diameter of the cable. *Page 846*

90. Before working on any electronic component containing integrated circuit devices, wear a wrist strap that connects your body to electrical _____ . *Page 846*

91. When electronic equipment has been installed or removed from an aircraft, appropriate changes must be made in the _____ records. *Page 846*

92. Heat from the electronic equipment installed in a large aircraft is removed by cold air produced in the _____ system. *Page 847*

93. Bonding jumpers for connecting a shock-mounted equipment rack to the aircraft structure are normally made of braided _____ . *Page 847*

Continued

94. If electronic equipment is installed beneath a seat, the seat must not deflect to closer than _____ inch(es) from the equipment when the seat is loaded with 6.6 time the load it is designed to hold. *Page 847*

95. Static dischargers help eliminate radio interference by dissipating static electricity into the atmosphere at a _____ (high or low) current level. *Page 848*

96. The VHF V-dipole antenna mounted on top of the cabin or on the vertical fin is used by the _____ and the _____ . *Page 850*

97. The antenna for the marker beacon is mounted on the _____ (top or bottom) of the fuselage. *Page 850*

98. When a hole is cut in the aircraft skin for an antenna, the strength that has been lost is replaced by riveting a/an _____ in place inside the skin. *Page 852*

99. Commercial broadcast stations are usually received by the ADF _____ (loop or sense) antenna. *Page 851*

100. Before installing a rigid antenna on a vertical fin, the installation must be carefully evaluated for _____ and _____ characteristics. *Page 852*

101. When an automatic direction finder is installed on a particular type of aircraft for the first time, it is important that the loop antenna be checked for _____ error. *Page 852*

102. The preferred location for a VOR antenna on a single-engine aircraft is on top of the cabin, with the apex of the V pointing _____ (aft or forward). *Page 850*

103. The DME antenna is normally mounted on the center line of the aircraft fuselage on the _____ (bottom or top). *Page 851*

Answers to Communication and Navigation Systems Study Questions

1. Federal Communications Commission
2. restricted radio telephone permit
3. crystal
4. receiver
5. VHF
6. HF
7. HF
8. narrower
9. a. magnetic
   b. electric
10. 186,000, 300,000,000
11. vertically
12. 2.2
13. space
14. a. length
    b. polarization
    c. directivity
15. $\frac{1}{2}$
16. is
17. coaxial
18. Aircraft Communication Addressing and Reporting System (ACARS)
19. Selective Calling (SELCAL)
20. cabin depressurization
21. 121.5, 243
22. a self contained battery
23. longitudinal
24. aft
25. 48
26. 50
27. transmitter case
28. 121.5
29. 5
30. low
31. low, medium
32. loop, sense
33. is

34. does
35. VHF
36. horizontally
37. localizer
38. does not
39. TO
40. magnetic
41. LF
42. ADF
43. localizer
44. VHF
45. more
46. UHF
47. 75
48. does not
49. pulse
50. UHF
51. is not
52. C
53. 24
54. VORTAC
55. linear
56. LF
57. are
58. loran, GPS
59. is not
60. SHF
61. the ground
62. aural
63. landing gear, flap
64. water
65. red
66. does not
67. a. central processing unit
    b. memory
    c. input/output devices
68. a. ROM (Read Only Memory)
    b. RAM (Random Access Memory)

69. does
70. volatile
71. BITE
72. LRU
73. symbol generator
74. display controller
75. a. electronic attitude director indicator (EADI)
    b. electronic horizontal situation indicator (EHSI)
76. inoperative
77. a. EGT
    b. EPR
    c. N_1 speed
78. failure-related
79. true airspeed
80. Mach number
81. flight management computer system
82. minor
83. 337
84. alternator
85. wiring
86. shielded
87. should not
88. 2
89. 10
90. ground
91. weight and balance
92. air conditioning
93. tinned copper
94. 1
95. low
96. VOR, localizer
97. bottom
98. doubler
99. sense
100. flutter, vibration
101. quadrantal
102. forward
103. bottom

ICE CONTROL AND RAIN REMOVAL SYSTEMS

![12]

ICE CONTROL AND RAIN REMOVAL SYSTEMS

12

Ice Control Systems

Ice affects both engines and airframes and accounts for a large number of aircraft accidents. Reciprocating-engine-powered aircraft are susceptible to carburetor ice, which shuts off the airflow to the engine. Structural ice forms on the airfoil surfaces and adds weight, as well as disturbing the smooth flow of air needed to produce lift.

There are two types of ice control systems: anti-icing systems, which prevent the formation of ice, and deicing systems, which remove ice after it has formed. Both of these systems are discussed here.

A complete ice control system consists of:

- Surface deicers
- Windshield ice control
- Powerplant ice control
- Brake deicers
- Heated pitot heads

Dangers of In-Flight Icing

Some aircraft are certificated for flight into known icing conditions, but wise pilots know that in reality, the ice control systems on these aircraft only give them time to fly out of the icing conditions, not enough to remain in them deliberately. No aircraft can withstand unrestricted exposure to icing.

Three types of structural ice affect aircraft in flight: rime ice, glaze ice, and frost. Rime ice is a rough, opaque ice that forms when small droplets of water freeze immediately upon striking the aircraft. It builds up slowly, causes a great deal of drag, and deforms the airfoil, increasing the stall speed of the aircraft. Rime ice is relatively easy to break loose with deicer boots.

Glaze ice is the most dangerous ice. It forms on aircraft flying through supercooled water or freezing rain. Glaze ice adds a great amount of weight and is difficult for the boots to break loose.

Three factors must be present for rime or glaze ice to form on an aircraft in flight. There must be visible moisture in the air, which can be in the form of rain, drizzle, or clouds. The surface of the aircraft must be below the freezing temperature of water, and the drops of water must be of the appropriate size for the formation of ice.

rime ice. A rough ice that forms on aircraft flying through visible moisture, such as a cloud, when the temperature is below freezing. Rime ice disturbs the smooth airflow as well as adding weight.

glaze ice. Ice that forms when large drops of water strike a surface whose temperature is below freezing. Glaze ice is clear and heavy.

frost. Ice crystal deposits formed by sublimation when the temperature and dew point are below freezing.

supercooled water. Water in its liquid form at a temperature well below its natural freezing temperature. When supercooled water is disturbed, it immediately freezes.

sublimation. A process in which a solid material changes directly into a vapor without passing through the liquid stage.

ethylene glycol. A form of alcohol used as a coolant for liquid-cooled engines and as an anti-icing agent.

isopropyl alcohol. A colorless liquid used in the manufacture of acetone and its derivatives and as a solvent and anti-icing agent.

Frost forms on an aircraft when the surface temperature is below freezing and water sublimates from the air, or changes directly from water vapor into ice crystals without passing through the liquid state. Frost does not add appreciable weight, but the tiny ice crystals create a rough surface that increases the thickness of the boundary layer and adds so much drag that flight may be impossible. All traces of frost must be removed before flight. Do this by sweeping it off with a long-handled push broom or by spraying the aircraft with a mixture of ethylene glycol and isopropyl alcohol.

Types of Ice Control Systems

Three types of ice control systems are considered here: ice detection systems, anti-ice systems, and deice systems.

Ice Detection Systems

Ice control systems should be turned on when needed, but not used when there is no danger of ice formation. Ice is easy to see in some conditions, but some locations on the aircraft are not visible and require other methods besides visual detection.

Ice on the windshield and on the wings in the daytime is easy to see before it builds up to a dangerous level. Aircraft manufacturers recognize the importance of visual ice detection and provide ice lights on the outside of the aircraft cabin that shine out along the wings' leading edges so that ice build-up can be detected at night.

Some jet transport aircraft have electronic ice detectors mounted in critical locations that are not visible to the flight crew. These detectors are small probes that vibrate at a specific frequency monitored by a small built-in dedicated computer. When ice forms on the probe its vibrating frequency decreases, and when it drops to a predetermined value the computer turns on an ice-warning light. This alerts the flight crew so they can turn on the appropriate ice control system. At the same time, current is sent through heaters surrounding the probe to melt the ice so the probe can again vibrate freely. As long as the probe continues to detect ice, the ice-warning light remains on, but when it no longer ices up, the ice warning light goes out.

Anti-Icing Systems

anti-icer system. A system that prevents the formation of ice on an aircraft structure.

Critical areas on an aircraft where ice should not be allowed to form include carburetors, pitot tubes, windshields, turbine engine air inlets, and any components that are located ahead of the these inlets. On some aircraft, such as the Boeing 727, this includes the upper VOR antenna. Anti-icing systems prevent ice from forming on these components. There are three types of anti-icing systems: electrical, thermal, and chemical.

Deicing Systems

Components of an aircraft that do not lend themselves to anti-icing are protected by deicing systems. Ice is allowed to form, and then its bond with the surface is broken and the ice is removed by the air flowing over the surface or by centrifugal force. Most airfoils and propellers are protected by deicing systems.

Pitot-Static System Ice Protection

Pitot heads installed on aircraft that are likely to encounter icing have an electrical heater built into them to prevent ice clogging their air inlet. This heater produces enough heat to damage the head if there is no cooling air flowing over it, so it should not be turned on while the aircraft is on the ground except for brief preflight checking.

You can ensure that the heater is operating properly in flight by watching the ammeter when the pitot heat is turned on. The heater draws enough current that the ammeter will show its operation.

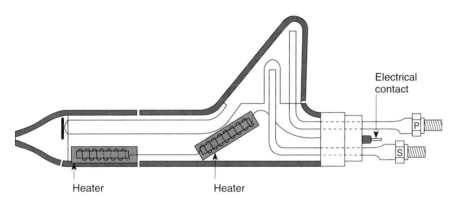

Figure 12-1. *The heater in a pitot-static head effectively prevents ice from blocking the source of pitot and static air pressures.*

Some flush static ports have heaters built into them, but on most aircraft there are two separate ports located at widely separated locations. It is unlikely that both ports will ice over at the same time. In the unlikely event that both should become plugged, the system is equipped with an alternate static air source valve that allows the pilot to select alternate air. This picks up static air from a location inside the aircraft where ice will not form.

deicer system. A system that removes ice after it has formed on an aircraft structure.

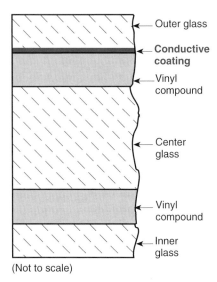

(Not to scale)

Figure 12-2. *The heated windshield of a jet transport aircraft is made of several layers of glass and vinyl with a conductive film deposited on the inner surface of the outer glass.*

thermistor. A special form of electrical resistor whose resistance varies with its temperature.

tempered glass. Glass that has been heat-treated to increase its strength. Tempered glass is used in birdproof heated windshields for high-speed aircraft.

Windshield Ice Protection

Aircraft that routinely fly into icing conditions have some method of preventing ice from forming on the windshield and obstructing the pilot's visibility. Three types of ice control are: double-panel windshields with warm air blown through the space between the panels, anti-icing fluid sprayed on the outside of the windshield, and electrically heated windshields. Most modern aircraft use electrically heated windshields.

Windshields for jet transport aircraft are extremely strong, as they must not only withstand all of the air loads but must be strong enough to withstand, without penetration, a direct strike by a four-pound bird at the designed cruising speed of the aircraft. In addition to preventing the formation of ice on these windshields, the heat keeps the thermoplastic vinyl layers from becoming brittle, and this prevents the windshield from shattering if it should be struck by a bird in flight.

Figure 12-2 shows the makeup of a jet transport windshield. It is made of three layers of tempered glass with inner layers of a thermoplastic vinyl compound. An electrically conductive film is deposited on the inside surface of the outer glass.

Windshields like the one in Figure 12-2 use 400-Hz AC. Voltage is increased by autotransformers to force enough current through the high resistance of the conductive film to produce the required heat. Thermistor-type temperature sensors laminated into the windshield measure its temperature and send this data to the AC controller, which sends just enough current through the conductive film to keep the windshield at the correct temperature.

Surface scratches or tiny chips in the tempered glass often cause stresses inside the panel that break the electrically conductive film. This allows arcing across the breaks which can cause local hot spots. If arcing occurs near one of the heat sensors, it can distort the heat control system.

Some business jet and turboprop airplanes have windshields made of two layers of tempered glass with a layer of a vinyl compound between them. A fine-wire heating element is embedded in this vinyl material.

The heating element is supplied with DC through a two-position switch and a temperature controller. Thermistor-type sensors embedded in the vinyl layer sense the windshield temperature. When the windshield anti-ice switch is in the NORMAL position, the sensors cause the controller to send current into the heating element until the windshield temperature rises to approximately 110°F. When this temperature is reached, current stops until the windshield cools to 90°F. The controller cycles current through the heating element to maintain the temperature within the set limits.

When severe icing is encountered, the switch can be moved to the HIGH position. This sends additional current through a small section of the heating element to raise the temperature of a critical area of the windshield.

This type of windshield ice control is strictly anti-icing, as it does not produce enough heat to melt off a heavy accumulation of ice that could form before the heat is turned on. Enough heat is generated, however, that this system should not be turned on while the aircraft is on the ground except for a momentary check of its operation. An adequate flow of air is required over the windshield to prevent damage.

Some of the smaller general aviation aircraft have heated anti-icing panels on the outside of the windshield. A panel of this type is shown in Figure 12-3. This panel is made of two sheets of plate glass separated by a layer of vinyl compound. A fine resistance wire embedded in the vinyl is heated with DC, supplied through a connector enclosed in a streamlined housing near the panel. The panel is removable and is installed only on flights when icing conditions are likely. Prior to entering possible icing conditions, the system is turned on, and once it is in operation, temperature sensors cycle the power to maintain a temperature of approximately 100°F.

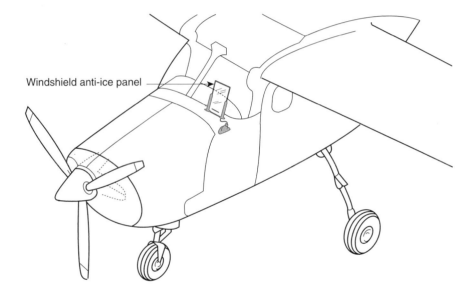

Windshield anti-ice panel

Figure 12-3. *A removable heated panel may be installed on some of the smaller general aviation aircraft to provide an ice-free area in the windshield directly in front of the pilot.*

Airfoil Ice Protection

Ice formation on the wings of early aircraft was one of the hindrances to scheduled airline flights. Ford Trimotors and Curtiss Condors, with their exposed wires and struts, had so many places to collect ice that there would not have been much profit in deicing the airfoil surfaces. But when the streamlined, slick-skin, cantilever airplanes such as the Boeing 247, the Douglas DC-2, and the Northrop *Alpha*, started flying in airline service, engineers and operators realized that if they could remove ice from the wings

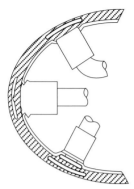

A When system is not operating, suction holds all three tubes deflated and tight against leading edge.

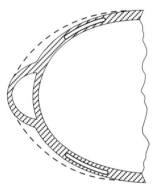

B When system is first turned on, center tube inflates and cracks the ice. Center tube remains inflated for specific number of seconds, then deflates.

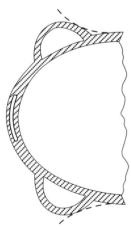

C Outer two tubes inflate and raise cracked ice from surface so wind can blow it away.

Figure 12-4. *The operating cycle of a typical three-spanwise-tube deicer boot*

of these airplanes, all-weather flight schedules could be realistic. In about 1932, the B.F. Goodrich Company developed the inflatable boot deicer that is still in use today.

Turbine-powered aircraft have a ready supply of hot compressed air from their engine compressors, and these aircraft often used thermal deicers and anti-icers for their wings.

Pneumatic Deicer System

Pneumatic deicer systems have boots made of soft pliable rubber or rubberized fabric attached to the leading edges of the wings and empennage. These boots contain inflatable tubes. There are several boot designs, some having as few as three and others as many as 10 spanwise tubes. Other boots have chordwise tubes.

The surface ply of the boots is made electrically conductive so it will dissipate the static electrical charges that build up as air flows over them. If this charge did not flow off the boot, the voltage could build up high enough to discharge through the boot to the skin, and in doing so burn a hole in the boot.

The typical three-spanwise-tube boot in Figure 12-4 shows the operation of this system. When the system is not in operation, suction from the engine-driven vacuum pump holds the tubes deflated and tight against the leading edge (A).

When icing is encountered in flight, the pilot allows ice to form over the boots, then turns the system on. Air from the discharge side of the vacuum pump inflates the center tube in the boot (B) to crack the ice. The timer holds the center tube inflated for a specific number of seconds, then deflates it and inflates the two outer tubes. These tubes lift the cracked ice so air can get under it and blow it from the surface (C).

When the pneumatic deicer system was first developed, there were no good adhesives to bond the boots to the wing, and the B.F. Goodrich Company devised the Rivnut to provide a threaded hole in the thin metal of the leading edges of the wings and empennage. Some of the older installations still use machine screws and Rivnuts to secure the boots. These installations are easily identified by a metal fairing strip that covers the edges of the boots.

All modern installations use an adhesive to bond the boots to the surface. When a surface-bonded boot is installed, all the paint must be removed from the area to which the boot is to be bonded. The metal must be perfectly clean, and the bonding material must be applied in strict accordance with the instructions furnished by the maker of the boots.

Deicer boots are made of rubber and should be cleaned with a mild soap and water solution. Any grease or oil must be removed with a rag damp with naphtha or varsol, and then the entire area washed with soap and water.

Small holes in the boots may be patched with cold patches similar to those used for bicycle tubes, but not the same material. Use only patching material provided by the boot manufacturer and follow their repair procedures in detail.

The boots may be periodically resurfaced with a black, conductive neoprene cement to seal any tiny pinholes and ensure that the boots remain electrically conductive.

Single-Engine Airplane Deicing System

Small aircraft equipped for flight into known icing conditions have a wing and empennage deicing system similar to the one in Figure 12-5. The air pump used for the instruments supplies the necessary 18- to 20-psi positive pressure to operate the boots and the suction used to hold them tight against the leading edges when the system is not operating.

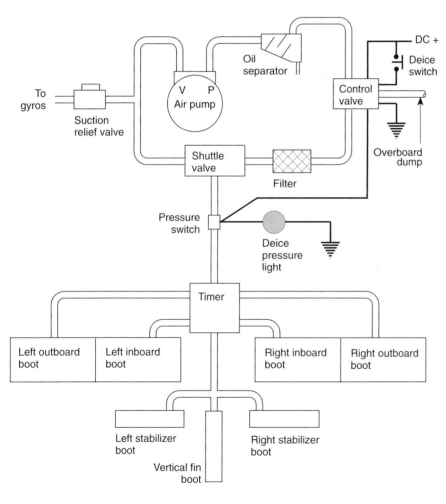

Figure 12-5. *Wing and empennage deicing system for a single-engine airplane that is approved for flight into known icing conditions*

If the air pump uses engine oil as a lubricant ("wet"-type), an oil separator must be installed in its discharge side to remove the lubricating oil. This oil collects on a series of baffles and drains back into the engine crankcase. Dry-type air pumps have carbon vanes and require no lubrication, and so do not require an oil separator.

When the deicing system is not operating, the shuttle valve is held over so that suction from the air pump holds the boots deflated and tight against the leading edges of the surfaces.

When ice has formed on the wings, the pilot depresses the momentary-on deice switch. This opens the control valve, allowing air pressure to reach the shuttle valve and move the shuttle over so air pressure can reach the timer. The timer begins a sequence of operation that inflates the empennage boots for about six seconds, then the inboard wing boots for six seconds, and finally the outboard wing boots for six seconds. When there is sufficient pressure at the boots for proper inflation, the deice pressure light on the instrument panel illuminates. When the cycle is completed, the control valve opens the passage to the overboard dump, and the shuttle moves over so the suction can again hold the boots tightly against the skin.

Multi-Engine Airplane Deicing System

The pneumatic deicing system used on large aircraft works in the same way as the system just described, except there are larger boots and more components. Figure 12-6 diagrams a typical deicing system for a twin-engine airplane. This system has wet-type air pumps on both engines. The discharge air from these pumps flows through oil separators and check valves into the deicer control valve. When the system is turned OFF, the air discharges overboard, and when it is turned ON, the air flows to the distributor valve/timer. An electric motor drives the distributor valve in a timed sequence to the center tube of the outboard boots, then to the outer tubes of the outboard boots. The boots on the empennage then inflate and deflate, then the center tubes, and finally the outer tubes on the inboard wing boots inflate and deflate.

The boots actuate symmetrically to keep the airflow disturbances even on both sides of the aircraft. This minimizes any flight or control problems caused by these disturbances.

When the system is turned OFF, the distributor valve connects the suction side of the air pumps to the boots to hold them tightly against the leading edges. A suction-relief valve installed between the check valves and the distributor valve regulates the amount of suction that is applied to the boots.

Proper actuation of the deicer system may be determined by watching the pressure and suction gages. The pressure gage fluctuates as the timer sequences the different boots, but the suction gage remains steady since the vacuum side of the pump is not used during normal operation of the system.

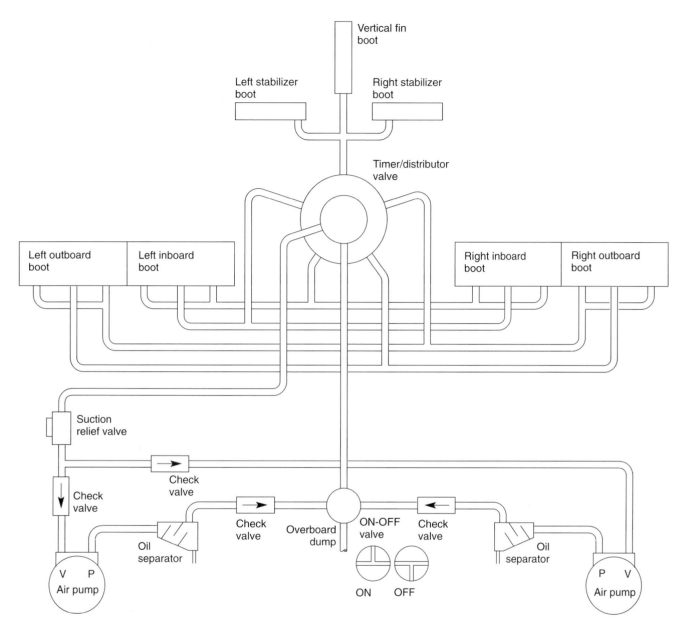

Figure 12-6. *A pneumatic deicing system for a twin-engine airplane*

Turbine-engine aircraft have a ready source of warm compressor bleed air for anti-icing, and they normally use thermal ice control. Some of the smaller turbine engines do not have an adequate quantity of bleed air for thermal ice control, but do have enough for inflating pneumatic deicing boots. Systems that use compressor bleed air for this purpose have a pressure regulator that lowers the pressure to the correct value and a venturi downstream of the regulator that produces suction when the boots are not inflated. This suction holds the tubes deflated and tight against the leading edges.

Thermal Ice Control Systems

Large turbine-engine-powered aircraft use hot compressor bleed air to prevent the formation of ice on the airfoils. This anti-icing system is operated in flight when icing conditions are first encountered or when they are expected to occur. It keeps the leading-edge devices warm with a continuous flow of heated air.

Some thermal ice control systems may be used as deicers as well as anti-icers. These systems allow much hotter air to flow through the leading edges, but for shorter periods of time and in a cyclic sequence. When these are used as deicers, ice is allowed to accumulate, then the leading edge is heated, and the ice breaks off.

The Boeing 727 uses hot air to protect the wings, engines, and upper VHF antenna from ice. Hot compressor bleed air flows from the two outboard engines through wing anti-ice control valves to a common manifold and then to the wing anti-ice ducts. The two inboard leading-edge flap sections and all eight leading edge slats are protected. After passing through the leading-edge flaps, the air is vented into the wing leading edge cavity, and air from the slats is vented into the inner slat cavity and then overboard through the slat-track openings and drain holes.

Overheat warning switches in the wing anti-ice ducting warn of overheating when the system is operating either on the ground or in the air. Temperature sensors are installed in the bleed air supply ducts downstream of the anti-ice valves, and this temperature is shown on the flight engineer's panel.

Some hot air is tapped off from the wing anti-ice ducting and used to provide anti-ice protection to the upper VHF radio antenna. This antenna is mounted on top of the fuselage in such a location that if ice were to form on it and break off, it would be ingested into the center engine.

Some large reciprocating-engine-powered airplanes use thermal ice control systems with the heat supplied by either combustion heaters or augmenter tubes installed around the exhaust system.

Combustion heaters burn aviation gasoline from the main fuel tanks, and the amount of heat they produce is controlled by thermoswitches. These switches turn the fuel off when the temperature reaches the upper limit and turn it back on when the lower control temperature is reached.

Brake Deice System

Some aircraft operate in climates where they regularly encounter freezing rain that can cause the brakes to seize. When the brake deice system is actuated, compressor bleed air is directed through the brake assemblies to melt any ice that may have formed.

Brake deice systems can be used at any time the aircraft is on the ground, but should not be used when the outside air temperature is well above freezing. In flight, a timer prevents them from being used for more than approximately 10 minutes. This prevents overheating in the wheel well.

augmenter tube. A long, stainless steel tube around the discharge of the exhaust pipes of a reciprocating engine. Exhaust gases flow through the augmenter tube and produce a low pressure that pulls additional cooling air through the engine. Heat may be taken from the augmenter tubes and directed through the leading edges of the wings for thermal anti-icing.

Powerplant Ice Protection

Powerplant ice affects both reciprocating and turbine engines. Most reciprocating engines are prone to carburetor or induction system icing, and turbine engines are mostly bothered by ingestion of ice that has broken off of some portion of the aircraft ahead of the intake.

Reciprocating Engines

Carburetor ice is the most prevalent type of powerplant ice and it can affect the safety of flight when there is no visible moisture in the air and no danger of other types of ice forming. A float-type carburetor acts as a very effective mechanical refrigerator. Liquid fuel is sprayed into the induction air in the form of tiny droplets that evaporate, or change from a liquid into a vapor. Heat is required to make this change, and it comes from the air flowing through the carburetor. When heat energy is removed from the air, the air's temperature drops enough to cause moisture to condense out and freeze in the throat of the carburetor. This ice chokes off the air flowing into the cylinders and causes the engine to lose power. Severe carburetor icing can cause engine failure. There is about a 70°F drop in temperature when the fuel evaporates, and carburetor ice can form when the outside air temperature is as high as 100°F if the humidity is high.

Carburetor ice is typically prevented by heating the air before it is taken into the carburetor. Aircraft certificated under Federal Aviation Regulation Part 23, which have a sea-level engine with a venturi carburetor, must be able to increase the temperature of the induction air by 90°F. Aircraft with altitude engines must be able to provide a temperature rise of 120°F. This heating is normally done by routing the air around the outside of some part of the exhaust system before taking it into the carburetor. The heated air bypasses the inlet air filter, and carburetor heat should not be used for ground operation.

Fuel-injected engines are not bothered by carburetor ice, but ice can form on the intake air filter and choke off the air flowing into the engine. These aircraft typically have an alternate air valve that allows air from inside the engine cowling to be taken into the fuel injection unit if the screen should ice over.

Some larger engines spray isopropyl alcohol into the throat of the carburetor. This coats the venturi and throttle valves so ice will not stick to the carburetor.

Most carburetor ice forms at the point the liquid fuel droplets evaporate, and this is in the carburetor body where the airflow would be disturbed by a temperature probe. Flight tests have shown a definite relationship between the temperature of the air entering the carburetor and the temperature of the air

sea-level engine. A reciprocating engine whose rated takeoff power can be produced only at sea level.

altitude engine. A reciprocating engine whose rated sea level takeoff power can be produced to an established higher altitude.

at the point of fuel evaporation. A temperature probe can be installed at the carburetor air inlet, and as long as the air temperature it senses remains above a specific value, there is little chance of carburetor ice forming. The pilot can control the temperature of this air by using the carburetor heat control.

Turbine Engines

Turbine engines are susceptible to damage from chunks of ice that get into the compressor, so anti-icing systems are used to prevent the formation of ice ahead of the compressor inlet. Many aircraft have air passages in the compressor inlet case, inlet guide vanes, nose dome, and nose cowling. Hot compressor bleed air flows through these passages to prevent the formation of ice.

Ice can form when the engine is operated at high speed on the ground when the temperature is as high as 45°F if the air is moist. The high velocity of the inlet air creates a pressure drop that lowers the temperature of the air enough for ice to form.

In flight the anti-icing system is turned on before entering areas of visible moisture (rain or clouds) when the inlet temperature is between about 40°F and 5°F. Below 5°F, there is so little moisture in the air that ice is not likely to form.

Sometimes turbine-powered aircraft sit on the ground and water collects in the compressor and freezes. If this should happen, direct a flow of warm air through the engine until all of the ice is melted and the rotating parts turn freely.

Propellers

Ice on a propeller changes its airfoil shape and creates an unbalanced condition. Both of these conditions produce vibration and can damage the engine as well as the airframe. The earliest propeller ice control, and a system that is still in use, is chemical anti-icing. A mixture of isopropyl alcohol and ethylene glycol is carried in a tank in the aircraft and when icing conditions are anticipated, some of it is pumped into a slinger ring around the hub of the propeller and then out along the leading edges of the blades. Some propellers have molded rubber feed shoes bonded to the blade roots to help concentrate the flow of fluid along the portions of the blade that are most susceptible to ice formation. Keeping the blade surfaces perfectly smooth and waxed assists in preventing ice from sticking when it forms.

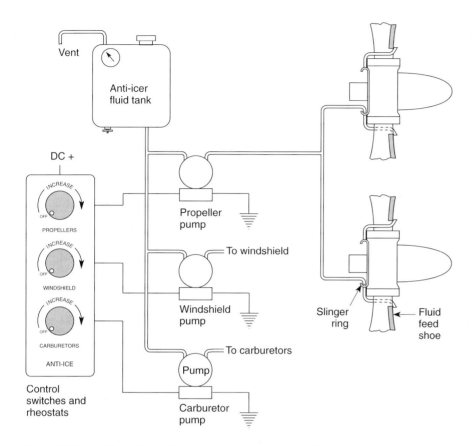

Figure 12-7. *A typical chemical anti-icing system for a propeller*

Propellers are deiced with an electrothermal system that has rubber boots bonded to the leading edge of the blades. These boots have electrical heating elements embedded in them that are supplied with current from a propeller deicing timer.

Figure 12-8 is the electrical schematic diagram of a typical electrothermal deicing system used on a twin turboprop airplane. Current flows from the bus through the 20-amp Auto Prop Deice circuit breaker/switch into the deicer timer unit. When the manual-override relays are not energized, this current flows through brushes riding on slip rings mounted on the propeller spinner bulkhead into the heating elements bonded to the propeller blades. The slip rings are connected to the heater elements through flexible conductors that allow the blades to change their pitch angle. *See* Figure 12-8 on the next page.

The timer sends current through the right propeller for about 90 seconds, then switches over and sends current through the left propeller for 90 seconds.

Some propeller deicing systems have two separate heating elements on each blade. Current flows through the right propeller outboard element for somewhere around 30 seconds, then through the right propeller inboard element for the same length of time. After the right propeller is deiced, the timer shifts over and sends current through the left propeller outboard elements and then through the left propeller inboard elements.

Current cycles of the two propellers are controlled by the timer as long as the propeller Auto Prop Deice switch is ON. When the Manual Prop Deicer switch is held in its momentary ON position, the two manual-override relays are energized and current flows directly from the bus to the blades without going through the timer.

The pilot can easily tell whether the deicing system is operating correctly in the AUTOMATIC mode by watching the propeller ammeter. It will show a flow of current each time one of the heater elements draws current.

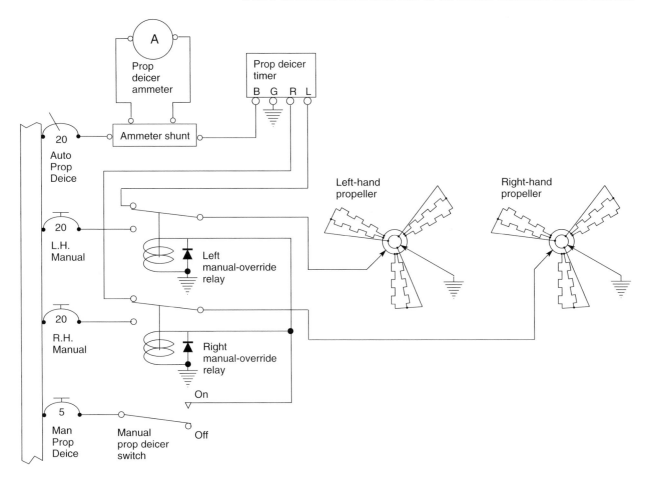

Figure 12-8. *Electrothermal propeller deicing system*

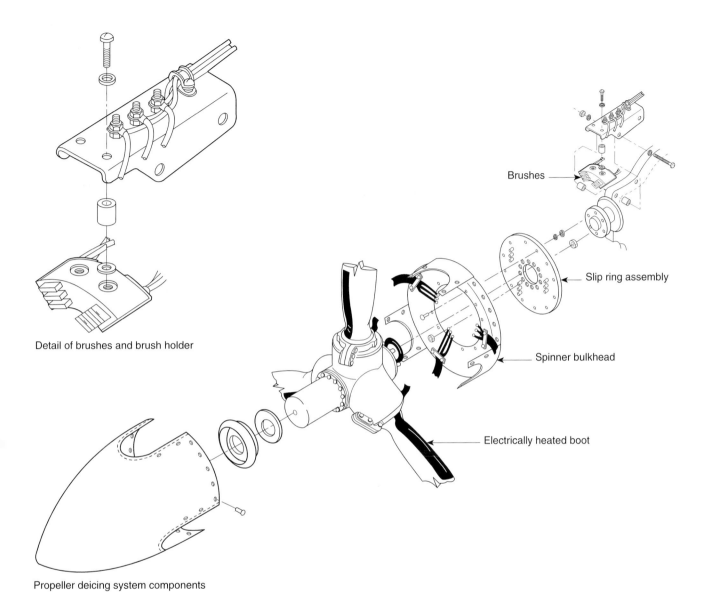

Detail of brushes and brush holder

Brushes

Slip ring assembly

Spinner bulkhead

Electrically heated boot

Propeller deicing system components

Figure 12-9. *Electrothermally deiced propeller*

Water Drain System Ice Protection

The water lines, drain masts, toilet drain lines, and waste water drains that are located in areas where they are exposed to freezing temperatures in flight are protected by electrically heated hoses or by ribbon or blanket heaters. All of these heaters have thermostats built into them that prevent them from overheating.

Ground Deicing and Anti-Icing

Aircraft operating in the winter months are often faced with the problem of taking off into conditions of snow and ice. Federal Aviation Regulations prohibit takeoff when snow, ice, or frost is adhering to the wings, and it is the responsibility of the aviation maintenance technician to operate the equipment that deices and anti-ices the aircraft.

Test data shows that ice, snow, or frost formations with a thickness and surface roughness similar to medium or coarse sandpaper on the leading edge and upper surface of a wing can reduce wing lift by as much as 30 percent and increase drag by as much as 40 percent. For this reason, all snow, ice, and frost must be removed.

Small aircraft that have been sitting in the open and are covered with snow may be prepared for flight by sweeping the snow off with a brush or broom, making very sure that there is no frost left on the surface. Frost, while adding very little weight, roughens the surface enough to destroy lift. An engine heater that blows warm air through a large hose may be used for deicing, but take care to prevent melted ice from running down inside the aircraft structure and refreezing.

There are two methods of ground ice control for large aircraft: deicing and anti-icing, and there are two types of freezing-point depressant (FPD) fluids in use: Type I and Type II. Deicing and anti-icing may be accomplished by two procedures: the one-step procedure and two-step procedure.

Deicing is the removal of ice that has already formed on the surface, and anti-icing is the protection of the surface from the subsequent formation of ice. Just before takeoff large aircraft are both deiced and anti-iced.

The FPD fluids used for icing protection are made up of propylene/diethylene and ethylene glycols with certain additives. These fluids are mixed with water to give them the proper characteristics.

Type I FPD fluids contain a minimum of 80% glycols and are considered "unthickened" because of their relative low viscosity. Type I fluid is used primarily for deicing, because it provides very limited anti-icing protection.

Type II FPD fluids contain a minimum of 50% glycols and are considered "thickened" because of added agents that enable the fluid to be deposited in a thicker film and to remain on the aircraft surfaces until time of takeoff. These fluids are used for deicing and anti-icing and provide greater protection than Type I fluids against ice, frost, or snow formation on the ground.

FPD. Freezing point depressant

Deicing and anti-icing may be done with the one-step or the two-step procedure. In the one-step procedure, the FPD fluid is mixed with water that is heated to a nozzle temperature of 140°F (60°C) and sprayed on the surface. The heated fluid is very effective for deicing, but the residual FPD fluid film has very limited anti-icing protection. Anti-icing protection is enhanced by using cold fluids. In some instances, the final coat of fluid is applied in a fine mist, using a high trajectory to allow the fluid to cool before it touches the aircraft skin.

For the two-step procedure, the first step is deicing, and heated fluid is used. The second step is anti-icing and cold fluid is used, so it will remain on the surface for a longer period of time.

STUDY QUESTIONS: ICE CONTROL SYSTEMS

Answers begin on Page 880. Page numbers refer to chapter text.

1. Two types of ice control are:
   a. _____
   b. _____
   Page 859

2. The ice control system that prevents the formation of ice is the _____ system. *Page 859*

3. The ice control system that removes ice after it has formed is the _____ system. *Page 859*

4. Frost on an aircraft wing _____ (does or does not) constitute a hazard to flight. *Page 860*

5. A pitot head is anti-iced with a/an _____ (electric or hot air) heater. *Page 861*

6. An operational check of a pitot-static tube heater may be made by watching the _____ when the heater is turned on. *Page 861*

7. Frost may be removed from an aircraft by spraying it with a deicing fluid that normally contains _____ and _____ . *Page 860*

8. Electrically heated windshields that use a conductive film as the heating element are energized with _____ (AC or DC). *Page 862*

9. The temperature of an electrically heated windshield is sensed by _____-type sensors laminated between the glass panels. *Page 862*

Continued

---

10. A breakdown of the electrically conductive film inside an electrically heated windshield can cause _____ . *Page 862*

11. Three methods of preventing ice from forming on a windshield and obstructing pilot visibility are:
    a. _____
    b. _____
    c. _____
    Page 862

12. The fluid that is used for anti-icing propeller blades is a mixture of _____ and _____ . *Page 870*

13. Current for the heating elements in an electrothermal deicing system for a propeller is carried from the airframe into the propeller through _____ and _____ . *Page 871*

14. Reciprocating-engine-powered aircraft get the air for inflating the deicer boots from a/an _____ . *Page 865*

15. Deicing systems are turned on _____ (before or after) icing is encountered. *Page 864*

16. Deicer boots are attached to modern aircraft leading edges with a/an _____ . *Page 864*

17. Before installing a surface-bonded deicer boot to the leading edge of an aircraft wing, the paint must be _____ (cleaned or removed). *Page 864*

18. The oil that is used to lubricate a "wet" vacuum pump is removed from the discharge air by a/an _____ . *Page 866*

19. Deicer boots should be cleaned with _____ . *Page 864*

20. Deicer boots are actuated symmetrically to minimize control problems caused by disturbance of the _____ . *Page 866*

21. The inflation sequence of a pneumatic deicer boot system is controlled by a _____ /timer. *Page 866*

22. The amount of suction used to hold the deicing boots deflated when the system is not operating is controlled by a/an _____ valve. *Page 866*

23. During normal operation of a pneumatic deicer system, the air pressure gage will _____ (fluctuate or remain steady). *Page 866*

24. During normal operation of a pneumatic deicer system, the suction gage will _____ (fluctuate or remain steady). *Page 866*

25. The component in a multi-engine pneumatic deicing system that directs suction into the boots when the system is not operating is the _____ . *Page 866*

26. Two sources of heat for thermal ice control on reciprocating-engine-powered aircraft are:
   a. _____
   b. _____
   Page 868

27. The temperature of the air produced by a combustion heater is controlled by cycling the _____ (fuel or ignition) on and off. *Page 868*

28. Carburetor ice _____ (can or cannot) form when the outside air temperature is above 70°F. *Page 869*

29. Visible moisture _____ (is or is not) required for the formation of carburetor ice. *Page 869*

30. The heat for eliminating carburetor ice normally comes from the _____ . *Page 869*

31. Fuel-injected engines have an alternate source of induction system air to use in the event the _____ ices over. *Page 869*

32. When carburetor heat is used, the intake air _____ (is or is not) filtered. *Page 869*

33. A carburetor heater system for a sea-level engine should be able to increase the temperature of the air by _____°F. *Page 869*

34. Ice is prevented from sticking to the throttle valve and venturi in a carburetor by spraying _____ into the carburetor inlet. *Page 869*

35. If the compressor of a turbine engine is immobile because of ice, the ice should be melted with _____ . *Page 870*

Continued

36. Type I FPD fluids are used primarily for _____ (anti-icing or deicing). *Page 874*

37. Heated FPD fluids are most effective for _____ (anti-icing or deicing). *Page 875*

38. For most effective anti-icing, the FPD fluid is applied _____ (hot or cold). *Page 875*

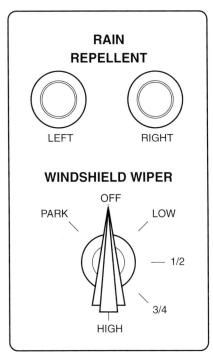

Figure 12-10. *Rain control panel located in the overhead control area of a jet transport cockpit*

Rain Removal Systems

Rain removal systems are used in most larger aircraft to keep the windshield free of water so the pilot can see for the approach and to maneuver the aircraft safely on the ground.

Small general aviation aircraft have acrylic windshields that are easy to scratch, so windshield wipers are not used. Rain is prevented from obstructing visibility on these aircraft by keeping the windshield waxed with a good grade of paste wax. Water does not spread out on the waxed surface, but balls up and is blown away by the propeller blast.

Large aircraft have tempered glass windshields and a rain removal system that may be mechanical, chemical, or pneumatic.

Mechanical systems use windshield wipers similar to those used on automobiles except that they are able to withstand the high air loads caused by the speed of the aircraft. The wipers for the pilot and the copilot are driven independently, so if one drive malfunctions, there will still be clear visibility on the other side. The wipers may be driven by electric motors or hydraulic or pneumatic actuators, and all systems have speed controls and a position on the control switch that drives the blades to a stowed, or park, position.

Windshield wipers should never be operated on a dry windshield because they will scratch the expensive glass. When you must operate them for maintenance purposes, flush the windshield with water and operate the wipers while the glass is wet.

Chemical rain repellent is a syrupy liquid carried in pressurized cans in the rain repellent system. When flying in heavy rain with the windshield wipers operating, the pilot depresses the rain repellent buttons. This opens solenoid valves for a specific length of time and allows the correct amount of liquid to spray out along the lower portion of the windshield. The windshield wipers then spread the repellent evenly over the glass, and when rain strikes the treated surface it balls up rather than spreading out. The water is carried away by the high velocity of the air flowing over the windshield.

Chemical rain repellent should not be discharged onto a dry windshield because it will smear and be difficult to remove. It can restrict visibility if it is sprayed on the windshield when there is not enough rain to allow it to be spread out smoothly.

Another method of controlling rain on aircraft windshields is the use of a blast of high-velocity hot turbine engine compressor bleed air. This air is blown across the windshield from ducts similar to that in Figure 12-11. The air forms a barrier that prevents the rain from hitting the windshield glass.

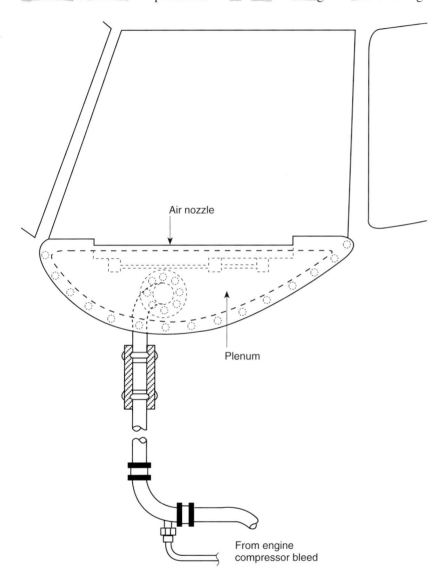

plenum. An enclosed chamber in which air can be held at a pressure higher than that of the surrounding air.

Figure 12-11. *Pneumatic rain removal system*

Answers begin below. **Page numbers refer to chapter text.**

39. Acrylic plastic windshields on small general aviation aircraft are treated to ease the removal of rain by coating them with a smooth coat of _____ . *Page 878*

40. Three types of rain removal systems for large aircraft are:
    a. _____
    b. _____
    c. _____
    Page 878

41. Chemical rain repellent _____ (should or should not) be applied to a dry windshield. *Page 878*

42. The air for a pneumatic rain removal system comes from the _____ . *Page 879*

Answers to Ice Control and Rain Removal Systems Study Questions

1. a. anti-ice system
   b. deice system
2. anti-ice
3. deice
4. does
5. electric
6. ammeter
7. ethylene glycol, isopropyl alcohol
8. AC
9. thermistor
10. arcing
11. a. warm air blown between laminated glass panels
    b. chemical anti-icing fluid sprayed on the outside
    c. electrically heated windshields
12. isopropyl alcohol, ethylene glycol
13. brushes, slip rings
14. vacuum pump
15. after
16. adhesive
17. removed
18. oil separator
19. soap and water
20. airflow
21. distributor valve
22. suction relief
23. fluctuate
24. remain steady
25. distributor valve
26. a. combustion heaters
    b. augmenter tubes around the exhaust
27. fuel
28. can
29. is not
30. exhaust system
31. air filter
32. is not
33. 90
34. isopropyl alcohol
35. warm air
36. deicing
37. deicing
38. cold
39. wax
40. a. mechanical
    b. chemical
    c. pneumatic
41. should not
42. turbine engine compressor

FIRE PROTECTION SYSTEMS

13

Continued

FIRE PROTECTION SYSTEMS

13

Fire Protection

Aircraft carry large volumes of highly flammable fuel in a lightweight, vibration-prone structure. This structure also carries engines that continually produce extremely hot exhaust gases. Add a complex electrical system with motors and relays that produce sparks, and radio and radar transmitters that emit electromagnetic radiation, and you have an ideal environment for fires.

Yet the fire detection and protection systems available in modern aircraft are so effective, there are relatively few fires in the air.

Requirements for Fire

Fire is the result of a chemical reaction between some type of fuel and oxygen. When this reaction occurs, energy is released in the form of heat and light.

For a fire to start, there must be fuel, oxygen, and a high enough temperature to start the reaction. Fires may be extinguished by removing the fuel or oxygen or by reducing the temperature to a level below that needed for the reaction.

The National Fire Protection Association has categorized fires and identified the types of extinguishing agents best used on each type. The four categories are Classes A, B, C, and D.

Class A fires are fueled by solid combustible materials such as wood, paper, and cloth. These fires typically occur in aircraft cabins and cockpits, so any extinguishing agent used for Class-A fires must be safe for the occupants.

Class B fires are fueled by combustible liquids such as gasoline, turbine-engine fuel, lubricating oil, and hydraulic fluid. Class-B fires typically occur in engine compartments.

Class C fires involve energized electrical equipment. These fires can occur in almost any part of an aircraft and they demand special care because of the danger of electrical shock.

Class D fires are those in which some metal such as magnesium burns. These fires typically occur in the brakes and wheels, and burn with a ferocious intensity. Never use water on a burning metal, it only intensifies the fire.

Fire Detection Systems

A complete fire detection system consists of fire detectors, overheat detectors, rate-of-temperature-rise detectors, smoke detectors, and carbon monoxide detectors. We will discuss each of these.

Requirements for a fire detection system:

1. The system must not give false warnings under any flight or ground operating condition.

2. The system must give a rapid indication of a fire and accurately identify its location.

3. The system must accurately indicate when a fire has been extinguished.

4. The system must sound a warning if a fire re-ignites.

5. The system must continue to indicate the presence of a fire as long as the fire exists.

6. The integrity of the system must be able to be tested from the cockpit.

7. Detectors must not be damaged by exposure to oil, water, vibration, extremes of temperature, and the handling encountered in normal maintenance.

8. Detectors must be lightweight and adaptable to any mounting position.

9. Detector circuitry must operate directly from the aircraft electrical system.

10. The detector circuitry must require a minimum of electrical current when it is not indicating a fire.

11. Each detection system should actuate an audible alarm and a cockpit light that shows the location of the fire.

12. There must be a separate detection system for each engine.

Fire Detectors and Overheat Detection Systems

A fire detector system warns the flight crew of the presence of a fire that raises the temperature of a particular location to a predetermined high value. An overheat detector initiates a warning when there is a lesser increase in temperature over a larger area. Most of these detection systems turn on a red light and sound a fire-warning bell.

Thermoswitch-Type Fire Detection System

The single-terminal bimetallic thermoswitch-type spot detector circuit uses a number of spot detectors such as the one in Figure 13-1 installed in a circuit like the one in Figure 13-2. When a fire occurs in the area protected by one of the detectors, the detector is heated, and strips on which the contacts are mounted distort and close the contacts, completing the circuit between the loop and ground.

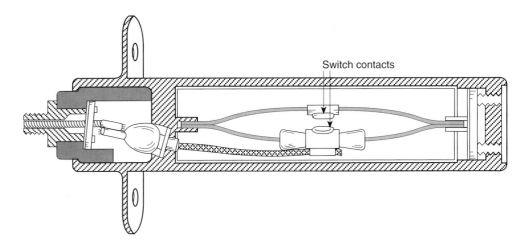

Figure 13-1. *A single-terminal bimetallic thermoswitch fire detector*

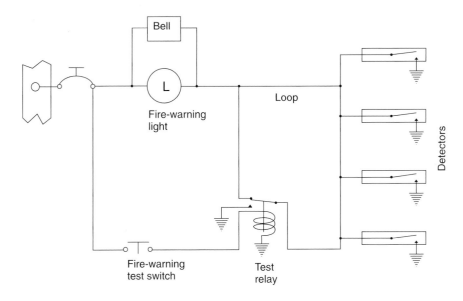

Figure 13-2. *Circuit for a single-terminal thermoswitch fire detector system*

The circuit in Figure 13-2 will signal the presence of a fire even if the loop of wire connecting the detectors is broken. During normal operation the detectors get their power from both ends of the loop, and if the loop is broken at any one point, all of the detectors still have power. If any one detector senses a fire, its contacts will close and provide a ground for the fire-warning light.

Closing the fire-warning test switch energizes the test relay, removes power from one end of the loop and grounds it, turning on the fire-warning light and sounding the bell. If there is an open in the wire between the detectors, there will be no ground for the warning light, and it will not illuminate.

Another type of thermoswitch spot detector installed in some aircraft have two terminals. Instead of completing the circuit to ground when a fire is detected, the detector completes the circuit between the two conductors connected to their terminals. These two-terminal thermoswitches are connected between two loops, and the system can tolerate either an open circuit or a short to ground in either of the loops without affecting the operation of the system.

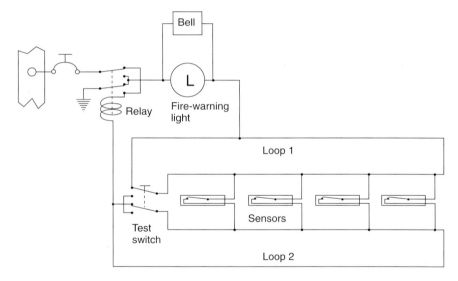

Figure 13-3. *Circuit for a two-terminal thermoswitch fire detector system*

two-terminal spot-type fire detection system. A fire detection system that uses individual thermoswitches installed around the inside of the area to be protected.

These thermoswitches are wired in parallel between two separate circuits. A short or an open circuit can exist in either circuit without causing a fire warning.

thermocouple. An electrical device consisting of a loop made of two different types of wire. A voltage is generated in a thermocouple that is proportional to the difference in the temperatures of the two points where the dissimilar wires join. This voltage difference causes current to flow.

Follow the circuit in Figure 13-3 to see the way the two-terminal thermoswitch system works. When there is no fire, Loop 2 is connected to the positive voltage, and Loop 1 is connected to ground, both through the normally-closed contacts of the relay.

If there is a short to ground in Loop 1, nothing happens because Loop 1 is already at ground potential. If there is a short to ground in Loop 2, the fault current energizes the relay and places Loop 2 at ground potential. The relay makes Loop 1 positive, or "hot."

Both ends of the two loops are connected to the test switch, and a single open in either of the loops has no effect on the operation of the system.

When the test switch is depressed, the circuit between the two loops is completed. Current flows through the relay coil, all of Loops 1 and 2, and back to ground through the fire-warning light and bell. Pressing the test switch checks the integrity of the entire system.

Rate-of-Temperature-Rise Detection System

A thermoswitch-type detection system initiates a fire warning when any of the individual detectors reaches a predetermined temperature. But because a fire can have a good start before this temperature is reached, the thermocouple-type fire-warning system is used. This system initiates a fire warning when the temperature at any specific location in the monitored compartment rises a great deal faster than the temperature of the entire compartment. Thermocouple-type fire-warning systems are often installed in engine compartments where normal operating temperatures are quite high, but the rise to this temperature is gradual.

A thermocouple is made of two different types of wire welded together, and the point at which the wires are joined is called a junction. When several thermocouples are connected in series in a circuit, a voltage will exist within the circuit that is proportional to the difference in the temperatures of the various junctions.

The sensors used with a thermocouple system are similar to the one in Figure 13-4. These sensors have a piece of each of the two thermocouple wires, typically iron and constantan, welded together and mounted in the housing that protects them from physical damage, yet allows free circulation of air around the wires. They form the measuring junctions of the thermocouple, and all of them are connected in series with the coil of a sensitive relay and a test thermocouple.

thermocouple fire detection system. A fire detection system that works on the principle of the rate-of-temperature-rise. Thermocouples are installed around the area to be protected, and one thermocouple is surrounded by insulation that prevents its temperature changing rapidly.

In the event of a fire, the temperature of all the thermocouples except the protected one will rise immediately and a fire warning will be initiated. In the case of a general overheat condition, the temperature of all the thermocouples will rise uniformly and there will be no fire warning.

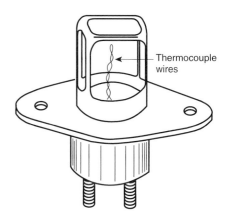

Figure 13-4. *A thermocouple fire sensor*

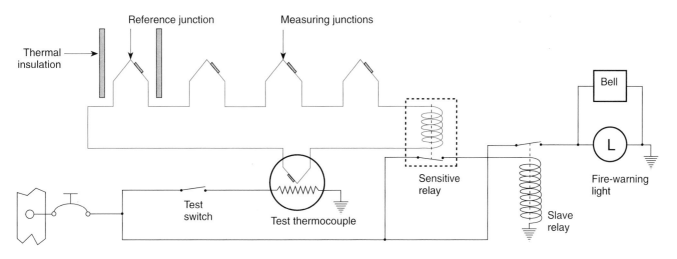

Figure 13-5. *A rate-of-temperature-rise fire-detection circuit*

The sensors are mounted at strategic locations around the monitored compartment. One sensor is mounted inside a thermal insulating shield that protects it from direct air circulation, yet allows it to reach the temperature of the air within the compartment. This sensor is called the reference junction.

When there is no fire, all of the junctions are the same temperature and no current flows in the thermocouple circuit. When the engine is started and the temperature of the engine compartment rises, the temperatures of all of the thermocouples rise together and there is still no current flow. But if there is a fire, the temperature of one or more of the thermocouples will rise immediately while the temperature of the insulated reference thermocouple rises much more slowly. As long as there is a difference in temperatures between any of the junctions, there is a difference in voltage between them. Not much current, but enough to energize the sealed sensitive relay, flows in the thermocouple circuit. The contacts of the sensitive relay close and carry enough current to the coil of the slave relay to close its contacts and allow current to flow to the fire-warning light and bell.

A thermocouple fire detection system is tested by closing the test switch and holding it closed for a specified number of seconds. Current flows through the heater inside the test thermocouple housing and heats the test junction. Since this junction is in series with all the other junctions, there is a voltage difference, and thus enough current flows to energize the sensitive relay and initiate a fire warning.

Continuous-Loop Detector Systems

Engine compartments, APU installations, and wheel wells are difficult locations to monitor for fire, and continuous-loop-type detectors are often used in these areas rather than individual detectors such as thermoswitches or thermocouples. There are two types of continuous-loop fire and overheat detection systems: thermistor and pneumatic.

Thermistor-Type Continuous-Loop Systems

There are two configurations of thermistor-type continuous loop elements: single-conductor and two-conductor elements.

The single-conductor element has a center conductor supported in a thin-wall inconel tube by ceramic beads. An electrical connection is made to the conductor, and the outside tube is grounded to the airframe. The space between the beads is filled with a eutectic (low melting-point) salt whose resistance drops drastically when it melts. When any portion of the tube gets hot enough to melt the salt, the resistance between the center conductor and the outside tube drops, and signal current flows to initiate a fire warning. When the fire is extinguished, the molten salt solidifies and its resistance increases enough that the fire-warning current no longer flows.

continuous-loop fire-detection system. A fire-detection system that uses a continuous loop of two conductors separated with a thermistor-type insulation.

Under normal temperature conditions, the thermistor material is an insulator, but if it is exposed to a fire, the thermistor changes into a conductor and completes the circuit between the two conductors, initiating a fire warning.

eutectic material. An alloy or solution that has the lowest possible melting point.

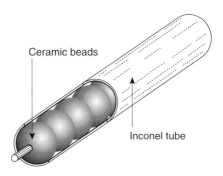

Ceramic beads

Inconel tube

Figure 13-6. *A single-conductor continuous-loop fire detector element*

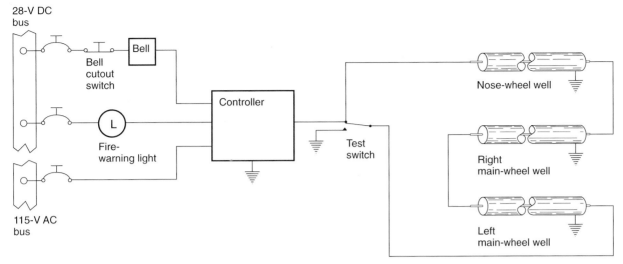

Figure 13-7. *Single-conductor continuous-loop fire detection circuit*

Single-wire continuous-loop detectors

The two-conductor loop is also mounted in an inconel tube, and it has two parallel wires embedded in a thermistor material whose resistance decreases as its temperature increases. One of the wires is grounded to the outer tube, and the other terminates in a connector and is connected to a control unit that continuously measures the total resistance of the sensing loop. By monitoring the resistance, this unit will detect a general overheat condition as well as a single hot spot.

Pneumatic-Type Continuous-Loop System

The pneumatic fire detection system also uses a continuous loop for the detection element, but this loop is made of a sealed stainless steel tube that contains an element which absorbs gas when it is cold, but releases this gas when it is heated.

One type of pneumatic fire detection system is the Lindberg system. The stainless steel tube which makes up the loop contains the gas-absorbing element and the gas, and is connected to a pressure switch as is seen in Figure 13-9. When the loop, which is installed around the monitored area, is heated in a local area by a fire or by a general overheat condition, the gas is released and its pressure closes the pressure switch. Closing this switch completes the circuit for one of the windings of a transformer and allows the 115-volt, 400-Hz power from the aircraft electrical system to illuminate the fire-warning light and sound the fire-warning bell.

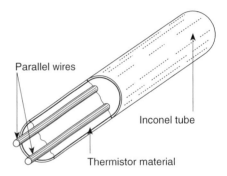

Figure 13-8. *Two-conductor continuous-loop fire detector element*

thermistor material. A material with a negative temperature coefficient that causes its resistance to decrease as its temperature increases.

This system is tested by closing the test switch. This allows low-voltage AC to flow through the tubing in the loop. This current heats the loop and causes the release of enough gas to close the pressure switch and initiate a fire warning.

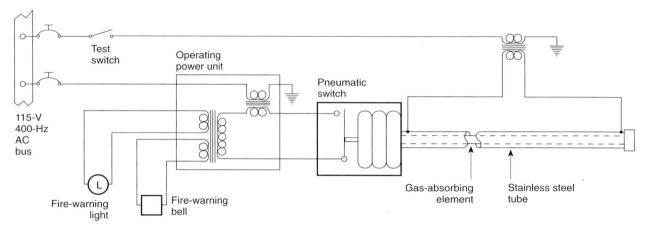

Figure 13-9. *The operating principle of a Lindberg pneumatic fire detector*

The Systron-Donner pneumatic fire detection system also uses a continuous loop for the detection element, but this loop contains two gases and a titanium center wire with the capacity to absorb an amount of hydrogen gas that is proportional to its temperature.

The tube is filled with helium gas under pressure, and at normal temperature, the helium produces a pressure that is proportional to the average temperature of the entire tube. When the average temperature of the tube reaches the value for which the warning system is set, the pressure of the helium gas becomes great enough to close a set of normally open contacts in the detector housing and initiate a fire-warning signal.

Any time an actual fire increases the temperature of a localized area of the tube, the center wire will release enough hydrogen gas to increase the pressure inside the housing to close the contacts and initiate a fire warning.

When the fire is extinguished, the temperature drops and the center wire absorbs enough hydrogen gas to lower the pressure in the housing so the contacts can snap open and restore the system to a condition to detect the fire if it should re-ignite.

There are two switches in the housing; one is normally open, and it closes to signal the presence of a fire when the pressure of either the hydrogen or helium gas increases enough to close it. The other is called the integrity switch and it is held closed by the normal pressure of the helium gas in the tube. If a break should occur in the tube and the helium pressure is lost, the integrity switch will open, and when the test switch is closed, no current can flow to initiate the fire-warning system. The failure of the warning light to illuminate shows that the system is faulty.

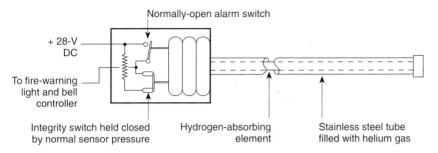

Normally-open alarm switch

+ 28-V
DC

To fire-warning
light and bell
controller

Integrity switch held closed
by normal sensor pressure

Hydrogen-absorbing
element

Stainless steel tube
filled with helium gas

Figure 13-10. *Operating principle of a Systron-Donner pneumatic fire and overheat detector*

Smoke and Flame Detectors

Certain areas in an aircraft can produce a great deal of smoke before any flames actually appear, and it is important in these areas to detect the first indication of smoke. Baggage and cargo compartments are typically protected by smoke detectors, of which there are four types: CO detectors, photoelectric detectors, ionization-type detectors, and visual detectors. CO detectors measure the level of carbon monoxide in the air. Photoelectric detectors measure the amount the smoke in a sample of air obstructs or refracts a beam of light. Ionization-type detectors measure the current that flows through ionized air, and visual detectors detect the presence of smoke by actually viewing samples of air that are drawn through the smoke detector chamber.

Flame detectors are usually light detectors that are sensitive to infrared radiation. These detectors are mounted in an electrical circuit that amplifies their voltage enough to initiate a fire-warning signal.

Carbon Monoxide Detectors

Carbon monoxide is a colorless, odorless gas that is a byproduct of incomplete combustion of almost all hydrocarbon fuels and is present in all smoke. It is lethal even in small concentrations, and its presence must be detected early.

CO detectors are not usually used in cargo and baggage compartments as are other smoke detectors, but are used in the cabin and cockpit areas. The most widely used CO detectors are small cards with a transparent pocket containing silica gel crystals that are treated with a chemical that changes color when it is exposed to CO. Normally the crystals are yellow or tan, but when they are exposed to CO, they change color to green or black. The more drastic the change, the higher the content of CO in the air. These small detectors have an adhesive backing that allows them to be attached to the instrument panel, in easy view of the flight crew to warn of the presence of CO. They must be periodically replaced with fresh indicators.

smoke detector. A device that warns the flight crew of the presence of smoke in cargo and/or baggage compartments. Some smoke detectors are of the visual type, others are photoelectric or ionization devices.

infrared radiation. Electromagnetic radiation whose wavelengths are longer than those of visible light.

carbon monoxide detector. A packet of chemical crystals mounted in the aircraft cockpit or cabin where they are easily visible. The crystals change their color from yellow to green when they are exposed to carbon monoxide.

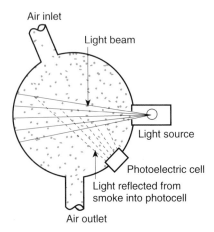

Figure 13-11. *A photoelectric smoke detector allows a current to flow that is proportional to the amount of light refracted by the smoke particles in the detector chamber.*

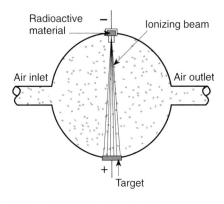

Figure 13-12. *Smoke in the detector chamber of an ionization-type smoke detector lowers the degree of ionization and decreases the current flowing to the external circuit.*

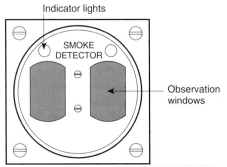

Photoelectric Smoke Detectors

Air from the monitored compartment is drawn through the detector chamber and a light beam is shone on it. A photoelectric cell installed in the chamber senses the light that is refracted by smoke particles. The photocell is installed in a bridge circuit that measures any changes in the amount of current it conducts. When there is no smoke in the air flowing through the chamber, no light is refracted, and the photocell conducts a reference amount of current. When there is smoke in the air, some of the light is refracted and sensed by the photocell, and its conductivity changes, changing the amount of current. These changes in current are amplified and used to initiate a smoke-warning signal.

Ionization-Type Smoke Detectors

Ionization-type smoke detectors work on the basic principle of those detectors found in many homes. A tiny amount of radioactive material is mounted on one side of the detector chamber. This material bombards the oxygen and nitrogen molecules in the air flowing through the chamber and ionizes it to the extent that a reference amount of current can flow across the chamber through the ionized gas to an external circuit. Smoke flowing through the chamber changes the level of ionization and decreases the current. When the current is reduced to a specific amount, the external circuit initiates a smoke-warning signal.

Visual Smoke Detectors

Some jet transport aircraft have visual-type smoke detectors similar to the one in Figure 13-13 installed on the flight engineer's panel. The inside of the chamber is painted nonreflective black, and glass observation windows let the flight engineer see inside the chamber. A light shines across the chamber in such a way that it will illuminate any smoke that is present. Air, pulled from the compartments that are being monitored, flows through the detection chamber. When there is no smoke in this air, no light is visible in the window, but when there is smoke, the light strikes it, and can be seen in the window.

Since no light is visible when there is no smoke, a green indicator light on the front of the detector illuminates to show the flight engineer when the light is on.

Figure 13-13. *Visual-type smoke indicator allows the flight engineer to actually observe the air sampled from a compartment for traces of smoke.*

Answers begin on Page 905. Page numbers refer to chapter text.

1. Three requirements for a fire are:
   a. _____
   b. _____
   c. _____
   Page 883

2. A fire that involves solid combustibles such as paper and upholstery is a Class _____ fire. *Page 883*

3. A fire that involves burning metals is a Class _____ fire. *Page 883*

4. A fire that involves energized electrical equipment is a Class _____ fire. *Page 883*

5. A fire that involves liquid fuels such as gasoline and oil is a Class _____ fire. *Page 883*

6. In thermoswitch fire-detection systems using several thermoswitches and a single indicator light, the switches are wired in _____ (series or parallel) with each other, and the entire combination of switches is in _____ (series or parallel) with the light. *Page 885*

7. The fire detection system that can operate properly when there is either an open or a short circuit in either of its two loops is the _____ (single-terminal or two-terminal) thermoswitch system. *Page 886*

8. The fire detection system that initiates a fire warning when there is an excessive rate of temperature rise in the monitored compartment is the _____ (thermocouple or thermoswitch) system. *Page 887*

9. Current flows in a fire-warning thermocouple circuit because of the voltage produced by the difference in the _____ of any of the junctions. *Page 887*

10. The two-conductor continuous-loop fire detector _____ (does or does not) detect a general overheat condition as well as a local hot spot. *Page 889*

11. A pneumatic fire detection system _____ (does or does not) warn of a general overheat condition as well as a fire. *Page 889*

12. Carbon monoxide is usually detected by chemical crystals that change their _____ (color or electrical resistance) when they are exposed to CO. *Page 891*

Continued

13. Flame detectors are light detectors that are sensitive to _____ (visual light or infrared radiation). *Page 891*

14. Photoelectric smoke detectors are usually used to monitor _____ (engine or cargo) compartments. *Page 891*

15. Some of the air in an ionization-type smoke detector is ionized by a tiny piece of _____ material. *Page 892*

16. The light that actuates a visual smoke indicator _____ (is or is not) visible to the flight crew. *Page 892*

Fire-Extinguishing Systems

Fire protection systems divide themselves logically into two categories: fire detection and fire extinguishing. The fire-extinguishing systems furthermore divide into hand-held and installed systems. Here we will consider the various types of fire-extinguishing agents, then the hand-held extinguishers, and finally, the installed systems.

Fire-Extinguishing Agents

Since fire is the chemical reaction between a fuel with oxygen, it can be controlled by interfering with this reaction. This can involve removing the fuel, smothering the fuel with a substance that excludes the oxygen, or lowering the temperature of the fuel. The most effective method for extinguishing aircraft fires involves using a chemical compound that combines with the oxygen to prevent it from combining with the fuel.

Water

Class A fires can be extinguished with an agent, such as water, that lowers the temperature of the fuel. Small hand-held fire extinguishers contain water that is adequately protected with an antifreeze agent. When the handle of these extinguishers is twisted, the seal in a carbon dioxide (CO_2) cartridge is broken, and the CO_2 pressurizes the water and discharges it in the form of a spray. When the water changes from a liquid to a vapor, it absorbs heat from the air above the fire and drops its temperature enough to cool the fuel enough to cause the fire to go out.

Never use water on Class B, C, or D fires. Most flammable liquids float on water, and the use of water on Class B fires will only spread the fire. Water conducts electricity, and its use on a Class C fire constitutes a definite danger of electrocution. Water sprayed on the burning metal in a Class D fire will actually intensify the fire rather than extinguish it.

Inert Cold Gas Agents

Carbon dioxide (CO_2) and liquid nitrogen (N_2) are both effective fire-extinguishing agents. They both have very low toxicity.

Carbon Dioxide

CO_2 is heavier than air, and when it is sprayed on a fire it remains on the surface and excludes oxygen from the combustion process, and the fire goes out. CO_2 has been a favored extinguishing agent for many years. It is relatively inexpensive, nontoxic, safe to handle, and has a long life in storage.

CO_2 extinguishers are found in almost all maintenance shops, on most flight lines, and in most ground vehicles. Most of the older aircraft had hand-held CO_2 extinguishers mounted in fixtures in the cabins and cockpits and fixed CO_2 extinguishing systems in the engine nacelles. These airborne extinguishers have been replaced in modern aircraft by more efficient types. Hand-held CO_2 extinguishers can be used to extinguish fires in energized electrical equipment, but they should not be used unless the nozzles are made of a nonconductive material. Fortunately most nozzles are made of pressed nonconductive fiber.

CO_2 is usually a gas, and it is stored in steel bottles under pressure. When it is released, it expands and cools enough to change into a finely divided snow of dry ice. CO_2 may also be produced directly on a fire by covering the fire with a dry powder such as sodium bicarbonate, potassium bicarbonate, or ammonium phosphate. Dry powder is useful for Class D fires such as fires in an aircraft brake.

dry ice. Solidified carbon dioxide. Dry ice sublimates, or changes from a solid directly into a gas, at a temperature of -110°F (-78.5°C).

Liquid Nitrogen (N₂)

N_2 is more effective than CO_2, but because it is a cryogenic liquid, it must be kept in a Dewar bottle. Some military aircraft use N_2 for inerting fuel tanks and have it available for use in fire-extinguishing systems, primarily for use in extinguishing powerplant fires.

cryogenic liquid. A liquid which boils at temperatures of less than about 110°K (-163°C) at normal atmospheric pressures.

Halogenated Hydrocarbons

This classification of fire-extinguishing agents includes the most widely used agents today, as well as some of the agents used in the past that are no longer considered suitable.

These agents are hydrocarbon compounds in which one or more of the hydrogen atoms have been replaced with an atom of one of the halogen elements such as fluorine, chlorine, or bromine.

Dewar bottle. A vessel designed to hold liquefied gases. It has double walls with the space between being evacuated to prevent the transfer of heat. The surfaces in the vacuum area are made heat-reflective.

In the process of combustion, the molecules of the fuel combine with those of oxygen in an orderly fashion, but if one of the halogen compounds is mixed with the oxygen this combination is interrupted and may be stopped entirely; the fire will go out.

One of the earliest halogenated hydrocarbons to find widespread use as a fire-extinguishing agent for use in aircraft was carbon tetrachloride, generally known as carbon tet or by its trade name, Pyrene. When a stream of liquid Pyrene is sprayed on a fire from a hand-pump-type extinguisher, it evaporates and extinguishes the flame. There are serious drawbacks to carbon tet; it is unstable in the temperatures of the flame and it converts into a poisonous gas known as phosgene. It also has a harmful cumulative toxic effect on the human body, and so is no longer used as a fire-extinguishing agent nor as a dry-cleaning fluid.

The two most widely used halogenated hydrocarbons are bromotrifluoromethane ($CBrF_3$), widely known as Halon 1301, and bromochlorodifluoromethane ($CBrClF_2$), known as Halon 1211. Both of these compounds, often called by the trade name Freon, have a very low toxicity. Halon 1301 is the least toxic of all commonly used agents. Both are very effective as fire-extinguishing agents. They are noncorrosive, evaporate rapidly, leave no residue, and require no cleanup or neutralization. Halon 1301 does not require any pressurizing agent, but Halon 1211 may be pressurized with nitrogen or with 1301.

Hand-Held Fire Extinguishers

Federal Aviation Regulations Part 135 *Air Taxi Operators and Commercial Operators* requires that passenger-carrying aircraft operated under this part have at least one hand-held fire extinguisher located on the flight deck and at least one in the passenger compartment. For years, the most popular extinguishers have been CO_2 type, but modern developments have made Halon 1301 and Halon 1211 the extinguishers of choice. These extinguishing agents are the least toxic of all and they are effective on almost all types of fires likely to be encountered in an aircraft cabin. These extinguishers are available in small, medium, and large sizes. The small extinguishers are adequate for fires of up to one square foot in area, medium extinguishers are adequate for fires up to two square feet in area, and the large sizes are adequate for fires up to five square feet.

Extinguishers using Halon 1211 use compressed nitrogen for a propellant, but Halon 1301 has enough pressure that it does not require a separate propelling agent. All Halon extinguishers have built-in pressure gages to indicate the pressure of the extinguishant.

Hand-held CO_2 extinguishers are still used in many aircraft. The two-pound size is usually installed in aircraft cabins. The state of charge of a CO_2 extinguisher is determined by weighing it. The weight of the empty container and nozzle is stamped on the valve.

Halon 1301. A halogenated hydrocarbon fire-extinguishing agent that is one of the best for extinguishing cabin and powerplant fires. It is highly effective and is the least toxic of the extinguishing agents available. The technical name for Halon 1301 is bromotrifluoromethane.

Halon 1211. A halogenated hydrocarbon fire-extinguishing agent used in many HRD fire-extinguishing systems for powerplant protection. The technical name for Halon 1211 is bromochlorodifluoromethane.

Freon. The registered trade name for many of the halogenated hydrocarbons used as fire extinguishants and refrigerants.

Dry chemical fire extinguishers use compressed nitrogen to expel a dry powder such as sodium bicarbonate or potassium bicarbonate. Dry powder is an effective extinguishing agent, but should never be used in an aircraft cockpit in-flight, as the loose powder in the air obstructs visibility.

Installed Fire-Extinguishing Systems

Aircraft use two types of installed fire-extinguishing systems: the CO_2 systems installed in the engine compartments of older aircraft, and the high-rate-discharge (HRD) systems used on most modern jet transport aircraft.

Carbon Dioxide Extinguishing Systems

Installed CO_2 systems were the primary systems for most twin-engine and four-engine transport aircraft up through the World War II era.

CO_2 is carried in steel bottles and is often pressurized with compressed nitrogen to aid in expelling the CO_2 under very low temperature conditions. The bottles have a remotely operated valve and are connected to a selector handle that allows the pilot to select the engine into which the CO_2 will be discharged. When the engine is selected, the T-shaped handle is pulled. The bottle is emptied into the power section of the engine through a perforated aluminum tube that surrounds the engine. Some of the larger systems had two bottles that allowed the pilot to release the second bottle into the fire if it was not extinguished by the first one.

CO_2 systems have two indicator disks, one red and one yellow, located on the outside of the fuselage near the bottles. If the bottles are discharged by the pilot actuating the T-handle, the yellow disk will blow out. If the area around the bottles becomes overheated enough to raise the pressure of the gas to a dangerous level, the red disk will blow out and the system will automatically discharge. On the normal walk-around inspection, the flight crewmember can tell, from these disks, the condition of the CO_2 system.

High-Rate-Discharge (HRD) Extinguishing Systems

Most modern turbine-engine-powered aircraft have their powerplant areas protected by two or more spherical or cylindrical HRD bottles of Halon 1211 or 1301. A charge of compressed nitrogen is usually placed in the container to ensure that the agent is dispersed in the shortest time possible. The containers are sealed with a frangible disk that is broken when a cutter is fired into it by a powder charge, or squib, which is ignited when the pilot closes the agent discharge switch. The entire contents of the bottle are discharged within about 0.08 second after the agent discharge switch is closed.

Figure 13-14 (Page 898) shows a cross-sectional view of a typical spherical HRD bottle. The cartridge is electrically ignited, which drives the cutter into the disk and releases the agent. The strainer prevents any of the broken disk from getting into the distribution system.

HRD. High-rate-discharge

frangible. Breakable, or easily broken.

squib. An explosive device in the discharge valve of a high-rate-discharge container of fire-extinguishing agent. The squib drives a cutter into the seal in the container to discharge the agent.

The safety plug is connected to a red indicator disk on the outside of the engine compartment. If the temperature of the compartment in which the bottle is mounted rises enough to increase the pressure of the gas enough to become dangerous, the safety plug melts and releases the gas. As the gas vents to the atmosphere, it blows out the red indicator disk, showing that the bottle has been discharged because of an overheat condition. If the bottle is discharged by normal operation of the system, a yellow indicator disk blows out. The gage shows the pressure of the agent and the gas in the container.

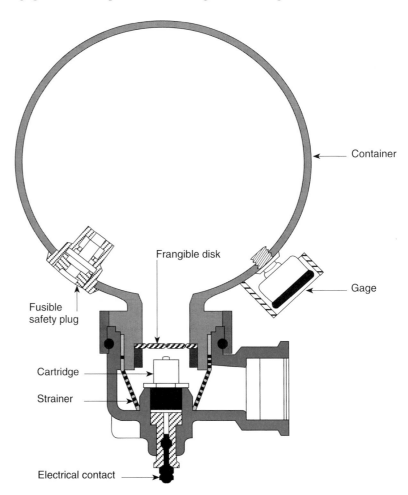

Figure 13-14. *A typical HRD container for protecting an engine compartment*

Answers begin on Page 905. Page numbers refer to chapter text.

17. A water fire extinguisher _____ (should or should not) be used on a burning metal. *Page 894*

18. CO_2 fire extinguishers should not be used on an electrical fire unless the discharge horn is made of a _____ (metal or nonmetallic material). *Page 895*

19. A dry-powder fire-extinguishing agent extinguishes a fire by producing _____ gas. *Page 895*

20. A dry-powder fire extinguisher _____ (is or is not) suitable for extinguishing inflight cockpit fires. *Page 897*

21. The proper fire-extinguishing agent to use to extinguish a fire in an aircraft brake is _____ . *Page 895*

22. A fire-extinguishing agent that is also used to inert fuel tanks is _____ . *Page 895*

23. Carbon tetrachloride is _____ (toxic or nontoxic). *Page 896*

24. The least toxic of all popular fire-extinguishing agents other than water is _____ . *Page 896*

25. The state of charge of a hand-held fire extinguisher may be determined by weighing it. This is true of a _____ (CO_2 or Halon) extinguisher. *Page 896*

26. The state of charge of a hand-held fire extinguisher may be determined by a pressure gage built into the valve head. This is true of a _____ (CO_2 or Halon) extinguisher. *Page 896*

27. If an installed CO_2 fire-extinguishing system is discharged in the normal manner, the _____ (yellow or red) disk on the outside of the fuselage is blown out. *Page 897*

28. The agent in an HRD container is discharged when the sealing disk is ruptured by a cutter driven by a _____ . *Page 897*

29. The Freon, or Halon, fire-extinguishing agent in an HRD bottle is propelled from the bottle by a charge of compressed _____ . *Page 897*

30. If an HRD fire extinguisher bottle is discharged because of an overheat condition, the _____ (yellow or red) disk on the outside of the fuselage is blown out. *Page 898*

31. Halon 1301 _____ (is or is not) corrosive to aluminum. *Page 896*

Complete Fire Protection System

A complete fire protection system incorporates both the detection and the extinguishing systems. In this section, we will consider the complete fire protection system in a typical three-engine jet transport aircraft.

Each of the three engines has two continuous-loop fire detector sensors, one mounted on the firewall, and the other mounted on the engine itself. The wheel wells have sensors that detect a fire or overheat condition, and the APU has a fire-detector loop and a complete fire-extinguishing system. Red fire-warning lights in the fire pull handles on the captain's and the first officer's glare shield illuminate when any of the engine sensors detect a fire, and a fire-warning bell sounds. The first officer can silence the bell by depressing the "Bell Cutout" switch.

A light on the glare shield illuminates and the fire warning sounds if the loop detectors in any of the three wheel wells detect a fire or an overheat condition.

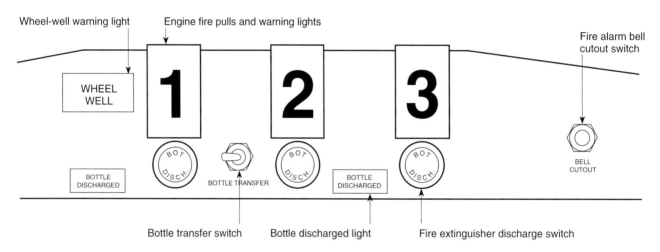

Figure 13-15. *Typical fire-warning and fire-extinguishing controls located on the glare shield*

If a fire occurs in any of the engines, the light in the combination fire-warning light and fire-pull handle for the appropriate engine illuminates, and the fire-warning bell sounds. The pilot or first officer can pull the fire-pull handle. This does six things:

1. Closes the engine fuel shutoff valve
2. Trips the generator field relay after a delay of 5 to 10 seconds
3. Closes the engine bleed air valves
4. Closes the wing or cowl anti-ice valves as is appropriate
5. Closes the hydraulic supply shutoff valves
6. Turns off hydraulic pump low-pressure warning lights

If the fire-warning light does not go out, the bottle discharge button is depressed and the selected bottle is discharged to the affected engine. The "Bottle Discharged" light then comes on. If the fire-warning light still remains illuminated, indicating that the fire has not been extinguished, the bottle transfer switch can be operated to select the other bottle and the bottle discharge button again depressed. This will discharge the other bottle and its "Bottle Discharged" light will come on.

Figure 13-16 is a schematic diagram of a typical HRD fire extinguisher system installed in a three-engine jet transport airplane. Two bottles are connected through check valves to a manifold to which the three engines are connected. In this diagram the extinguisher discharge switch for Engine 2 has been depressed. Current flows through the switch to ignite the squib to discharge the left bottle and to open the solenoid valve for Engine 2. When the bottle discharges, the Bottle Discharged light illuminates and the yellow discharge indicator disk is blown out. To discharge the second bottle, the bottle transfer switch is shifted. This not only selects the other bottle, but takes the current through a different circuit breaker.

The plumbing that carries the fire-extinguishing agent from the bottles to the engines is marked with brown color-coding tape that has a series of diamonds to aid technicians who are color-blind or for use in dim light.

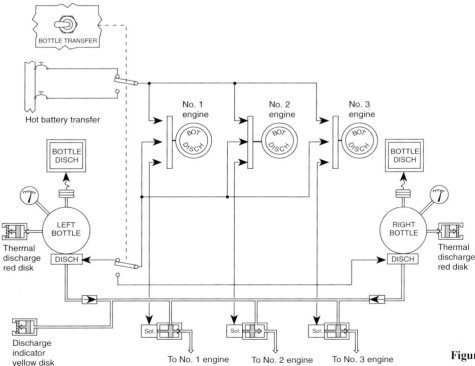

Figure 13-16. *Schematic of the three-engine jet transport fire-extinguishing system*

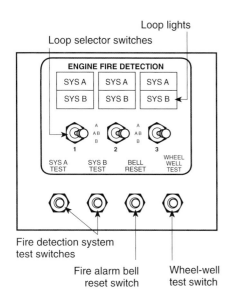

Figure 13-17. *Fire detection test light and switch panel*

APU. Auxiliary power unit

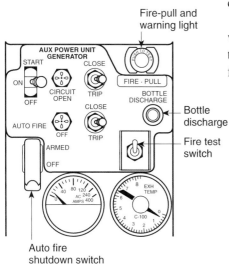

Figure 13-18. *APU fire-warning panel at the flight engineer station*

The flight engineer has a panel with engine fire detection test lights and switches. *See* Figure 13-17. The Loop Selector switch allows the flight engineer to select either loop separately, or both loops together. The Loop Lights above these switches illuminate to show when any of the loops is energized by a fire signal, a test signal, or by a fault. The two Fire Detection System Test switches check the continuity of the selected loop. The Fire Alarm Bell Reset switch silences the fire-warning bell after the alarm is sounded. The Wheel-Well Test switch checks the continuity of the wheel-well detection loop.

The Auxiliary Power Unit (APU) is protected by its own fire-detection and extinguishing system. Figure 13-18 shows the APU fire control panel that is accessible to the flight engineer.

When a fire is detected in the APU shroud, the APU automatically shuts down, the cockpit fire-warning bell is activated, the warning light on the APU fire-warning panel illuminates, the fire-warning light in the APU ground control panel in the left wheel well flashes, and the intermittent fire-warning horn in the nosewheel well sounds.

Pulling the APU fire-pull handle closes the fuel valve to the APU, trips the APU generator field relay, and arms the APU fire-bottle discharge switch. If the fire-warning light does not go out, the bottle discharge switch may be pressed to discharge the HRD bottle.

When the Fire Test switch is placed in the TEST position, it heats the pneumatic detector loop to trigger a test fire warning. When it is placed in the RESET position, it silences the fire-warning bell and horn and resets the control circuits that enables the APU to be restarted after the fire test.

When the Auto Fire Shutdown switch is in the ARMED position, a fire warning or actuation of the test switch will shut down the APU. When it is in the OFF position, the automatic shutdown is disabled to allow testing of the fire-detection system.

Maintenance and Servicing of Fire-Detector Systems

The detector elements used in fire and overheat protection systems are precision devices that require special care and attention for their installation and servicing. About the only maintenance required by a fire detection system is replacing damaged sensors and ensuring that all of the wiring is properly supported and in good condition.

The sensors used in the continuous-loop-type systems are particularly subject to damage from careless handling during routine engine maintenance. They should be carefully checked for dented, kinked, or crushed sections, as any damage of this type can cause a false fire warning. When replacing continuous-loop sensor elements, be sure to follow the instructions in the aircraft service manual in detail. Support the elements as shown the service manual and be sure to maintain the required clearance between the elements and the aircraft structure.

The locations for all of the components in a fire detection system have been chosen with special care by the engineers of the aircraft manufacturer, and all the components must be maintained in the exact location specified. Detectors actuate at different temperatures, and it is especially important to use only detectors with the correct part number when replacing one.

Some of the specific items to inspect are:

1. Check for abrasion of the loop caused by the elements rubbing on the cowling, accessories, or structural members.

2. Be sure that there are no pieces of safety wire or metal particles that could short-circuit a spot detector.

3. Be sure that no rubber grommets in the mounting clamps have an indication of damage from oil or overheating, and be sure that all grommets are properly installed. The slit in the grommet should face the outside of the nearest bend to prevent the element from chafing on the clamp. *See* Figure 13-19.

4. Check for loose nuts or broken safety wire at the ends of the sensing elements. Follow the manufacturer's instructions regarding the torque to use and the types of washers, if any, that are to be used. *See* Figure 13-20.

5. When replacing a thermocouple sensor, be sure that the wires are connected to the proper terminal of the sensor. The fact that the two elements of the thermocouple are made of different metals makes this important.

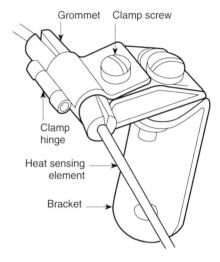

Figure 13-19. *Typical fire-detector loop clamp showing the correct way of installing the grommet*

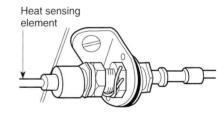

Figure 13-20. *Correct attachment of a fire-detector loop to the aircraft structure*

Container Pressure Versus Temperature		
Temperature °F	Container Pressure (PSIG)	
	Minimum	Maximum
-40	60	145
-30	83	465
-20	105	188
-10	125	210
0	145	230
10	167	252
20	188	275
30	209	295
40	230	317
50	255	342
60	284	370
70	319	405
80	356	443
90	395	483
100	438	523

Figure 13-21. *Fire extinguisher pressure/ temperature chart*

Maintenance and Servicing of Fire-Extinguishing Systems

Bottles of fire-extinguishing agent must be kept fully charged. Most of these bottles have gages mounted directly on them. The pressure of the agent varies with its temperature, and for this pressure to be meaningful, a correction must be made. Figure 13-21 is a typical chart showing the allowable limits for the indicated pressure. If the pressure falls outside of the allowable range, the container must be removed and replaced with one that is properly charged.

To find the allowable pressure range for an agent temperature of 33°F, see Figure 13-21.

For this problem, we must interpolate:

33°F is 0.3 of the way between 30° and 40°.

215 psig (pounds per square inch, gage) is 0.3 of the way between 209 and 230 Psgi.

302 psig is 0.3 of the way between 295 and 317 Psgi.

For 33°F, the acceptable pressure range is between 215 and 302 psig.

The discharge cartridges for an HRD container are life-limited components, and the replacement date is measured from the date stamped on the cartridge.

Fire extinguisher discharge cartridges are not normally interchangeable between valves. The distance the contact point protrudes from the cartridge may vary from one cartridge to another, and care must be taken if a cartridge is removed from the discharge valve that the correct cartridge is reinstalled in the valve. If the wrong cartridge is used, there is a possibility that there will not be electrical continuity.

It is extremely important when checking the electrical connections to the container to use the recommendations of the manufacturer. Make sure that the current used to test the wiring is less than that required to detonate the squib.

STUDY QUESTIONS: MAINTENANCE AND SERVICING OF FIRE PROTECTION SYSTEMS

Answers begin on Page 905. Page numbers refer to chapter text.

32. Six things that happen when the Fire-Pull in the cockpit is pulled are:

a. _____

b. _____

c. _____

d. _____

e. _____

f. _____

Page 900

33. The fire-extinguishing agent _____ (is or is not) discharged when the fire-pull handle is pulled. *Page 901*

34. The tubing that carries fire-extinguishing agents is color coded with a stripe of _____ (what color) tape and a series of _____ (what symbol). *Page 901*

35. Maintenance of a fire detection system consists of _____ (repair or replacement) of damaged components. *Page 903*

36. Based on the chart in Figure 13-21, the allowable range of agent pressure at a temperature of 85°F is _____ to _____ psig. *Page 904*

37. If the pressure gage on an HRD bottle shows that the container pressure is too low for the existing temperature, the technician must _____ (replace or refill) the container. *Page 904*

38. Fire extinguisher discharge cartridges _____ (are or are not) normally interchangeable between valves. *Page 904*

Answers to Fire Protection Systems Study Questions

1. a. fuel
   b. oxygen
   c. high enough temperature
2. A
3. D
4. C
5. B
6. parallel; series
7. two-terminal
8. thermocouple
9. temperature
10. does
11. does
12. color
13. infrared radiation
14. cargo
15. radioactive

16. is not
17. should not
18. nonmetallic material
19. carbon dioxide
20. is not
21. dry powder
22. nitrogen
23. toxic
24. Halon 1301
25. CO_2
26. Halon
27. yellow
28. powder charge
29. nitrogen
30. red
31. is not

32. a. Closes engine fuel shutoff valve
    b. Trips generator field relay
    c. Closes engine bleed air valves
    d. Closes anti-icer valves
    e. Closes hydraulic supply shutoff valves
    f. Turns off hydraulic pump low-pressure light
33. is not
34. brown, diamonds
35. replacement
36. 376, 463
37. replace
38. are not

AIRCRAFT INSPECTION

AIRCRAFT INSPECTION

14

Inspections

Inspection is one of the most important functions of an aviation maintenance technician. As aircraft grow in complexity, it becomes more important to detect any possible trouble before it gets serious. To assist the technician in this important function, aircraft manufacturers furnish a detailed inspection check list in the service manual for each aircraft. In addition, the Federal Aviation Administration has listed in Appendix D of FAR Part 43 *Maintenance, Preventive Maintenance, Rebuilding, and Alteration*, the scope and detail of items to be included in annual and 100-hour inspections. Appendix E of this same FAR gives the requirements for altimeter system tests and inspections, and Appendix F gives the requirements for ATC transponder tests and inspections.

Chapter 12 of the *General* textbook of this *Aviation Maintenance Technician Series* covers the requirements for the various inspections, primarily from the legal standpoint. It discusses the authorization needed to conduct the inspections, how often they must be conducted, and what records must be kept. In this section of the Airframe text, we want to look at inspections from the practical standpoint and refer you to the General text for the legal implications.

Required Inspections

We will consider the inspections in order of their complexity, from the preflight inspection to some of the special inspections, and finally to inspections that involve the entire aircraft.

Preflight Inspection

The preflight inspection is not a maintenance inspection, but many pilots do not know how to give an aircraft a good preflight. You may be able to help a pilot learn just what to look for. The inspection described here is typical for light airplanes, and should always be modified to agree with the information furnished in the pilot's operating handbook for the particular aircraft.

preflight inspection. A required inspection to determine the condition of the aircraft for the flight to be conducted. It is conducted by the pilot-in-command.

Preflight Inspection Sequence

1. Begin the inspection inside the cabin. Check to be sure the ignition switch or magneto switches are OFF, and the flight controls are unlocked. Turn the master switch ON and check the indication of the fuel quantity indicator. Turn the master switch OFF, and be sure that the avionics master switch is OFF so the sensitive electronic equipment will not be damaged during the engine start procedure.

Check to be sure that the proper paperwork is in the aircraft and that the aircraft has been inspected within the required time interval for the type of inspection under which it is operating. There should be a current registration certificate, a certificate of airworthiness, and a radio-station license. If the aircraft is not operating for hire, it should have had an annual inspection within the past 12 months. If it is operating for hire, it should also have had a 100-hour inspection within the past 100 hours of operation or evidence of being operated under a progressive inspection system.

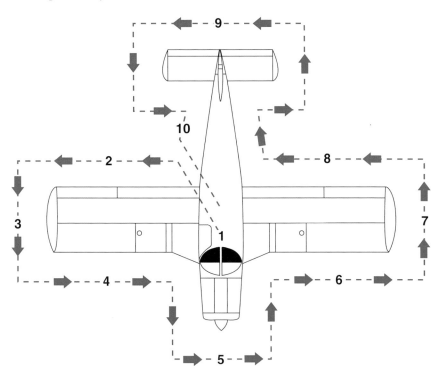

Figure 14-1. *Recommended preflight walk-around inspection of a small training airplane*

2. Walk along the trailing edge of the right wing and check the flap and aileron. The flap should be in its fully up position and there should be no looseness that could indicate worn attachment fittings. You should be able to move the aileron through its full travel without any binding or any unusual noise. The aileron should not be loose on its hinges, which would indicate worn hinges or hinge bolts. If the bolt that connects the control cable to the aileron horn is visible, it should be checked for proper safety. Check the cable to be sure that its fitting pivots freely on the horn.

3. Walk around the wing tip and check it for any indication of "hangar rash." The wing tip light should be secure and show no indication of damage.

4. Walk along the leading edge and check top and bottom for any indication of dents or damage. There should be no dirt or anything that could disrupt the smooth airflow over the top of the wing. Remove the chain, cable, or rope used to tie the aircraft down.

Drain a sample of fuel from the fuel tank quick-drain. This fuel should be clean and free from any trace of water, and its color should indicate that it is of the grade specified for the aircraft. Grade 100 fuel is green, 100-low lead is blue, and grade 80 is red. Dispose of this fuel sample using whatever method is allowed by the airport.

Remove the fuel cap and look at the amount of fuel in the tank. Fuel gages are not known for their accuracy, and this is the one chance the pilot has to be absolutely positive of the amount of fuel in the tanks. Be sure to replace the fuel cap properly.

Check the condition of the landing gear. Most fixed-gear airplanes have wheel pants installed, so you will not be able to inspect the tire thoroughly, but check it to see that its inflation appears to be proper. The shock strut should have several inches of piston visible, and the torsion links should not be loose, indicating excessive wear. The hydraulic line going to the brake should show no sign of wear or leakage, and there should be no indication of leaking hydraulic fluid around the brake. The wheel pant should be secure, with no cracks or looseness. There should be no mud that could interfere with the wheel.

Continued

control horn. The arm on a control surface to which the control cable or push-pull rod attaches to move the surface.

hangar rash. Scrapes, bends, and dents in an aircraft structure caused by careless handling.

5. Walk around the nose of the aircraft. Check the windshield for cleanliness and for any indication of cracks, scratches, or other damage.

   Check the engine oil quantity, and be sure the dipstick is properly secured. Check as much of the engine as is visible for any indication of oil or fuel leakage, or anything that may be loose. Check the air inlets for any kind of obstruction. If the aircraft has been tied down outside for any length of time, check especially for any indication of bird nests that have been built inside the cowling.

   Drain a sample of fuel from the main strainer and check it for indication of water.

   If it is winter, check the end of the crankcase breather to be sure it is not clogged with ice.

   Check the propeller and spinner. There should be no nicks or pits along the leading edge of the blades, and there should be no looseness in the spinner. Propeller spinner bulkheads are noted for cracking and they should be checked for any indication of cracks or missing screws.

   Check the nosewheel. There should be no looseness or cracks in the wheel pant, and the torsion links and the shimmy damper should show no indication of excessive looseness or wear. The shock strut should show the proper amount of extension, and when the nose is depressed, the strut should return to its original extension.

6., 7. and 8. Walk around the left wing, noting the same things as on the right wing. On many airplanes, the stall warning pickup is in the leading edge of the left wing. Check this for freedom and proper operation.

9. Walk around the empennage. Check the movable surfaces for freedom of movement and for any indication of looseness or wear. Remove the tail tie-down.

   Pay particular attention to the trim tab or stabilizer adjustment mechanism. Trim tab hinges are subject to a good deal of wear, and worn tab hinges can allow the tab to flutter.

   Check the ELT antenna for security of mounting.

10. Check the baggage compartment to be sure that there is nothing in it that should not be there, and that everything in the compartment is properly secured. Check to see that the door closes and locks securely so it will not cause any airflow distortion.

10. *(Continued)* When you return to the cockpit, check all of the controls for freedom of movement, and be sure that when the wheel is rotated to the left, the left aileron moves up and the right aileron moves down. When the wheel is pulled back, the trailing edge of the movable surface should move up. The flaps should move smoothly through their entire range of travel. The trim tab should operate smoothly and the indicator should show its position. It should be positioned correctly for takeoff. When the master switch is turned on, the electric gyros should begin to spin up without any excessive noise. When the radio is turned on, tune it to 121.5 MHz temporarily to be sure the ELT has not been inadvertently triggered into operation.

The seat belts and shoulder harness should be in good condition, and the cabin door should close tightly and the door lock should operate freely.

Special Inspections

You must give special inspections to any aircraft that has experienced a rough or overweight landing or flown into severe turbulence. Inspect the powerplant according to the manufacturer's recommendations after a propeller strike or a sudden stoppage. These inspections are described in the *Powerplant* textbook of the *Aviation Maintenance Technician Series*.

If an aircraft has experienced a rough or overweight landing, jack it up and inspect the entire landing gear for damage. Remove the tires and the check wheels by eddy current inspection, especially in the bead seat area. Check the inside of the tires for any indication of broken cords.

If the aircraft has flown through severe turbulence, check the entire structure for any indication of deformation or cracks. Check the skins for any waviness and the rows of rivets for any indication of rivets that have tipped. You'll need to do further in-depth inspection if you find any of these problems.

Altimeters and Static Systems

FAR 91.411 specifies that no person may operate an airplane or helicopter in controlled airspace under Instrument Flight Rules unless, within the preceding 24 calendar months, each static pressure system, each altimeter instrument, and each automatic pressure altitude reporting system has been tested and inspected and found to comply with the provisions of FAR Part 43, Appendix E.

calendar month. A measurement of time used by the FAA for inspection and certification purposes. One calendar month from a given day extends from that day until midnight of the last day of that month.

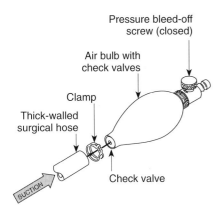

Figure 14-2. *Equipment for checking an instrument static system for leaks*

Static System Check

The check of the static system is described in FAR 23.1325. It may be conducted by a certified technician holding an airframe rating (FAR 91.411(b)(3)).

For unpressurized aircraft, the static air system is evacuated to a pressure of one inch of mercury or until the altimeter indicates an increase of 1,000 feet. The pressure is trapped and held for one minute, and the altimeter should not change its indication by more than 100 feet.

For pressurized aircraft, the system is evacuated to a pressure that is equal to the maximum certificated cabin differential pressure. This is held for one minute, and the altimeter should not change its indication by more than 2% of the equivalent altitude of the maximum cabin differential pressure, or 100 feet, whichever is greater.

An air bulb like the one in Figure 14-2 can generate an adequate source of suction to check the static system. You can obtain the bulb, which is the type used for measuring blood pressure, and the thick-walled surgical tubing from a surgical supply company.

To perform the static system check on an unpressurized aircraft, follow these steps:

1. Seal off one of the static ports with pressure-sensitive tape. Black electrical tape is good for this purpose because it is highly visible, and you are not likely to forget and leave it in place when the check is completed. Do not use transparent tape, because it is too easy to forget to remove it.

2. Check the alternate static source valve to be sure that it is in the closed, or normal, position.

3. Squeeze the air bulb (*see* Figure 14-2) to expel as much air as possible and hold the suction hose firmly against the static port opening.

4. Slowly release the bulb to apply suction to the system until the altimeter shows an increase of 1,000 feet. (On a pressurized aircraft, this increase must be the altitude equivalent of the maximum cabin differential pressure for which the aircraft is certificated.)

5. Pinch the hose tightly to trap the suction in the system and hold it for one minute. The altimeter should not change its indication more than 100 feet. (The altimeter indication in a pressurized aircraft is allowed to change 2% of the altitude increase used for the test).

6. If the altimeter does not change its indication more than the allowable amount, carefully tilt the hose away from the static port, allowing air to enter the system slowly.

7. Remove the tape from the unused static port.

The altimeter or automatic pressure altitude reporting equipment must be checked by the manufacturer of the airplane or helicopter or by a certificated repair station properly equipped and approved for this procedure.

The tests specified in FAR 43, Appendix E are:

- Scale error to the maximum normally expected operating altitude of the aircraft
- Hysteresis
- After effect
- Friction
- Case leak
- Barometric scale error

ATC Transponder

An aircraft's ATC transponder must be inspected once every 24 calendar months according to the requirements in FAR Part 43, Appendix F. These inspections must be conducted by a certificated repair station having the proper equipment and approved for this specific function.

The tests specified in FAR 43, Appendix F are:

- Radio reply frequency
- Suppression
- Receiver sensitivity
- Radio-frequency peak output power
- Mode S diversity transmission channel isolation
- Mode S address
- Mode S formats
- Mode S all-call interrogations
- ATCRBS-only all-call interrogations
- Squitter

Major Inspections

The FAA requires all certificated aircraft to have a major inspection on a periodic basis. These inspections are all similar in content but differ in how often they are performed and in who is authorized to perform them.

The FAA requires in FAR Part 43.15 that each annual and 100-hour inspection be conducted by following a checklist. This checklist may be compiled by the technician performing the inspection or may be one furnished by the manufacturer of the aircraft. Progressive inspections require a description of the work to be done, and this description must be followed in detail. All of these inspections must include at least all of the items listed in Appendix D of FAR Part 43, which are reproduced in Figure 14-3 on the next page.

You can substitute a progressive inspection for the annual and 100-hour inspection under certain conditions.

Appendix D—Scope and Detail of Items (as Applicable to the Particular Aircraft) To Be Included in Annual and 100-Hour Inspections

(a) Each person performing an annual or 100-hour inspection shall, before that inspection, remove or open all necessary inspection plates, access doors, fairing, and cowling. He shall thoroughly clean the aircraft and aircraft engine.

(b) Each person performing an annual or 100-hour inspection shall inspect (where applicable) the following components of the fuselage and hull group:

(1) Fabric and skin—for deterioration, distortion, other evidence of failure, and defective or insecure attachment of fittings.

(2) Systems and components—for improper installation, apparent defects, and unsatisfactory operation.

(3) Envelope, gas bags, ballast tanks, and related parts—for poor condition.

(c) Each person performing an annual inspection shall inspect (where applicable) the following components of the cabin and cockpit group:

(1) Generally—for uncleanliness and loose equipment that might foul the controls.

(2) Seats and safety belts—for poor condition and apparent defect.

(3) Windows and windshields—for deterioration and breakage.

(4) Instruments—for poor condition, mounting, marking, and (where practicable) improper operation.

(5) Flight and engine controls—for improper installation and improper operation.

(6) Batteries—for improper installation and improper charge.

(7) All systems—for improper installation, poor general condition, apparent and obvious defects, and insecurity of attachment.

(d) Each person performing an annual or 100-hour inspection shall inspect (where applicable) components of the engine and nacelle group as follows:

(1) Engine section—for visual evidence of excessive oil, fuel, or hydraulic leaks, and sources of such leaks.

(2) Studs and nuts—for improper torquing and obvious defects.

(3) Internal engine—for cylinder compression and for metal particles or foreign matter on screens and sump drain plugs. If there is weak cylinder compression, for improper internal condition and improper internal tolerances.

(4) Engine mount—for cracks, looseness of mounting, and looseness of engine to mount.

(5) Flexible vibration dampeners—for poor condition and deterioration.

(6) Engine controls—for defects, improper travel, and improper safetying.

(7) Lines, hoses, and clamps—for leaks, improper condition and looseness.

(8) Exhaust stacks—for cracks, defects, and insecure attachment.

(9) Accessories—for apparent defects in security of mounting.

(10) All systems—for improper installation, poor general condition, defects, and insecure attachment.

(11) Cowling—for cracks, and defects.

(e) Each person performing an annual or 100-hour inspection shall inspect (where applicable) the following components of the landing gear group:

(1) All units—for poor condition and insecurity of attachment.

(2) Shock absorbing devices—for improper oleo fluid level.

(3) Linkages, trusses, and members—for undue or excessive wear fatigue, and distortion.

(4) Retracting and locking mechanism—for improper operation.

(5) Hydraulic lines—for leakage.

(6) Electrical system—for chafing and improper operation of switches.

(7) Wheels—for cracks, defects, and condition of bearings.

(8) Tires—for wear and cuts.

(9) Brakes—for improper adjustment.

(10) Floats and skis—for insecure attachment and obvious or apparent defects.

(f) Each person performing an annual or 100-hour inspection shall inspect (where applicable) all components of the wing and center section assembly for poor general condition, fabric or skin deterioration, distortion, evidence of failure, and insecurity of attachment.

(g) Each person performing an annual or 100-hour inspection shall inspect (where applicable) all components and systems that make up the complete empennage assembly for poor general condition, fabric or skin deterioration, distortion, evidence of failure, insecure attachment, improper component installation, and improper component operation.

(h) Each person performing an annual or 100-hour inspection shall inspect (where applicable) the following components of the propeller group:

(1) Propeller assembly—for cracks, nicks, binds, and oil leakage.

(2) Bolts—for improper torquing and lack of safetying.

(3) Anti-icing devices—for improper operations and obvious defects.

(4) Control mechanisms—for improper operation, insecure mounting, and restricted travel.

(i) Each person performing an annual or 100-hour inspection shall inspect (where applicable) the following components of the radio group:

(1) Radio and electronic equipment—for improper installation and insecure mounting.

(2) Wiring and conduits—for improper routing, insecure mounting, and obvious defects.

(3) Bonding and shielding—for improper installation and poor condition.

(4) Antenna including trailing antenna—for poor condition, insecure mounting, and improper operation.

(j) Each person performing an annual or 100-hour inspection shall inspect (where applicable) each installed miscellaneous item that is not otherwise covered by this listing for improper installation and improper operation.

Figure 14-3. *Items that must be checked on each annual, 100-hour, or progressive inspection. This is Appendix D of FAR Part 43.*

Large airplanes, turbojet multi-engine airplanes, turbopropeller-powered multi-engine airplanes, and turbine-powered rotorcraft must be inspected on an inspection program similar to that used by air carriers.

These programs are adapted to the aircraft and to the specific conditions under which they operate, and they may be taken from:

1. The continuous airworthiness inspection program currently in use by an air carrier operating under FAR Part 121, 127, or 135.

2. An aircraft inspection program approved for a carrier operating under FAR Part 135.

3. A current inspection program recommended by the aircraft manufacturer.

4. Any other inspection program established by the registered owner or operator and approved by the Administrator.

Continuous Airworthiness Inspection Program. An inspection program that is part of a continuous airworthiness maintenance program approved for certain large airplanes (to which FAR Part 125 is not applicable), turbojet multi-engine airplanes, turbopropeller-powered multi-engine airplanes, and turbine-powered rotorcraft.

Annual Inspection

All aircraft operating under FAR Part 91, except large and turbine-powered multi-engine airplanes and those operating under a progressive inspection, must have an annual inspection and be approved for return to service once every 12 calendar months. The requirements for these inspections are covered in FAR Part 91.409.

An annual inspection is identical to a 100-hour inspection except that it must be conducted by an A&P technician who holds an Inspection Authorization (IA). The technician conducting a 100-hour inspection does not need to hold an Inspection Authorization.

An aircraft due for an annual inspection can be flown to a point where the inspection can be conducted only if the FAA issues a special flight permit for the flight.

air carrier. An organization or person involved in the business of transporting people or cargo by air for compensation or hire.

One-Hundred-Hour Inspection

All aircraft operated for hire and all aircraft used for flight instruction for hire are required by FAR 91.409(b) to have a complete inspection once every 100 hours of flight. This inspection, which includes both the airframe and the powerplant, is identical to the annual inspection except that it may be performed by a certificated technician who holds both airframe and powerplant ratings, but it does not require an Inspection Authorization (IA).

An annual inspection can take the place of a required 100-hour inspection, and each 100-hour inspection can be used as an annual inspection if it is conducted by a technician holding an Inspection Authorization.

The 100-hour limitation can be exceeded by not more than 10 hours while en route to a place where the inspection can be performed. But if the time is extended, the extension must be subtracted from the time to the next inspection. If an inspection is due at 1,200 hours, but at this time the airplane is away from its home base, it has until 1,210 hours, if needed, to reach the place where the inspection can be performed. The excess time used must be

Inspection Authorization (IA). An authorization that may be issued to an experienced aviation maintenance technician who holds both an Airframe and Powerplant rating. It allows the holder to conduct annual inspections and to approve an aircraft or aircraft engine for return to service after a major repair or major alteration.

included in the time for the next 100-hour inspection. If the inspection was performed at 1,208 hours, the next 100-hour inspection would still be due at 1,300 hours.

Progressive Inspection

Progressive inspections may be used instead of annual and 100-hour inspections to keep the downtime to a minimum while performing the inspection. The inspection is conducted in small increments under an approved schedule that will ensure that the complete inspection equivalent to an annual inspection is completed within a period of 12 calendar months.

To put an aircraft on a progressive inspection program, the owner or operator must submit a written request to the local FAA Flight Standards District Office (FSDO). This request must include:

1. The name of the certificated technician holding an Inspection Authorization who will supervise or conduct the progressive inspection;

2. A detailed inspection procedures manual including:

    a. An explanation of the progressive inspection, including the continuity of inspection responsibility, the making of reports and the keeping of records, and technical reference materials,

    b. An inspection schedule, specifying the interval in hours or days when routine and detailed inspections will be performed and including instructions for exceeding an inspection interval by not more than 10 hours while en route, and for changing an inspection interval because of service experience, and

    c. Sample routine and detailed inspection forms and instructions for their use;

3. Description of the housing and equipment for disassembly and proper inspection of the aircraft; and

4. Statement that the appropriate current technical information for the aircraft is available.

The frequency and detail of the progressive inspection must ensure that the aircraft, at all times, will be airworthy and will conform to all applicable FAA Aircraft Specifications, Type Certificate Data Sheets, Airworthiness Directives, and other approved data.

If the progressive inspection is discontinued, the owner or operator must immediately notify the local FAA FSDO in writing of the discontinuance. After discontinuance, the first annual inspection is due within 12 calendar months after the last complete inspection under the progressive program. If 100-hour inspections are required, they are required based upon the date the annual inspection was completed.

---

progressive inspection. An inspection that may be used in place of an annual or 100-hour inspection. It has the same scope as an annual inspection, but it may be performed in increments so the aircraft will not have to be out of service for a lengthy period of time.

downtime. Any time during which an aircraft is out of commission and unable to be operated.

Type Certificate Data Sheets (TCDS). The official specifications of an aircraft, engine, or propeller issued by the Federal Aviation Administration.

TCDS lists pertinent specifications for the device, and it is the responsibility of the mechanic and/or inspector to assure, on each inspection, that the device meets these specifications.

Airworthiness Directive (AD note). A notice sent out by the FAA to the registered owner of an aircraft notifying him or her of an unsafe condition that has been found on his aircraft. Compliance with AD notes is compulsory.

Large Aircraft Inspections

Large airplanes, turbojet multi-engine airplanes, turbopropeller-powered multi-engine airplanes, and turbine-powered rotorcraft operated under FAR Part 91 must be inspected on an inspection program specified in FAR 91.409 (e) and (f). This inspection program is not the same as the progressive inspection described in FAR Part 43.15(d).

These programs are adapted to the aircraft and to the specific conditions under which they operate, and they may be taken from:

1. The continuous airworthiness inspection program currently in use by an air carrier operating under FAR Part 121, 127, or 135;

2. An aircraft inspection program approved for a carrier operating under FAR Part 135;

3. A current inspection program recommended by the aircraft manufacturer; or

4. Any other inspection program established by the registered owner or operator and approved by the Administrator.

The Conduct of an Annual or 100-Hour Inspection

All annual, 100-hour, and progressive inspections begin with an examination of the aircraft records, a survey of the appropriate maintenance information, the actual inspection of the aircraft, and the completion of the required records. Here, we will examine each of these steps.

Examination of the Aircraft Records

All the aircraft records must be examined, and these include:

- Type of inspection program and time since last inspection;
- Total time on the airframe;
- Current status of life-limited parts;
- Time since last overhaul of parts required to be overhauled on a specific time basis;
- List of current major alterations to the airframe, engine, propeller, rotor, or any appliance; and
- Status of any applicable Airworthiness Directives. This must show the date and method of compliance, and if it is a recurring AD, the date the next compliance is required.

These records may be in the form of a logbook or some other method that has been approved by the FAA. Keeping these records on computers is a modern practice.

Survey of Maintenance Information

Airworthiness Alert. A notice sent by the FAA to certain interested maintenance personnel, identifying problems with aircraft gathered from Malfunction and Defect Reports. These problems are being studied at the time the Airworthiness Alert is issued but have not been fully evaluated at the time the material went to press.

Supplemental Type Certificate (STC). An approval issued by the FAA for a modification to a type certificated airframe, engine, or component.

More than one STC can be issued for the same basic alteration, but each holder must prove to the FAA that the alteration meets all of the requirements of the original type certificate.

The Type Certificate Data Sheets for the aircraft, engine, and propeller must be available to allow the technician to be sure the aircraft adheres to its specifications for certification.

All the Airworthiness Directives that apply to the aircraft, engine, propeller, and all appliances must be researched. It is extremely important that no applicable AD be missed, and with the large number of ADs currently issued, it is wise to subscribe to a service that compiles all the ADs and service bulletins and makes them available in the form of loose-leaf record books, microfiche, or computer data.

Check Airworthiness Alerts and manufacturer's service bulletins and letters to find out whether or not the aircraft needs special attention in any area.

Some equipment may have been installed according to a Supplemental Type Certificate (STC). The installation must conform to the data furnished with the STC.

Inspection of the Aircraft

Before starting the actual inspection, run up the engine to check the operation of all its systems and to get warm fresh oil covering the cylinder walls for the compression test. Check every airframe control for proper operation and operate all systems to detect any problems that may need correction.

Follow the written checklist specified for the aircraft. This list must include at least all of the items listed in FAR Part 43, Appendix D. This is the information in Figure 14-3. The requirements for a powerplant inspection are covered in the *Powerplant* textbook of the *Aviation Maintenance Technician Series*.

The more important airframe items to be checked on a typical high-performance single-engine airplane during an annual, 100-hour, or progressive inspection are listed here with notes showing some of the things to look for.

Fuel System

1. **Fuel strainers.** Drain all fuel strainers, clean the bowls and filters, and replace them. Pressure-check the system for leaks. Safety the filters.

2. **Fuel sump drains.** Drain a quantity of fuel from all of the tank and system sump drains. Check the drained fuel for indications of water or other contaminants. Check the drain for leakage.

3. **Fuel selector valve and placards.** Check for freedom of movement of the selector valve control. Determine that there is a definite feel for the valve in each position. There should be no indication of fuel leakage around the selector valve or the lines attached to it. All the required placards should be installed and legible.

4. **Auxiliary fuel pump.** This pump should operate properly with no indication of leaks. The electric wires going to the pump should be properly supported and in good condition.

5. **Engine-driven fuel pump.** This pump should be securely mounted on the engine with no indication of oil leaks around the base or fuel leaks around the lines attached to it.

6. **Fuel quantity indicators and sensing units.** These should be checked for any indication of fuel leakage, and the wires should be securely attached and supported. The indicator should agree with the amount of fuel known to be in the tank.

7. **Fuel lines.** Check all lines for security of mounting and for any indication of chafing. Check for fuel dye stains around all fittings.

8. **Engine primer.** The primer typically uses a small-diameter copper line that is susceptible to breakage after it has been hardened from vibration. Check it at the primer pump and at the engine. Tug on the line to see if it will pull out of the fitting. Check the entire system for indication of fuel leaks.

Landing Gear

1. **Brake wheel units.** Check the brake linings for excessive wear. Check the calipers for freedom and for any indication of corrosion or rust. Check the hydraulic line for indication of leaks. Check the disk for indications of rust or pitting and for any indication of warpage.

2. **Tires.** Check for any indication of weather-checking of the sidewall, cuts across any of the tread lands, and any indication of uneven wear. Check the tread depth. Check the inflation pressure when the loaded weight of the aircraft is on the wheels.

3. **Main gear wheels.** Check for any indication of damage to the flanges and for any indication of cracks. Check the balance weights for security of mounting.

4. **Wheel bearings.** Remove the bearings, clean them, and check all of the rollers and races for indication of flaking or brinelling. Repack the bearings with the proper grease, and torque the axle nut according to the aircraft manufacturer's instructions, and safety it.

5. **Shock absorbers.** Check the oleo strut for proper extension and for any indication of rust or corrosion. Check the torsion links for looseness or wear and for any indication of damage. Check for proper safety of all bolts securing the torsion links. Lubricate the torsion links as specified by the aircraft manufacturer.

Continued

6. **Nose gear.** Check the nose-gear shock strut, torsion links, and shimmy damper for any indication of excessive wear or looseness. Check the tire for uneven wear and for any evidence of damage. Clean, inspect, and pack the nose-gear wheel bearings and torque the axle nut and safety it. Check the entire nose-gear steering mechanism for looseness and for freedom of all of the bearings in the steering links.

7. **Landing gear retraction.** Place retractable landing gear aircraft on jacks to perform a gear retraction test. Be sure to follow all of the manufacturer's instructions for jacking the aircraft, and use the proper power supply for performing the retraction test.

   Systematically check all of the wiring and switches in the indicating system for security of mounting and the integrity of all connections. Check all of the hydraulic lines for any indication of leakage or wear. Check the uplocks, downlocks, and all of the door operating linkage for proper rigging and alignment. Lubricate any components specified by the aircraft manufacturer.

   Perform the number of retraction and extension cycles specified by the manufacturer, and check to be sure that there is the required clearance between all parts of the landing gear and the structure when the gear is retracted. Check to be sure that the doors are all flush with the structure when the gear is up. Check to be sure that the hydraulic reservoir is full of the proper type of hydraulic fluid.

Airframe

1. **Exterior.** Inspect all of the external portions of the aircraft for any indication of damage or corrosion. Remove all of the fairings and inspection covers. Examine the edges of all of the skins for any indication of deformed rivets or puffed paint which would indicate corrosion under the paint. Sight along the surface of the skins for any indication of wrinkles.

2. **Windshield and windows.** Check all transparent plastic for scratches, cracks, or crazing and for any evidence of damage. All windows that can be opened should function smoothly and close and lock completely.

3. **Doors.** Check all door hinges and locks. The locks should secure the door properly and function with no binding. Check all of the door seals for proper functioning.

4. **Bilge areas.** Remove all of the inspection covers below the floor rug, and carefully examine the bilge area for entrapped dirt or water and for any indication of corrosion. Make sure that all drain holes are open. Check all of the control cables in this area and perform any lubrication specified by the manufacturer.

5. **Seats and seat rails.** Carefully examine the seat rails for any indication of worn holes and for cracks or damages to the rails. Examine the seat locking pins to be sure that they are working properly and are not worn. The pin should easily and smoothly extend for the correct distance into the holes in the rail.

6. **Seat belts and harness.** Examine the seat belts and shoulder harness for any indication of fraying or wearing. The attachment points should be secure, and the belts and harnesses should be of the proper approved type.

7. **Control columns, chains, and cables.** Examine the controls for full and unobstructed travel. Examine the chains and sprockets to be sure that the sprockets are secure on the control yoke and the chains ride freely over the sprockets. Examine all of the control cables, especially as they pass over pulleys, to be sure that the cable is not frayed and the pulleys turn freely. Check all of the turnbuckles for the proper safety.

8. **Rudder pedals and brake cylinders.** Check the rudder pedals for any indication of wear or looseness. Check the brake master cylinders for indication of leakage and for the condition of the hoses. Fill the brake reservoirs with the proper fluid.

9. **Avionics equipment.** Check to be sure that all avionics equipment listed in the current equipment list is actually installed and that no equipment is installed that is not included in the equipment list. Check all of the avionics for operation.

10. **Instruments.** Check all instruments for loose or broken glass and for any indication of damage. All required range marking should be in place. Be sure that a current compensation card is installed for the compass and for any other instruments that require such a card. Check behind the panel to see that no hoses or wires are chafing or are obstructing the free movement of the controls.

    When the master switch is turned on, the electrical gyro instruments should begin to spin up. They should operate with no excessive noise, and when the power is turned off, they should have the coast-down time specified in the service manual.

11. **Air filters.** Clean or replace all of the air filters in the gyro instruments.

12. **Instrument panel.** Check the shock mounts to be sure that they are adequately supporting the instrument panel and do not allow it to contact the structure. Check the bonding straps that electrically connect the instrument panel to the aircraft structure. Be sure that all of the required placards are on the panel.

13. **Heating and defrosting systems.** Check all of the ducting and controls for the heating and defrosting system. The controls should work freely and all of the hoses should be of the proper type and correctly installed.

Continued

14. **Lights, switches, and circuit breakers.** Check all interior and exterior lights to be sure they operate as they should. All switches should operate properly and should be properly labeled. All circuit breakers should be labeled, and the wires attached to them should be secure. If the aircraft uses fuses, the correct fuses should be installed and the proper spare fuses should be available.

15. **Pitot-static system.** If the aircraft is operated under Instrument Flight Rules, the altimeter and static system must be checked every 24 months as described in the section under special inspections. If these special checks do not have to be made, at least check the static system for leaks. Check the pitot system to be sure that it does not have any leaks. Check the pitot heater. Turn it on for a few seconds and then turn it off. The pitot head should be warm.

16. **Stall warning system.** Check the stall warning system for operation. If an electrical system is used, check the stall-warning vane for freedom and be sure that the stall-warning horn or light operates when the vane is lifted. If the mechanical-reed type of system is used, be sure that it sounds when a suction is placed over its entry hole.

17. **Antennas and cables.** All antennas should be securely mounted on the aircraft, and the coaxial cables firmly attached. There should be no corrosion or indication of water leaking into the structure around the antenna, and there should be no cracks in the structure that could be caused by the antenna vibrating. The coaxial cable should be secured to the structure and it should not interfere with any of the controls or control cables.

18. **Battery, battery box, and cables.** Check the battery box and the area surrounding it for any indication of corrosion. The inside of the box should be adequately protected with a tar-based paint or with polyurethane enamel. The battery should be secure in the box with no looseness. There should be no corrosion on the battery cables and the cables should be tight. Lead-acid batteries should be checked for proper water level. Check all of the hardware on nickel-cadmium batteries for condition and for any indication of burning.

19. **Emergency Locator Transmitter.** Check the ELT for security of mounting and connection to its antenna. The ELT should be of the approved type and the battery replacement or recharge date should be legibly marked on the outside of the case. The battery must have been replaced or recharged within the allowable time. Turn on the VHF radio receiver and tune it to 121.5 to be sure that the ELT is not transmitting.

20. **Oxygen system.** Check the oxygen bottles to be sure that they are the correct type and that they have been hydrostatically tested within the required time interval. The bottles should be filled. The masks and hoses should be in good condition and be properly stowed.

21. **Deicer system.** The deicer boots should be checked for condition and security of attachment. The distributor valve and all plumbing should be checked, and during engine run-up, the system should be checked for proper operation.

Control System

1. **Cables and control surfaces.** Systematically check all of the control cables, turnbuckles, pulleys, brackets, cable guards, and fairleads. Begin at the cockpit control and go all the way to the horn on the control surface. There should be no rust or corrosion on the cables, and all pulleys should turn freely. Be sure that the control surfaces move in the correct direction when the cockpit control is moved. Be sure that no part of the control system rubs against the structure during full travel of the controls.

2. **Control surface travel.** Check the control surface travel to be sure that it is the same as that specified in the Type Certificate Data Sheets for the aircraft. The stop on the control surface should be reached before the stop in the cockpit, and there should be a slight amount of springback in the control system.

3. **Flaps.** The wing flaps should operate freely throughout all of their range, and electric flaps with automatic stops should stop at the correct number of degrees. The flap tracks should show no excessive wear or looseness.

4. **Trim adjustment devices.** The trim tabs or adjustable stabilizer jackscrews should be inspected for security and for any indication of binding or unusual wear. There should be no looseness in any tab actuating mechanism as this can lead to flutter. The indicator in the cockpit should agree with the position of the tabs.

Record of the Inspection

After the inspection is complete, it must be recorded in the aircraft maintenance records as specified in FAR Part 43.11. The record must be concluded with a statement like the one in Figure 14-4 if the aircraft passed, and the one in Figure 14-5 if it failed.

An annual inspection is valid for 12 calendar months, and a calendar month ends at midnight of the last day of the month in which the inspection is completed. If an annual is completed on June 4 of this year, it will expire at midnight of June 30 next year.

Date _____

I certify that this aircraft has been inspected in accordance with a/an (insert type) inspection and was determined to be in an airworthy condition.

Signed _____
Certificate type and number _____

Figure 14-4. *Typical statement approving an aircraft for return to service after it has passed an annual or 100-hour inspection.*

Failed Inspection

If the aircraft does not pass the inspection, a signed and dated list of all the discrepancies and items that keep it from meeting its airworthiness requirements must be furnished to the owner or lessee, FAR 43.11(b). These discrepancies do not have to be corrected by the technician performing the inspection, but can be corrected by any technician who holds the appropriate certification. When they are corrected and signed off in the maintenance record, the aircraft is legal for flight.

If any of the discrepancies require a major repair, an AMT may make the repair and initiate an FAA Form 337, but the repair must be checked for compliance with approved data. The aircraft must be approved for return to service and the Form 337 signed by an AMT holding an Inspection Authorization.

FAA Form 337. The FAA form that must be filled in and submitted to the FAA when a major repair or major alteration has been completed.

Date _____

I certify that this aircraft has been inspected in accordance with a/an (insert type) inspection and a list of discrepancies and unairworthy items dated (date) has been provided for the aircraft owner or operator.

Signed _____
Certificate type and number _____

Figure 14-5. *Typical statement disapproving an aircraft for return to service after it has failed an annual or 100-hour inspection.*

STUDY QUESTIONS: AIRCRAFT INSPECTIONS

Answers begin on Page 929. Page numbers refer to chapter text.

1. A preflight inspection _____ (is or is not) considered to be a maintenance inspection.
   Page 909

2. The method of nondestructive inspection best suited for checking wheels after an overweight landing is the _____ method. *Page 913*

3. A maintenance technician holding an airframe rating can conduct the _____ (static system or altimeter) tests required by FAR 91.411. *Page 914*

4. The maximum leakage that is allowed for a static air system that has been evacuated until the altimeter indicates a change of 1,000 feet is _____ feet in one minute. *Page 914*

5. Altimeters used in IFR flight must be checked for accuracy every _____ calendar months. *Page 913*

6. The tests required for an altimeter are described in FAR Part _____ Appendix E. *Page 913*

7. An ATC transponder must be checked every _____ calendar months. *Page 915*

8. An Aviation Maintenance Technician certificate with an Airframe rating _____ (is or is not) the authorization needed to perform the required tests on an ATC transponder. *Page 915*

9. An annual inspection _____ (is or is not) more comprehensive than a 100-hour inspection. *Page 917*

10. An aircraft that is due for an annual inspection may be flown to a place where the inspection can be performed if the FAA grants a/an _____ permit for the flight. *Page 917*

11. A 100-hour inspection of an aircraft _____ (does or does not) include an inspection of the powerplant. *Page 917*

12. A person conducting a 100-hour inspection on an aircraft must hold both an Airframe and Powerplant rating. An Inspection Authorization _____ (is or is not) required. *Page 917*

13. A person conducting an annual inspection on an aircraft must hold both an Airframe and Powerplant rating. An Inspection Authorization _____ (is or is not) required. *Page 917*

14. An aircraft operating under the 100-hour inspection system of FAR 91 can be operated for a maximum of _____ hours beyond the 100-hour inspection period, if necessary, in order to reach a place where the inspection can be performed. *Page 917*

15. The operating conditions that make a 100-hour inspection mandatory are found in FAR Part _____ . *Page 917*

16. An annual inspection _____ (can or cannot) be substituted for a 100-hour inspection. *Page 917*

17. A 100-hour inspection can be treated as an annual inspection if the inspector holds a/an _____ . *Page 917*

18. An entire progressive inspection must be completed within _____ calendar months. *Page 918*

19. The record of compliance with all applicable Airworthiness Directives must include the date and _____ of their compliance. *Page 919*

Continued

20. The permanent records of an aircraft must include these things:

    a. _____

    b. _____

    c. _____

    d. _____

    e. _____

    f. _____

    Page 919

21. The recommended statement for approving or disapproving an aircraft for return to service after a 100-hour or annual inspection is found in FAR _____ . *Page 925*

22. An annual inspection that is completed on March 15 of this year will expire on midnight of March _____ next year. *Page 925*

23. If an aircraft fails an annual or 100-hour inspection, a signed and dated list of all the discrepancies and unairworthy items that keep it from meeting its airworthiness requirements must be furnished to the _____ or _____ . *Page 926*

24. If an aircraft fails an annual inspection because of a discrepancy that requires a major repair, the repair can be made by an appropriately rated mechanic. The person returning the aircraft for return to service _____ (is or is not) required to hold an Inspection Authorization (IA). *Page 926*

25. If an aircraft has failed an annual inspection because of several items that require minor repairs, the repairs can be made and the aircraft approved for return to service by an appropriately rated AMT. The AMT approving the aircraft for return to service _____ (is or is not) required to hold an Inspection Authorization. *Page 926*

26. Large airplanes and turbine-powered multi-engine aircraft operated under FAR Part 91 must be inspected in accordance with an inspection program authorized under Subpart E of FAR 91.409 (e) and (f). This inspection _____ (is or is not) the same as the progressive inspection covered in FAR Part 43.15 (d). *Page 919*

Answers to Aircraft Inspection Study Questions

1. is not
2. eddy current
3. static system
4. 100
5. 24
6. 43
7. 24
8. is not
9. is not
10. special flight
11. does
12. is not
13. is
14. 10
15. 91
16. can
17. Inspection Authorization
18. 12
19. method

20. a. Type of inspection program
    b. Total time on airframe
    c. Current status of life-limited parts
    d. Time since last overhaul of parts required to be overhauled on a specific time basis
    e. List of current major alterations
    f. Status of applicable Airworthiness Directives
21. 43
22. 31
23. owner, lessee
24. is
25. is not
26. is not

GLOSSARY

aborted takeoff. A takeoff that is terminated prematurely when it is determined that some condition exists that makes takeoff or further flight dangerous.

absolute pressure. Pressure measured from zero pressure, or a vacuum.

absolute pressure regulator. A valve used in a pneumatic system at the pump inlet to regulate the compressor inlet air pressure to prevent excessive speed variation and/or overspeeding of the compressor.

absolute zero. The point at which all molecular motion ceases. Absolute zero is -460°F and -273°C.

AC 43.13-1A. The advisory circular used by technicians that contains examples of accepted methods, techniques, and practices for aircraft inspection and repair.

ACARS (Aircraft Communication Addressing and Reporting System). A two-way communication link between an airliner in flight and the airline's main ground facilities. Data is collected in the aircraft by digital sensors and is transmitted to the ground facilities. Replies from the ground may be printed out so the appropriate flight crewmember can have a hard copy of the response.

accumulator. A hydraulic component that consists of two compartments separated by a movable component such as a piston, diaphragm, or bladder. One compartment is filled with compressed air or nitrogen, and the other is filled with hydraulic fluid and is connected into the system pressure manifold.

An accumulator allows an incompressible fluid to be stored under pressure by the force produced by a compressible fluid. Its primary purposes are to act as a shock absorber in the system, and to provide a source of additional hydraulic power when heavy demands are placed on the system.

accumulator air preload. Compressed air or nitrogen in one side of an accumulator. The air preload is usually about one third of the system hydraulic pressure. When fluid is pumped into the oil side of the accumulator, the air is further compressed, and the air pressure and the fluid pressure become the same.

If an air preload pressure is too low, there will be almost no time between the regulator reaching its kick-in and kick-out pressures, and the system will cycle far more frequently than it should.

The amount of air preload is found by reducing the hydraulic pressure to zero and observing the reading on the accumulator air gage. If there is no air gage, slowly bleed the hydraulic pressure off the system while watching the hydraulic pressure gage. The pressure will drop slowly, until a point is reached at which it drops suddenly. This point is the air preload pressure.

actuator. A fluid power device that changes fluid pressure into mechanical motion.

ADC. Air Data Computer.

ADF. Automatic Direction Finder.

ADI. Attitude Director Indicator.

advancing blade. The blade on a helicopter rotor whose tip is moving in the same direction the helicopter is moving.

adverse yaw. A condition of flight at the beginning of a turn in which the nose of an airplane momentarily yaws in the opposite direction from the direction in which the turn is to be made.

aerodynamic drag. The total resistance to the movement of an object through the air. Aerodynamic drag is composed of both induced drag and parasite drag. *See* induced drag and parasite drag.

aerodynamic lift. The force produced by air moving over a specially shaped surface called an airfoil. Aerodynamic lift acts in a direction perpendicular to the direction the air is moving.

aeroelastic tailoring. The design of an aerodynamic surface whose strength and stiffness are matched to the aerodynamic loads that will be imposed upon it.

aging. A change in the characteristics of a material with time. Certain aluminum alloys do not have their full strength when they are first removed from the quench bath after they have been heat-treated, but they gain this strength after a few days by the natural process of aging.

agonic line. A line drawn on an aeronautical chart along which there is no angular difference between the magnetic and geographic north poles.

air carrier. An organization or person involved in the business of transporting people or cargo by air for compensation or hire.

air-cycle cooling system. A system for cooling the air in the cabin of a turbojet-powered aircraft. Compressor bleed air passes through two heat exchangers where it gives up some of its heat; then it drives an expansion turbine where it loses still more of its heat energy as the turbine drives a compressor. When the air leaves the turbine it expands and its pressure and temperature are both low.

airfoil. Any surface designed to obtain a useful reaction, or lift, from air passing over it.

airspeed indicator. A flight instrument that measures the pressure differential between the pitot, or ram, air pressure and the static pressure of the air surrounding the aircraft. This differential pressure is shown in units of miles per hour, knots, or kilometers per hour.

Airworthiness Alert. A notice sent by the FAA to certain interested maintenance personnel, identifying problems with aircraft that have been gathered from Malfunction and Defect Reports. These problems are being studied at the time the Airworthiness Alert is issued but have not been fully evaluated by the time the material went to press.

Airworthiness Directive (AD note). A notice sent out by the FAA to the registered owner of an aircraft notifying him or her of an unsafe condition that has been found on the aircraft. Compliance with AD notes is mandatory.

Alclad. A registered trade name for clad aluminum alloy.

Alodine. The registered trade name for a popular conversion coating chemical used to produce a hard, airtight, oxide film on aluminum alloy for corrosion protection.

alphanumeric symbols. Symbols made up of all of the letters in our alphabet, numerals, punctuation marks, and certain other special symbols.

alternator. An electrical generator that produces alternating current. The popular DC alternator used on light aircraft produces three-phase AC in its stator windings. This AC is changed into DC by a six-diode, solid-state rectifier before it leaves the alternator.

altimeter setting. The barometric pressure at a given location corrected to mean (average) sea level.

altitude engine. A reciprocating engine whose rated sea-level takeoff power can be produced to an established higher altitude.

alumel. An alloy of nickel, aluminum, manganese, and silicon that is the negative element in a thermocouple used to measure exhaust gas temperature.

ambient pressure. The pressure of the air surrounding a person or an object.

ambient temperature. The temperature of the air surrounding a person or an object.

American Wire Gage. The system of measurement of wire size used in aircraft electrical systems.

amphibian. An airplane with landing gear that allows it to operate from both water and land surfaces.

amplifier. An electronic circuit in which a small change in voltage or current controls a much larger change in voltage or current.

analog electronics. Electronics in which values change in a linear fashion. Output values vary in direct relationship to changes of input values.

analog-type indicator. An electrical meter that indicates values by the amount a pointer moves across a graduated, numerical scale.

aneroid. The sensitive component in an altimeter or barometer that measures the absolute pressure of the air. The aneroid is a sealed, flat capsule made of thin corrugated disks of metal soldered together and evacuated by pumping all of the air out of it. Evacuating the aneroid allows it to expand or collapse as the air pressure on the outside changes.

angle of attack (α). The acute angle formed between the chord line of an airfoil and the direction of the air that strikes the airfoil.

angle-of-attack indicator. An instrument that measures the angle between the local airflow around the direction detector and the fuselage reference plane.

angle of incidence. The acute angle formed between the chord line of an airfoil and the longitudinal axis of the aircraft on which it is mounted.

annual rings. The rings that appear in the end of a log cut from a tree. The number of annual rings per inch gives an indication of the strength of the wood. The more rings there are and the closer they are together, the stronger the wood.

The pattern of alternating light and dark rings is caused by the seasonal variations in the growth rate of the tree. A tree grows quickly in the spring and produces the light-colored, less dense rings. The slower growth during the summer, or latter part of the growing season, produces the dark-colored, denser rings.

annunciator panel. A panel of warning lights in plain sight of the pilot. These lights are identified by the name of the system they represent and are usually covered with colored lenses to show the meaning of the condition they announce.

anodizing. The electrolytic process in which a hard, airtight, oxide film is deposited on aluminum alloy for corrosion protection.

antenna. A special device used with electronic communication and navigation systems to radiate and receive electromagnetic energy.

anti-icer system. A system that prevents the formation of ice on an aircraft structure.

anti-icing additive. A chemical added to the turbine-engine fuel used in some aircraft. This additive mixes with water that condenses from the fuel and lowers its freezing temperature so it will not freeze and block the fuel filters. It also acts as a biocidal agent and prevents the formation of microbial contamination in the tanks.

antidrag wire. A structural wire inside a Pratt truss airplane wing between the spars. Antidrag wires run from the rear spar inboard, to the front spar at the next bay outboard. Antidrag wires oppose the forces that try to pull the wing forward.

antiservo tab. A tab installed on the trailing edge of a stabilator to make it less sensitive. The tab automatically moves in the same direction as the stabilator to produce an aerodynamic force that tries to bring the surface back to a streamline position. This tab is also called an anti-balance tab.

antiskid brake system. An electrohydraulic system in an airplane's power brake system that senses the deceleration rate of every main landing gear wheel. If any wheel decelerates too rapidly, indicating an impending skid, pressure to that brake is released and the wheel stops decelerating. Pressure is then reapplied at a slightly lower value.

antitear strip. Strips of aircraft fabric laid under the reinforcing tape before the fabric is stitched to an aircraft wing.

APU (Auxiliary Power Unit). A small turbine or reciprocating engine that drives a generator, hydraulic pump, and air pump. The APU is installed in the aircraft and is used to supply electrical power, compressed air, and hydraulic pressure when the main engines are not running.

arbor press. A press with either a mechanically or hydraulically operated ram used in a maintenance shop for a variety of pressing functions.

arcing. Sparking between a commutator and brush or between switch contacts that is caused by induced current when a circuit is broken.

area. The number of square units in a surface.

ARINC (Aeronautical Radio Incorporated). A corporation whose principal stockholders are the airlines. Its function is to operate certain communication links between airliners in flight and the airline ground facilities. ARINC also sets standards for communication equipment used by the airlines.

aspect ratio. The ratio of the length, or span, of an airplane wing to its width, or chord. For a nonrectangular wing, the aspect ratio is found by dividing the square of the span of the wing by its area. Aspect Ratio = span² ÷ area

asymmetrical airfoil. An airfoil section that is not the same on both sides of the chord line.

asymmetrical lift. A condition of uneven lift produced by the rotor when a helicopter is in forward flight. Asymmetrical lift is caused by the difference between the airspeed of the advancing blade and that of the retreating blade.

attenuate. To weaken, or lessen the intensity of, an activity.

attitude indicator. A gyroscopic flight instrument that gives the pilot an indication of the attitude of the aircraft relative to its pitch and roll axes.

The attitude indicator in an autopilot is in the sensing system that detects deviation from a level-flight attitude.

augmenter tube. A long, stainless steel tube around the discharge of the exhaust pipes of a reciprocating engine. Exhaust gases flow through the augmenter tube and produce a low pressure that pulls additional cooling air through the engine compartment. Heat may be taken from the augmenter tubes and directed through the leading edges of the wings for thermal anti-icing.

autoclave. A pressure vessel inside of which air can be heated to a high temperature and pressure raised to a high value.

Autoclaves are used in the composite manufacturing industry to apply heat and pressure for curing resins.

autogiro. A heavier-than-air rotor-wing aircraft sustained in the air by rotors turned by aerodynamic forces rather than by engine power. When the name Autogiro is spelled with a capital A, it refers to a specific series of machines built by Juan de la Cierva or his successors.

autoignition system. A system on a turbine engine that automatically energizes the igniters to provide a relight if the engine should flame out.

automatic adjuster. A subsystem in an aircraft disk brake that compensates for disk or lining wear. Each time the brakes are applied, the automatic adjuster is reset for zero clearance, and when the brakes are released, the clearance between the disks or the disk and lining is returned to a preset value.

A malfunctioning automatic adjuster in a multiple-disk brake can cause sluggish and jerky operation.

automatic flight control system (AFCS). The full system of automatic flight control that includes the autopilot, flight director, horizontal situation indicator, air data sensors, and other avionics inputs.

automatic pilot (autopilot). An automatic flight control device that controls an aircraft about one or more of its three axes. The primary purpose of an autopilot is to relieve the pilot of the control of the aircraft during long periods of flight.

autorotation. Descent of a helicopter without the use of engine power. An aerodynamic force causes the rotors to rotate.

Autosyn system. A synchro system used in remote indicating instruments. The rotors in an Autosyn system are two-pole electromagnets, and the stators are delta-connected, three-phase, distributed-pole windings in the stator housings.

The rotors in the transmitters and indicators are connected in parallel and are excited with 26-volt, 400-Hz AC. The rotor in the indicator follows the movement of the rotor in the transmitter.

aviation snips. Compound-action hand shears used for cutting sheet metal. Aviation snips come in sets of three. One pair cuts to the left, one pair cuts to the right, and the third pair of snips cuts straight.

aviators oxygen. Oxygen that has had almost all of the water and water vapor removed from it.

avionics. The branch of technology that deals with the design, production, installation, use, and servicing of electronic equipment mounted in aircraft.

azimuth. A horizontal angular distance, measured clockwise from a fixed reference direction to an object.

back course. The reciprocal of the localizer course for an ILS (Instrument Landing System). When flying a back-course approach, the aircraft approaches the instrument runway from the end on which the localizer antennas are installed.

backhand welding. Welding in which the torch is pointed away from the direction the weld is progressing.

backplate (brake component). A floating plate on which the wheel cylinder and the brake shoes attach on an energizing-type brake.

backup ring. A flat leather or Teflon ring installed in the groove in which an O-ring or T-seal is placed. The backup ring is on the side of the seal away from the pressure, and it prevents the pressure extruding the seal between the piston and the cylinder wall.

balance cable. A cable in the aileron system of an airplane that connects to one side of each aileron. When the control wheel is rotated, a cable from the cockpit pulls one aileron down and relaxes the cable going to the other aileron. The balance cable pulls the other aileron up.

balance panel. A flat panel hinged to the leading edge of some ailerons that produces a force which assists the pilot in holding the ailerons deflected. The balance panel divides a chamber ahead of the aileron in such a way that when the aileron is deflected downward, for example, air flowing over its top surface produces a low pressure that acts on the balance panel and causes it to apply an upward force to the aileron leading edge.

balance tab. An adjustable tab mounted on the trailing edge of a control surface to produce a force that aids the pilot in moving the surface. The tab is automatically actuated in such a way it moves in the direction opposite to the direction the control surface on which it is mounted moves.

balanced actuator. A linear hydraulic or pneumatic actuator that has the same area on each side of the piston.

banana oil. Nitrocellulose dissolved in amyl acetate, so named because it smells like bananas.

bank (*verb*). The act of rotating an aircraft about its longitudinal axis.

barometric scale. A small window in the dial of a sensitive altimeter in which the pilot sets the barometric pressure level from which the altitude shown on the altimeter is measured. This window is sometimes called the "Kollsman" window.

base. The electrode of a bipolar transistor between the emitter and the collector. Varying a small flow of electrons moving into or out of the base controls a much larger flow of electrons between the emitter and the collector.

bead (tire component). The high-strength carbon-steel wire bundles that give an aircraft tire its strength and stiffness where it mounts on the wheel.

bead seat area. The flat surface on the inside of the rim of an aircraft wheel on which the bead of the tire seats.

bearing strength (sheet metal characteristic). The amount of pull needed to cause a piece of sheet metal to tear at the points at which it is held together with rivets. The bearing strength of a material is affected by both its thickness and the diameter of the rivet.

beehive spring. A hardened-steel, coil-spring retainer used to hold a rivet set in a pneumatic rivet gun.

This spring gets its name from its shape. It screws onto the end of the rivet gun and allows the set to move back and forth, but prevents it being driven from the gun.

bend allowance. The amount of material actually used to make a bend in a piece of sheet metal. Bend allowance depends upon the thickness of the metal and the radius of the bend, and is normally found in a bend allowance chart.

bend radius. The radius of the inside of a bend.

bend tangent line. A line made in a sheet metal layout that indicates the point at which the bend starts.

Bernoulli's principle. The basic principle that explains the relation between kinetic energy and potential energy in fluids that are in motion.

When the total energy in a column of moving fluid remains constant, any increase in the kinetic energy of the fluid (its velocity) results in a corresponding decrease in its potential energy (its pressure).

bezel. The rim that holds the glass cover in the case of an aircraft instrument.

bias-cut surface tape. A fabric tape in which the threads run at an angle of 45° to the length of the tape. Bias-cut tape may be stretched around a compound curve such as a wing tip bow without wrinkling.

bilge area. A low portion in an aircraft structure in which water and contaminants collect. The area under the cabin floorboards is normally called the bilge.

bipolar transistor. A solid-state component in which the flow of current between its emitter and collector is controlled by a much smaller flow of current into or out of its base. Bipolar transistors may be of either the NPN or PNP type.

BITE. Built-In Test Equipment.

black box. A term used for any portion of an electrical or electronic system that can be removed as a unit. A black box does not have to be a physical box.

bladder-type fuel cell. A plastic-impregnated fabric bag supported in a portion of an aircraft structure so that it forms a cell in which fuel is carried.

blade track. The condition of a helicopter rotor in which each blade follows in exactly the same path as the blade ahead of it.

bleeder. A material such as glass cloth or mat that is placed over a composite lay-up to absorb the excess resin forced out of the ply fibers when pressure is applied.

bleeding dope. Dope whose pigments are soluble in the solvents or thinners used in the finishing system. The color will bleed up through the finish coats.

bleeding of brakes. The maintenance procedure of removing air entrapped in hydraulic fluid in the brakes. Fluid is bled from the brake system until fluid with no bubbles flows out.

blimp. A cigar-shaped, nonrigid lighter-than-air flying machine.

blush. A defect in a lacquer or dope finish caused by moisture condensing on the surface before the finish dries.

If the humidity of the air is high, the evaporation of the solvents cools the air enough to cause the moisture to condense. The water condensed from the air mixes with the lacquer or dope and forms a dull, porous, chalky-looking finish called blush. A blushed finish is neither attractive nor protective.

bonding. The process of electrically connecting all isolated components to the aircraft structure. Bonding provides a path for return current from electrical components, and a low-impedance path to ground to minimize static electrical charges.

Shock-mounted components have bonding braids connected across the shock mounts.

boost pump. An electrically driven centrifugal pump mounted in the bottom of the fuel tanks in large aircraft. Boost pumps provide a positive flow of fuel under pressure to the engine for starting and serve as an emergency backup in the event an engine-driven pump should fail. They are also used to transfer fuel from one tank to another and to pump fuel overboard when it is being dumped.

Boost pumps prevent vapor locks by holding pressure on the fuel in the line to the engine-driven pump.

Centrifugal boost pumps have a small agitator propeller on top of the impeller to force vapors from the fuel before it leaves the tank.

boundary layer. The layer of air that flows next to an aerodynamic surface. Because of the design of the surface and local surface roughness, the boundary layer often has a random flow pattern, sometimes even flowing in a direction opposite to the direction of flight. A turbulent boundary layer causes a great deal of aerodynamic drag.

Bourdon tube. A pressure-indicating mechanism used in most oil pressure and hydraulic pressure gages. It consists of a sealed, curved tube with an elliptical cross section. Pressure inside the tube tries to straighten it, and as it straightens, it moves a pointer across a calibrated dial.

Bourdon-tube pressure gages are used to measure temperature by measuring the vapor pressure in a sealed container of a volatile liquid, such as methyl chloride, whose vapor pressure varies directly with its temperature.

brazing. A method of thermally joining metal parts by wetting the surface with a molten nonferrous alloy. When the molten material cools and solidifies, it holds the pieces together.

Brazing materials melt at a temperature higher than 800°F, but lower than the melting temperature of the metal on which they are used.

(Btu) British thermal unit. The amount of heat energy needed to raise the temperature of one pound of pure water 1°F.

bucking bar. A heavy steel bar with smooth, hardened surfaces, or faces. The bucking bar is held against the end of the rivet shank when it is driven with a pneumatic rivet gun, and the shop head is formed against the bucking bar.

buffeting. Turbulent movement of the air over an aerodynamic surface.

bulb angle. An L-shaped metal extrusion having an enlarged, rounded edge that resembles a bulb on one of its legs.

bulkhead. A structural partition that divides the fuselage of an aircraft into compartments, or bays.

bungee shock cord. A cushioning material used with the non-shock absorbing landing gears installed on older aircraft.

Bungee cord is made up of many small rubber bands encased in a loose-woven cotton braid.

burnish (verb). To smooth the surface of metal that has been damaged by a deep scratch or gouge. The metal piled up at the edge of the damage is pushed back into the damage with a smooth, hard steel burnishing tool.

burr. A sharp rough edge of a piece of metal left when the metal was sheared, punched, or drilled.

bus. A point within an electrical system from which the individual circuits get their power.

buttock line. A line used to locate a position to the right or left of the center line of an aircraft structure.

Butyl. The trade name for a synthetic rubber product made by the polymerization of isobutylene.

Butyl withstands such potent chemicals as phosphate ester-base (Skydrol) hydraulic fluids.

cage (verb). To lock the gimbals of a gyroscopic instrument so it will not be damaged by abrupt flight maneuvers or rough handling.

calendar month. A measurement of time used by the FAA for inspection and certification purposes. One calendar month from a given day extends from that day until midnight of the last day of that month.

calender (fabric treatment). To pass fabric through a series of heated rollers to give it a smooth shiny surface.

calibrated airspeed (CAS). Indicated airspeed corrected for position error. *See* position error.

calorie. The amount of heat energy needed to raise the temperature of one gram of pure water 1°C.

camber (wheel alignment). The amount the wheels of an aircraft are tilted, or inclined, from the vertical. If the top of the wheel tilts outward, the camber is positive. If the top of the wheel tilts inward, the camber is negative.

canard. A horizontal control surface mounted ahead of the wing to provide longitudinal stability and control.

canted rate gyro. A rate gyro whose gimbal axis is tilted so it can sense rotation of the aircraft about its roll axis as well as its yaw axis.

cantilever wing. A wing that is supported by its internal structure and requires no external supports. The wing spars are built in such a way that they carry all the bending and torsional loads.

cap strip. The main top and bottom members of a wing rib. The cap strips give the rib its aerodynamic shape.

capacitance-type fuel quantity measuring system. A popular type of electronic fuel quantity indicating system that has no moving parts in the fuel tank. The tank units are cylindrical capacitors, called probes, mounted across the tank, from top to bottom.

The dielectric between the plates of the probes is either fuel or the air above the fuel, and the capacitance of the probe varies with the amount of fuel in the tank.

The indicator is a servo-type instrument driven by the amplified output of a capacitance bridge.

capillary tube. A soft copper tube with a small inside diameter. The capillary tube used with a vapor-pressure thermometer connects the temperature sensing bulb to the Bourdon tube. The capillary tube is protected from physical damage by enclosing it in a braided metal wire jacket.

carbon monoxide detector. A packet of chemical crystals mounted in the aircraft cockpit or cabin where they are easily visible. The crystals change their color from yellow to green when they are exposed to carbon monoxide.

carbon-pile voltage regulator. A type of voltage regulator used with high-output DC generators.

Field current is controlled by varying the resistance of a stack of thin carbon disks. This resistance is varied by controlling the amount the stack is compressed by a spring whose force is opposed by the pull of an electromagnet. The electromagnet's strength is proportional to the generator's output voltage.

carburizing flame. An oxyacetylene flame produced by an excess of acetylene. This flame is identified by a feather around the inner cone. A carburizing flame is also called a reducing flame.

carcass (tire component). The layers of rubberized fabric that make up the body of an aircraft tire.

case pressure. A low pressure that is maintained inside the case of a hydraulic pump.

If a seal becomes damaged, hydraulic fluid will be forced out of the pump rather than allowing air to be drawn into the pump.

cathode-ray tube. A display tube used for oscilloscopes and computer video displays.

An electron gun emits a stream of electrons that is attracted to a positively charged inner surface of the face of the tube. Acceleration and focusing grids speed the movement of the electrons and shape the beam into a pinpoint size. Electrostatic or electromagnetic forces caused by deflection plates or coils move the beam over the face of the tube.

The inside surface of the face of the tube is treated with a phosphor material that emits light when the beam of electrons strikes it.

cavitation. A condition that exists in a hydraulic pump when there is not enough pressure in the reservoir to force fluid to the inlet of the pump. The pump picks up air instead of fluid.

CDI. Course Deviation Indicator.

CDU. Control Display Unit.

centering cam. A cam in the nose-gear shock strut that causes the piston to center when the strut fully extends.

When the aircraft takes off and the strut extends, the wheel is straightened in its fore-and-aft position so it can be retracted into the wheel well.

center of gravity. The location on an aircraft about which the force of gravity is concentrated.

center of lift. The location on the chord line of an airfoil at which all the lift forces produced by the airfoil are considered to be concentrated.

center of pressure. The point on the chord line of an airfoil where all of the aerodynamic forces are considered to be concentrated.

charging stand (air conditioning service equipment). A handy and compact arrangement of air conditioning servicing equipment. A charging stand contains a vacuum pump, a manifold gage set, and a method of measuring and dispensing the refrigerant.

chatter. A type of rapid vibration of a hydraulic pump caused by the pump taking in some air along with the hydraulic fluid.

check (wood defect). Longitudinal cracks that extend, in general, across a log's annual rings.

check valve. A hydraulic or pneumatic system component that allows full flow of fluid in one direction but blocks all flow in the opposite direction.

chemical oxygen candle system. An oxygen system used for emergency or backup use.

Solid blocks of a material that release oxygen when they are burned are carried in special fireproof fixtures. When oxygen is needed, the candles are ignited with an integral igniter, and oxygen flows into the tubing leading to the masks.

chevron seal. A form of one-way seal used in some fluid-power actuators. A chevron seal is made of a resilient material whose cross section is in the shape of the letter V. The pressure being sealed must be applied to the open side of the V.

chromel. An alloy of nickel and chromium used as the positive element in a thermocouple for measuring exhaust gas temperature.

circle. A closed plane figure with every point an equal distance from the center. A circle has the greatest area for its circumference of any enclosed shape.

circuit breaker. An electrical component that automatically opens a circuit any time excessive current flows through it.

A circuit breaker may be reset to restore the circuit after the fault causing the excessive current has been corrected.

clad aluminum. A sheet of aluminum alloy that has a coating of pure aluminum rolled on one or both of its surfaces for corrosion protection.

clamp-on ammeter. An electrical instrument used to measure current without opening the circuit through which it is flowing.

    The jaws of the ammeter are opened, slipped over the current-carrying wire, and then clamped shut. Current flowing through the wire produces a magnetic field which induces a voltage in the ammeter that is proportional to the amount of current.

Cleco fastener. A patented spring-type fastener used to hold metal sheets in position until they can be permanently riveted together.

close-quarter iron. A small hand-held iron with an accurately calibrated thermostat. This iron is used for heat-shrinking polyester fabrics in areas that would be difficult to work with a large iron.

closed angle. An angle formed in sheet metal that has been bent through more than 90°.

closed assembly time. The time elapsing between the assembly of glued joints and the application of pressure.

closed-center hydraulic system. A hydraulic system in which the selector valves are installed in parallel with each other. When no unit is actuated, fluid circulates from the pump back to the reservoir without flowing through any of the selector valves.

closed-center selector valve. A type of flow-control valve used to direct pressurized fluid into one side of an actuator, and at the same time, direct the return fluid from the other side of the actuator to the fluid reservoir.

    Closed-center selector valves are connected in parallel between the pressure manifold and the return manifold.

coaxial. Rotating about the same axis. Coaxial rotors of a helicopter are mounted on concentric shafts in such a way that they turn in opposite directions to cancel torque.

coaxial cable. A special type of electrical cable that consists of a central conductor held rigidly in the center of a braided outer conductor.

    Coaxial cable, or coax, as it is normally called, is used for attaching radio receivers and transmitters to their antenna.

coefficient of drag. A dimensionless number used in the formula for determining induced drag as it relates to the angle of attack.

coefficient of lift. A dimensionless number relating to the angle of attack used in the formula for aerodynamic lift.

coin dimpling. A process of preparing a hole in sheet metal for flush riveting. A coining die is pressed into the rivet hole to form a sharp-edged depression into which the rivet head fits.

collective pitch control. The helicopter control that changes the pitch of all of the rotor blades at the same time. Movement of the collective pitch control increases or decreases the lift produced by the entire rotor disk.

collodion. Cellulose nitrate used as a film base for certain aircraft dopes.

combustion heater. A type of cabin heater used in some aircraft. Gasoline from the aircraft fuel tanks is burned in the heater.

compass fluid. A highly refined, water-clear petroleum product similar to kerosine. Compass fluid is used to damp the oscillations of magnetic compasses.

compass rose. A location on an airport where an aircraft can be taken to have its compasses "swung." Lines are painted on the rose to mark the magnetic directions in 30° increments.

compass swinging. A maintenance procedure that minimizes deviation error in a magnetic compass. The aircraft is aligned on a compass rose, and the compensating magnets in the compass case are adjusted so the compass card indicates the direction marked on the rose. After the deviation error is minimized on all headings, a compass correction card is completed and mounted on the instrument panel next to the compass.

compensated fuel pump. A vane-type, engine-driven fuel pump that has a diaphragm connected to the pressure-regulating valve. The chamber above the diaphragm is vented to the carburetor upper deck where it senses the pressure of the air as it enters the engine.

    The diaphragm allows the fuel pump to compensate for altitude changes and keeps the carburetor inlet fuel pressure a constant amount higher than the carburetor inlet air pressure.

compensator port (brake system component). A small hole between a hydraulic brake master cylinder and the reservoir. When the brakes are released, this port is uncovered and the fluid in the master cylinder is vented to the reservoir.

    When the brake is applied, the master-cylinder piston covers the compensator port and allows pressure in the line to the brake to build up and apply the brakes. When the brake is released, the piston uncovers the compensator port. If any fluid has been lost from the brake, the reservoir will refill the master cylinder.

A restricted compensator port will cause the brakes to drag or cause them to be slow to release.

composite. Something made up of different materials combined in such a way that the characteristics of the resulting material are different from those of any of the components.

compound curve. A curve formed in more than one plane. The surface of a sphere is a compound curve.

compound gage (air conditioning servicing equipment). A pressure gage used to measure the pressure in the low side of an air conditioning system. A compound gage is calibrated from zero to 30-inches of mercury vacuum, and from zero to about 150-psi positive gage pressure.

compressibility effect. The sudden increase in the total drag of an airfoil in transonic flight caused by formation of shock waves on the surface.

compression failure. A type of structural failure in wood caused by the application of too great a compressive load. A compression failure shows up as a faint line running at right angles to the grain of the wood.

compression strut. A heavy structural member, often in the form of a steel tube, used to hold the spars of a Pratt truss airplane wing apart. A compression strut opposes the compressive loads between the spars arising from the tensile loads produced by the drag and antidrag wires.

compression wood. A defect in wood that causes it to have a high specific gravity and the appearance of an excessive growth of summerwood. In most species, there is little difference between the color of the springwood and summerwood.

Any material containing compression wood is unsuited for aircraft structural use and must be rejected.

compressor (air conditioning system component). The component in a vapor-cycle cooling system in which the low-pressure refrigerant vapors, after they leave the evaporator, are compressed to increase both their temperature and pressure before they pass into the condenser.

Some compressors are driven by electric motors, others by hydraulic motors and, in the case of most light airplanes, are belt driven from the engine.

concave surface. A surface that is curved inward. The outer edges are higher than the center.

condenser (air conditioning system component). The component in a vapor-cycle cooling system in which the heat taken from the aircraft cabin is given up to the ambient air outside the aircraft.

conductor (electrical). A material that allows electrons to move freely from one atom to another within the material.

coning angle. The angle formed between the plane of rotation of a helicopter rotor blade when it is producing lift and a line perpendicular to the rotor shaft.

The degree of the coning angle is determined by the relationship between the centrifugal force acting on the blades and the aerodynamic lift produced by the blades.

constant (mathematical). A value used in a mathematical computation that is the same every time it is used.

For example, the relationship between the length of the circumference of a circle and the length of its diameter is a constant, 3.1416. This constant is called by the Greek name of pi (π).

constant differential mode (cabin pressurization). The mode of pressurization in which the cabin pressure is maintained a constant amount higher than the outside air pressure. The maximum differential pressure is determined by the structural strength of the aircraft cabin.

constant-displacement pump. A fluid pump that moves a specific volume of fluid each time it rotates; the faster the pump turns, the more fluid it moves.

Some form of pressure regulator or relief valve must be used with a constant-displacement pump when it is driven by an aircraft engine.

constant-speed drive (CSD). A special drive system used to connect an alternating current generator to an aircraft engine. The drive holds the generator speed (and thus its frequency) constant as the engine speed varies.

constantan. A copper-nickel alloy used as the negative lead of a thermocouple for measuring the cylinder head temperature of a reciprocating engine.

contactor (electrical component). A remotely actuated, heavy-duty electrical switch. Contactors are used in an aircraft electrical system to connect the battery to the main bus.

continuity tester. A troubleshooting tool that consists of a battery, a light bulb, and test leads.

The test leads are connected to each end of the conductor under test, and if the bulb lights up, there is continuity. If it does not light up, the conductor is open.

Continuous Airworthiness Inspection Program. An inspection program that is part of a continuous airworthiness maintenance program approved for certain large airplanes (to which FAR Part 125 is not applicable), turbojet multi-engine airplanes, turbopropeller-powered multi-engine airplanes, and turbine-powered rotorcraft.

continuous-duty solenoid. A solenoid-type switch designed to be kept energized by current flowing through its coil for an indefinite period of time. The battery contactor in an aircraft electrical system is a continuous-duty solenoid. Current flows through its coil all the time the battery is connected to the electrical system.

continuous-flow oxygen system. A type of oxygen system that allows a metered amount of oxygen to continuously flow into the mask. A rebreather-type mask is used with a continuous-flow system.

The simplest form of continuous-flow oxygen systems regulates the flow by a calibrated orifice in the outlet to the mask, but most systems use either a manual or automatic regulator to vary the pressure across the orifice proportional to the altitude being flown.

continuous-loop fire-detection system. A fire-detection system that uses a continuous loop of two conductors separated with a thermistor-type insulation.

Under normal temperature conditions, the thermistor material is an insulator, but if it is exposed to a fire, the thermistor changes into a conductor and completes the circuit between the two conductors, initiating a fire warning.

control horn. The arm on a control surface to which the control cable or push-pull rod attaches to move the surface.

controllability. The characteristic of an aircraft that allows it to change its flight attitude in response to the pilot's movement of the cockpit controls.

control stick. The type of control device used in some airplanes. A vertical stick in the cockpit controlls the ailerons by side-to-side movement and the elevators by fore-and-aft movement.

control yoke. The movable column on which an airplane control wheel is mounted. The yoke may be moved in or out to actuate the elevators, and the control wheel may be rotated to actuate the ailerons.

conventional current. An imaginary flow of electricity that is said to flow from the positive terminal of a power source, through the external circuit to its negative terminal. The arrowheads in semiconductor symbols point in the direction of conventional current flow.

converging duct. A duct, or passage, whose cross-sectional area decreases in the direction of fluid flow.

conversion coating. A chemical solution used to form an airtight oxide or phosphate film on the surface of aluminum or magnesium parts. The conversion coating prevents air reaching the metal and keeps it from corroding.

convex surface. A surface that is curved outward. The outer edges are lower than the center.

coriolis effect. The change in rotor blade velocity to compensate for a change in the distance between the center of mass of the rotor blade and the axis rotation of the blade as the blades flap in flight.

cornice brake. A large shop tool used to make straight bends across a sheet of metal. Cornice brakes are often called leaf brakes.

corrugated metal. Sheets of metal that have been made more rigid by forming a series of parallel ridges or waves in its surface.

cotter pin. A split metal pin used to safety a castellated or slotted nut on a bolt. The pin is passed through the hole in the shank of the bolt and the slots in the nut, and the ends of the pin are spread to prevent it backing out of the hole.

countersinking. Preparation of a rivet hole for a flush rivet by beveling the edges of the holes with a cutter of the correct angle.

Coverite surface thermometer. A small surface-type bimetallic thermometer that calibrates the temperature of an iron used to heat-shrink polyester fabrics.

crabbing. Pointing the nose of an aircraft into the wind to compensate for wind drift.

crazing. A form of stress-caused damage that occurs in a transparent thermoplastic material. Crazing appears as a series of tiny, hair-like cracks just below the surface of the plastic.

critical Mach number. The flight Mach number at which there is the first indication of supersonic airflow over any part of the aircraft structure.

cross coat. A double coat of aircraft finishing material in which the second coat is sprayed at right angles to the first coat, before the solvents have evaporated from the first coat.

cross-feed valve (fuel system component). A valve in a fuel system that allows any engines of a multi-engine aircraft to draw fuel from any fuel tank.

Cross-feed systems are used to allow a multi-engine aircraft to maintain a balanced fuel condition.

cross-flow valve. An automatic flow-control valve installed between the gear-up and gear-down lines of the landing gear of some large airplanes.

When the landing gear is released from its uplocks, its weight causes it to fall faster than the hydraulic system can supply fluid to the gear-down side of the actuation cylinder. The cross-flow valve opens and directs fluid from the gear-up side into the gear-down side. This allows the gear to move down with a smooth motion.

CRT. Cathode-Ray Tube.

cryogenic liquid. A liquid which boils at temperatures of less than about 110°K (-163°C) at normal atmospheric pressures.

Cuno filter. The registered trade name for a particular style of edge-type fluid filter.

Cuno filters are made up of a stack of thin metal disks that are separated by thin scraper blades. Contaminants collect on the edge of the disks, and they are periodically scraped out and allowed to collect in the bottom of the filter case for future removal.

current. A general term used for electrical flow. *See* conventional current.

current limiter. An electrical component used to limit the amount of current a generator can produce. Some current limiters are a type of slow-blow fuse in the generator output. Other current limiters reduce the generator output voltage if the generator tries to put out more than its rated current.

cusp. A pointed end.

cyclic pitch control. The helicopter control that allows the pilot to change the pitch of the rotor blades individually, at a specific point in their rotation. The cyclic pitch control allows the pilot to tilt the plane of rotation of the rotor disk to change the direction of lift produced by the rotor.

Dacron. The registered trade name for a cloth woven from polyester fibers.

damped oscillation. Oscillation whose amplitude decreases with time.

database. A body of information that is available on any particular subject.

data bus. A wire or group of wires that are used to move data within a computer system.

debooster valve. A valve in a power brake system between the power brake control valve and the wheel cylinder. This valve lowers the pressure of the fluid going to the brake and increases its volume.

A debooster valve increases the smoothness of brake application and aids in rapid release of the brakes.

decay. Decomposition. The breakdown of the structure of wood fibers. Wood that shows any indication of decay must be rejected for use in aircraft structure.

deciduous. A type of tree that sheds its foliage at the end of the growing season. Hardwoods come from deciduous trees.

dedicated computer. A small digital computer, often built into an instrument or control device, that contains a built-in program that causes it to perform a specific function.

deep-vacuum pump. A vacuum pump capable of removing almost all of the air from a refrigeration system. A deep-vacuum pump can reduce the pressure inside the system to a few microns of pressure.

deflator cap. A cap for a tire, strut, or accumulator air valve that, when screwed onto the valve, depresses the valve stem and allows the air to escape safely through a hole in the side of the cap.

deicer system. A system that removes ice after it has formed on an aircraft.

delamination. The separation of the layers of a laminated material.

delivery air duct check valve. An isolation valve at the discharge side of the air turbine that prevents the loss of pressurization through a disengaged cabin air compressor.

delta airplane. An airplane with a triangular-shaped wing. This wing has an extreme amount of sweepback on its leading edge, and a trailing edge that is almost perpendicular to the longitudinal axis of the airplane.

delta connection (electrical connection). A method of connecting three electrical coils into a ring or, as they are drawn on a schematic diagram as a triangle, a delta (D).

denier. A measure of the fineness of the yarns in a fabric.

density altitude. The altitude in standard air at which the density is the same as that of the existing air.

density ratio (σ). The ratio of the density of the air at a given altitude to the density of the air at sea level under standard conditions.

derated (electrical specification). Reduction in the rated voltage or current of an electrical component. Derating is done to extend the life or reliability of the device.

desiccant (air conditioning component). A drying agent used in an air conditioning system to remove water from the refrigerant. A desiccant is made of silica-gel or some similar material.

detent. A spring-loaded pin or tab that enters a hole or groove when the device to which it is attached is in a certain position. Detents are used on a fuel valve to provide a positive means of identifying the fully on and fully off position of the valve.

detonation. An explosion, or uncontrolled burning of the fuel-air mixture inside the cylinder of a reciprocating engine. Detonation occurs when the pressure and temperature inside the cylinder become higher than the critical pressure and temperature of the fuel. Detonation is often confused with preignition. *See* preignition.

deviation error. An error in a magnetic compass caused by localized magnetic fields in the aircraft.

Deviation error, which is different on each heading, is compensated by the technician "swinging" the compass.

A compass must be compensated so the deviation error on any heading is no greater than 10 degrees.

Dewar bottle. A vessel designed to hold liquefied gases. It has double walls with the space between being evacuated to prevent the transfer of heat. The surfaces in the vacuum area are made heat-reflective.

differential aileron travel. Aileron movement in which the upward-moving aileron deflects a greater distance than the one moving downward. The up aileron produces parasite drag to counteract the induced drag caused by the down aileron.

Differential aileron travel is used to counteract adverse yaw.

differential pressure. The difference between two pressures. An airspeed indicator is a differential-pressure gage. It measures the difference between static air pressure and pitot air pressure.

differential-voltage reverse-current cutout. A type of reverse-current cutout switch used with heavy-duty electrical systems. This switch connects the generator to the electrical bus when the generator voltage is a specific amount higher than the battery voltage.

digital multimeter. An electrical test instrument that can be used to measure voltage, current, and resistance. The indication is in the form of a liquid crystal display in discrete numbers.

dihedral. The positive angle formed between the lateral axis of an airplane and a line that passes through the center of the wing or horizontal stabilizer. Dihedral increases the lateral stability of an airplane.

diluter-demand oxygen system. A popular type of oxygen system in which the oxygen is metered to the mask, where it is diluted with cabin air by an airflow-metering aneroid assembly which regulates the amount of air allowed to dilute the oxygen on the basis of cabin altitude.

The mixture of oxygen and air flows only when the wearer of the mask inhales. The percentage of oxygen in the air delivered to the mask is regulated, on the basis of altitude, by the regulator.

A diluter-demand regulator has an emergency position which allows 100% oxygen to flow to the mask, bypassing the regulating mechanism.

dipole antenna. A half-wavelength, center-fed radio antenna. The length of each of the two arms is approximately one fourth of the wavelength of the center frequency for which the antenna is designed.

dirigible. A large, cigar-shaped, rigid, lighter-than-air flying machine. Dirigibles are made of a rigid truss structure covered with fabric. Gas bags inside the structure contain the lifting gas, which is either helium or hydrogen.

disc area (helicopter specification). The total area swept by the blades of a helicopter main rotor.

divergent oscillation. Oscillation whose amplitude increases with time.

diverging duct. A duct, or passage, whose cross-sectional area increases in the direction of fluid flow.

DME. Distance Measuring Equipment.

dope proofing. The treatment of a structure to be covered with fabric to keep the solvents in the dope from softening the protective coating on the structure.

dope roping. A condition of aircraft dope brushed onto a surface in such a way that it forms a stringy, uneven surface rather than flowing out smoothly.

double-acting actuator (hydraulic system component). A linear actuator moved in both directions by fluid power.

double-acting hand pump (hydraulic system component). A hand-operated fluid pump that moves fluid during both strokes of the pump handle.

doubler. A piece of sheet metal used to strengthen and stiffen a repair in a sheet metal structure.

downtime. Any time during which an aircraft is out of commission and unable to be operated.

downwash. Air forced down by aerodynamic action below and behind the wing of an airplane or the rotor of a helicopter. Aerodynamic lift is produced when the air is deflected downward. The upward force on the aircraft is the same as the downward force on the air.

drag (helicopter rotor blade movement). Fore-and-aft movement of the tip of a helicopter rotor blade in its plane of rotation.

dragging brakes. Brakes that do not fully release when the brake pedal is released. The brakes are partially applied all the time, which causes excessive lining wear and heat.

drag wire. A structural wire inside a Pratt truss airplane wing between the spars. Drag wires run from the front spar inboard, to the rear spar at the next bay outboard. Drag wires oppose the forces that try to drag the wing backward.

drill motor. An electric or pneumatic motor that drives a chuck that holds a twist drill. The best drill motors produce high torque, and their speed can be controlled.

drip stick. A fuel quantity indicator used to measure the fuel level in the tank when the aircraft is on the ground.

The drip stick is pulled down from the bottom of the tank until fuel drips from its open end. This indicates that the top of the gage inside the tank is at the level of the fuel. Note the number of inches read on the outside of the gage at the point it contacts the bottom of the tank, and use a drip-stick table to convert this measurement into gallons of fuel in the tank.

dry air pump. An engine-driven air pump which uses carbon vanes. Dry pumps do not use any lubrication, and the vanes are extremely susceptible to damage from solid airborne particles. These pumps must be operated with filters in their inlet so they will take in only filtered air.

dry ice. Solidified carbon dioxide. Dry ice sublimates, or changes from a solid directly into a gas, at a temperature of -110°F (-78.5°C).

dry rot. Decomposition of wood fibers caused by fungi. Dry rot destroys all strength in the wood.

ductility. The property of a material that allows it to be drawn into a thin section without breaking.

dummy load (electrical load). A noninductive, high-power, 50-ohm resistor that can be connected to a transmission line in place of the antenna. The transmitter can be operated into the dummy load without transmitting any signal.

Duralumin. The name for the original alloy of aluminum, magnesium, manganese, and copper. Duralumin is the same as the modern 2017 aluminum alloy.

Dutch roll. An undesirable, low-amplitude coupled oscillation about both the yaw and roll axes that affects many swept wing airplanes. Dutch roll is minimized by the use of a yaw damper.

Dutchman shears. A common name for compound-action sheet metal shears.

dynamic pressure (q). The pressure a moving fluid would have if it were stopped. Dynamic pressure is measured in pounds per square foot.

dynamic stability. The stability that causes an aircraft to return to a condition of straight and level flight after it has been disturbed from this condition.

When an aircraft is disturbed from straight and level flight, its static stability starts it back in the correct direction; but it overshoots, and the corrective forces are applied in the opposite direction. The aircraft oscillates back and forth on both sides of the correct condition, with each oscillation smaller than the one before it. Dynamic stability is the decreasing of these restorative oscillations.

EADI. Electronic Attitude Director Indicator.

ECAM. Electronic Centralized Aircraft Monitor.

eccentric bushing. A special bushing used between the rear spar of certain cantilever airplane wings and the wing attachment fitting on the fuselage. The portion of the bushing that fits through the hole in the spar is slightly offset from that which passes through the holes in the fitting. By rotating the bushing, the rear spar may be moved up or down to adjust the root incidence of the wing.

eddy current damping (electrical instrument damping). Decreasing the amplitude of oscillations by the interaction of magnetic fields.

In the case of a vertical-card magnetic compass, flux from the oscillating permanent magnet produces eddy currents in a damping disk or cup. The magnetic flux produced by the eddy currents opposes the flux from the permanent magnet and decreases the oscillations.

edge distance. The distance between the center of a rivet hole and the edge of the sheet of metal.

EFIS. Electronic Flight Instrument System.

EHSI. Electronic Horizontal Situation Indicator.

EICAS. Engine Indicating and Crew Alerting System.

ejector. A form of jet pump used to pick up a liquid and move it to another location. Ejectors are used to assure that the compartment in which the boost pumps are mounted is kept full of fuel. Part of the fuel from the boost pump flowing through the ejector produces a low pressure that pulls fuel from the main tank and forces it into the boost-pump sump area.

elastic limit. The maximum amount of tensile load, in pounds per square inch, a material is able to withstand without being permanently deformed.

electromotive force (EMF). The force that causes electrons to move from one atom to another within an electrical circuit. Electromotive force is an electrical pressure, and it is measured in volts.

electron current. The actual flow of electrons in a circuit. Electrons flow from the negative terminal of a power source through the external circuit to its positive terminal. The arrowheads in semiconductor symbols point in the direction opposite to the flow of electron current.

elevator downspring. A spring in the elevator control system that produces a mechanical force that tries to lower the elevator. In normal flight this spring force is overcome by the aerodynamic force from the elevator trim tab. But in slow flight with an aft CG position, the trim tab loses its effectiveness and the downspring lowers the nose to prevent a stall.

elevons. Movable control surfaces on the trailing edge of a delta wing or a flying wing airplane. These surfaces operate together to serve as elevators, and differentially to act as ailerons.

ELT (Emergency Locator Transmitter). A self-contained radio transmitter that automatically begins transmitting on the emergency frequencies any time it is triggered by a severe impact parallel to the longitudinal axis of the aircraft.

EMI. Electromagnetic Interference.

empennage. The tail section of an airplane.

enamel. A type of finishing material that flows out to form a smooth surface. Enamel is usually made of a pigment suspended in some form of resin. When the resin cures, it leaves a smooth, glossy protective surface.

energizing brake. A brake that uses the momentum of the aircraft to increase its effectiveness by wedging the shoe against the brake drum.

Energizing brakes are also called servo brakes. A single-servo brake is energizing only when moving in the forward direction, and a duo-servo brake is energizing when the aircraft is moving either forward or backward.

epoxy. A flexible, thermosetting resin that is made by polymerization of an epoxide.

Epoxy has wide application as a matrix for composite materials and as an adhesive that bonds many different types of materials. It is noted for its durability and its chemical resistance.

equalizing resistor. A large resistor in the ground circuit of a heavy-duty aircraft generator through which all of the generator output current flows.

The voltage drop across this resistor is used to produce the current in the paralleling circuit that forces the generators to share the electrical load equally.

ethylene dibromide. A chemical compound added to aviation gasoline to convert some of the deposits left by the tetraethyl lead into lead bromides. These bromides are volatile and will pass out of the engine with the exhaust gases.

ethylene glycol. A form of alcohol used as a coolant for liquid-cooled engines and as an anti-icing agent.

eutectic material. An alloy or solution that has the lowest possible melting point.

evacuation (air conditioning servicing procedure). A procedure in servicing vapor-cycle cooling systems. A vacuum pump removes all the air from the system. Evacuation removes all traces of water vapor that could condense out, freeze, and block the system.

evaporator (air conditioning component). The component in a vapor-cycle cooling system in which heat from the aircraft cabin is absorbed into the refrigerant. As the heat is absorbed, the refrigerant evaporates, or changes from a liquid into a vapor. The function of the evaporator is to lower the cabin air temperature.

expander-tube brake. A brake that uses hydraulic fluid inside a synthetic rubber tube around the brake hub to force rectangular blocks of brake-lining material against the rotating brake drum. Friction between the brake drum and the lining material slows the aircraft.

expansion wave. The change in pressure and velocity of a supersonic flow of air as it passes over a surface which drops away from the flow. As the surface drops away, the air tries to follow it. In changing its direction, the air speeds up to a higher supersonic velocity and its static pressure decreases. There is no change in the total energy as the air passes through an expansion wave, and so there is no sound as there is when air passes through a shock wave.

extruded angle. A structural angle formed by passing metal heated to its plastic state through specially shaped dies.

FAA Form 337. The FAA form that must be filled in and submitted to the FAA when a major repair or major alteration has been completed.

FAA FSDO. Federal Aviation Administration Flight Standards District Office. An FAA field office serving an assigned geographical area staffed with Flight Standards personnel who serve the aviation industry and the general public on matters relating to certification and operation of air carrier and general aviation aircraft.

fading of brakes. The decrease in the amount of braking action that occurs with some types of brakes that are applied for a long period of time.

True fading occurs with overheated drum-type brakes. As the drum is heated, it expands in a bell-mouthed fashion. This decreases the amount of drum in contact with the brake shoes and decreases the braking action. A condition similar to brake fading occurs when there is an internal leak in the brake master cylinder. The brakes are applied, but as the pedal is held down, fluid leaks past the piston, and the brakes slowly release.

fairing. A part of a structure whose primary purpose is to produce a smooth surface or a smooth junction where two surfaces join.

fairlead. A plastic or wooden guide used to prevent a steel control cable rubbing against an aircraft structure.

FCC. Federal Communications Commission.

FCC. Flight Control Computer.

feather (helicopter rotor blade movement). Rotation of a helicopter rotor blade about its pitch-change axis.

ferrous metal. Any metal that contains iron and has magnetic characteristics.

fiber stop nut. A form of self-locking nut that has a fiber insert crimped into a recess above the threads. The hole in the insert is slightly smaller than the minor diameter of the threads. When the nut is screwed down over the bolt threads, the opposition caused by the fiber insert produces a force that prevents vibration loosening the nut.

file. A hand-held cutting tool used to remove a small amount of metal with each stroke.

fill threads. Threads in a piece of fabric that run across the width of the fabric, interweaving with the warp threads. Fill threads are often called woof, or weft, threads.

fillet. A fairing used to give shape but not strength to an object. A fillet produces a smooth junction where two surfaces meet.

finishing tape. Another name for surface tape. *See* surface tape.

fire pull handle. The handle in an aircraft cockpit that is pulled at the first indication of an engine fire. Pulling this handle removes the generator from the electrical system, shuts off the fuel and hydraulic fluid to the engine, and closes the compressor bleed air valve. The fire extinguisher agent discharge switch is uncovered, but it is not automatically closed.

fire zone. A portion of an aircraft designated by the manufacturer to require fire-detection and/or fire-extinguishing equipment and a high degree of inherent fire resistance.

fishmouth splice. A type of splice used in a welded tubular structure in which the end of the tube whose inside diameter is the same as the outside diameter of the tube being spliced is cut in the shape of a V, or a fishmouth, and is slipped over the smaller tube and welded. A fishmouth splice has more weld area than a butt splice and allows the stresses from one tube to transfer into the other tube gradually.

fitting. An attachment device that is used to connect components to an aircraft structure.

fixed fire-extinguishing system. A fire-extinguishing system installed in an aircraft.

flameout. A condition in the operation of a gas turbine engine in which the fire in the engine unintentionally goes out.

flap (aircraft control). A secondary control on an airplane wing that changes its camber to increase both its lift and its drag.

flap (helicopter rotor blade movement). Up-and-down movement of the tip of a helicopter rotor blade.

flap overload valve. A valve in the flap system of an airplane that prevents the flaps being lowered at an airspeed which could cause structural damage. If the pilot tries to extend the flaps when the airspeed is too high, the opposition caused by the airflow will open the overload valve and return the fluid to the reservoir.

flash point. The temperature to which a material must be raised for it to ignite, but not continue to burn, when a flame is passed above it.

flat pattern layout. The pattern for a sheet metal part that has the material used for each flat surface, and for all of the bends, marked out with bend-tangent lines drawn between the flats and bend allowances.

flight controller. The component in an autopilot system that allows the pilot to maneuver the aircraft manually when the autopilot is engaged.

fluid. A form of material whose molecules are able to flow past one another without destroying the material. Gases and liquids are both fluids.

fluid power. The transmission of force by the movement of a fluid.

The most familiar examples of fluid power systems are hydraulic and pneumatic systems.

flutter. Rapid and uncontrolled oscillation of a flight control surface on an aircraft that is caused by a dynamically unbalanced condition.

fly-by-wire. A method of control used by some modern aircraft in which control movement or pressures exerted by the pilot are directed into a digital computer where they are input into a program tailored to the flight characteristics of the aircraft. The computer output signal is sent to actuators at the control surfaces to move them the optimum amount for the desired maneuver.

flying boat. An airplane whose fuselage is built in the form of a boat hull to allow it to land and takeoff from water. In the past, flying boats were a popular form of large airplane.

flying wing. A type of heavier-than-air aircraft that has no fuselage or separate tail surfaces. The engines and useful load are carried inside the wing, and movable control surfaces on the trailing edge provide both pitch and roll control.

FMC. Flight Management Computer.

follow-up signal. A signal in an autopilot system that nulls out the input signal to the servo when the correct amount of control surface deflection has been reached.

foot-pound. A measure of work accomplished when a force of 1 pound moves an object a distance of 1 foot.

force. Energy brought to bear on an object that tends to cause motion or to change motion.

forehand welding. Welding in which the torch is pointed in the direction the weld is progressing.

form drag. Parasite drag caused by the form of the object passing through the air.

former. An aircraft structural member used to give a fuselage its shape.

forward bias. A condition of operation of a semiconductor device such as a diode or transistor in which a positive voltage is connected to the P-type material and a negative voltage to the N-type material.

FPD. Freezing point depressant.

fractional distillation. A method of separating the various components from a physical mixture of liquids.

The material to be separated is put into a container and its temperature is increased. The components having the lowest boiling points boil off first and are condensed. Then as the temperature is further raised, other components are removed. Kerosine, gasoline and other petroleum products are obtained by fractional distillation of crude oil.

frangible. Breakable, or easily broken.

Freon. The registered trade name for the refrigerant used in a vapor-cycle cooling system. Freon-12 is the most commonly used refrigerant.

Frise aileron. An aileron with its hinge line set back from the leading edge so that when it is deflected upward, part of the leading edge projects below the wing and produces parasite drag to help overcome adverse yaw.

frost. Ice crystal deposits formed by sublimation when the temperature and dew point are below freezing.

fuel-flow transmitter. A device in the fuel line between the engine-driven fuel pump and the carburetor that measures the rate of flow of the fuel. It converts this flow rate into an electrical signal and sends it to an indicator in the instrument panel.

fuel jettison system. A system installed in most large aircraft that allows the flight crew to jettison, or dump, fuel to lower the gross weight of the aircraft to its allowable landing weight.

Boost pumps in the fuel tanks move the fuel from the tank into a fuel manifold. From the fuel manifold it flows away from the aircraft through dump chutes in each wing tip.

The fuel jettison system must be so designed and constructed that it is free from fire hazards.

fuel totalizer. A fuel quantity indicator that gives the total amount of fuel remaining on board the aircraft on one instrument. The totalizer adds the quantities of fuel in all of the tanks.

full-bodied. Not thinned.

fully articulated rotor. A helicopter rotor whose blades are attached to the hub in such a way that they are free to flap, drag, and feather. See each of these terms.

fungus (*plural* **fungi**). Any of several types of plant life that include yeasts, molds, and mildew.

fusible plugs. Plugs in the wheels of high-performance airplanes that use tubeless tires. The centers of the plugs are filled with a metal that melts at a relatively low temperature.

If a takeoff is aborted and the pilot uses the brakes excessively, the heat transferred into the wheel will melt the center of the fusible plugs and allow the air to escape from the tire before it builds up enough pressure to cause an explosion.

gage pressure. Pressure referenced from the existing atmospheric pressure.

gage (rivet). The distance between rows of rivets in a multirow seam. Gage is also called transverse pitch.

galling. Fretting or pulling out chunks of a surface by sliding contact with another surface or body.

gasket. A seal between two parts where there is no relative motion.

gear-type pump. A constant-displacement fluid pump that contains two meshing large-tooth spur gears. Fluid is drawn into the pump as the teeth separate and is carried around the inside of the housing with the teeth and is forced from the pump when the teeth come together.

General Aviation Airworthiness Alerts. Documents published by the FAA that provide an economical interchange of service experience and cooperation in the improvement of aeronautical product durability, reliability, and safety. Alerts include items that have been reported to be significant, but which have not been fully evaluated at the time the material went to press.

generator. A mechanical device that transforms mechanical energy into electrical energy by rotating a coil inside a magnetic field. As the conductors in the coil cut across the lines of magnetic flux, a voltage is generated that causes current to flow.

generator series field. A set of heavy field windings in a generator connected in series with the armature. The magnetic field produced by the series windings is used to change the characteristics of the generator.

generator shunt field. A set of field windings in a generator connected in parallel with the armature. Varying the amount of current flowing in the shunt field windings controls the voltage output of the generator.

gerotor pump. A form of constant-displacement gear pump. A gerotor pump uses an external-tooth spur gear that rides inside of and drives an internal-tooth rotor gear. There is one more tooth space inside the rotor than there are teeth on the drive gear.

As the gears rotate, the volume of the space between two of the teeth on the inlet side of the pump increases, while the volume of the space between the two teeth on the opposite side of the pump decreases.

GHz (gigahertz). 1,000,000,000 cycles per second

gimbal. A support that allows a gyroscope to remain in an upright condition when its base is tilted.

glass cockpit. An aircraft instrument system that uses a few cathode-ray-tube displays to replace a large number of mechanically actuated instruments.

glaze ice. Ice that forms when large drops of water strike a surface whose temperature is below freezing. Glaze ice is clear and heavy.

glide slope. The portion of an ILS (Instrument Landing System) that provides the vertical path along which an aircraft descends on an instrument landing.

goniometer. Electronic circuitry in an ADF system that uses the output of a fixed loop antenna to sense the angle between a fixed reference, usually the nose of the aircraft, and the direction from which the radio signal is being received.

gram. The basic unit of weight or mass in the metric system. One gram equals about 0.035 ounce.

graphite. A form of carbon. Structural graphite is used in composite structure because of its strength and stiffness.

greige (pronounced "gray"). The unshrunk condition of a polyester fabric as it is removed from the loom.

ground. The voltage reference point in an aircraft electrical system. Ground has zero electrical potential. Voltage values, both positive and negative, are measured from ground. In the United Kingdom, ground is spoken of as "earth."

ground effect. The increased aerodynamic lift produced when an airplane or helicopter is flown nearer than a half wing span or rotor span to the ground. This additional lift is caused by an effective increase in angle of attack without the accompanying increase in induced drag, which is caused by the deflection of the downwashed air.

ground-power unit (GPU). A service component used to supply electrical power to an aircraft when it is being operated on the ground.

guncotton. A highly explosive material made by treating cotton fibers with nitric and sulfuric acids. Guncotton is used in making the film base of nitrate dope.

gusset. A small plate attached to two or more members of a truss structure. A gusset strengthens the truss.

gyro (gyroscope). The sensing device in an autopilot system. A gyroscope is a rapidly spinning wheel with its weight concentrated around its rim. Gyroscopes have two basic characteristics that make them useful in aircraft instruments: rigidity in space and precession. *See* rigidity in space and precession.

gyroscopic precession. The characteristic of a gyroscope that causes it to react to an applied force as though the force were applied at a point 90° in the direction of rotation from the actual point of application.

The rotor of a helicopter acts in much the same way as a gyroscope and is affected by gyroscopic precession.

Halon 1211. A halogenated hydrocarbon fire-extinguishing agent used in many HRD fire-extinguishing systems for powerplant protection. The technical name for Halon 1211 is bromochlorodifluoromethane.

Halon 1301. A halogenated hydrocarbon fire-extinguishing agent that is one of the best for extinguishing cabin and powerplant fires. It is highly effective and is the least toxic of the extinguishing agents available. The technical name for Halon 1301 is bromotrifluoromethane.

hangar rash. Scrapes, bends, and dents in an aircraft structure caused by careless handling.

hardwood. Wood from a broadleaf tree that sheds its leaves each year.

heading indicator. A gyroscopic flight instrument that gives the pilot an indication of the heading of the aircraft.

heat exchanger. A device used to exchange heat from one medium to another. Radiators, condensers, and evaporators are all examples of heat exchangers. Heat always moves from the object or medium having the greatest level of heat energy to a medium or object having a lower level.

helix. A screw-like, or spiral, curve.

hertz. One cycle per second.

holding relay. An electrical relay that is closed by sending a pulse of current through the coil. It remains closed until the current flowing through its contacts is interrupted.

homebuilt aircraft. Aircraft that are built by individuals as a hobby rather than by factories as commercial products. Homebuilt, or amateur-built, aircraft are not required to meet the stringent requirements imposed on the manufacture of FAA-certificated aircraft.

horsepower. A unit of mechanical power that is equal to 33,000 foot-pounds of work done in 1 minute, or 550 foot-pounds of work done in 1 second.

hot dimpling. A process used to dimple, or indent, the hole into which a flush rivet is to be installed. Hot dimpling is done by clamping the metal between heating elements and forcing the dies through the holes in the softened metal. Hot dimpling prevents hard metal from cracking when it is dimpled.

hot-wire cutter. A cutter used to shape blocks of Styrofoam. The wire is stretched tight between the arms of a frame and heated by electrical current. The hot wire melts its way through the foam.

HRD. High-rate-discharge.

HSI. Horizontal Situation Indicator.

hydraulic actuator. The component in a hydraulic system that converts hydraulic pressure into mechanical force. The two main types of hydraulic actuators are linear actuators (cylinders and pistons) and rotary actuators (hydraulic motors).

hydraulic fuse. A type of flow control valve that allows a normal flow of fluid in the system but, if the flow rate is excessive, or if too much fluid flows for normal operation, the fuse will shut off all further flow.

hydraulic motor. A hydraulic actuator that converts fluid pressure into rotary motion.

Hydraulic motors have an advantage in aircraft installations over electric motors, because they can operate in a stalled condition without the danger of a fire.

hydraulic powerpack. A small, self-contained hydraulic system that consists of a reservoir, pump, selector valves, and relief valves. The powerpack is removable from the aircraft as a unit to facilitate maintenance and service.

hydraulics. The system of fluid power which transmits force through an incompressible fluid.

hydrocarbon. An organic compound that contains only carbon and hydrogen. The vast majority of our fossil fuels such as gasoline and turbine-engine fuel are hydrocarbons.

hydroplaning. A condition that exists when a high-speed airplane is landed on a water-covered runway. When the brakes are applied, the wheels lock up and the tires skid on the surface of the water in much the same way a water ski rides on the surface. Hydroplaning develops enough heat in a tire to ruin it.

hydrostatic test. A pressure test used to determine the serviceability of high-pressure oxygen cylinders. The cylinders are filled with water and pressurized to 5/3 of their working pressure.

Standard-weight cylinders (DOT 3AA) must be hydrostatically tested every five years, and lightweight cylinders (DOT 3HT) must be tested every three years.

hyperbolic navigation. Electronic navigation systems that determine aircraft location by the time difference between the reception of two signals.

Signals from two stations at different locations will be received in the aircraft at different times. A line plotted between the two stations along which the time difference is the same forms a hyperbola.

hypersonic speed. Speed of greater than Mach 5 (5 times the speed of sound).

hypoxia. A physiological condition in which a person is deprived of the needed oxygen. The effects of hypoxia normally disappear as soon as the person is able to breathe air containing sufficient oxygen.

ICAO. The International Civil Aviation Organization.

IFR. Instrument Flight Rules.

icebox rivet. A solid rivet made of 2017 or 2024 aluminum alloy. These rivets are too hard to drive in the condition they are received from the factory, and must be heat-treated to soften them. They are heated in a furnace and then quenched in cold water. Immediately after quenching they are soft, but within a few hours at room temperature they become quite hard. The hardening can be delayed for several days by storing them in a sub-freezing icebox and holding them at this low temperature until they are to be used.

inch-pound. A measure of work accomplished when a force of 1 pound moves an object a distance of 1 inch.

indicated airspeed (IAS). The airspeed as shown on an airspeed indicator with no corrections applied.

induced current. Electrical current produced in a conductor when it is moved through or crossed by a magnetic field.

induced drag. Aerodynamic drag produced by an airfoil when it is producing lift. Induced drag is affected by the same factors that affect induced lift.

induction time. The time allowed an epoxy or polyurethane material between its initial mixing and its application. This time allows the materials to begin their cure.

infrared radiation. Electromagnetic radiation whose wavelengths are longer than those of visible light.

ingot. A large block of metal that was molded as it was poured from the furnace. Ingots are further processed into sheets, bars, tubes, or structural beams.

INS. Inertial Navigation System.

Inspection Authorization (IA). An authorization that may be issued to an experienced aviation maintenance technician who holds both an Airframe and Powerplant rating. It allows the holder to conduct annual inspections and to approve an aircraft or aircraft engine for return to service after a major repair or major alteration.

integral fuel tank. A fuel tank which is formed by sealing off part of the aircraft structure and using it as a fuel tank. An integral wing tank is called a "wet wing." Integral tanks are used because of their large weight saving.

The only way of repairing an integral fuel tank is by replacing damaged sealant and making riveted repairs, as is done with any other part of the aircraft structure.

interference drag. Parasite drag caused by air flowing over one portion of the airframe interfering with the smooth flow of air over another portion.

intermittent-duty solenoid. A solenoid-type switch whose coil is designed for current to flow through it for only a short period of time. The coil will overheat if current flows through it too long.

IRS. Inertial Reference System.

IRU. Inertial Reference Unit.

iso-octane. A hydrocarbon, C_8H_{18}, which has a very high critical pressure and temperature. Iso-octane is used as the high reference for measuring the anti-detonation characteristics of a fuel.

isobaric mode. The mode of pressurization in which the cabin pressure is maintained at a constant value regardless of the outside air pressure.

isogonic line. A line drawn on an aeronautical chart along which the angular difference between the magnetic and geographic north poles is the same.

isopropyl alcohol. A colorless liquid used in the manufacture of acetone and its derivatives and as a solvent and anti-icing agent.

jackscrew. A hardened steel rod with strong threads cut into it. A jackscrew is rotated by hand or with a motor to apply a force or to lift an object.

jet pump. A special venturi in a line carrying air from certain areas in an aircraft that need an augmented flow of air through them.

High-velocity compressor bleed air is blown into the throat of a venturi where it produces a low pressure that pulls air from the area to which it is connected.

Jet pumps are often used in the lines that pull air through galleys and toilet areas.

joggle. A small offset near the edge of a piece of sheet metal. It allows one sheet of metal to overlap another sheet while maintaining a flush surface.

jointer. A woodworking power tool used to smooth the edges of a piece of wood.

K-factor. A factor used in sheet metal work to determine the setback for other than a 90° bend.

Setback = K · (bend radius + metal thickness).

For bends of less than 90° the value of K is less than 1; for bends greater than 90° the value of K is greater than 1.

Kevlar. A patented synthetic aramid fiber noted for its flexibility and light weight. It is to a great extent replacing fiberglass as a reinforcing fabric for composite construction.

key (*verb*). To initiate an action by depressing a key or a button.

kHz (kilohertz). 1,000 cycles per second.

kick-in pressure. The pressure at which an unloading valve causes a hydraulic pump to direct its fluid into the system manifold.

kick-out pressure. The pressure at which an unloading valve shuts off the flow of fluid into the system pressure manifold and directs it back to the reservoir under a much reduced pressure.

kilogram. One thousand grams.

kinetic energy. Energy that exists because of motion.

knot (wood defect). A hard, usually round section of a tree branch embedded in a board. The grain of the knot is perpendicular to the grain of the board.

Knots decrease the strength of the board and should be avoided where strength is needed.

knot (measure of speed). A speed measurement that is equal to one nautical mile per hour. One knot is equal to 1.15 statute mile per hour.

Kollsman window. The barometric scale window of a sensitive altimeter. *See* barometric scale.

Koroseal lacing. A plastic lacing material available in round or rectangular cross sections and used for holding wire bundles and tubing together. It holds tension on knots indefinitely and is impervious to petroleum products.

kraft paper. A tough brown wrapping paper like that used for paper bags.

labyrinth seal. A type of seal in a Roots blower cabin supercharger that is made in the form of knife edges riding in step-shaped grooves. Air pressure is dropped in each section of the seal, and any oil in the air is trapped in the grooves.

lacquer. A finishing material made of a film base, solvents, plasticizers, and thinners. The film base forms a tough film over the surface when it dries. The solvents dissolve the film base so it can be applied as a liquid. The plasticizers give the film base the needed resilience, and the thinners dilute the lacquer so it can be applied with a spray gun. Lacquer is sprayed on the surface as a liquid, and when the solvents and thinners evaporate, the film base remains as a tough decorative and protective coating.

laminar flow. Airflow in which the air passes over the surface in smooth layers with a minimum of turbulence.

laminated wood. A type of wood made by gluing several pieces of thin wood together. The grain of all pieces runs in the same direction.

landing gear warning system. A system of lights used to indicate the condition of the landing gear. A red light illuminates when any of the gears are in an unsafe condition, a green light shows when all of the gears are down and locked, and no light is lit when the gears are all up and locked.

An aural warning system is installed that sounds a horn if any of the landing gears are not down and locked when the throttles are retarded for landing.

latent heat. Heat that is added to a material that causes a change in its state without changing its temperature.

lateral axis. An imaginary line, passing through the center of gravity of an airplane, and extending across it from wing tip to wing tip.

lay-up. The placement of the various layers of resin-impregnated fabric in the mold for a piece of laminated composite material.

L/D ratio. A measure of efficiency of an airfoil. It is the ratio of the lift to the total drag at a specified angle of attack.

left-right indicator. The course-deviation indicator used with a VOR navigation system.

lightening hole. A hole cut in a piece of structural material to get rid of weight without losing any strength. A hole several inches in diameter may be cut in a piece of metal at a point where the metal is not needed for strength, and the edges of the hole are flanged to give it rigidity. A piece of metal with properly flanged lightening holes is more rigid than the metal before the holes were cut.

linear actuator. A fluid power actuator that uses a piston moving inside a cylinder to change pressure into linear, or straight-line, motion.

linear change. A change in which the output is directly proportional to the input.

loadmeter. A current meter used in some aircraft electrical systems to show the amount of current the generator or alternator is producing. Loadmeters are calibrated in percent of the generator rated output.

localizer. The portion of an ILS (Instrument Landing System) that directs the pilot along the center line of the instrument runway.

lodestone. A magnetized piece of natural iron oxide.

logic flow chart. A type of graphic chart that can be made up for a specific process or procedure to help follow the process through all of its logical steps.

longitudinal axis. An imaginary line, passing through the center of gravity of an airplane, and extending lengthwise through it from nose to tail.

longitudinal stability. Stability of an aircraft along its longitudinal axis and about its lateral axis. Longitudinal stability is also called pitch stability.

Loran A. LOng Range Aid to Navigation. A hyperbolic navigation system that operates with frequencies of 1,950 kHz, 1,850 kHz, and 1,900 kHz.

Loran C. The Loran system used in aircraft. It operates on a frequency of 100 kHz.

LRU. Line Replaceable Unit.

lubber line. A reference on a magnetic compass and directional gyro that represents the nose of the aircraft. The heading of the aircraft is shown on the compass card opposite the lubber line.

Mach number. A measurement of speed based on the ratio of the speed of the aircraft to the speed of sound under the same atmospheric conditions. An airplane flying at Mach 1 is flying at the speed of sound.

Magnesyn system. The registered trade name of a synchro system used for remote indicating instruments. The rotors in a Magnesyn system are permanent magnets, and the stators are tapped toroidal coils, excited with 26-volt, 400-hertz AC. The rotor in the indicator accurately follows the movement of the rotor in the transmitter.

major alteration. An alteration not listed in the aircraft, aircraft engine, or propeller specifications. It is one that might appreciably affect weight, balance, structural strength performance, powerplant operation, flight characteristics, or other qualities affecting airworthiness, or that cannot be made with elementary operations.

major repair. A repair to an aircraft structure or component that if improperly made might appreciably affect weight, balance, structural strength, performance, powerplant operation, flight characteristics, or other qualities affecting airworthiness, or that is not done according to accepted practices, or cannot be made with elementary operations.

manifold cross-feed fuel system. A type of fuel system commonly used in large transport category aircraft. All fuel tanks feed into a common manifold, and the dump chutes and the single-point fueling valves are connected to the manifold. Fuel lines to each engine are taken from the manifold.

manifold pressure. The absolute pressure of the air in the induction system of a reciprocating engine.

manifold pressure gage. A pressure gage that measures the absolute pressure inside the induction system of a reciprocating engine. When the engine is not operating, this instrument shows the existing atmospheric pressure.

master switch. A switch in an aircraft electrical system that can disconnect the battery from the bus and open the generator or alternator field circuit.

matrix. The material used in composite construction to bond the fibers together and to transmit the forces into the fibers. Resins are the most widely used matrix materials.

mean camber. A line that is drawn midway between the upper and lower camber of an airfoil section. The mean camber determines the aerodynamic characteristics of the airfoil.

MEK. Methyl-ethyl-ketone, an organic chemical solvent that is soluble in water and is used as a solvent for vinyl and nitrocellulose films. MEK is an efficient cleaner for preparing surfaces for priming or painting.

mercerize. A treatment given to cotton thread to make it strong and lustrous. The thread is stretched while it is soaked in a solution of caustic soda.

MFD. Multi-Function Display.

MHz (megahertz). 1,000,000 cycles per second.

microballoons. Tiny, hollow spheres of glass or phenolic material used to add body to a resin.

microbial contaminants. The scum that forms inside the fuel tanks of turbine-engine-powered aircraft that is caused by micro-organisms.

These micro-organisms live in water that condenses from the fuel, and they feed on the fuel. The scum they form clogs fuel filters, lines, and fuel controls and holds water in contact with the aluminum alloy structure. This causes corrosion.

Micro-Mesh. A patented graduated series of cloth-backed cushioned sheets that contain abrasive crystals. Micro-Mesh is used for polishing and restoring transparency to acrylic plastic windows and windshields.

micron ("micro meter"). A unit of linear measurement equal to one millionth of a meter, or one thousandth of a millimeter, or 0.000 039 inch. A micron is also called a micrometer.

Micronic filter. The registered trade name of a type of fluid filter whose filtering element is a specially treated cellulose paper formed into vertical convolutions, or wrinkles. Micronic filters prevent the passage of solids larger than about 10 microns.

    Micronic filters are normally replaced with new filters rather being cleaned.

micro-organism. An organism, normally bacteria or fungus, of microscopic size.

Microswitch. The registered trade name for a precision switch that uses a short throw of the control plunger to actuate the contacts. Microswitches are used primarily as limit switches to control electrical units automatically.

MIG welding. Metal inert gas welding is a form of electric arc welding in which the electrode is an expenable wire. MIG welding is now called GMA (Gas Metal Arc) welding.

mil. One thousandth of an inch (0.001 inch). Paint film thickness is usually measured in mils.

mildew. A gray or white fungus growth that forms on organic materials. Mildew forms on cotton and linen aircraft fabric and destroys its strength.

millivoltmeter. An electrical instrument that measures voltage in units of millivolts (thousandths of a volt).

mist coat. A very light coat of zinc chromate primer. It is so thin that the metal is still visible, but the primer makes pencil marks easy to see.

moisture separator. A component in a high-pressure pneumatic system that removes most of the water vapor from the compressed air.

    When the compressed air is used, its pressure drops, and this pressure drop causes a drop in temperature. If any moisture were allowed to remain in the air, it would freeze and block the system.

mold line. A line used in the development of a flat pattern for a formed piece of sheet metal. The mold line is an extension of the flat side of a part beyond the radius. The mold line dimension of a part is the dimension made to the intersection of mold lines and is the dimension the part would have if its corners had no radius.

mold point. The intersection of two mold lines of a part. Mold line dimensions are made between mold points.

moment. A force that causes or tries to cause an object to rotate. The value of a moment is the product of the weight of an object (or the force), multiplied by the distance between the center of gravity of the object (or the point of application of the force) and the fulcrum about which the object rotates.

Monel. An alloy of nickel, copper, and aluminum or silicon.

monocoque. A single-shell type of aircraft structure in which all of the flight loads are carried in the outside skin of the structure.

MSDS. Material Safety Data Sheets. MSDS are required by the Federal Government to be available in workplaces to inform workers of the dangers that may exist from contact with certain materials.

MSL. Mean sea level. When the letters MSL are used with an altitude, it means that the altitude is measured from mean, or average, sea level.

MTBF. Mean Time Between Failures.

multiple-disk brakes. Aircraft brakes in which one set of disks is keyed to the axle and remains stationary. Between each stationary disk there is a rotating disk that is keyed to the inside of the wheel. When the brakes are applied, the stationary disks are forced together, clamping the rotating disks between them. The friction between the disks slows the aircraft.

multimeter. An electrical test instrument that consists of a single current-measuring meter and all of the needed components to allow the meter to be used to measure voltage, resistance, and current. Multimeters are available with either analog- or digital-type displays.

nailing strip. A method of applying pressure to the glue in a scarf joint repair in a plywood skin. A strip of thin plywood is nailed over the glued scarf joint with the nails extending into a supporting structure beneath the skin. The strip is installed over vinyl sheeting to prevent it sticking to the skin. When the glue is thoroughly dry, the nailing strip is broken away and the nails removed.

nap of the fabric. The ends of the fibers in a fabric. The first coat of dope on cotton or linen fabric raises the nap, and the fiber ends stick up. These ends must be carefully removed by sanding to get a smooth finish.

naphtha. A volatile and flammable hydrocarbon liquid used chiefly as a solvent or as a cleaning fluid.

NDB. Nondirectional Beacons.

negative pressure relief valve (pressurization component). A valve that opens anytime the outside air pressure is greater than the cabin pressure. It prevents the cabin altitude ever becoming greater than the aircraft flight altitude.

neutral axis (neutral plane). A line through a piece of material that is bent. The material in the outside of the bend is stretched and that on the inside of the bend is shrunk. The material along the neutral plane is neither shrunk nor stretched.

neutral flame. An oxyacetylene flame produced when the ratio of oxygen and acetylene is chemically correct and there is no excess of oxygen or carbon. A neutral flame has a rounded inner cone and no feather around it.

noise (electrical). An unwanted electrical signal within a piece of electronic equipment.

Nomex. A patented nylon material used to make the honeycomb core for certain types of sandwich materials.

nonenergizing brake. A brake that does not use the momentum of the aircraft to increase the friction.

nonvolatile memory. Memory in a computer that is not lost when power to the computer is lost.

normal heptane. A hydrocarbon, C_7H_{16}, with a very low critical pressure and temperature. Normal heptane is used as the low reference in measuring the anti-detonation characteristics of a fuel.

normal shock wave. A shock wave that forms ahead of a blunt object moving through the air at the speed of sound. The shock wave is normal (perpendicular) to the air approaching the object.

Air passing through a normal shock wave is slowed to a subsonic speed and its static pressure is increased.

normalizing. A process of strain-relieving steel that has been welded and left in a strained condition. The steel is heated to a specified temperature, usually red hot, and allowed to cool in still air to room temperature.

nose-gear centering cam. A cam in the nose-gear shock strut that causes the piston to center when the strut fully extends.

When the aircraft takes off and the strut extends, the wheel is straightened in its fore-and-aft position so it can be retracted into the wheel well.

NPN transistor. A bipolar transistor made of a thin base of P-type silicon or germanium sandwiched between a collector and an emitter, both of which are made of N-type material.

null position. The position of an ADF loop antenna when the signal being received is canceled in the two sides of the loop and the signal strength is the weakest.

oblique shock wave. A shock wave that forms on a sharp-pointed object moving through the air at a speed greater than the speed of sound. Air passing through an oblique shock wave is slowed down, but not to a subsonic speed, and its static pressure is increased.

octane rating. A rating of the antidetonation characteristics of a reciprocating engine fuel. It is based on the performance of the fuel in a special test engine. When a fuel is given a dual rating such as 80/87, the first number is its antidetonating rating with a lean fuel-air mixture, and the higher number is its rating with a rich mixture.

oleo shock absorber. A shock absorber used on aircraft landing gear. The initial landing impact is absorbed by oil transferring from one compartment in the shock strut into another compartment through a metering orifice. The shocks of taxiing are taken up by a cushion of compressed air.

open angle. An angle in which sheet metal is bent less than 90°.

open assembly time. The period of time between the application of the glue and the assembly of the joint components.

open-center hydraulic system. A fluid power system in which the selector valves are arranged in series with each other. Fluid flows from the pump through the center of the selector valves, back into the reservoir when no unit is being actuated.

open-center selector valve. A type of selector valve that functions as an unloading valve as well as a selector valve.

Open-center selector valves are installed in series, and when no unit is actuated, fluid from the pump flows through the centers of all the valves and returns to the reservoir.

When a unit is selected for actuation, the center of the selector valve is shut off and the fluid from the pump goes through the selector valve into one side of the actuator. Fluid from the other side of the actuator returns to the valve and goes back to the reservoir through the other selector valves. When the actuation is completed, the selector valve is placed in its neutral position. Its center opens, and fluid from the pump flows straight through the valve.

open wiring. An electrical wiring installation in which the wires are tied together in bundles and clamped to the aircraft structure rather than being enclosed in conduit.

orifice check valve. A component in a hydraulic or pneumatic system that allows unrestricted flow in one direction, and restricted flow in the opposite direction.

O-ring. A widely used type of seal made in the form of a rubber ring with a round cross section. An O-ring seals in both directions, and it can be used as a packing or a gasket.

ornithopter. A heavier-than-air flying machine that produces lift by flapping its wings. No practical ornithopter has been built.

oscilloscope. An electrical instrument that displays on the face of a cathode-ray tube the waveform of the electrical signal it is measuring.

outflow valve (pressurization component). A valve in the cabin of a pressurized aircraft that controls the cabin pressure by opening to relieve all pressure above that for which the cabin pressure control is set.

overvoltage protector. A component in an aircraft electrical system that opens the alternator field circuit any time the alternator output voltage is too high.

oxidizing flame. An oxyacetylene flame in which there is an excess of oxygen. The inner cone is pointed and often a hissing sound is heard.

ozone. An unstable form of oxygen produced when an electric spark passes through the air. Ozone is harmful to rubber products.

packing. A seal between two parts where there is relative motion.

paint. A covering applied to an object or structure to protect it and improve its appearance. Paint consists of a pigment suspended in a vehicle such as oil or water. When the vehicle dries by evaporation or curing, the pigment is left as a film on the surface.

parabolic reflector. A reflector whose surface is made in the form of a parabola.

parallel circuit. A method of connecting electrical components so that each component is in a path between the terminals of the source of electrical energy.

paralleling circuit. A circuit in a multi-engine aircraft electrical system that causes the generators or alternators to share the electrical load equally.

paralleling relay. A relay in a multi-engine aircraft electrical system that controls a flow of control current which is used to keep the generators or alternators sharing the electrical load equally.

The relay opens automatically to shut off the flow of paralleling current any time the output of either alternator or generator drops to zero.

parasite drag. A form of aerodynamic drag caused by friction between the air and the surface over which it is flowing.

parent metal. The metal being welded. This term is used to distinguish between the metal being welded and the welding rod.

partial pressure. The percentage of the total pressure of a mixture of gases produced by each of the individual gases in the mixture.

parting film. A layer of thin plastic material placed between a composite lay-up and the heating blanket. It prevents the blanket from sticking to the fabric.

Pascal's law. A basic law of fluid power which states that the pressure in an enclosed container is transmitted equally and undiminished to all points of the container, and the force acts at right angles to the enclosing walls.

performance number. The anti-detonation rating of a fuel that has a higher critical pressure and temperature than iso-octane (a rating of 100). Iso-octane that has been treated with varying amounts of tetraethyl lead is used as the reference fuel.

petrolatum-zinc dust compound. A special abrasive compound used inside an aluminum wire terminal being swaged onto a piece of aluminum electrical wire. When the terminal is compressed, the zinc dust abrades the oxides from the wire, and the petrolatum prevents oxygen reaching the wire so no more oxides can form.

petroleum fractions. The various components of a hydrocarbon fuel that are separated by boiling them off at different temperatures in the process of fractional distillation.

phased array antenna. A complex antenna which consists of a number of elements. A beam of energy is formed by the superimposition of the signals radiating from the elements. The direction of the beam can be changed by varying the relative phase of the signals applied to each of the elements.

phenolic plastic. A plastic material made of a thermosetting phenol-formaldehyde resin, reinforced with cloth or paper. Phenolic plastic materials are used for electrical insulators and for chemical-resistant table tops.

pilot hole. A small hole punched or drilled in a piece of sheet metal to locate a rivet hole.

pin knot cluster. A group of knots, all having a diameter of less than approximately $\frac{1}{16}$ inch.

pinion. A small gear that meshes with a larger gear, a sector of a gear, or a toothed rack.

pinked-edge tape. Cloth tape whose edges have small V-shaped notches cut along their length. The pinked edges prevent the tape from raveling.

pinking shears. Shears used to cut aircraft fabric with a series of small notches along the cut edge.

piston. A sliding plug in an actuating cylinder used to convert pressure into force and then into work.

pitch (aircraft maneuver). Rotation of an aircraft about its lateral axis.

pitch (rivet). The distance between the centers of adjacent rivets installed in the same row.

pitch pocket (wood defect). Pockets of pitch that appear in the growth rings of a piece of wood.

pitot pressure. Ram air pressure used to measure airspeed. The pitot tube faces directly into the air flowing around the aircraft. It stops the air and measures its pressure.

plain-weave fabric. Fabric in which each warp thread passes over one fill thread and under the next. Plain-weave fabric typically has the same strength in both warp and fill directions.

planer. A woodworking power tool used to smooth the surfaces of a piece of wood.

plasticizer. A constituent in dope or lacquer that gives its film flexibility and resilience.

plastic media blasting (PMB). A method of removing paint from an aircraft surface by dry-blasting it with tiny plastic beads.

plastics. The generic name for any of the organic materials produced by polymerization. Plastics can be shaped by molding or drawing.

plenum. An enclosed chamber in which air can be held at a pressure higher than that of the surrounding air.

ply rating. The rating of an aircraft tire that indicates its relative strength. The ply rating does not indicate the actual number of plies of fabric in the tire; rather it indicates the number of plies of cotton fabric needed to produce the same strength as the actual plies.

plywood. A wood product made by gluing several pieces of thin wood veneer together. The grain of the wood in each layer runs at 90° or 45° to the grain of the layer next to it.

pneumatics. The system of fluid power which transmits force by the use of a compressible fluid.

PNP transistor. A bipolar transistor made of a thin base of N-type silicon or germanium sandwiched between a collector and an emitter, both of which are made of P-type material.

polyester fibers. A synthetic fiber made by the polymerization process in which tiny molecules are united to form a long chain of molecules.

Polyester fibers are woven into fabrics that are known by their trade names of Dacron, Fortrel, and Kodel. Polyester film and sheet are known as Mylar and Celenar.

polyester resin. A thermosetting resin used as a matrix for much of the fiberglass used in composite construction.

polyurethane enamel. A hard, chemically resistant finish used on aircraft. Polyurethane enamel is resistant to damage from all types of hydraulic fluid.

polyvinyl chloride. A thermoplastic resin used in the manufacture of transparent tubing for electrical insulation and fluid lines which are subject to low pressures.

position error. The error in pitot-static instruments caused by the static ports not sensing true static air pressure. Position error changes with airspeed and is usually greatest at low airspeeds.

potential energy. Energy possessed in an object because of its position, chemical composition, shape, or configuration.

potentiometer. A variable resistor having connections to both ends of the resistance element and to the wiper that moves across the resistance.

pot life. The length of time a resin will remain workable after the catalyst has been added. If a catalyzed material is not used within its usable pot life, it must be discarded and a new batch mixed.

power. The time rate of doing work. Power is force multiplied by distance (work), divided by time.

power brakes. Aircraft brakes that use the main hydraulic system to supply fluid for the brake actuation.

Aircraft that require a large amount of fluid for their brake actuation normally use power brakes, and the volume of fluid sent to the brakes is increased by the use of deboosters.

power control valve. A hand-operated hydraulic pump unloading valve.

When the valve is open, fluid flows from the pump to the reservoir with little opposition. To actuate a unit, turn the selector valve, and manually close the power control valve. Pressurized fluid flows to the unit, and when it is completely actuated, the power control valve automatically opens.

PPI (Plan Position Indicator). A type of radar scope that shows both the direction and distance of the target from the radar antenna. Some radar antenna rotate and their PPI scopes are circular. Other antenna oscillate and their PPI scopes are fan shaped.

precession. The characteristic of a gyroscope that causes a force to be felt, not at the point of application, but at a point 90° in the direction of rotation from that point.

precipitation heat treatment. A method of increasing the strength of heat-treated aluminum alloy. After the aluminum alloy has been solution-heat-treated by heating and quenching, it is returned to the oven and heated to a temperature lower than that used for the initial heat treatment. It is held at this temperature for a specified period of time and then removed from the oven and allowed to cool slowly.

preflight inspection. A required inspection to determine the condition of the aircraft for the flight to be conducted. It is conducted by the pilot-in-command.

prepreg. Preimpregnated fabric. A type of composite material in which the reinforcing fibers are encapsulated in an uncured resin. Prepreg materials must be kept refrigerated to prevent them from curing before they are used.

press-to-test light fixture. An indicator light fixture whose lens can be pressed in to complete a circuit that tests the filament of the light bulb.

pressure. Force per unit area. Hydraulic and pneumatic pressure are normally given in units of pounds per square inch (psi).

pressure altitude. The altitude in standard air at which the pressure is the same as that of the existing air. Pressure altitude is read on an altimeter when the barometric scale is set to the standard sea level pressure of 29.92 inches of mercury.

pressure-demand oxygen system. A type of oxygen system used by aircraft that fly at very high altitude. This system functions as a diluter-demand system (*See* diluter-demand oxygen system) until, at about 40,000 feet, the output to the mask is pressurized enough to force the needed oxygen into the lungs, rather than depending on the low pressure produced when the wearer of the mask inhales to pull in the oxygen.

pressure fueling. The method of fueling used by almost all transport aircraft. The fuel is put into the aircraft through a single underwing fueling port. The fuel tanks are filled to the desired quantity and in the sequence selected by the person conducting the fueling operation.

Pressure fueling saves servicing time by using a single point to fuel the entire aircraft, and it reduces the chances for fuel contamination.

pressure manifold (hydraulic system component). The portion of a fluid power system from which the selector valves receive their pressurized fluid.

pressure plate (brake component). A strong, heavy plate used in a multiple-disk brake. The pressure plate receives the force from the brake cylinders and transmits this force to the disks.

pressure reducing valve (oxygen system component). A valve used in an oxygen system to change high cylinder pressure to low system pressure.

pressure relief valve (oxygen system component). A valve in an oxygen system that relieves the pressure if the pressure reducing valve should fail.

pressure vessel. The strengthened portion of an aircraft structure that is sealed and pressurized in flight.

primer (finishing system component). A component in a finishing system that provides a good bond between the surface and the material used for the topcoats.

profile drag. Aerodynamic drag produced by skin friction. Profile drag is a form of parasite drag.

progressive inspection. An inspection that may be used in place of an annual or 100-hour inspection. It has the same scope as an annual inspection, but it may be performed in increments so the aircraft will not have to be out of service for a lengthy period of time.

pump control valve. A control valve in a hydraulic system that allows the pilot to manually direct the output of the hydraulic pump back to the reservoir when no unit is being actuated.

Pureclad. A registered trade name for clad aluminum alloy.

purge (air conditioning system operation). To remove all of the moisture and air from a cooling system by flushing the system with a dry gaseous refrigerant.

pusher powerplant. A powerplant whose propeller is mounted at the rear of the airplane and pushes, rather than pulls, the airplane through the air.

PVC. Polyvinylchloride. A thermoplastic resin used to make transparent tubing for insulating electrical wires.

quartersawed wood. Wood sawed from a tree in such a way that the annual rings cross the plank at an angle greater than 45°.

quick-disconnect connector. A type of wire connector used in aircraft electrical systems. The wires terminate inside an insulated plug with pins or sockets that mate with the opposite type of terminals in a similar plug. The two halves of the connector push together and are held tight with a special nut.

quick-disconnect fitting. A hydraulic line fitting that seals the line when the fitting is disconnected. Quick-disconnect fittings are used on the lines connected to the engine-driven hydraulic pump. They allow the pump to be disconnected and an auxiliary hydraulic power system connected to perform checks requiring hydraulic power while the aircraft is in the hangar.

rack-and-pinion actuator. A form of rotary actuator where the fluid acts on a piston on which a rack of gear teeth is cut. As the piston moves, it rotates a pinion gear which is mated with the teeth cut in the rack.

radial. A directional line radiating outward from a radio facility, usually a VOR.

When an aircraft is flying outbound on the 330° radial, it is flying away from the station on a line that has a magnetic direction of 330° from the station.

radius dimpling. A process of preparing a hole in sheet metal for flush riveting. A cone-shaped male die forces the edges of the rivet hole into the depression in a female die. Radius dimpling forms a round-edged depression into which the rivet head fits.

range markings. Colored marks on an instrument dial that identify certain ranges of operation as specified in the aircraft maintenance or flight manual and listed in the appropriate aircraft Type Certificate Data Sheets or Aircraft Specifications. Color coding directs attention to approaching operating difficulties.

Airspeed indicators and most pressure and temperature indicators are marked to show the various ranges of operation.

These ranges and colors are the most generally used:
Red radial line, do not exceed.
Green arc, normal operating range.
Yellow arc, caution range.
Blue radial line, used on airspeed indicators to show best single-engine rate of climb speed.
White arc, used on airspeed indicators to show flap operating range.

RDF. Radio Direction Finding.

rebreather oxygen mask. A type of oxygen mask used with a continuous-flow oxygen system. Oxygen continuously flows into the bottom of the loose-fitting rebreather bag on the mask. The wearer of the mask exhales into the top of the bag. The first air exhaled contains some oxygen, and this air goes into the bag first. The last air to leave the lungs contains little oxygen, and it is forced out of the bag as the bag is filled with fresh oxygen. Each time the wearer of the mask inhales, the air first exhaled, along with fresh oxygen, is taken into the lungs.

receiver-dryer. The component in a vapor-cycle cooling system that serves as a reservoir for the liquid refrigerant. The receiver-dryer contains a desiccant that absorbs any moisture that may be in the system.

rectangle. A plane surface with four sides whose opposite sides are parallel and whose angles are all right angles.

rectification (arc welding condition). A condition in AC-electric arc welding in which oxides on the surface of the metal act as a rectifier and prevent electrons flowing from the metal to the electrode during the half cycle when the electrode is positive.

reducing flame. *See* carburizing flame.

reed valve. A thin, leaf-type valve mounted in the valve plate of an air conditioning compressor to control the flow of refrigerant gases into and out of the compressor cylinders.

reinforcing tape. A narrow strip of woven fabric material placed over the fabric as it is being attached to the aircraft structure with rib lacing cord. This tape carries a large amount of the load and prevents the fabric tearing at the stitches.

rejuvenator. A finishing material used to restore resilience to an old dope film. Rejuvenator contains strong solvents to open the dried-out film and plasticizers to restore resilience to the old dope.

relative wind. The direction the wind strikes an airfoil.

relay. An electrical component which uses a small amount of current flowing through a coil to produce a magnetic pull to close a set of contacts through which a large amount of current can flow. The core in a relay coil is fixed.

relief hole. A hole drilled at the point at which two bend lines meet in a piece of sheet metal. This hole spreads the stresses caused by the bends and prevents the metal cracking.

relief valve. A pressure-control valve that relieves any pressure over the amount for which it is set. They are damage-preventing units used in both hydraulic and pneumatic systems.

In an aircraft hydraulic system, pressure relief valves prevent damaging high pressures that could be caused by a malfunctioning pressure regulator, or by thermal expansion of fluid trapped in portions of the system.

repair. A maintenance procedure in which a damaged component is restored to its original condition, or at least to a condition that allows it to fulfill its design function.

restrictor. A fluid power system component that controls the rate of actuator movement by restricting the flow of fluid into or out of the actuator.

retard breaker points. A set of breaker points in certain aircraft magnetos that are used to provide a late (retarded) spark for starting the engine.

retarder (finishing system component). Dope thinner that contains certain additives that slow its rate of evaporation enough to prevent the dope blushing.

retread. The replacement of the tread rubber on an aircraft tire.

retreating blade. The blade on a helicopter rotor whose tip is moving in the direction opposite to that in which the helicopter is moving.

retreating blade stall. The stall of a helicopter rotor disc that occurs near the tip of the retreating blade. A retreating blade stall occurs when the flight airspeed is high and the retreating blade airspeed is low. This results in a high angle of attack, causing the stall.

return manifold. The portion of a fluid power system through which the fluid is returned to the reservoir.

reverse bias. A voltage placed across the PN junction in a semiconductor device with the positive voltage connected to the N-type material and the negative voltage to the P-type material.

reverse polarity welding. DC-electric arc welding in which the electrode is positive with respect to the work.

rib tread. A series of circumferential grooves cut into the tread of a tire. This tread pattern provides superior traction and directional stability on hard-surfaced runways.

ribbon direction. The direction in a piece of honeycomb material that is parallel to the length of the strips of material that make up the core.

rigid conduit. Aluminum alloy tubing used to house electrical wires in areas where they are subject to mechanical damage.

rigidity in space. The characteristic of a gyroscope that prevents its axis of rotation tilting as the earth rotates. This characteristic is used for attitude gyro instruments.

rime ice. A rough ice that forms on aircraft flying through visible moisture, such as a cloud, when the temperature is below freezing. Rime ice disturbs the smooth airflow as well as adding weight.

rivet cutters. Special cutting pliers that resemble diagonal cutters except that the jaws are ground in such a way that they cut the rivet shank, or stem, off square.

rivet set. A tool used to drive aircraft solid rivets. It is a piece of hardened steel with a recess the shape of the rivet head in one end. The other end fits into the rivet gun.

RMI. Radio Magnetic Indicator.

rocking shaft. A shaft used in the mechanism of a pressure-measuring instrument to change the direction of movement by 90° and to amplify the amount of movement.

roll (aircraft maneuver). Rotation of an aircraft about its longitudinal axis.

Roots-type air compressor. A positive-displacement air pump that uses two intermeshing figure-8-shaped rotors to move the air.

rosette weld. A method of securing one metal tube inside another by welding. Small holes are drilled in the outer tube and the inner tube is welded to it around the circumference of the holes.

rotary actuator. A fluid power actuator whose output is rotational. A hydraulic motor is a rotary actuator.

roving. A lightly twisted roll or strand of fibers.

RPM. Revolutions per minute.

ruddervators. The two movable surfaces on a V-tail empennage. When these two surfaces are moved together with the in-and-out movement of the control yoke, they act as elevators, and when they are moved differentially with the rudder pedals, they act as the rudder.

saddle gusset. A piece of plywood glued to an aircraft structural member. The saddle gusset has a cutout to hold a backing block or strip tightly against the skin to allow a nailing strip to be used to apply pressure to a glued joint in the skin.

sailplane. A high-performance glider.

sandwich material. A type of composite structural material in which a core material is bonded between face sheets of metal or resin-impregnated fabric.

satin-weave fabric. Fabric in which the warp threads pass under one fill thread and over several others. Satin-weave fabrics are used when the lay-up must be made over complex shapes.

scarf joint. A joint in a wood structure in which the ends to be joined are cut in a long taper, normally about 12:1, and fastened together by gluing. A glued scarf joint makes a strong splice because the joint is made along the side of the wood fibers rather than along their ends.

schematic diagram. A diagram of an electrical system in which the system components are represented by symbols rather than drawings or pictures of the actual devices.

Schrader valve. A type of service valve used in an air conditioning system. This is a spring-loaded valve much like the valve used to put air into a tire.

scissors. A name commonly used for torque links. *See* torque links.

scupper. A recess around the filler neck of an aircraft fuel tank. Any fuel spilled when the tank is being serviced collects in the scupper and drains to the ground through a drain line rather than flowing into the aircraft structure.

sea-level engine. A reciprocating engine whose rated takeoff power can be produced only at sea level.

sector gear. A part of a gear wheel containing the hub and a portion of the rim with teeth.

segmented-rotor brake. A heavy-duty, multiple-disk brake used on large, high-speed aircraft.

Stators that are surfaced with a material that retains its friction characteristics at high temperatures are keyed to the axle. Rotors which are keyed into the wheels mesh with the stators.

The rotors are made in segments to allow for cooling and for their large amounts of expansion.

selcal system. Selective calling system. Each aircraft operated by an airline is assigned a particular four-tone audio combination for identification purposes. A ground station keys the signal whenever contact with that particular aircraft is desired. The signal is decoded by the airborne selcal decoder and the crew alerted by the selcal warning system.

selector valve. A flow control valve used in hydraulic systems that directs pressurized fluid into one side of an actuator, and at the same time directs return fluid from the other side of the actuator back to the reservoir.

There are two basic types of selector valves: open-center valves and closed-center valves. The four-port

closed-center valve is the most frequently used type.

See closed-center selector valve and open-center selector valve.

Selsyn system. A DC synchro system used in remote indicating instruments. The rotor in the indicator is a permanent magnet and the stator is a tapped toroidal coil. The transmitter is a circular potentiometer with DC power fed into its wiper which is moved by the object being monitored. The transmitter is connected to the indicator in such a way that rotation of the transmitter shaft varies the current in the sections of the indicator toroidal coil. The magnet in the indicator on which the pointer is mounted locks with the magnetic field produced by the coils and follows the rotation of the transmitter shaft.

selvage edge. The woven edge of fabric used to prevent the material unraveling during normal handling. The selvage edge, which runs the length of the fabric parallel to the warp threads, is usually removed from materials used in composite construction.

semiconductor diode. A two-element electrical component that allows current to pass through it in one direction, but blocks its passage in the opposite direction. A diode acts in an electrical system in the same way a check valve acts in a hydraulic system.

semimonocoque structure. A form of aircraft stressed skin structure. Most of the strength of a semimonocoque structure is in the skin, but the skin is supported on a substructure of formers and stringers that give the skin its shape and increase its rigidity.

sensible heat. Heat that is added to a liquid causing a change in its temperature but not its physical state.

sequence valve. A valve in a hydraulic system that requires a certain action to be completed before another action can begin.

Sequence valves are used to assure that the hydraulically actuated wheel-well doors are completely open before pressure is directed to the landing gear to lower it.

series circuit. A method of connecting electrical components in such a way that all the current flows through each of the components. There is only one path for current to flow.

series-parallel circuit. An electrical circuit in which some of the components are connected in parallel and others are connected in series.

servo. An electrical or hydraulic actuator connected into a flight control system. A small force on the cockpit control is amplified by the servo and provides a large force to move the control surface.

servo amplifier. An electronic amplifier in an autopilot system that increases the signal from the autopilot enough that it can operate the servos that move the control surfaces.

servo tab. A small movable tab built into the trailing edge of a primary control surface of an airplane. The cockpit controls move the tab in such a direction that it produces an aerodynamic force moving the surface on which it is mounted.

setback. The distance the jaws of a brake must be set back from the mold line to form a bend. Setback for a 90° bend is equal to the inside radius of the bend plus the thickness of the metal being bent. For a bend other than 90°, a K-factor must be used. *See also* K-factor.

shake (wood defect). Longitudinal cracks in a piece of wood, usually between two annual rings.

shear section. A necked-down section of the drive shaft of a constant-displacement engine-driven fluid pump. If the pump should seize, the shear section will break and prevent the pump from being destroyed or the engine from being damaged.

Some pumps use a shear pin rather than a shear section.

shear strength. The strength of a riveted joint in a sheet metal structure in which the rivets shear before the metal tears at the rivet holes.

shelf life. The length of time a product is good when it remains in its original unopened container.

SHF. Superhigh Frequency

shielded wire. Electrical wire enclosed in a braided metal jacket. Electromagnetic energy radiated from the wire is trapped by the braid and is carried to ground.

shimmy. Abnormal, and often violent, vibration of the nose wheel of an airplane. Shimmying is usually caused by looseness of the nose wheel support mechanism or an unbalanced wheel.

shimmy damper. A small hydraulic shock absorber installed between the nose wheel fork and the nose wheel cylinder attached to the aircraft structure.

shock mounts. Resilient mounting pads used to protect electronic equipment by absorbing low-frequency, high-amplitude vibrations.

shock wave. A pressure wave formed in the air by a flight vehicle moving at a speed greater than the speed of sound.

As the vehicle passes through the air, it produces sound waves that spread out in all directions. But since the vehicle is flying faster than these waves are moving, they build up and form a pressure wave at the front and rear of the vehicle.

As the air passes through a shock wave it slows down, its static pressure increases, and its total energy decreases.

shop head. The head of a rivet which is formed when the shank is upset.

show-type finish. The type of finish put on fabric-covered aircraft intended for show. This finish is usually made up of many coats of dope, with much sanding and rubbing of the surface between coats.

shunt winding. Field coils in an electric motor or generator that are connected in parallel with the armature.

shuttle valve. An automatic selector valve mounted on critical components such as landing gear actuation cylinders and brake cylinders.

For normal operation, system fluid flows into the actuator through the shuttle valve, but if normal system pressure is lost, emergency system pressure forces the shuttle over and emergency fluid flows into the actuator.

sidestick controller. A cockpit flight control used on some of the fly-by-wire equipped airplanes. The stick is mounted rigidly on the side console of the cockpit, and pressures exerted on the stick by the pilot produce electrical signals that are sent to the computer that flies the airplane.

sight glass (air conditioning system component). A small window in the high side of a vapor-cycle cooling system. Liquid refrigerant flows past the sight glass, and if the charge of refrigerant is low, bubbles will be seen. A fully charged system has no bubbles in the refrigerant.

sight line. A line drawn on a sheet metal layout that is one bend radius from the bend-tangent line. The sight line is lined up directly below the nose of the radius bar in a cornice brake. When the metal is clamped in this position, the bend tangent line is in the correct position for the start of the bend.

silicon controlled rectifier (SCR). A semiconductor electron control device. An SCR blocks current flow in both directions until a pulse of positive voltage is applied to its gate. It then conducts in its forward direction, while continuing to block current in its reverse direction.

silicone rubber. An elastomeric material made from silicone elastomers. Silicone rubber is compatible with fluids that attack other natural or synthetic rubbers.

single-acting actuator. A linear hydraulic or pneumatic actuator that uses fluid power for movement in one direction and a spring force for its return.

single-action hand pump. A hand-operated fluid pump that moves fluid only during one stroke of the pump handle. One stroke pulls the fluid into the pump and the other forces the fluid out.

single-disk brakes. Aircraft brakes in which a single steel disk rotates with the wheel between two brake-lining blocks. When the brake is applied, the disk is clamped tightly between the lining blocks, and the friction slows the aircraft.

single-servo brakes. Brakes that uses the momentum of the aircraft rolling forward to help apply the brakes by wedging the brake shoe against the brake drum.

sintered metal. A porous material made by fusing powdered metal under heat and pressure.

skip distance. The distance from a radio transmitting antenna to the point on the surface of the earth the reflected sky wave first touches after it has bounced off of the ionosphere.

Skydrol hydraulic fluid. The registered trade name for a synthetic, non-flammable, phosphate ester-base hydraulic fluid used in modern high-temperature hydraulic systems.

slat. A secondary control on an aircraft that allows it to fly at a high angle of attack without stalling. A slat is a section of the leading edge of the wing mounted on curved tracks that move into and out of the wing on rollers.

slip roll former. A shop tool used to form large radius curves in sheet metal.

slippage mark. A paint mark extending across the edge of an aircraft wheel onto a tube-type tire. When this mark is broken, it indicates the tire has slipped on the wheel, and there is good reason to believe the tube has been damaged.

slipstream area. For the purpose of rib stitch spacing, the slipstream area is considered to be the diameter of the propeller plus one wing rib on each side.

slot (aerodynamic device). A fixed, nozzle-like opening near the leading edge of an airplane wing ahead of the aileron.

A slot acts as a duct to force high-energy air down on the upper surface of the wing when the airplane is flying at a high angle of attack. The slot, which is located ahead of the aileron, causes the inboard portion of the wing to stall first, allowing the aileron to remain effective throughout the stall.

slow-blow fuse. An electrical fuse that allows a large amount of current to flow for a short length of time but melts to open the circuit if more than its rated current flows for a longer period.

smoke detector. A device that warns the flight crew of the presence of smoke in cargo and/or baggage compartments. Some smoke detectors are of the visual type, others are photoelectric or ionization devices.

snubber. A device in a hydraulic or pneumatic component that absorbs shock and/or vibration. A snubber is installed in the line to a hydraulic pressure gage to prevent the pointer fluctuating.

softwood. Wood from a tree that bears cones and has needles rather than leaves.

soldering. A method of thermally joining metal parts with a molten nonferrous alloy that melts at a temperature below 800°F. The molten alloy is pulled up between close-fitting parts by capillary action. When the alloy cools and hardens, it forms a strong, leak-proof connection.

solenoid. An electrical component using a small amount of current flowing through a coil to produce a magnetic force that pulls an iron core into the center of the coil. The core may be attached to a set of heavy-duty electrical contacts, or it may be used to move a valve or other mechanical device.

solidity (helicopter rotor characteristic). The solidity of a helicopter rotor system is the ratio of the total blade area to the disc area.

solution heat treatment. A type of heat treatment in which the metal is heated in a furnace until it has a uniform temperature throughout. It is then removed and quenched in cold water.

When the metal is hot, the alloying elements enter into a solid solution with the base metal to become part of its basic structure. When the metal is quenched, these elements are locked into place.

sonic venturi. A venturi in a line between a turbine engine or turbocharger and a pressurization system. When the air flowing through the venturi reaches the speed of sound, a shock wave forms across the throat of the venturi and limits the flow. A sonic venturi is also called a flow limiter.

specific heat. The number of Btu's of heat energy needed to change the temperature of one pound of a substance 1°F.

speed brakes. A secondary control of an airplane that produces drag without causing a change in the pitch attitude of the airplane. Speed brakes allow an airplane to make a steep descent without building up excessive forward airspeed.

spike knot. A knot that runs through the depth of a beam perpendicular to the annual rings. Spike knots appear most frequently in quartersawed wood.

spin. A flight maneuver in which an airplane descends in a corkscrew fashion. One wing is stalled and the other is producing lift.

spirit level. A curved glass tube partially filled with a liquid, but with a bubble in it. When the device in which the tube is mounted is level, the bubble will be in the center of the tube.

splayed patch (wood structure repair). A type of patch made in an aircraft plywood structure in which the edges of the patch are tapered for approximately five times the thickness of the plywood. A splayed patch is not recommended for use on plywood less than 1/10 inch thick.

split (wood defect). A longitudinal crack in a piece of wood caused by externally induced stress.

split bus. A type of electrical bus that allows all of the voltage-sensitive avionic equipment to be isolated from the rest of the aircraft electrical system when the engine is being started or when the ground-power unit is connected.

split-rocker switch. An electrical switch whose operating rocker is split so one half of the switch can be opened without affecting the other half.

Split-rocker switches are used as aircraft master switches. The battery can be turned on without turning on the alternator, but the alternator cannot be turned on without also turning on the battery. The alternator can be turned off without turning off the battery, but the battery cannot be turned off without also turning off the alternator.

spoilers. Flight controls that are raised up from the upper surface of a wing to destroy, or spoil, lift. Flight spoilers are used in conjunction with the ailerons to decrease lift and increase drag on the descending wing. Ground spoilers are used to produce a great amount of drag to slow the airplane on its landing roll.

spongy brakes. Hydraulic brakes whose pedal has a spongy feel because of air trapped in the fluid.

spontaneous combustion. Self-ignition of a material caused by heat produced in the material as it combines with oxygen from the air.

springwood. The portion of an annual ring in a piece of wood formed principally during the first part of the growing season, the spring of the year. Springwood is softer, more porous, and lighter than the summerwood.

square. A four-sided plane figure whose sides are all the same length, whose opposite sides are parallel, and whose angles are all right angles.

squat switch. An electrical switch actuated by the landing gear scissors on the oleo strut. When no weight is on the landing gear, the oleo piston is extended and the switch is in one position, but when weight is on the gear, the oleo strut compresses and the switch changes its position.

Squat switches are used in antiskid brake systems, landing gear safety circuits, and cabin pressurization systems.

squib. An explosive device in the discharge valve of a high-rate-discharge container of fire-extinguishing agent. The squib drives a cutter into the seal in the container to discharge the agent.

SRM. Structural Repair Manual.

stabilator. A flight control on the empennage of an airplane that acts as both a stabilizer and an elevator. The entire horizontal tail surface pivots and is moved as a unit.

stability. The characteristic of an aircraft that causes it to return to its original flight condition after it has been disturbed.

stabilons. Small wing-like horizontal surfaces mounted on the aft fuselage to improve longitudinal stability of airplanes that have an exceptionally wide center of gravity range.

stagnation point. The point on the leading edge of a wing at which the airflow separates, with some flowing over the top of the wing and the rest below the wing.

stall. A flight condition in which an angle of attack is reached at which the air ceases to flow smoothly over the upper surface of an airfoil. The air becomes turbulent and lift is lost.

stall strip. A small triangular metal strip installed along the leading edge of an airplane wing near the wing root. Stall strips cause the root section of the wing to stall before the portion of the wing ahead of the ailerons.

standpipe. A pipe sticking up in a tank or reservoir that allows part of the tank to be used as a reserve, or standby, source of fluid.

starter-generator. A single-component starter and generator used on many of the smaller gas-turbine engines.

It is used as a starter, and when the engine is running, its circuitry is shifted so that it acts as a generator.

static. Still, not moving

static air pressure. Pressure of the ambient air surrounding the aircraft. Static pressure does not take into consideration any air movement.

static dischargers. Devices connected to the trailing edges of control surfaces to discharge static electricity harmlessly into the air. They discharge the static charges before they can build up high enough to cause radio receiver interference.

static stability. The characteristic of an aircraft that causes it to return to straight and level flight after it has been disturbed from that condition.

Stoddard solvent. A petroleum product, similar to naphtha, used as a solvent and a cleaning fluid.

STOL. Short Takeoff and Landing

stop drilling. A method of stopping the growth of a crack in a piece of metal or transparent plastic by drilling a small hole at the end of the crack.

   The stresses are spread out all around the circumference of the hole rather than concentrated at the end of the crack.

straight polarity welding. DC-electric arc welding in which the electrode is negative with respect to the work.

strain. A deformation or physical change in a material caused by a stress.

stress. A force set up within an object that tries to prevent an outside force from changing its shape.

stressed skin structure. A type of aircraft structure in which all or most of the stresses are carried in the outside skin. A stressed skin structure has a minimum of internal structure.

stress riser. A location where the cross-sectional area of the part changes abruptly. Stresses concentrate at such a location and failure is likely.

   A scratch, gouge, or tool mark in the surface of a highly stressed part can change the area enough to concentrate the stresses and become a stress riser.

stringer. A part of an aircraft structure used to give the fuselage its shape and, in some types of structure, to provide a small part of the fuselage strength.

   Formers give the fuselage its cross-sectional shape and stringers fill in the shape between the formers.

stroboscopic tachometer. A tachometer used to measure the speed of any rotating device without physical contact. A highly accurate variable-frequency oscillator triggers a high-intensity strobe light. When the lamp is flashing at the same frequency the device is rotating, the device appears to stand still.

sublimation. A process in which a solid material changes directly into a vapor without passing through the liquid stage.

subsonic flight. Flight at an airspeed in which all air flowing over the aircraft is moving at a speed below the speed of sound.

summerwood. The less porous, usually harder portion of an annual ring that forms in the latter part of the growing season, the summer of the year.

sump. A low point in an aircraft fuel tank in which water and other contaminants can collect and be held until they can be drained out.

supercooled water. Water in its liquid form at a temperature well below its natural freezing temperature. When supercooled water is disturbed, it immediately freezes.

superheat. Heat energy that is added to a refrigerant after it changes from a liquid to a vapor.

superheterodyne circuit. A sensitive radio receiver circuit in which a local oscillator produces a frequency that is a specific difference from the received signal frequency. The desired signal and the output from the oscillator are mixed, and they produce a single, constant intermediate frequency. This IF is amplified, demodulated, and detected to produce the audio frequency that is used to drive the speaker.

supersonic flight. Flight at an airspeed in which all air flowing over the aircraft is moving at a speed greater than the speed of sound.

Supplemental Type Certificate (STC). An approval issued by the FAA for a modification to a type certificated airframe, engine, or component.

   More than one STC can be issued for the same basic alteration, but each holder must prove to the FAA that the alteration meets all the requirements of the original type certificate.

surface tape. Strips of aircraft fabric that are doped over all seams and places where the fabric is stitched to the aircraft structure. Surface tape is also doped over the wing leading edges where abrasive wear occurs.

   The edges of surface tape are pinked, or notched, to keep them from raveling before the dope is applied.

surfactant. A surface active agent, or partially soluble contaminant, which is a by-product of fuel processing or of fuel additives. Surfactants adhere to other contaminants and cause them to drop out of the fuel and settle to the bottom of the fuel tank as sludge.

surveyor's transit. An instrument consisting of a telescope mounted on a flat, graduated, circular plate on a tripod. The plate can be adjusted so it is level, and its graduations oriented to magnetic north. When an object is viewed through the telescope, its azimuth and elevation may be determined.

swashplate. The component in a helicopter control system that consists basically of two bearing races with ball bearings between them.

The lower, or nonrotating, race is tilted by the cyclic control, and the upper, or rotating, race has arms which connect to the control horns on the rotor blades.

Movement of the cyclic pitch control is transmitted to the rotor blades through the swashplate. Movement of the collective pitch control raises or lowers the entire swashplate assembly to change the pitch of all of the blades at the same time.

symmetrical airfoil. An airfoil that has the same shape on both sides of its chord line, or center line.

symmetry check. A check of an airframe to determine that the wings and tail are symmetrical about the longitudinal axis.

synchro system. A remote instrument indicating system. A synchro transmitter is actuated by the device whose movement is to be measured, and it is connected electrically with wires to a synchro indicator whose pointer follows the movement of the shaft of the transmitter.

system-pressure regulator (hydraulic system component). A type of hydraulic system-pressure control valve. When the system pressure is low, as it is when some unit is actuated, the output of the constant-delivery pump is directed into the system. When the actuation is completed and the pressure builds up to a specified kick-out pressure, the pressure regulator shifts. A check valve seals the system off and the pressure is maintained by the accumulator. The pump is unloaded and its output is directed back into the reservoir with very little opposition. The pump output pressure drops, but the volume of flow remains the same. When the system pressure drops to the specified kick-in pressure, the regulator again shifts and directs fluid into the system.

Spool-type and balanced-pressure-type system pressure regulators are completely automatic in their operation and require no attention on the part of the flight crew.

TACAN (Tactical Air Navigation). A radio navigation facility used by military aircraft for both direction and distance information. Civilian aircraft receive distance information from a TACAN on their DME.

tack coat. A coat of finishing material sprayed on the surface and allowed to dry until the solvents evaporate. As soon as the solvents evaporate, a wet full-bodied coat of material is sprayed over it.

tack rag. A clean, lintless rag, slightly damp with thinner. A tack rag is used to wipe a surface to prepare it to receive a coat of finishing material.

tack weld. A method of holding parts together before they are permanently welded. The parts are assembled, and small spots of weld are placed at strategic locations to hold them in position.

tacky. Slightly sticky to the touch.

tailets. Small vertical surfaces mounted underside of the horizontal stabilizer of some airplanes to increase the directional stability.

takeoff warning system. An aural warning system that provides audio warning signals when the thrust levers are advanced for takeoff if the stabilizer, flaps, or speed brakes are in an unsafe condition for takeoff.

tang. A tapered shank sticking out from the blade of a knife or a file. The handle of a knife or file is mounted on the tang.

TCAS. Traffic Alert Collision Avoidance System.

Teflon. The registered trade name for a fluorocarbon resin used to make hydraulic and pneumatic seals, hoses, and backup rings.

tempered glass. Glass that has been heat-treated to increase its strength. Tempered glass is used in birdproof, heated windshields for high-speed aircraft.

terminal strips. A group of threaded studs mounted in a strip of insulating plastic. Electrical wires with crimped-on terminals are placed over the studs and secured with nuts.

terminal VOR. A low-powered VOR that is normally located on an airport.

tetraethyl lead (TEL). A heavy, oily, poisonous liquid, $Pb(C_2H_5)_4$, that is mixed into aviation gasoline to increase its critical pressure and temperature.

therapeutic mask adapter. A calibrated orifice in the mask adapter for a continuous-flow oxygen system that increases the flow of oxygen to a mask being used by a passenger who is known to have a heart or respiratory problem.

thermal dimpling. *See* hot dimpling.

thermal relief valve. A relief valve in a hydraulic system that relieves pressure that builds up in an isolated part of the system because of heat. Thermal relief valves are set at a higher pressure than the system pressure relief valve.

thermistor. A special form of electrical resistor whose resistance varies with its temperature.

thermistor material. A material with a negative temperature coefficient that causes its resistance to decrease as its temperature increases.

thermocouple. A loop consisting of two kinds of wire, joined at the hot, or measuring, junction and at the cold junction in the instrument. The voltage difference between the two junctions is proportional to the temperature difference between the junctions.

In order for the current to be meaningful, the resistance of the thermocouple is critical, and the leads are designed for a specific installation. Their length should not be altered. Thermocouples used to measure cylinder head temperature are usually made of iron and constantan, and thermocouples that measure exhaust gas temperature for turbine engines are made of chromel and alumel.

thermocouple fire detection system. A fire detection system that works on the principle of the rate-of-temperature rise. Thermocouples are installed around the area to be protected, and one thermocouple is surrounded by thermal insulation that prevents its temperature changing rapidly.

In the event of a fire, the temperature of all the thermocouples except the protected one will rise immediately and a fire warning will be initiated. In the case of a general overheat condition, the temperature of all the thermocouples will rise uniformly and there will be no fire warning.

thermoplastic resin. A type of plastic material that becomes soft when heated and hardens when cooled.

thermosetting resin. A type of plastic material that, when once hardened by heat, cannot be softened by being heated again.

thermostatic expansion valve (TXV). The component in a vapor-cycle cooling system that meters the refrigerant into the evaporator.

The amount of refrigerant metered by the TXV is determined by the temperature and pressure of the refrigerant as it leaves the evaporator coils.

The TXV changes the refrigerant from a high-pressure liquid into a low-pressure liquid.

thixotropic agents. Materials, such as microballoons, added to a resin to give it body and increase its workability.

TIG welding. Tungsten inert gas welding is a form of electric arc welding in which the electrode is a nonconsumable tungsten wire. TIG welding is now called GTA (Gas Tungsten Arc) Welding.

TMC. Thrust Management Computer.

toe-in. A condition of landing gear alignment in which the front of the tires are closer together than the rear. When the aircraft rolls forward, the wheels try to move closer together.

toe-out. A condition of landing gear alignment in which the front of the tires are farther apart than the rear. When the aircraft rolls forward, the wheels try to move farther apart.

toroidal coil. An electrical coil wound around a ring-shaped core of highly permeable material.

torque. A force that produces or tries to produce rotation.

torque links. The hinged link between the piston and cylinder of an oleo-type landing gear shock absorber. The torque links allow the piston to move freely in and out of the landing gear cylinder, but prevent it rotating. The torque links can be adjusted to achieve and maintain the correct wheel alignment. Torque links are also called scissors and nutcrackers.

torque tube. A tube in an aircraft control system that transmits a torsional force from the operating control to the control surface.

torsion rod. A device in a spring tab to which the control horn is attached. For normal operation, the torsion rod acts as a fixed attachment point, but when the control surface loads are high, the torsion rod twists and allows the control horn to deflect the spring tab.

total air pressure. The pressure a column of moving air will have if it is stopped.

total air temperature. The temperature a column of moving air will have if it is stopped.

TR unit. A transformer-rectifier unit. A TR unit reduces the voltage of alternating current and changes it into direct current.

tractor powerplant. An airplane powerplant in which the propeller is mounted in the front, and its thrust pulls the airplane rather than pushes it.

trammel (*verb*). To square up the Pratt truss used in an airplane wing. Trammel points are set on the trammel bar so they measure the distance between the center of the front spar, at the inboard compression strut, and the center of the rear spar at the next compression strut outboard. The drag and antidrag wires are adjusted until the distance between the center of the rear spar at the inboard compression strut and the center of the front spar at the next outboard compression strut is exactly the same as that between the first points measured.

trammel bar. A wood or metal bar on which trammel points are mounted to compare distances.

trammel points. A set of sharp-pointed pins that protrude from the sides of a trammel bar.

transducer. A device that changes energy from one form to another. Commonly used transducers change mechanical movement or pressures into electrical signals.

transformer rectifier. A component in a large aircraft electrical system used to reduce the AC voltage and change it into DC for charging the battery and for operating DC equipment in the aircraft.

translational lift. The additional lift produced by a helicopter rotor as the helicopter changes from hovering to forward flight.

transonic flight. Flight at an airspeed in which some air flowing over the aircraft is moving at a speed below the speed of sound, and other air is moving at a speed greater than the speed of sound.

transverse pitch. *See* gage.

triangle. A three-sided, closed plane figure. The sum of the three angles in a triangle is always equal to 180°.

tricresyl phosphate (TCP). A chemical compound, $(CH_3C_6H_4O)_3PO$, used in aviation gasoline to assist in scavenging the lead deposits left from the tetraethyl lead.

trimmed flight. A flight condition in which the aerodynamic forces acting on the control surfaces are balanced and the aircraft is able to fly straight and level with no control input.

trim tab. A small control tab mounted on the trailing edge of a movable control surface. The tab may be adjusted to provide an aerodynamic force to hold the surface on which it is mounted deflected in order to trim the airplane for hands-off flight at a specified airspeed.

trip-free circuit breaker. A circuit breaker that opens a circuit any time an excessive amount of current flows regardless of the position of the circuit breaker's operating handle.

troubleshooting. A procedure used in aircraft maintenance in which the operation of a malfunctioning system is analyzed to find the reason for the malfunction and to find a method for returning the system to its condition of normal operation.

true airspeed (TAS). Airspeed shown on the airspeed indicator (indicated airspeed) corrected for position error and nonstandard air temperature and pressure.

trunnion. Projections from the cylinder of a retractable landing gear strut about which the strut pivots retract.

truss-type structure. A type of structure made up of longitudinal beams and cross braces. Compression loads between the main beams are carried by rigid cross braces. Tension loads are carried by stays, or wires, that go from one main beam to the other and cross between the cross braces.

turbine. A rotary device actuated by impulse or reaction of a fluid flowing through vanes or blades that are arranged around a central shaft.

turn and slip indicator. A rate gyroscopic flight instrument that gives the pilot an indication of the rate of rotation of the aircraft about its vertical axis.

A ball in a curved glass tube shows the pilot the relationship between the centrifugal force and the force of gravity. This indicates whether or not the angle of bank is proper for the rate of turn.

The turn and slip indicator shows the trim condition of the aircraft and serves as an emergency source of bank information in case the attitude gyro fails. Turn and slip indicators were formerly called needle and ball and turn and bank indicators.

turnbuckle. A component in an aircraft control system used to adjust cable tension. A turnbuckle consists of a brass tubular barrel with right-hand threads in one end and left-hand in the other end. Control cable terminals screw into the two ends of the barrel, and turning the barrel pulls the terminals together, shortening the cable.

twist drill. A metal cutting tool turned in a drill press or hand-held drill motor. A twist drill has a straight shank and spiraled flutes. The cutting edge is ground on the end of the spiraled flutes.

twist stripe. A stripe of paint on flexible hose that runs the length of the hose. If this stripe spirals around the hose after it is installed, it indicates the hose was twisted when it was installed. Twist stripes are also called lay lines.

two-terminal spot-type fire detection system. A fire detection system that uses individual thermoswitches installed around the inside of the area to be protected.

These thermoswitches are wired in parallel between two separate circuits. A short or an open circuit can exist in either circuit without causing a fire warning.

Type Certificate Data Sheets (TCDS). The official specifications of an aircraft, engine, or propeller issued by the Federal Aviation Administration.

TCDS lists pertinent specifications for the device, and it is the responsibility of the mechanic and/or inspector to assure, on each inspection, that the device meets these specifications.

UHF. Ultrahigh Frequency.

ultimate tensile strength. The tensile strength required to cause a material to break or to continue to deform under a decreasing load.

ultraviolet-blocking dope. Dope that contains aluminum powder or some other pigment that blocks the passage of ultraviolet rays of the sun. This coat of dope protects the organic fabrics and clear dope from deterioration by these rays.

undamped oscillation. Oscillation that continues with an unchanging amplitude once it has started.

underslung rotor. A helicopter rotor whose center of gravity is below the point at which it is attached to the mast.

unidirectional fabric. Fabric in which all the threads run in the same direction. These threads are often bound with a few fibers run at right angles, just enough to hold the yarns together and prevent their bunching.

unloading valve. This is another name for system pressure regulator. *See* system pressure regulator.

utility finish. The finish of an aircraft that gives the necessary tautness and fill to the fabric and the necessary protection to the metal, but does not have the glossy appearance of a show-type finish.

vapor lock. A condition in which vapors form in the fuel lines and block the flow of fuel to the carburetor.

vapor pressure. The pressure of the vapor above a liquid needed to prevent the liquid evaporating. Vapor pressure is always specified at a specific temperature.

variable displacement pump. A fluid pump whose output is controlled by the demands of the system. These pumps normally have a built-in system pressure regulator. When the demands of the system are low, the pump moves very little fluid, but when the demands are high, the pump moves a lot of fluid. Most variable displacement pumps used in aircraft hydraulic systems are piston-type pumps.

varnish (aircraft finishing material). A material used to produce an attractive and protective coating on wood or metal. Varnish is made of a resin dissolved in a solvent and thinned until it has the proper viscosity to spray or brush. The varnish is spread evenly over the surface to be coated, and when the solvents evaporate, a tough film is left.

varsol. A petroleum product similar to naphtha used as a solvent and a cleaning fluid.

veneer. Thin sheets of wood "peeled" from a log. A wide-blade knife held against the surface of the log peels away the veneer as the log is rotated in the cutter.

Veneer is used for making plywood. Several sheets of veneer are glued together, with the grain of each sheet placed at 45° or 90° to the grain of the sheets next to it.

vertical axis. An imaginary line, passing vertically through the center of gravity of an airplane.

vertical fin. The fixed vertical surface in the empennage of an airplane. The vertical fin acts as a weathervane to give the airplane directional stability.

VFR. Visual Flight Rules.

VHF. Very High Frequency.

vibrator-type voltage regulator. A type of voltage regulator used with a generator or alternator that intermittently places a resistance in the field circuit to control the voltage. A set of vibrating contacts puts the resistor in the circuit and takes it out several times a second.

viscosity. The resistance of a fluid to flow. Viscosity refers to the "stiffness" of the fluid, or its internal friction.

viscosity cup. A specially shaped cup with an accurately sized hole in its bottom. The cup is submerged in the liquid to completely fill it. It is then lifted from the liquid and the time in seconds is measured from the beginning of the flow through the hole until the first break in this flow. The viscosity of the liquid relates to this time.

vixen file. A metal-cutting hand file that has curved teeth across its faces. Vixen files are used to remove large amounts of soft metal.

V_{NE}. Never-exceed speed. The maximum speed the aircraft is allowed to attain in any conditions of flight.

volatile liquid. A liquid that easily changes into a vapor.

voltmeter multiplier. A precision resistor in series with a voltmeter mechanism used to extend the range of the basic meter or to allow a single meter to measure several ranges of voltage.

VOR. Very high frequency Omni Range navigation

VORTAC. An electronic navigation system that contains both a VOR and a TACAN facility.

vortex (*plural* vortices). A whirling motion in a fluid.

vortex generator. Small low-aspect-ratio airfoils installed in pairs on the upper surface of a wing, on both sides of the vertical fin just ahead of the rudder, and on the underside of the vertical stabilizers of some airplanes. Their function is to pull high-energy air down to the surface to energize the boundary layer and prevent airflow separation until the surface reaches a higher angle of attack.

warp clock. An alignment indicator included in a structural repair manual to show the orientation of the plies of a composite material. The ply direction is shown in relation to a reference direction.

warp threads. Threads that run the length of the roll of fabric, parallel to the selvage edge. Warp threads are often stronger than fill threads.

warp tracers. Threads of a different color from the warp threads that are woven into a material to identify the direction of the warp threads.

wash in. A twist in an airplane wing that increases its angle of incidence near the tip.

wash out. A twist in an airplane wing that decreases its angle of incidence near the tip.

watt. The basic unit of electrical power. One watt is equal to 1/746 horsepower.

way point. A phantom location created in certain electronic navigation systems by measuring direction and distance from a VORTAC station or by latitude and longitude coordinates from Loran or GPS.

web of a spar. The part of a spar between the caps.

weft threads. *See* fill threads.

wet-type vacuum pump. An engine-driven air pump that uses steel vanes. These pumps are lubricated by engine oil drawn in through holes in the pump base. The oil passes through the pump and is exhausted with the air. Wet-type pumps must have oil separators in their discharge line to trap the oil and return it to the engine crankcase.

wing fences. Vertical vanes that extend chordwise across the upper surface of an airplane wing to prevent spanwise airflow.

wing heavy. An out-of-trim flight condition in which an airplane flies hands off, with one wing low.

wire bundle. A compact group of electrical wires held together with special wrapping devices or with waxed string. These bundles are secured to the aircraft structure with special clamps.

woof threads. *See* fill threads.

work. The product of force times distance.

yaw. Rotation of an aircraft about its vertical axis.

yaw damper. An automatic flight control system that counteracts the rolling and yawing produced by Dutch roll. *See* Dutch roll.
A yaw damper senses yaw with a rate gyro and moves the rudder an amount proportional to the rate of yaw, but in the opposite direction.

yield strength. The amount of stress needed to permanently deform a material.

zener diode. A special type of solid-state diode designed to have a specific breakdown voltage and to operate with current flowing through it in its reverse direction.

Zeppelin. The name of large rigid lighter-than-air ships built by the Zeppelin Company in Germany prior to and during World War I.

zero-center ammeter. An ammeter in a light aircraft electrical system located between the battery and the main bus. This ammeter shows the current flowing into or out of the battery.

INDEX

air transformer, *224*

air valves, high-pressure, *374*

AIS (Audio Integrating System), *803*

Alclad, *73*

alloy steel, *74*

Alodine, *215*

alodizing, *73*

alphanumeric, *818*

alternator, *511–514*

altimeter inspection, *913*

altimeter, drum-pointer-type, *761*

altimeter, encoding, *761*

altimeter, pneumatic, *720*

altimeter, sensitive, *760*

altimeter setting, *760*

altitude, density, *8*

altitude engine, *869*

alumel, *730*

aluminum alloy, *70–73, 75*

aluminum, clad, *73*

AM (Amplitude Modulation), *795*

amateur-built aircraft, *235*

American Wire Gage, *550*

ammeter, *520, 526*

ammeter, clamp-on, *572, 574*

amphibian, *421*

amphibious floats, *422*

amplifier, *502*

AND gate, *732*

aneroid, *720*

angle drill, *96*

angle of attack, *10, 17, 18, 738*

angle of attack, critical, *17*

angle of attack indicator, *738–740*

angle of incidence, *40, 273, 293*

An Introduction to Aircraft Electrical Systems: Study Questions, *505*

An Introduction to Fluid Power Systems: Study Questions, *333*

annealing, *72*

annual inspection, *915, 917*

annunciator panel, *540*

anodizing, *73*

antenna, *791, 797–798, 800–802, 809, 849–852*

antenna, dipole, *800*

antenna installation, *849–852*

antenna, long-wire, *802,*

antenna, loop, *801, 809*

antenna polarization, *798*

antenna, sense, *809*

antenna, vertical whip, *801*

anti-icing additive, *591*

anti-icing, ground, *874*

anti-icing system, *860*

antidrag wire, *190*

antiservo tab, *279, 280*

antiskid brake system, *455–461, 537*

antitear strip, *196*

antitorque pedals, *54, 303*

APU (Auxiliary Power Unit), *547*

arbor press, *112*

area measurement, *324*

area navigation, *820*

ARINC (Aeronautical Radio INCorporated), *802*

aromatic additives, *590*

artificial aging, *71*

aspect ratio, *22, 24*

Assembly and Rigging: Answers to Study Questions, *317*

ATC transponder inspection, *915*

atmospheric conditions, standard, *657*

attitude indicator, *750*

augmenter tube, *868*

Aural Warning Systems: Study Questions, *777*

aural warning systems, *776*

auto-brake system, *463*

autoclave, *243, 244*

autogiro, *44*

autoignition system, *540, 541*

Automatic Flight Control Systems: Study Questions, *775*

automatic pilot, *323, 768*

autopilot correction subsystem, *771*

autopilot error sensing subsystem, *770*

autopilot follow-up subsystem, *773*

autopilot servos, *772*

autorotation, *48*

Autosyn system, *637, 734, 735*

auxiliary power unit, *407*

avionics cooling, *847*

avionics, *544, 545, 791, 847*

axes of an aircraft, *9, 27, 32, 269–271*

axis, lateral, *27, 271*

axis, longitudinal, *269*

axis, vertical, *32, 270*

backup ring, *384, 385*

balance cable, *269*

balance panel, *270, 280*

balance tab, *278*

balanced surface, *278*

balancer/analyzer, Chadwick-Helmuth, *314*

balsa wood, *241*

band saw, *91*

barometer, mercury, *720*

barometric scale *720*

Basic Aerodynamics: Answers to Study Questions, *58*

Basic Aircraft Hydraulic Systems: Study Questions, *341*

Basic Fixed-Wing Aerodynamics: Study Questions, *32*

Basic High-Speed Aerodynamics: Study Questions, *43*

battery contactor, *500, 508, 510*

bead seat area, *469*

float repair, *135*

flow equalizer valve, *365, 366*

flow multiplier, *683*

fluid, *323*

fluid line installation, *398*

fluid lines, flexible, *393*

fluid lines, rigid, *389*

fluid power, *323, 332*

Fluid Power System Lines and Fittings: Study Questions, *400*

flush patch, *131*

flush riveting, NACA *125*

flush rivets, *120*

flux-gate compass, *746, 748*

flux valve, *746, 747*

fly-by-light, *285*

fly-by-wire, *285*

flying wing, *27*

FM (Frequency Modulation), *795*

FMCS (Flight Management Computer System), *841*

forming block, *112*

forward-swept wing, *40*

fractional distillation, *588*

free-turbine engine, *311*

freewheeling unit, *312*

Frise aileron, *30, 270*

frost, *859*

FSDO (Flight Standards District Office), *918*

fuel dumping, *606*

fuel filter, micronic-type, *625*

Fuel Filters and Strainers: Study Questions, *626*

fuel filter, wafer-type, *626*

fuel flowmeter, *636–639*

fuel grade, *647*

fuel heaters, *629, 630*

Fuel Heaters: Study Questions, *631*

fueling and defueling, *644*

Fueling and Defueling: Study Questions, *645*

fuel-injected engine, *597, 599*

fuel jettisoning system, *595, 606, 643*

Fuel Jettisoning System: Study Questions, *643*

fuel pressure warning system, *640*

fuel pump, centrifugal-type, *617, 618*

fuel pump, diaphragm-type, *620*

fuel pump, ejector-type, *618, 619*

fuel pump, gear-type, *622*

fuel pump, plunger-type, *616*

fuel pump, vane-type, *620, 621*

Fuel Pumps: Study Questions, *623*

fuel quantity gage, capacitance-type, *633–635*

fuel quantity gage, direct reading, *631*

fuel quantity gage, drip gage, *636*

fuel quantity gage, electrical resistance-type, *632, 633*

fuel strainer, gascolator, *624*

fuel system contamination, *646*

Fuel System Instruments: Study Questions, *640*

fuel system, manifold cross-feed, *601, 602*

fuel system plumbing, *641–642*

Fuel System Plumbing: Study Questions, *642*

Fuel System Requirements: Study Questions, *595*

fuel system troubleshooting, *648*

Fuel System Troubleshooting: Study Questions, *648*

fuel tank, bladder-type, *592, 603, 609, 612, 613*

fuel tank filler caps, *613, 614*

fuel tank, integral, *609, 611, 612*

Fuel Tanks: Study Questions, *615*

fuel tank sump, *610*

fuel temperature indicators, *640*

fuel, turbine engine, *588, 590*

fuel valve, electric motor operated, *628*

fuel valve, plug-type, *627*

fuel valve, poppet-type, *627*

fuel valve, solenoid operated, *628, 629*

Fuel Valves: Study Questions, *629*

fuse, *509,*

fuse, electrical, *562*

fuse, slow-blow, *509, 522*

gaseous oxygen cylinders, *675*

gasket, *383*

Gas Welding, Cutting, Brazing, and Soldering: Study Questions, *153*

generator, *511, 518*

generator series field, *522*

generator shunt field, *522*

gerotor pump, *354*

glass cockpit, *836*

glass, tempered, *862*

glaze, ice, *859,*

glide slope, *815, 817*

glue, *178*

glue, plastic resin, *178*

glue, resorcinol, *178*

GMAW (Gas Metal Arc Welding), *156*

goniometer, *810*

GPS (Global Positioning System), *822*

GPU (Ground-Power Unit), *510*

GPWS (Ground Proximity Warning System), *825*

graphite, *235, 237, 241, 252*

ground crew call, *804*

ground effect, *19, 49, 50*

Grumman X-*29, 41, 237, 243*

GTAW (Gas Tungsten Arc Welding), *156, 157, 158, 160*

outflow valve, *681*

overheat detection systems, *884*

overvoltage protector, *513, 515–517*

oxyacetylene cutting, *150*

oxyacetylene flames, *145*

oxyacetylene welding, *138*

oxygen, *139*

oxygen, aviators, *668*

oxygen characteristics, *658*

oxygen functions, *659*

oxygen, mechanically separated, *669*

oxygen regulator, *140, 674–675*

oxygen regulator, diluter-demand, *674*

oxygen regulator, pressure-demand, *675*

oxygen servicing trailer, *676*

oxygen storage cylinder, *140*

oxygen system, continuous-flow, *670, 671*

oxygen system leak testing, *676*

oxygen system purging, *676*

oxyhydrogen welding, *138*

packing, *383*

paint equipment, electrostatic, *224*

paint pressure pot, *225, 227*

paint spray gun, *224, 225, 227–229*

paint spray gun cleaning, *229*

paint spray gun problems, *228, 229*

paint spray pattern, *228*

paint stripping, *212*

parallel circuit, *504*

paralleling circuit, *517*

paralleling relay, *521*

partial pressure, *658, 667*

parting film, *248*

Pascal's law, *329*

passenger address system, *804*

passenger entertainment system, *804*

performance number, *589*

Perspex, *255*

petroleum fractions, *590*

pin knot clusters, *177*

pin punch, *88, 89*

pinholes, *221*

pipe fittings, *395*

piston pump, *354, 355*

pitch, *271, 287*

pitot static system, *756, 757*

Pitot-Static Systems: Study Questions, *762*

pitot-static head, *755, 861*

plastic resin glue, *178*

plastics, *234*

Plexiglas, *255*

plywood, *176*

plywood repair, *182*

plywood structure inspection, *182*

PMB (Plastic Media Blasting), *213, 214*

pneumatic deicer system, *402*

pneumatic gyro power system, *403*

pneumatics, *323*

pneumatic system, high-pressure, *404*

pneumatic system, low-pressure, *402*

Pneumatic Systems: Study Questions, *407*

Poly-Fiber, *186, 202, 203*

polyester resin, *235, 240*

polyethylene sheeting, *223*

polyurethane enamel, *217, 218*

polyvinyl chloride, *345*

position error, *759*

potentiometer, *502*

power, *326*

power brake control valve, *453, 454, 538*

power brakes, *452*

power control valve, *338, 339*

power pack retraction system, *433–435*

power transfer unit, *407*

precession, *51, 751*

precipitation heat treatment, *71*

preimpregnated material, *241, 244*

prepreg, *241, 249*

pressure, *327*

pressure, absolute, *665, 720*

pressure altitude, *8, 660, 760*

pressure, dynamic, *13*

pressure fueling and defueling, *604, 606*

pressure, gage, *665, 720*

Pressure Measuring Instruments: Study Questions, *724*

pressure manifold, *340*

pressure reducer valve, *371*

pressure vessel repair, *135*

pressure vessel, *135, 681*

pressurization, constant-differential mode, *684*

pressurization, isobaric mode, *684, 686*

prick punch, *88, 89, 119*

priority valve, *364*

propeller chemical anti-icing, *871*

propeller deicer, electrothermal, *539*

propeller electrothermal deicing, *872*

propeller protractor, *298*

pulleys, *282, 283*

pump, boost, *600*

pump, constant-displacement, *338, 352*

pump control valve, *338*

pump, deep-vacuum, *706*

pump, ejector, *600*

pump, gerotor, *354*

pump, piston, *354, 355*

pump, variable-displacement, *352, 356–357*

punch, center, *88, 89, 119*

punch, pin, *88, 89*

punch, prick, *88, 89, 119*

punch, transfer, *88, 89*

Pureclad, *73*

push-pull rod, *284*

quick-disconnect connector, *554*

quick-disconnect fittings, *397*

radar, *826*

radar altimeter, *824*

radar beacon transponder, *818*

radar, doppler navigation, *828*

radar, weather, *829*

radio altimeter, *824*

radio frequency allocation, *798, 799*

radio receiver, *792*

radio transmitter, *792*

radio wave propagation, *797, 800*

radio wavelength, *798*

rain removal system, chemical, *878*

rain removal system, mechanic, *878*

rain removal system, pneumatic, *879*

Rain Removal Systems: Study
    Questions, *880*

rain repellant, chemical, *878*

ram air turbine, *408*

rate, gyros, *751*

ratiometer, *727*

rebreather oxygen mask, *671*

refrigerant R-12, *663, 695, 696, 706*

refrigerant R-134a, *706*

refrigeration oil, *707, 710*

refueling controls, *606–608*

registration numbers, *229–231*

reinforced shell structure, *66*

reinforcing tape, *196, 197*

rejuvenator, *220, 222*

relative wind, *11, 48*

relaxed static stability, *27*

relay, *499*

relief hole, *111*

relief valve, *338, 369*

repair approval, *136*

Repair of Aircraft Structure by
    Welding: Study Questions, *167*

Repair of Sheet Metal Structure:
    Study Questions, *137*

resistor, equalizing, *523, 524*

resorcinol glue, *178*

retard breaker points, *542*

retarder, *220, 221*

retractable landing gear, *421, 423*

retreating blade, *46*

retreating blade stall, *48, 49*

return manifold, *340*

reverse-current cutout, *519*

reverse-current cutout, differential-
    voltage, *522, 523*

rib stitching, *196, 198*

rib stitch spacing, *197*

rigid tube bending, *392*

rigidity in space, *750*

rime, ice, *859*

ringworms, *222*

riveter, compression, *102*

rivet evaluation, *124*

rivet gage, *116*

rivet gun, *99, 100, 122*

rivet, Hi-Shear, *83, 84*

riveting, compression, *121*

rivet pitch, *116*

rivet removal, *125*

rivet set, *100, 101, 122*

rivets, flush *120*

rivets, icebox, *79*

rivets, solid, *79, 115*

Rivnut, *83*

RMI (Radio Magnetic Indicator), *814*

RNAV (Area Navigation), *820*

Rockwell hardness tester, *74*

rod-end bearings, *284*

roll, *287*

room-temperature cure repair, *246*

rosette weld, *148*

rotor, rigid, *311*

rotor thrust, *45*

rotor, underslung, *3*

Rotorwing Aerodynamics: Study
    Questions, *57*

rudder, *274, 300, 301*

ruddervator, *29, 273*

safety, oxygen system, *677*

sandbag, *98*

sandwich construction, *241*

satin-weave fabric, *238, 239*

scales, steel, *87*

Schrader valves, *704*

scissors, *425*

SCR (Silicon Controlled Rectifier),
    502, 503

scroll shear, *90*

scupper, *610*

sea-level engine, *869*

seal, O ring, *384*

seams, machine-sewed, *195*

seaplane hull repair, *135*

SELCAL (Selective Calling), *803*

selector valve, *337, 362–363*

selector valve, poppet-type, *362*

selector valve, spool-type, *363*

Selsyn system, *732*

semiconductor diodes, *498, 499*

semimonocoque structure, *65*

semirigid rotor, *310*

sensible heat, *662*

sequence valve, *363*

series circuit, *496, 504*

service interphone, *804*

servo actuator, *382*

servo tab, *270, 279*

setback, *106, 109*

settling with power, *52*

Seyboth fabric tester, *188, 189*

shear, *69*

shear section, *351*

shear strength, *75, 117*

Sheet Metal Aircraft Construction: Study Questions, *69*

sheet metal damage appraisal, *127*

sheet metal damage classification, *128*

Sheet Metal Joints Using Solid Rivets: Study Questions, *126*

shimmy damper, *430, 431*

Shock Absorbers: Study Questions, *432*

shock mounts, *780, 781, 847*

shock wave, *12*

shock wave, normal, *40, 41*

shock wave, oblique, *42*

shuttle valve, *404, 436*

sidestick controller, *285*

sight line, *110*

silicone rubber, *345*

silver soldering, *152*

Sitka spruce, *175, 177*

skip distance, *800*

skis, retractable, *422*

ski, wheel-replacement, *422*

slats, *20, 276, 277, 286*

slip roll former, *98*

slot, *20, 23*

SMAW (Shielded Metal Arc Welding), *155*

smoke detector, *891–892*

smoke detector, ionization-type, *892*

smoke detector, photoelectric, *892*

smoke detector, visual, *892*

snubber, *413*

softwood, *175*

soldering, *151–152*

soldering, soft, *152*

solenoid, *499*

solenoid, continuous-duty, *531*

solenoid, intermittent-duty, *531*

solidity ratio, *45*

solution heat treatment, *71*

sonic venturi, *681*

sound barrier, *37*

specific heat, *662*

speed brakes, *270*

split bus, *544*

split-rocker switch, *514*

spoilers, *269, 276–277, 286*

spoilers, ground, *277, 286*

sprag clutch, *312*

spring tab, *279*

springwood, *176*

squaring shear, *89, 90*

squat switch, *457, 537*

SRM (Structural Repair Manual), *245, 247–249*

SSB (Single-Sideband), *795, 796*

stabilator, *28, 272*

stability, *26–27, 29, 31, 277*

stability augmentation system, *56*

stability, directional, *31*

stability, dynamic, *26*

stability, lateral, *29*

stability, longitudinal, *27*

stabilizer, *273*

stabilizer, adjustable, *280*

stabilizer bar, *55, 309*

stall strip, *24*

stall-warning indicator, *739*

standard atmosphere, *7*

standpipe, *340*

starter, *531*

starter-generator, *525*

static air pressure, *723*

static dischargers, *848*

static stability, *25, 26*

static system inspection, *913–915*

static system leak checks, *781*

STC (Supplemental Type Certificate), *187, 201, 202, 844, 920*

steel, corrosion-resistant, *74*

Stoddard solvent, *344*

Stormscope, *829, 830*

strain, *67*

Stratopower variable-displacement pump, *356–357*

stratosphere, *7*

stress, *67*

stressed-skin replacement, *136*

stressed-skin structure, *234*

stress riser, *470*

stringer repair, *133*

structure, monocoque, *65, 234*

Styrofoam, *242*

sublimation, *860*

subsonic flight, *39*

summerwood, *176*

supercooled water, *859*

Superflite, *186, 204, 205*

superheterodyne receiver, *793*

supersonic airflow, *41*

supersonic flight, *39*

surface patch for stressed skin, *129*

surface tape, *192, 200*

surface tape, bias-cut, *192*

surfactant, *624*

surge tank, *604*

swashplate, *304*

sweepback, *31, 40*

switch derating, *561*

switches, *561*

symmetry check, *294*

synchro system *732*

synchroscope, *738*

system pressure regulator, *339*

T seal, *385*

tab, antiservo, *279, 280*

tab, balance, *278*

tab, spring, *279*

tab, trim, *278*

TACAN, *819*

tachometer, *736–737*

tachometer, electric, *736*

tachometer, magnetic drag, *736*

tachometer, stroboscopic, *737*

tack coat, *218*

tail rotor, *308*

tail wheel landing gear, *423, 429*

TAS (True AirSpeed), *759*

TCAS (Traffic Alert Collision Avoidance System), *826*

team riveting, *125*

teetering hinge, *310*

Teflon, *345, 384, 385, 394*

Teflon hose, *394*

Temperature Measuring Instruments: Study Questions, *731*

temperature, *664, 665*

tension, *67*

tetraethyl lead, *589*

The Physics of Cabin Atmosphere Control: Study Questions, *666*

therapeutic oxygen mask adapter, *671*

thermal ice control, *868*

thermal relief valve, *369*

thermistor, *862*

thermocouple, *728, 729*

thermometer, bimetallic strip, *725*

thermometer, electrical resistance change, *726*

thermoplastic resin, *240*

thermosetting resin, *240*

throatless shear, *89, 90*

thrust, *9*

tire bead, *474, 479*

tire carcass, *474*

tire inflation, *476*

tire retreading, *480*

tire sidewall, *476, 477*

tire storage, *481*

tire tread, *475, 477*

titanium, *74*

toe in, *427*

toe out, *427*

Tools for Sheet Metal Construction and Repair: Study Questions, *104*

toroidal coil, *733*

torque links, *424*

torque tube, *284*

torque, *46, 307*

torsion, *68*

TR (Transformer-Rectifier), *547*

trammel, *191*

transfer punch, *88, 89*

transistor, bipolar, *500*

transistor, NPN, *500, 501*

transistor, PNP, *500, 501*

translational lift, *50*

transmission line, *80, 846*

transonic flight, *39, 40*

Transparent Plastics: Study Questions, *262*

transverse flow effect, *51*

transverse pitch, *116*

tricresyl posphate, *589*

trim tab, *278*

troposphere, *7*

troubleshooting, *565–570*

true airspeed indicator, *758*

tubeless tires, *482*

tubing cutter, *390*

tubing double flare, *390*

tubing single flare, *390*

turbine, *323*

turn and slip indicator, *752*

turnbuckle, *298–299*

turnbuckle safetying, *299*

turn coordinator, *753*

twist drill, *94, 95, 119*

TXV (Thermostatic Expansion Valve), *700, 702*

Type Certificate Data Sheets, *290, 918*

unloading valve, *339, 370*

urethane foam, *242*

vacuum bag, *244*

vacuum pump, *706, 765*

vacuum pump, wet, *765*

valve, cross-feed, *600*

vapor lock, *588*

vapor pressure, *588*

vapor-cycle cooling system, *695–711*

variable-displacement pump, *352, 356–357*

variation error, *743*

varsol, *344*

veneer, *176*

venturi tee, *348*

venturi tube, *764*

vertical fin, *294*

vertical speed indicator, *761*

viscosity cup, *226*

volt-ammeter, *527*

voltage regulator, *513–519*

voltage regulator, carbon-pile, *522, 524*

voltage regulator, vibrator-type, *520*

voltmeter, *526*

volume, *325*

VOR (Very high frequency Omnidirectional Range), *811–813*

vortex generator, *21, 22*

warp clock, *248*

wash in, *40, 293*

wash out, *40, 293*

wash primer, *216*

way point, *838*

weight and balance, *846*

weight, *10*

weld characteristics, *149*

welded aircraft repairs, *163–166*

welding, backhand, *147*

welding, electric arc, *138, 155*

welding, electric resistance, *138, 161*

welding filler rod, *143*

welding, forehand, *146, 147*

welding, gas, *138*

welding, gas shielded arc, *155*

welding goggles, *143*

welding hoses, *141*

welding, MIG, *155*

welding, seam, *162*

welding, spot, *162*

welding, TIG, *155*

welding torch lighter, *143*

welding torch tips, *143*

welding torch, balanced-pressure, *142*

welding torch, injector, *142*

welding torches, *142*

Wheatstone bridge, *727*

wheel alignment, *427, 429*

wheel balancing, *483*

wheel bearings, *471*

wheel camber, *427, 428*

wheel, drop-center, *468*

windshield, electrically heated, *862*

wing fences, *20, 40*

winglets, *24*

wing-tip vortices, *24*

wire, shielded, *552*

wire, twisted pair, *553*

wood, balsa, *241*

wood, compression, *177*

wood, flat grain, *176*

wood, laminated, *176*

wood, quartersawed, *176, 177*

wood, vertical grain, *176*

wood wing rib repair, *181*

wood wing spar repair, *180*

work, *326*

yaw, *270, 273, 287*

yaw damper, *288, 769*

yield strength, *74, 75*

zener diode, *498*

Zeppelin, *5*

zinc chromate primer, *118, 215, 217*

AVIATION MAINTENANCE TECHNICIAN SERIES
AIRFRAME

Copy Editing	Janice Bultmann, Kitty Crane
Design & Production	Dora McClurkin Muir
Editing & Production	Jennifer Trerise
Illustration & Production	Dan McArdle, Jennifer Shontz
Additional Illustration	Glen Greenwood, Virginia Wright

Produced at
ASA's Graphic Design & Publications Department
in Times and Helvetica Black
using Microsoft Word, Aldus FreeHand, Adobe Illustrator,
Hewlett Packard DeskScan II, Zedcor DeskPaint, Adobe PhotoShop
and Aldus PageMaker

Product names are trademarks or registered trademarks of their respective holders.

READER RESPONSE

Dear Aviation Maintenance Technician:

You have made an investment in your future by purchasing this textbook from ASA's *Aviation Maintenance Technician Series*. We hope you were pleased with your selection. Your input is invaluable to us. Please take a moment to provide us with your comments and suggestions. Include your name and address so we can thank you.

— Aviation Supplies & Academics, Inc.

Please print clearly.

NAME _____ DATE _____

TITLE *(Student, Instructor, other)* _____

BUSINESS/SCHOOL _____

ADDRESS _____

CITY _____ STATE _____ ZIP CODE/POSTAL CODE _____

COUNTRY _____ TELEPHONE *(optional)* _____

WHERE DID YOU PURCHASE THIS **AIRFRAME** AVIATION MAINTENANCE TEXT? _____

WAS THE TEXT RECOMMENDED TO YOU? _____ BY WHOM? _____

DO YOU INTEND TO PURCHASE ASA'S TWO ADDITIONAL TEXTS IN THE SERIES? GENERAL _____ POWERPLANT _____

COMMENTS AND SUGGESTIONS
Please tell us what you liked or disliked about the text: content, subject matter, ease-of-use, illustrations and figures, etc.

_____

_____

_____

_____

_____

_____

_____

MAIL THIS FORM TO:

Aviation Supplies & Academics, Inc.
7005 132nd Place SE
Newcastle, Washington 98059-3153

✂ *Please photocopy or remove this page.*